James Clerk Maxwell.

THE SCIENTIFIC PAPERS OF

JAMES CLERK MAXWELL

EDITED BY W. D. NIVEN, M.A., F.R.S.

TWO VOLUMES BOUND AS ONE

DOVER PUBLICATIONS, INC., NEW YORK

Published in Canada by General Publishing Company, Ltd., 30 Lesmill Road, Don Mills, Toronto, Ontario.

Published in the United Kingdom by Constable and Company, Ltd., 10 Orange Street, London W. C. 2.

This Dover edition, first published in 1965, is an unabridged and unaltered republication of the work first published by Cambridge University Press in 1890. This edition is published by special arrangement with Cambridge University Press.

The work was originally published in two separate volumes, but is now published in two volumes bound as one.

Library of Congress Catalog Card Number: A53-9813

Manufactured in the United States of America

Dover Publications, Inc.
180 Varick Street
New York, N. Y. 10014

THE SCIENTIFIC PAPERS OF

JAMES CLERK MAXWELL

EDITED BY W. D. NIVEN, M.A., F.R.S.

VOLUME ONE

SHORTLY after the death of Professor James Clerk Maxwell a Committee was formed, consisting of graduate members of the University of Cambridge and of other friends and admirers, for the purpose of securing a fitting memorial of him.

The Committee had in view two objects: to obtain a likeness of Professor Clerk Maxwell, which should be placed in some public building of the University; and to collect and publish his scattered scientific writings, copies of which, so far as the funds at the disposal of the Committee would allow, should be presented to learned Societies and Libraries at home and abroad.

It was decided that the likeness should take the form of a marble bust. This was executed by Sir J. E. Boehm, R.A., and is now placed in the apparatus room of the Cavendish Laboratory.

In carrying out the second part of their programme the Committee obtained the cordial assistance of the Syndics of the University Press, who willingly consented to publish the present work. At the request of the Syndics, Mr W. D. Niven, M.A., Fellow and Assistant Tutor of Trinity College and now Director of Studies at the Royal Naval College, Greenwich, undertook the duties of Editor.

The Committee and the Syndics desire to take this opportunity of acknowledging their obligation to Messrs Adam and Charles Black, Publishers of the ninth Edition of the *Encyclopædia Britannica*, to Messrs Taylor and Francis, Publishers of the *London, Edinburgh, and Dublin Philosophical Magazine and Journal of Science*, to Messrs Macmillan and Co., Publishers of *Nature* and of the *Cambridge and Dublin Mathematical Journal*, to Messrs Metcalfe and Co., Publishers of the *Quarterly Journal of Pure and Applied Mathematics*, and to the Lords of the Committee of Council on Education, Proprietors of the *Handbooks* of the South Kensington Museum, for their courteous consent to allow the articles which Clerk Maxwell had contributed to these publications to be included in the present work; to Mr Norman Lockyer for the assistance which he rendered in the selection of the articles re-printed from *Nature*; and their further obligation to Messrs Macmillan and Co. for permission to use in this work the steel engravings of Faraday, Clerk Maxwell, and Helmholtz from the *Nature* Series of Portraits.

Numerous and important Papers, contributed by Clerk Maxwell to the *Transactions* or *Proceedings* of the Royal Societies of London and of Edinburgh, of the Cambridge Philosophical Society, of the Royal Scottish Society of Arts, and of the London Mathematical Society; Lectures delivered by Clerk Maxwell at the Royal Institution of Great Britain published in its *Proceedings*; as well as Communications and Addresses to the British Association published in its *Reports,* are also included in the present work with the sanction of the above mentioned learned bodies.

The Essay which gained the Adams Prize for the year 1856 in the University of Cambridge, the introductory Lecture on the Study of Experimental Physics delivered in the Cavendish Laboratory, and the Rede Lecture delivered before the University in 1878, complete this collection of Clerk Maxwell's scientific writings.

The diagrams in this work have been re-produced by a photographic process from the original diagrams in Clerk Maxwell's Papers by the Cambridge Scientific Instrument Company.

It only remains to add that the footnotes inserted by the Editor are enclosed between square brackets.

CAMBRIDGE, *August,* 1890.

PREFACE.

CLERK MAXWELL'S biography has been written by Professors Lewis Campbell and Wm. Garnett with so much skill and appreciation of their subject that nothing further remains to be told. It would therefore be presumption on the part of the editor of his papers to attempt any lengthened narrative of a biographical character. At the same time a memorial edition of an author's collected writings would hardly be complete without some account however slight of his life and works. Accordingly the principal events of Clerk Maxwell's career will be recounted in the following brief sketch, and the reader who wishes to obtain further and more detailed information or to study his character in its social relations may consult the interesting work to which reference has been made.

James Clerk Maxwell was descended from the Clerks of Penicuick in Midlothian, a well-known Scottish family whose history can be traced back to the 16th century. The first baronet served in the parliament of Scotland. His eldest son, a man of learning, was a Baron of the Exchequer in Scotland. In later times John Clerk of Eldin a member of the family claimed the credit of having invented a new method of breaking the enemy's line in naval warfare, an invention said to have been adopted by Lord Rodney in the battle which he gained over the French in 1782. Another John Clerk, son of the naval tactitian, was a lawyer of much acumen and became a Lord of the Court of Session. He was distinguished among his Edinburgh contemporaries by his ready and sarcastic wit.

The father of the subject of this memoir was John, brother to Sir George Clerk of Penicuick. He adopted the surname of Maxwell on succeeding to an estate in Kirkcudbrightshire which came into the Clerk family through marriage with a Miss Maxwell. It cannot be said that he was possessed of the energy and activity of mind which lead to distinction. He was in truth a somewhat easy-going but shrewd and intelligent man, whose most notable characteristics were his perfect sincerity and extreme benevolence. He took an enlightened interest in mechanical and scientific pursuits and was of an essentially practical turn of mind. On leaving the University he had devoted himself to law and was called to the Scottish Bar. It does not appear however that he met with any great success in that profession. At all events, a quiet life in the country presented so many attractions to his wife as well as to himself that he was easily induced to relinquish his prospects at the bar. He had been married to Frances, daughter of Robert Cay of N. Charlton, Northumberland, a lady of strong good sense and resolute character.

The country house which was their home after they left Edinburgh was designed by John Clerk Maxwell himself and was built on his estate. The house, which was named Glenlair, was surrounded by fine scenery, of which the water of Urr with its rocky and wooded banks formed the principal charm.

James was born at Edinburgh on the 13th of June, 1831, but it was at Glenlair that the greater part of his childhood was passed. In that pleasant spot under healthful influences of all kinds the child developed into a hardy and courageous boy. Not precociously clever at books he was yet not without some signs of future intellectual strength, being remarkable for a spirit of inquiry into the causes and connections of the phenomena around him. It was remembered afterwards when he had become distinguished, that the questions he put as a child shewed an amount of thoughtfulness which for his years was very unusual.

At the age of ten, James, who had lost his mother, was placed under the charge of relatives in Edinburgh that he might attend the Edinburgh Academy. A charming account of his school days is given in the narrative of Professor Campbell who was Maxwell's schoolfellow and in after life an intimate friend and constant correspondent. The child is father to the man, and those who were privileged to know the man Maxwell will easily recognise Mr Campbell's picture of the boy on his first appearance at school,—the home-made garments more serviceable than fashionable, the rustic speech and curiously quaint but often humorous manner of conveying his meaning, his bewilderment on first undergoing the routine of schoolwork, and his Spartan conduct under various trials at the hands of his schoolfellows. They will further feel how accurate is the sketch of the boy become accustomed to his surroundings and rapidly assuming the place at school to which his mental powers entitled him, while his superfluous energy finds vent privately in carrying out mechanical contrivances and geometrical constructions, in reading and even trying his hand at composing ballads, and in sending to his father letters richly embellished with grotesquely elaborate borders and drawings.

An event of his school-days, worth recording, was his invention of a mechanical method of drawing certain classes of Ovals. An account of this method was printed in the Proceedings of the Royal Society of Edinburgh and forms the first of his writings collected in the present work. The subject was introduced to the notice of the Society by the celebrated Professor James Forbes, who from the first took the greatest possible interest in Maxwell's progress. Professor Tait, another schoolfellow, mentions that at the time when the paper on the Ovals was written, Maxwell had received no instruction in Mathematics beyond a little Euclid and Algebra.

In 1847 Maxwell entered the University of Edinburgh where he remained for three sessions. He attended the lectures of Kelland in Mathematics, Forbes in Natural Philosophy, Gregory in Chemistry, Sir W. Hamilton in Mental Philosophy, Wilson (Christopher North) in Moral Philosophy. The lectures of Sir W. Hamilton made a strong impression upon him, in stimulating the love of speculation to which his mind was prone, but, as might have been expected, it was the Professor of Natural Philosophy who obtained the chief share of his devotion. The enthusiasm which so distinguished a man as Forbes naturally inspired in young and ardent disciples, evoked a feeling of personal attachment, and the Professor, on his part, took special interest in his pupil and gave to him the altogether unusual privilege of working with his fine apparatus.

What was the nature of this experimental work we may conjecture from a perusal of his paper on Elastic Solids, written at that time, in which he describes some experiments made with the view of verifying the deductions of his theory in its application to Optics. Maxwell would seem to have been led to the study of this subject by the following circumstance. He was taken by his uncle John Cay to see William Nicol, the inventor of the polarising prism which bears his name, and was shewn by Nicol the colours of unannealed glass in the polariscope. This incited Maxwell to study the laws of polarised light and to construct a rough polariscope in which the polariser and analyser were simple glass reflectors. By means of this instrument he was able to obtain the colour bands of unannealed glass. These he copied on paper in water colours and sent to Nicol. It is gratifying to find that this spirited attempt at experimenting on the part of a mere boy was duly appreciated by Nicol, who at once encouraged and delighted him by a present of a couple of his prisms.

The paper alluded to, viz. that entitled "On the Equilibrium of Elastic Solids," was read to the Royal Society of Edinburgh in 1850. It forms the third paper which Maxwell addressed to that Society. The first in 1846 on Ovals has been already mentioned. The second, under the title "The Theory of Rolling Curves," was presented by Kelland in 1849.

It is obvious that a youth of nineteen years who had been capable of these efforts must have been gifted with rare originality and with great power of sustained exertion. But his singular self-concentration led him into habits of solitude and seclusion, the tendency of which was to confirm his peculiarities of speech and of manner. He was shy and reserved with strangers, and his utterances were often obscure both in substance and in his manner of expressing himself, so many remote and unexpected allusions perpetually obtruding themselves. Though really most sociable and even fond of society he was essentially reticent and reserved. Mr Campbell thinks it is to be regretted that Maxwell did not begin his Cambridge career earlier for the sake of the social intercourse which he would have found it difficult to avoid there. It is a question, however, whether in losing the opportunity of using Professor Forbes' apparatus he would not thereby have lost what was perhaps the most valuable part of his early scientific training.

It was originally intended that Maxwell should follow his father's profession of advocate, but this intention was abandoned as soon as it became obvious that his tastes lay in a direction so decidedly scientific. It was at length determined to send him to Cambridge and accordingly in October, 1850, he commenced residence in Peterhouse, where however he resided during the Michaelmas Term only. On December 14 of the same year he migrated to Trinity College.

It may readily be supposed that his preparatory training for the Cambridge course was far removed from the ordinary type. There had indeed for some time been practically no restraint upon his plan of study and his mind had been allowed to follow its natural bent towards science, though not to an extent so absorbing as to withdraw him from other pursuits. Though he was not a sportsman,—indeed sport so called was always repugnant to him—he was yet exceedingly fond of a country life. He was a good horseman and a good swimmer. Whence however he derived his chief enjoyment may be gathered from the account which Mr Campbell gives of the zest with which he quoted on one occasion the lines of Burns which describe the poet finding inspiration while wandering along the banks of a stream in the free indulgence of his fancies. Maxwell was not only a lover of poetry but himself a poet, as the fine pieces gathered together by Mr Campbell abundantly testify. He saw however that his true calling was Science and never regarded these poetical efforts as other than mere pastime. Devotion to science, already stimulated by successful endeavour, a tendency to ponder over philosophical problems and an attachment to English literature, particularly to English poetry,—these tastes, implanted in a mind of singular strength and purity, may be said to have been the endowments with which young Maxwell began his Cambridge career. Besides this, his scientific reading, as we may gather from his papers to the Royal Society of Edinburgh referred to above, was already extensive and varied. He brought with him, says Professor Tait, a mass of knowledge which was really immense for so young a man but in a state of disorder appalling to his methodical private tutor.

Maxwell's undergraduate career was not marked by any specially notable feature. His private speculations had in some measure to be laid aside in favour of more systematic study. Yet his mind was steadily ripening for the work of his later years. Among those with whom he was brought into daily contact by his position, as a Scholar of Trinity College, were some of the brightest and most cultivated young men in the University. In the genial fellowship of the Scholars' table Maxwell's kindly humour found ready play, while in the more select coterie of the Apostle Club, formed for mutual cultivation, he found a field for the exercise of his love of speculation in essays on subjects beyond the lines of the ordinary University course. The composition of these essays doubtless laid the foundation of that literary finish which is one of the characteristics of Maxwell's scientific writings. His biographers have preserved several extracts on a variety of subjects chiefly of a speculative character. They are remarkable mainly for the weight of thought contained in them but occasionally also for smart epigrams and for a vein of dry and sarcastic humour.

These glimpses into Maxwell's character may prepare us to believe that, with all his shyness, he was not without confidence in his own powers, as also appears from the account which was given by the late Master of Trinity College, Dr Thompson, who was Tutor when Maxwell personally applied to him for permission to migrate to that College. He appeared to be a shy and diffident youth, but presently surprised Dr Thompson by producing a bundle of papers, doubtless copies of those we have already mentioned, remarking "Perhaps these may shew you that I am not unfit to enter at your College."

He became a pupil of the celebrated William Hopkins of Peterhouse, under whom his course of study became more systematic. One striking characteristic was remarked by his contemporaries. Whenever the subject admitted of it he had recourse to diagrams, though his fellow students might solve the question more easily by a train of analysis. Many illustrations of this manner of proceeding might be taken from his writings, but in truth it was only one phase of his mental attitude towards scientific questions, which led him to proceed from one distinct idea to another instead of trusting to symbols and equations.

Maxwell's published contributions to Mathematical Science during his undergraduate career were few and of no great importance. He found time however to carry his investigations into regions outside the prescribed Cambridge course. At the lectures of Professor Stokes* he was regular in his attendance. Indeed it appears from the paper on Elastic Solids, mentioned above, that he was acquainted with some of the writings of Stokes before he entered Cambridge. Before 1850, Stokes had published some of his most important contributions to Hydromechanics and Optics ; and Sir W. Thomson, who was nine years' Maxwell's senior in University standing, had, among other remarkable investigations, called special attention to the mathematical analogy between Heat-conduction and Statical Electricity. There is no doubt that these authors as well as Faraday, of whose experimental researches he had made a careful study, exercised a powerful directive influence on his mind.

In January, 1854, Maxwell's undergraduate career closed. He was second wrangler, but shared with Dr Routh, who was senior wrangler, the honours of the First Smith's Prize. In due course he was elected Fellow of Trinity and placed on the staff of College Lecturers.

No sooner was he released from the restraints imposed by the Trinity Fellowship Examination than he plunged headlong into original work. There were several questions he was anxious to deal with, and first of all he completed an investigation on the Transformation of Surfaces by Bending, a purely geometrical problem. This memoir he presented to the Cambridge Philosophical Society in the following March. At this period he also set about an enquiry into the quantitative measurement of mixtures of colours and the causes of colour-blindness. During his undergraduateship he had, as we have seen, found time for the study of Electricity. This had already borne fruit and now resulted in the first of his important memoirs on that subject,—the memoir on Faraday's Lines of Force.

* Now Sir George Gabriel Stokes, Bart., M.P. for the University.

The number and importance of his papers, published in 1855—6, bear witness to his assiduity during this period. With these labours, and in the preparation of his College lectures, on which he entered with much enthusiasm, his mind was fully occupied and the work was congenial. He had formed a number of valued friendships, and he had a variety of interests, scientific and literary, attaching him to the University. Nevertheless, when the chair of Natural Philosophy in Marischal College, Aberdeen, fell vacant, Maxwell became a candidate. This step was probably taken in deference to his father's wishes, as the long summer vacation of the Scottish College would enable him to reside with his father at Glenlair for half the year continuously. He obtained the professorship, but unhappily the kind intentions which prompted him to apply for it were frustrated by the death of his father, which took place in April, 1856.

It is doubtful whether the change from the Trinity lectureship to the Aberdeen professorship was altogether prudent. The advantages were the possession of a laboratory and the long uninterrupted summer vacation. But the labour of drilling classes composed chiefly of comparatively young and untrained lads, in the elements of mechanics and physics, was not the work for which Maxwell was specially fitted. On the other hand, in a large college like Trinity there could not fail to have been among its undergraduate members, some of the most promising young mathematicians of the University, capable of appreciating his original genius and immense knowledge, by instructing whom he would himself have derived advantage.

In 1856 Maxwell entered upon his duties as Professor of Natural Philosophy at Marischal College, and two years afterwards he married Katharine Mary Dewar, daughter of the Principal of the College. He in consequence ceased to be a Fellow of Trinity College, but was afterwards elected an honorary Fellow, at the same time as Professor Cayley.

During the years 1856—60 he was still actively employed upon the subject of colour sensation, to which he contributed a new method of measurement in the ingenious instrument known as the colour-box. The most serious demands upon his powers and upon his time were made by his investigations on the Stability of Saturn's Rings. This was the subject chosen by the Examiners for the Adams Prize Essay to be adjudged in 1857, and was advertised in the following terms:—

"The Problem may be treated on the supposition that the system of Rings is exactly or very approximately concentric with Saturn and symmetrically disposed about the plane of his equator and different hypotheses may be made respecting the physical constitution of the Rings. It may be supposed (1) that they are rigid; (2) that they are fluid and in part aeriform; (3) that they consist of masses of matter not materially coherent. The question will be considered to be answered by ascertaining on these hypotheses severally whether the conditions of mechanical stability are satisfied by the mutual attractions and motions of the Planet and the Rings."

"It is desirable that an attempt should also be made to determine on which of the above hypotheses the appearances both of the bright rings and the recently discovered dark ring may be most satisfactorily explained; and to indicate any causes to which a change of form such as is supposed from a comparison of modern with the earlier observations to have taken place, may be attributed."

It is sufficient to mention here that Maxwell bestowed an immense amount of labour in working out the theory as proposed, and that he arrived at the conclusion that "the only system of rings which can exist is one composed of an indefinite number of unconnected particles revolving round the planet with different velocities according to their respective distances. These particles may be arranged in a series of narrow rings, or they may move about through each other irregularly. In the first case the destruction of the system will be very slow, in the second case it will be more rapid, but there may be a tendency towards an arrangement in narrow rings which may retard the process."

Part of the work, dealing with the oscillatory waves set up in a ring of satellites, was illustrated by an ingenious mechanical contrivance which was greatly admired when exhibited before the Royal Society of Edinburgh.

This essay, besides securing the prize, obtained for its author great credit among scientific men. It was characterized by Sir George Airy as one of the most remarkable applications of Mathematics to Physics that he had ever seen.

The suggestion has been made that it was the irregular motions of the particles which compose the Rings of Saturn resulting on the whole in apparent regularity and uniformity, which led Maxwell to the investigation of the Kinetic Theory of Gases, his first contribution to which was read to the British Association in 1859. This is not unlikely, but it must also be borne in mind that Bernoulli's Theory had recently been revived by Herapath, Joule and Clausius whose writings may have drawn Maxwell's attention to the subject.

In 1860 King's College and Marischal College were joined together as one institution, now known as the University of Aberdeen. The new chair of Natural Philosophy thus created was filled up by the appointment of David Thomson, formerly Professor at King's College and Maxwell's senior. Professor Thomson, though not comparable to Maxwell as a physicist, was nevertheless a remarkable man. He was distinguished by singular force of character and great administrative faculty and he had been prominent in bringing about the fusion of the Colleges. He was also an admirable lecturer and teacher and had done much to raise the standard of scientific education in the north of Scotland. Thus the choice made by the Commissioners, though almost inevitable, had the effect of making it appear that Maxwell failed as a teacher. There seems however to be no evidence to support such an inference. On the contrary, if we may judge from the number of voluntary students attending his classes in his last College session, he would seem to have been as popular as a professor as he was personally estimable.

This is also borne out by the fact that he was soon afterwards elected Professor of Natural Philosophy and Astronomy in King's College, London. The new appointment had the advantage of bringing him much more into contact with men in his own department of science, especially with Faraday, with whose electrical work his own was so intimately connected. In 1862—63 he took a prominent part in the experiments organised by a Committee of the British Association for the determination of electrical resistance in absolute measure and for placing electrical measurements on a satisfactory basis. In the experiments which were conducted in the laboratory of King's College upon a plan due to Sir W. Thomson, two long series of measurements were taken in successive years. In the first year, the working members were Maxwell, Balfour Stewart and Fleeming Jenkin; in the second, Charles Hockin took the place of Balfour Stewart. The work of this Committee was communicated in the form of reports to the British Association and was afterwards republished in one volume by Fleeming Jenkin.

Maxwell was a professor in King's College from 1860 to 1865, and this period of his life is distinguished by the production of his most important papers. The second memoir on Colours made its appearance in 1860. In the same year his first papers on the Kinetic Theory of Gases were published. In 1861 came his papers on Physical Lines of Force and in 1864 his greatest memoir on Electricity,—a Dynamical Theory of the Electromagnetic Field. He must have been occupied with the Dynamical Theory of Gases in 1865, as two important papers appeared in the following year, first the Bakerian lecture on the Viscosity of Gases, and next the memoir on the Dynamical Theory of Gases.

The mental strain involved in the production of so much valuable work, combined with the duties of his professorship which required his attention during nine months of the year, seems to have influenced him in a resolution which in 1865 he at length adopted of resigning his chair and retiring to his country seat. Shortly after this he had a severe illness. On his recovery he continued his work on the Dynamical Theory of Gases, to which reference has just been made. For the next few years he led a quiet and secluded life at Glenlair, varied by annual visits to London, attendances at the British Association meetings and by a tour in Italy in 1867. He was also Moderator or Examiner in the Mathematical Tripos at Cambridge on several occasions, offices which entailed a few weeks' residence at the University in winter. His chief employment during those years was the preparation of his now celebrated treatise on Electricity and Magnetism which, however, was not published till 1873. He also wrote a treatise on Heat which was published in 1871.

In 1871 Maxwell was, with some reluctance, induced to quit his retreat in the country and to enter upon a new career. The University of Cambridge had recently resolved to found a professorship of physical science, especially for the cultivation and teaching of the subjects of Heat, Electricity and Magnetism. In furtherance of this object her Chancellor, the Duke of Devonshire, had most generously undertaken to build a laboratory and furnish it with the necessary apparatus. Maxwell was invited to fill the new chair thus formed and to superintend the erection of the laboratory. In October, 1871, he delivered his inaugural lecture.

The Cavendish Laboratory, so called after its founder, the present venerable chief of the family which produced the great physicist of the same name, was not completed for practical work until 1874. In June of that year it was formally presented to the University by the Chancellor. The building itself and the fittings of the several rooms were admirably contrived mainly by Maxwell himself, but the stock of apparatus was smaller than accorded with the generous intentions of the Chancellor. This defect must be attributed to the anxiety of the Professor to procure only instruments by the best makers and with such improvements as he could himself suggest. Such a defect therefore required time for its removal and afterwards in great measure disappeared, apparatus being constantly added to the stock as occasion demanded.

One of the chief tasks which Maxwell undertook was that of superintending and directing the energies of such young Bachelors of Arts as became his pupils after having acquired good positions in the University examinations. Several pupils, who have since acquired distinction, carried out valuable experiments under the guidance of the Professor. It must be admitted, however, that the numbers were at first small, but perhaps this was only to be expected from the traditions of so many years. The Professor was singularly kind and helpful to these pupils. He would hold long conversations with them, opening up to them the stores of his mind, giving them hints as to what they might try and what avoid, and was always ready with some ingenious remedy for the experimental troubles which beset them. These conversations, always delightful and instructive, were, according to the account of one of his pupils, a liberal education in themselves, and were repaid in the minds of the pupils by a grateful affection rarely accorded to any teacher.

Besides discharging the duties of his chair, Maxwell took an active part in conducting the general business of the University and more particularly in regulating the courses of study in Mathematics and Physics.

For some years previous to 1866 when Maxwell returned to Cambridge as Moderator in the Mathematical Tripos, the studies in the University had lost touch with the great scientific movements going on outside her walls. It was said that some of the subjects most in vogue had but little interest for the present generation, and loud complaints began to be heard that while such branches of knowledge as Heat, Electricity and Magnetism, were left out of the Tripos examination, the candidates were wasting their time and energy upon mathematical trifles barren of scientific interest and of practical results. Into the movement for reform Maxwell entered warmly. By his questions in 1866 and subsequent years he infused new life into the examination; he took an active part in drafting the new scheme introduced in 1873; but most of all by his writings he exerted a powerful influence on the younger members of the University, and was largely instrumental in bringing about the change which has been now effected.

In the first few years at Cambridge Maxwell was busy in giving the final touches to his great work on Electricity and Magnetism and in passing it through the press. This work was published in 1873, and it seems to have occupied the most of his attention for the two previous years, as the few papers published by him during that period relate chiefly to subjects forming part of the contents. After this publication his contributions to scientific journals became more numerous, those on the Dynamical Theory of Gases being perhaps the most important. He also wrote a great many short articles and reviews which made their appearance in *Nature* and the *Encyclopædia Britannica*. Some of these essays are charming expositions of scientific subjects, some are general criticisms of the works of contemporary writers and others are brief and appreciative biographies of fellow workers in the same fields of research.

An undertaking in which he was long engaged and which, though it proved exceedingly interesting, entailed much labour, was the editing of the "Electrical Researches" of the Hon. Henry Cavendish. This work, published in 1879, has had the effect of increasing the reputation of Cavendish, disclosing as it does the unsuspected advances which that acute physicist had made in the Theory of Electricity, especially in the measurement of electrical quantities. The work is enriched by a variety of valuable notes in which Cavendish's views and results are examined by the light of modern theory and methods. Especially valuable are the methods applied to the determination of the electrical capacities of conductors and condensers, a subject in which Cavendish himself shewed considerable skill both of a mathematical and experimental character.

The importance of the task undertaken by Maxwell in connection with Cavendish's papers will be understood from the following extract from his introduction to them.

"It is somewhat difficult to account for the fact that though Cavendish had prepared a complete description of his experiments on the charges of bodies, and had even taken the trouble to write out a fair copy, and though all this seems to have been done before 1774 and he continued to make experiments in Electricity till 1781 and lived on till 1810, he kept his manuscript by him and never published it."

"Cavendish cared more for investigation than for publication. He would undertake the most laborious researches in order to clear up a difficulty which no one but himself could appreciate or was even aware of, and we cannot doubt that the result of his enquiries, when successful, gave him a certain degree of satisfaction. But it did not excite in him that desire to communicate the discovery to others which in the case of ordinary men of science, generally ensures the publication of their results. How completely these researches of Cavendish remained unknown to other men of science is shewn by the external history of electricity."

It will probably be thought a matter of some difficulty to place oneself in the position of a physicist of a century ago and to ascertain the exact bearing of his experiments. But Maxwell entered upon this undertaking with the utmost enthusiasm and succeeded in completely identifying himself with Cavendish's methods. He shewed that Cavendish had really anticipated several of the discoveries in electrical science which have been made since his time. Cavendish was the first to form the conception of and to measure Electrostatic Capacity and Specific Inductive Capacity; he also anticipated Ohm's law.

The Cavendish papers were no sooner disposed of than Maxwell set about preparing a new edition of his work on Electricity and Magnetism; but unhappily in the summer term of 1879 his health gave way. Hopes were however entertained that when he returned to the bracing air of his country home he would soon recover. But he lingered through the summer months with no signs of improvement and his spirits gradually sank. He was finally informed by his old fellow-student, Professor Sanders, that he could not live more than a few weeks. As a last resort he was brought back to Cambridge in October that he might be under the charge of his favourite physician, Dr Paget*. Nothing however could be done for · his malady, and, after a painful illness, he died on the 5th of November, 1879, in his 49th year.

Maxwell was thus cut off in the prime of his powers, and at a time when the departments of science, which he had contributed so much to develop, were being every day extended by fresh discoveries. His death was deplored as an irreparable loss to science and to the University, in which his amiable disposition was as universally esteemed as his genius was admired.

It is not intended in this preface to enter at length into a discussion of the relation which Maxwell's work bears historically to that of his predecessors, or to attempt to estimate the effect which it has had on the scientific thought of the present day. In some of his papers he has given more than usually copious references to the works of those by whom he had been influenced; and in his later papers, especially those of a more popular nature which appeared in the *Encyclopædia Britannica*, he has given full historical outlines of some of the most prominent fields in which he laboured. Nor does it appear to the present editor that the time has yet arrived when the quickening influence of Maxwell's mind on modern scientific thought can be duly estimated. He therefore proposes to himself the duty of recalling briefly, according to subjects, the most important speculations in which Maxwell engaged.

His works have been arranged as far as possible in chronological order but they fall naturally under a few leading heads; and perhaps we shall not be far wrong if we place first in importance his work in Electricity.

His first paper on this subject bearing the title "On Faraday's Lines of Force" was read before the Cambridge Philosophical Society on Dec. 11th, 1855. He had been previously attracted by Faraday's method of expressing electrical laws, and he here set before himself the task of shewing that the ideas which had guided Faraday's researches were not inconsistent with the mathematical formulæ in which Poisson and others had cast the laws of

* Now Sir George Edward Paget, K.C.B.

Electricity. His object, he says, is to find a physical analogy which shall help the mind to grasp the results of previous investigations "without being committed to any theory founded on the physical science from which that conception is borrowed, so that it is neither drawn aside from the subject in the pursuit of analytical subtleties nor carried beyond the truth by a favorite hypothesis."

The laws of electricity are therefore compared with the properties of an incompressible fluid the motion of which is retarded by a force proportional to the velocity, and the fluid is supposed to possess no inertia. He shews the analogy which the lines of flow of such a fluid would have with the lines of force, and deduces not merely the laws of Statical Electricity in a single medium but also a method of representing what takes place when the action passes from one dielectric into another.

In the latter part of the paper he proceeds to consider the phenomena of Electro-magnetism and shews how the laws discovered by Ampère lead to conclusions identical with those of Faraday. In this paper three expressions are introduced which he identifies with the components of Faraday's electrotonic state, though the author admits that he has not been able to frame a physical theory which would give a clear mental picture of the various connections expressed by the equations.

Altogether this paper is most important for the light which it throws on the principles which guided Maxwell at the outset of his electrical work. The idea of the electrotonic state had already taken a firm hold of his mind though as yet he had formed no physical explanation of it. In the paper "On Physical Lines of Force" printed in the *Philosophical Magazine*, Vol. XXI. he resumes his speculations. He explains that in his former paper he had found the geometrical significance of the Electrotonic state but that he now proposes "to examine magnetic phenomena from a mechanical point of view." Accordingly he propounds his remarkable speculation as to the magnetic field being occupied by molecular vortices, the axes of which coincide with the lines of force. The cells within which these vortices rotate are supposed to be separated by layers of particles which serve the double purpose of transmitting motion from one cell to another and by their own motions constituting an electric current. This theory, the parent of several working models which have been devised to represent the motions of the dielectric, is remarkable for the detail with which it is worked out and made to explain the various laws not only of magnetic and electromagnetic action, but also the various forms of electrostatic action. As Maxwell subsequently gave a more general theory of the Electromagnetic Field, it may be inferred that he did not desire it to be supposed that he adhered to the views set forth in this paper in every particular; but there is no doubt that in some of its main features, especially the existence of rotation round the lines of magnetic force, it expressed his permanent convictions. In his treatise on " Electricity and Magnetism," Vol. II. p. 416, (2nd edition 427) after quoting from Sir W. Thomson on the explanation of the magnetic rotation of the plane of the polarisation of light, he goes on to say of the present paper,

"A theory of molecular vortices which I worked out at considerable length was published in the *Phil. Mag.* for March, April and May, 1861, Jan. and Feb. 1862."

"I think we have good evidence for the opinion that some phenomenon of rotation is going on in the magnetic field, that this rotation is performed by a great number of very small portions of matter, each rotating on its own axis, that axis being parallel to the direction of the magnetic force, and that the rotations of these various vortices are made to depend on one another by means of some mechanism between them."

"The attempt which I then made to imagine a working model of this mechanism must be taken for no more than it really is, a demonstration that mechanism may be imagined capable of producing a connection mechanically equivalent to the actual connection of the parts of the Electromagnetic Field."

This paper is also important as containing the first hint of the Electromagnetic Theory of Light which was to be more fully developed afterwards in his third great memoir "On the Dynamical Theory of the Electromagnetic Field." This memoir, which was presented to the Royal Society on the 27th October, 1864, contains Maxwell's mature thoughts on a subject which had so long occupied his mind. It was afterwards reproduced in his Treatise with trifling modifications in the treatment of its parts, but without substantial changes in its main features. In this paper Maxwell reverses the mode of treating electrical phenomena adopted by previous mathematical writers; for while they had sought to build up the laws of the subject by starting from the principles discovered by Ampère, and deducing the induction of currents from the conservation of energy, Maxwell adopts the method of first arriving at the laws of induction and then deducing the mechanical attractions and repulsions.

After recalling the general phenomena of the mutual action of currents and magnets and the induction produced in a circuit by any variation of the strength of the field in which it lies, the propagation of light through a luminiferous medium, the properties of dielectrics and other phenomena which point to a medium capable of transmitting force and motion, he proceeds.—

"Thus then we are led to the conception of a complicated mechanism capable of a vast variety of motions but at the same time so connected that the motion of one part depends, according to definite relations, on the motion of other parts, these motions being communicated by forces arising from the relative displacement of their connected parts, in virtue of their elasticity. Such a mechanism must be subject to the laws of Dynamics."

On applying dynamical principles to such a connected system he attains certain general propositions which, on being compared with the laws of induced currents, enable him to identify certain features of the mechanism with properties of currents. The induction of currents and their electromagnetic attraction are thus explained and connected.

In a subsequent part of the memoir he proceeds to establish from these premises the general equations of the Field and obtains the usual formulæ for the mechanical force on currents, magnets and bodies possessing an electrostatic charge.

He also returns to and elaborates more fully the electromagnetic Theory of Light. His equations shew that dielectrics can transmit only transverse vibrations, the speed of propagation of which in air as deduced from electrical data comes out practically identical with the known velocity of light. For other dielectrics the index of refraction is equal to the square root of the product of the specific inductive capacity by the coefficient of magnetic induction, which last factor is for most bodies practically unity. Various comparisons have been made with the view of testing this deduction. In the case of paraffin wax and some of the hydrocarbons, theory and experiment agree, but this is not the case with glass and some other substances. Maxwell has also applied his theory to media which are not perfect insulators, and finds an expression for the loss of light in passing through a stratum of given thickness. He remarks in confirmation of his result that most good conductors are opaque while insulators are transparent, but he also adds that electrolytes which transmit a current freely are often transparent, while a piece of gold leaf whose resistance was determined by Mr Hockin allowed far too great an amount of light to pass. He observes however that it is possible "there is less loss of energy when the electromotive forces are reversed with the rapidity of light than when they act for sensible times as in our experiments." A similar explanation may be given of the discordance between the calculated and observed values of the specific inductive capacity. Prof. J. J. Thomson in the *Proceedings of the Royal Society*, Vol. 46, has described an experiment by which he has obtained the specific inductive capacities of various dielectrics when acted on by alternating electric forces whose frequency is 25,000,000 per second. He finds that under these conditions the specific inductive capacity of glass is very nearly the same as the square of the refractive index, and very much less than the value for slow rates of reversals. In illustration of these remarks may be quoted the observations of Prof. Hertz who has shewn that vulcanite and pitch are transparent for waves, whose periods of vibration are about three hundred millionths of a second. The investigations of Hertz have shewn that electro-dynamic radiations are transmitted in waves with a velocity, which, if not equal to, is comparable with that of light, and have thus given conclusive proof that a satisfactory theory of Electricity must take into account in some form or other the action of the dielectric. But this does not prove that Maxwell's theory is to be accepted in every particular. A peculiarity of his theory is, as he himself points out in his treatise, that the variation of the electric displacement is to be treated as part of the current as well as the current of conduction, and that it is the total amount due to the sum of these which flows as if electricity were an incompressible fluid, and which determines external electrodynamic actions. In this respect it differs from the theory of Helmholtz which also takes into account the action of the dielectric. Professor J. J. Thomson ، in his Review of Electric Theories has entered into a full discussion of the points at issue between the two above mentioned theories, and the reader is referred to his paper for further information *. Maxwell in the memoir before us has also applied his theory to the passage of light through crystals, and gets rid at once of the wave of normal vibrations which has hitherto proved the stumbling block in other theories of light.

The electromagnetic Theory of Light has received numerous developments at the hands of Lord Rayleigh, Mr Glazebrook, Professor J. J. Thomson and others. These volumes also contain various shorter papers on Electrical Science, though perhaps the most complete record of Maxwell's work in this department is to be found in his Treatise on Electricity and Magnetism in which they were afterwards embodied.

Another series of papers of hardly less importance than those on Electricity are the various memoirs on the Dynamical Theory of Gases. The idea that the properties of matter might be explained by the motions and impacts of their ultimate atoms is as old as the time of the Greeks, and Maxwell has given in his paper on "Atoms" a full sketch of the ancient controversies to which it gave rise. The mathematical difficulties of the speculation however were so great that it made little real progress till it was taken up by Clausius and shortly afterwards by Maxwell. The first paper by Maxwell on the subject is entitled "Illustrations of the Dynamical Theory of Gases" and was published in the *Philosophical Magazine* for January and July, 1860, having been read at a meeting of the British Association of the previous year. Although the methods developed in this paper were afterwards abandoned for others, the paper itself is most interesting, as it indicates clearly the problems in the theory which Maxwell proposed to himself for solution, and so far contains the germs of much that was treated of in his next memoir. It is also epoch-making, inasmuch as it for the first time enumerates various propositions which are characteristic of Maxwell's work in this subject. It contains the first statement of the distribution of velocities according to the law of errors. It also foreshadows the theorem that when two gases are in thermal equilibrium the mean kinetic energy of the molecules of each system is the same; and for the first time the question of the viscosity of gases is treated dynamically.

In his great memoir "On the Dynamical Theory of Gases" published in the *Philosophical Transactions of the Royal Society* and read before the Society in May, 1866, he returns to this subject and lays down for the first time the general dynamical methods appropriate for its treatment. Though to some extent the same ground is traversed as in his former paper, the methods are widely different. He here abandons his former hypothesis that the molecules are hard elastic spheres, and supposes them to repel each other with forces varying inversely as the fifth power of the distance. His chief reason for assuming this law of action appears to be that it simplifies considerably the calculation of the collisions between the molecules, and it leads to the conclusion that the coefficient of viscosity is directly proportional to the absolute temperature. He himself undertook an experimental enquiry for the purpose of verifying this conclusion, and, in his paper on the Viscosity of Gases, he satisfied himself of its correctness. A re-examination of the numerical

---

* *British Association Report*, 1885.

reductions made in the course of his work discloses however an inaccuracy which materially affects the values of the coefficient of viscosity obtained. Subsequent experiments also seem to shew that the concise relation he endeavoured to establish is by no means so near the truth as he supposed, and it is more than doubtful whether the action between two molecules can be represented by any law of so simple a character.

In the same memoir he gives a fresh demonstration of the law of distribution of velocities, but though the method is of permanent value, it labours under the defect of assuming that the distribution of velocities in the neighbourhood of a point is the same in every direction, whatever actions may be taking place within the gas. This flaw in the argument, first pointed out by Boltzmann, seems to have been recognised by Maxwell, who in his next paper "On the Stresses in Rarefied Gases arising from inequalities of Temperature," published in the *Philosophical Transactions* for 1879, Part I., adopts a form of the distribution function of a somewhat different shape. The object of this paper was to arrive at a theory of the effects observed in Crookes's Radiometer. The results of the investigation are stated by Maxwell in the introduction to the paper, from which it would appear that the observed motion cannot be explained on the Dynamical Theory, unless it be supposed that the gas in contact with a solid can slide along the surface with a finite velocity between places whose temperatures are different. In an appendix to the paper he shews that on certain assumptions regarding the nature of the contact of the solid and gas, there will be, when the pressure is constant, a flow of gas along the surface from the colder to the hotter parts. The last of his longer papers on this subject is one on Boltzmann's Theorem. Throughout these volumes will be found numerous shorter essays on kindred subjects, published chiefly in *Nature* and in the *Encyclopædia Britannica*. Some of these contain more or less popular expositions of this subject which Maxwell had himself in great part created, while others deal with the work of other writers in the same field. They are profoundly suggestive in almost every page, and abound in acute criticisms of speculations which he could not accept. They are always interesting; for although the larger papers are sometimes difficult to follow, Maxwell's more popular writings are characterized by extreme lucidity and simplicity of style.

The first of Maxwell's papers on Colour Perception is taken from the Transactions of the Royal Scottish Society of Arts and is in the form of a letter to Dr G. Wilson dated Jan. 4, 1855. It was followed directly afterwards by a communication to the Royal Society of Edinburgh, and the subject occupied his attention for some years. The most important of his subsequent work is to be found in the papers entitled "An account of Experiments on the Perception of Colour" published in the *Philosophical Magazine*, Vol. XIV. and "On the Theory of Compound Colours and its relation to the colours of the spectrum" in the *Philosophical Transactions* for the year 1860. We may also refer to two lectures delivered at the Royal Institution, in which he recapitulates and enforces his main positions in his usual luminous style. Maxwell from the first adopts Young's Theory of Colour Sensation, according to which all colours may ultimately be reduced to three, a red, a green and a violet. This theory had been revived by Helmholtz who endeavoured to find for it a physiological basis. Maxwell however devoted himself chiefly to the invention of accurate methods for combining and recording mixtures of colours. His first method of obtaining mixtures, that of the Colour Top, is an adaptation of one formerly employed, but in Maxwell's hands it became an instrument capable of giving precise numerical results by means which he added of varying and measuring the amounts of colour which were blended in the eye. In the representation of colours diagrammatically he followed Young in employing an equilateral triangle at the angles of which the fundamental colours were placed. All colours, white included, which may be obtained by mixing the fundamental colours in any proportions will then be represented by points lying within the triangle. Points without the triangle represent colours which must be mixed with one of the fundamental tints to produce a mixture of the other two, or with which two of them must be mixed to produce the third.

In his later papers, notably in that printed in the *Philosophical Transactions*, he adopts the method of the Colour Box, by which different parts of the spectrum may be mixed in different proportions and matched with white, the intensity of which has been suitably diminished. In this way a series of colour equations are obtained which can be used to evaluate any colour in terms of the three fundamental colours. These observations on which Maxwell expended great care and labour, constitute by far the most important data regarding the combinations of colour sensations which have been yet obtained, and are of permanent value whatever theory may ultimately be adopted of the physiology of the perception of colour.

In connection with these researches into the sensations of the normal eye, may be mentioned the subject of colour-blindness, which also engaged Maxwell's attention, and is discussed at considerable length in several of his papers.

Geometrical Optics was another subject in which Maxwell took much interest. At an early period of his career he commenced a treatise on Optics, which however was never completed. His first paper "On the general laws of optical instruments," appeared in 1858, but a brief account of the first part of it had been previously communicated to the Cambridge Philosophical Society. He therein lays down the conditions which a perfect optical instrument must fulfil, and shews that if an instrument produce perfect images of an object, i.e. images free from astigmatism, curvature and distortion, for two different positions of the object, it will give perfect images at all distances. On this result as a basis, he finds the relations between the foci of the incident and emergent pencils, the magnifying power and other characteristic quantities. The subject of refraction through optical combinations was afterwards treated by him in a different manner, in three papers communicated to the London Mathematical Society. In the first (1873), "On the focal lines of a refracted pencil," he applies Hamilton's characteristic function to determine the focal lines of a thin pencil refracted from one isotropic medium into another at any surface of separation. In the second (1874), "On

Hamilton's characteristic function for a narrow beam of light," he considers the more general question of the passage of a ray from one isotropic medium into another, the two media being separated by a third which may be of a heterogeneous character. He finds the most general form of Hamilton's characteristic function from one point to another, the first being in the medium in which the pencil is incident and the second in the medium in which it is emergent, and both points near the principal ray of the pencil. This result is then applied in two particular cases, viz. to determine the emergent pencil (1) from a spectroscope, (2) from an optical instrument symmetrical about its axis. In the third paper (1875) he resumes the last-mentioned application, discussing this case more fully under a somewhat simplified analysis.

It may be remarked that all these papers are connected by the same idea, which was— first to study the optical effects of the entire instrument without examining the mechanism by which these effects are produced, and then, as in the paper in 1858, to supply whatever data may be necessary by experiments upon the instrument itself.

Connected to some extent with the above papers is an investigation which was published in 1868 "On the cyclide." As the name imports, this paper deals chiefly with the geometrical properties of the surface named, but other matters are touched on, such as its conjugate isothermal functions. Primarily however the investigation is on the orthogonal surfaces to a system of rays passing accurately through two lines. In a footnote to this paper Maxwell describes the stereoscope which he invented and which is now in the Cavendish Laboratory.

In 1868 was also published a short but important article entitled "On the best arrangement for producing a pure spectrum on a screen."

The various papers relating to the stresses experienced by a system of pieces joined together so as to form a frame and acted on by forces form an important group connected with one another. The first in order was "On reciprocal figures and diagrams of forces," published in 1864. It was immediately followed by a paper on a kindred subject, "On the calculation of the equilibrium and stiffness of frames." In the first of these Maxwell demonstrates certain reciprocal properties in the geometry of two polygons which are related to one another in a particular way, and establishes his well-known theorem in Graphical Statics on the stresses in frames. In the second he employs the principle of work to problems connected with the stresses in frames and structures and with the deflections arising from extensions in any of the connecting pieces.

A third paper "On the equilibrium of a spherical envelope," published in 1867, may here be referred to. The author therein considers the stresses set up in the envelope by a system of forces applied at its surface, and ultimately solves the problem for two normal forces applied at any two points. The solution, in which he makes use of the principle of inversion as it is applied in various electrical questions, turns ultimately on the determination of a certain function first introduced by Sir George Airy, and called by Maxwell

Airy's Function of Stress. The methods which in this paper were attended with so much success, seem to have suggested to Maxwell a reconsideration of his former work, with the view of extending the character of the reciprocity therein established. Accordingly in 1870 there appeared his fourth contribution to the subject, "On reciprocal figures, frames and diagrams of forces." This important memoir was published in the Transactions of the Royal Society of Edinburgh, and its author received for it the Keith Prize. He begins with a remarkably beautiful construction for drawing plane reciprocal diagrams, and then proceeds to discuss the geometry and the degrees of freedom and constraint of polyhedral frames, his object being to lead up to the limiting case when the faces of the polyhedron become infinitely small and form parts of a continuous surface. In the course of this work he obtains certain results of a general character relating to inextensible surfaces and certain others of practical utility relating to loaded frames. He then attacks the general problem of representing graphically the internal stress of a body and by an extension of the meaning of "Diagram of Stress," he gives a construction for finding a diagram which has mechanical as well as geometrical reciprocal properties with the figure supposed to be under stress. It is impossible with brevity to give an account of this reciprocity, the development of which in Maxwell's hands forms a very beautiful example of analysis. It will be sufficient to state that under restricted conditions this diagram of stress leads to a solution for the components of stress in terms of a single function analogous to Airy's Function of Stress. In the remaining parts of the memoir there is a discussion of the equations of stress, and it is shewn that the general solution may be expressed in terms of three functions analogous to Airy's single function in two dimensions. These results are then applied to special cases, and in particular the stresses in a horizontal beam with a uniform load on its upper surface are fully investigated.

On the subjects in which Maxwell's investigations were the most numerous it has been thought necessary, in the observations which have been made, to sketch out briefly the connections of the various papers on each subject with one another. It is not however intended to enter into an account of the contents of his other contributions to science, and this is the less necessary as the reader may readily obtain the information he may require in Maxwell's own language. It was usually his habit to explain by way of introduction to any paper his exact position with regard to the subject matter and to give a brief account of the nature of the work he was contributing. There are however several memoirs which though unconnected with others are exceedingly interesting in themselves. Of these the essay on Saturn's Rings will probably be thought the most important as containing the solution of a difficult cosmical problem; there are also various papers on Dynamics, Hydromechanics and subjects of pure mathematics, which are most useful contributions on the subjects of which they treat.

The remaining miscellaneous papers may be classified under the following heads: (a) Lectures and Addresses, (b) Essays or Short Treatises, (c) Biographical Sketches, (d) Criticisms and Reviews.

Class (*a*) comprises his addresses to the British Association, to the London Mathematical Society, the Rede Lecture at Cambridge, his address at the opening of the Cavendish Laboratory and his Lectures at the Royal Institution and to the Chemical Society.

Class (*b*) includes all but one of the articles which he contributed to the *Encyclopædia Britannica* and several others of a kindred character to *Nature*.

Class (*c*) contains such articles as "Faraday" in the *Encyclopædia Britannica* and "Helmholtz" in *Nature*.

Class (*d*) is chiefly occupied with the reviews of scientific books as they were published. These appeared in *Nature* and the most important have been reprinted in these pages.

In some of these writings, particularly those in class (*b*), the author allowed himself a greater latitude in the use of mathematical symbols and processes than in others, as for instance in the article "Capillary Attraction," which is in fact a treatise on that subject treated mathematically. The lectures were upon one or other of the three departments of Physics with which he had mainly occupied himself;—Colour Perception, Action through a Medium, Molecular Physics; and on this account they are the more valuable. In the whole series of these more popular sketches we find the same clear, graceful delineation of principles, the same beauty in arrangement of subject, the same force and precision in expounding proofs and illustrations. The style is simple and singularly free from any kind of haze or obscurity, rising occasionally, as in his lectures, to a strain of subdued eloquence when the emotional aspects of the subject overcome the purely speculative.

The books which were written or edited by Maxwell and published in his lifetime but which are not included in this collection were the "Theory of Heat" (1st edition, 1871); "Electricity and Magnetism" (1st edition, 1873); "The Electrical Researches of the Honourable Henry Cavendish, F.R.S., written between 1771 and 1781, edited from the original manuscripts in the possession of the Duke of Devonshire, K.G." (1879). To these may be added a graceful little introductory treatise on Dynamics entitled "Matter and Motion" (published in 1876 by the Society for promoting Christian Knowledge). Maxwell also contributed part of the British Association Report on Electrical Units which was afterwards published in book form by Fleeming Jenkin.

The "Theory of Heat" appeared in the Text Books of Science series published by Longmans, Green and Co., and was at once hailed as a beautiful exposition of a subject, part of which, and that the most interesting part, the mechanical theory, had as yet but commenced the existence which it owed to the genius and labours of Rankine, Thomson and Clausius. There is a certain charm in Maxwell's treatise, due to the freshness and originality of its expositions which has rendered it a great favourite with students of Heat.

After his death an "Elementary Treatise on Electricity," the greater part of which he had written, was completed by Professor Garnett and published in 1881. The aim of this treatise and its position relatively to his larger work may be gathered from the following extract from Maxwell's preface.

> "In this smaller book I have endeavoured to present, in as compact a form as I can, those phenomena which appear to throw light on the theory of electricity and to use them, each in its place, for the development of electrical ideas in the mind of the reader."

> "In the larger treatise I sometimes made use of methods which I do not think the best in themselves, but without which the student cannot follow the investigations of the founders of the Mathematical Theory of Electricity. I have since become more convinced of the superiority of methods akin to those of Faraday, and have therefore adopted them from the first."

Of the "Electricity and Magnetism" it is difficult to predict the future, but there is no doubt that since its publication it has given direction and colour to the study of Electrical Science. It was the master's last word upon a subject to which he had devoted several years of his life, and most of what he wrote found its proper place in the treatise. Several of the chapters, notably those on Electromagnetism, are practically reproductions of his memoirs in a modified or improved form. The treatise is also remarkable for the handling of the mathematical details no less than for the exposition of physical principles, and is enriched incidentally by chapters of much originality on mathematical subjects touched on in the course of the work. Among these may be mentioned the dissertations on Spherical Harmonics and Lagrange's Equations in Dynamics.

The origin and growth of Maxwell's ideas and conceptions of electrical action, culminating in his treatise where all these ideas are arranged in due connection, form an interesting chapter not only in the history of an individual mind but in the history of electrical science. The importance of Faraday's discoveries and speculations can hardly be overrated in their influence on Maxwell, who tells us that before he began the study of electricity he resolved to read none of the mathematics of the subject till he had first mastered the "Experimental Researches." He was also at first under deep obligations to the ideas contained in the exceedingly important papers of Sir W. Thomson on the analogy between Heat-Conduction and Statical Electricity and on the Mathematical Theory of Electricity in Equilibrium. In his subsequent efforts we must perceive in Maxwell, possessed of Faraday's views and embued with his spirit, a vigorous intellect bringing to bear on a subject still full of obscurity the steady light of patient thought and expending upon it all the resources of a never failing ingenuity.

ROYAL NAVAL COLLEGE,
    GREENWICH,
        August, 1890.

TABLE OF CONTENTS.

ERRATA.

Page 40. In the first of equations (12), second group of terms, read

$$\frac{d^2}{dx^2}\,\delta x + \frac{d^2}{dy^2}\,\delta x + \frac{d^2}{dz^2}\,\delta x$$

instead of

$$\frac{d^2}{dx^2}\,\delta x + \frac{d^2}{dy^2}\,\delta y + \frac{d^2}{dz^2}\,\delta z$$

with corresponding changes in the other two equations.

Page 153, five lines from bottom of page, read 127 instead of 276.

Page 591, four lines from bottom of page the equation should be

$$\frac{d^2M}{da^2} + \frac{d^2M}{db^2} - \frac{1}{a}\frac{dM}{da} = 0.$$

Page 592, in the first line of the expression for L change

$$-\frac{\pi}{3}\cos 2\theta \quad \text{into} \quad -\frac{\pi}{3}\operatorname{cosec} 2\theta.$$

[From the *Proceedings of the Royal Society of Edinburgh,* Vol. II. April, 1846.]

I. *On the Description of Oval Curves, and those having a plurality of Foci; with remarks by Professor Forbes.* Communicated by Professor Forbes.

Mr Clerk Maxwell ingeniously suggests the extension of the common theory of the foci of the conic sections to curves of a higher degree of complication in the following manner :—

(1) As in the ellipse and hyperbola, any point in the curve has the *sum* or *difference* of two lines drawn from two points or *foci* = a constant quantity, so the author infers, that curves to a certain degree analogous, may be described and determined by the condition that the simple distance from one focus *plus* a multiple distance from the other, may be = a constant quantity; or more generally, *m* times the one distance + *n* times the other = constant.

(2) The author devised a simple mechanical means, by the wrapping of a thread round pins, for producing these curves. See Figs. 1 and 2. He

Fig. 1.   Two Foci.   Ratios 1, 2.　　　　　Fig. 2.   Two Foci.   Ratios 2, 3.

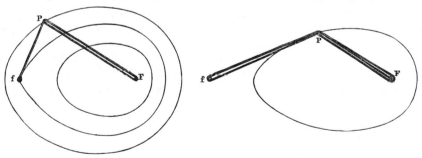

then thought of extending the principle to other curves, whose property should be, that the sum of the simple or multiple distances of any point of the curve from three or more points or foci, should be = a constant quantity; and this, too, he has effected mechanically, by a very simple arrangement of a string of given length passing round three or more fixed pins, and constraining a tracing point, P. See Fig. 3. Farther, the author regards curves

Fig. 3.   Three Foci.   Ratios of Equality.

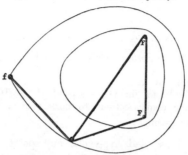

of the first kind as constituting a particular class of curves of the second kind, two or more foci coinciding in one, a focus in which two strings meet being considered a double focus; when three strings meet a treble focus, &c.

Professor Forbes observed that the equation to curves of the first class is easily found, having the form

$$\sqrt{x^2+y^2}=a+b\sqrt{(x-c)^2+y^2},$$

which is that of the curve known under the name of the First Oval of Descartes*. Mr Maxwell had already observed that when one of the foci was at an infinite distance (or the thread moved parallel to itself, and was confined in respect of length by the edge of a board), a curve resembling an ellipse was traced; from which property Professor Forbes was led first to infer the identity of the oval with the Cartesian oval, which is well known to have this property. But the simplest analogy of all is that derived from the method of description, r and r' being the radients to any point of the curve from the two foci;

$$mr+nr'=\text{constant},$$

which in fact at once expresses on the undulatory theory of light the optical character of the surface in question, namely, that light diverging from one focus F without the medium, shall be correctly convergent at another point f

* Herschel, *On Light*, Art. 232; Lloyd, *On Light and Vision*, Chap. VII.

within it; and in this case the ratio $\dfrac{n}{m}$ expresses the index of refraction of the medium*.

If we denote by *the power of either focus* the number of strings leading to it by Mr Maxwell's construction, and if one of the foci be removed to an infinite distance, if the powers of the two foci be *equal* the curve is a parabola; if the power of the nearer focus be *greater* than the other, the curve is an ellipse; if the power of the infinitely distant focus be the greater, the curve is a hyperbola. The first case evidently corresponds to the case of the reflection of parallel rays to a focus, the velocity being unchanged after reflection; the second, to the refraction of parallel rays to a focus in a dense medium (in which light moves slower); the third case to refraction into a rarer medium.

The ovals of Descartes were described in his *Geometry*, where he has also given a mechanical method of describing one of them†, but only in a particular case, and the method is less simple than Mr Maxwell's. The *demonstration* of the optical properties was given by Newton in the *Principia*, Book I., prop. 97, by the law of the sines; and by Huyghens in 1690, on the Theory of Undulations in his *Traité de la Lumière*. It probably has not been suspected that so easy and elegant a method exists of describing these curves by the use of a thread and pins whenever the powers of the foci are commensurable. For instance, the curve, Fig. 2, drawn with powers 3 and 2 respectively, give the proper form for a refracting surface of a glass, whose index of refraction is 1·50, in order that rays diverging from f may be refracted to F.

As to the higher classes of curves with three or more focal points, we cannot at present invest them with equally clear and curious physical properties, but the method of drawing a curve by so simple a contrivance, which shall satisfy the condition

$$mr + nr' + pr'' + \&c. = \text{constant},$$

is in itself not a little interesting; and if we regard, with Mr Maxwell, the ovals above described, as the limiting case of the others by the coalescence of two or more foci, we have a farther generalization of the same kind as that so highly recommended by Montucla‡, by which Descartes elucidated the conic sections as particular cases of his oval curves.

---

* This was perfectly well shewn by Huyghens in his *Traité de la Lumière*, p. 111.   (1690.)
† Edit. 1683.   *Geometria*, Lib. II. p. 54.
‡ *Histoire des Mathématiques.*   First Edit. II. 102.

[From the *Transactions of the Royal Society of Edinburgh*, Vol. XVI. Part V.]

II. *On the Theory of Rolling Curves.* Communicated by the Rev. Professor KELLAND.

THERE is an important geometrical problem which proposes to find a curve having a given relation to a series of curves described according to a given law. This is the problem of Trajectories in its general form.

The series of curves is obtained from the general equation to a curve by the variation of its parameters. In the general case, this variation may change the form of the curve, but, in the case which we are about to consider, the curve is changed only in position.

This change of position takes place partly by rotation, and partly by transference through space. The rolling of one curve on another is an example of this compound motion.

As examples of the way in which the new curve may be related to the series of curves, we may take the following :—

1. The new curve may cut the series of curves at a given angle. When this angle becomes zero, the curve is the envelope of the series of curves.

2. It may pass through corresponding points in the series of curves. There are many other relations which may be imagined, but we shall confine our attention to this, partly because it affords the means of tracing various curves, and partly on account of the connection which it has with many geometrical problems.

Therefore the subject of this paper will be the consideration of the relations of three curves, one of which is fixed, while the second rolls upon it and traces the third. The subject of rolling curves is by no means a new one. The first idea of the cycloid is attributed to Aristotle, and involutes and evolutes have been long known.

In the *History of the Royal Academy of Sciences* for 1704, page 97, there is a memoir entitled "Nouvelle formation des Spirales," by M. Varignon, in which he shews how to construct a polar curve from a curve referred to rectangular co-ordinates by substituting the radius vector for the abscissa, and a circular arc for the ordinate. After each curve, he gives the curve into which it is "unrolled," by which he means the curve which the spiral must be rolled upon in order that its pole may trace a straight line; but as this is not the principal subject of his paper, he does not discuss it very fully.

There is also a memoir by M. de la Hire, in the volume for 1706, Part II., page 489, entitled "Methode generale pour réduire toutes les Lignes courbes à des Roulettes, leur generatrice ou leur base étant donnée telle qu'on voudra."

M. de la Hire treats curves as if they were polygons, and gives geometrical constructions for finding the fixed curve or the rolling curve, the other two being given; but he does not work any examples.

In the volume for 1707, page 79, there is a paper entitled, "Methode generale pour déterminer la nature des Courbes formées par le roulement de toutes sortes de Courbes sur une autre Courbe quelconque." Par M. Nicole.

M. Nicole takes the equations of the three curves referred to rectangular co-ordinates, and finds three general equations to connect them. He takes the tracing-point either at the origin of the co-ordinates of the rolled curve or not. He then shews how these equations may be simplified in several particular cases. These cases are—

(1) When the tracing-point is the origin of the rolled curve.
(2) When the fixed curve is the same as the rolling curve.
(3) When both of these conditions are satisfied.
(4) When the fixed line is straight.

He then says, that if we roll a geometric curve on itself, we obtain a new geometric curve, and that we may thus obtain an infinite number of geometric curves.

The examples which he gives of the application of his method are all taken from the cycloid and epicycloid, except one which relates to a parabola, rolling on itself, and tracing a cissoid with its vertex. The reason of so small a number of examples being worked may be, that it is not easy to eliminate the co-ordinates of the fixed and rolling curves from his equations.

The case in which one curve rolling on another produces a circle is treated of in Willis's *Principles of Mechanism*. Class C. *Rolling Contact*.

He employs the same method of finding the one curve from the other which is used here, and he attributes it to Euler (see the *Acta Petropolitana*, Vol. v.).

Thus, nearly all the simple cases have been treated of by different authors; but the subject is still far from being exhausted, for the equations have been applied to very few curves, and we may easily obtain new and elegant properties from any curve we please.

Almost all the more notable curves may be thus linked together in a great variety of ways, so that there are scarcely two curves, however dissimilar, between which we cannot form a chain of connected curves.

This will appear in the list of examples given at the end of this paper.

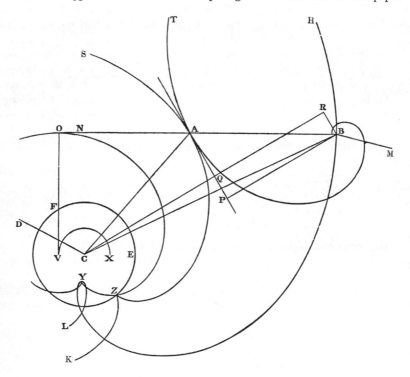

Let there be a curve *KAS*, whose pole is at *C*.

Let the angle $DCA = \theta_1$ and $CA = r_1$ and let
$$\theta_1 = \phi_1(r_1).$$
Let this curve remain fixed to the paper.

Let there be another curve BAT, whose pole is B.

Let the angle $MBA = \theta_2$, and $BA = r_2$, and let
$$\theta_2 = \phi_2(r_2).$$
Let this curve roll along the curve KAS without slipping.

Then the pole B will describe a third curve, whose pole is C.

Let the angle $DCB = \theta_3$, and $CB = r_3$, and let
$$\theta_3 = \phi_3(r_3).$$

We have here six unknown quantities $\theta_1 \theta_2 \theta_3 r_1 r_2 r_3$; but we have only three equations given to connect them, therefore the other three must be sought for in the enunciation.

But before proceeding to the investigation of these three equations, we must premise that the three curves will be denominated as follows:—

The Fixed Curve, Equation, $\theta_1 = \phi_1(r_1)$.

The Rolled Curve, Equation, $\theta_2 = \phi_2(r_2)$.

The Traced Curve, Equation, $\theta_3 = \phi_3(r_3)$.

When it is more convenient to make use of equations between rectangular co-ordinates, we shall use the letters $x_1 y_1$, $x_2 y_2$, $x_3 y_3$. We shall always employ the letters $s_1 s_2 s_3$ to denote the length of the curve from the pole, $p_1 p_2 p_3$ for the perpendiculars from the pole on the tangent, and $q_1 q_2 q_3$ for the intercepted part of the tangent.

Between these quantities, we have the following equations:—

$$r = \sqrt{x^2 + y^2}, \qquad\qquad \theta = \tan^{-1}\frac{y}{x},$$

$$x = r\cos\theta, \qquad\qquad y = r\sin\theta,$$

$$s = \int \sqrt{r^2 + \left(\frac{dr}{d\theta}\right)^2}\, d\theta, \qquad\qquad s = \int \sqrt{1 + \left(\frac{dy}{dx}\right)^2}\, dx,$$

$$p = \frac{r^2}{\sqrt{r^2 + \left(\frac{dr}{d\theta}\right)^2}}, \qquad\qquad p = \frac{y\,dx - x\,dy}{\sqrt{(dx)^2 + (dy)^2}},$$

$$q = \frac{r\frac{dr}{d\theta}}{\sqrt{r^2 + \left(\frac{dr}{d\theta}\right)^2}}, \qquad q = \frac{x\,dx + y\,dy}{\sqrt{(dx)^2 + (dy)^2}},$$

$$R = \frac{\left\{r^2 + \left(\frac{dr}{d\theta}\right)^2\right\}^{\frac{3}{2}}}{r^2 + 2\left(\frac{dr}{d\theta}\right)^2 - r\frac{d^2r}{d\theta^2}}, \qquad R = \frac{\left\{1 + \left(\frac{dy}{dx}\right)^2\right\}^{\frac{3}{2}}}{\frac{d^2y}{dx^2}}.$$

We come now to consider the three equations of rolling which are involved in the enunciation. Since the second curve rolls upon the first *without slipping*, the length of the fixed curve at the point of contact is the measure of the length of the rolled curve, therefore we have the following equation to connect the fixed curve and the rolled curve—

$$s_1 = s_2.$$

Now, by combining this equation with the two equations

$$\begin{cases} \theta_1 = \phi_1(r_1) \\ \theta_2 = \phi_2(r_2) \end{cases} \text{ or } \begin{cases} x_1 = \psi_1(y_1) \\ x_2 = \psi_2(y_2) \end{cases},$$

it is evident that from any of the four quantities $\theta_1 r_1 \theta_2 r_2$ or $x_1 y_1 x_2 y_2$, we can obtain the other three, therefore we may consider these quantities as known functions of each other.

Since the curve *rolls* on the fixed curve, they must have a common tangent.

Let PA be this tangent, draw BP, CQ perpendicular to PA, produce CQ, and draw BR perpendicular to it, then we have $CA = r_1$, $BA = r_2$, and $CB = r_3$; $CQ = p_1$, $PB = p_2$, and $BN = p_3$; $AQ = q_1$, $AP = q_2$, and $CN = q_3$.

Also
$$r_3^2 = CB^2 = CR^2 + RB^2 = (CQ + PB)^2 + (AP - AQ)^2$$
$$= (p_1 + p_2)^2 + (q_2 - q_1)^2$$
$$= p_1^2 + 2p_1p_2 + p_2^2 + r_2^2 - p_2^2 - 2q_1q_2 + r_1^2 - p_1^2$$
$$r_3^2 = r_1^2 + r_2^2 + 2p_1p_2 - 2q_1q_2.$$

Since the first curve is fixed to the paper, we may find the angle θ_3.

Thus
$$\theta_3 = DCB = DCA + ACQ + RCB$$

$$= \theta_1 + \tan^{-1}\frac{q_1}{p_1} + \tan^{-1}\frac{RB}{RC}$$

$$\theta_3 = \theta_1 + \tan^{-1}\frac{dr_1}{r_1 d\theta_1} + \tan^{-1}\frac{q_2 - q_1}{p_2 + p_1}.$$

Thus we have found three independent equations, which, together with the equations of the curves, make up six equations, of which each may be deduced from the others. There is an equation connecting the radii of curvature of the three curves which is sometimes of use.

The angle through which the rolled curve revolves during the description of the element ds_3, is equal to the angle of contact of the fixed curve and the rolling curve, or to the sum of their curvatures,

$$\therefore \frac{ds_3}{r_2} = \frac{ds_1}{R_1} + \frac{ds_2}{R_2}.$$

But the radius of the rolled curve has revolved in the opposite direction through an angle equal to $d\theta_2$, therefore the angle between two successive positions of r_2 is equal to $\frac{ds_3}{r_2} - d\theta_2$. Now this angle is the angle between two successive positions of the normal to the traced curve, therefore, if O be the centre of curvature of the traced curve, it is the angle which ds_3 or ds_1 subtends at O. Let $OA = T$, then

$$\frac{ds_3}{R_3} = \frac{r_2 d\theta_2}{T} = \frac{ds_3}{r_2} - d\theta_2 = \frac{ds_2}{R_1} + \frac{ds_2}{R_2} - d\theta_2,$$

$$\therefore r_2 \frac{d\theta_2}{ds_2} \frac{1}{T} = \frac{1}{R_1} + \frac{1}{R_2} - \frac{d\theta_2}{ds_2},$$

$$\therefore \frac{p_2}{r_2} \left(\frac{1}{T} + \frac{1}{r_2} \right) = \frac{1}{R_1} + \frac{1}{R_2}.$$

As an example of the use of this equation, we may examine a property of the logarithmic spiral.

In this curve, $p = mr$, and $R = \frac{r}{m}$, therefore if the rolled curve be the logarithmic spiral

$$m \left(\frac{1}{T} + \frac{1}{r_2} \right) = \frac{1}{R_1} + \frac{m}{r_2},$$

$$\frac{m}{T} = \frac{1}{R_1},$$

therefore AO in the figure $= mR_1$, and $\frac{AO}{R_1} = m$.

Let the locus of O, or the evolute of the traced curve $LYBH$, be the curve OZY, and let the evolute of the fixed curve $KZAS$ be FEZ, and let us consider FEZ as the fixed curve, and OZY as the traced curve.

Then in the triangles BPA, AOF, we have $OAF = PBA$, and $\dfrac{OA}{AF} = m = \dfrac{BP}{AB}$, therefore the triangles are similar, and $FOA = APB = \dfrac{\pi}{2}$, therefore OF is perpendicular to OA, the tangent to the curve OZY, therefore OF is the radius of the curve which when rolled on FEZ traces OZY, and the angle which the curve makes with this radius is $OFA = PAB = \sin^{-1} m$, which is constant, therefore the curve, which, when rolled on FEZ, traces OZY, is the logarithmic spiral. Thus we have proved the following proposition: "The involute of the curve traced by the pole of a logarithmic spiral which rolls upon any curve, is the curve traced by the pole of the same logarithmic spiral when rolled on the involute of the primary curve."

It follows from this, that if we roll on any curve a curve having the property $p_1 = m_1 r_1$, and roll another curve having $p_2 = m_2 r_2$ on the curve traced, and so on, it is immaterial in what order we roll these curves. Thus, if we roll a logarithmic spiral, in which $p = mr$, on the nth involute of a circle whose radius is a, the curve traced is the $n+1$th involute of a circle whose radius is $\sqrt{1 - m^2}$.

Or, if we roll successively m logarithmic spirals, the resulting curve is the $n+m$th involute of a circle, whose radius is

$$a \sqrt{1 - m_1^2} \ \sqrt{1 - m_2^2}, \ \sqrt{\&c.}$$

We now proceed to the cases in which the solution of the problem may be simplified. This simplification is generally effected by the consideration that the radius vector of the rolled curve is the normal drawn from the traced curve to the fixed curve.

In the case in which the curve is rolled on a straight line, the perpendicular on the tangent of the rolled curve is the distance of the tracing point from the straight line; therefore, if the traced curve be defined by an equation in x_3 and y_3,

$$x_3 = p_2 = \frac{r_2^2}{\sqrt{r_2^2 + \left(\dfrac{dr_2}{d\theta_2}\right)^2}} \quad \dots\dots\dots\dots\dots\dots\dots\dots (1),$$

and

$$r_2 = x_3 \sqrt{\left(\dfrac{dx_3}{dy_3}\right)^2 + 1} \quad \dots\dots\dots\dots\dots\dots (2).$$

By substituting for r_2 in the first equation, its value, as derived from the second, we obtain

$$x_3^2 \left(\frac{dx_3}{dy_3}\right)^2 \left[\left(\frac{dx_3}{dy_3}\right)^2 + 1\right] = \left(\frac{dr_2}{d\theta_2}\right)^2.$$

If we know the equation to the rolled curve, we may find $\left(\frac{dr_2}{d\theta_2}\right)^2$ in terms of r_2, then by substituting for r_2 its value in the second equation, we have an equation containing x_3 and $\frac{dx_3}{dy_3}$, from which we find the value of $\frac{dx_3}{dy_3}$ in terms of x_3; the integration of this gives the equation of the traced curve.

As an example, we may find the curve traced by the pole of a hyperbolic spiral which rolls on a straight line.

The equation of the rolled curve is $\theta_2 = \frac{a}{r_2}$,

$$\therefore \left(\frac{dr_2}{d\theta_2}\right)^2 = \frac{r_2^4}{a^2}$$

$$= x_3^2 \left(\frac{dx_3}{dy_3}\right)^2 \left[\left(\frac{dx_3}{dy_3}\right)^2 + 1\right] = \frac{x_3^4}{a^2} \left[\left(\frac{dx_3}{dy_3}\right)^2 + 1\right]^2,$$

$$\therefore a^2 \left(\frac{dx_3}{dy_3}\right)^2 = x_3^2 \left[\left(\frac{dx_3}{dy_3}\right)^2 + 1\right],$$

$$\therefore \frac{dx_3}{dy_3} = \frac{x_3}{\sqrt{a^2 - x_3^2}}.$$

This is the differential equation of the tractory of the straight line, which is the curve traced by the pole of the hyperbolic spiral.

By eliminating x_3 in the two equations, we obtain

$$\frac{dr_2}{d\theta_2} = r_2 \left(\frac{dx_3}{dy_3}\right).$$

This equation serves to determine the rolled curve when the traced curve is given.

As an example we shall find the curve, which being rolled on a straight line, traces a common catenary.

Let the equation to the catenary be

$$x = \frac{a}{2} \left(e^{\frac{y}{a}} + e^{-\frac{y}{a}}\right).$$

Then
$$\frac{dx_3}{dy_3} = \sqrt{\frac{x_3^2}{a^2} - 1},$$

$$\therefore \left(\frac{dr_2}{d\theta_2}\right)^2 = \frac{r_2^2}{a^2} \frac{r_2^4}{\left(\frac{dr_2}{d\theta_2}\right)^2 + r_2^2} - r_2^2,$$

$$\therefore \left[\left(\frac{dr_2}{d\theta_2}\right)^2 + r_2^2\right]^2 = \left(\frac{r_2^3}{a}\right)^2,$$

$$\therefore \left(\frac{dr_2}{d\theta_2}\right)^2 = \frac{r_2^2}{a}\,(r_2 - a),$$

$$\therefore \frac{d\theta}{dr} = \frac{1}{r\sqrt{\dfrac{r}{a} - 1}},$$

then by integration
$$\theta = \cos^{-1}\left(\frac{2a}{r} - 1\right),$$

$$r = \frac{2a}{1 + \cos\theta}.$$

This is the polar equation of the parabola, the focus being the pole; therefore, if we roll a parabola on a straight line, its focus will trace a catenary.

The rectangular equation of this parabola is $x^2 = 4ay$, and we shall now consider what curve must be rolled along the axis of y to trace the parabola.

By the second equation (2),

$$r_2 = x_3 \sqrt{\frac{4a^2}{x_3^2} + 1}, \quad \text{but } x_3 = p_2,$$

$$\therefore r_2 = \sqrt{4a^2 + p_2^2},$$

$$\therefore r_2^2 = p_2^2 + 4a^2,$$

$$\therefore 2a = \sqrt{r_2^2 - p_2^2} = q_2,$$

but q_2 is the perpendicular on the normal, therefore the normal to the curve always touches a circle whose radius is $2a$, therefore the curve is the involute of this circle.

Therefore we have the following method of describing a catenary by continued motion.

Describe a circle whose radius is twice the parameter of the catenary; roll a straight line on this circle, then any point in the line will describe an involute of the circle; roll this curve on a straight line, and the centre of the circle will describe a parabola; roll this parabola on a straight line, and its focus will trace the catenary required.

We come now to the case in which a straight line rolls on a curve.

When the tracing-point is in the straight line, the problem becomes that of involutes and evolutes, which we need not enter upon; and when the tracing-point is not in the straight line, the calculation is somewhat complex; we shall therefore consider only the relations between the curves described in the first and second cases.

Definition.—The curve which cuts at a given angle all the circles of a given radius whose centres are in a given curve, is called a tractory of the given curve.

Let a straight line roll on a curve A, and let a point in the straight line describe a curve B, and let another point, whose distance from the first point is b, and from the straight line a, describe a curve C, then it is evident that the curve B cuts the circle whose centre is in C, and whose radius is b, at an angle whose sine is equal to $\dfrac{a}{b}$, therefore the curve B is a tractory of the curve C.

When $a = b$, the curve B is the orthogonal tractory of the curve C. If tangents equal to a be drawn to the curve B, they will be terminated in the curve C; and if one end of a thread be carried along the curve C, the other end will trace the curve B.

When $a = 0$, the curves B and C are both involutes of the curve A, they are always equidistant from each other, and if a circle, whose radius is b, be rolled on the one, its centre will trace the other.

If the curve A is such that, if the distance between two points measured along the curve is equal to b, the two points are similarly situate, then the curve B is the same with the curve C. Thus, the curve A may be a re-entrant curve, the circumference of which is equal to b.

When the curve A is a circle, the curves B and C are always the same.

The equations between the radii of curvature become

$$\frac{1}{T} + \frac{1}{r_2} = \frac{r}{aR_1}.$$

When $a = 0$, $T = 0$, or the centre of curvature of the curve B is at the point of contact. Now, the normal to the curve C passes through this point, therefore—

"The normal to any curve passes through the centre of curvature of its tractory."

In the next case, one curve, by rolling on another, produces a straight line. Let this straight line be the axis of y, then, since the radius of the rolled curve is perpendicular to it, and terminates in the fixed curve, and since these curves have a common tangent, we have this equation,

$$x_1 \frac{dy_1}{dx_1} = r_2^2 \frac{d\theta_2}{dr_2}.$$

If the equation of the rolled curve be given, find $\frac{d\theta_2}{dr_2}$ in terms of r_2, substitute x_1 for r_2, and multiply by x_1, equate the result to $\frac{dy_1}{dx_1}$, and integrate.

Thus, if the equation of the rolled curve be

$$\theta = Ar^{-n} + \&c. + Kr^{-2} + Lr^{-1} + M \log r + Nr + \&c. + Zr^n,$$

$$\frac{d\theta}{dr} = -nAr^{-(n+1)} - \&c. - 2Kr^{-3} - Lr^{-2} + Mr^{-1} + N + \&c. + nZr^{n-1},$$

$$\frac{dy}{dx} = -nAx^{-n} - \&c. - 2Kx^{-2} - Lx^{-1} + M + Nx + \&c. + nZx^n,$$

$$y = \frac{n}{n-1}Ax^{1-n} + \&c. + 2Kx^{-1} - L \log x + Mx + \tfrac{1}{2}Nx^2 + \&c. + \frac{n}{n+1}Zx^{n+1},$$

which is the equation of the fixed curve.

If the equation of the fixed curve be given, find $\frac{dy}{dx}$ in terms of x, substitute r for x, and divide by r, equate the result to $\frac{d\theta}{dr}$, and integrate.

Thus, if the fixed curve be the orthogonal tractory of the straight line, whose equation is

$$y = a \log \frac{x}{a + \sqrt{a^2 - x^2}} + \sqrt{a^2 - x^2},$$

$$\frac{dy}{dx} = \frac{\sqrt{a^2 - x^2}}{x},$$

$$\frac{d\theta}{dr} = \frac{\sqrt{a^2 - r^2}}{r^2},$$

$$\theta = \cos^{-1}\frac{r}{a} - \sqrt{\frac{a^2}{r^2} - 1},$$

this is the equation to the orthogonal tractory of a circle whose diameter is equal to the constant tangent of the fixed curve, and its constant tangent equal to half that of the fixed curve.

This property of the tractory of the circle may be proved geometrically, thus—Let P be the centre of a circle whose radius is PD, and let CD be a line constantly equal to the radius. Let BCP be the curve described by the point C when the point D is moved along the circumference of the circle, then if tangents equal to CD be drawn to the curve, their extremities will be in the circle. Let ACH be the curve on which BCP rolls, and let OPE be the straight line traced by the pole, let CDE be the common tangent, let it cut the circle in D, and the straight line in E.

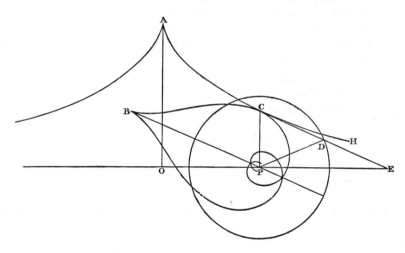

Then $CD = PD$, ∴ $\angle DCP = \angle DPC$, and CP is perpendicular to OE, ∴ $\angle CPE = \angle DCP + \angle DEP$. Take away $\angle DCP = \angle DPC$, and there remains $DPE = DEP$, ∴ $PD = DE$, ∴ $CE = 2PD$.

Therefore the curve ACH has a constant tangent equal to the diameter of the circle, therefore ACH is the orthogonal tractory of the straight line, which is the tractrix or equitangential curve.

The operation of finding the fixed curve from the rolled curve is what Sir John Leslie calls "divesting a curve of its radiated structure."

The method of finding the curve which must be rolled on a circle to trace a given curve is mentioned here because it generally leads to a double result, for the normal to the traced curve cuts the circle in two points, either of which may be a point in the rolled curve.

Thus, if the traced curve be the involute of a circle concentric with the given circle, the rolled curve is one of two similar logarithmic spirals.

If the curve traced be the spiral of Archimedes, the rolled curve may be either the hyperbolic spiral or the straight line.

In the next case, one curve rolls on another and traces a circle.

Since the curve traced is a circle, the distance between the poles of the fixed curve and the rolled curve is always the same; therefore, if we fix the rolled curve and roll the fixed curve, the curve traced will still be a circle, and, if we fix the poles of both the curves, we may roll them on each other without friction.

Let a be the radius of the traced circle, then the sum or difference of the radii of the other curves is equal to a, and the angles which they make with the radius at the point of contact are equal,

$$\therefore \ r_1 = \pm(a \pm r_2) \text{ and } r_1 \frac{d\theta_1}{dr_1} = r_2 \frac{d\theta_2}{dr_2}.$$

$$\therefore \ \frac{d\theta_2}{dr_2} = \frac{\pm(a \pm r_2)}{r_2} \frac{d\theta_1}{dr_1}.$$

If we know the equation between θ_1 and r_1, we may find $\frac{d\theta_1}{dr_1}$ in terms of r_1, substitute $\pm(a \pm r_2)$ for r_1, multiply by $\frac{\pm(a \pm r_2)}{r_2}$, and integrate.

Thus, if the equation between θ_1 and r_1 be

$$r_1 = a \sec \theta_1,$$

which is the polar equation of a straight line touching the traced circle whose equation is $r = a$, then

$$\frac{d\theta}{dr_1} = \frac{a}{r_1 \sqrt{r_1^2 - a^2}}$$

$$= \frac{a}{(r_2 \pm a) \sqrt{r_2^2 \pm 2r_2 a}},$$

$$\frac{d\theta_2}{dr_2} = \frac{r_2 \pm a}{r_2} \frac{a}{(r_2 \pm a) \sqrt{r_2^2 \pm 2r_2 a}}$$

$$= \frac{a}{r_2 \sqrt{r_2^2 \pm 2ar_2}},$$

$$\theta_2 = \pm \sqrt{1 \pm 2\frac{a}{r_2}},$$

$$r_2 = \frac{2a}{\theta_2^2 - 1} = \frac{2a}{\theta^2 - 1}.$$

Now, since the rolling curve is a straight line, and the tracing point is not in its direction, we may apply to this example the observations which have been made upon tractories.

Let, therefore, the curve $r = \dfrac{2a}{\theta^2 - 1}$ be denoted by A, its involute by B, and the circle traced by C, then B is the tractory of C; therefore the involute of the curve $r = \dfrac{2a}{\theta^2 - 1}$ is the tractory of the circle, the equation of which is $\theta = \cos^{-1}\dfrac{r}{a} - \sqrt{\dfrac{a^2}{r^2} - 1}$. The curve whose equation is $r = \dfrac{2a}{\theta^2 - 1}$ seems to be among spirals what the catenary is among curves whose equations are between rectangular co-ordinates; for, if we represent the vertical direction by the radius vector, the tangent of the angle which the curve makes with this line is proportional to the length of the curve reckoned from the origin; the point at the distance a from a straight line rolled on this curve generates a circle, and when rolled on the catenary produces a straight line; the involute of this curve is the tractory of the circle, and that of the catenary is the tractory of the straight line, and the tractory of the circle rolled on that of the straight line traces the straight line; if this curve is rolled on the catenary, it produces the straight line touching the catenary at its vertex; the method of drawing tangents is the same as in the catenary, namely, by describing a circle whose radius is a on the production of the radius vector, and drawing a tangent to the circle from the given point.

In the next case the rolled curve is the same as the fixed curve. It is evident that the traced curve will be similar to the locus of the intersection of the tangent with the perpendicular from the pole; the magnitude, however, of the traced curve will be double that of the other curve; therefore, if we call $r_0 = \phi_0 \theta_0$ the equation to the fixed curve, $r_1 = \phi_1 \theta_1$ that of the traced curve, we have

$$r_1 = 2p_0, \qquad \theta_1 = \theta_0 - \cos^{-1} \frac{p_0}{r_0} = \theta_0 - \frac{\pi}{2} + \sin^{-1} \frac{p_0}{r_0},$$

also,
$$\frac{p_1}{r_1} = \frac{p_0}{r_0}.$$

Similarly, $\quad r_2 = 2p_1 = 2r_1 \dfrac{p_0}{r_0} = 4 \dfrac{p_0^2}{r_0} \; 4r_0 \left(\dfrac{p_0}{r_0}\right)^2, \quad \theta_2 = \theta_0 - 2\cos^{-1} \dfrac{p_0}{r_0}.$

Similarly, $\quad r_n = 2p_{n-1} = 2r_{n-1} \dfrac{p_0}{r_0} \;$ &c. $\; = 2^n r_0 \left(\dfrac{p_0}{r_0}\right)^n,$

and
$$\frac{p_n}{r_n} = \frac{p_0}{r_0},$$

$$\theta_n = \theta_0 - n \cos^{-1} \frac{p_0}{r_0},$$

$$\theta_n = \theta_0 - n \cos^{-1} \frac{p_n}{r_n}. \qquad .$$

Let θ_n become θ_n^1; θ_0, θ_0^1 and $\dfrac{p_0}{r_0}$, $\dfrac{p_0^1}{r_0^1}$. Let $\theta_n^1 - \theta_n = a,$

$$\theta_n^1 = \theta_0^1 - n \cos^{-1} \frac{p^1}{r_n^1},$$

$$a = \theta_n^1 - \theta_n = \theta_0^1 - \theta_0 - n \cos^{-1} \frac{p_n^1}{r_n^1} + n \cos^{-1} \frac{p_n}{r_n};$$

$$\therefore \; \cos^{-1} \frac{p_n}{r_n} - \cos^{-1} \frac{p_n^1}{r_n^1} = \frac{a}{n} + \frac{\theta_0 - \theta_0^1}{n}.$$

Now, $\cos^{-1} \dfrac{p_n}{r_n}$ is the complement of the angle at which the curve cuts the radius vector, and $\cos^{-1} \dfrac{p_n}{r_n} - \cos^{-1} \dfrac{p_n^{1}}{r_n^{1}}$ is the variation of this angle when θ_n varies by an angle equal to a. Let this variation $= \phi$; then if $\theta_0 - \theta_0^{1} = \beta$,

$$\phi = \frac{a}{n} + \frac{\beta}{n}.$$

Now, if n increases, ϕ will diminish; and if n becomes infinite,

$$\phi = \frac{a}{\infty} + \frac{\beta}{\infty} = 0 \text{ when } a \text{ and } \beta \text{ are finite.}$$

Therefore, when n is infinite, ϕ vanishes; therefore the curve cuts the radius vector at a constant angle; therefore the curve is the logarithmic spiral.

Therefore, if any curve be rolled on itself, and the operation repeated an infinite number of times, the resulting curve is the logarithmic spiral.

Hence we may find, analytically, the curve which, being rolled on itself, traces itself.

For the curve which has this property, if rolled on itself, and the operation repeated an infinite number of times, will still trace itself.

But, by this proposition, the resulting curve is the logarithmic spiral; therefore the curve required is the logarithmic spiral. As an example of a curve rolling on itself, we will take the curve whose equation is

$$r_0 = 2^n a \left(\cos \frac{\theta_0}{n} \right)^n.$$

Here

$$-\frac{dr_0}{d\theta_0} = 2^n a \left(\sin \frac{\theta_0}{n} \right) \left(\cos \frac{\theta_0}{n} \right)^{n-1};$$

$$\therefore r_1 = 2p_0 = 2 \frac{2^{2n} a^2 \left(\cos \dfrac{\theta_0}{n} \right)^{2n}}{\sqrt{2^{2n} a^2 \left(\cos \dfrac{\theta_0}{n} \right)^{2n} + 2^{2n} a^2 \left(\sin \dfrac{\theta_0}{n} \right) \left(\cos \dfrac{\theta_0}{n} \right)^{2n-2}}},$$

$$r_1 = 2 \frac{2^n a \left(\cos \dfrac{\theta_0}{n} \right)^{n+1}}{\sqrt{\left(\cos \dfrac{\theta_0}{n} \right)^2 + \left(\sin \dfrac{\theta_0}{n} \right)^2}} = 2^{n+1} a \left(\cos \frac{\theta_0}{n} \right)^{n+1}.$$

Now $\theta_1 - \theta_0 = -\cos^{-1}\dfrac{p_0}{r_0} = -\cos^{-1}\cos\dfrac{\theta_0}{n} = \dfrac{\theta_0}{n}$,

$$\therefore \;\; \theta_0 = \theta_1 \dfrac{n}{n+1} ;$$

substituting this value of θ_0 in the expression for r_1,

$$r_1 = 2^{n+1}a\left(\cos\dfrac{\theta_1}{n+1}\right)^{n+1},$$

similarly, if the operation be repeated m times, the resulting curve is

$$r_m = 2^{n+m}a\left(\cos\dfrac{\theta_m}{n+m}\right)^{n+m}$$

When $n = 1$, the curve is

$$r = 2a\cos\theta,$$

the equation to a circle, the pole being in the circumference.

When $n = 2$, it is the equation to the cardioid

$$r = 4a\left(\cos\dfrac{\theta}{2}\right)^2.$$

In order to obtain the cardioid from the circle, we roll the circle upon itself, and thus obtain it by one operation; but there is an operation which, being performed on a circle, and again on the resulting curve, will produce a cardioid, and the intermediate curve between the circle and cardioid is

$$r = 2^{\frac{3}{2}}a\left(\cos\dfrac{2\theta}{3}\right)^{\frac{3}{2}}.$$

As the operation of rolling a curve on itself is represented by changing n into $(n+1)$ in the equation, so this operation may be represented by changing n into $(n+\frac{1}{2})$.

Similarly there may be many other fractional operations performed upon the curves comprehended under the equation

$$r = 2^n a\left(\cos\dfrac{\theta}{n}\right)^n.$$

We may also find the curve, which, being rolled on itself, will produce a given curve, by making $n = -1$.

We may likewise prove by the same method as before, that the result of performing this inverse operation an infinite number of times is the logarithmic spiral.

As an example of the inverse method, let the traced line be straight, let its equation be

$$r_0 = 2a \sec \theta_0,$$

then

$$\frac{p_{-1}}{r_{-1}} = \frac{p_0}{r_0} = \frac{2a}{r_0} = \frac{2a}{2p_{-1}},$$

$$\therefore p^2_{-1} = a r_{-1},$$

therefore suppressing the suffix,

$$\frac{r^4}{r^2 + \dfrac{dr^2}{d\theta^2}} = ar,$$

$$\therefore \left(\frac{dr}{d\theta}\right)^2 = \frac{r^3}{a} - r^2,$$

$$\therefore \frac{d\theta}{dr} = \frac{1}{r\sqrt{\dfrac{r}{a} - 1}},$$

$$\therefore \theta = \cos^{-1}\left(\frac{2a}{r} - 1\right),$$

$$r = \frac{2a}{1 - \cos\theta},$$

he polar equation of the parabola whose parameter is $4a$.

The last case which we shall here consider affords the means of constructing wo wheels whose centres are fixed, and which shall roll on each other, so that he angle described by the first shall be a given function of the angle described y the second.

Let $\theta_2 = \phi\theta_1$, then $r_1 + r_2 = a$, and $\dfrac{d\theta_2}{d\theta_1} = \dfrac{r_1}{r_2}$;

$$\therefore \frac{d(\phi\theta_1)}{d\theta_1} = \frac{r_1}{a - r_1}.$$

Let us take as an example, the pair of wheels which will represent the ngular motion of a comet in a parabola.

Here $\qquad \theta_2 = \tan \dfrac{\theta_1}{2}, \quad \therefore \dfrac{d\theta_2}{d\theta_1} = \dfrac{1}{2 \cos^2 \dfrac{\theta_1}{2}} = \dfrac{r_1}{a - r_1},$

$$\therefore \; \frac{r_1}{a} = \frac{1}{2 + \cos \theta_1},$$

therefore the first wheel is an ellipse, whose major axis is equal to $\frac{4}{3}$ of the distance between the centres of the wheels, and in which the distance between the foci is half the major axis.

Now since $\qquad \theta_1 = 2 \tan^{-1} \theta_2 \text{ and } r_1 = a - r_2,$

$$\frac{r}{a} = 1 + \frac{1}{2 \left(2 - \theta^4 \right)},$$

$$\theta^4 = 2 - \frac{1}{\dfrac{2r}{a} - 2},$$

which is the equation to the wheel which revolves with constant angular velocity.

Before proceeding to give a list of examples of rolling curves, we shall state a theorem which is almost self-evident after what has been shewn previously.

Let there be three curves, A, B, and C. Let the curve A, when rolled on itself, produce the curve B, and when rolled on a straight line let it produce the curve C, then, if the dimensions of C be doubled, and B be rolled on it, it will trace a straight line.

A Collection of Examples of Rolling Curves.

First. Examples of a curve rolling on a straight line.

Ex. 1. When the rolling curve is a circle whose tracing-point is in the circumference, the curve traced is a cycloid, and when the point is not in the circumference, the cycloid becomes a trochoid.

Ex. 2. When the rolling curve is the involute of the circle whose radius is $2a$, the traced curve is a parabola whose parameter is $4a$.

Ex. 3. When the rolled curve is the parabola whose parameter is $4a$, the traced curve is a catenary whose parameter is a, and whose vertex is distant a from the straight line.

Ex. 4. When the rolled curve is a logarithmic spiral, the pole traces a straight line which cuts the fixed line at the same angle as the spiral cuts the radius vector.

Ex. 5. When the rolled curve is the hyperbolic spiral, the traced curve is the tractory of the straight line.

Ex. 6. When the rolled curve is the polar catenary

$$\theta = \pm \sqrt{1 \pm \frac{2a}{r}},$$

the traced curve is a circle whose radius is a, and which touches the straight line.

Ex. 7. When the equation of the rolled curve is

$$\theta = \log\left(\sqrt{\frac{r^4}{a^4} - 1} + \frac{r^2}{a^2}\right) - \log\left(\sqrt{\frac{a^4}{r^4} + 1} - \frac{a^2}{r^2}\right),$$

the traced curve is the hyperbola whose equation is

$$y^2 = a^2 + x^2.$$

Second. In the examples of a straight line rolling on a curve, we shall use the letters A, B, and C to denote the three curves treated of in page 22.

Ex. 1. When the curve A is a circle whose radius is a, then the curve B is the involute of that circle, and the curve C is the spiral of Archimedes, $r = a\theta$.

Ex. 2. When the curve A is a catenary whose equation is

$$x = \frac{a}{2}\left(e^{\frac{y}{a}} + e^{-\frac{y}{a}}\right),$$

the curve B is the tractory of the straight line, whose equation is

$$y = a \log \frac{x}{a + \sqrt{a^2 - x^2}} + \sqrt{a^2 - x^2},$$

and C is a straight line at a distance a from the vertex of the catenary.

Ex. 3.   When the curve A is the polar catenary

$$\theta = \pm \sqrt{1 \pm \frac{2a}{r}},$$

the curve B is the tractory of the circle

$$\theta = \cos^{-1}\frac{r}{a} - \sqrt{\frac{a^2}{r^2} - 1},$$

and the curve C is a circle of which the radius is $\frac{a}{2}$.

Third.   Examples of one curve rolling on another, and tracing a straight line.

Ex. 1.   The curve whose equation is

$$\theta = Ar^{-n} + \&c. + Kr^{-2} + Lr^{-1} + M\log r + Nr + \&c. + Zr^r,$$

when rolled on the curve whose equation is

$$y = \frac{n}{n-1}Ax^{1-n} + \&c. + 2Kx^{-1} - L\log x + Mx + \tfrac{1}{2}Nx^2 + \&c. + \frac{n}{n+1}Zx^{n+1},$$

traces the axis of y.

Ex. 2.   The circle whose equation is $r = a\cos\theta$ rolled on the circle whose radius is a traces a diameter of the circle.

Ex. 3.   The curve whose equation is

$$\theta = \sqrt{\frac{2a}{r} - 1} - \text{versin}^{-1}\frac{r}{a},$$

rolled on the circle whose radius is a, traces the tangent to the circle.

Ex. 4.   If the fixed curve be a parabola whose parameter is $4a$, and if we roll on it the spiral of Archimedes $r = a\theta$, the pole will trace the axis of the parabola.

Ex. 5.   If we roll an equal parabola on it, the focus will trace the directrix of the first parabola.

Ex. 6.   If we roll on it the curve $r = \frac{a}{4\theta^2}$ the pole will trace the tangent at the vertex of the parabola.

Ex. 7. If we roll the curve whose equation is

$$r = a \cos \left(\frac{a}{b} \theta \right)$$

on the ellipse whose equation is

$$\frac{x^2}{a^2} + \frac{y^2}{b^2} = 1,$$

the pole will trace the axis b.

Ex. 8. If we roll the curve whose equation is

$$r = \frac{a}{2} \left(e^{\frac{a\theta}{b}} - e^{-\frac{a\theta}{b}} \right)$$

on the hyperbola whose equation is

$$\frac{y^2}{b^2} - \frac{x^2}{a^2} = 1,$$

the pole will trace the axis b.

Ex. 9. If we roll the lituus, whose equation is

$$r^2 = \frac{a^2}{3\theta},$$

on the hyperbola whose equation is

$$xy = a^2,$$

the pole will trace the asymptote.

Ex. 10. The cardioid whose equation is

$$r = a \left(1 + \cos \theta \right),$$

rolled on the cycloid whose equation is

$$y = a \operatorname{versin}^{-1} \frac{x}{a} + \sqrt{2ax - x^2},$$

traces the base of the cycloid.

Ex. 11. The curve whose equation is

$$\theta = \operatorname{versin}^{-1} \frac{r}{a} + 2 \sqrt{\frac{2a}{r} - 1},$$

rolled on the cycloid, traces the tangent at the vertex.

Ex. 12. The straight line whose equation is

$$r = a \sec \theta,$$

rolled on a catenary whose parameter is a, traces a line whose distance from the vertex is a.

Ex. 13. The part of the polar catenary whose equation is

$$\theta = \pm \sqrt{1 + \frac{2a}{r}},$$

rolled on the catenary, traces the tangent at the vertex.

Ex. 14. The other part of the polar catenary whose equation is

$$\theta = \pm \sqrt{1 - \frac{2a}{r}},$$

rolled on the catenary, traces a line whose distance from the vertex is equal to $2a$.

Ex. 15. The tractory of the circle whose diameter is a, rolled on the tractory of the straight line whose constant tangent is a, produces the straight line.

Ex. 16. The hyperbolic spiral whose equation is

$$r = \frac{a}{\theta},$$

rolled on the logarithmic curve whose equation is

$$y = a \log \frac{x}{a},$$

traces the axis of y or the asymptote.

Ex. 17. The involute of the circle whose radius is a, rolled on an orthogonal trajectory of the catenary whose equation is

$$y = \frac{x}{2a} \sqrt{x^2 - a^2} + \frac{a}{2} \log \left(\sqrt{\frac{x^2}{a^2} - 1} + \frac{x}{a} \right),$$

traces the axis of y.

Ex. 18. The curve whose equation is

$$\theta = \left(\frac{a}{r} + 1 \right) \sqrt{2 \frac{a}{r} + 1},$$

rolled on the witch, whose equation is

$$y = 2a \sqrt{\frac{2a}{x} - 1},$$

traces the asymptote.

Ex. 19. The curve whose equation is

$$r = a \tan \theta,$$

rolled on the curve whose equation is

$$y = \frac{a}{2} \log \left(\frac{x^2}{a^2} - 1 \right),$$

traces the axis of y.

Ex. 20. The curve whose equation is

$$\theta = \frac{2r}{\sqrt{a^2 - r^2}},$$

rolled on the curve whose equation is

$$y = \frac{x^2}{\sqrt{a^2 - x^2}}, \quad \text{or} \quad r = a \tan \theta,$$

traces the axis of y.

Ex. 21. The curve whose equation is

$$r = a \left(\sec \theta - \tan \theta \right),$$

rolled on the curve whose equation is

$$y = a \log \left(\frac{x^2}{a^2} + 1 \right),$$

traces the axis of y.

Fourth. Examples of pairs of rolling curves which have their poles at a fixed distance $= a$.

Ex. 1. $\begin{cases} \text{The straight line whose equation is} \quad \theta = \sec^{-1} \dfrac{r}{a}. \\ \text{The polar catenary whose equation is} \quad \theta = \pm \sqrt{1 \pm \dfrac{2a}{r}}. \end{cases}$

Ex. 2. Two equal ellipses or hyperbolas centered at the foci.

Ex. 3. Two equal logarithmic spirals.

Ex. 4. $\begin{cases} \text{Circle whose equation is} \quad r = 2a \cos \theta. \\ \text{Curve whose equation is} \quad \theta = \sqrt{2\dfrac{a}{r} - 1} + \text{versin}^{-1} \dfrac{r}{a}. \end{cases}$

Ex. 5. $\begin{cases}\text{Cardioid whose equation is} \\ \\ \text{Curve whose equation is}\end{cases}$ $\quad\begin{aligned}&r = 2a\,(1 + \cos\theta). \\ \\ &\theta = \sin^{-1}\frac{r}{a} + \log\frac{r}{\sqrt{a^2 - r^2} + a}.\end{aligned}$

Ex. 6. $\begin{cases}\text{Conchoid,} \\ \\ \text{Curve,}\end{cases}$ $\quad\begin{aligned}&r = a\,(\sec\theta - 1). \\ \\ &\theta = \sqrt{1 - \frac{a^2}{r^2}} + \sec^{-1}\frac{r}{a}.\end{aligned}$

Ex. 7. $\begin{cases}\text{Spiral of Archimedes,} \\ \\ \text{Curve,}\end{cases}$ $\quad\begin{aligned}&r = a\theta. \\ \\ &\theta = \frac{r}{a} + \log\frac{r}{a}.\end{aligned}$

Ex. 8. $\begin{cases}\text{Hyperbolic spiral,} \\ \\ \text{Curve,}\end{cases}$ $\quad\begin{aligned}&r = \frac{a}{\theta}. \\ \\ &r = \frac{a}{e^\theta + 1}.\end{aligned}$

Ex. 9. $\begin{cases}\text{Ellipse whose equation is} \\ \\ \text{Curve,}\end{cases}$ $\quad\begin{aligned}&r = a\,\frac{1}{2 + \cos\theta}. \\ \\ &r = a\left(1 + \frac{1}{2\,(2 - \theta^4)}\right).\end{aligned}$

Ex. 10. $\begin{cases}\text{Involute of circle,} \\ \\ \text{Curve,}\end{cases}$ $\quad\begin{aligned}&\theta = \sqrt{\frac{r^2}{a^2} - 1}\,\sec^{-1}\frac{r}{a}. \\ \\ &\theta = \sqrt{\frac{r^2}{a^2} \pm 2\,\frac{r}{a}} \pm \log\left(\frac{r}{a} \pm 1 + \sqrt{\frac{r^2}{a^2} \pm 2\,\frac{r}{a}}\right).\end{aligned}$

Fifth.   Examples of curves rolling on themselves.

Ex. 1.   When the curve which rolls on itself is a circle, equation

$$r = a\cos\theta,$$

the traced curve is a cardioid, equation $r = a\,(1 + \cos\theta)$.

Ex. 2.   When it is the curve whose equation is

$$r = 2^n a \left(\cos\frac{\theta}{r}\right)^n,$$

the equation of the traced curve is

$$r = 2^{n+1} a \left(\cos\frac{\theta}{n+1}\right)^{n+1}.$$

Ex. 3.   When it is the involute of the circle, the traced curve is the spiral of Archimedes.

Ex. 4. When it is a parabola, the focus traces the directrix, and the vertex traces the cissoid.

Ex. 5. When it is the hyperbolic spiral, the traced curve is the tractory of the circle.

Ex. 6. When it is the polar catenary, the equation of the traced curve is

$$\theta = \sqrt{\frac{2a}{r} - 1} - \text{versin}^{-1} \frac{r}{a}.$$

Ex. 7. When it is the curve whose equation is

$$\theta = \log\left(\sqrt{\frac{r^4}{a^4} - 1} + \frac{r^2}{a^2}\right) - \log\left(\sqrt{1 + \frac{a^4}{r^4}} - \frac{a^2}{r^2}\right),$$

the equation of the traced curve is $r = a\left(e^\theta - e^{-\theta}\right)$.

This paper commenced with an outline of the nature and history of the problem of rolling curves, and it was shewn that the subject had been discussed previously, by several geometers, amongst whom were De la Hire and Nicolè in the *Mémoires de l'Académie*, Euler, Professor Willis, in his *Principles of Mechanism*, and the Rev. H. Holditch in the *Cambridge Philosophical Transactions*.

None of these authors, however, except the two last, had made any application of their methods; and the principal object of the present communication was to find how far the general equations could be simplified in particular cases, and to apply the results to practice.

Several problems were then worked out, of which some were applicable to the generation of curves, and some to wheelwork; while others were interesting as shewing the relations which exist between different curves; and, finally, a collection of examples was added, as an illustration of the fertility of the methods employed.

[From the *Transactions of the Royal Society of Edinburgh*, Vol. xx. Part i.]

III.—*On the Equilibrium of Elastic Solids.*

THERE are few parts of mechanics in which theory has differed more from experiment than in the theory of elastic solids.

Mathematicians, setting out from very plausible assumptions with respect to the constitution of bodies, and the laws of molecular action, came to conclusions which were shewn to be erroneous by the observations of experimental philosophers. The experiments of Œrsted proved to be at variance with the mathematical theories of Navier, Poisson, and Lamé and Clapeyron, and apparently deprived this practically important branch of mechanics of all assistance from mathematics.

The assumption on which these theories were founded may be stated thus:—

Solid bodies are composed of distinct molecules, which are kept at a certain distance from each other by the opposing principles of attraction and heat. When the distance between two molecules is changed, they act on each other with a force whose direction is in the line joining the centres of the molecules, and whose magnitude is equal to the change of distance multiplied into a function of the distance which vanishes when that distance becomes sensible.

The equations of elasticity deduced from this assumption contain only one coefficient, which varies with the nature of the substance.

The insufficiency of one coefficient may be proved from the existence of bodies of different degrees of solidity.

No effort is required to retain a liquid in any form, if its volume remain unchanged; but when the form of a solid is changed, a force is called into action which tends to restore its former figure; and this constitutes the difference between elastic solids and fluids. Both tend to recover their *volume*, but fluids do not tend to recover their *shape*.

Now, since there are in nature bodies which are in every intermediate state from perfect solidity to perfect liquidity, these two elastic powers cannot exist in every body in the same proportion, and therefore all theories which assign to them an invariable ratio must be erroneous.

I have therefore substituted for the assumption of Navier the following axioms as the results of experiments.

If three pressures in three rectangular axes be applied at a point in an elastic solid,—

1. *The sum of the three pressures is proportional to the sum of the compressions which they produce.*

2. *The difference between two of the pressures is proportional to the difference of the compressions which they produce.*

The equations deduced from these axioms contain two coefficients, and differ from those of Navier only in not assuming any invariable ratio between the cubical and linear elasticity. They are the same as those obtained by Professor Stokes from his equations of fluid motion, and they agree with all the laws of elasticity which have been deduced from experiments.

In this paper *pressures* are expressed by the number of units of weight to the unit of surface; if in English measure, in pounds to the square inch, or in atmospheres of 15 pounds to the square inch.

Compression is the proportional change of any dimension of the solid caused by pressure, and is expressed by the quotient of the change of dimension divided by the dimension compressed*.

Pressure will be understood to include tension, and compression dilatation; pressure and compression being reckoned positive.

Elasticity is the force which opposes pressure, and the *equations of elasticity* are those which express the relation of pressure to compression†.

Of those who have treated of elastic solids, some have confined themselves to the investigation of the laws of the bending and twisting of rods, without

---

* The laws of pressure and compression may be found in the Memoir of Lamé and Clapeyron. See note A.

† See note B.

considering the relation of the coefficients which occur in these two cases; while others have treated of the general problem of a solid body exposed to any forces.

The investigations of Leibnitz, Bernoulli, Euler, Varignon, Young, La Hire, and Lagrange, are confined to the equilibrium of bent rods; but those of Navier, Poisson, Lamé and Clapeyron, Cauchy, Stokes, and Wertheim, are principally directed to the formation and application of the general equations.

The investigations of Navier are contained in the seventh volume of the *Memoirs of the Institute*, page 373; and in the *Annales de Chimie et de Physique*, 2ᵉ Série, xv. 264, and xxxviii. 435; *L'Application de la Mécanique*, Tom. i.

Those of Poisson in *Mém. de l'Institut*, viii. 429; *Annales de Chimie*, 2ᵉ Série, xxxvi. 334; xxxvii. 337; xxxviii. 338; xlii. *Journal de l'École Polytechnique*, cahier xx., with an abstract in *Annales de Chimie* for 1829.

The memoir of MM. Lamé and Clapeyron is contained in Crelle's *Mathematical Journal*, Vol. vii.; and some observations on elasticity are to be found in Lamé's *Cours de Physique*.

M. Cauchy's investigations are contained in his *Exercices d'Analyse*, Vol. iii. p. 180, published in 1828.

Instead of supposing each pressure proportional to the linear compression which it produces, he supposes it to consist of two parts, one of which is proportional to the linear compression in the direction of the pressure, while the other is proportional to the diminution of volume. As this hypothesis admits two coefficients, it differs from that of this paper only in the values of the coefficients selected. They are denoted by K and k, and $K = \mu - \frac{1}{3}m$, $k = m$.

The theory of Professor Stokes is contained in Vol. viii. Part 3, of the *Cambridge Philosophical Transactions*, and was read April 14, 1845.

He states his general principles thus:—"The capability which solids possess of being put into a state of isochronous vibration, shews that the pressures called into action by small displacements depend on homogeneous functions of those displacements of one dimension. I shall suppose, moreover, according to the general principle of the superposition of small quantities, that the pressures due to different displacements are superimposed, and, consequently, that the pressures are linear functions of the displacements."

Having assumed the proportionality of pressure to compression, he proceeds to define his coefficients.—"Let $-A\delta$ be the pressures corresponding to a uniform linear dilatation δ when the solid is in equilibrium, and suppose that it becomes $mA\delta$, in consequence of the heat developed when the solid is in a state of rapid vibration. Suppose, also, that a displacement of shifting parallel to the plane xy, for which $\delta x = kx$, $\delta y = -ky$, and $\delta z = 0$, calls into action a pressure $-Bk$ on a plane perpendicular to the axis of x, and a pressure Bk on a plane perpendicular to the axis of y; the pressure on these planes being equal and of contrary signs; that on a plane perpendicular to z being zero, and the tangential forces on those planes being zero." The coefficients A and B, thus defined, when expressed as in this paper, are $A = 3\mu$, $B = \dfrac{m}{2}$.

Professor Stokes does not enter into the solution of his equations, but gives their results in some particular cases.

1. A body exposed to a uniform pressure on its whole surface.

2. A rod extended in the direction of its length.

3. A cylinder twisted by a statical couple.

He then points out the method of finding A and B from the last two cases.

While explaining why the equations of motion of the luminiferous ether are the same as those of incompressible elastic solids, he has mentioned the property of *plasticity* or the tendency which a constrained body has to relieve itself from a state of constraint, by its molecules assuming new positions of equilibrium. This property is opposed to linear elasticity; and these two properties exist in all bodies, but in variable ratio.

M. Wertheim, in *Annales de Chimie*, 3ᵉ Série, XXIII., has given the results of some experiments on caoutchouc, from which he finds that $K = k$, or $\mu = \frac{4}{3} m$; and concludes that $k = K$ in all substances. In his equations, μ is therefore made equal to $\frac{4}{3} m$.

The accounts of experimental researches on the values of the coefficients are so numerous that I can mention only a few.

Canton, Perkins, Œrsted, Aimé, Colladon and Sturm, and Regnault, have determined the cubical compressibilities of substances; Coulomb, Duleau, and Giulio, have calculated the linear elasticity from the torsion of wires; and a great many observations have been made on the elongation and bending of beams.

I have found no account of any experiments on the relation between the doubly refracting power communicated to glass and other elastic solids by compression, and the pressure which produces it*; but the phenomena of bent glass seem to prove, that, in homogeneous singly-refracting substances exposed to pressures, the principal axes of pressure coincide with the principal axes of double refraction; and that the difference of pressures in any two axes is proportional to the difference of the velocities of the oppositely polarised rays whose directions are parallel to the third axis. On this principle I have calculated the phenomena seen by polarised light in the cases where the solid is bounded by parallel planes.

In the following pages I have endeavoured to apply a theory identical with that of Stokes to the solution of problems which have been selected on account of the possibility of fulfilling the conditions. I have not attempted to extend the theory to the case of imperfectly elastic bodies, or to the laws of permanent bending and breaking. The solids here considered are supposed not to be compressed beyond the limits of perfect elasticity.

The equations employed in the transformation of co-ordinates may be found in Gregory's *Solid Geometry*.

I have denoted the displacements by δx, δy, δz. They are generally denoted by a, β, γ; but as I had employed these letters to denote the principal axes at any point, and as this had been done throughout the paper, I did not alter a notation which to me appears natural and intelligible.

The laws of elasticity express the relation between the changes of the dimensions of a body and the forces which produce them.

These forces are called Pressures, and their effects Compressions. Pressures are estimated in pounds on the square inch, and compressions in fractions of the dimensions compressed.

Let the position of material points in space be expressed by their co-ordinates x, y, and z, then any change in a system of such points is expressed by giving to these co-ordinates the variations δx, δy, δz, these variations being functions of x, y, z.

* See note C.

The quantities δx, δy, δz, represent the absolute motion of each point in the directions of the three co-ordinates; but as compression depends not on absolute, but on relative displacement, we have to consider only the nine quantities—

$$\frac{d\delta x}{dx}, \quad \frac{d\delta x}{dy}, \quad \frac{d\delta x}{dz},$$

$$\frac{d\delta y}{dx}, \quad \frac{d\delta y}{dy}, \quad \frac{d\delta y}{dz},$$

$$\frac{d\delta z}{dx}, \quad \frac{d\delta z}{dy}, \quad \frac{d\delta z}{dz}.$$

Since the number of these quantities is nine, if nine other independent quantities of the same kind can be found, the one set may be found in terms of the other. The quantities which we shall assume for this purpose are—

1. Three compressions, $\dfrac{\delta a}{a}$, $\dfrac{\delta \beta}{\beta}$, $\dfrac{\delta \gamma}{\gamma}$, in the directions of three principal axes a, β, γ.

2. The nine *direction-cosines* of these axes, with the *six connecting equations*, leaving three independent quantities. (See Gregory's *Solid Geometry*.)

3. The small angles of rotation of this system of axes about the axes of x, y, z.

The cosines of the angles which the axes of x, y, z make with those of a, β, γ are

$$\cos(a0x) = a_1, \quad \cos(\beta 0x) = b_1, \quad \cos(\gamma 0x) = c_1,$$
$$\cos(a0y) = a_2, \quad \cos(\beta 0y) = b_2, \quad \cos(\gamma 0y) = c_2,$$
$$\cos(a0z) = a_3, \quad \cos(\beta 0z) = b_3, \quad \cos(\gamma 0z) = c_3.$$

These *direction-cosines* are connected by the six equations,

$$a_1^2 + b_1^2 + c_1^2 = 1, \qquad a_1 a_2 + b_1 b_2 + c_1 c_2 = 0,$$
$$a_2^2 + b_2^2 + c_2^2 = 1, \qquad a_2 a_3 + b_2 b_3 + c_2 c_3 = 0,$$
$$a_3^2 + b_3^2 + c_3^2 = 1, \qquad a_3 a_1 + b_3 b_1 + c_3 c_1 = 0.$$

The rotation of the system of axes a, β, γ, round the axis of

$$x, \text{ from } y \text{ to } z, \ = \delta\theta_1,$$
$$y, \text{ from } z \text{ to } x, \ = \delta\theta_2,$$
$$z, \text{ from } x \text{ to } y, \ = \delta\theta_3;$$

By resolving the displacements $\delta\alpha$, $\delta\beta$, $\delta\gamma$, $\delta\theta_1$, $\delta\theta_2$, $\delta\theta_3$, in the directions of the axes x, y, z, the displacements in these axes are found to be

$$\delta x = a_1\delta\alpha + b_1\delta\beta + c_1\delta\gamma - \delta\theta_3 z + \delta\theta_2 y,$$
$$\delta y = a_2\delta\alpha + b_2\delta\beta + c_2\delta\gamma - \delta\theta_3 x + \delta\theta_1 z,$$
$$\delta z = a_3\delta\alpha + b_3\delta\beta + c_3\delta\gamma - \delta\theta_1 y + \delta\theta_2 x.$$

But
$$\delta\alpha = \alpha\frac{\delta a}{a}, \quad \delta\beta = \beta\frac{\delta\beta}{\beta}, \text{ and } \delta\gamma = \gamma\frac{\delta\gamma}{\gamma},$$

and
$$\alpha = a_1 x + a_2 y + a_3 z, \quad \beta = b_1 x + b_2 y + b_3 z, \text{ and } \gamma = c_1 x + c_2 y + c_3 z.$$

Substituting these values of $\delta\alpha$, $\delta\beta$, and $\delta\gamma$ in the expressions for δx, δy, δz, and differentiating with respect to x, y, and z, in each equation, we obtain the equations

$$\left.\begin{array}{l}
\dfrac{d\delta x}{dx} = \dfrac{\delta a}{a}a_1^2 + \dfrac{\delta\beta}{\beta}b_1^2 + \dfrac{\delta\gamma}{\gamma}c_1^2 \\[2mm]
\dfrac{d\delta y}{dy} = \dfrac{\delta a}{a}a_2^2 + \dfrac{\delta\beta}{\beta}b_2^2 + \dfrac{\delta\gamma}{\gamma}c_2^2 \\[2mm]
\dfrac{d\delta z}{dz} = \dfrac{\delta a}{a}a_3^2 + \dfrac{\delta\beta}{\beta}b_3^2 + \dfrac{\delta\gamma}{\gamma}c_3^2
\end{array}\right\} \quad\dots\dots\dots\dots(1).$$

Equations of compression.

$$\left.\begin{array}{l}
\dfrac{d\delta x}{dy} = \dfrac{\delta a}{a}a_1 a_2 + \dfrac{\delta\beta}{\beta}b_1 b_2 + \dfrac{\delta\gamma}{\gamma}c_1 c_2 + \delta\theta_3 \\[2mm]
\dfrac{d\delta x}{dz} = \dfrac{\delta a}{a}a_1 a_3 + \dfrac{\delta\beta}{\beta}b_1 b_3 + \dfrac{\delta\gamma}{\gamma}c_1 c_3 - \delta\theta_2 \\[2mm]
\dfrac{d\delta y}{dz} = \dfrac{\delta a}{a}a_2 a_3 + \dfrac{\delta\beta}{\beta}b_2 b_3 + \dfrac{\delta\gamma}{\gamma}c_2 c_3 + \delta\theta_1 \\[2mm]
\dfrac{d\delta y}{dx} = \dfrac{\delta a}{a}a_2 a_1 + \dfrac{\delta\beta}{\beta}b_2 b_1 + \dfrac{\delta\gamma}{\gamma}c_2 c_1 - \delta\theta_3 \\[2mm]
\dfrac{d\delta z}{dx} = \dfrac{\delta a}{a}a_3 a_1 + \dfrac{\delta\beta}{\beta}b_3 b_1 + \dfrac{\delta\gamma}{\gamma}c_3 c_1 + \delta\theta_2 \\[2mm]
\dfrac{d\delta z}{dy} = \dfrac{\delta a}{a}a_3 a_2 + \dfrac{\delta\beta}{\beta}b_3 b_2 + \dfrac{\delta\gamma}{\gamma}c_3 c_2 - \delta\theta_1
\end{array}\right\} \quad\dots\dots\dots\dots(2).$$

Equations of the equilibrium of an element of the solid.

The forces which may act on a particle of the solid are :—

1. Three attractions in the direction of the axes, represented by X, Y, Z.
2. Six pressures on the six faces.

3. Two tangential actions on each face.

Let the six faces of the small parallelopiped be denoted by x_1, y_1, z_1, x_2, y_2, and z_2, then the forces acting on x_1 are :—

1. A normal pressure p_1 acting in the direction of x on the area $dydz$.

2. A tangential force q_3 acting in the direction of y on the same area.

3. A tangential force q_2^1 acting in the direction of z on the same area, and so on for the other five faces, thus :—

Forces which act in the direction of the axes of

	x	y	z
On the face x_1	$-p_1 dydz$	$-q_3 dydz$	$-q_2^1 dydz$
... ... x_2	$\left(p_1 + \dfrac{dp_1}{dx} dx\right) dydz$	$\left(q_3 + \dfrac{dq_3}{dx} dx\right) dydx$	$\left(q_2^1 + \dfrac{dq_2^1}{dx} dx\right) dydz$
... ... y_1	$-q_3^1 dzdx$	$-p_2 dzdx$	$-q_1 dzdx$
... ... y_2	$\left(q_3^1 + \dfrac{dq_3^1}{dy} dy\right) dzdx$	$\left(p_2 + \dfrac{dp_2}{dy} dy\right) dzdx$	$\left(q_1 + \dfrac{dq_1}{dy} dy\right) dzdx$
... ... z_1	$-q_2 dxdy$	$-q^1 dxdy$	$-p_3 dxdy$
... ... z_2	$\left(q_2 + \dfrac{dq_2}{dz} dz\right) dxdy$	$\left(q^1 + \dfrac{dq^1}{dz} dz\right) dxdy$	$\left(p_3 + \dfrac{dp_3}{dz} dz\right) dxdy$
Attractions,	$\rho X dxdydz$	$\rho Y dxdydz$	$\rho Z dxdydz$

Taking the moments of these forces round the axes of the particle, we find

$$q_1^1 = q_1, \quad q_2^1 = q_2, \quad q_3^1 = q_3;$$

and then equating the forces in the directions of the three axes, and dividing by dx, dy, dz, we find the equations of pressures,

$$\left. \begin{aligned} \frac{dp_1}{dx} + \frac{dq_3}{dy} + \frac{dq_2}{dz} + \rho X &= 0 \\ \frac{dp_2}{dy} + \frac{dq_1}{dz} + \frac{dq_3}{dx} + \rho Y &= 0 \\ \frac{dp_3}{dz} + \frac{dq_2}{dx} + \frac{dq_1}{dy} + \rho Z &= 0 \end{aligned} \right\} \text{Equations of Pressures.} \quad \dots\dots\dots\dots\dots\dots\dots (3).$$

The resistance which the solid opposes to these pressures is called Elasticity, and is of two kinds, for it opposes either change of *volume* or change of *figure*. These two kinds of elasticity have no necessary connection, for they are possessed in very different ratios by different substances. Thus *jelly* has a cubical elasticity little different from that of water, and a linear elasticity as small as we please; while *cork*, whose cubical elasticity is very small, has a much greater linear elasticity than jelly.

Hooke discovered that the elastic forces are proportional to the changes that excite them, or as he expressed it, "Ut tensio sic vis."

To fix our ideas, let us suppose the compressed body to be a parallelopiped, and let pressures P_1, P_2, P_3 act on its faces in the direction of the axes a, β, γ, which will become the principal axes of compression, and the compressions will be $\dfrac{\delta a}{a}$, $\dfrac{\delta \beta}{\beta}$, $\dfrac{\delta \gamma}{\gamma}$.

The fundamental assumption from which the following equations are deduced is an extension of Hooke's law, and consists of two parts.

I. The sum of the compressions is proportional to the sum of the pressures.

II. The difference of the compressions is proportional to the difference of the pressures.

These laws are expressed by the following equations :—

$$\text{I.} \quad (P_1 + P_2 + P_3) = 3\mu \left(\frac{\delta a}{a} + \frac{\delta \beta}{\beta} + \frac{\delta \gamma}{\gamma} \right) \quad \dots\dots\dots\dots\dots\dots (4).$$

$$\text{II.} \quad \left\{ \begin{array}{l} (P_1 - P_2) = m \left(\dfrac{\delta a}{a} - \dfrac{\delta \beta}{\beta} \right) \\[2mm] (P_2 - P_3) = m \left(\dfrac{\delta \beta}{\beta} - \dfrac{\delta \gamma}{\gamma} \right) \\[2mm] (P_3 - P_1) = m \left(\dfrac{\delta \gamma}{\gamma} - \dfrac{\delta a}{a} \right) \end{array} \right\} \quad \dots\dots\dots\dots\dots\dots\dots\dots (5).$$

Equations of Elasticity.

The quantity μ is the coefficient of cubical elasticity, and m that of linear elasticity.

By solving these equations, the values of the pressures P_1, P_2, P_3, and the compressions $\dfrac{\delta a}{a}$, $\dfrac{\delta \beta}{\beta}$, $\dfrac{\delta \gamma}{\gamma}$ may be found.

$$\left.\begin{array}{l} P_1 = \left(\mu - \tfrac{1}{3}m\right)\left(\dfrac{\delta a}{a} + \dfrac{\delta \beta}{\beta} + \dfrac{\delta \gamma}{\gamma}\right) + m\,\dfrac{\delta a}{a} \\[2mm] P_2 = \left(\mu - \tfrac{1}{3}m\right)\left(\dfrac{\delta a}{a} + \dfrac{\delta \beta}{\beta} + \dfrac{\delta \gamma}{\gamma}\right) + m\,\dfrac{\delta \beta}{\beta} \\[2mm] P_3 = \left(\mu - \tfrac{1}{3}m\right)\left(\dfrac{\delta a}{a} + \dfrac{\delta \beta}{\beta} + \dfrac{\delta \gamma}{\gamma}\right) + m\,\dfrac{\delta \gamma}{\gamma} \end{array}\right\} \dots\dots\dots\dots\dots (6).$$

$$\left.\begin{array}{l} \dfrac{\delta a}{a} = \left(\dfrac{1}{9\mu} - \dfrac{1}{3m}\right)(P_1 + P_2 + P_3) + \dfrac{1}{m}\,P_1 \\[2mm] \dfrac{\delta \beta}{\beta} = \left(\dfrac{1}{9\mu} - \dfrac{1}{3m}\right)(P_1 + P_2 + P_3) + \dfrac{1}{m}\,P_2 \\[2mm] \dfrac{\delta \gamma}{\gamma} = \left(\dfrac{1}{9\mu} - \dfrac{1}{3m}\right)(P_1 + P_2 + P_3) + \dfrac{1}{m}\,P_3 \end{array}\right\} \dots\dots\dots\dots\dots (7).$$

From these values of the pressures in the axes a, β, γ, may be obtained the equations for the axes x, y, z, by resolutions of pressures and compressions[*].

For
$$p = a^2 P_1 + b^2 P_2 + c^2 P_3$$
and
$$q = aa P_1 + bb P_2 + cc P_3 ;$$

$$\left.\begin{array}{l} p_1 = \left(\mu - \tfrac{1}{3}m\right)\left(\dfrac{d\delta x}{dx} + \dfrac{d\delta y}{dy} + \dfrac{d\delta z}{dz}\right) + m\,\dfrac{d\delta x}{dx} \\[2mm] p_2 = \left(\mu - \tfrac{1}{3}m\right)\left(\dfrac{d\delta x}{dx} + \dfrac{d\delta y}{dy} + \dfrac{d\delta z}{dz}\right) + m\,\dfrac{d\delta y}{dy} \\[2mm] p_3 = \left(\mu - \tfrac{1}{3}m\right)\left(\dfrac{d\delta x}{dx} + \dfrac{d\delta y}{dy} + \dfrac{d\delta z}{dz}\right) + m\,\dfrac{d\delta z}{dz} \end{array}\right\} \dots\dots\dots\dots (8).$$

$$\left.\begin{array}{l} q_1 = \dfrac{m}{2}\left(\dfrac{d\delta y}{dz} + \dfrac{d\delta z}{dy}\right) \\[2mm] q_2 = \dfrac{m}{2}\left(\dfrac{d\delta z}{dx} + \dfrac{d\delta x}{dz}\right) \\[2mm] q_3 = \dfrac{m}{2}\left(\dfrac{d\delta x}{dy} + \dfrac{d\delta y}{dx}\right) \end{array}\right\} \dots\dots\dots\dots\dots\dots(9).$$

[*] See the Memoir of Lamé and Clapeyron, and note A.

$$\left.\begin{aligned}
\frac{d\delta x}{dx} &= \left(\frac{1}{9\mu} - \frac{1}{3m}\right)(p_1 + p_2 + p_3) + \frac{1}{m}\,p_1 \\
\frac{d\delta y}{dy} &= \left(\frac{1}{9\mu} - \frac{1}{3m}\right)(p_1 + p_2 + p_3) + \frac{1}{m}\,p_2 \\
\frac{d\delta z}{dz} &= \left(\frac{1}{9\mu} - \frac{1}{3m}\right)(p_1 + p_2 + p_3) + \frac{1}{m}\,p_3
\end{aligned}\right\} \quad \cdots\cdots\cdots\cdots (10).$$

$$\left.\begin{aligned}
\frac{d\delta x}{dy} - \delta\theta_3 &= \frac{d\delta y}{dx} + \delta\theta_3 = \frac{1}{m}\,q_3 \\
\frac{d\delta y}{dz} - \delta\theta_1 &= \frac{d\delta z}{dy} + \delta\theta_1 = \frac{1}{m}\,q_1 \\
\frac{d\delta z}{dx} - \delta\theta_2 &= \frac{d\delta x}{dz} + \delta\theta_2 = \frac{1}{m}\,q_2
\end{aligned}\right\} \quad \cdots\cdots\cdots\cdots\cdots (11).$$

By substituting in Equations (3) the values of the forces given in Equations (8) and (9), they become

$$\left.\begin{aligned}
\left(\mu + \frac{1}{6}m\right)\left\{\frac{d}{dx}\left(\frac{d\delta x}{dx} + \frac{d\delta y}{dy} + \frac{d\delta z}{dz}\right)\right\} + \frac{m}{2}\left(\frac{d^2}{dx^2}\,\delta x + \frac{d^2}{dy^2}\,\delta y + \frac{d^2}{dz^2}\,\delta z\right) + \rho X = 0 \\
\left(\mu + \frac{1}{6}m\right)\left\{\frac{d}{dy}\left(\frac{d\delta x}{dx} + \frac{d\delta y}{dy} + \frac{d\delta z}{dz}\right)\right\} + \frac{m}{2}\left(\frac{d^2}{dx^2}\,\delta x + \frac{d^2}{dy^2}\,\delta y + \frac{d^2}{dz^2}\,\delta z\right) + \rho Y = 0 \\
\left(\mu + \frac{1}{6}m\right)\left\{\frac{d}{dz}\left(\frac{d\delta x}{dx} + \frac{d\delta y}{dy} + \frac{d\delta z}{dz}\right)\right\} + \frac{m}{2}\left(\frac{d^2}{dx^2}\,\delta x + \frac{d^2}{dy^2}\,\delta y + \frac{d^2}{dz^2}\,\delta z\right) + \rho Z = 0
\end{aligned}\right\} \cdots (12).$$

These are the general equations of elasticity, and are identical with those of M. Cauchy, in his *Exercices d'Analyse*, Vol. III., p. 180, published in 1828, where k stands for m, and K for $\mu - \dfrac{m}{2}$, and those of Mr Stokes, given in the *Cambridge Philosophical Transactions*, Vol. VIII., part 3, and numbered (30); in his equations $A = 3\mu$, $B = \dfrac{m}{2}$.

If the temperature is variable from one part to another of the elastic solid, the compressions $\dfrac{d\delta x}{dx}$, $\dfrac{d\delta y}{dy}$, $\dfrac{d\delta z}{dz}$, at any point will be diminished by a quantity proportional to the temperature at that point. This principle is applied in Cases X. and XI. Equations (10) then become

$$\left.\begin{aligned}
\frac{d\delta x}{dx} &= \left(\frac{1}{9\mu} - \frac{1}{3m}\right)(p_1 + p_2 + p_3) + c_3 v + \frac{1}{m}p_1 \\
\frac{d\delta y}{dy} &= \left(\frac{1}{9\mu} - \frac{1}{3m}\right)(p_1 + p_2 + p_3) + c_3 v + \frac{1}{m}p_2 \\
\frac{d\delta x}{dz} &= \left(\frac{1}{9\mu} - \frac{1}{3m}\right)(p_1 + p_2 + p_3) + c_3 v + \frac{1}{m}p_3
\end{aligned}\right\} \dots\dots\dots (13),$$

$c_3 v$ being the linear expansion for the temperature v.

Having found the general equations of the equilibrium of elastic solids, I proceed to work some examples of their application, which afford the means of determining the coefficients μ, m, and ω, and of calculating the stiffness of solid figures. I begin with those cases in which the elastic solid is a hollow cylinder exposed to given forces on the two concentric cylindric surfaces, and the two parallel terminating planes.

In these cases the co-ordinates x, y, z are replaced by the co-ordinates

$x = x$, measured along the axis of the cylinder.

$y = r$, the radius of any point, or the distance from the axis.

$z = r\theta$, the arc of a circle measured from a fixed plane passing through the axis.

$\dfrac{d\delta x}{dx} = \dfrac{d\delta x}{dx}$, $p_1 = o$, are the compression and pressure in the direction of the axis at any point.

$\dfrac{d\delta y}{dy} = \dfrac{d\delta r}{dr}$, $p_2 = p$, are the compression and pressure in the direction of the radius.

$\dfrac{d\delta z}{dz} = \dfrac{d\delta r\theta}{dr\theta} = \dfrac{\delta r}{r}$, $p_3 = q$, are the compression and pressure in the direction of the tangent.

Equations (9) become, when expressed in terms of these co-ordinates—

$$\left.\begin{aligned}
q_1 &= \frac{m}{2}\, r\, \frac{d\delta\theta}{dr} \\
q_2 &= \frac{m}{2}\, r\, \frac{d\delta\theta}{dx} \\
q_3 &= \frac{m}{2}\cdot \frac{d\delta x}{dr}
\end{aligned}\right\} \dots\dots\dots\dots\dots\dots\dots (14).$$

The length of the cylinder is b, and the two radii a_1 and a_2 in every case.

CASE I.

The first equation is applicable to the case of a hollow cylinder, of which the outer surface is fixed, while the inner surface is made to turn through a small angle $\delta\theta$, by a couple whose moment is M.

The twisting force M is resisted only by the elasticity of the solid, and therefore the whole resistance, in every concentric cylindric surface, must be equal to M.

The resistance at any point, multiplied into the radius at which it acts, is expressed by

$$rq_1 = \frac{m}{2} r^2 \frac{d\delta\theta}{dr}.$$

Therefore for the whole cylindric surface

$$\frac{d\delta\theta}{dr} m\pi r^3 b = M.$$

Whence
$$\delta\theta = \frac{M}{2\pi mb}\left(\frac{1}{a_1^2} - \frac{1}{a_2^2}\right),$$

and
$$m = \frac{M}{2\pi b\delta\theta}\left(\frac{1}{a_1^2} - \frac{1}{a_2^2}\right) \quad\dots\dots\dots\dots\dots\dots\dots (16).$$

The optical effect of the pressure of any point is expressed by

$$I = \omega q_1 b = \omega \cdot \frac{Mb}{2\pi r^2} \quad\dots\dots\dots\dots\dots\dots\dots (15).$$

Therefore, if the solid be viewed by polarized light (transmitted parallel to the axis), the difference of retardation of the oppositely polarized rays at any point in the solid will be inversely proportional to the square of the distance from the axis of the cylinder, and the planes of polarization of these rays will be inclined 45° to the radius at that point.

The general appearance is therefore a system of coloured rings arranged oppositely to the rings in uniaxal crystals, the tints ascending in the scale as they approach the centre, and the distance between the rings decreasing towards the centre. The whole system is crossed by two dark bands inclined 45° to the plane of primitive polarization, when the plane of the analysing plate is perpendicular to that of the first polarizing plate.

A jelly of isinglass poured when hot between two concentric cylinders forms, when cold, a convenient solid for this experiment; and the diameters of the rings may be varied at pleasure by changing the force of torsion applied to the interior cylinder.

By continuing the force of torsion while the jelly is allowed to dry, a hard plate of isinglass is obtained, which still acts in the same way on polarized light, even when the force of torsion is removed.

It seems that this action cannot be accounted for by supposing the interior parts kept in a state of constraint by the exterior parts, as in, unannealed and heated glass; for the optical properties of the plate of isinglass are such as would indicate a strain preserving in every part of the plate the direction of the original strain, so that the strain on one part of the plate cannot be maintained by an opposite strain on another part.

Two other uncrystallised substances have the power of retaining the polarizing structure developed by compression. The first is a mixture of wax and resin pressed into a thin plate between two plates of glass, as described by Sir David Brewster, in the *Philosophical Transactions* for 1815 and 1830.

When a compressed plate of this substance is examined with polarized light, it is observed to have no action on light at a perpendicular incidence; but when inclined, it shews the segments of coloured rings. This property does not belong to the plate as a whole, but is possessed by every part of it. It is therefore similar to a plate cut from a uniaxal crystal perpendicular to the axis.

I find that its action on light is like that of a *positive* crystal, while that of a plate of isinglass similarly treated would be *negative*.

The other substance which possesses similar properties is gutta percha. This substance in its ordinary state, when cold, is not transparent even in thin films; but if a thin film be drawn out gradually, it may be extended to more than double its length. It then possesses a powerful double refraction, which it retains so strongly that it has been used for polarizing light*. As one of its refractive indices is nearly the same as that of Canada balsam, while the other is very different, the common surface of the gutta percha and Canada balsam will transmit one set of rays much more readily than the other, so that a film of extended gutta percha placed between two layers of Canada balsam acts like

* By Dr Wright, I believe.

a plate of nitre treated in the same way. That these films are in a state of constraint may be proved by heating them slightly, when they recover their original dimensions.

As all these permanently compressed substances have passed their limit of perfect elasticity, they do not belong to the class of elastic solids treated of in this paper; and as I cannot explain the method by which an uncrystallised body maintains itself in a state of constraint, I go on to the next case of twisting, which has more practical importance than any other. This is the case of a cylinder fixed at one end, and twisted at the other by a couple whose moment is M.

CASE II.

In this case let $\delta\theta$ be the angle of torsion at any point, then the resistance to torsion in any circular section of the cylinder is equal to the twisting force M.

The resistance at any point in the circular section is given by the second Equation of (14).

$$q_2 = \frac{m}{2} r \frac{d\delta\theta}{dx} .$$

This force acts at the distance r from the axis; therefore its resistance to torsion will be $q_2 r$, and the resistance in a circular annulus will be

$$q_2 r 2\pi r dr = m\pi r^3 \frac{d\delta\theta}{dx} dr$$

and the whole resistance for the hollow cylinder will be expressed by

$$M = \frac{m\pi}{4} \frac{d\delta\theta}{dx} (a_1^4 - a_2^4) \dots\dots\dots\dots\dots\dots\dots\dots(16).$$

$$m = 4M \frac{1}{\pi \dfrac{\delta\theta}{b} (a_1^4 - a_2^4)} .$$

$$m = \frac{720}{\pi^2} \frac{M}{n} \left(\frac{b}{a_1^4 - a_2^4} \right) \dots\dots\dots\dots\dots\dots\dots\dots(17).$$

In this equation, m is the coefficient of linear elasticity; a_1 and a_2 are the radii of the exterior and interior surfaces of the hollow cylinder in inches; M is the moment of torsion produced by a weight acting on a lever, and is expressed by the product of the number of pounds in the weight into the number of inches in the lever; b is the distance of two points on the cylinder whose angular motion is measured by means of indices, or more accurately by small mirrors attached to the cylinder; n is the difference of the angle of rotation of the two indices in degrees.

This is the most accurate method for the determination of m independently of μ, and it seems to answer best with thick cylinders which cannot be used with the balance of torsion, as the oscillations are too short, and produce a vibration of the whole apparatus.

Case III.

A hollow cylinder exposed to normal pressures only. When the pressures parallel to the axis, radius, and tangent are substituted for p_1, p_2, and p_3, Equations (10) become

$$\frac{d\delta x}{dx} = \left(\frac{1}{9\mu} - \frac{1}{3m}\right)(o + p + q) + \frac{1}{m}o \quad\dots\dots\dots\dots(18).$$

$$\frac{d\delta r}{dr} = \left(\frac{1}{9\mu} - \frac{1}{3m}\right)(o + p + q) + \frac{1}{m}p \quad\dots\dots\dots\dots(19).$$

$$\frac{d\delta(r\theta)}{d(r\theta)} = \frac{\delta r}{r} = \left(\frac{1}{9\mu} - \frac{1}{3m}\right)(o + p + q) + \frac{1}{m}q \quad\dots\dots\dots\dots(20).$$

By multiplying Equation (20) by r, differentiating with respect to r, and comparing this value of $\frac{d\delta r}{dr}$ with that of Equation (19),

$$\frac{p - q}{rm} = \left(\frac{1}{9\mu} - \frac{1}{3m}\right)\left(\frac{do}{dr} + \frac{dp}{dr} + \frac{dq}{dr}\right) - \frac{1}{m}\frac{dq}{dr}.$$

The equation of the equilibrium of an element of the solid is obtained by considering the forces which act on it in the direction of the radius. By equating the forces which press it outwards with those pressing it inwards, we find the equation of the equilibrium of the element,

$$\frac{q - p}{r} = \frac{dp}{dr} \quad\dots\dots\dots\dots\dots\dots\dots\dots\dots\dots(21).$$

By comparing this equation with the last, we find

$$\left(\frac{1}{9\mu} - \frac{1}{3m}\right)\frac{do}{dr} + \left(\frac{1}{9\mu} + \frac{2}{3m}\right)\left(\frac{dp}{dr} + \frac{dq}{dr}\right) = 0.$$

Integrating,

$$\left(\frac{1}{9\mu} - \frac{1}{3m}\right)o + \left(\frac{1}{9\mu} + \frac{2}{3m}\right)(p+q) = c_1.$$

Since o, the longitudinal pressure, is supposed constant, we may assume

$$c_2 = \frac{c_1 - \left(\dfrac{1}{9\mu} - \dfrac{1}{3m}\right)o}{\dfrac{1}{9\mu} + \dfrac{2}{3m}} = (p+q).$$

Therefore $\qquad q - p = c_2 - 2p,$ therefore by (21),

$$\frac{dp}{dr} + \frac{2p}{r} = \frac{c_2}{r},$$

a linear equation, which gives

$$p = c_3\frac{1}{r^2} + \frac{c_2}{2}.$$

The coefficients c_2 and c_3 must be found from the conditions of the surface of the solid. If the pressure on the exterior cylindric surface whose radius is a_1 be denoted by h_1, and that on the interior surface whose radius is a_2 by h_2,

then $p = h_1$ when $r = a_1$

and $p = h_2$ when $r = a_2$

and the general value of p is

$$p = \frac{a_1^2 h_1 - a_2^2 h_2}{a_1^2 - a_2^2} - \frac{a_1^2 a_2^2}{r^2}\frac{h_1 - h_2}{a_1^2 - a_2^2} \quad\dotfill(22).$$

$$r\frac{dp}{dr} = q - p = 2\frac{a_1^2 a_2^2}{r^2}\frac{h_1 - h_2}{a_1^2 - a_2^2} \text{ by (21).}$$

$$q = \frac{a_1^2 h_1 - a_2^2 h}{a_1^2 - a_2^2} + \frac{a_1^2 a_2^2}{r^2}\frac{h_1 - h_2}{a_1^2 - a_2^2} \quad\dotfill(23).$$

$$I = b\omega(p - q) = -2b\omega\frac{a_1^2 a_2^2}{r^2}\frac{h_1 - h_2}{a_1^2 - a_2^2}\dotfill(24).$$

This last equation gives the optical effect of the pressure at any point. The law of the magnitude of this quantity is the inverse square of the radius, as in

Case I.; but the direction of the principal axes is different, as in this case they are parallel and perpendicular to the radius. The dark bands seen by polarized light will therefore be parallel and perpendicular to the plane of polarization, instead of being inclined at an angle of 45°, as in Case I.

By substituting in Equations (18) and (20), the values of p and q given in (22) and (23), we find that when $r = a_1$,

$$
\left.
\begin{aligned}
\frac{\delta x}{x} &= \left(\frac{1}{9\mu}\right)\left(o + 2\frac{a_1^2 h_1 - a_2^2 h_2}{a_1^2 - a_2^2}\right) + \frac{2}{3m}\left(o - \frac{a_1^2 h_1 - a_2^2 h_2}{a_1^2 - a_2^2}\right) \\
&= o\left(\frac{1}{9\mu} + \frac{2}{3m}\right) + 2\left(h_1 a_1^2 - h_1 a_2^2\right)\frac{1}{a_1^2 - a_2^2}\left(\frac{1}{9\mu} - \frac{1}{3m}\right)
\end{aligned}
\right\}
\quad\ldots\ldots\ldots(25).
$$

When $r = a_1$,

$$
\left.
\begin{aligned}
\frac{\delta r}{r} &= \frac{1}{9\mu}\left(o + 2\frac{a_1^2 h_1 - a_2^2 h_2}{a_1^2 - a_2^2}\right) + \frac{1}{3m}\left(\frac{a_1^2 h_1 + 3a_2^2 h_1 - 4a_2^2 h_2}{a_1^2 - a_2^2} - o\right) \\
&= o\left(\frac{1}{9\mu} - \frac{1}{3m}\right) + h_1\frac{1}{a_1^2 - a_2^2}\left(\frac{2a_1^2}{9\mu} + \frac{a_1^2 + 3a_2^2}{3m}\right) - h_2\frac{a_2^2}{a_1^2 - a_2^2}\left(\frac{2}{9\mu} + \frac{4}{3m}\right)
\end{aligned}
\right\}
\quad\ldots(26).
$$

From these equations it appears that the longitudinal compression of cylindric tubes is proportional to the longitudinal pressure referred to unit of surface when the lateral pressures are constant, so that for a given pressure the compression is inversely as the sectional area of the tube.

These equations may be simplified in the following cases:—

1. When the external and internal pressures are equal, or $h_1 = h_2$.

2. When the external pressure is to the internal pressure as the square of the interior diameter is to that of the exterior diameter, or when $a_1^2 h_1 = a_2^2 h_2$.

3. When the cylinder is solid, or when $a_2 = 0$.

4. When the solid becomes an indefinitely extended plate with a cylindric hole in it, or when a_2 becomes infinite.

5. When pressure is applied only at the plane surfaces of the solid cylinder, and the cylindric surface is prevented from expanding by being inclosed in a strong case, or when $\dfrac{\delta r}{r} = 0$.

6. When pressure is applied to the cylindric surface, and the ends are retained at an invariable distance, or when $\dfrac{\delta x}{x} = 0$.

1. When $h_1 = h_2$, the equations of compression become

$$
\begin{aligned}
\frac{\delta x}{x} &= \frac{1}{9\mu}(o + 2h_1) + \frac{2}{3m}(o - h_1) \\
&= o\left(\frac{1}{9\mu} + \frac{2}{3m}\right) + 2h_1\left(\frac{1}{9\mu} - \frac{1}{3m}\right) \\
\frac{\delta r}{r} &= \frac{1}{9\mu}(o + 2h_1) + \frac{1}{3m}(h_1 - o) \\
&= o\left(\frac{1}{9\mu} - \frac{1}{3m}\right) + h_1\left(\frac{2}{9\mu} + \frac{1}{3m}\right)
\end{aligned}
\right\} \quad \dots\dots\dots\dots\dots (27).
$$

When $h_1 = h_2 = o$, then

$$
\frac{\delta x}{x} = \frac{\delta r}{r} = \frac{h_1}{3\mu}.
$$

The compression of a cylindrical vessel exposed on all sides to the same hydrostatic pressure is therefore independent of m, and it may be shewn that the same is true for a vessel of any shape.

2. When $a_1^2 h_1 = a_2^2 h_2$,

$$
\begin{aligned}
\frac{\delta x}{x} &= o\left(\frac{1}{9\mu} + \frac{2}{3m}\right) \\
\frac{\delta r}{r} &= \frac{1}{9\mu}(o) + \frac{1}{3m}(3h_1 - o) \\
&= o\left(\frac{1}{9\mu} - \frac{1}{3m}\right) + h_1\frac{1}{m}
\end{aligned}
\right\} \quad \dots\dots\dots\dots\dots (28).
$$

In this case, when $o = 0$, the compressions are independent of μ.

3. In a solid cylinder, $a_2 = 0$,

$$
p = q = h_1.
$$

The expressions for $\dfrac{\delta x}{x}$ and $\dfrac{\delta r}{r}$ are the same as those in the first case, when $h_1 = h_2$.

When the longitudinal pressure o vanishes,

$$
\frac{\delta x}{x} = 2h_1\left(\frac{1}{9\mu} - \frac{1}{3m}\right),
$$

$$
\frac{\delta r}{r} = h_1\left(\frac{2}{9\mu} - \frac{1}{3m}\right).
$$

When the cylinder is pressed on the plane sides only,

$$\frac{\delta x}{x} = o\left(\frac{1}{9\mu} + \frac{2}{3m}\right),$$

$$\frac{\delta r}{r} = o\left(\frac{1}{9\mu} - \frac{1}{3m}\right).$$

4. When the solid is infinite, or when a_1 is infinite,

$$\left.\begin{aligned}
p &= h_1 - \frac{1}{r^2} a_2^2 (h_1 - h_2) \\
q &= h_1 + \frac{1}{r^2} a_2^2 (h_1 - h_2) \\
I &= \omega (p - q) = -\frac{2\omega}{r^2} a_2^2 (h_1 - h_2) \\
\frac{\delta x}{x} &= \frac{1}{9\mu} (o + 2h_1) + \frac{2}{3m} (o - h_1) \\
&= o\left(\frac{1}{9\mu} + \frac{2}{3m}\right) + 2h_1\left(\frac{1}{9\mu} - \frac{1}{3m}\right) \\
\frac{\delta r}{r} &= \frac{1}{9\mu} (o + 2h_1) + \frac{1}{3m} (h_1 - o) \\
&= o\left(\frac{1}{9\mu} - \frac{1}{3m}\right) + h_1\left(\frac{2}{9\mu} + \frac{1}{3m}\right).
\end{aligned}\right\} \quad \ldots\ldots\ldots\ldots (29).$$

5. When $\delta r = 0$ in a solid cylinder,

$$\left.\begin{aligned}
\frac{\delta x}{x} &= \frac{3o}{2m + 3\mu} \\
\frac{\delta x}{x} &= 0, \quad \frac{\delta r}{r} = \frac{3h}{m + 6\mu}
\end{aligned}\right\} \quad \ldots\ldots\ldots\ldots\ldots(30).$$

6. When

Since the expression for the effect of a longitudinal strain is

$$\frac{\delta x}{x} = o\left(\frac{1}{9\mu} + \frac{2}{3m}\right),$$

if we make $\qquad E = \frac{9m\mu}{m + 6\mu}, \quad$ then $\quad \frac{\delta x}{x} = o\,\frac{1}{E} \ldots\ldots\ldots\ldots\ldots (31).$

The quantity E may be deduced from experiment on the extension of wires or rods of the substance, and μ is given in terms of m and E by the equation,

$$\mu = \frac{Em}{9m - 6E} \dots\dots\dots\dots\dots\dots\dots\dots\dots\dots\dots (32),$$

and

$$E = \frac{Pb}{s\delta x} \dots\dots\dots\dots\dots\dots\dots\dots\dots\dots\dots\dots (33),$$

P being the extending force, b the length of the rod, s the sectional area, and δx the elongation, which may be determined by the deflection of a wire, as in the apparatus of S' Gravesande, or by direct measurement.

Case IV.

The only known direct method of finding the compressibility of liquids is that employed by Canton, Œrsted, Perkins, Aimé, &c.

The liquid is confined in a vessel with a narrow neck, then pressure is applied, and the descent of the liquid in the tube is observed, so that the difference between the change of volume of liquid and the change of internal capacity of the vessel may be determined.

Now, since the substance of which the vessel is formed is compressible, a change of the internal capacity is possible. If the pressure be applied only to the contained liquid, it is evident that the vessel will be distended, and the compressibility of the liquid will appear too great. The pressure, therefore, is commonly applied externally and internally at the same time, by means of a hydrostatic pressure produced by water compressed either in a strong vessel or in the depths of the sea.

As it does not necessarily follow, from the equality of the external and internal pressures, that the capacity does not change, the equilibrium of the vessel must be determined theoretically. Œrsted, therefore, obtained from Poisson his solution of the problem, and applied it to the case of a vessel of lead. To find the cubical elasticity of lead, he applied the theory of Poisson to the numerical results of Tredgold. As the compressibility of lead thus found was greater than that of water, Œrsted expected that the apparent compressibility of water in a lead vessel would be *negative*. On making the experiment the apparent compressibility was *greater* in lead than in glass. The quantity found by Tredgold from the extension of rods was that denoted by E, and the value of μ deduced from E alone by the formulæ of Poisson cannot be true, unless $\frac{\mu}{m} = \frac{5}{6}$; and as $\frac{\mu}{m}$ for lead is probably more than 3, the calculated compressibility is much too great.

A similar experiment was made by Professor Forbes, who used a vessel of caoutchouc. As in this case the apparent compressibility vanishes, it appears that the cubical compressibility of caoutchouc is equal to that of water.

Some who reject the mathematical theories as unsatisfactory, have conjectured that if the sides of the vessel be sufficiently thin, the pressure on both sides being equal, the compressibility of the vessel will not affect the result. The following calculations shew that the apparent compressibility of the liquid depends on the compressibility of the vessel, and is independent of the thickness when the pressures are equal.

A hollow sphere, whose external and internal radii are a_1 and a_2, is acted on by external and internal normal pressures h_1 and h_2, it is required to determine the equilibrium of the elastic solid.

The pressures at any point in the solid are :—

1. A pressure p in the direction of the radius.
2. A pressure q in the perpendicular plane.

These pressures depend on the distance from the centre, which is denoted by r.

The compressions at any point are $\frac{d\delta r}{dr}$ in the radial direction, and $\frac{\delta r}{r}$ in the tangent plane, the values of these compressions are :—

$$\frac{d\delta r}{dr} = \left(\frac{1}{9\mu} - \frac{1}{3m}\right)(p + 2q) + \frac{1}{m} \, p \quad\text{......................} (34).$$

$$\frac{\delta r}{r} = \left(\frac{1}{9\mu} - \frac{1}{3m}\right)(p + 2q) + \frac{1}{m} \, q \quad\text{......................} (35).$$

Multiplying the last equation by r, differentiating with respect to r, and equating the result with that of the first equation, we find

$$r\left(\frac{1}{9\mu} - \frac{1}{3m}\right)\left(\frac{dp}{dr} + 2\frac{dq}{dr}\right) + \frac{1}{m}\left(r\frac{dq}{dr} + q - p\right) = 0.$$

Since the forces which act on the particle in the direction of the radius must balance one another, or

$$2qdrd\theta + p\,(rd\theta)^2 = \left(p + \frac{dp}{dr}\,dr\right)(r+dr)^2\theta,$$

therefore

$$q - p = \frac{r}{2}\frac{dp}{dr} \dots\dots\dots\dots\dots\dots\dots\dots (36).$$

Substituting this value of $q-p$ in the preceding equation, and reducing,

therefore

$$\frac{dp}{dr} + 2\frac{dq}{dr} = 0.$$

Integrating,

$$p + 2q = c_1.$$

But

$$q = \frac{r}{2}\frac{dp}{dr} + p,$$

and the equation becomes

$$\frac{dp}{dr} + 3\frac{p}{r} - \frac{c_1}{r} = 0,$$

therefore

$$p = c_2\frac{1}{r^3} + \frac{c_1}{3}.$$

Since $p = h_1$ when $r = a_1$, and $p = h_2$ when $r = a_2$, the value of p at any distance is found to be

$$p = \frac{a_1^3 h_1 - a_2^3 h_2}{a_1^3 - a_2^3} - \frac{a_1^3 a_2^3}{r^3}\frac{h_1 - h_2}{a_1^3 - a_2^3} \dots\dots\dots\dots\dots (37).$$

$$q = \frac{a_1^3 h_1 - a_2^3 h_2}{a_1^3 - a_2^3} + \tfrac{1}{2}\frac{a_1^3 a_2^3}{r^3}\frac{h_1 - h_2}{a_1^3 - a_2^3} \dots\dots\dots\dots\dots(38).$$

$$\frac{\delta V}{V} = 3\frac{\delta r}{r} = \frac{a_1^3 h_1 - a_2^3 h_2}{a_1^3 - a_2^3}\frac{1}{\mu} + \tfrac{3}{2}\frac{a_1^3 a_2^3}{r^3}\frac{h_1 - h_2}{a_1^3 - a_2^3}\frac{1}{m}$$

$$\left.\begin{array}{l}\text{When } r = a_1,\ \dfrac{\delta V}{V} = \dfrac{a_1^3 h_1 - a_2^3 h_2}{a_1^3 - a_2^3}\dfrac{1}{\mu} + \tfrac{3}{2}\,a_2^3\dfrac{h_1 - h_2}{a_1^3 - a_2^3}\dfrac{1}{m} \\[2mm] \qquad = \dfrac{h_1}{a_1^3 - a_2^3}\left(\dfrac{a_1^3}{\mu} + \dfrac{3a_2^3}{2m}\right) - \dfrac{h_2 a_2^3}{a_1^3 - a_2^3}\left(\dfrac{1}{\mu} - \dfrac{3}{2m}\right)\end{array}\right\} \dots\dots\dots(39).$$

When the external and internal pressures are equal

$$h_1 = h_2 = p = q,\ \text{ and }\ \frac{\delta V}{V} = \frac{h_1}{\mu} \dots\dots\dots\dots\dots(40),$$

the change of internal capacity depends entirely on the cubical elasticity of the vessel, and not on its thickness or linear elasticity.

When the external and internal pressures are inversely as the cubes of the radii of the surfaces on which they act,

$$a_1^3 h_1 = a_2^3 h_2, \quad p = \frac{a^3}{r^3} h_1, \quad q = -\tfrac{1}{2} \frac{a_1^3}{r^3} h_1$$
$$\frac{\delta V}{V} = -\tfrac{3}{2} \frac{a_1^3}{r^3} \frac{h_1}{m} \qquad \left.\right\} \quad \dots\dots\dots\dots (41).$$
$$\text{when } r = a_1, \quad \frac{\delta V}{V} = -\tfrac{3}{2} \frac{h_1}{m}$$

In this case the change of capacity depends on the linear elasticity alone.

M. Regnault, in his researches on the theory of the steam engine, has given an account of the experiments which he made in order to determine with accuracy the compressibility of mercury.

He considers the mathematical formulæ very uncertain, because the theories of molecular forces from which they are deduced are probably far from the truth; and even were the equations free from error, there would be much uncertainty in the ordinary method by measuring the elongation of a rod of the substance, for it is difficult to ensure that the material of the rod is the same as that of the hollow sphere.

He has, therefore, availed himself of the results of M. Lamé for a hollow sphere in three different cases, in the first of which the pressure acts on the interior and exterior surface at the same time, while in the other two cases the pressure is applied to the exterior or interior surface alone. Equation (39) becomes in these cases,—

1.   When $h_1 = h_2, \dfrac{\delta V}{V} = \dfrac{h_1}{\mu}$ and the compressibility of the enclosed liquid being μ_2, and the apparent diminution of volume $\delta' V$,

$$\frac{\delta' V}{V} = h_1 \left(\frac{1}{\mu_2} - \frac{1}{\mu} \right) \dots\dots\dots\dots\dots\dots (42).$$

2.   When $h_1 = 0$,

$$\frac{\delta V}{V} = \frac{\delta' V}{V} = -h_2 \frac{a_2^3}{a_1^3 - a_2^3} \left(\frac{1}{\mu} + \frac{3}{2m} \right) \dots\dots\dots\dots (43).$$

3.   When $h_2 = 0$,

$$\frac{\delta V}{V} = \frac{h_1}{a_1{}^3 - a_2{}^3} \left(\frac{a_1{}^3}{\mu} + \tfrac{3}{2} \frac{a_2{}^3}{V} \right),$$

$$\frac{\delta V}{V} = \frac{h_1}{a_1{}^3 - a_2{}^3} \left\{ \frac{a_1{}^3}{\mu} + \tfrac{3}{2} \frac{a_2{}^3}{m} + \left(a_2{}^3 - a_1{}^3 \right) \frac{1}{\mu_2} \right\}.$$

M. Lamé's equations differ from these only in assuming that $\mu = \tfrac{5}{8}m$. If this assumption be correct, then the coefficients μ, m, and μ_2, may be found from two of these equations; but since one of these equations may be derived from the other two, the *three* coefficients cannot be found when μ is supposed independent of m. In Equations (39), the quantities which may be varied at pleasure are h_1 and h_2, and the quantities which may be deduced from the apparent compressions are,

$$c_1 = \left(\frac{1}{\mu} + \frac{3}{2m} \right) \text{ and } \left(\frac{1}{\mu} - \frac{1}{\mu_2} \right) = c_2,$$

therefore some independent equation between these quantities must be found, and this cannot be done by means of the sphere alone; some other experiment must be made on the liquid, or on another portion of the substance of which the vessel is made.

The value of μ_2, the elasticity of the liquid, may be previously known.

The linear elasticity m of the vessel may be found by twisting a rod of the material of which it is made;

Or, the value of E may be found by the elongation or bending of the rod, and $\dfrac{1}{E} = \dfrac{1}{9\mu} + \dfrac{2}{3m}$.

We have here five quantities, which may be determined by experiment.

$$(43) \quad 1. \qquad c_1 = \left(\frac{1}{\mu} + \frac{3}{2m} \right) \text{ by external pressure} \left.\vphantom{\begin{array}{c} a \\ b \\ c \end{array}}\right\}$$

on sphere.

$$(42) \quad 2. \qquad c_2 = \left(\frac{1}{\mu} - \frac{1}{\mu_2} \right) \text{ equal pressures.}$$

$$(31) \quad 3. \qquad \frac{1}{E} = \left(\frac{1}{9m} + \frac{2}{3m} \right) \text{ by elongation of a rod.}$$

$(17) \quad 4. \qquad\quad m \qquad\qquad$ by twisting the rod.

$\qquad\quad\; 5. \qquad\quad \mu_2 \qquad\qquad$ the elasticity of the liquid.

When the elastic sphere is solid, the internal radius a_2 vanishes, and $h_1 = p = q$, and $\dfrac{\delta V}{V} = \dfrac{h_1}{\mu}$.

When the case becomes that of a spherical cavity in an infinite solid, the external radius a_1 becomes infinite, and

$$
\left.
\begin{aligned}
p &= h_1 - \frac{a_2^{\,3}}{r^3}\,(h_1 - h_2) \\[2mm]
q &= h_1 + \tfrac{1}{2}\,\frac{a_2^{\,3}}{r^2}\,(h_1 - h_2) \\[2mm]
\frac{\delta r}{r} &= h_1 \frac{1}{3\mu} + \tfrac{1}{2}\frac{a_2^{\,3}}{r^3}\,(h_1 - h_2)\frac{1}{m} \\[2mm]
\frac{\delta V}{V} &= \frac{h_1}{\mu} + \tfrac{3}{2}\frac{h_1 - h_2}{m}
\end{aligned}
\right\} \quad \ldots\ldots\ldots\ldots\ldots\ldots (44).
$$

The effect of pressure on the surface of a spherical cavity on any other part of an elastic solid is therefore inversely proportional to the cube of its distance from the centre of the cavity.

When one of the surfaces of an elastic hollow sphere has its radius rendered invariable by the support of an incompressible sphere, whose radius is a_1, then

$$
\frac{\delta r}{r} = 0, \quad \text{when } r = a_1,
$$

therefore

$$
\left.
\begin{aligned}
p &= h_2 \frac{3a_2^{\,3}\mu}{2a_1^{\,3}m + 3a_2^{\,3}\mu} + h_2 \frac{a_1^{\,3}a_2^{\,3}}{r^3}\frac{2m}{2a_1^{\,3}m + 3a_2^{\,3}\mu} \\[2mm]
q &= h_2 \frac{3a_2^{\,3}\mu}{2a_1^{\,3}m + 3a_2^{\,3}\mu} - \tfrac{1}{2}h_2 \frac{a_1^{\,3}a_2^{\,3}}{r^3}\frac{m}{2a_1^{\,3}m + 3a_2^{\,3}\mu} \\[2mm]
\frac{\delta r}{r} &= h_2 \frac{a_2^{\,3}}{2a_1^{\,3}m + 3a_2^{\,3}\mu} - h_2 \frac{a_1^{\,3}a_2^{\,3}}{r^3}\frac{1}{2a_1^{\,3}m + 3a_2^{\,3}\mu}
\end{aligned}
\right\} \quad \ldots\ldots\ldots\ldots\ldots\ldots (45).
$$

When $r = a_2$, $\dfrac{\delta V}{V} = h_2 \dfrac{3a_2^{\,3} - 3a_1^{\,3}}{2a_1^{\,3}m + 3a_2^{\,3}\mu}$

Case V.

On the equilibrium of an elastic beam of rectangular section uniformly bent.

By supposing the bent beam to be produced till it returns into itself, we may treat it as a hollow cylinder.

Let a rectangular elastic beam, whose length is $2\pi c$, be bent into a circular form, so as to be a section of a hollow cylinder, those parts of the beam which lie towards the centre of the circle will be longitudinally compressed, while the opposite parts will be extended.

The expression for the tangential compression is therefore

$$\frac{\delta r}{r} = \frac{r-c}{c}.$$

Comparing this value of $\frac{\delta r}{r}$ with that of Equation (20),

$$\frac{r-c}{r} = \left(\frac{1}{9\mu} - \frac{1}{3m}\right)(o+p+q) + \frac{1}{m}\, q,$$

and by (21), $$q = p + r\,\frac{dp}{dr}.$$

By substituting for q its value, and dividing by $r\left(\frac{1}{9\mu} + \frac{2}{3m}\right)$, the equation becomes

$$\frac{dp}{dr} + \frac{2m+3\mu}{m+6\mu}\frac{p}{r} = \frac{9m\mu - (m-3\mu)\,o}{(m+6\mu)\,r} - \frac{9m\mu}{(m+6\mu)}\frac{c}{r^2},$$

a linear differential equation, which gives

$$p = C_1 r^{-\frac{2m+3\mu}{m+6\mu}} - \frac{9m\mu}{m-3\mu}\frac{c}{r} + \frac{9\mu m - (m-3\mu)\,o}{2m+3\mu} \ \ldots\ldots\ldots\ldots (46).$$

C_1 may be found by assuming that when $r = a_1$, $p = h_1$, and q may be found from p by equation (21).

As the expressions thus found are long and cumbrous, it is better to use the following approximations :—

$$q = -\left(\frac{9m\mu}{m+6\mu}\right)\frac{y}{c} \ \ldots\ldots\ldots\ldots\ldots\ldots\ldots\ldots\ldots\ldots (47).$$

$$p = \left(\frac{9m\mu}{m+6\mu}\right)\frac{1}{2c}\left(\frac{c^2 - a^2}{y+c} + c - y\right) \ \ldots\ldots\ldots\ldots\ldots (48).$$

In these expressions a is half the depth of the beam, and y is the distance of any part of the beam from the neutral surface, which in this case is a cylindric surface, whose radius is c.

These expressions suppose c to be large compared with a, since most substances break when $\frac{a}{c}$ exceeds a certain small quantity.

Let b be the breadth of the beam, then the force with which the beam resists flexure $= M$.

$$M = \int byq = \frac{9m\mu}{m+6\mu} \frac{b}{c} \frac{a^3}{3} = E \frac{a^3 b}{3c} \dots\dots\dots\dots\dots(49),$$

which is the ordinary expression for the stiffness of a rectangular beam.

The stiffness of a beam of any section, the form of which is expressed by an equation between x and y, the axis of x being perpendicular to the plane of flexure, or the osculating plane of the axis of the beam at any point, is expressed by

$$Mc = E \int y^2 dx \dots\dots\dots\dots\dots\dots(50),$$

M being the moment of the force which bends the beam, and c the radius of the circle into which it is bent.

CASE VI.

At the meeting of the British Association in 1839, Mr James Nasmyth described his method of making concave specula of silvered glass by bending.

A circular piece of silvered plate-glass was cemented to the opening of an iron vessel, from which the air was afterwards exhausted. The mirror then became concave, and the focal distance depended on the pressure of the air.

Buffon proposed to make burning-mirrors in this way, and to produce the partial vacuum by the combustion of the air in the vessel, which was to be effected by igniting sulphur in the interior of the vessel by means of a burning-glass. Although sulphur evidently would not answer for this purpose, phosphorus might; but the simplest way of removing the air is by means of the air-pump. The mirrors which were actually made by Buffon, were bent by means of a screw acting on the centre of the glass.

To find an expression for the curvature produced in a flat, circular, elastic plate, by the difference of the hydrostatic pressures which act on each side of it,—

Let t be the thickness of the plate, which must be small compared with its diameter.

Let the form of the middle surface of the plate, after the curvature is produced, be expressed by an equation between r, the distance of any point from the axis, or normal to the centre of the plate, and x the distance of the point from the plane in which the middle of the plate originally was, and let

$$ds = \sqrt{(dx)^2 + (dr)^2}.$$

Let h_1 be the pressure on one side of the plate, and h_2 that on the other.

Let p and q be the pressures in the plane of the plate at any point, p acting in the direction of a tangent to the section of the plate by a plane passing through the axis, and q acting in the direction perpendicular to that plane.

By equating the forces which act on any particle in a direction parallel to the axis, we find

$$tp\frac{dr}{ds}\frac{dx}{ds}+tr\frac{dp}{ds}\frac{dx}{ds}+trp\frac{d^2x}{ds^2}+r\left(h_1-h_2\right)\frac{dr}{ds}=0.$$

By making $p=0$ when $r=0$ in this equation, when integrated,

$$p=-\frac{r}{2t}\frac{ds}{dx}(h_1-h_2)\dots\dots\dots\dots\dots(51).$$

The forces perpendicular to the axis are

$$tp\left(\frac{dr}{ds}\right)^2+tr\frac{dp}{ds}\frac{dr}{ds}+trp\frac{d^2r}{ds^2}-(h_1-h_2)\,r\frac{dx}{ds}-qt=0.$$

Substituting for p its value, the equation gives

$$q=-\frac{(h_1-h_2)}{t}\,r\left(\frac{dr}{ds}\frac{dr}{dx}+\frac{dx}{ds}\right)+\frac{(h_1-h_2)}{2t}\,r^2\left(\frac{dr}{dx}\frac{ds}{dx}\frac{d^2x}{ds^2}-\frac{ds}{dx}\frac{d^2r}{ds^2}\right)\dots(52).$$

The equations of elasticity become

$$\frac{d\delta s}{ds}=\left(\frac{1}{9\mu}-\frac{1}{3m}\right)\left(p+q+\frac{h_1+h_2}{2}\right)+\frac{p}{m}\,,$$

$$\frac{\delta r}{r}=\left(\frac{1}{9\mu}-\frac{1}{3m}\right)\left(p+q+\frac{h_1+h_2}{2}\right)+\frac{q}{m}\,.$$

Differentiating $\dfrac{d\delta r}{dr}=\dfrac{d}{dr}\left(\dfrac{\delta r}{r}r\right)$, and in this case

$$\frac{d\delta r}{dr}=1-\frac{dr}{ds}+\frac{dr}{ds}\frac{d\delta s}{ds}\,.$$

By a comparison of these values of $\dfrac{d\delta r}{ds}$,

$$\left(1-\frac{dr}{ds}\right)\left(\frac{1}{9\mu}-\frac{1}{3m}\right)\left(p+q+\frac{h_1+h_2}{2}\right)+\frac{q}{m}+\frac{dr}{ds}\frac{p}{m}+r\left(\frac{1}{9\mu}-\frac{1}{3m}\right)\left(\frac{dp}{dr}+\frac{dq}{dr}\right)$$
$$+\frac{r}{m}\frac{dq}{dr}+\frac{dr}{ds}-1=0.$$

To obtain an expression for the curvature of the plate at the vertex, let a be the radius of curvature, then, as an approximation to the equation of the plate, let

$$x = \frac{r^2}{2a} .$$

By substituting the value of x in the values of p and q, and in the equation of elasticity, the approximate value of a is found to be

$$a = \frac{t}{h_1 - h_2} \frac{(h_1 + h_2)\left(\dfrac{1}{9\mu} - \dfrac{1}{3m}\right) - 2}{10\left(\dfrac{1}{9\mu} - \dfrac{1}{3m}\right) + \dfrac{9}{m}} ,$$

$$a = \frac{t}{h_1 - h_2} \frac{-18m\mu}{10m + 51\mu} + t \frac{h_1 + h_2}{h_1 - h_2} \frac{m - 3\mu}{10m + 51\mu} \dots\dots\dots\dots(53).$$

Since the focal distance of the mirror, or $\frac{a}{2}$, depends on the difference of pressures, a telescope on Mr Nasmyth's principle would act as an aneroid barometer, the focal distance varying inversely as the pressure of the atmosphere.

Case VII.

To find the conditions of torsion of a cylinder composed of a great number of parallel wires bound together without adhering to one another.

Let x be the length of the cylinder, a its radius, r the radius at any point, $\delta\theta$ the angle of torsion, M the force producing torsion, δx the change of length, and P the longitudinal force. Each of the wires becomes a helix whose radius is r, its angular rotation $\delta\theta$, and its length along the axis $x - \delta x$.

Its length is therefore $\sqrt{(r\delta\theta)^2 + x^2\left(1 - \dfrac{\delta x}{x}\right)^2}$,

and the tension is $= E\left\{1 - \sqrt{\left(1 - \dfrac{\delta x}{x}\right)^2 + r^2\left(\dfrac{\delta\theta}{x}\right)^2}\right\} .$

This force, resolved parallel to the axis, is

$$\frac{1}{r}\frac{d}{d\theta}\frac{d}{dr}P = E\left\{\frac{1}{\sqrt{\left(1 - \dfrac{\delta x}{x}\right)^2 + r^2\left(\dfrac{\delta\theta}{x}\right)^2}} - 1\right\},$$

and since $\dfrac{\delta x}{x}$ and $r\dfrac{\delta\theta}{x}$ are small, we may assume

$$\frac{d}{d\theta}\frac{d}{dr}P = Er\left\{\frac{\delta x}{x} - \frac{r^2}{2}\left(\frac{\delta\theta}{x}\right)^2\right\},$$

$$P = \pi E\left\{r^3\frac{\delta x}{x} - \frac{r^4}{4}\left(\frac{\delta\theta}{x}\right)^2\right\} \quad\ldots\ldots\ldots\ldots\ldots\ldots (54),$$

The force, when resolved in the tangential direction, is approximately

$$\frac{1}{r}\frac{d}{d\theta}\frac{d}{dr}M = Er\left\{r\frac{\delta\theta}{x}\frac{\delta x}{x} - \frac{r^3}{2}\left(\frac{\delta\theta}{x}\right)^3\right\},$$

$$M = \pi E\left\{\frac{r^4}{2}\frac{\delta\theta}{x}\frac{\delta x}{x} - \frac{r^6}{6}\left(\frac{\delta\theta}{x}\right)^3\right\} \quad\ldots\ldots\ldots\ldots\ldots\ldots\ldots\ldots (55).$$

By eliminating $\dfrac{\delta x}{x}$ between (54) and (55) we have

$$M = \frac{r^2}{2}\frac{\delta\theta}{x}P - E\pi\frac{r^6}{24}\left(\frac{\delta\theta}{x}\right)^3 \quad\ldots\ldots\ldots\ldots\ldots\ldots (56).$$

When $P = 0$, M depends on the sixth power of the radius and the cube of the angle of torsion, when the cylinder is composed of separate filaments.

Since the force of torsion for a homogeneous cylinder depends on the fourth power of the radius and the first power of the angle of torsion, the torsion of a wire having a fibrous texture will depend on both these laws.

The parts of the force of torsion which depend on these two laws may be found by experiment, and thus the difference of the elasticities in the direction of the axis and in the perpendicular directions may be determined.

A calculation of the force of torsion, on this supposition, may be found in Young's *Mathematical Principles of Natural Philosophy*; and it is introduced here to account for the variations from the law of Case II., which may be observed in a twisted rod.

CASE VIII.

It is well known that grindstones and fly-wheels are often broken by the centrifugal force produced by their rapid rotation. I have therefore calculated the strains and pressure acting on an elastic cylinder revolving round its axis, and acted on by the centrifugal force alone.

The equation of the equilibrium of a particle [see Equation (21)], becomes

$$q - p = r \frac{dp}{dr} - \frac{4\pi^2 k}{gt^2} r^2 ;$$

where q and p are the tangential and radial pressures, k is the weight in pounds of a cubic inch of the substance, g is twice the height in inches that a body falls in a second, t is the time of revolution of the cylinder in seconds.

By substituting the value of q and $\frac{dq}{dr}$ in Equations (19), (20), and neglecting o,

$$0 = \left(\frac{1}{9\mu} - \frac{1}{3m} \right) \left(3 \frac{dp}{dr} - 2 \frac{4\pi^2 k}{gt^2} r + r \frac{d^2 p}{dr^2} \right) + \frac{1}{m} \left(3 \frac{dp}{dr} - 3 \frac{4\pi^2 k}{gt^2} r + r \frac{d^2 p}{dr^2} \right)$$

which gives

$$p = c_1 \frac{1}{r^2} + \frac{\pi^2 k}{2gt^2} \left(2 + \frac{E}{m} \right) r^2 + c_2$$

$$\therefore \quad q - p = - c_1 \frac{1}{r^2} + \frac{\pi^2 k}{2gt} \left(-4 + \frac{2E}{m} \right) r^2$$

$$q = - c_1 \frac{1}{r^2} + \frac{\pi^2 k}{2gt^2} \left(-2 + \frac{3E}{m_3} \right) r^2 + c_2$$

\left. \right\} \quad .... (57).

If the radii of the surfaces of the hollow cylinder be a_1 and a_2, and the pressures acting on them h_1 and h_2, then the values of c_1 and c_2 are

$$c_1 = a_1^2 a_2^2 \frac{\pi^2 k}{2gt^2} \left(2 + \frac{E}{m} \right) - a_1^2 a_2^2 \frac{h_1 - h_2}{a_1^2 - a_2^2}$$

$$c_2 = \frac{a_1^2 h_1 - a_2^2 h_2}{a_1^2 - a_2^2} - \left(a_1^2 + a_2^2 \right) \frac{\pi^2 k}{2gt^2} \left(2 + \frac{E}{m} \right)$$

\left. \right\} \quad .... (58).

When $a_2 = 0$, as in the case of a solid cylinder, $c_1 = 0$, and

$$c_2 = h_1 - a_1^2 \frac{\pi^2 k}{2gt^2} \left(2 + \frac{E}{m} \right),$$

$$q = h_1 + \frac{\pi^2 k}{2gt^2} \left\{ 2 \left(r^2 + a_1^2 \right) + \frac{E}{m} \left(3r^2 - a_1^2 \right) \right\} .... (59).$$

When $h_1 = 0$, and $r = a_1$,

$$q = \frac{\pi^2 k a_1^2}{gt^2} \left(\frac{E}{m} - 2 \right) ....(60).$$

When q exceeds the tenacity of the substance in pounds per square inch, the cylinder will give way; and by making q equal to the number of pounds which a square inch of the substance will support, the velocity may be found which the bursting of the cylinder will take place.

Since $I = b\omega(q-p) = \dfrac{\pi^2 k\omega}{gt}\left(\dfrac{E}{m} - 2\right)br^2$, a transparent revolving cylinder, when polarized light is transmitted parallel to the axis, will exhibit rings whose diameters are as the square roots of an arithmetical progression, and brushes parallel and perpendicular to the plane of polarization.

CASE IX.

A hollow cylinder or tube is surrounded by a medium of a constant temperature while a liquid of a different temperature is made to flow through it. The exterior and interior surfaces are thus kept each at a constant temperature till the transference of heat through the cylinder becomes uniform.

Let v be the temperature at any point, then when this quantity has reached its limit,

$$\frac{r\,dv}{dr} = c_1,$$

$$v = c_1 \log r + c_2 \dots\dots\dots\dots\dots\dots\dots\dots (61).$$

Let the temperatures at the surfaces be θ_1 and θ_2, and the radii of the surfaces a_1 and a_2, then

$$c_1 = \frac{\theta_1 - \theta_2}{\log a_1 - \log a_2}, \quad c_2 = \frac{\log a_1 \theta_2 - \log a_2 \theta_1}{\log a_1 - \log a_2}.$$

Let the coefficient of linear dilatation of the substance be c_3, then the proportional dilatation at any point will be expressed by $c_3 v$, and the equations of elasticity (18), (19), (20), become

$$\frac{d\delta x}{dx} = \left(\frac{1}{9\mu} - \frac{1}{3m}\right)(o + p + q) + \frac{o}{m} - c_3 v,$$

$$\frac{d\delta r}{dr} = \left(\frac{1}{9\mu} - \frac{1}{3m}\right)(o + p + q) + \frac{p}{m} - c_3 v,$$

$$\frac{\delta r}{r} = \left(\frac{1}{9\mu} - \frac{1}{3m}\right)(o + p + q) + \frac{q}{m} - c_3 v.$$

The equation of equilibrium is

$$q = p + r\frac{dp}{dr} \dots\dots\dots\dots\dots\dots\dots\dots (21),$$

and since the tube is supposed to be of a considerable length

$$\frac{d\delta x}{dx} = c_4 \text{ a constant quantity.}$$

From these equations we find that

$$0 = \cfrac{c_4 + c_3 v - \left(\cfrac{1}{9\mu} - \cfrac{1}{3m}\right)\left(2p + r\cfrac{dp}{dr}\right)}{\cfrac{1}{9\mu} + \cfrac{2}{3m}},$$

and hence $v = c_1 \log r + c_2$, p may be found in terms of r.

$$p = \left(\frac{2}{9\mu} + \frac{1}{3m}\right)^{-1} c_1 c_3 \log r + c_5 \frac{1}{r^2} + c_6.$$

Hence $\qquad q = \left(\dfrac{2}{9\mu} + \dfrac{1}{3m}\right)^{-1} c_1 c_3 \log r - c_5 \dfrac{1}{r^2} + c_6 + \left(\dfrac{2}{9\mu} + \dfrac{1}{3m}\right) c_1 c_3.$

Since $\qquad I = b\omega(q - p) = b\omega\left(\dfrac{2}{9\mu} + \dfrac{1}{3m}\right)^{-1} c_1 c_3 - 2b\omega c_5 \dfrac{1}{r^2},$

the rings seen in this case will differ from those described in Case III. only by the addition of a constant quantity.

When no pressures act on the exterior and interior surfaces of the tube $h_1 = h_2 = 0$, and

$$\left.\begin{aligned}
p &= \left(\frac{2}{9\mu} + \frac{1}{3m}\right)^{-1} c_1 c_3 \left(\log r + \frac{a_1^2 a_2^2}{r^2}\frac{\log a_1 - \log a_2}{a_1^2 - a_2^2} + \frac{a_1^2 \log a_1 - a_2^2 \log a_2}{a_1^2 - a_2^2}\right), \\
q &= \left(\frac{2}{9\mu} + \frac{1}{3m}\right)^{-1} c_1 c_3 \left(\log r - \frac{a_1^2 a_2^2}{r^2}\frac{\log a_1 - \log a_2}{a_1^2 - a_2^2} + \frac{a_1^2 \log a_1 - a_2^2 \log a_2}{a_1^2 - a_2^2} + 1\right), \\
I &= b\left(\frac{2}{9\mu} + \frac{1}{3m}\right)^{-1} c_1 c_3 \omega \left(1 - 2\frac{a_1^2 a_2^2}{r^2}\frac{\log a_1 - \log a_2}{a_1^2 - a_2^2}\right).
\end{aligned}\right\} \dots (62).$$

There will, therefore, be no action on polarized light for the ring whose radius is r when

$$r^2 = 2\frac{a_1^2 a_2^2}{a_1^2 - a_2^2}\log\frac{a_1}{a_2}.$$

Case X.

Sir David Brewster has observed (*Edinburgh Transactions*, Vol. VIII.), that when a solid cylinder of glass is suddenly heated at the cylindric surface a polarizing force is developed, which is at any point proportional to the square of the distance from the axis of the cylinder; that is to say, that the difference of retardation of the oppositely polarized rays of light is proportional to the square of the radius r, or

$$I = bc_1\omega r^2 = b\omega\,(q-p) = b\omega r\,\frac{dp}{dr}\,,$$

$$\therefore\ \frac{dp}{dr} = c_1 r, \quad \therefore\ p = \frac{c_1}{2}\,r^2 + c_{2}.$$

Since if a be the radius of the cylinder, $p=0$ when $r=a$,

$$p = \frac{c_1}{2}\,(r^2 - a^2).$$

Hence

$$q = \frac{c_1}{2}\,(3r^2 - a^2).$$

By substituting these values of p and q in equations (19) and (20), and making $\dfrac{d}{dr}\,\dfrac{\delta r}{r}\,r = \dfrac{d\delta r}{dr}\,$, I find,

$$v = \frac{2c_1}{c_3}\left(\frac{1}{9\mu} + \frac{2}{3m}\right)r^2 + c_4, \quad\ldots\ldots\ldots\ldots\ldots(63).$$

c_4 being the temperature of the axis of the cylinder, and c_3 the coefficient of linear expansion for glass.

CASE XI.

Heat is passing uniformly through the sides of a spherical vessel, such as the ball of a thermometer, it is required to determine the mechanical state of the sphere. As the methods are nearly the same as in Case IX., it will be sufficient to give the results, using the same notation.

$$r^2\,\frac{dv}{dr} = c_1, \quad \therefore\ v = c_2 - \frac{c_1}{r}\,,$$

$$c_1 = a_1 a_2\,\frac{\theta_1 - \theta_2}{a_1 - a_2}, \quad c_2 = \frac{\theta_1 a_1 - \theta_2 a_2}{a_1 - a_2}\,,$$

$$p = c_4\,\frac{1}{r^3} - \left(\frac{2}{9\mu} + \frac{1}{3m}\right)^{-1}c_1 c_3\,\frac{1}{r} + c_{5}.$$

When $h_1 = h_2 = 0$ the expression for p becomes

$$p = \left(\frac{2}{9\mu} + \frac{1}{3m}\right)^{-1}c_3\,(\theta_1 - \theta_2)\left\{\frac{a_1^3 a_2^3}{a_1^3 - a_2^3}\,\frac{1}{r^3} - \frac{a_1 a_2}{a_1 - a_2}\,\frac{1}{r} + a_1 a_2\,\frac{a_1^2 - a_2^2}{(a_1 - a_2)\,(a_1^3 - a_2^3)}\right\}\ \ldots\ldots\,(64).$$

From this value of p the other quantities may be found, as in Case IX., from the equations of Case IV.

Case XII.

When a long beam is bent into the form of a closed circular ring (as in Case V.), all the pressures act either parallel or perpendicular to the direction of the length of the beam, so that if the beam were divided into planks, there would be no tendency of the planks to slide on one another.

But when the beam does not form a closed circle, the planks into which it may be supposed to be divided will have a tendency to slide on one another, and the amount of sliding is determined by the linear elasticity of the substance. The deflection of the beam thus arises partly from the bending of the whole beam, and partly from the sliding of the planks; and since each of these deflections is small compared with the length of the beam, the total deflection will be the sum of the deflections due to bending and sliding.

Let
$$A = Mc = E \int xy^2 dy \dots\dots\dots\dots\dots\dots\dots(65).$$

A is the stiffness of the beam as found in Case V., the equation of the transverse section being expressed in terms of x and y, y being measured from the neutral surface.

Let a horizontal beam, whose length is $2l$, and whose weight is $2w$, be supported at the extremities and loaded at the middle with a weight W.

Let the deflection at any point be expressed by $\delta_1 y$, and let this quantity be small compared with the length of the beam.

At the middle of the beam, $\delta_1 y$ is found by the usual methods to be

$$\delta_1 y = \frac{1}{A} \left(\tfrac{5}{24} l^3 w + \tfrac{1}{6} l^3 W \right) \dots\dots\dots\dots\dots\dots (66).$$

Let
$$B = \frac{m}{2} \int x \, dy = \frac{m}{2} \text{ (sectional area)} \dots\dots\dots\dots\dots(67).$$

B is the resistance of the beam to the sliding of the planks. The deflection of the beam arising from this cause is

$$\delta_2 y = \frac{l}{2B} (w + W) \dots\dots\dots\dots\dots\dots\dots(68).$$

This quantity is small compared with $\delta_1 y$, when the depth of the beam is small compared with its length.

The whole deflection $\Delta y = \delta_1 y + \delta_2 y$

$$\Delta y = \frac{l^3}{6A}\left(\tfrac{5}{4}w + W\right) + \frac{l}{2B}\left(w + W\right)$$

$$\Delta y = w\left(\tfrac{5}{24}\frac{l^3}{A} + \tfrac{1}{2}\frac{l}{B}\right) + W\left(\frac{l^3}{6A} + \tfrac{1}{2}\frac{l}{B}\right) \quad\ldots\ldots\ldots\ldots\ldots\ldots(69).$$

CASE XIII.

When the values of the compressions at any point have been found, when two different sets of forces act on a solid separately, the compressions, when the forces act at the same time, may be found by the composition of compressions, because the small compressions are independent of one another.

It appears from Case I., that if a cylinder be twisted as there described, the compressions will be inversely proportional to the square of the distance from the centre.

If *two* cylindric surfaces, whose axes are perpendicular to the plane of an indefinite elastic plate, be equally twisted in the same direction, the resultant compression in any direction may be found by adding the compression due to each resolved in that direction.

The result of this operation may be thus stated geometrically. Let A_1 and A_2 (Fig. 1) be the centres of the twisted cylinders. Join $A_1 A_2$, and bisect $A_1 A_2$ in O. Draw OBC at right angles, and cut off OB_1 and OB_2 each equal to OA_1.

Then the difference of the retardation of oppositely polarized rays of light passing perpendicularly through any point of the plane varies directly as the product of its distances from B_1 and B_2, and inversely as the square of the product of its distances from A_1 and A_2.

The isochromatic lines are represented in the figure.

The retardation is infinite at the points A_1 and A_2; it vanishes at B_1 and B_2; and if the retardation at O be taken for unity, the isochromatic curves 2, 4, surround A_1 and A_2; that in which the retardation is unity has two loops, and passes through O; the curves $\frac{1}{2}$, $\frac{1}{4}$ are continuous, and have points of contrary flexure; the curve $\frac{1}{8}$ has multiple points at C_1 and C_2, where

$A_1 C_1 = A_1 A_2$, and two loops surrounding B_1 and B_2; the other curves, for which $I = \frac{1}{16}$, $\frac{1}{32}$, &c., consist each of two ovals surrounding B_1 and B_2, and an exterior portion surrounding all the former curves.

Fig. 1.

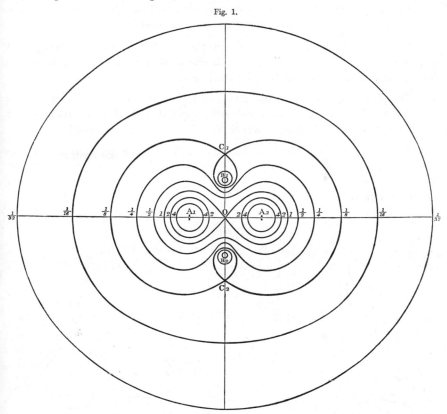

I have produced these curves in the jelly of isinglass described in Case I. They are best seen by using circularly polarized light, as the curves are then seen without interruption, and their resemblance to the calculated curves is more apparent. To avoid crowding the curves toward the centre of the figure, I have taken the values of I for the different curves, not in an arithmetical, but in a geometrical progression, ascending by powers of 2.

Case XIV.

On the determination of the pressures which act in the interior of transparent solids, from observations of the action of the solid on polarized light.

Sir David Brewster has pointed out the method by which polarized light might be made to indicate the strains in elastic solids; and his experiments on bent glass confirm the theories of the bending of beams.

The phenomena of heated and unannealed glass are of a much more complex nature, and they cannot be predicted and explained without a knowledge of the laws of cooling and solidification, combined with those of elastic equilibrium.

In Case X. I have given an example of the inverse problem, in the case of a cylinder in which the action on light followed a simple law; and I now go on to describe the method of determining the pressures in a general case, applying it to the case of a triangle of unannealed plate-glass.

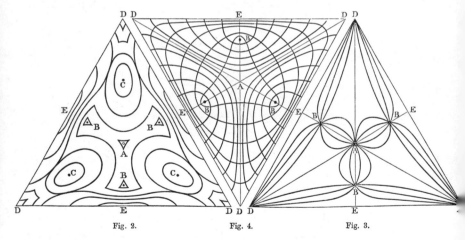

Fig. 2.   Fig. 4.   Fig. 3.

The lines of equal intensity of the action on light are seen without interruption, by using circularly polarized light. They are represented in Fig. 2, where *A, BBB, DDD* are the neutral points, or points of no action on light, and *CCC, EEE* are the points where that action is greatest; and the intensity of the action at any other point is determined by its position with respect to the isochromatic curves.

The direction of the principal axes of pressure at any point is found by transmitting plane polarized light, and analysing it in the plane perpendicular to that of polarization. The light is then restored in every part of the triangle, except in those points at which one of the principal axes is parallel to the plane of polarization. A dark band formed of all these points is seen, which shifts its position as the triangle is turned round in its own plane. Fig. 3 represents these curves for every fifteenth degree of inclination. They correspond to the lines of equal variation of the needle in a magnetic chart.

From these curves others may be found which shall indicate, by their own direction, the direction of the principal axes at any point. These curves of direction of compression and dilatation are represented in Fig. 4; the curves whose direction corresponds to that of *compression* are concave toward the centre of the triangle, and intersect at right angles the curves of dilatation.

Let the isochromatic lines in Fig. 2 be determined by the equation

$$\phi_1(x, y) = I\frac{1}{z} = \omega\,(q-p)\,\frac{1}{z}\,,$$

where I is the difference of retardation of the oppositely polarized rays, and q and p the pressures in the principal axes at any point, z being the thickness of the plate.

Let the lines of equal inclination be determined by the equation

$$\phi_2\,(x,\,y) = \tan\theta,$$

θ being the angle of inclination of the principal axes; then the differential equation of the curves of direction of compression and dilatation (Fig. 4) is

$$\phi_2\,(x,\,y) = \frac{dy}{dx}\,.$$

By considering any particle of the plate as a portion of a cylinder whose axis passes through the centre of curvature of the curve of compression, we find

$$q - p = r\,\frac{dp}{dr} \dotfill (21).$$

Let R denote the radius of curvature of the curve of compression at any point, and let S denote the length of the curve of dilatation at the same point,

$$\phi_3(x, y) = R, \qquad \phi_4(x, y) = S,$$

$$q - p = R \frac{dp}{dS},$$

and since $(q-p)$, R and S are known, and since at the surface, where $\phi_5(x, y) = 0$, $p = 0$, all the data are given for determining the absolute value of p by integration.

Though this is the best method of finding p and q by graphic construction, it is much better, when the equations of the curves have been found, that is, when ϕ_1 and ϕ_2 are known, to resolve the pressures in the direction of the axes.

The new quantities are p_1, p_2, and q_3; and the equations are

$$\tan \theta = \frac{q_3}{p_1 - p_2}, \quad (p - q)^2 = q_3^2 + (p_1 - p_2)^2, \quad p_1 + p_2 = p + q.$$

It is therefore possible to find the pressures from the curves of equal tint and equal inclination, in any case in which it may be required. In the meantime the curves of Figs. 2, 3, 4 shew the correctness of Sir John Herschell's ingenious explanation of the phenomena of heated and unannealed glass.

Note A.

As the mathematical laws of compressions and pressures have been very thoroughly investigated, and as they are demonstrated with great elegance in the very complete and elaborate memoir of MM. Lamé and Clapeyron, I shall state as briefly as possible their results.

Let a solid be subjected to compressions or pressures of any kind, then, if through any point in the solid lines be drawn whose lengths, measured from the given point, are proportional to the compression or pressure at the point resolved in the directions in which the lines are drawn, the extremities of such lines will be in the surface of an ellipsoid, whose centre is the given point.

The properties of the system of compressions or pressures may be deduced from those of the ellipsoid.

There are three diameters having perpendicular ordinates, which are called the *principal axes* of the ellipsoid.

Similarly, there are always three directions in the compressed particle in which there is no tangential action, or tendency of the parts to slide on one another. These directions are called the *principal axes* of *compression* or of *pressure,* and in homogeneous solids they always coincide with each other.

The compression or pressure in any other direction is equal to the sum of the products of the compressions or pressures in the principal axes multiplied into the squares of the cosines of the angles which they respectively make with that direction.

NOTE B.

The fundamental equations of this paper differ from those of Navier, Poisson, &c., only in not assuming an invariable ratio between the linear and the cubical elasticity; but since I have not attempted to deduce them from the laws of molecular action, some other reasons must be given for adopting them.

The experiments from which the laws are deduced are—

1st. Elastic solids put into motion vibrate isochronously, so that the sound does not vary with the amplitude of the vibrations.

2nd. Regnault's experiments on hollow spheres shew that both linear and cubic compressions are proportional to the pressures.

3rd. Experiments on the elongation of rods and tubes immersed in water, prove that the elongation, the decrease of diameter, and the increase of volume, are proportional to the tension.

4th. In Coulomb's balance of torsion, the angles of torsion are proportional to the twisting forces.

It would appear from these experiments, that compressions are always proportional to pressures.

Professor Stokes has expressed this by making one of his coefficients depend on the cubical elasticity, while the other is deduced from the displacement of shifting produced by a given tangential force.

M. Cauchy makes one coefficient depend on the linear compression produced by a force acting in one direction, and the other on the change of volume produced by the same force.

Both of these methods lead to a correct result; but the coefficients of Stokes seem to have more of a real signification than those of Cauchy; I have therefore adopted those of Stokes, using the symbols m and μ, and the fundamental equations (4) and (5), which define them.

NOTE C.

As the coefficient ω, which determines the optical effect of pressure on a substance, varies from one substance to another, and is probably a function of the linear elasticity, a determination of its value in different substances might lead to some explanation of the action of media on light.

This paper commenced by pointing out the insufficiency of all theories of elastic solids, in which the equations do not contain two independent constants deduced from experiments. One of these constants is common to liquids and solids, and is called the modulus of *cubical* elasticity. The other is peculiar to solids, and is here called the modulus of *linear* elasticity. The equations of Navier, Poisson, and Lamé and Clapeyron, contain only one coefficient; and Professor G. G. Stokes of Cambridge, seems to have formed the first theory of elastic solids which recognised the independence of cubical and linear elasticity, although M. Cauchy seems to have suggested a modification of the old theories, which made the ratio of linear to cubical elasticity the same for all substances. Professor Stokes has deduced the theory of elastic solids from that of the motion of fluids, and his equations are identical with those of this paper, which are deduced from the two following assumptions.

In an element of an elastic solid, acted on by three pressures at right angles to one another, as long as the compressions do not pass the limits of perfect elasticity—

1st. The sum of the pressures, in three rectangular axes, is proportional to the sum of the compressions in those axes.

2nd. The difference of the pressures in two axes at right angles to one another, is proportional to the difference of the compressions in those axes.

Or, in symbols:

$$1. \quad (P_1 + P_2 + P_3) = 3\mu \left(\frac{\delta x}{x} + \frac{\delta y}{y} + \frac{\delta z}{z} \right).$$

$$2. \quad \begin{cases} (P_1 - P_2) = m \left(\dfrac{\delta x}{x} - \dfrac{\delta y}{y} \right), \\[2mm] (P_2 - P_3) = m \left(\dfrac{\delta y}{y} - \dfrac{\delta z}{z} \right), \\[2mm] (P_3 - P_1) = m \left(\dfrac{\delta z}{z} - \dfrac{\delta x}{x} \right), \end{cases}$$

μ being the modulus of *cubical*, and m that of *linear* elasticity.

These equations are found to be very convenient for the solution of problems, some of which were given in the latter part of the paper.

These particular cases were—

That of an elastic hollow cylinder, the exterior surface of which was fixed, while the interior was turned through a small angle. The action of a transparent solid thus twisted on polarized light, was calculated, and the calculation confirmed by experiment.

The second case related to the torsion of cylindric rods, and a method was given by which m may be found. The quantity $E = \dfrac{9mn}{m + 6n}$ was found by elongating, or by bending the rod used to determine m, and μ is found by the equation,

$$\mu = \frac{Em}{9m - 6E}.$$

The effect of pressure on the surfaces of a hollow sphere or cylinder was calculated, and the result applied to the determination of the cubical compressibility of liquids and solids.

An expression was found for the curvature of an elastic plate exposed to pressure on one side; and the state of cylinders acted on by centrifugal force and by heat was determined.

The principle of the superposition of compressions and pressures was applied to the case of a bent beam, and a formula was given to determine E from the deflection of a beam supported at both ends and loaded at the middle.

The paper concluded with a conjecture, that as the quantity ω (which expresses the relation of the inequality of pressure in a solid to the doubly-refracting force produced) is probably a function of m, the determination of these quantities for different substances might lead to a more complete theory of double refraction, and extend our knowledge of the laws of optics.

[Extracted from the *Cambridge and Dublin Mathematical Journal*, Vol. VIII. p. 188, *February*, 1854.]

Solutions of Problems.

1. If from a point in the circumference of a vertical circle two heavy particles be successively projected along the curve, their initial velocities being equal and either in the same or in opposite directions, the subsequent motion will be such that a straight line joining the particles at any instant will touch a circle.

Note. The particles are supposed not to interfere with each other's motion.

THE direct analytical proof would involve the properties of elliptic integrals, but it may be made to depend upon the following geometrical theorems.

(1) If from a point in one of two circles a right line be drawn cutting the other, the rectangle contained by the segments so formed is double of the rectangle contained by a line drawn from the point perpendicular to the *radical axis* of the two circles, and the line joining their centres.

The radical axis is the line joining the points of intersection of the two circles. It is always a real line, whether the points of intersection of the circles be real or imaginary, and it has the geometrical property—that if from any point on the radical axis, straight lines be drawn cutting the circles, the rectangle contained by the segments formed by one of the circles is equal to the rectangle contained by the segments formed by the other.

The analytical proof of these propositions is very simple, and may be resorted to if a geometrical proof does not suggest itself as soon as the requisite figure is constructed.

If A, B be the centres of the circles, P the given point in the circle whose centre is A, a line drawn from P cuts the first circle in p, the second in Q

and q, and the radical axis in R. If PH be drawn perpendicular to the radical axis, then

$$PQ \cdot Pq = 2AB \cdot HP.$$

Cor. If the line be drawn from P to *touch* the circle in T, instead of cutting it in Q and q, then the square of the tangent PT is equal to the rectangle $2AB \cdot HP$.

Similarly, if ph be drawn from p perpendicular to the radical axis

$$pT^2 = 2AB \cdot hp.$$

Hence, if a line be drawn touching one circle in T, and cutting the other in P and p, then

$$(PT)^2 : (pT)^2 :: HP : hp.$$

(2) If two straight lines touching one circle and cutting another be made to approach each other indefinitely, the small arcs intercepted by their intersections with the second circle will be ultimately proportional to their distances from the point of contact.

This result may easily be deduced from the properties of the similar triangles $P'TP$ and $p'pT$.

Cor. If particles P, p be constrained to move in the circle A, while the line Pp joining them continually touches the circle B, then the velocity of P at any instant is to that of p as PT to pT; and conversely, if the velocity of P at any instant be to that of P as PT to pT, then the line Pp will continue to be a tangent to the circle B.

Now let the plane of the circles be vertical and the radical axis horizontal, and let gravity act on the particles P, p. The particles were projected from the same point with the same velocity. Let this velocity be that due to the depth of the point of projection below the radical axis. Then the square of the velocity at any other point will be proportional to the perpendicular from that point on the radical axis; or, by the corollary to (1), if P and p be at any time at the extremities of the line PTp, the square of the velocity of P will be to the square of the velocity of p as PH to ph, that is, as $(PT)^2$ to $(pT)^2$. Hence, the velocities of P and p are in the proportion of PT to pT, and therefore, by the corollary to (2), the line joining them will continue a tangent to the circle B during each instant, and will therefore remain a tangent during the motion.

The circle A, the radical axis, and one position of the line Pp, are given by the circumstances of projection of P and p. From these data it is easy to determine the circle B by a geometrical construction.

It is evident that the character of the motion will determine the position of the circle B. If the motion is oscillatory, B will intersect A. If P and p make complete revolutions in the same direction, B will lie entirely within A, but if they move in opposite directions, B will lie entirely above the radical axis.

If any number of such particles be projected from the same point at equal intervals of time with the same direction and velocity, the lines joining successive particles at any instant will be tangents to the same circle; and if the time of a complete revolution, or oscillation, contain n of these intervals, then these lines will form a polygon of n sides, and as this is true at any instant, any number of such polygons may be formed.

Hence, the following geometrical theorem is true:

"If two circles be such that n lines can be drawn touching one of them and having their successive intersections, including that of the last and first, on the circumference of the other, the construction of such a system of lines will be possible, at whatever point of the first circle we draw the first tangent."

---

2. A transparent medium is such that the path of a ray of light within it is a given circle, the index of refraction being a function of the distance from a given point in the plane of the circle.

Find the form of this function and shew that for light of the same refrangibility—

(1) The path of *every ray within the medium* is a circle.

(2) All the rays proceeding from any point in the medium will meet accurately in another point.

(3) If rays diverge from a point without the medium and enter it through a spherical surface having that point for its centre, they will be made to converge accurately to a point within the medium.

LEMMA I. Let a transparent medium be so constituted, that the refractive index is the same at the same distance from a fixed point, then the path of any ray of light within the medium will be in one plane, and the perpendicular from the fixed point on the tangent to the path of the ray at any point will vary inversely as the refractive index of the medium at that point.

We may easily prove that when a ray of light passes through a spherical surface, separating a medium whose refractive index is μ_1 from another where it is μ_2, the plane of incidence and refraction passes through the centre of the sphere, and the perpendiculars on the direction of the ray before and after refraction are in the ratio of μ_2 to μ_1. Since this is true of any number of spherical shells of different refractive powers, it is also true when the index of refraction varies continuously from one shell to another, and therefore the proposition is true.

LEMMA II. If from any fixed point in the plane of a circle, a perpendicular be drawn to the tangent at any point of the circumference, the rectangle contained by this perpendicular and the diameter of the circle is equal to the square of the line joining the point of contact with the fixed point, together with the rectangle contained by the segments of any chord through the fixed point.

Let APB be the circle, O the fixed point; then

$$OY \cdot PR = OP^2 + AO \cdot OB.$$

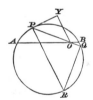

Produce PO to Q, and join QR, then the triangles OYP, PQR are similar; therefore

$$OY \cdot PR = OP \cdot PQ$$
$$= OP^2 + OP \cdot OQ;$$
$$\therefore \ OY \cdot PR = OP^2 + AO \cdot OB.$$

If we put in this expression $AO \cdot OB = a^2$,

$$PO = r, \quad OY = p, \quad PR = 2\rho,$$

it becomes

$$2p\rho = r^2 + a^2,$$
$$p = \frac{r^2 + a^2}{2\rho}.$$

To find the law of the index of refraction of the medium, so that a ray from A may describe the circle APB, μ must be made to vary inversely as p by Lemma I.

Let $AO = r_1$, and let the refractive index at $A = \mu_1$; then generally

$$\mu = \frac{C}{p} = \frac{2C\rho}{a^2 + r^2};$$

but at A

$$\mu_1 = \frac{2C\rho}{a^2 + r_1^2},$$

therefore

$$\mu = \mu_1 \frac{a^2 + r_1^2}{a^2 + r^2}.$$

The value of μ at any point is therefore independent of ρ, the radius of the given circle; so that the same law of refractive index will cause any other ray to describe another circle, for which the value of a^2 is the same. The value of OB is $\dfrac{a^2}{r}$, which is also independent of ρ; so that every ray which proceeds from A must pass through B.

Again, if we assume μ_0 as the value of μ when $r = 0$,

$$\mu_0 = \mu_1 \frac{a^2 + r_1^2}{a^2};$$

therefore

$$\mu = \mu_0 \frac{a^2}{a^2 + r^2},$$

a result independent of r_1. This shews that any point A' may be taken as the origin of the ray instead of A, and that the path of the ray will still be circular, and will pass through another point B' on the other side of O, such that $OB' = \dfrac{a^2}{OA'}$.

Next, let CP be a ray from C, a point without the medium, falling at P on a spherical surface whose centre is C.

Let O be the fixed point in the medium as before. Join PO, and produce to Q till $OQ = \dfrac{a^2}{OP}$. Through Q draw a circle touching CP in P, and cutting CO in A and B; then PBQ is the path of the ray within the medium.

Since CP touches the circle, we have

$$CP^2 = CA \cdot CB,$$
$$= (CO - OA)(CO + OB);$$

but
$$OA = \frac{a^2}{OB};$$

therefore
$$CP^2 = CO^2 + CO\left(OB - \frac{a^2}{OB}\right) - a^2,$$

an equation whence OB may be found, B being the point in the medium through which all rays from C pass.

Note. The possibility of the existence of a medium of this kind possessing remarkable optical properties, was suggested by the contemplation of the structure of the crystalline lens in fish; and the method of searching for these properties was deduced by analogy from Newton's *Principia*, Lib. I. Prop. VII.

It would require a more accurate investigation into the law of the refractive index of the different coats of the lens to test its agreement with the supposed medium, which is an optical instrument theoretically perfect for homogeneous light, and might be made achromatic by proper adaptation of the dispersive power of each coat.

On the other hand, we find that the law of the index of refraction which would give a minimum of aberration for a sphere of this kind placed in water, gives results not discordant with facts, so far as they can be readily ascertained.

[From the *Transactions of the Cambridge Philosophical Society*, Vol. IX. Part IV.]

IV. *On the Transformation of Surfaces by Bending.*

EUCLID has given two definitions of a surface, which may be taken as examples of the two methods of investigating their properties.

That in the first book of the Elements is—

" A superficies is that which has only length and breadth."

The superficies differs from a line in having breadth as well as length, and the conception of a third dimension is excluded without being explicitly introduced.

In the eleventh book, where the definition of a solid is first formally given, the definition of the superficies is made to depend on that of the solid—

" That which bounds a solid is a superficies."

Here the conception of three dimensions in space is employed in forming a definition more perfect than that belonging to plane Geometry.

In our analytical treatises on geometry a surface is defined by a function of three independent variables equated to zero. The surface is therefore the boundary between the portion of space in which the value of the function is positive, and that in which it is negative ; so that we may now define a surface to be the boundary of any assigned portion of space.

Surfaces are thus considered rather with reference to the figures which they limit than as having any properties belonging to themselves.

But the conception of a surface which we most readily form is that of a portion of matter, extended in length and breadth, but of which the thickness may be neglected. By excluding the thickness altogether, we arrive at Euclid's first definition, which we may state thus—

"A surface is a lamina of which the thickness is diminished so as to become evanescent."

We are thus enabled to consider a surface by itself, without reference to the portion of space of which it is a boundary. By drawing figures on the surface, and investigating their properties, we might construct a system of theorems, which would be true independently of the position of the surface in space, and which might remain the same even when the form of the solid of which it is the boundary is changed.

When the properties of a surface with respect to space are changed, while the relations of lines and figures in the surface itself are unaltered, the surface may be said to preserve its identity, so that we may consider it, after the change has taken place, as the same surface.

When a thin material lamina is made to assume a new form it is said to be *bent*. In certain cases this process of bending is called *development*, and when one surface is bent so as to coincide with another it is said to be *applied* to it.

By considering the lamina as deprived of rigidity, elasticity, and other mechanical properties, and neglecting the thickness, we arrive at a mathematical definition of this kind of transformation.

"The operation of bending is a continuous change of the form of a surface, without extension or contraction of any part of it."

The following investigations were undertaken with the hope of obtaining more definite conceptions of the nature of such transformations by the aid of those geometrical methods which appear most suitable to each particular case. The order of arrangement is that in which the different parts of the subject presented themselves at first for examination, and the methods employed form parts of the original plan, but much assistance in other matters has been derived from the works of Gauss[*], Liouville[†], Bertrand[‡], Puiseux[§], &c., references to which will be given in the course of the investigation.

---

[*] *Disquisitiones générales circa superficies curvas.* Presented to the Royal Society of Gottingen, 8th October, 1827. *Commentationes Recentiores,* Tom. VI.

[†] Liouville's *Journal,* XII.   [‡] *Ibid.* XIII.   [§] *Ibid.*

I.

On the Bending of Surfaces generated by the motion of a straight line in space.

If a straight line can be drawn in any surface, we may suppose that part of the surface which is on one side of the straight line to be fixed, while the other part is turned about the straight line as an axis.

In this way the surface may be bent about any number of generating lines as axes successively, till the form of every part of the surface is altered.

The mathematical conditions of this kind of bending may be obtained in the following manner.

Let the equations of the generating line be expressed so that the constants involved in them are functions of one independent variable u, by the variation of which we pass from one position of the line to another.

If in the equations of the generating line Aa, $u = u_1$, then in the equations of the line Bb we may put $u = u_2$, and from the equations of these lines we may find by the common methods the equations of the shortest line PQ between Aa and Bb, and its length, which we may call $\delta\zeta$. We may also find the angle between the directions of Aa and Bb, and let this angle be $\delta\theta$.

In the same way from the equations of Cc, in which $u = u_3$, we may deduce the equations of RS, the shortest line between Bb and Cc, its length $\delta\zeta_2$, and the angle $\delta\theta_2$ between the directions of Bb and Cc. We may also find the value of QR, the distance between the points at which PQ and RS cut Bb. Let $QR = \delta\sigma$, and let the angle between the directions of PQ and RS be $\delta\phi$.

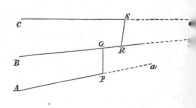

Now suppose the part of the surface between the lines Aa and Bb to be fixed, while the part between Bb and Cc is turned round Bb as an axis. The line RS will then revolve round the point R, remaining perpendicular to Bb and Cc will still be at the same distance from Bb, and will make the same angle with it. Hence of the four quantities $\delta\zeta_2$, $\delta\theta_2$, $\delta\sigma$ and $\delta\phi$, $\delta\phi$ alone will be changed by the process of bending. $\delta\phi$, however, may be varied in perfectly arbitrary manner, and may even be made to vanish.

For, PQ and RS being both perpendicular to Bb, RS may be turned about Bb till it is parallel to PQ, in which case $\delta\phi$ becomes $=0$.

By repeating this process, we may make all the "shortest lines" parallel to one another, and then all the generating lines will be parallel to the same plane.

We have hitherto considered generating lines situated at finite distances from one another; but what we have proved will be equally true when their distances are indefinitely diminished. Then in the limit

$$\frac{\delta\zeta}{u_2 - u_1} \text{ becomes } \frac{d\zeta}{du},$$

$$\frac{\delta\theta}{u_2 - u_1} \quad " \quad \frac{d\theta}{du},$$

$$\frac{\delta\sigma}{u_2 - u_1} \quad " \quad \frac{d\sigma}{du},$$

$$\frac{\delta\phi}{u_2 - u_1} \quad " \quad \frac{d\phi}{du}.$$

All these quantities being functions of u, ζ, θ, σ and ϕ, are functions of u and of each other; and if the forms of these functions be known, the positions of all the generating lines may be successively determined, and the equation to the surface may be found by integrating the equations containing the values of ζ, θ, σ and ϕ.

When the surface is bent in any manner about the generating lines, ζ, θ, and σ remain unaltered, but ϕ is changed at every point.

The form of ϕ as a function of u will depend on the nature of the bending; but since this is perfectly arbitrary, ϕ may be any arbitrary function of u. In this way we may find the form of any surface produced by bending the given surface along its generating lines.

By making $\phi = 0$, we make all the generating lines parallel to the same plane. Let this plane be that of xy, and let the first generating line coincide with the axis of x, then ζ will be the height of any other generating line above the plane of xy, and θ the angle which its projection on that plane makes with the axis of x. The ultimate intersections of the projections of the generating lines on the plane of xy will form a curve, whose length, measured from the axis of x, will be σ.

Since in this case the quantities ζ, θ, and σ are represented by distinct geometrical quantities, we may simplify the consideration of all surfaces generated by straight lines by reducing them by bending to the case in which those lines are parallel to a given plane.

In the class of surfaces in which the generating lines ultimately intersect, $\frac{d\zeta}{du} = 0$, and ζ constant. If these surfaces be bent so that $\phi = 0$, the whole of the generating lines will lie in one plane, and their ultimate intersections will form a plane curve. The surface is thus reduced to one plane, and therefore belongs to the class usually described as "developable surfaces." The form of a developable surface may be defined by means of the three quantities θ, σ and ϕ. The generating lines form by their ultimate intersections a curve of double curvature to which they are all tangents. This curve has been called the cuspidal edge. The length of this curve is represented by σ, its absolute curvature at any point by $\frac{d\theta}{d\sigma}$, and its torsion at the same point by $\frac{d\phi}{d\sigma}$.

When the surface is developed, the cuspidal edge becomes a plane curve, and every part of the surface coincides with the plane. But it does not follow that every part of the plane is capable of being bent into the original form of the surface. This may be easily seen by considering the surface when the position of the cuspidal edge nearly coincides with the plane curve but is not confounded with it. It is evident that if from any point in space a tangent can be drawn to the cuspidal edge, a sheet of the surface passes through that point. Hence the number of sheets which pass through one point is the same as the number of tangents to the cuspidal edge which pass through that point; and since the same is true in the limit, the number of sheets which coincide at any point of the plane is the same as the number of tangents which can be drawn from that point to the plane curve. In constructing a developable surface of paper, we must remove those parts of the sheet from which no real tangents can be drawn, and provide additional sheets where more than one tangent can be drawn.

In the case of developable surfaces we see the importance of attending to the position of the lines of bending; for though all developable surfaces may be produced from the same plane surface, their distinguishing properties depend on the form of the plane curve which determines the lines of bending.

II.

On the Bending of Surfaces of Revolution.

In the cases previously considered, the bending in one part of the surface may take place independently of that in any other part. In the case now before us the bending must be simultaneous over the whole surface, and its nature must be investigated by a different method.

The position of any point P on a surface of revolution may be determined by the distance PV from the vertex, measured along a generating line, and the angle AVO which the plane of the generating line makes with a fixed plane through the axis. Let $PV = s$ and $AVO = \theta$. Let r be the distance (Pp) of P from the axis; r will be a function of s depending on the form of the generating curve.

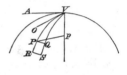

Now consider the small rectangular element of the surface at P. Its length $PR = \delta s$, and its breadth $PQ = r\delta\theta$, where r is a function of s.

If in another surface of revolution r' is some other function of s, then the length and breadth of the new element will be δs and $r'\delta\theta'$, and if

$$r' = \mu r, \quad \text{and} \quad \theta' = \frac{1}{\mu}\theta,$$
$$r'\delta\theta' = r\delta\theta,$$

and the dimensions of the two elements will be the same.

Hence the one element may be applied to the other, and the one surface may be applied to the other surface, element to element, by bending it. To effect this, the surface must be divided by cutting it along one of the generating lines, and the parts opened out, or made to overlap, according as μ is greater or less than unity.

To find the effect of this transformation on the form of the surface we must find the equation to the original form of the generating line in terms of s and r, then putting $r' = \mu r$, the equation between s and r' will give the form of the generating line after bending.

When μ is greater than 1 it may happen that for some values of s, $\dfrac{dr}{ds}$ is greater than $\dfrac{1}{\mu}$. In this case

$$\frac{dr'}{ds} = \mu \frac{dr}{ds} \text{ is greater than } 1 \; ;$$

a result which indicates that the curve becomes impossible for such values of s and μ.

The transformation is therefore impossible for the corresponding part of the surface. If, however, that portion of the original surface be removed, the remainder may be subjected to the required transformation.

The theory of bending when applied to the case of surfaces of revolution presents no geometrical difficulty, and little variety; but when we pass to the consideration of surfaces of a more general kind, we discover the insufficiency of the methods hitherto employed, by the vagueness of our ideas with respect to the nature of bending in such cases. In the former case the bending is of one kind only, and depends on the variation of one variable; but the surfaces we have now to consider may be bent in an infinite variety of ways, depending on the variation of three variables, of which we do not yet know the nature or interdependence.

We have therefore to discover some method sufficiently general to be applicable to every possible case, and yet so definite as to limit each particular case to one kind of bending easily understood.

The method adopted in the following investigations is deduced from the consideration of the surface as the limit of the inscribed polyhedron, when the size of the sides is indefinitely diminished, and their number indefinitely increased.

A method is then described by which such a polyhedron may be inscribed in any surface so that all the sides shall be triangles, and all the solid angles composed of six plane angles.

The problem of the bending of such a polyhedron is a question of trigonometry, and equations might be found connecting the angles of the different edges which meet in each solid angle of the polyhedron. It will be shewn that the conditions thus obtained would be equivalent to three equations between the six angles of the edges belonging to each solid angle. Hence three additional conditions would be necessary to determine the value of every such angle, and the problem would remain as indefinite as before. But if by any means we can reduce the number of edges meeting in a point to four, only one condition would be necessary to determine them all, and the problem would be reduced to the consideration of one kind of bending only.

This may be done by drawing the polyhedron in such a manner that the planes of adjacent triangles coincide two and two, and form quadrilateral facets, four of which meet in every solid angle. The bending of such a polyhedron can take place only in one way, by the increase of the angles of two of the edges which meet in a point, and the diminution of the angles of the other two.

The condition of such a polyhedron being inscribed in any surface is then found, and it is shewn that when two forms of the same surface are given, a perfectly definite rule may be given by which two corresponding polyhedrons of this kind may be inscribed, one in each surface.

Since the *kind* of bending completely defines the nature of the quadrilateral polyhedron which must be described, the lines formed by the edges of the quadrilateral may be taken as an indication of the kind of bending performed on the surface.

These lines are therefore defined as "*Lines of Bending.*"

When the lines of bending are given, the forms of the quadrilateral facets are completely determined; and if we know the angle which any two adjacent facets make with one another, we may determine the angles of the three edges which meet it at one of its extremities. From each of these we may find the angles of three other edges, and so on, so that the form of the polyhedron after bending will be completely determined when the angle of one edge is given. The bending is thus made to depend on the change of one variable only.

In this way the angle of any edge may be calculated from that of any given edge; but since this may be done in two different ways, by passing along two different sets of edges, we must have the condition that these results may be consistent with each other. This condition is satisfied by the method of inscribing the polyhedron. Another condition will be necessary that the *change* of the angle of any edge due to a small change of the given angle, produced by bending, may be the same by both calculations. This is the condition of "Instantaneous Lines of Bending." That this condition may continue to be satisfied during the whole process we must have another, which is the condition for "Permanent Lines of Bending."

The use of these lines of bending in simplifying the theory of surfaces is the only part of the present method which is new, although the investigations connected with them naturally led to the employment of other methods which had been used by those who have already treated of this subject. A statement of the principal methods and results of these mathematicians will save repetition, and will indicate the different points of view under which the subject may present itself.

The first and most complete memoir on the subject is that of M. Gauss already referred to.

The method which he employs consists in referring every point of the surface to a corresponding point of a sphere whose radius is unity. Normals are drawn at the several points of the surface toward the same side of it then lines drawn through the centre of the sphere in the direction of each of these normals intersect the surface of the sphere in points corresponding to those points of the original surface at which the normals were drawn.

If any line be drawn on the surface, each of its points will have a corresponding point on the sphere, so that there will be a corresponding line on the sphere.

If the line on the surface return into itself, so as to enclose a finite area of the surface, the corresponding curve on the sphere will enclose an area on the sphere, the extent of which will depend on the form of the surface.

This area on the sphere has been defined by M. Gauss as the measure of the "entire curvature" of the area on the surface. This mathematical quantity is of great use in the theory of surfaces, for it is the only quantity connected with curvature which is capable of being expressed as the sum of all its parts.

The sum of the entire curvatures of any number of areas is the entire curvature of their sum, and the entire curvature of any area depends on the form of its boundary only, and is not altered by any change in the form of the surface within the boundary line.

The curvature of the surface may even be discontinuous, so that we may speak of the entire curvature of a portion of a polyhedron, and calculate its amount.

If the dimensions of the closed curve be diminished so that it may be treated as an element of the surface, the ultimate ratio of the entire curvature to the area of the element on the surface is taken as the measure of the "specific curvature" at that point of the surface.

The terms "entire" and "specific" curvature when used in this paper are adopted from M. Gauss, although the use of the sphere and the areas on its surface formed an essential part of the original design. The use of these terms will save much explanation, and supersede several very cumbrous expressions.

M. Gauss then proceeds to find several analytical expressions for the measure of specific curvature at any point of a surface, by the consideration of three points very near each other.

The co-ordinates adopted are first rectangular, x and y, or x, y and z, being regarded as independent variables.

Then the points on the surface are referred to two systems of curves drawn on the surface, and their position is defined by the values of two independent variables p and q, such that by varying p while q remains constant, we obtain the different points of a line of the first system, while p constant and q variable defines a line of the second system.

By means of these variables, points on the surface may be referred to lines on the surface itself instead of arbitrary co-ordinates, and the measure of curvature may be found in terms of p and q when the surface is known.

In this way it is shewn that the specific curvature at any point is the reciprocal of the product of the principal radii of curvature at that point, a result of great interest.

From the condition of bending, that the length of any element of the curve must not be altered, it is shewn that the specific curvature at any point is not altered by bending.

The rest of the memoir is occupied with the consideration of particular modes of describing the two systems of lines. One case is when the lines of the first system are geodesic, or "shortest" lines having their origin in a point, and the second system is drawn so as to cut off equal lengths from the curves of the first system.

The angle which the tangent at the origin of a line of the first system makes with a fixed line is taken as one of the co-ordinates, and the distance of the point measured along that line as the other.

It is shewn that the two systems intersect at right angles, and a simple expression is found for the specific curvature at any point.

M. Liouville (*Journal*, Tom. XII.) has adopted a different mode of simplifying the problem. He has shewn that on every surface it is possible to find two systems of curves intersecting at right angles, such that the length and breadth of every element into which the surface is thus divided shall be equal, and that an infinite number of such systems may be found. By means of these curves he has found a much simpler expression for the specific curvature than that given by M. Gauss.

He has also given, in a note to his edition of Monge, a method of testing two given surfaces in order to determine whether they are applicable to one another. He first draws on both surfaces lines of equal specific curvature, and determines the distance between two corresponding consecutive lines of curvature in both surfaces.

If by assuming the origin properly these distances can be made equal for every part of the surface, the two surfaces can be applied to each other. He has developed the theorem analytically, of which this is only the geometrical interpretation.

When the lines of equal specific curvature are equidistant throughout their whole length, as in the case of surfaces of revolution, the surfaces may be applied to one another in an infinite variety of ways.

When the specific curvature at every point of the surface is positive and equal to a^2, the surface may be applied to a sphere of radius a, and when the specific curvature is negative $= -a^2$ it may be applied to the surface of revolution which cuts at right angles all the spheres of radius a, and whose centres are in a straight line.

M. Bertrand has given in the XIIIth Vol. of Liouville's *Journal* a very simple and elegant proof of the theorem of M. Gauss about the product of the radii of curvature.

He supposes one extremity of an inextensible thread to be fixed at a point in a surface, and a closed curve to be described on the surface by the other extremity, the thread being stretched all the while. It is evident that the length of such a curve cannot be altered by bending the surface. He then calculates the length of this curve, considering the length of the thread small, and finds that it depends on the product of the principal radii of curvature of the surface at the fixed point. His memoir is followed by a note of M. Diguet, who deduces the same result from a consideration of the area of the same curve; and by an independent memoir of M. Puiseux, who seems to give the same proof at somewhat greater length.

NOTE. Since this paper was written, I have seen the Rev. Professor Jellett's Memoir, *On the Properties of Inextensible Surfaces.* It is to be found in the *Transactions of the Royal Irish Academy,* Vol. XXII. *Science,* &c., and was read May 23, 1853.

Professor Jellett has obtained a system of three partial differential equations which express the conditions to which the displacements of a continuous inextensible membrane are subject. From these he has deduced the two theorems of Gauss, relating to the invariability of the product of the radii of curvature at any point, and of the "entire curvature" of a finite portion of the surface.

He has then applied his method to the consideration of cases in which the flexibility of the surface is limited by certain conditions, and he has obtained the following results :—

If the displacements of an inextensible surface be all parallel to the same plane, the surface moves as a rigid body.

Or, more generally,

If the movement of an inextensible surface, parallel to any one line, be that of a rigid body, the entire movement is that of a rigid body.

The following theorems relate to the case in which a curve traced on the surface is rendered rigid :—

If any curve be traced upon an inextensible surface whose principal radii of curvature are finite and of the same sign, and if this curve be rendered immoveable, the entire surface will become immoveable also.

In a developable surface composed of an inextensible membrane, any one of its rectilinear sections may be fixed without destroying the flexibility of the membrane.

In convexo-concave surfaces, there are two directions passing through every point of the surface, such that the curvature of a normal section taken in these directions vanishes. We may therefore conceive the entire surface to be crossed by two series of curves, such that a tangent drawn to either of them at any point shall coincide with one of these directions. These curves Professor Jellett has denominated *Curves of Flexure,* from the following properties :—

Any curve of flexure may be fixed without destroying the flexibility of the surface.

If an arc of a curve traced upon an inextensible surface be rendered fixed or rigid, the entire of the quadrilateral, formed by drawing the two curves of flexure through each extremity of the curve, becomes fixed or rigid also.

Professor Jellett has also investigated the properties of partially inextensible surfaces, and of thin material laminæ whose extensibility is small, and in a note he has demonstrated the following theorem :—

If a closed oval surface be perfectly inextensible, it is also perfectly rigid.

A demonstration of one of Professor Jellett's theorems will be found at the end of this paper.

J. C. M.

Aug. 30, 1854.

ON THE PROPERTIES OF A SURFACE CONSIDERED AS THE LIMIT OF THE INSCRIBED POLYHEDRON.

1. *To inscribe a polyhedron in a given surface, all whose sides shall be triangles, and all whose solid angles shall be hexahedral.*

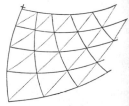

On the given surface describe a series of curves according to any assumed law. Describe a second series intersecting these in any manner, so as to divide the whole surface into quadrilaterals. Lastly, describe a third series (the dotted lines in the figure), so as to pass through all the intersections of the first and second series, forming the diagonals of the quadrilaterals.

The surface is now covered with a network of curvilinear triangles. The plane triangles which have the same angular points will form a polyhedron fulfilling the required conditions. By increasing the number of the curves in each series, and diminishing their distance, we may make the polyhedron approximate to the surface without limit. At the same time the polygons formed by the edges of the polyhedron will approximate to the three systems of intersecting curves.

2. *To find the measure of the "entire curvature" of a solid angle of the polyhedron, and of a finite portion of its surface.*

From the centre of a sphere whose radius is unity draw perpendiculars to the planes of the six sides forming the solid angle. These lines will meet the surface in six points on the same side of the centre, which being joined by arcs of great circles will form a hexagon on the surface of the sphere.

The area of this hexagon represents the entire curvature of the solid angle.

It is plain by spherical geometry that the angles of this hexagon are the supplements of the six plane angles which form the solid angle, and that the arcs forming the sides are the supplements of those subtended by the angles of the six edges formed by adjacent sides.

The area of the hexagon is equal to the excess of the sum of its angles above eight right angles, or to the defect of the sum of the six plane angles from four right angles, which is the same thing. Since these angles are invariable, the bending of the polyhedron cannot alter the measure of curvature of each of its solid angles.

If perpendiculars be drawn to the sides of the polyhedron which contain other solid angles, additional points on the sphere will be found, and if these be joined by arcs of great circles, a network of hexagons will be formed on the sphere, each of which corresponds to a solid angle of the polyhedron and represents its "entire curvature."

The entire curvature of any assigned portion of the polyhedron is the sum of the entire curvatures of the solid angles it contains. It is therefore represented by a polygon on the sphere, which is composed of all the hexagons corresponding to its solid angles.

If a polygon composed of the edges of the polyhedron be taken as the boundary of the assigned portion, the sum of its exterior angles will be the same as the sum of the exterior angles of the polygon on the sphere; but the area of a spherical polygon is equal to the defect of the sum of its exterior angles from four right angles, and this is the measure of entire curvature.

Therefore the entire curvature of the portion of the polyhedron enclosed by the polygon is equal to the defect of the sum of its exterior angles from four right angles.

Since the entire curvature of each solid angle is unaltered by bending, that of a finite portion of the surface must be also invariable.

3.   *On the "Conic of Contact," and its use in determining the curvature of normal sections of a surface.*

Suppose the plane of one of the triangular facets of the polyhedron to be produced till it cuts the surface. The form of the curve of intersection will depend on the nature of the surface, and when the size of the triangle is indefinitely diminished, it will approximate to the form of a conic section.

For we may suppose a surface of the second order constructed so as to have a contact of the second order with the given surface at a point within the angular points of the triangle. The curve of intersection with this surface will be the conic section to which the other curve of intersection approaches. This curve will be henceforth called the "Conic of Contact," for want of a better name.

To find the radius of curvature of a normal section of the surface.

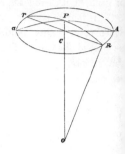

Let ARa be the conic of contact, C its centre, and CP perpendicular to its plane. rPR a normal section, and O its centre of curvature, then

$$PO = \tfrac{1}{2}\frac{PR^2}{CP}$$

$$= \tfrac{1}{2}\frac{CR^2}{CP} \text{ in the limit, when } CR \text{ and } PR \text{ coincide,}$$

$$= \tfrac{1}{8}\frac{rR^2}{CP},$$

or calling CP the "sagitta," we have this theorem:

"The radius of curvature of a normal section is equal to the square of the corresponding diameter of the conic of contact divided by eight times the sagitta."

4. *To inscribe a polyhedron in a given surface, all whose sides shall be plane quadrilaterals, and all whose solid angles shall be tetrahedral.*

Suppose the three systems of curves drawn as described in sect. (1), then each of the quadrilaterals formed by the intersection of the first and second systems is divided into two triangles by the third system. If the planes of these two triangles coincide, they form a plane quadrilateral, and if every such pair of triangles coincide, the polyhedron will satisfy the required condition.

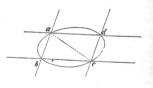

Let abc be one of these triangles, and acd the other, which is to be in the same plane with abc. Then if the plane of abc be produced to meet the surface in the conic of contact, the curve will pass through abc and d. Hence $abcd$ must be a quadrilateral inscribed in the conic of contact.

But since ab and dc belong to the same system of curves, they will be ultimately parallel when the size of the facets is diminished, and for a similar reason, ad and bc will be ultimately parallel. Hence $abcd$ will become a parallelogram, but the sides of a parallelogram inscribed in a conic are parallel to conjugate diameters.

Therefore the directions of two curves of the first and second system at their point of intersection must be parallel to two conjugate diameters of the conic of contact at that point in order that such a polyhedron may be inscribed.

Systems of curves intersecting in this manner will be referred to as "conjugate systems."

5. *On the elementary conditions of the applicability of two surfaces.*

It is evident, that if one surface is capable of being applied to another by bending, every point, line, or angle in the first has its corresponding point, line, or angle in the second.

If the transformation of the surface be effected without the extension or contraction of any part, no line drawn on the surface can experience any change in its length, and if this condition be fulfilled, there can be no extension or contraction.

Therefore the condition of bending is, that if any line whatever be drawn on the first surface, the corresponding curve on the second surface is equal to it in length. All other conditions of bending may be deduced from this.

6. *If two curves on the first surface intersect, the corresponding curves on the second surface intersect at the same angle.*

On the first surface draw any curve, so as to form a triangle with the curves already drawn, and let the sides of this triangle be indefinitely diminished, by making the new curve approach to the intersection of the former curves. Let the same thing be done on the second surface. We shall then have two corresponding triangles whose sides are equal each to each, by (5), and since their sides are indefinitely small, we may regard them as straight lines. Therefore by Euclid I. 8, the angle of the first triangle formed by the intersection of the two curves is equal to the corresponding angle of the second.

7. *At any given point of the first surface, two directions can be found, which are conjugate to each other with respect to the conic of contact at that point, and continue to be conjugate to each other when the first surface is transformed into the second.*

For let the first surface be transferred, without changing its form, to a position such that the given point coincides with the corresponding point of the second surface, and the normal to the first surface coincides with that of the second at the same point. Then let the first surface be turned about the normal as an axis till the tangent of any line through the point coincides with the tangent of the corresponding line in the second surface.

Then by (6) any pair of corresponding lines passing through the point will have a common tangent, and will therefore coincide in direction at that point.

If we now draw the conics of contact belonging to each surface we shall have two conics with the same centre, and the problem is to determine a pair of conjugate diameters of the first which coincide with a pair of conjugate diameters of the second. The analytical solution gives two directions, real, coincident, or impossible, for the diameters required.

In our investigations we can be concerned only with the case in which these directions are real.

When the conics intersect in four points, P, Q, R, S, $PQRS$ is a parallelogram inscribed in both conics, and the axes CA, CB, parallel to the sides, are conjugate in both conics.

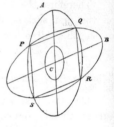

If the conics do not intersect, describe, through any point P of the second conic, a conic similar to and concentric with the first. If the conics intersect in four points, we must proceed as before; if they touch in two points, the diameter through those points and its conjugate must be taken. If they intersect in two points only, then the problem is impossible; and if they coincide altogether, the conics are similar and similarly situated, and the problem is indeterminate.

8. *Two surfaces being given as before, one pair of conjugate systems of curves may be drawn on the first surface, which shall correspond to a pair of conjugate systems on the second surface.*

By article (7) we may find at every point of the first surface two directions conjugate to one another, corresponding to two conjugate directions on the second surface. These directions indicate the directions of the two systems of curves which pass through that point.

Knowing the direction which every curve of each system must have at every point of its course, the systems of curves may be either drawn by some direct geometrical method, or constructed from their equations, which may be found by solving their differential equations.

Two systems of curves being drawn on the first surface, the corresponding systems may be drawn on the second surface. These systems being conjugate to each other, fulfil the condition of Art. (4), and may therefore be made the means of constructing a polyhedron with quadrilateral facets, by the bending of which the transformation may be effected.

These systems of curves will be referred to as the "first and second systems of Lines of Bending."

9. *General considerations applicable to Lines of Bending.*

It has been shewn that when two forms of a surface are given, one of which may be transformed into the other by bending, the nature of the lines of bending is completely determined. Supposing the problem reduced to its analytical expression, the equations of these curves would appear under the form of double solutions of differential equations of the first order and second degree, each of which would involve one arbitrary quantity, by the variation of which we should pass from one curve to another of the same system.

Hence the position of any curve of either system depends on the value assumed for the arbitrary constant; to distinguish the systems, let us call one the first system, and the other the second, and let all quantities relating to the second system be denoted by accented letters.

Let the arbitrary constants introduced by integration be u for the first system, and u' for the second.

Then the value of u will determine the position of a curve of the first system, and that of u' a curve of the second system, and therefore u and u' will suffice to determine the point of intersection of these two curves.

Hence we may conceive the position of any point on the surface to be determined by the values of u and u' for the curves of the two systems which intersect at that point.

By taking into account the equation to the surface, we may suppose x, y, and z the co-ordinates of any point, to be determined as functions of the two variables u and u'. This being done, we shall have materials for calculating everything connected with the surface, and its lines of bending. But before entering on such calculations let us examine the principal properties of these lines which we must take into account.

Suppose a series of values to be given to u and u', and the corresponding curves to be drawn on the surface.

The surface will then be covered with a system of quadrilaterals, the size of which may be diminished indefinitely by interpolating values of u and u' between those already assumed; and in the limit each quadrilateral may be regarded as a parallelogram coinciding with a facet of the inscribed polyhedron.

The *length*, the *breadth*, and the *angle* of these parallelograms will vary at different parts of the surface, and will therefore depend on the values of u and u'.

The *curvature* of a line drawn on a surface may be investigated by considering the curvature of two other lines depending on it.

The first is the projection of the line on a tangent plane to the surface at a given point in the line. The curvature of the projection at the point of contact may be called the *tangential curvature* of the line on the surface. It has also been called the *geodesic* curvature, because it is the measure of its deviation from a geodesic or shortest line on the surface.

The other projection necessary to define the curvature of a line on the surface is on a plane passing through the tangent to the curve and the normal to the surface at the point of contact. The curvature of this projection at that point may be called the *normal curvature* of the line on the surface.

It is easy to shew that this normal curvature is the same as the curvature of a normal section of the surface passing through a tangent to the curve at the same point.

10. *General considerations applicable to the inscribed polyhedron.*

When two series of lines of bending belonging to the first and second systems have been described on the surface, we may proceed, as in Art. (1), to describe a third series of curves so as to pass through all their intersections and form the diagonals of the quadrilaterals formed by the first pair of systems.

Plane triangles may then be constituted within the surface, having these points of intersection for angles, and the size of the facets of this polyhedron may be diminished indefinitely by increasing the number of curves in each series.

But by Art. (8) the first and second systems of lines of bending are conjugate to each other, and therefore by Art. (4) the polygon just constructed will have every pair of triangular facets in the same plane, and may therefore be considered as a polyhedron with plane quadrilateral facets all whose solid angles are formed by four of these facets meeting in a point.

When the number of curves in each system is increased and their distance diminished indefinitely, the plane facets of the polyhedron will ultimately coincide with the curved surface, and the polygons formed by the successive edges between the facets, will coincide with the lines of bending.

These quadrilaterals may then be considered as parallelograms, the length of which is determined by the portion of a curve of the second system intercepted between two curves of the first, while the breadth is the distance of two curves of the second system measured along a curve of the first. The expressions for these quantities will be given when we come to the calculation of our results along with the other particulars which we only specify at present.

The angle of the sides of these parallelograms will be ultimately the same as the angle of intersection of the first and second systems, which we may call ϕ; but if we suppose the dimensions of the facets to be small quantities of the first order, the angles of the four facets which meet in a point will differ from the angle of intersection of the curves at that point by small angles of the first order depending on the tangential curvature of the lines of bending. The sum of these four angles will differ from four right angles by a small angle of the second order, the circular measure of which expresses the entire curvature of the solid angle as in Art. (2).

The angle of inclination of two adjacent facets will depend on the normal curvature of the lines of bending, and will be that of the projection of two consecutive sides of the polygon of one system on a plane perpendicular to a side of the other system.

11. *Explanation of the Notation to be employed in calculation.*

Suppose each system of lines of bending to be determined by an equation containing one arbitrary parameter.

Let this parameter be u for the first system, and u' for the second.

Let two curves, one from each system, be selected as curves of reference, and let their parameters be u_0 and u'_0.

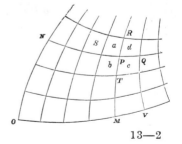

Let ON and OM in the figure represent these two curves.

Let PM be any curve of the first system whose parameter is u, and PN any curve of the second whose parameter is u', then their intersection P may be defined as the point (u, u'), and all quantities referring to the point P may be expressed as functions of u and u'.

Let PN, the length of a curve of the second system (u'), from N (u_0) to P (u), be expressed by s, and PM the length of the curve (u) from (u'_0) to (u'), by s', then s and s' will be functions of u and u'.

Let $(u + \delta u)$ be the parameter of the curve QV of the first system consecutive to PM. Then the length of PQ, the part of the curve of the second system intercepted between the curves (u) and $(u + \delta u)$, will be

$$\frac{ds}{du}\,\delta u.$$

Similarly PR may be expressed by

$$\frac{ds'}{du'}\,\delta u'.$$

These values of PQ and PR will be the ultimate values of the length and breadth of a quadrilateral facet.

The angle between these lines will be ultimately equal to ϕ, the angle of intersection of the system; but when the values of δu and $\delta u'$ are considered as finite though small, the angles a, b, c, d of the facets which form a solid angle will depend on the tangential curvature of the two systems of lines.

Let r be the tangential curvature of a curve of the first system at the given point measured in the direction in which u increases, and let r', that of the second system, be measured in the direction in which u' increases.

Then we shall have for the values of the four plane angles which meet at P,

$$a = \pi - \phi + \frac{1}{2r}\frac{ds'}{du'}\,\delta u' - \frac{1}{2r'}\frac{ds}{du}\delta u,$$

$$b = \phi \quad + \frac{1}{2r}\frac{ds'}{du'}\,\delta u' + \frac{1}{2r'}\frac{ds}{du}\,\delta u,$$

$$c = \pi - \phi - \frac{1}{2r}\frac{ds'}{du'}\,\delta u' + \frac{1}{2r'}\frac{ds}{du}\,\delta u,$$

$$d = \phi \quad - \frac{1}{2r}\frac{ds'}{du'}\,\delta u' - \frac{1}{2r'}\frac{ds}{du}\,\delta u.$$

These values are correct as far as the first order of small quantities. Those corrections which depend on the curvature of the surface are of the second order.

Let ρ be the normal curvature of a curve of the first system, and ρ' that of a curve of the second, then the inclination l of the plane facets a and b, separated by a curve of the second system, will be

$$l = \frac{1}{\rho \sin \phi} \frac{ds'}{du'} \delta u',$$

as far as the first order of small angles, and the inclination l' of b and c will be

$$l' = \frac{1}{\rho' \sin \phi} \frac{ds}{du} \delta u$$

to the same order of exactness.

12. *On the corresponding polygon on the surface of the sphere of reference.*

By the method described in Art. (2) we may find a point on the sphere corresponding to each facet of the polyhedron.

In the annexed figure, let a, b, c, d be the points on the sphere corresponding to the four facets which meet at the solid angle P. Then the area of the spherical quadrilateral a, b, c, d will be the measure of the entire curvature of the solid angle P.

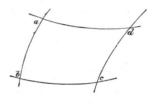

This area is measured by the defect of the sum of the exterior angles from four right angles; but these exterior angles are equal to the four angles a, b, c, d, which form the solid angle P, therefore the entire curvature is measured by

$$k = 2\pi - (a + b + c + d).$$

Since a, b, c, d are invariable, it is evident, as in Art. (2), that the entire curvature at P is not altered by bending.

By the last article it appears that when the facets are small the angles b and d are approximately equal to ϕ, and a and c to $(\pi - \phi)$, and since the sides of the quadrilateral on the sphere are small, we may regard it as approximately a plane parallelogram whose angle $bad = \phi$.

The sides of this parallelogram will be l and l', the supplements of the angles of the edges of the polyhedron, and we may therefore express its area as a plane parallelogram

$$k = ll' \sin \phi.$$

By the expression for l and l' in the last article, we find

$$k = \frac{1}{\rho\rho' \sin \phi} \frac{ds}{du} \frac{ds'}{du'} \delta u \, \delta u'$$

for the entire curvature of one solid angle.

Since the whole number of solid angles is equal to the whole number of facets, we may suppose a quarter of each of the facets of which it is composed to be assigned to each solid angle. The area of these will be the same as that of one whole facet, namely,

$$\sin \phi \frac{ds}{du} \frac{ds'}{du'} \delta u \, \delta u' \; ;$$

therefore dividing the expression for k by this quantity, we find for the value of the specific curvature at P

$$p = \frac{1}{\rho\rho' \sin^2 \phi} \; ;$$

which gives the specific curvature in terms of the normal curvatures of the lines of bending and their angle of intersection.

13.   *Further reduction of this expression by means of the " Conic of Contact," as defined in Art.* (3).

Let a and b be the semiaxes of the conic of contact, and h the sagitta or perpendicular to its plane from the centre to the surface.

Let CP, CQ be semidiameters parallel to the lines of bending of the first and second systems, and therefore conjugate to each other.

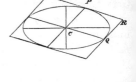

By (Art. 3), $\rho = \frac{1}{2} \dfrac{CP^2}{h}$,

and $\rho' = \frac{1}{2} \dfrac{CQ^2}{h}$;

and the expression for p in Art. (12), becomes

$$p = \frac{4h^2}{(CP \cdot CQ \sin \phi)^2} \cdot$$

But $CP \cdot CQ \sin \phi$ is the area of the parallelogram $CPRQ$, which is one quarter of the circumscribed parallelogram, and therefore by a well-known theorem

$$CP \cdot CQ \sin \phi = ab,$$

and the expression for p becomes

$$p = \frac{4h^2}{a^2b^2};$$

or if the area of the circumscribing parallelogram be called A,

$$p = \frac{16h^2}{A^2}.$$

The principal radii of curvature of the surface are parallel to the axes of the conic of contact. Let R and R' denote these radii, then

$$R = \tfrac{1}{2}\frac{a^2}{h} \text{ and } R' = \tfrac{1}{2}\frac{b^2}{h};$$

and therefore substituting in the expression for p,

$$p = \frac{1}{RR'};$$

or the specific curvature is the reciprocal of the product of the principal radii of curvature.

This remarkable expression was introduced by Gauss in the memoir referred to in a former part of this paper. His method of investigation, though not so elementary, is more direct than that here given, and will shew how this result can be obtained without reference to the geometrical methods necessary to a more extended inquiry into the *modes* of bending.

14. *On the variation of normal curvature of the lines of bending as we pass from one point of the surface to another.*

We have determined the relation between the normal curvatures of the lines of bending of the two systems at their points of intersection; we have now to find the variation of normal curvature when we pass from one line of the first system to another, along a line of the second.

In analytical language we have to find the value of

$$\frac{d}{du}\left(\frac{1}{\rho}\right).$$

Referring to the figure in Art. (11), we shall see that this may be done if we can determine the difference between the angle of inclination of the facets a and b, and that of c and d: for the angle l between a and b is

$$l = \frac{1}{\rho \sin \phi}\frac{ds'}{du'}\delta u'.$$

and therefore the difference between the angle of a and b and that of c and d is

$$\delta l = \frac{dl}{du}\,\delta u = \frac{d}{du}\left(\frac{1}{\rho\sin\phi}\,\frac{ds'}{du'}\right)\delta u\,\delta u';$$

whence the differential of ρ with respect to u may be found.

We must therefore find δl, and this is done by means of the quadrilateral on the sphere described in Art. (12).

15.   *To find the values of δl and $\delta l'$.*

In the annexed figure let $abcd$ represent the small quadrilateral on the surface of the sphere. The exterior angles a, b, c, d are equal to those of the four facets which meet at the point P of the surface, and the sides represent the angles which the planes of those facets make with each other; so that

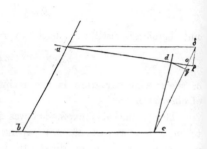

$$ab = l,\quad bc = l',\quad cd = l + \delta l,\quad da = l' + \delta l',$$

and the problem is to determine δl and $\delta l'$ in terms of the sides l and l' and the angles a, b, c, d.

On the sides ba, bc complete the parallelogram $abcd$.

Produce ad to p, so that $ap = a\delta$.   Join δp.

Make $cq = cd$ and join dq.

then $\delta l = cd - ab,$

$$= cq - c\delta,$$

$$= -(qo + o\delta).$$

Now $qo = qd \tan qdo$

$$= cd \sin qcd \cot qod,$$

but $cd = l$ nearly, $\sin qcd = qcd = (c + b - \pi)$ and $qod = \phi$;

$$\therefore\ qo = l\,(c + b - \pi)\cot\phi.$$

Also $o\delta = \dfrac{p\delta}{\sin \delta op}$

$$= a\delta \left(\delta ap \right) \dfrac{1}{\sin \phi}$$

$$= l' \left(a + b - \pi \right) \dfrac{1}{\sin \phi}.$$

Substituting the values of a, b, c, d from Art. (11),

$$\delta l = - \left(qo + o\delta \right)$$

$$= - l \,\dfrac{1}{r'} \,\dfrac{ds}{du} \cot \phi \delta u - l' \,\dfrac{1}{r} \,\dfrac{ds'}{du'} \,\dfrac{1}{\sin \phi} \,\delta u'.$$

Finally, substituting the values of l, l', and δl from Art. (14),

$$\dfrac{d}{du} \left(\dfrac{1}{\rho \sin \phi} \,\dfrac{ds'}{du'} \right) \delta u \,\delta u' = - \dfrac{\cot \phi}{\rho \sin \phi} \,\dfrac{ds'}{du'} \,\dfrac{1}{r'} \,\dfrac{ds}{du} \,\delta u \,\delta u' - \dfrac{1}{\rho' \sin^2 \phi} \,\dfrac{ds}{du} \,\dfrac{1}{r} \,\dfrac{ds'}{du'} \,\delta u \,\delta u';$$

which may be put under the more convenient form

$$\dfrac{d}{du} \left(\log \rho \right) = \dfrac{d}{du} \log \left(\dfrac{1}{\sin \phi} \,\dfrac{ds'}{du'} \right) + \dfrac{1}{r'} \,\dfrac{ds}{du} \cot \phi + \dfrac{\rho}{\rho'} \,\dfrac{1}{r} \,\dfrac{ds}{du} \,\dfrac{1}{\sin \phi} \,;$$

and from the value of $\delta l'$ we may similarly obtain

$$\dfrac{d}{du'} \left(\log \rho' \right) = \dfrac{d}{du'} \log \left(\dfrac{1}{\sin \phi} \,\dfrac{ds}{du} \right) + \dfrac{1}{r} \,\dfrac{ds'}{du'} \cot \phi + \dfrac{\rho'}{\rho} \,\dfrac{1}{r'} \,\dfrac{ds'}{du'} \,\dfrac{1}{\sin \phi} \,.$$

We may simplify these equations by putting p for the specific curvature of the surface, and q for the ratio $\dfrac{\rho}{\rho'}$, which is the only quantity altered by bending.

We have then

$$p = \dfrac{1}{\rho \rho' \sin^2 \phi}, \quad \text{and} \quad q = \dfrac{\rho}{\rho'},$$

whence $\rho^2 = q \,\dfrac{1}{p \sin^2 \phi}, \qquad \rho'^2 = \dfrac{1}{q} \,\dfrac{1}{p \sin^2 \phi},$

and the equations become

$$\dfrac{d}{du} \left(\log q \right) = \dfrac{d}{du} \log \left(p \,\overline{\dfrac{ds'}{du'}} \Big|^2 \right) + \dfrac{2}{r'} \,\dfrac{ds}{du} \cot \phi + \dfrac{2}{r} \,\dfrac{ds}{du} \,\dfrac{1}{\sin \phi} \, q,$$

$$\dfrac{d}{du'} \left(\log q \right) = - \dfrac{d}{du'} \log \left(p \,\overline{\dfrac{ds}{du}} \Big|^2 \right) - \dfrac{2}{r} \,\dfrac{ds'}{du'} \cot \phi - \dfrac{2}{r'} \,\dfrac{ds'}{du'} \,\dfrac{1}{\sin \phi} \,\dfrac{1}{q}.$$

In this way we may reduce the problem of bending a surface to the consideration of one variable q, by means of the lines of bending.

16. *To obtain the condition of Instantaneous lines of bending.*

We have now obtained the values of the differential coefficients of q with respect to each of the variables u, u'.

From the equation

$$\frac{d^2}{du\,du'}(\log q) = \frac{d^2}{du'\,du}(\log q),$$

we might find an equation which would give certain conditions of lines of bending. These conditions however would be equivalent to those which we have already assumed when we drew the systems of lines so as to be conjugate to each other.

To find the true conditions of bending we must suppose the form of the surface to vary continuously, so as to depend on some variable t which we may call the time.

Of the different quantities which enter into our equations, none are changed by the operation of bending except q, so that in differentiating with respect to t all the rest may be considered constant, q being the only variable.

Differentiating the equations of last article with respect to t, we obtain

$$\frac{d^2}{du\,dt}(\log q) = \frac{2}{r}\frac{ds}{du}\frac{1}{\sin\phi}\,q\,\frac{d}{dt}(\log q),$$

$$\frac{d^2}{du'\,dt}(\log q) = \frac{2}{r'}\frac{ds'}{du'}\frac{1}{\sin\phi}\frac{1}{q}\frac{d}{dt}(\log q).$$

Whence

$$\frac{d^3}{du\,du'\,dt}(\log q) =$$

$$\left\{\frac{d}{du'}\left(\frac{2}{r}\frac{ds}{du}\frac{1}{\sin\phi}\right) + \frac{2}{r}\frac{ds}{du}\frac{1}{\sin\phi}\frac{d}{du'}(\log q)\right\}q\,\frac{d}{dt}(\log q) + \frac{2}{r}\frac{ds}{du}\frac{1}{\sin\phi}\,q\,\frac{d}{du'dt}(\log q),$$

and

$$\frac{d^3}{du\,du'\,dt}(\log q) =$$

$$\left\{\frac{d}{du}\left(\frac{2}{r'}\frac{ds'}{du'}\frac{1}{\sin\phi}\right) - \frac{2}{r'}\frac{ds'}{du'}\frac{1}{\sin\phi}\frac{d}{du}\log q\right\}\frac{1}{q}\frac{d}{dt}(\log q) + \frac{2}{r'}\frac{ds'}{du'}\frac{1}{\sin\phi}\frac{1}{q}\frac{d}{du\,dt}(\log q),$$

two independent values of the same quantity, whence the required conditions may be obtained.

Substituting in these equations the values of those quantities which occur in the original equations, we obtain

$$q\,\frac{1}{r}\frac{ds}{du}\left\{\frac{d}{du'}\log\left(pr\,\frac{ds}{du}\sin\phi\right)+\frac{2}{r}\frac{ds'}{du'}\cot\phi\right\}$$

$$=\frac{1}{q}\frac{1}{r'}\frac{ds'}{du'}\left\{\frac{d}{du'}\log\left(pr'\,\frac{ds'}{du'}\sin\phi\right)+\frac{2}{r'}\frac{ds}{du}\cot\phi\right\},$$

which is the condition which must hold at every instant during the process of bending for the lines about which the bending takes place at that instant. When the bending is such that the position of the lines of bending on the surface alters at every instant, this is the only condition which is required. It is therefore called the condition of Instantaneous lines of bending.

17. *To find the condition of Permanent lines of bending.*

Since q changes with the time, the equation of last article will not be satisfied for any finite time unless both sides are separately equal to zero. In that case we have the two conditions

$$\left.\begin{aligned}\frac{d}{du'}\log\left(pr\,\frac{ds}{du}\sin\phi\right)+\frac{2}{r}\frac{ds'}{du'}\cot\phi=0,\\[4pt]\text{or}\quad\frac{1}{r}\frac{ds}{du}=0.\end{aligned}\right\}\dotfill(1).$$

$$\left.\begin{aligned}\frac{d}{du}\log\left(pr'\,\frac{ds'}{du'}\sin\phi\right)+\frac{2}{r'}\frac{ds}{du}\cot\phi=0,\\[4pt]\text{or}\quad\frac{1}{r'}\frac{ds'}{du'}=0.\end{aligned}\right\}\dotfill(2).$$

If the lines of bending satisfy these conditions, a finite amount of bending may take place without changing the position of the system on the surface. Such lines are therefore called Permanent lines of bending.

The only case in which the phenomena of bending may be exhibited by means of the polyhedron with quadrilateral facets is that in which permanent lines of bending are chosen as the boundaries of the facets. In all other cases the bending takes place about an instantaneous system of lines which is continually in motion with respect to the surface, so that the nature of the polyhedron would need to be altered at every instant.

We are now able to determine whether any system of lines drawn on a given surface is a system of instantaneous or permanent lines of bending.

We are also able, by the method of Article (8), to deduce from two consecutive forms of a surface, the lines of bending about which the transformation must have taken place.

If our analytical methods were sufficiently powerful, we might apply our results to the determination of such systems of lines on any known surface, but the necessary calculations even in the simplest cases are so complicated, that, even if useful results were obtained, they would be out of place in a paper of this kind, which is intended to afford the means of forming distinct conceptions rather than to exhibit the results of mathematical labour.

18. *On the application of the ordinary methods of analytical geometry to the consideration of lines of bending.*

It may be interesting to those who may hesitate to accept results derived from the consideration of a polyhedron, when applied to a curved surface, to inquire whether the same results may not be obtained by some independent method.

As the following method involves only those operations which are most familiar to the analyst, it will be sufficient to give the rough outline, which may be filled up at pleasure.

The proof of the invariability of the specific curvature may be taken from any of the memoirs above referred to, and its value in terms of the equation of the surface will be found in the memoir of Gauss.

Let the equation to the surface be put under the form

$$z = f(xy),$$

then the value of the specific curvature is

$$p = \frac{\dfrac{d^2z}{dx^2}\dfrac{d^2z}{dy^2} - \overline{\dfrac{d^2z}{dx\,dy}}\Big|^2}{\sqrt{1 + \overline{\dfrac{dz}{dx}}\Big|^2 + \overline{\dfrac{dz}{dy}}\Big|^2}}\,.$$

The definition of conjugate systems of curves may be rendered independent of the reasoning formerly employed by the following modification.

Let a tangent plane move along any line of the first system, then if the line of ultimate intersection of this plane with itself be always a tangent to some line of the second system, the second system is said to be conjugate to the first.

It is easy to show that the first system is also conjugate to the second.

Let the system of curves be projected on the plane of xy, and at the point (x, y) let α be the angle which a projected curve of the first system makes with the axis of x, and β the angle which the projected curve of the second system which intersects it at that point makes with the same axis. Then the condition of the systems being conjugate will be found to be

$$\frac{d^2z}{dx^2} \cos \alpha \cos \beta + \frac{d^2z}{dxdy} \sin (\alpha + \beta) + \frac{d^2z}{dy^2} \sin \alpha \sin \beta = 0 \; ;$$

α and β being known as functions of x and y, we may determine the nature of the curves projected on the plane of xy.

Supposing the surface to touch that plane at the origin, the length and tangential curvature of the lines on the surface near the point of contact may be taken the same as those of their projections on the plane, and any change of form of the surface due to bending will not alter the form of the projected lines indefinitely near the point of contact. We may therefore consider z as the only variable altered by bending; but in order to apply our analysis with facility, we may assume

$$\frac{d^2z}{dx^2} = PQ \sin^2 \alpha + PQ^{-1} \sin^2 \beta,$$

$$\frac{d^2z}{dxdy} = - PQ \sin \alpha \cos \alpha - PQ^{-1} \sin \beta \cos \beta,$$

$$\frac{d^2z}{dy^2} = PQ \cos^2 \alpha + PQ^{-1} \cos^2 \beta.$$

It will be seen that these values satisfy the condition last given. Near the origin we have

$$p = \frac{d^2z}{dx^2} \frac{d^2z}{dy^2} - \overline{\frac{d^2z}{dxdy}}\Big|^2 = P^2 \sin^2 (\alpha - \beta),$$

and $q = Q^{-2}.$

Differentiating these values of $\dfrac{d^2z}{dx^2}$, &c., we shall obtain two values of $\dfrac{d^2z}{dx^2\,dy}$ and of $\dfrac{d^2z}{dx\,dy^2}$, which being equated will give two equations of condition.

Now if s' be measured along a curve of the first system, and R be any function of x and y, then

$$\frac{dR}{ds'} = \frac{dR}{dx}\cos a + \frac{dR}{dy}\sin a,$$

$$\text{and } \frac{dR}{du'} = \frac{dR}{ds'}\frac{ds'}{du'}.$$

We may also show that

$$\frac{da}{ds'} = \frac{1}{r},$$

and that $\cos a\,\dfrac{da}{dy} - \sin a\,\dfrac{da}{dx} = \dfrac{d}{ds}\log\left(\dfrac{ds'}{du'}\sin\phi\right).$

By substituting these values in the equations thus obtained, they are reduced to the two equations given at the end of (Art. 15). This method of investigation introduces no difficulty except that of somewhat long equations, and is therefore satisfactory as supplementary to the geometrical method given at length.

As an example of the method given in page (2), we may apply it to the case of the surface whose equation is

$$\left(\frac{x}{c-z}\right) + \left(\frac{y}{c+z}\right)^2 = \left(\frac{a}{c}\right)^2.$$

This surface may be generated by the motion of a straight line whose equation is of the form

$$x = a\cos t\left(1 - \frac{z}{c}\right), \qquad y = a\sin t\left(1 + \frac{z}{c}\right),$$

t being the variable, by the change of which we pass from one position of the line to another. This line always passes through the circle

$$z = 0, \qquad x^2 + y^2 = a^2,$$

and the straight lines $z = c, \qquad x = 0,$

and $z = -c, \quad y = 0,$

which may therefore be taken as the directors of the surface.

Taking two consecutive positions of this line, in which the values of t are t and $t + \delta t$, we may find by the ordinary methods the equation to the shortest line between them, its length, and the co-ordinates of the point in which it intersects the first line.

Calling the length $\delta\zeta$,

$$\delta\zeta = \frac{ac}{\sqrt{a^2 + c^2}} \sin 2t \delta t,$$

and the co-ordinates of the point of intersection are

$$x = 2a \cos^3 t, \qquad y = 2a \sin^3 t, \qquad z = -c \cos 2t.$$

The angle $\delta\theta$ between the consecutive lines is

$$\delta\theta = \frac{a}{\sqrt{a^2 + c^2}} \delta t.$$

The distance $\delta\sigma$ between consecutive shortest lines is

$$\delta\sigma = \frac{3a^2 + 2c^2}{\sqrt{a^2 + c^2}} \sin 2t \delta t,$$

and the angle $\delta\phi$ between these latter lines is

$$\delta\phi = \frac{c}{\sqrt{a^2 + c^2}} \delta t.$$

Hence if we suppose ζ, θ, σ, ϕ, and t to vanish together, we shall have by integration

$$\zeta = \frac{ac}{2\sqrt{a^2 + c^2}} (1 - \cos 2t),$$

$$\theta = \frac{a}{\sqrt{a^2 + c^2}} t,$$

$$\sigma = \frac{3a^2 + 2c^2}{2\sqrt{a^2 + c^2}} (1 - \cos 2t),$$

$$\phi = \frac{c}{\sqrt{a^2 + c^2}} t.$$

By bending the surface about its generating lines we alter the value of ϕ in any manner without changing ζ, θ, or σ. For instance, making $\phi = 0$, all the generating lines become parallel to the same plane. Let this plane be that of xy, then ζ is the distance of a generating line from that plane. The projections of the generating lines on the plane of xy will, by their ultimate intersections, form a curve, the length of which is measured by σ, and the angle which its tangent makes with the axis of x by θ, θ and σ being connected by the equation

$$\sigma = \frac{3a^2 + 2c^2}{2\sqrt{a^2 + c^2}}\left(1 - \cos\frac{2\sqrt{a^2 + c^2}}{a}\theta\right),$$

which shows the curve to be an epicycloid.

The generating lines of the surface when bent into this form are therefore tangents to a cylindrical surface on an epicycloidal base, touching that surface along a curve which is always equally inclined to the plane of the base, the tangents themselves being drawn parallel to the base.

We may now consider the bending of the surface of revolution

$$\sqrt[3]{x^2 + y^2} + z^{\frac{2}{3}} = c^{\frac{2}{3}}.$$

Putting $r = \sqrt{x^2 + y^2}$, then the equation of the generating line is

$$r^{\frac{2}{3}} + z^{\frac{2}{3}} = c^{\frac{2}{3}}.$$

This is the well-known hypocycloid of four cusps.

Let s be the length of the curve measured from the cusp in the axis of z then,

$$s = \tfrac{3}{2}c^{\frac{1}{3}}r^{\frac{2}{3}},$$

wherefore,

$$r = \left(\tfrac{2}{3}\right)^{\frac{3}{2}} c^{-\frac{1}{2}} s^{\frac{3}{2}}.$$

Let θ be the angle which the plane of any generating line makes with that of xz, then s and θ determine the position of any point on the surface The length and breadth of an element of the surface will be δs and $r\delta\theta$.

Now let the surface be bent in the manner formerly described, so that becomes θ', and r, r', when

$$\theta' = \mu\theta \text{ and } r' = \frac{1}{\mu}r,$$

then

$$r' = \left(\tfrac{2}{3}\right)^{\frac{3}{2}} c^{-\frac{1}{2}} \mu^{-1} s^{\frac{3}{2}}$$

$$= \left(\tfrac{2}{3}\right)^{\frac{3}{2}} c'^{-\frac{1}{2}} s^{\frac{3}{2}},$$

provided

$$c' = \mu^2 c.$$

The equation between r' and s being of the same form as that betwee r and s shows that the surface when bent is similar to the original surface, i dimensions being multiplied by μ^2.

This, however, is true only for one half of the surface when bent. The other half is precisely symmetrical, but belongs to a surface which is not continuous with the first.

The surface in its original form is divided by the plane of xy into two parts which meet in that plane, forming a kind of cuspidal edge of a circular form which limits the possible value of s and r.

After being bent, the surface still consists of the same two parts, but the edge in which they meet is no longer of the cuspidal form, but has a finite angle $= 2 \cos^{-1} \dfrac{1}{\mu}$, and the two sheets of the surface become parts of two different surfaces which meet but are not continuous.

NOTE.

As an example of the application of the more general theory of "lines of bending," let us consider the problem which has been already solved by Professor Jellett.

To determine the conditions under which one portion of a surface may be rendered rigid, while the remainder is flexible.

Suppose the lines of bending to be traced on the surface, and the corresponding polyhedron to be formed, as in (9) and (10), then if the angle of one of the four edges which meet at any solid angle of the polyhedron be altered by bending, those of the other three must be also altered. These edges terminate in other solid angles, the forms of which will also be changed, and therefore the effect of the alteration of one angle of the polyhedron will be communicated to every other angle within the system of lines of bending which defines the form of the polyhedron.

If any portion of the surface remains unaltered it must lie beyond the limits of the system of lines of bending. We must therefore investigate the conditions of such a system being bounded.

The boundary of any system of lines on a surface is the curve formed by the ultimate intersection of those lines, and therefore at any given point coincides in direction with the curve of the system which passes through that point. In this case there are two systems of lines of bending, which are necessarily coincident in extent, and must therefore have the same boundary. At any point of this boundary therefore the directions of the lines of bending of the first and second systems are coincident.

But, by (7), these two directions must be "conjugate" to each other, that is, must correspond to conjugate diameters of the "Conic of Contact." Now the only case in which conjugate diameters of a conic can coincide, is when the conic is an hyperbola, and both diameters coincide with one of the asymptotes; therefore the boundary of the system of lines of bending must be a curve at every point of which the conic of contact is an hyperbola, one of whose asymptotes lies in the direction of the curve. The radius of "normal curvature" must therefore by (3) be infinite at every point of the curve. This is the geometrical property of what Professor Jellett calls a " Curve of Flexure," so that we may express the result as follows :

If one portion of a surface be fixed, while the remainder is bent, the boundary of the fixed portion is a curve of flexure.

This theorem includes those given at p. (92), relative to a fixed curve on a surface, for in a surface whose curvatures are of the same sign, there can be no "curves of flexure," and in a developable surface, they are the rectilinear sections. Although the cuspidal edge, or *arête de rebroussement*, satisfies the analytical condition of a curve of flexure, yet, since its form determines that of the whole surface, it cannot remain fixed while the form of the surface is changed.

In concavo-convex surfaces, the curves of flexure must either have tangential curvature or be straight lines. Now if we put $\phi = 0$ in the equations of Art. (17), we find that the lines of bending of both systems have no tangential curvature at the point where they touch the curve of flexure. They must therefore lie entirely on the convex side of that curve, and therefore

If a curve of flexure be fixed, the surface on the concave side of the curve is not flexible.

I have not yet been able to determine whether the surface is inflexible on the convex side of the curve. It certainly is so in some cases which I have been able to work out, but I have no general proof.

When a surface has one or more rectilinear sections, the portions of the surface between them may revolve as rigid bodies round those lines as axes in any manner, but no other motion is possible. The case in which the rectilinear sections form an infinite series has been discussed in Sect. (I.).

[From the *Cambridge and Dublin Mathematical Journal*, Vol. IX.]

V. *On a particular case of the descent of a heavy body in a resisting
medium.*

EVERY one must have observed that when a slip of paper falls through
the air, its motion, though undecided and wavering at first, sometimes becomes
regular. Its general path is not in the vertical direction, but inclined to it
at an angle which remains nearly constant, and its fluttering appearance will
be found to be due to a rapid rotation round a horizontal axis. The direction
of deviation from the vertical depends on the direction of rotation.

If the positive directions of an axis be toward the right hand and upwards,
and the positive angular direction opposite to the direction of motion of the
hands of a watch, then, if the rotation is in the positive direction, the horizontal part of the mean motion will be positive.

These effects are commonly attributed to some accidental peculiarity in the
form of the paper, but a few experiments with a rectangular slip of paper
(about two inches long and one broad), will shew that the direction of rotation
is determined, not by the irregularities of the paper, but by the initial circumstances of projection, and that the symmetry of the form of the paper greatly
increases the distinctness of the phenomena. We may therefore assume that
if the form of the body were accurately that of a plane rectangle, the same
effects would be produced.

The following investigation is intended as a general explanation of the true
cause of the phenomenon.

I suppose the resistance of the air caused by the motion of the plane to
be in the direction of the normal and to vary as the square of the velocity
estimated in that direction.

Now though this may be taken as a sufficiently near approximation to the
magnitude of the resisting force on the plane taken as a whole, the pressure

on any given element of the surface will vary with its position so that the resultant force will not generally pass through the centre of gravity.

It is found by experiment that the position of the centre of pressure depends on the tangential part of the motion, that it lies on that side of the centre of gravity towards which the tangential motion of the plane is directed, and that its distance from that point increases as the tangential velocity increases.

I am not aware of any mathematical investigation of this effect. The explanation may be deduced from experiment.

Place a body similar in shape to the slip of paper obliquely in a current of some visible fluid. Call the edge where the fluid first meets the plane the first edge, and the edge where it leaves the plane, the second edge, then we may observe that

(1) On the anterior side of the plane the velocity of the fluid increases as it moves along the surface from the first to the second edge, and therefore by a known law in hydrodynamics, the pressure must diminish from the first to the second edge.

(2) The motion of the fluid behind the plane is very unsteady, but may be observed to consist of a series of eddies diminishing in rapidity as they pass behind the plane from the first to the second edge, and therefore relieving the posterior pressure most at the first edge.

Both these causes tend to make the total resistance greatest at the first edge, and therefore to bring the centre of pressure nearest to that edge.

Hence the moment of the resistance about the centre of gravity will always tend to turn the plane towards a position perpendicular to the direction of the current, or, in the case of the slip of paper, to the path of the body itself. It will be shewn that it is this moment that maintains the rotatory motion of the falling paper.

When the plane has a motion of rotation, the resistance will be modified on account of the unequal velocities of different parts of the surface. The magnitude of the whole resistance at any instant will not be sensibly altered if the velocity of any point due to angular motion be small compared with that due to the motion of the centre of gravity. But there will be an additional moment of the resistance round the centre of gravity, which will always act in the direction opposite to that of rotation, and will vary directly as the normal and angular velocities together.

The part of the moment due to the obliquity of the motion will remain nearly the same as before.

We are now prepared to give a general explanation of the motion of the slip of paper after it has become regular.

Let the angular position of the paper be determined by the angle between the normal to its surface and the axis of x, and let the angular motion be such that the normal, at first coinciding with the axis of x, passes towards that of y.

The motion, speaking roughly, is one of descent, that is, in the negative direction along the axis of y.

The resolved part of the resistance in the vertical direction will always act upwards, being greatest when the plane of the paper is horizontal, and vanishing when it is vertical.

When the motion has become regular, the effect of this force during a whole revolution will be equal and opposite to that of gravity during the same time.

Since the resisting force increases while the normal is in its first and third quadrants, and diminishes when it is in its second and fourth, the maxima of velocity will occur when the normal is in its first and third quadrants, and the minima when it is in the second and fourth.

The resolved part of the resistance in the horizontal direction will act in the positive direction along the axis of x in the first and third quadrants, and in the negative direction during the second and fourth; but since the resistance increases with the velocity, the whole effect during the first and third quadrants will be greater than the whole effect during the second and fourth. Hence the horizontal part of the resistance will act on the whole in the positive direction, and will therefore cause the general path of the body to incline in that direction, that is, toward the right.

That part of the moment of the resistance about the centre of gravity which depends on the angular velocity will vary in magnitude, but will always act in the negative direction. The other part, which depends on the obliquity of the plane of the paper to the direction of motion, will be positive in the first and third quadrants and negative in the second and fourth; but as its magnitude increases with the velocity, the positive effect will be greater than the negative.

When the motion has become regular, the effect of this excess in the positive direction will be equal and opposite to the negative effect due to the angular velocity during a whole revolution.

The motion will then consist of a succession of equal and similar parts performed in the same manner, each part corresponding to half a revolution of the paper.

These considerations will serve to explain the lateral motion of the paper, and the maintenance of the rotatory motion.

Similar reasoning will shew that whatever be the initial motion of the paper, it cannot remain uniform.

Any accidental oscillations will increase till their amplitude exceeds half a revolution. The motion will then become one of rotation, and will continually approximate to that which we have just considered.

It may be also shewn that this motion will be unstable unless it take place about the longer axis of the rectangle.

If this axis is inclined to the horizon, or if one end of the slip of paper be different from the other, the path will not be straight, but in the form of a helix. There will be no other essential difference between this case and that of the symmetrical arrangement.

Trinity College, April 5, 1853.

[From the *Transactions of the Royal Scottish Society of Arts,* Vol. IV. Part III.]

VI. *On the Theory of Colours in relation to Colour-Blindness.*
A letter to Dr G. Wilson.

DEAR SIR,—As you seemed to think that the results which I have obtained in the theory of colours might be of service to you, I have endeavoured to arrange them for you in a more convenient form than that in which I first obtained them. I must premise, that the first distinct statement of the theory of colour which I adopt, is to be found in *Young's Lectures on Natural Philosophy* (p. 345, Kelland's Edition); and the most philosophical enquiry into it which I have seen is that of Helmholtz, which may be found in the Annals of Philosophy for 1852.

It is well known that a ray of light, from any source, may be divided by means of a prism into a number of rays of different refrangibility, forming a series called a spectrum. The intensity of the light is different at different points of this spectrum; and the law of intensity for different refrangibilities differs according to the nature of the incident light. In Sir John F. W. Herschel's *Treatise on Light*, diagrams will be found, each of which represents completely, by means of a curve, the law of the intensity and refrangibility of a beam of solar light after passing through various coloured media.

I have mentioned this mode of defining and registering a beam of light, because it is the perfect expression of what a beam of light is in itself, considered with respect to all its properties as ascertained by the most refined instruments. When a beam of light falls on the human eye, certain sensations are produced, from which the possessor of that organ judges of the colour and intensity of the light. Now, though every one experiences these sensations, and though they are the foundation of all the phenomena of sight, yet, on account of their absolute simplicity, they are incapable of analysis, and can never become in themselves objects of thought. If we attempt to discover them, we must do so by artificial means; and our reasonings on them must be guided by some theory.

The most general form in which the existing theory can be stated is this,—

There are certain sensations, finite in number, but infinitely variable in degree, which may be excited by the different kinds of light. The compound sensation resulting from all these is the object of consciousness, is a simple act of vision.

It is easy to see that the *number* of these sensations corresponds to what may be called in mathematical language the number of independent variables, of which sensible colour is a function.

This will be readily understood by attending to the following cases:—

1. When objects are illuminated by homogeneous yellow light, the only thing which can be distinguished by the eye is difference of intensity or brightness.

If we take a horizontal line, and colour it black at one end, with increasing degrees of intensity of yellow light towards the other, then every visible object will have a brightness corresponding to some point in this line.

In this case there is nothing to prove the existence of more than one sensation in vision.

In those photographic pictures in which there is only one tint of which the different intensities correspond to the different degrees of illumination of the object, we have another illustration of an optical effect depending on one variable only.

2. Now, suppose that different kinds of light are emanating from different sources, but that each of these sources gives out perfectly homogeneous light, then there will be two things on which the nature of each ray will depend:—
(1) its intensity or brightness; (2) its hue, which may be estimated by its position in the spectrum, and measured by its wave length.

If we take a rectangular plane, and illuminate it with the different kinds of homogeneous light, the intensity at any point being proportional to its horizontal distance along the plane, and its wave length being proportional to its height above the foot of the plane, then the plane will display every possible variety of homogeneous light, and will furnish an instance of an optical effect depending on two variables.

3. Now, let us take the case of nature. We find that colours differ not only in intensity and hue, but also in tint; that is, they are more or less pure. We might arrange the varieties of each colour along a line, which should begin with the homogeneous colour as seen in the spectrum, and pass through all gradations of tint, so as to become continually purer, and terminate in white.

We have, therefore, three elements in our sensation of colour, each of which may vary independently. For distinctness sake I have spoken of intensity, hue, and tint; but if any other three independent qualities had been chosen, the one set might have been expressed in terms of the other, and the results identified.

The theory which I adopt assumes the existence of three elementary sensations, by the combination of which all the actual sensations of colour are produced. It will be shewn that it is not necessary to specify any given colours as typical of these sensations. Young has called them red, green, and violet; but any other three colours might have been chosen, provided that white resulted from their combination in proper proportions.

Before going farther I would observe, that the important part of the theory is not that three elements enter into our sensation of colour, but that there are only three. Optically, there are as many elements in the composition of a ray of light as there are different kinds of light in its spectrum; and, therefore, strictly speaking, its nature depends on an infinite number of independent variables.

I now go on to the geometrical form into which the theory may be thrown. Let it be granted that the three pure sensations correspond to the colours red, green, and violet, and that we can estimate the intensity of each of these sensations numerically.

Let v, r, g be the angular points of a triangle, and conceive the three sensations as having their positions at these points. If we find the numerical measure of the red, green, and violet parts of the sensation of a given colour, and then place weights proportional to these parts at r, g, and v, and find the centre of gravity of the three weights by the ordinary process, that point will be the position of the given colour, and the numerical measure of its intensity will be the sum of the three primitive sensations.

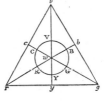

In this way, every possible colour may have its position and intensity ascertained; and it is easy to see that when two compound colours are combined, their centre of gravity is the position of the new colour.

The idea of this geometrical method of investigating colours is to be found in Newton's *Opticks* (Book I., Part 2, Prop. 6), but I am not aware that it has been ever employed in practice, except in the reduction of the experiments which I have just made. The accuracy of the method depends entirely on the truth of the theory of three sensations, and therefore its success is a testimony in favour of that theory.

Every possible colour must be included within the triangle *rgv*. White will be found at some point, *w*, within the triangle. If lines be drawn through *w* to any point, the colour at that point will vary in hue according to the angular position of the line drawn to *w*, and the purity of the tint will depend on the length of that line.

Though the homogeneous rays of the prismatic spectrum are absolutely pure in themselves, yet they do not give rise to the "pure sensations" of which we are speaking. Every ray of the spectrum gives rise to all three sensations, though in different proportions; hence the position of the colours of the spectrum is not at the boundary of the triangle, but in some curve *C R Y G B V* considerably within the triangle. The nature of this curve is not yet determined, but may form the subject of a future investigation*.

All natural colours must be within this curve, and all ordinary pigments do in fact lie very much within it. The experiments on the colours of the spectrum which I have made are not brought to the same degree of accuracy as those on coloured papers. I therefore proceed at once to describe the mode of making those experiments which I have found most simple and convenient.

The coloured paper is cut into the form of discs, each with a small hole in the centre, and divided along a radius, so as to admit of several of them being placed on the same axis, so that part of each is exposed. By slipping one disc over another, we can expose any given portion of each colour. These discs are placed on a little top or teetotum, consisting of a flat disc of tin-plate and a vertical axis of ivory. This  axis passes through the centre of the discs, and the quantity of each colour exposed is measured by a graduation on the rim of the disc, which is divided into 100 parts.

* [See the author's Memoir in the *Philosophical Transactions*, 1860, on the Theory of Compound Colours, and on the relations of the Colours of the Spectrum.]

By spinning the top, each colour is presented to the eye for a time proportional to the angle of the sector exposed, and I have found by independent experiments, that the colour produced by fast spinning is identical with that produced by causing the light of the different colours to fall on the retina at once.

By properly arranging the discs, any given colour may be imitated and afterwards registered by the graduation on the rim of the top. The principal use of the top is to obtain colour-equations. These are got by producing, by two different combinations of colours, the same mixed tint. For this purpose there is another set of discs, half the diameter of the others, which lie above them, and by which the second combination of colours is formed.

The two combinations being close together, may be accurately compared, and when they are made sensibly identical, the proportions of the different colours in each is registered, and the results equated.

These equations in the case of ordinary vision, are always between four colours, not including black.

From them, by a very simple rule, the different colours and compounds have their places assigned on the triangle of colours. The rule for finding the position is this:—Assume any three points as the positions of your three standard colours, whatever they are; then form an equation between the three standard colours, the given colour and black, by arranging these colours on the inner and outer circles so as to produce an identity when spun. Bring the given colour to the left-hand side of the equation, and the three standard colours to the right hand, leaving out black, then the position of the given colour is the centre of gravity of three masses, whose weights are as the number of degrees of each of the standard colours, taken positive or negative, as the case may be.

In this way the triangle of colours may be constructed by scale and compass from experiments on ordinary vision. I now proceed to state the results of experiments on Colour-Blind vision.

If we find two combinations of colours which appear identical to a Colour-Blind person, and mark their positions on the triangle of colours, then the straight line passing through these points will pass through all points corresponding to other colours, which, to such a person, appear identical with the first two.

We may in the same way find other lines passing through the series of colours which appear alike to the Colour-Blind. All these lines either pass through one point or are parallel, according to the standard colours which we have assumed, and the other arbitrary assumptions we may have made. Knowing this law of Colour-Blind vision, we may predict any number of equations which will be true for eyes having this defect.

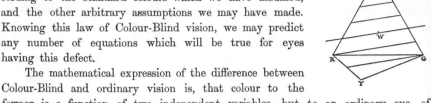

The mathematical expression of the difference between Colour-Blind and ordinary vision is, that colour to the former is a function of two independent variables, but to an ordinary eye, of three; and that the relation of the two kinds of vision is not arbitrary, but indicates the absence of a determinate sensation, depending perhaps upon some undiscovered structure or organic arrangement, which forms one-third of the apparatus by which we receive sensations of colour.

Suppose the absent structure to be that which is brought most into play when red light falls on our eyes, then to the Colour-Blind red light will be visible only so far as it affects the other two sensations, say of blue and green. It will, therefore, appear to them much less bright than to us, and will excite a sensation not distinguishable from that of a bluish-green light.

I cannot at present recover the results of all my experiments; but I recollect that the neutral colours for a Colour-Blind person may be produced by combining 6 degrees of ultramarine with 94 of vermilion, or 60 of emerald-green with 40 of ultramarine. The first of these, I suppose to represent to our eyes the kind of red which belongs to the red sensation. It excites the other two sensations, and is, therefore, visible to the Colour-Blind, but it appears very dark to them and of no definite colour. I therefore suspect that one of the three sensations in perfect vision will be found to correspond to a red of the same hue, but of much greater purity of tint. Of the nature of the other two, I can say nothing definite, except that one must correspond to a blue, and the other to a green, verging to yellow.

I hope that what I have written may help you in any way in your experiments. I have put down many things simply to indicate a way of thinking about colours which belongs to this theory of triple sensation. We are indebted to Newton for the original design; to Young for the suggestion of the means of working it out; to Prof. Forbes* for a scientific history of its application

*Phil. Mag. 1848.

to practice ; to Helmholtz for a rigorous examination of the facts on which it rests ; and to Prof. Grassman (in the *Phil. Mag.* for 1852), for an admirable theoretical exposition of the subject. The colours given in Hay's *Nomenclature of Colours* are illustrations of a similar theory applied to mixtures of pigments, but the results are often different from those in which the colours are combined by the eye alone. I hope soon to have results with pigments compared with those given by the prismatic spectrum, and then, perhaps, some more definite results may be obtained. Yours truly,

J. C. MAXWELL.

EDINBURGH, 4th *Jan.* 1855.

[From the *Transactions of the Royal Society of Edinburgh*, Vol. XXI. Part II.]

VII. *Experiments on Colour, as perceived by the Eye, with remarks on Colour-Blindness.* Communicated by Dr Gregory.

THE object of the following communication is to describe a method by which every variety of visible colour may be exhibited to the eye in such a form as to admit of accurate comparison; to shew how experiments so made may be registered numerically; and to deduce from these numerical results certain laws of vision.

The different tints are produced by means of a combination of discs of paper, painted with the pigments commonly used in the arts, and arranged round an axis, so that a sector of any required angular magnitude of each colour may be exposed. When this system of discs is set in rapid rotation, the sectors of the different colours become indistinguishable, and the whole appears of one uniform tint. The resultant tints of two different combinations of colours may be compared by using a second set of discs of a smaller size, and placing these over the centre of the first set, so as to leave the outer portion of the larger discs exposed. The resultant tint of the first combination will then appear in a ring round that of the second, and may be very carefully compared with it.

The form in which the experiment is most manageable is that of the common top. An axis, of which the lower extremity is conical, carries a circular plate, which serves as a support for the discs of coloured paper. The circumference of this plate is divided into 100 equal parts, for the purpose of ascertaining the proportions of the different colours which form the combination. When the discs have been properly arranged, the upper part of the axis is screwed down so as to prevent any alteration in the proportions of the colours.

The instrument used in the first series of experiments (at Cambridge, in November, 1854) was constructed by myself, with coloured papers procured from

Mr D. R. Hay. The experiments made in the present year were with the improved top made by Mr J. M. Bryson, Edinburgh, and coloured papers prepared by Mr T. Purdie, with the unmixed pigments used in the arts. A number of Mr Bryson's tops, with Mr Purdie's coloured papers has been prepared, so as to afford different observers the means of testing and comparing results independently obtained.

The colour used for Mr Purdie's papers were—

Vermilion	.	.	V	Ultramarine	.	.	U	Emerald Green . . EG
Carmine .	.	.	C	Prussian Blue .	.	PB	Brunswick Green . . BG
Red Lead	.	.	RL	Verditer Blue .	.	VB	Mixture of Ultramarine
Orange Orpiment	.	OO					and Chrome . . UC
Orange Chrome	.	OC					
Chrome Yellow	.	CY					
Gamboge	.	.	Gam				
Pale Chrome .	.	PC					

Ivory Black . . Bk
Snow White . . SW
White Paper (Pirie, Aberdeen).

The colours in the first column are reds, oranges, and yellows; those in the second, blues; and those in the third, greens. Vermilion, ultramarine, and emerald green, seem the best colours to adopt in referring the rest to a uniform standard. They are therefore put at the head of the list, as types of three convenient divisions of colour, red, blue, and green.

It may be asked, why some variety of yellow was not chosen in place of green, which is commonly placed among the secondary colours, while yellow ranks as a primary? The reason for this deviation from the received system is, that the colours on the discs do not represent primary colours at all, but are simply specimens of different kinds of paint, and the choice of these was determined solely by the power of forming the requisite variety of combinations. Now, if red, blue, and yellow, had been adopted, there would have been a difficulty in forming green by any compound of blue and yellow, while the yellow formed by vermilion and emerald green is tolerably distinct. This will be more clearly perceived after the experiments have been discussed, by referring to the diagram.

As an example of the method of experimenting, let us endeavour to form a neutral gray by the combination of vermilion, ultramarine, and emerald green. The most perfect results are obtained by two persons acting in concert, when the operator arranges the colours and spins the top, leaving the eye of the observer free from the distracting effect of the bright colours of the papers when at rest.

After placing discs of these three colours on the circular plate of the top, and smaller discs of white and black above them, the operator must spin the top, and demand the opinion of the observer respecting the relation of the outer ring to the inner circle. He will be told that the outer circle is too red, too blue, or too green, as the case may be, and that the inner one is too light or too dark, as compared with the outer. The arrangement must then be changed, so as to render the resultant tint of the outer and inner circles more nearly alike. Sometimes the observer will see the inner circle tinted with the complementary colour of the outer one. In this case the operator must interpret the observation with respect to the outer circle, as the inner circle contains only black and white.

By a little experience the operator will learn how to put his questions, and how to interpret their answers. The observer should not look at the coloured papers, nor be told the proportions of the colours during the experiments. When these adjustments have been properly made, the resultant tints of the outer and inner circles ought to be perfectly indistinguishable, when the top has a sufficient velocity of rotation. The number of divisions occupied by the different colours must then be read off on the edge of the plate, and registered in the form of an equation. Thus, in the preceding experiment we have vermilion, ultramarine, and emerald green outside, and black and white inside. The numbers, as given by an experiment on the 6th March 1855, in daylight without sun, are—

$$\cdot37 \; V + \cdot27 \; U + \cdot36 \; EG = \cdot28 \; SW + \cdot72 \; Bk \ldots\ldots\ldots\ldots(1).$$

The method of treating these equations will be given when we come to the theoretical view of the subject.

In this way we have formed a neutral gray by the combination of the three standard colours. We may also form neutral grays of different intensities by the combination of vermilion and ultramarine with the other greens, and thus obtain the quantities of each necessary to neutralize a given quantity of the proposed green. By substituting for each standard colour in succession one of the colours which stand under it, we may obtain equations, each of which contains two standard colours, and one of the remaining colours.

Thus, in the case of pale chrome, we have, from the same set of experiments,

$$\cdot34 \text{ PC} + \cdot55 \text{ U} + \cdot12 \text{ EG} = \cdot37 \text{ SW} + \cdot63 \text{ Bk}\dots\dots\dots\dots(2).$$

We may also make experiments in which the resulting tint is not a neutral gray, but a decided colour. Thus we may combine ultramarine, pale chrome, and black, so as to produce a tint identical with that of a compound of vermilion and emerald-green. Experiments of this sort are more difficult, both from the inability of the observer to express the difference which he detects in two tints which have, perhaps, the same hue and intensity, but differ in purity; and also from the complementary colours which are produced in the eye after gazing too long at the colours to be compared.

The best method of arriving at a result in the case before us, is to render the *hue* of the red and green combination something like that of the yellow, to reduce the *purity* of the yellow by the admixture of blue, and to diminish its *intensity* by the addition of black. These operations must be repeated and adjusted, till the two tints are not merely varieties of the same colour, but absolutely the same. An experiment made 5th March gives—

$$\cdot39 \text{ PC} + \cdot21 \text{ U} + \cdot40 \text{ Bk} = \cdot59 \text{ V} + \cdot41 \text{ EG} \dots\dots\dots\dots (3).$$

That these experiments are really evidence relating to the constitution of the eye, and not mere comparisons of two things which are in themselves identical, may be shewn by observing these resultant tints through coloured glasses, or by using gas-light instead of day-light. The tints which before appeared identical will now be manifestly different, and will require alteration, to reduce them to equality.

Thus, in the case of carmine, we have by day-light,

$$\cdot44 \text{ C} + \cdot22 \text{ U} + \cdot34 \text{ EG} = \cdot17 \text{ SW} + \cdot83 \text{ Bk},$$

while by gas-light (Edinburgh)

$$\cdot47 \text{ C} + \cdot08 \text{ U} + \cdot45 \text{ EG} = \cdot25 \text{ SW} + \cdot75 \text{ Bk},$$

which shews that the yellowing effect of the gas-light tells more on the white than on the combination of colours. If we examine the two resulting tints which appeared identical in experiment (3), observing the whirling discs through a blue glass, the combination of yellow, blue, and black, appears redder than the other, while through a yellow glass, the red and green mixture appears redder. So also a red glass makes the first side of the equation too dark, and a green glass makes it too light.

The apparent identity of the tints in these experiments is therefore not real, but a consequence of a determinate constitution of the eye, and hence arises the importance of the results, as indicating the laws of human vision.

The first result which is worthy of notice is, that the equations, as observed by different persons of ordinary vision, agree in a remarkable manner. If care be taken to secure the same kind of light in all the experiments, the equations, as determined by two independent observers, will seldom shew a difference of more than three divisions in any part of the equation containing the bright standard colours. As the duller colours are less active in changing the resultant tint, their true proportions cannot be so well ascertained. The accuracy of vision of each observer may be tested by repeating the same experiment at different times, and comparing the equations so found.

Experiments of this kind, made at Cambridge in November 1854, shew that of ten observers, the best were accurate to within $1\frac{1}{2}$ division, and agreed within 1 division of the mean of all; and the worst contradicted themselves to the extent of 6 degrees, but still were never more than 4 or 5 from the mean of all the observations.

We are thus led to conclude—

1st. That the human eye is capable of estimating the likeness of colours with a precision which in some cases is very great.

2nd. That the judgment thus formed is determined, not by the real identity of the colours, but by a cause residing in the eye of the observer.

3rd. That the eyes of different observers vary in accuracy, but agree with each other so nearly as to leave no doubt that the law of colour-vision is identical for all ordinary eyes.

Investigation of the Law of the Perception of Colour.

Before proceeding to the deduction of the elementary laws of the perception of colour from the numerical results previously obtained, it will be desirable to point out some general features of the experiments which indicate the form which these laws must assume.

Returning to experiment (1), in which a neutral gray was produced from red, blue, and green, we may observe, that, while the adjustments were incomplete, the difference of the tints could be detected only by one circle appearing more red, more green, or more blue than the other, or by being lighter or darker, that is, having an excess or defect of all the three colours together. Hence it appears that the nature of a colour may be considered as dependent on *three* things, as, for instance, redness, blueness, and greenness. This is confirmed by the fact that any tint may be imitated by mixing red, blue, and green alone, provided that tint does not exceed a certain brilliancy.

Another way of shewing that colour depends on *three* things is by considering how two tints, say two lilacs, may differ. In the first place, one may be *lighter* or *darker* than the other, that is, the tints may differ in *shade*. Secondly, one may be more *blue* or more *red* than the other, that is, they may differ in *hue*. Thirdly, one may be more or less *decided* in its colour; it may vary from purity on the one hand, to neutrality on the other. This is sometimes expressed by saying that they may differ in *tint*.

Thus, in shade, hue, and tint, we have another mode of reducing the elements of colour to three. It will be shewn that these two methods of considering colour may be deduced one from the other, and are capable of exact numerical comparison.

On a Geographical Method of Exhibiting the Relations of Colours.

The method which exhibits to the eye most clearly the results of this theory of the three elements of colour, is that which supposes each colour to be represented by a point in space, whose distances from three co-ordinate planes are proportional to the three elements of colour. But as any method by which the operations are confined to a plane is preferable to one requiring space of three dimensions, we shall only consider for the present that which has been adopted for convenience, founded on Newton's Circle of colours and Mayer and Young's Triangle.

Vermilion, ultramarine, and emerald-green, being taken (for convenience) as standard colours, are conceived to be represented by three points, taken (for convenience) at the angles of an equilateral triangle. Any colour compounded of these three is to be represented by a point found by conceiving masses proportional to the several components of the colour placed at their respective angular points, and taking the centre of gravity of the three masses. In this way, each

17—2

colour will indicate by its position the proportions of the elements of which it is composed. The total intensity of the colour is to be measured by the whole number of divisions of V, U, and EG, of which it is composed. This may be indicated by a number or coefficient appended to the name of the colour, by which the number of divisions it occupies must be multiplied to obtain its mass in calculating the results of new combinations.

This will be best explained by an example on the diagram (No. 1). We have, by experiment (1),

$$\cdot 37 \text{ V} + \cdot 27 \text{ U} + \cdot 36 \text{ EG} = \cdot 28 \text{ SW} + \cdot 72 \text{ Bk}.$$

To find the position of the resultant neutral tint, we must conceive a mass of ·37 at V, of ·27 at U, and of ·36 at EG, and find the centre of gravity. This may be done by taking the line UV, and dividing it in the proportion of ·37 to ·27 at the point a, where

$$aV : aU :: \cdot 27 : \cdot 37.$$

Then, joining a with EG, divide the joining line in W in the proportion of ·36 to (·37 + ·27), W will be the position of the neutral tint required, which is not white, but 0·28 of white, diluted with 0·72 of black, which has hardly any effect whatever, except in decreasing the amount of the other colour. The total intensity of our white paper will be represented by $\frac{1}{0 \cdot 28} = 3 \cdot 57$; so that, whenever white enters into an equation, the number of divisions must be multiplied by the coefficient 3·57 before any true results can be obtained.

We may take, as the next example, the method of representing the relation of pale chrome to the standard colours on our diagram, by making use of experiment (2), in which pale chrome, ultramarine, and emerald-green, produced a neutral gray. The resulting equation was

$$\cdot 33 \text{ PC} + \cdot 55 \text{ U} + \cdot 12 \text{ EG} = \cdot 37 \text{ SW} + \cdot 63 \text{ Bk} \dots\dots\dots\dots\dots\dots(2).$$

In order to obtain the total intensity of white, we must multiply the number of divisions, ·37, by the proper coefficient, which is 3·57. The result is 1·32, which therefore measures the total intensity on both sides of the equation.

Subtracting the intensity of ·55 U + ·12 EG, or ·67 from 1·32, we obtain ·65 as the *corrected* value of ·33 PC. It will be convenient to use these corrected values of the different colours, taking care to distinguish them by small initials instead of capitals.

Equation (2) then becomes

$$\cdot 65 \text{ pc} + \cdot 55 \text{ U} + \cdot 12 \text{ EG} = 1 \cdot 32 \text{ w}.$$

Hence pc must be situated at a point such that w is the centre of gravity of $\cdot 65$ pc $+ \cdot 55$ U $+ \cdot 12$ EG.

To find it, we begin by determining β the centre of gravity of $\cdot 55$ U $+ \cdot 12$ EG, then, joining βw, the point we are seeking must lie at a certain distance on the other side of w from c. This distance may be found from the proportion,

$$\cdot 65 \; : \; (\cdot 55 + \cdot 12) \; :: \; \overline{\beta \text{w}} \; : \; \overline{\text{w pc}},$$

which determines the position of pc. The proper coefficient, by which the observed values of PC must be corrected, is $\frac{65}{33}$, or $1 \cdot 97$.

We have thus determined the position and coefficient of a colour by a single experiment, in which it was made to produce a neutral tint along with two of the standard colours. As this may be done with every possible colour, the method is applicable wherever we can obtain a disc of the proposed colour. In this way the diagram (No. 1) has been laid down from observations made in daylight, by a good eye of the ordinary type.

It has been observed that experiments, in which the resultant tint is neutral, are more accurate than those in which the resulting tint has a decided colour, as in experiment (3), owing to the effects of accidental colours produced in the eye in the latter case. These experiments, however, may be repeated till a very good mean result has been obtained.

But since the elements of every colour have been already fixed by our previous observations and calculations, the agreement of these results with those calculated from the diagram forms a test of the correctness of our method.

By experiment (No. 3), made at the same time with (1) and (2), we have

$$\cdot 39 \text{ PC} + \cdot 21 \text{ U} + \cdot 40 \text{ Bk} = \cdot 59 \text{ V} + \cdot 41 \text{ EG} \dots \dots \dots \dots \dots \text{ (3)}.$$

Now, joining U with pc, and V with EG, the only common point is that at which they cross, namely γ.

Measuring the parts of the line $\overline{\text{V EG}}$, we find them in the proportion of

$$\cdot 58 \text{ V} \text{ and } \cdot 42 \text{ EG} = 1 \cdot 00 \gamma.$$

Similarly, the line $\overline{\text{U pc}}$ is divided in the proportion

$$\cdot 78 \text{ pc} \text{ and } \cdot 22 \text{ U} = 1 \cdot 00 \gamma.$$

But ·78 pc must be divided by 1·97, to reduce it to PC, as was previously explained. The result of calculation is, therefore,

$$·39 \text{ PC} + ·22 \text{ U} + ·39 \text{ Bk} = ·58 \text{ V} + ·42 \text{ EG},$$

the black being introduced simply to fill up the circle.

This result differs very little from that of experiment (3), and it must be recollected that these are single experiments, made independently of theory, and chosen at random.

Experiments made at Cambridge, with all the combinations of five colours, shew that theory agrees with calculation always within 0·012 of the whole, and sometimes within 0·002. By the repetition of these experiments at the numerous opportunities which present themselves, the accuracy of the results may be rendered still greater. As it is, I am not aware that the judgments of the human eye with respect to colour have been supposed capable of so severe a test.

Further consideration of the Diagram of Colours.

We have seen how the composition of any tint, in terms of our three standard colours, determines its position on the diagram and its proper coefficient. In the same way, the result of mixing any other colours, situated at other points of the diagram, is to be found by taking the centre of gravity of their *reduced masses*, as was done in the last calculation (experiment 3).

We have now to turn our attention to the general aspect of the diagram.

The standard colours, V, U, and EG, occupy the angles of an equilateral triangle, and the rest are arranged in the order in which they participate in red, blue, and green, the neutral tint being at the point w within the triangle. If we now draw lines through w to the different colours ranged round it, we shall find that, if we pass from one line to another in the order in which they lie from red to green, and through blue back again to red, the order will be—

	Coefficient.			Coefficient.
Carmine .	0·4	Pale Chrome .		2·0
Vermilion .	1·0	Mixed Green (U C) .		0·4
Red Lead .	1·3	Brunswick Green .		0·2
Orange Orpiment .	1·0	*Emerald Green* .		1·0
Orange Chrome .	1·6	Verditer Blue .		0·8
Chrome Yellow .	1·5	Prussian Blue .		0·1
Gamboge .	1·8	*Ultramarine* .		1·0

It may be easily seen that this arrangement of the colours corresponds to that of the prismatic spectrum; the only difference being that the spectrum is deficient in those fine purples which lie between ultramarine and vermilion. and which are easily produced by mixture. The experiments necessary for determining the exact relation of this list to the lines in the spectrum are not yet completed.

If we examine the colours represented by different points in one of these lines through w, we shall find the purest and most decided colours at its outer extremity, and the faint tints approaching to neutrality nearer to w.

If we also study the coefficients attached to each colour, we shall find that the brighter and more luminous colours have higher numbers for their coefficients than those which are dark.

In this way, the qualities which we have already distinguished as hue, tint, and shade, are represented on the diagram by angular position with respect to w, distance from w, and coefficient; and the relation between the two methods of reducing the elements of colour to three becomes a matter of geometry.

Theory of the Perception of Colour.

Opticians have long been divided on this point; those who trusted to popular notions and their own impressions adopting some theory of three primary colours, while those who studied the phenomena of light itself proved that no such theory could explain the constitution of the spectrum. Newton, who was the first to demonstrate the actual existence of a series of kinds of light, countless in number, yet all perfectly distinct, was also the first to propound a method of calculating the effect of the mixture of various coloured light; and this method was substantially the same as that which we have just verified. It is true, that the directions which he gives for the construction of his circle of colours are somewhat arbitrary, being probably only intended as an indication of the general nature of the method, but the method itself is mathematically reducible to the theory of three elements of the colour-sensation[*].

* See Note III. For a confirmation of Newton's analysis of Light, see Helmholtz, Pogg. *Ann.* 1852; and *Phil. Mag.* 1852, Part II.

Young, who made the next great step in the establishment of the theory of light, seems also to have been the first to follow out the necessary consequences of Newton's suggestion on the mixture of colours. He saw that, since this triplicity has no foundation in the theory of light, its cause must be looked for in the constitution of the eye; and, by one of those bold assumptions which sometimes express the result of speculation better than any cautious trains of reasoning, he attributed it to the existence of three distinct modes of sensation in the retina, each of which he supposed to be produced in different degrees by the different rays. These three elementary effects, according to his view, correspond to the three sensations of red, green, and violet, and would separately convey to the sensorium the sensation of a red, a green, and a violet picture; so that by the superposition of these pictures, the actual variegated world is represented*.

In order fully to understand Young's theory, the function which he attributes to each system of nerves must be carefully borne in mind. Each nerve acts, not, as some have thought, by conveying to the mind the knowledge of the length of an undulation of light, or of its periodic time, but simply by being *more* or *less* affected by the rays which fall on it. The sensation of each elementary nerve is capable only of increase and diminution, and of no other change. We must also observe, that the nerves corresponding to the red sensation are affected chiefly by the red rays, but in some degree also by those of every other part of the spectrum; just as red glass transmits red rays freely, but also suffers those of other colours to pass in smaller quantity.

This theory of colour may be illustrated by a supposed case taken from the art of photography. Let it be required to ascertain the colours of a landscape, by means of impressions taken on a preparation equally sensitive to rays of every colour.

Let a plate of red glass be placed before the camera, and an impression taken. The positive of this will be transparent wherever the red light has been abundant in the landscape, and opaque where it has been wanting. Let it now be put in a magic lantern, along with the red glass, and a red picture will be thrown on the screen.

Let this operation be repeated with a green and a violet glass, and, by

---

* Young's *Lectures*, p. 345, Kelland's Edition. See also Helmholtz's statement of Young's Theory, in his Paper referred to in Note I.; and Herschel's *Light*, Art. 518.

means of three magic lanterns, let the three images be superimposed on the screen. The colour of any point on the screen will then depend on that of the corresponding point of the landscape; and, by properly adjusting the intensities of the lights, &c., a complete copy of the landscape, as far as visible colour is concerned, will be thrown on the screen. The only apparent difference will be, that the copy will be more subdued, or less pure in tint, than the original. Here, however, we have the process performed twice—first on the screen, and then on the retina.

This illustration will shew how the functions which Young attributes to the three systems of nerves may be imitated by optical apparatus. It is therefore unnecessary to search for any direct connection between the lengths of the undulations of the various rays of light and the sensations as felt by us, as the threefold partition of the properties of light may be effected by physical means. The remarkable correspondence between the results of experiments on different individuals would indicate some anatomical contrivance identical in all. As there is little hope of detecting it by dissection, we may be content at present with any subsidiary evidence which we may possess. Such evidence is furnished by those individuals who have the defect of vision which was described by Dalton, and which is a variety of that which Dr G. Wilson has lately investigated, under the name of Colour-Blindness.

Testimony of the Colour-Blind with respect to Colour.

Dr George Wilson has described a great number of cases of colour-blindness, some of which involve a general indistinctness in the appreciation of colour, while in others, the errors of judgment are plainly more numerous in those colours which approach to red and green, than among those which approach to blue and yellow. In these more definite cases of colour-blindness, the phenomena can be tolerably well accounted for by the hypothesis of an insensibility to red light; and this is, to a certain extent, confirmed by the fact, that red objects appear to these eyes decidedly more obscure than to ordinary eyes. But by experiments made with the pure spectrum, it appears that though the red appears much more obscure than other colours, it is not wholly invisible, and, what is more curious, resembles the green more than any other colour. The spectrum to them appears faintly luminous in the red;

bright yellow from orange to yellow, bright but not coloured from yellow-green to blue, and then strongly coloured in the extreme blue and violet, after which it seems to approach the neutral obscure tint of the red. It is not easy to see why an insensibility to red *rays* should deprive the green rays, which have no *optical* connection with them, of their distinctive appearance. The phenomena seem rather to lead to the conclusion that it is the red *sensation* which is wanting, that is, that supposed system of nerves which is affected in various degrees by all light, but chiefly by red. We have fortunately the means of testing this hypothesis by numerical results.

Of the subjects of my experiments at Cambridge, four were decided cases of colour-blindness. Of these two, namely, Mr R. and Mr S., were not sufficiently critical in their observations to afford any results consistent within 10 divisions of the colour-top. The remaining two, Mr N. and Mr X., were as consistent in their observations as any persons of ordinary vision can be, while the results shewed all the more clearly how completely their sensations must differ from ours.

The method of experimenting was the same as that adopted with ordinary eyes, except that in these cases the operator can hardly influence the result by yielding to his own impressions, as he has no perception whatever of the similarity of the two tints as seen by the observer. The questions which he must ask are two, Which circle appears most blue or yellow? Which appears lightest and which darkest? By means of the answers to these questions he must adjust the resulting tints to equality in these respects as it appears to the observer, and then ascertain that these tints now present no difference of colour whatever to his eyes. The equations thus obtained do not require five colours including black, but four only. For instance, the mean of several observations gives—

$$\cdot19\ G + \cdot05\ B + \cdot76\ Bk = 100\ R \dots\dots\dots\dots\dots(4).$$

[In these experiments R, B, G, Y, stand for red, blue, green, and yellow papers prepared by Mr D. R. Hay. I am not certain that they are identical with his standard colours, but I believe so. Their relation to vermilion, ultramarine, and emerald-green is given in diagram (1). Their relations to each other are very accurately given in diagram (2).]

It appears, then, that the dark blue-green of the left side of the equation is equivalent to the full red of the right side.

Hence, if we divide the line BG in the proportion 19 to 5 at the point β, and join Rβ, the tint at β will differ from that at R (to the colour-blind) only in being more brilliant in the proportion of 100 to 24, and all intermediate tints on the line Rβ will appear to them of the same hue, but of intermediate intensities.

Now, if we take a point D, so that RD is to Rβ in the proportion of 24 to $100 - 24$, or 76, the tint of D, if producible, should be invisible to the colour-blind. D, therefore, represents the pure sensation which is unknown to the colour-blind, and the addition of this sensation to any others cannot alter it in their estimation. It is for them equivalent to black.

Hence, if we draw lines through D in different directions, the colours belonging to any line ought to differ only in intensity as seen by them, so that one of them may be reduced to the other by the addition of black only. If we draw DW and produce it, all colours on the upper side of DW will be varieties of blue, and those on the under side varieties of yellow, so that the line DW is a boundary line between their two kinds of colour, blue and yellow being the names by which they call them.

The accuracy of this theory will be evident from the comparison of the experiments which I had an opportunity of making on Mr N. and Mr X. with each other, and with measurements taken from the diagram No. 2, which was constructed from the observations of ordinary eyes only, the point D alone being ascertained from a series of observations by Mr N.

Taking the point γ, between R and B, it appears, by measurement of the lines Rγ and Bγ, that γ corresponds to

$$\cdot 07 \text{ B} + \cdot 93 \text{ R}.$$

By measurement of Wγ and Dγ, and correction by means of the coefficient of W, and calling D black in the colour-blind language, γ corresponds to

$$\cdot 105 \text{ W} + \cdot 895 \text{ Bk}.$$

Therefore

$$
\begin{array}{lll}
\text{By measurement} \dots\dots\dots\dots\dots & \cdot 93 \text{ R} + \cdot 07 \text{ B} = \cdot 105 \text{ W} + \cdot 895 \text{ Bk} & \\
\text{By observation N. \& X. together} & \cdot 94 \text{ R} + \cdot 06 \text{ B} = \cdot 10 \text{ W} + \cdot 90 \text{ Bk} & \left. \right\} \dots\dots(5). \\
\text{By X. alone} \dots\dots\dots\dots\dots\dots & \cdot 93 \text{ R} + \cdot 07 \text{ B} = \cdot 10 \text{ W} + \cdot 90 \text{ Bk} &
\end{array}
$$

The agreement here is as near as can be expected.

By a similar calculation with respect to the point δ, between B and G,

$$\left.\begin{array}{l}\text{By measurement} \quad\ldots\ldots\ldots\ldots\ldots\ \cdot43\ \text{B} + \cdot57\ \text{G} = \cdot335\ \text{W} + \cdot665\ \text{Bk} \\ \text{Observed by N. and X.} \ \ldots\ldots\ \cdot41\ \text{B} + \cdot59\ \text{G} = \cdot34\ \ \ \text{W} + \cdot66\ \ \text{Bk} \\ \text{By X. alone} \ \ldots\ldots\ldots\ldots\ldots\ldots\ \cdot42\ \text{B} + \cdot58\ \text{G} = \cdot32\ \ \ \text{W} + \cdot68\ \ \text{Bk}\end{array}\right\}\ldots\ldots(6).$$

We may also observe, that the line GD crosses RY. At the point of intersection we have—

$$\left.\begin{array}{l}\text{By calculation}\ldots\ldots\ldots\ldots\ldots\ldots\ldots\ \cdot87\ \text{R} + \cdot13\ \text{Y} = \cdot34\ \text{G} + \cdot66\ \text{Bk} \\ \text{Observed by N. and X.} \ \ldots\ldots\ldots\ \cdot86\ \text{R} + \cdot14\ \text{Y} = \cdot40\ \text{G} + \cdot60\ \text{Bk} \\ \quad\text{,,} \qquad\text{,,} \qquad\text{X.} \ \ldots\ldots\ldots\ \cdot84\ \text{R} + \cdot16\ \text{Y} = \cdot31\ \text{G} + \cdot69\ \text{Bk} \\ \quad\text{,,} \qquad\text{,,} \qquad\text{X.} \ \ldots\ldots\ldots\ \cdot90\ \text{R} + \cdot10\ \text{Y} = \cdot27\ \text{G} + \cdot73\ \text{Bk}\end{array}\right\}\ldots\ldots(7).$$

Here observations are at variance, owing to the decided colours produced affecting the state of the retina, but the mean agrees well with calculation.

Drawing the line BY, we find that it cuts lines through D drawn to every colour. Hence all colours appear to the colour-blind as if composed of blue and yellow. By measurement on the diagram, we find for red

$$\left.\begin{array}{l}\text{Measured} \ \ldots\ \ \ldots\ \cdot138\ \text{Y} + \cdot123\ \text{B} + \cdot749\ \text{Bk} = 100\ \text{R} \\ \text{Observed by N.}\ldots\ \cdot15\ \ \text{Y} + \cdot11\ \ \ \text{B} + \cdot74\ \ \ \text{Bk} = 100\ \text{R} \\ \quad\ldots\qquad\ \ \text{X.}\ldots\ \cdot13\ \ \text{Y} + \cdot11\ \ \ \text{B} + \cdot76\ \ \ \text{Bk} = 100\ \text{R}\end{array}\right\}\ldots\ldots\ldots(8).$$

For green we have in the same way—

$$\left.\begin{array}{l}\text{Measured} \ \ldots\ \ \ldots\ \cdot705\ \text{Y} + \cdot295\ \text{B} = \cdot95\ \text{G} + \cdot05\ \text{Bk} \\ \text{Observed by N.}\ldots\ \cdot70\ \ \text{Y} + \cdot30\ \ \text{B} = \cdot86\ \text{G} + \cdot14\ \text{Bk} \\ \quad\ldots\qquad\ \ \text{X.}\ldots\ \cdot70\ \ \text{Y} + \cdot30\ \ \text{B} = \cdot83\ \text{G} + \cdot17\ \text{Bk}\end{array}\right\}\ldots\ldots\ldots\ldots(9).$$

For white—

$$\begin{array}{l}\text{Measured} \ \ldots\ \ \ldots\ \cdot407\ \text{Y} + \cdot593\ \text{B} = \cdot326\ \text{W} + \cdot674\ \text{Bk} \\ \text{Observed by N.}\ldots\ \cdot40\ \ \text{Y} + \cdot60\ \ \text{B} = \cdot33\ \ \text{W} + \cdot67\ \ \text{Bk} \\ \quad\ldots\qquad\ \ \text{X.}\ldots\ \cdot44\ \ \text{Y} + \cdot56\ \ \text{B} = \cdot33\ \ \text{W} + \cdot67\ \ \text{Bk}\end{array}$$

The accuracy of these results shews that, whether the hypothesis of the want of one element out of three necessary to perfect vision be actually true or not, it affords a most trustworthy foundation on which to build a theory of colour-blindness, as it expresses completely the observed facts of the case. They also furnish us with a datum for our theory of perfect vision, namely, the point D, which points out the exact nature of the colour-sensation, which must be added to the colour-blind eye to render it perfect. I am not aware of any method of determining by a legitimate process the nature of the other two sensations, although Young's reasons for adopting something like green and violet appear to me worthy of attention.

The only remaining subject to which I would call the attention of the Society is the effect of coloured glasses on the colour-blind. Although they cannot distinguish reds and greens from varieties of gray, the transparency of red and green glasses for those kinds of light is very different. Hence, after finding a case such as that in equation (4), in which a red and a green appear identical, on looking through a red glass they see the red clearly and the green obscurely, while through a green glass the red appears dark and the green light.

By furnishing Mr X. with a red and a green glass, which he could distinguish only by their shape, I enabled him to make judgments in previously doubtful cases of colour with perfect certainty. I have since had a pair of spectacles constructed with one eye-glass red and the other green. These Mr X. intends to use for a length of time, and he hopes to acquire the habit of discriminating red from green tints by their different effects on his two eyes. Though he can never acquire our sensation of red, he may then discern for himself what things are red, and the mental process may become so familiar to him as to act unconsciously like a new sense.

In one experiment, after looking at a bright light, with a red glass over one eye and a green over the other, the two tints in experiment (4) appeared to him altered, so that the outer circle was lighter according to one eye, and the inner according to the other. As far as I could ascertain, it appeared as if the eye which had used the red glass saw the red circle brightest. This result, which seems at variance with what might be expected, I have had no opportunity of verifying.

This paper is already longer than was originally intended. For further information I would refer the reader to Newton's *Opticks*, Book I. Part II., to Young's *Lectures on Natural Philosophy*, page 345, to Mr D. R. Hay's works on Colours, and to Professor Forbes on the "Classification of Colours" (*Phil. Mag.*, March, 1849).

The most remarkable paper on the subject is that of M. Helmholtz, in the *Philosophical Magazine* for 1852, in which he discusses the different theories of primary colours, and describes his method of mixing the colours of the spectrum. An examination of the results of M. Helmholtz with reference to the theory of three elements of colour, by Professor Grassmann, is translated in the *Phil. Mag.*, April, 1854.

References to authors on colour-blindness are given in Dr G. Wilson's papers on that subject. A valuable Letter of Sir J. F. W. Herschel to Dalton on his peculiarity of vision, is to be found in the *Life of Dalton* by Dr Henry.

I had intended to describe some experiments on the propriety of the method of mixing colours by rotation, which might serve as an extension of Mr Swan's experiments on instantaneous impressions on the eye. These, together with the explanation of some phenomena which seem to be at variance with the theory of vision here adopted, must be deferred for the present. On some future occasion, I hope to be able to connect these simple experiments on the colours of pigments with others in which the pure hues of the spectrum are used. I have already constructed a model of apparatus for this purpose, and the results obtained are sufficiently remarkable to encourage perseverance.

NOTE I.

On different Methods of Exhibiting the Mixtures of Colours.

(1) *Mechanical Mixture of Coloured Powders.*

By grinding coloured powders together, the differently-coloured particles may be so intermingled that the eye cannot distinguish the colours of the separate powders, but receives the impression of a uniform tint, depending on the nature and proportions of the pigments used. In this way, Newton mixed the powders of orpiment, purple, bise, and *viride æris*, so as to form a gray, which, in sunlight, resembled white paper in the shade. (Newton's *Opticks,* Book I. Part II., Exp. xv.) This method of mixture, besides being adopted by all painters, has been employed by optical writers as a means of obtaining numerical results. The specimens of such mixtures given by D. R. Hay in his works on Colour, and the experiments of Professor J. D. Forbes on the same subject, shew the importance of the method as a means of classifying colours. There are two objections, however, to this method of exhibiting colours to the eye. When two powders of unequal fineness are mixed, the particles of the finer powder cover over those of the coarser, so as to produce more than their due effect in influencing the resultant tint. For instance, a small quantity of lamp-black, mixed with a large quantity of chalk, will produce a mixture which is nearly black. Although the powders generally used are not so different in this respect as lamp-black and chalk, the results of mixing given weights of any coloured powders must be greatly modified by the mode in which these powders have been prepared.

Again, the light which reaches the eye from the surface of the mixed powders consists partly of light which has fallen on one of the substances mixed without being modified by the other, and partly of light which, by repeated reflection or transmission, has been acted on by both substances. The colour of these rays will not be a mixture of those of the substances, but will be the result of the absorption due to both substances successively. Thus, a mixture of yellow and blue produces a neutral tint tending towards red, but the remainder of white light, after passing through both, is green ; and this green is generally sufficiently powerful to overpower the reddish gray due to the separate colours of the substances mixed. This curious result has been ably investigated by Professor Helmholtz of Königsberg, in his *Memoir on the Theory of Compound Colours*, a translation of which may be found in the *Annals of Philosophy* for 1852, Part 2.

(2) *Mixture of differently-coloured Beams of Light by Superposition on an Opaque Screen.*

When we can obtain light of sufficient intensity, this method produces the most beautiful results. The best series of experiments of this kind are to be found in Newton's *Opticks*, Book I. Part II. The different arrangements for mixing the rays of the spectrum on a screen, as described by Newton, form a very complete system of combinations of lenses and prisms, by which almost every possible modification of coloured light may be produced. The principal objections to the use of this method are—(1) The difficulty of obtaining a constant supply of uniformly intense light ; (2) The uncertainty of the effect of the position of the screen with respect to the incident beams and the eye of the observer ; (3) The possible change in the colour of the incident light due to the *fluorescence* of the substance of the screen. Professor Stokes has found that many substances, when illuminated by homogeneous light of one refrangibility, become themselves luminous, so as to emit light of lower refrangibility. This phenomenon must be carefully attended to when screens are used to exhibit light.

(3) *Union of Coloured Beams by a Prism so as to form one Beam.*

The mode of viewing the beam of light directly, without first throwing it on a screen, was not much used by the older experimenters, but it possesses the advantage of saving much light, and admits of examining the rays before they have been stopped in any way. In Newton's 11th proposition of the 2nd Book, an experiment is described, in which a beam is analysed by a prism, concentrated by a lens, and recombined by another prism, so as to form a beam of white light similar to the incident beam. By stopping the coloured rays at the lens, any proposed combination may be made to pass into the emergent beam, where it may be received directly by the eye, or on a screen, at pleasure.

The experiments of Helmholtz on the colours of the spectrum were made with the ordinary apparatus for directly viewing the pure spectrum, two oblique slits crossing one another being employed to admit the light instead of one vertical slit. Two pure spectra were then seen crossing each other, and so exhibiting at once a large number of combinations. The proportions of these combinations were altered by varying the inclination of the slits to the plane of refraction, and in this way a number of very remarkable results were obtained,— for which see his Memoir, before referred to.

In experiments of the same kind made by myself in August 1852 (independently of M. Helmholtz), I used a combination of three moveable vertical slits to admit the light, instead of two cross slits, and observed the compound ray through a slit made in a screen on which the pure spectrum is formed. In this way a considerable field of view was filled with the mixed light, and might be compared with another part of the field illuminated by light proceeding from a second system of slits, placed below the first set. The general character of the results agreed with those of M. Helmholtz. The chief difficulties seemed to arise from the defects of the optical apparatus of my own eye, which rendered apparent the compound nature of the light, by analysing it as a prism or an ordinary lens would do, whenever the lights mixed differed much in refrangibility.

(4) *Union of two beams by means of a transparent surface, which reflects the first and transmits the second.*

The simplest experiment of this kind is described by M. Helmholtz. He places two coloured wafers on a table, and then, taking a piece of transparent glass, he places it between them, so that the reflected image of one apparently coincides with the other as seen through the glass. The colours are thus mixed, and, by varying the angle of reflection, the relative intensities of the reflected and transmitted beams may be varied at pleasure.

In an instrument constructed by myself for photometrical purposes two reflecting plates were used. They were placed in a square tube, so as to polarize the incident light, which entered through holes in the sides of the tubes, and was reflected in the direction of the axis. In this way two beams oppositely polarized were mixed, either of which could be coloured in any way by coloured glasses placed over the holes in the tube. By means of a Nicol's prism placed at the end of the tube, the relative intensities of the two colours as they entered the eye could be altered at pleasure.

(5) *Union of two coloured beams by means of a doubly-refracting Prism.*

I am not aware that this method has been tried, although the opposite polarization of the emergent rays is favourable to the variation of the experiment.

(6) *Successive presentation of the different Colours to the Retina.*

It has long been known, that light does not produce its full effect on the eye at once, and that the effect, when produced, remains visible for some time after the light has ceased to act. In the case of the rotating disc, the various colours become indistinguishable, and the disc appears of a uniform tint, which is in some sense the resultant of the colours so blended. This method of combining colours has been used since the time of Newton, to exhibit the results of theory. The experiments of Professor J. D. Forbes, which I witnessed in 1849, first encouraged me to think that the laws of this kind of mixture might be discovered by special experiments. After repeating the well-known experiment in which a series of colours representing those of the spectrum are combined to form gray, Professor Forbes endeavoured to form a neutral tint, by the combination of three colours only. For this purpose, he combined the three so-called primary colours, red, blue, and yellow, but the resulting tint could not be rendered neutral by any combination of these colours; and the reason was found to be, that blue and yellow do not make green, but a pinkish tint, when neither prevails in the combination. It was plain, that no addition of red to this, could produce a neutral tint.

This result of mixing blue and yellow was, I believe, not previously known. It directly contradicted the received theory of colours, and seemed to be at variance with the fact, that the same blue and yellow paint, when ground together, do make green. Several experiments were proposed by Professor Forbes, in order to eliminate the effect of motion, but he was not then able to undertake them. One of these consisted in viewing alternate stripes of blue and yellow, with a telescope out of focus. I have tried this, and find the resultant tint pink as before*. I also found that the beams of light coloured by transmission through blue and yellow glasses appeared pink, when mixed on a screen, while a beam of light, after passing through both glasses, appeared green. By the help of the theory of absorption, given by Herschel†, I made out the complete explanation of this phenomenon. Those of pigments were, I think, first explained by Helmholtz in the manner above referred to‡.

It may still be asked, whether the effect of successive presentation to the eye is identical with that of simultaneous presentation, for if there is any action of the one kind of light on the other, it can take place only in the case of simultaneous presentation. An experiment tending to settle this point is recorded by Newton (Book I. Part II., Exp. 10). He used a comb with large teeth to intercept various rays of the spectrum. When it was moved slowly, the various colours could be perceived, but when the speed was increased the result was perfect whiteness. For another form of this experiment, see Newton's *Sixth Letter to Oldenburg* (Horsley's Edition, Vol. IV., page 335).

In order more fully to satisfy myself on this subject, I took a disc in which were cut a number of slits, so as to divide it into spokes. In a plane, nearly passing through the axis of this disc, I placed a blue glass, so that one

---

* See however *Encyc. Metropolitana*, Art. "Light," section 502.   † *Ib.* sect. 516.

‡ I have lately seen a passage in Moigno's *Cosmos*, stating that M. Plateau, in 1819, had obtained gray by whirling together gamboge and Prussian blue. *Correspondance Math. et Phys.* de M. Quetelet, Vol. v., p. 221.

half of the disc might be seen by transmitted light—blue, and the other by reflected light—white. In the course of the reflected light I placed a yellow glass, and in this way I had two nearly coincident images of the slits, one yellow and one blue. By turning the disc slowly, I observed that in some parts the yellow slits and the blue slits appeared to pass over the field alternately, while in others they appeared superimposed, so as to produce alternately their mixture, which was pale pink, and complete darkness. As long as the disc moved slowly I could perceive this, but when the speed became great, the whole field appeared uniformly coloured pink, so that those parts in which the colours were seen successively were indistinguishable from those in which they were presented together to the eye.

Another form in which the experiment may be tried requires only the colour-top above described. The disc should be covered with alternate sectors of any two colours, say red and green, disposed alternately in four quadrants. By placing a piece of glass above the top, in the plane of the axis, we make the image of one half seen by reflection coincide with that of the other seen by transmission. It will then be seen that, in the diameters of the top which are parallel and perpendicular to the plane of reflection, the transmitted green coincides with the reflected green, and the transmitted red with the reflected red, so that the result is always either pure red or pure green. But in the diameters intermediate to these, the transmitted red coincides with the reflected green, and *vice versa*, so that the pure colours are never seen, but only their mixtures. As long as the top is spun slowly, these parts of the disc will appear more steady in colour than those in which the greatest alternations take place; but when the speed is sufficiently increased, the disc appears perfectly uniform in colour. From these experiments it appears, that the apparent mixture of colours is not due to a mechanical superposition of vibrations, or to any mutual action of the mixed rays, but to some cause residing in the constitution of the apparatus of vision.

(7) *Presentation of the Colours to be mixed one to each Eye.*

This method is said not to succeed with some people; but I have always found that the mixture of *colours* was perfect, although it was difficult to conceive the *objects* seen by the two eyes as identical. In using the spectacles, of which one eye is green and the other red, I have found, when looking at an arrangement of green and red papers, that some looked metallic and others transparent. This arises from the very different relations of brightness of the two colours as seen by each eye through the spectacles, which suggests the false conclusion, that these differences are the result of reflection from a polished surface, or of light transmitted through a clear one.

NOTE II.

Results of Experiments with Mr Hay's *Papers at Cambridge, November,* 1854.

The mean of ten observations made by six observers gave

$$\cdot449 \text{ R} + \cdot299 \text{ G} + \cdot252 \text{ B} = \cdot224 \text{ W} + \cdot776 \text{ Bk} \dots\dots\dots(1).$$
$$\cdot696 \text{ R} + \cdot304 \text{ G} = \cdot181 \text{ B} + \cdot327 \text{ Y} + \cdot492 \text{ Bk} \dots\dots\dots(2).$$

These two equations served to determine the positions of white and yellow in diagram No. 2. The coefficient of W is 4·447, and that of yellow 2·506.

From these data we may deduce three other equations, either by calculation, or by measurement on the diagram (No. 2).

Eliminating green from the equations, we find

$$\cdot565 \text{ B} + \cdot435 \text{ Y} = \cdot307 \text{ R} + \cdot304 \text{ W} + \cdot389 \text{ Bk} \dots\dots\dots(3).$$

The mean of three observations by three different observers gives

$$\cdot573 \text{ B} + \cdot477 \text{ Y} = \cdot313 \text{ R} + \cdot297 \text{ W} + \cdot390 \text{ Bk}.$$

Errors of calculation $- \cdot008$ B $+ \cdot008$ Y $- \cdot006$ R $+ \cdot007$ W $- \cdot001$ Bk.

The point on the diagram to which this equation corresponds is the intersection of the lines BY and RW, and the resultant tint is a pinkish-gray.

Eliminating red from the equations, we obtain

Calculation	$\cdot533$ B $+ \cdot150$ G $+ \cdot317$ Y $= \cdot337$ W $+ \cdot663$ Bk	
By 10 observations	$\cdot537$ B $+ \cdot146$ G $+ \cdot317$ Y $= \cdot337$ W $+ \cdot663$ Bk	......(4).
Errors	$- \cdot004$ $+ \cdot004$ — — —	

Eliminating blue	$\cdot660$ R $+ \cdot340$ G $= \cdot218$ Y $+ \cdot108$ W $+ \cdot682$ Bk	
By 5 observations	$\cdot672$ R $+ \cdot328$ G $= \cdot224$ Y $+ \cdot094$ W $+ \cdot672$ Bk	......(5).
Errors	$- \cdot012$ $+ \cdot012$ $- \cdot006$ $+ \cdot014$ $+ \cdot008$	

Note III.

On the Theory of Compound Colours.

Newton's theorem on the mixture of colours is to be found in his *Opticks*, Book I., Part II., Prop. VI.

In a mixture of primary colours, the quantity and quality of each being given, to know the colour of the compound.

He divides the circumference of a circle into parts proportional to the seven musical intervals, in accordance with his opinion of the divisions of the spectrum. He then conceives the colours of the spectrum arranged round the circle, and at the centre of gravity of each of the seven arcs he places a little circle, the area of which represents the number of rays of the corresponding colour which enter into the given mixture. He takes the centre of gravity of all these circles to represent the colour formed by the mixture. The *hue* is determined by drawing a line through the centre of the circle and this point to the circumference. The position of this line points out the colour of the spectrum which the mixture most resembles, and the distance of the resultant tint from the centre determines the fulness of its colour.

Newton, by this construction (for which he gives no reasons), plainly shews that he considered it possible to find a place within his circle for every possible colour, and that the entire nature of any compound colour may be known from its place in the circle. It will be seen that the same colour may be compounded from the colours of the spectrum in an infinite variety of ways. The apparent identity of all these mixtures, which are optically different, as may be shewn by the prism, implies some law of vision not explicitly stated by Newton. This law, if Newton's method be true, must be that which I have endeavoured to establish, namely, the threefold nature of sensible colour.

With respect to Newton's construction, we now know that the proportions of the colours of the spectrum vary with the nature of the refracting medium. The only *absolute* index of the kind of light is the *time* of its vibration. The *length* of its vibration depends on the medium in which it is; and if any proportions are to be sought among the wave-lengths of the colours, they must be determined for those tissues of the eye in which their physical effects are supposed to terminate. It may be remarked, 'that the apparent colour of the spectrum changes most rapidly at three points, which lie respectively in the yellow, between blue and green, and between violet and blue. The wave-lengths of the corresponding rays *in water* are in the proportions of three geometric means between 1 and 2 very nearly. This result, however, is not to be considered established, unless confirmed by better observations than mine.

The only safe method of completing Newton's construction is by an examination of the colours of the spectrum and their mixtures, and subsequent calculation by the method used in the experiments with coloured papers. In this way I hope to determine the relative positions in the colour-diagram of every ray of the spectrum, and its relative intensity in the solar light. The spectrum will then form a curve not necessarily circular or even re-entrant, and its peculiarities so ascertained may form the foundation of a more complete theory of the colour-sensation.

On the relation of the pure rays of the Spectrum to the three assumed Elementary Sensations.

If we place the three elementary colour-sensations (which we may call, after Young, red, green, and violet) at the angles of a triangle, all colours which the eye can possibly perceive (whether by the action of light, or by pressure, disease, or imagination) must be somewhere within this triangle, those which lie farthest from the centre being the fullest and purest colours. Hence the colours which lie at the middle of the sides are the purest of their kind which the eye can see, although not so pure as the elementary sensations.

It is natural to suppose that the pure red, green, and violet rays of the spectrum produce the sensations which bear their names in the highest purity. But from this supposition it would follow that the yellow, composed of the red and green of the spectrum, would be the most intense yellow possible, while it is the result of experiment, that the yellow of the spectrum itself is much more full in colour. Hence the sensations produced by the pure red and green rays of the spectrum are not the pure sensations of our theory. Newton has remarked, that no two colours of the spectrum produce, when mixed, a colour equal in fulness to the intermediate colour. The colours of the spectrum are all more intense than any compound ones. Purple is the only colour which must be produced by combination. The experiments of Helmholtz lead to the same conclusion; and hence it would appear that we can find no part of the spectrum which produces a pure sensation.

An additional, though less satisfactory evidence of this, is supplied by the observation of the colours of the spectrum when excessively bright. They then appear to lose their peculiar colour, and to merge into pure whiteness. This is probably due to the want of capacity of the organ to take in so strong an impression; one sensation becomes first saturated, and the other two speedily follow it, the final effect being simple brightness.

From these facts I would conclude, that every ray of the spectrum is capable of producing all three pure sensations, though in different degrees. The curve, therefore, which we have supposed to represent the spectrum will be quite within the triangle of colour. All natural or artificial colours, being compounded of the colours of the spectrum, must lie within this curve, and, therefore, the colours corresponding to those parts of the triangle beyond this curve must be for ever unknown to us. The determination of the exact nature of the pure sensations, or of their relation to ordinary colours, is therefore impossible, unless we can prevent them from interfering with each other as they do. It may be possible to experience sensations more pure than those directly produced by the spectrum, by first exhausting the sensibility to one colour by protracted gazing, and then suddenly turning to its opposite. But if, as I suspect, colour-blindness be due to the absence of one of these sensations, then the point D in diagram (2), which indicates their absent sensation, indicates also our pure sensation, which we may call red, but which we can never experience, because all kinds of light excite the other sensations.

Newton has stated one objection to his theory, as follows:—"*Also, if only two of the primary colours, which in the circle are opposite to one another, be mixed in an equal proportion, the point Z*" (the resultant tint) "*shall fall upon the centre O*" (neutral tint); "*and yet the colour compounded of these two shall not be perfectly white, but some faint anonymous colour. For I could never yet, by mixing only two primary colours, produce a perfect white.*" This is confirmed by the experiments of Helmholtz; who, however, has succeeded better with some pairs of colours than with others.

In. my experiments on the spectrum, I came to the same result; but it appeared to me that the very peculiar appearance of the neutral tints produced was owing to some optical effect taking place in the transparent part of the eye on the mixture of two rays of very different refrangibility. Most eyes are by no means achromatic, so that the images of objects illuminated with mixed light of this kind appear divided into two different colours; and even when there is no distinct object, the mixtures become in some degree analysed, so as to present a very strange, and certainly "anonymous" appearance.

Additional Note on the more recent experiments of M. Helmholtz*.

In his former memoir on the Theory of Compound Colours†, M. Helmholtz arrived at the conclusion that only one pair of homogeneous colours, orange-yellow and indigo-blue, were strictly complementary. This result was shewn by Professor Grassmann‡ to be at variance with Newton's theory of compound colours; and although the reasoning was founded on intuitive rather than experimental truths, it pointed out the tests by which Newton's theory must be verified or overthrown. In applying these tests, M. Helmholtz made use of an apparatus similar to that described by M. Foucault§, by which a screen of white paper is illuminated by the mixed light. The field of mixed colour is much larger than in M. Helmholtz's former experiments, and the facility of forming combinations is much increased. In this memoir the mathematical theory of Newton's circle, and of the curve formed by the spectrum, with its possible transformations, is completely stated, and the form of this curve is in some degree indicated, as far as the determination of the colours which lie on opposite sides of white, and of those which lie opposite the part of the curve which is wanting. The colours between red and yellow-green are complementary to colours between blue-green and violet, and those between yellow-green and blue-green have no homogeneous complementaries, but must be neutralized by various hues of purple, i.e., mixtures of red and violet. The names of the complementary colours, with their wave-lengths in air, as deduced from Fraunhofer's measurements, are given in the following table:—

---

  * Poggendorff's *Annalen*, Bd. xciv. (I am indebted for the perusal of this Memoir to Professor Stokes.)

  † *Ib.* Bd. lxxxvii. *Annals of Philosophy*, 1852, Part ii.

  ‡ *Ib.* Bd. lxxxix. *Ann. Phil.*, 1854, April.

  § *Ib.* Bd. lxxxviii. Moigno, *Cosmos*, 1853, Tom. ii., p. 232.

Colour	Wave-length	Complementary Colour	Wave-length	Ratio of wave-lengths
Red	2425	Green-blue . .	1818	1·334
Orange . . .	2244	Blue	1809	1·240
Gold-yellow .	2162	Blue	1793	1·206
Gold yellow .	2120	Blue	1781	1·190
Yellow . . .	2095	Indigo-blue .	1716	1·221
Yellow . . .	2085	Indigo-blue .	1706	1·222
Green-yellow .	2082	Violet . . .	1600 −	1·301

(The wave-lengths are expressed in millionths of a Paris inch.)

(In order to reduce these wave-lengths to their actual lengths in the eye, each must be divided by the index of refraction for that kind of light in the medium in which the physical effect of the vibrations is supposed to take place.)

Although these experiments are not in themselves sufficient to give the complete theory of the curve of homogeneous colours, they determine the most important element of that theory in a way which seems very accurate, and I cannot doubt that when a philosopher who has so fully pointed out the importance of general theories in physics turns his attention to the theory of sensation, he will at least establish the principle that the laws of sensation can be successfully investigated only after the corresponding physical laws have been ascertained, and that the connection of these two kinds of laws can be apprehended only when the distinction between them is fully recognised.

NOTE IV.

Description of the Figures. Plate I.

No. 1. is the colour-diagram already referred to, representing, on Newton's principle, the relations of different coloured papers to the three standard colours—vermilion, emerald-green, and ultramarine. The initials denoting the colours are explained in the list at page 276, and the numbers belonging to them are their coefficients of intensity, the use of which has been explained. The initials H.R., H.B., and H.G., represent the red, blue and green papers of Mr HAY, and serve to connect this diagram with No. (2), which takes these colours for its standards.

No. 2. represents the relations of Mr HAY's red, blue, green, white, and yellow papers, as determined by a large number of experiments at Cambridge.—(See Note II.). The use of the point D, in calculating the results of colour-blindness, is explained in the Paper.

Fig. 3. represents a disc of the larger size, with its slit.

Fig. 4. shows the mode of combining two discs of the smaller size.

Fig. 5. shows the combination of discs, as placed on the top, in the first experiment described in the Paper.

Fig. 6. represents the method of spinning the top, when speed is required.

The last four figures are half the actual size.

Colour-tops of the kind used in these experiments, with paper discs of the colours whose relations are represented in No. 1, are to be had of Mr J. M. BRYSON, Optician, Edinburgh.

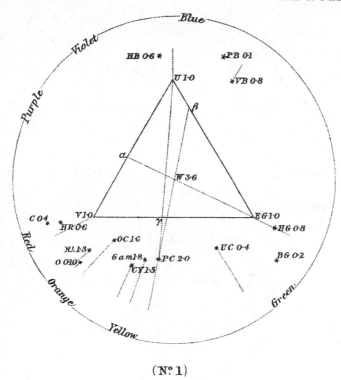

(Nº 1)

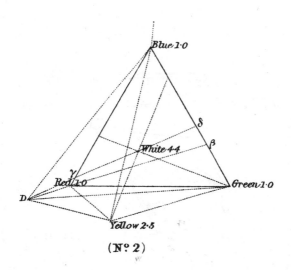

(Nº 2)

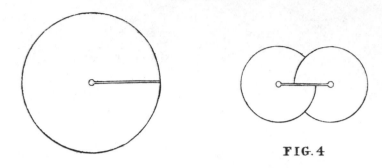

FIG. 3

FIG. 4

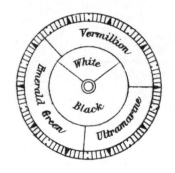

FIG. 5

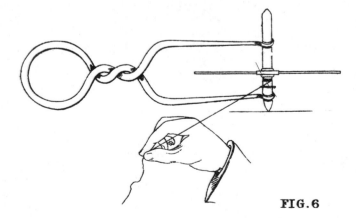

FIG. 6

[From the *Transactions of the Cambridge Philosophical Society*, Vol. x. Part i.]

VIII.   *On   Faraday's   Lines   of   Force.*

[Read *Dec.* 10, 1855, and *Feb.* 11, 1856.]

THE present state of electrical science seems peculiarly unfavourable to specu-
ation.   The laws of the distribution of electricity on the surface of conductors
ave been analytically deduced from experiment; some parts of the mathematical
eory of magnetism are established, while in other parts the experimental data
e wanting; the theory of the conduction of galvanism and that of the mutual
traction of conductors have been reduced to mathematical formulæ, but have
ot fallen into relation with the other parts of the science.   No electrical theory
n now be put forth, unless it shews the connexion not only between electricity
 rest and current electricity, but between the attractions and inductive effects
 electricity in both states.   Such a theory must accurately satisfy those laws,
e mathematical form of which is known, and must afford the means of calcu-
ting the effects in the limiting cases where the known formulæ are inapplicable.
 order therefore to appreciate the requirements of the science, the student
ust make himself familiar with a considerable body of most intricate mathe-
atics, the mere retention of which in the memory materially interferes with
rther progress.   The first process therefore in the effectual study of the science,
ist be one of simplification and reduction of the results of previous investiga-
n to a form in which the mind can grasp them.   The results of this simplifi-
ion may take the form of a purely mathematical formula or of a physical
pothesis.   In the first case we entirely lose sight of the phenomena to be
plained; and though we may trace out the consequences of given laws, we
 never obtain more extended views of the connexions of the subject.   If,
 the other hand, we adopt a physical hypothesis, we see the phenomena only
ough a medium, and are liable to that blindness to facts and rashness in

20—2

assumption which a partial explanation encourages. We must therefore discover some method of investigation which allows the mind at every step to lay hold of a clear physical conception, without being committed to any theory founded on the physical science from which that conception is borrowed, so that it is neither drawn aside from the subject in pursuit of analytical subtleties, nor carried beyond the truth by a favourite hypothesis.

In order to obtain physical ideas without adopting a physical theory we must make ourselves familiar with the existence of physical analogies. By a physical analogy I mean that partial similarity between the laws of one science and those of another which makes each of them illustrate the other. Thus all the mathematical sciences are founded on relations between physical laws and laws of numbers, so that the aim of exact science is to reduce the problems of nature to the determination of quantities by operations with numbers. Passing from the most universal of all analogies to a very partial one, we find the same resemblance in mathematical form between two different phenomena giving rise to a physical theory of light.

The changes of direction which light undergoes in passing from one medium to another, are identical with the deviations of the path of a particle in moving through a narrow space in which intense forces act. This analogy, which extends only to the direction, and not to the velocity of motion, was long believed to be the true explanation of the refraction of light; and we still find it useful in the solution of certain problems, in which we employ it without danger, as an artificial method. The other analogy, between light and the vibrations of an elastic medium, extends much farther, but, though its importance and fruitfulness cannot be over-estimated, we must recollect that it is founded only on a resemblance *in form* between the laws of light and those of vibrations. By stripping it of its physical dress and reducing it to a theory of "transverse alternations," we might obtain a system of truth strictly founded on observation, but probably deficient both in the vividness of its conceptions and the fertility of its method. I have said thus much on the disputed questions of Optics, as a preparation for the discussion of the almost universally admitted theory of attraction at a distance.

We have all acquired the mathematical conception of these attractions. We can reason about them and determine their appropriate forms or formulæ. These formulæ have a distinct mathematical significance, and their results are found to be in accordance with natural phenomena. There is no formula in applied mathematics more consistent with nature than the formula of attractions, and no theory better established in the minds of men than that of the action of bodies on one another at a distance. The laws of the conduction of heat in uniform media appear at first sight among the most different in their physical relations from those relating to attractions. The quantities which enter into them are *temperature, flow of heat, conductivity.* The word *force* is foreign to the subject. Yet we find that the mathematical laws of the uniform motion of heat in homogeneous media are identical in form with those of attractions varying inversely as the square of the distance. We have only to substitute *source of heat* for *centre of attraction, flow of heat* for *accelerating effect of attraction* at any point, and *temperature* for *potential,* and the solution of a problem in attractions is transformed into that of a problem in heat.

This analogy between the formulæ of heat and attraction was, I believe, first pointed out by Professor William Thomson in the *Camb. Math. Journal,* Vol. III.

Now the conduction of heat is supposed to proceed by an action between contiguous parts of a medium, while the force of attraction is a relation between distant bodies, and yet, if we knew nothing more than is expressed in the mathematical formulæ, there would be nothing to distinguish between the one set of phenomena and the other.

It is true, that if we introduce other considerations and observe additional facts, the two subjects will assume very different aspects, but the mathematical resemblance of some of their laws will remain, and may still be made useful in exciting appropriate mathematical ideas.

It is by the use of analogies of this kind that I have attempted to bring before the mind, in a convenient and manageable form, those mathematical ideas which are necessary to the study of the phenomena of electricity. The methods are generally those suggested by the processes of reasoning which are found in the researches of Faraday*, and which, though they have been interpreted mathematically by Prof. Thomson and others, are very generally supposed to be of an indefinite and unmathematical character, when compared with those employed by the professed mathematicians. By the method which I adopt, I hope to render it evident that I am not attempting to establish any physical theory of a science in which I have hardly made a single experiment, and that the limit of my design is to shew how, by a strict application of the ideas and

---

* See especially Series XXXVIII. of the *Experimental Researches,* and *Phil. Mag.* 1852.

methods of Faraday, the connexion of the very different orders of phenomena which he has discovered may be clearly placed before the mathematical mind. I shall therefore avoid as much as I can the introduction of anything which does not serve as a direct illustration of Faraday's methods, or of the mathematical deductions which may be made from them. In treating the simpler parts of the subject I shall use Faraday's mathematical methods as well as his ideas. When the complexity of the subject requires it, I shall use analytical notation, still confining myself to the development of ideas originated by the same philosopher.

I have in the first place to explain and illustrate the idea of "lines of force."

When a body is electrified in any manner, a small body charged with positive electricity, and placed in any given position, will experience a force urging it in a certain direction. If the small body be now negatively electrified, it will be urged by an equal force in a direction exactly opposite.

The same relations hold between a magnetic body and the north or south poles of a small magnet. If the north pole is urged in one direction, the south pole is urged in the opposite direction.

In this way we might find a line passing through any point of space, such that it represents the direction of the force acting on a positively electrified particle, or on an elementary north pole, and the reverse direction of the force on a negatively electrified particle or an elementary south pole. Since at every point of space such a direction may be found, if we commence at any point and draw a line so that, as we go along it, its direction at any point shall always coincide with that of the resultant force at that point, this curve will indicate the direction of that force for every point through which it passes, and might be called on that account a *line of force*. We might in the same way draw other lines of force, till we had filled all space with curves indicating by their direction that of the force at any assigned point.

We should thus obtain a geometrical model of the physical phenomena, which would tell us the *direction* of the force, but we should still require some method of indicating the *intensity* of the force at any point. If we consider these curves not as mere lines, but as fine tubes of variable section carrying an incompressible fluid, then, since the velocity of the fluid is inversely as the section of the tube, we may make the velocity vary according to any given law, by regulating the section of the tube, and in this way we might represent the intensity of the force as well as its direction by the motion of the fluid in these tubes. This method of representing the intensity of a force by the velocity of an imaginary fluid in a tube is applicable to any conceivable system of forces, but it is capable of great simplification in the case in which the forces are such as can be explained by the hypothesis of attractions varying inversely as the square of the distance, such as those observed in electrical and magnetic phenomena. In the case of a perfectly arbitrary system of forces, there will generally be interstices between the tubes; but in the case of electric and magnetic forces it is possible to arrange the tubes so as to leave no interstices. The tubes will then be mere surfaces, directing the motion of a fluid filling up the whole space. It has been usual to commence the investigation of the laws of these forces by at once assuming that the phenomena are due to attractive or repulsive forces acting between certain points. We may however obtain a different view of the subject, and one more suited to our more difficult inquiries, by adopting for the definition of the forces of which we treat, that they may be represented in magnitude and direction by the uniform motion of an incompressible fluid.

I propose, then, first to describe a method by which the motion of such a fluid can be clearly conceived; secondly to trace the consequences of assuming certain conditions of motion, and to point out the application of the method to some of the less complicated phenomena of electricity, magnetism, and galvanism; and lastly to shew how by an extension of these methods, and the introduction of another idea due to Faraday, the laws of the attractions and inductive actions of magnets and currents may be clearly conceived, without making any assumptions as to the physical nature of electricity, or adding anything to that which has been already proved by experiment.

By referring everything to the purely geometrical idea of the motion of an imaginary fluid, I hope to attain generality and precision, and to avoid the dangers arising from a premature theory professing to explain the cause of the phenomena. If the results of mere speculation which I have collected are found to be of any use to experimental philosophers, in arranging and interpreting their results, they will have served their purpose, and a mature theory, in which physical facts will be physically explained, will be formed by those who by interrogating Nature herself can obtain the only true solution of the questions which the mathematical theory suggests.

I.   *Theory of the Motion of an incompressible Fluid.*

(1)   The substance here treated of must not be assumed to possess any of the properties of ordinary fluids except those of freedom of motion and resistance to compression.   It is not even a hypothetical fluid which is introduced to explain actual phenomena.   It is merely a collection of imaginary properties which may be employed for establishing certain theorems in pure mathematics in a way more intelligible to many minds and more applicable to physical problems than that in which algebraic symbols alone are used.   The use of the word "Fluid" will not lead us into error, if we remember that it denotes a purely imaginary substance with the following property :

The portion of fluid which at any instant occupied a given volume, will at any succeeding instant occupy an equal volume.

This law expresses the incompressibility of the fluid, and furnishes us with a convenient measure of its quantity, namely its volume.   The unit of quantity of the fluid will therefore be the unit of volume.

(2)   The direction of motion of the fluid will in general be different at different points of the space which it occupies, but since the direction is determinate for every such point, we may conceive a line to begin at any point and to be continued so that every element of the line indicates by its direction the direction of motion at that point of space.   Lines drawn in such a manner that their direction always indicates the direction of fluid motion are called *lines of fluid motion.*

If the motion of the fluid be what is called *steady motion*, that is, if the direction and velocity of the motion at any fixed point be independent of the time, these curves will represent the paths of individual particles of the fluid, but if the motion be variable this will not generally be the case.   The cases of motion which will come under our notice will be those of steady motion.

(3)   If upon any surface which cuts the lines of fluid motion we draw a closed curve, and if from every point of this curve we draw a line of motion, these lines of motion will generate a tubular surface which we may call a *tube of fluid motion.*   Since this surface is generated by lines in the direction of fluid

motion no part of the fluid can flow across it, so that this imaginary surface is as impermeable to the fluid as a real tube.

(4) The quantity of fluid which in unit of time crosses any fixed section of the tube is the same at whatever part of the tube the section be taken. For the fluid is incompressible, and no part runs through the sides of the tube, therefore the quantity which escapes from the second section is equal to that which enters through the first.

If the tube be such that unit of volume passes through any section in unit of time it is called a *unit tube of fluid motion.*

(5) In what follows, various units will be referred to, and a finite number of lines or surfaces will be drawn, representing in terms of those units the motion of the fluid. Now in order to define the motion in every part of the fluid, an infinite number of lines would have to be drawn at indefinitely small intervals; but since the description of such a system of lines would involve continual reference to the theory of limits, it has been thought better to suppose the lines drawn at intervals depending on the assumed unit, and afterwards to assume the unit as small as we please by taking a small submultiple of the standard unit.

(6) To define the motion of the whole fluid by means of a system of unit tubes.

Take any fixed surface which cuts all the lines of fluid motion, and draw upon it any system of curves not intersecting one another. On the same surface draw a second system of curves intersecting the first system, and so arranged that the quantity of fluid which crosses the surface within each of the quadri-laterals formed by the intersection of the two systems of curves shall be unity in unit of time. From every point in a curve of the first system let a line of fluid motion be drawn. These lines will form a surface through which no fluid passes. Similar impermeable surfaces may be drawn for all the curves of the first system. The curves of the second system will give rise to a second system of impermeable surfaces, which, by their intersection with the first system, will form quadrilateral tubes, which will be tubes of fluid motion. Since each quadrilateral of the cutting surface transmits unity of fluid in unity of time, every tube in the system will transmit unity of fluid through any of its sections in unit of time. The motion of the fluid at every part of the space it occupies is determined by this system of unit tubes; for the direction of motion is that of the tube through the point in question, and the velocity is the reciprocal of the area of the section of the unit tube at that point.

(7) We have now obtained a geometrical construction which completely defines the motion of the fluid by dividing the space it occupies into a system of unit tubes. We have next to shew how by means of these tubes we may ascertain various points relating to the motion of the fluid.

A unit tube may either return into itself, or may begin and end at different points, and these may be either in the boundary of the space in which we investigate the motion, or within that space. In the first case there is a continual circulation of fluid in the tube, in the second the fluid enters at one end and flows out at the other. If the extremities of the tube are in the bounding surface, the fluid may be supposed to be continually supplied from without from an unknown source, and to flow out at the other into an unknown reservoir; but if the origin of the tube or its termination be within the space under consideration, then we must conceive the fluid to be supplied by a *source* within that space, capable of creating and emitting unity of fluid in unity of time, and to be afterwards swallowed up by a *sink* capable of receiving and destroying the same amount continually.

There is nothing self-contradictory in the conception of these sources where the fluid is created, and sinks where it is annihilated. The properties of the fluid are at our disposal, we have made it incompressible, and now we suppose it produced from nothing at certain points and reduced to nothing at others. The places of production will be called *sources*, and their numerical value will be the number of units of fluid which they produce in unit of time. The places of reduction will, for want of a better name, be called *sinks*, and will be estimated by the number of units of fluid absorbed in unit of time. Both places will sometimes be called sources, a source being understood to be a sink when its sign is negative.

(8) It is evident that the amount of fluid which passes any fixed surface is measured by the number of unit tubes which cut it, and the direction in which the fluid passes is determined by that of its motion in the tubes. If the surface be a closed one, then any tube whose terminations lie on the same side of the surface must cross the surface as many times in the one direction as in the other, and therefore must carry as much fluid out of the surface as

it carries in. A tube which begins within the surface and ends without it will carry out unity of fluid; and one which enters the surface and terminates within it will carry in the same quantity. In order therefore to estimate the amount of fluid which flows out of the closed surface, we must subtract the number of tubes which end within the surface from the number of tubes which begin there. If the result is negative the fluid will on the whole flow inwards.

If we call the beginning of a unit tube a unit source, and its termination a unit sink, then the quantity of fluid produced within the surface is estimated by the number of unit sources minus the number of unit sinks, and this must flow out of the surface on account of the incompressibility of the fluid.

In speaking of these unit tubes, sources and sinks, we must remember what was stated in (5) as to the magnitude of the unit, and how by diminishing their size and increasing their number we may distribute them according to any law however complicated.

(9) If we know the direction and velocity of the fluid at any point in two different cases, and if we conceive a third case in which the direction and velocity of the fluid at any point is the resultant of the velocities in the two former cases at corresponding points, then the amount of fluid which passes a given fixed surface in the third case will be the algebraic sum of the quantities which pass the same surface in the two former cases. For the rate at which the fluid crosses any surface is the resolved part of the velocity normal to the surface, and the resolved part of the resultant is equal to the sum of the resolved parts of the components.

Hence the number of unit tubes which cross the surface outwards in the third case must be the algebraical sum of the numbers which cross it in the two former cases, and the number of sources within any closed surface will be the sum of the numbers in the two former cases. Since the closed surface may be taken as small as we please, it is evident that the distribution of sources and sinks in the third case arises from the simple superposition of the distributions in the two former cases.

II. *Theory of the uniform motion of an imponderable incompressible fluid through a resisting medium.*

(10) The fluid is here supposed to have no inertia, and its motion is opposed by the action of a force which we may conceive to be due to the resistance of a

medium through which the fluid is supposed to flow. This resistance depends on the nature of the medium, and will in general depend on the direction in which the fluid moves, as well as on its velocity. For the present we may restrict ourselves to the case of a uniform medium, whose resistance is the same in all directions. The law which we assume is as follows.

Any portion of the fluid moving through the resisting medium is directly opposed by a retarding force proportional to its velocity.

If the velocity be represented by v, then the resistance will be a force equal to kv acting on unit of volume of the fluid in a direction contrary to that of motion. In order, therefore, that the velocity may be kept up, there must be a greater pressure behind any portion of the fluid than there is in front of it, so that the difference of pressures may neutralise the effect of the resistance. Conceive a cubical unit of fluid (which we may make as small as we please, by (5)), and let it move in a direction perpendicular to two of its faces. Then the resistance will be kv, and therefore the difference of pressures on the first and second faces is kv, so that the pressure diminishes in the direction of motion at the rate of kv for every unit of length measured along the line of motion; so that if we measure a length equal to h units, the difference of pressure at its extremities will be kvh.

(11) Since the pressure is supposed to vary continuously in the fluid, all the points at which the pressure is equal to a given pressure p will lie on a certain surface which we may call the *surface (p) of equal pressure*. If a series of these surfaces be constructed in the fluid corresponding to the pressures 0, 1, 2, 3 &c., then the number of the surface will indicate the pressure belonging to it, and the surface may be referred to as the surface 0, 1, 2 or 3. The unit of pressure is that pressure which is produced by unit of force acting on unit of surface. In order therefore to diminish the unit of pressure as in (5) we must diminish the unit of force in the same proportion.

(12) It is easy to see that these surfaces of equal pressure must be perpendicular to the lines of fluid motion; for if the fluid were to move in any other direction, there would be a resistance to its motion which could not be balanced by any difference of pressures. (We must remember that the fluid here considered has no inertia or mass, and that its properties are those only which are formally assigned to it, so that the resistances and pressures are the only things

to be considered.) There are therefore two sets of surfaces which by their inter-section form the system of unit tubes, and the system of surfaces of equal pressure cuts both the others at right angles.   Let h be the distance between two consecutive surfaces of equal pressure measured along a line of motion, then since the difference of pressures $= 1$,

$$kvh = 1,$$

which determines the relation of v to h, so that one can be found when the other is known.   Let s be the sectional area of a unit tube measured on a surface of equal pressure, then since by the definition of a unit tube

$$vs = 1,$$

we find by the last equation

$$s = kh.$$

(13) The surfaces of equal pressure cut the unit tubes into portions whose length is h and section s. These elementary portions of unit tubes will be called *unit cells*. In each of them unity of volume of fluid passes from a pressure p to a pressure $(p-1)$ in unit of time, and therefore overcomes unity of resistance in that time.   The work spent in overcoming resistance is therefore unity in every cell in every unit of time.

(14) If the surfaces of equal pressure are known, the direction and magni-tude of the velocity of the fluid at any point may be found, after which the complete system of unit tubes may be constructed, and the beginnings and end-ings of these tubes ascertained and marked out as the sources whence the fluid is derived, and the sinks where it disappears. In order to prove the converse of this, that if the distribution of sources be given, the pressure at every point may be found, we must lay down certain preliminary propositions.

(15) If we know the pressures at every point in the fluid in two different cases, and if we take a third case in which the pressure at any point is the sum of the pressures at corresponding points in the two former cases, then the velocity at any point in the third case is the resultant of the velocities in the other two, and the distribution of sources is that due to the simple superposition of the sources in the two former cases.

For the velocity in any direction is proportional to the rate of decrease of the pressure in that direction; so that if two systems of pressures be added together, since the rate of decrease of pressure along any line will be the sum of the combined rates, the velocity in the new system resolved in the same direction will be the sum of the resolved parts in the two original systems. The velocity in the new system will therefore be the resultant of the velocities at corresponding points in the two former systems.

It follows from this, by (9), that the quantity of fluid which crosses any fixed surface is, in the new system, the sum of the corresponding quantities in the old ones, and that the sources of the two original systems are simply combined to form the third.

It is evident that in the system in which the pressure is the difference of pressure in the two given systems the distribution of sources will be got by changing the sign of all the sources in the second system and adding them to those in the first.

(16) If the pressure at every point of a closed surface be the same and equal to p, and if there be no sources or sinks within the surface, then there will be no motion of the fluid within the surface, and the pressure within it will be uniform and equal to p.

For if there be motion of the fluid within the surface there will be tubes of fluid motion, and these tubes must either return into themselves or be terminated either within the surface or at its boundary. Now since the fluid always flows from places of greater pressure to places of less pressure, it cannot flow in a re-entering curve; since there are no sources or sinks within the surface, the tubes cannot begin or end except on the surface ; and since the pressure at all points of the surface is the same, there can be no motion in tubes having both extremities on the surface. Hence there is no motion within the surface, and therefore no difference of pressure which would cause motion, and since the pressure at the bounding surface is p, the pressure at any point within it is also p.

(17) If the pressure at every point of a given closed surface be known, and the distribution of sources within the surface be also known, then only one distribution of pressures can exist within the surface.

For if two different distributions of pressures satisfying these conditions could be found, a third distribution could be formed in which the pressure at any point should be the difference of the pressures in the two former distributions. In this case, since the pressures at the surface and the sources within it are the same in both distributions, the pressure at the surface in the third distribution would be zero, and all the sources within the surface would vanish, by (15).

Then by (16) the pressure at every point in the third distribution must be zero; but this is the difference of the pressures in the two former cases, and therefore these cases are the same, and there is only one distribution of pressure possible.

(18) Let us next determine the pressure at any point of an infinite body of fluid in the centre of which a unit source is placed, the pressure at an infinite distance from the source being supposed to be zero.

The fluid will flow out from the centre symmetrically, and since unity of volume flows out of every spherical surface surrounding the point in unit of time, the velocity at a distance r from the source will be

$$v = \frac{1}{4\pi r^2}.$$

The rate of decrease of pressure is therefore kv or $\frac{k}{4\pi r^2}$, and since the pressure $= 0$ when r is infinite, the actual pressure at any point will be

$$p = \frac{k}{4\pi r}.$$

The pressure is therefore inversely proportional to the distance from the source.

It is evident that the pressure due to a unit sink will be negative and equal to $-\frac{k}{4\pi r}$.

If we have a source formed by the coalition of S unit sources, then the resulting pressure will be $p = \frac{kS}{4\pi r}$, so that the pressure at a given distance varies as the resistance and number of sources conjointly.

(19) If a number of sources and sinks coexist in the fluid, then in order to determine the resultant pressure we have only to add the pressures which each source or sink produces. For by (15) this will be a solution of the problem, and by (17) it will be the only one. By this method we can determine the pressures due to any distribution of sources, as by the method

of (14) we can determine the distribution of sources to which a given distribution of pressures is due.

(20) We have next to shew that if we conceive any imaginary surface as fixed in space and intersecting the lines of motion of the fluid, we may substitute for the fluid on one side of this surface a distribution of sources upon the surface itself without altering in any way the motion of the fluid on the other side of the surface.

For if we describe the system of unit tubes which defines the motion of the fluid, and wherever a tube enters through the surface place a unit source, and wherever a tube goes out through the surface place a unit sink, and at the same time render the surface impermeable to the fluid, the motion of the fluid in the tubes will go on as before.

(21) If the system of pressures and the distribution of sources which produce them be known in a medium whose resistance is measured by k, then in order to produce the same system of pressures in a medium whose resistance is unity, the rate of production at each source must be multiplied by k. For the pressure at any point due to a given source varies as the rate of production and the resistance conjointly; therefore if the pressure be constant, the rate of production must vary inversely as the resistance.

(22) *On the conditions to be fulfilled at a surface which separates two media whose coefficients of resistance are k and k'.*

These are found from the consideration, that the quantity of fluid which flows out of the one medium at any point flows into the other, and that the pressure varies continuously from one medium to the other. The velocity normal to the surface is the same in both media, and therefore the rate of diminution of pressure is proportional to the resistance. The direction of the tubes of motion and the surfaces of equal pressure will be altered after passing through the surface, and the law of this refraction will be, that it takes place in the plane passing through the direction of incidence and the normal to the surface, and that the tangent of the angle of incidence is to the tangent of the angle of refraction as k' is to k.

(23) Let the space within a given closed surface be filled with a medium different from that exterior to it, and let the pressures at any point of this compound system due to a given distribution of sources within and without

the surface be given; it is required to determine a distribution of sources which would produce the same system of pressures in a medium whose coefficient of resistance is unity.

Construct the tubes of fluid motion, and wherever a unit tube enters either medium place a unit source, and wherever it leaves it place a unit sink. Then if we make the surface impermeable all will go on as before.

Let the resistance of the exterior medium be measured by k, and that of the interior by k'. Then if we multiply the rate of production of all the sources in the exterior medium (including those in the surface), by k, and make the coefficient of resistance unity, the pressures will remain as before, and the same will be true of the interior medium if we multiply all the sources in it by k', including those in the surface, and make its resistance unity.

Since the pressures on both sides of the surface are now equal, we may suppose it permeable if we please.

We have now the original system of pressures produced in a uniform medium by a combination of three systems of sources. The first of these is the given external system multiplied by k, the second is the given internal system multiplied by k', and the third is the system of sources and sinks on the surface itself. In the original case every source in the external medium had an equal sink in the internal medium on the other side of the surface, but now the source is multiplied by k and the sink by k', so that the result is for every external unit source on the surface, a source $= (k - k')$. By means of these three systems of sources the original system of pressures may be produced in a medium for which $k = 1$.

(24) Let there be no resistance in the medium within the closed surface, that is, let $k' = 0$, then the pressure within the closed surface is uniform and equal to p, and the pressure at the surface itself is also p. If by assuming any distribution of pairs of sources and sinks within the surface in addition to the given external and internal sources, and by supposing the medium the same within and without the surface, we can render the pressure at the surface uniform, the pressures so found for the external medium, together with the uniform pressure p in the internal medium, will be the true and only distribution of pressures which is possible.

For if two such distributions could be found by taking different imaginary distributions of pairs of sources and sinks within the medium, then by taking

22

the difference of the two for a third distribution, we should have the pressure of the bounding surface constant in the new system and as many sources as sinks within it, and therefore whatever fluid flows in at any point of the surface, an equal quantity must flow out at some other point.

In the external medium all the sources destroy one another, and we have an infinite medium without sources surrounding the internal medium. The pressure at infinity is zero, that at the surface is constant. If the pressure at the surface is positive, the motion of the fluid must be outwards from every point of the surface; if it be negative, it must flow inwards towards the surface. But it has been shewn that neither of these cases is possible, because if any fluid enters the surface an equal quantity must escape, and therefore the pressure at the surface is zero in the third system.

The pressure at all points in the boundary of the internal medium in the third case is therefore zero, and there are no sources, and therefore the pressure is everywhere zero, by (16).

The pressure in the bounding surface of the internal medium is also zero, and there is no resistance, therefore it is zero throughout; but the pressure in the third case is the difference of pressures in the two given cases, therefore these are equal, and there is only one distribution of pressure which is possible, namely, that due to the imaginary distribution of sources and sinks.

(25) When the resistance is infinite in the internal medium, there can be no passage of fluid through it or into it. The bounding surface may therefore be considered as impermeable to the fluid, and the tubes of fluid motion will run along it without cutting it.

If by assuming any arbitrary distribution of sources within the surface in addition to the given sources in the outer medium, and by calculating the resulting pressures and velocities as in the case of a uniform medium, we can fulfil the condition of there being no velocity across the surface, the system of pressures in the outer medium will be the true one. For since no fluid passes through the surface, the tubes in the interior are independent of those outside, and may be taken away without altering the external motion.

(26) If the extent of the internal medium be small, and if the difference of resistance in the two media be also small, then the position of the unit tubes will not be much altered from what it would be if the external medium filled the whole space.

On this supposition we can easily calculate the kind of alteration which the introduction of the internal medium will produce; for wherever a unit tube enters the surface we must conceive a source producing fluid at a rate $\dfrac{k'-k}{k}$, and wherever a tube leaves it we must place a sink annihilating fluid at the rate $\dfrac{k'-k}{k}$, then calculating pressures on the supposition that the resistance in both media is k, the same as in the external medium, we shall obtain the true distribution of pressures very approximately, and we may get a better result by repeating the process on the system of pressures thus obtained.

(27) If instead of an abrupt change from one coefficient of resistance to another we take a case in which the resistance varies continuously from point to point, we may treat the medium as if it were composed of thin shells each of which has uniform resistance. By properly assuming a distribution of sources over the surfaces of separation of the shells, we may treat the case as if the resistance were equal to unity throughout, as in (23). The sources will then be distributed continuously throughout the whole medium, and will be positive whenever the motion is from places of less to places of greater resistance, and negative when in the contrary direction.

(28) Hitherto we have supposed the resistance at a given point of the medium to be the same in whatever direction the motion of the fluid takes place; but we may conceive a case in which the resistance is different in different directions. In such cases the lines of motion will not in general be perpendicular to the surfaces of equal pressure. If a, b, c be the components of the velocity at any point, and α, β, γ the components of the resistance at the same point, these quantities will be connected by the following system of linear equations, which may be called "*equations of conduction*," and will be referred to by that name.

$$a = P_1\alpha + Q_3\beta + R_2\gamma,$$
$$b = P_2\beta + Q_1\gamma + R_3\alpha,$$
$$c = P_3\gamma + Q_2\alpha + R_1\beta.$$

In these equations there are nine independent coefficients of conductivity. In order to simplify the equations, let us put

$$Q_1 + R_1 = 2S_1, \quad Q_1 - R_1 = 2lT,$$
$$\dots\dots\dots\text{&c.} \quad \dots\dots\dots\text{&c.}$$

where $$4T^2 = (Q_1 - R_1)^2 + (Q_2 - R_2)^2 + (Q_3 - R_3)^2,$$

and l, m, n are direction-cosines of a certain fixed line in space.

The equations then become

$$a = P_1 a + S_3 \beta + S_2 \gamma + (n\beta - m\gamma)\, T,$$
$$b = P_2 \beta + S_1 \gamma + S_3 a + (l\gamma - na)\, T,$$
$$c = P_3 \gamma + S_2 a + S_1 \beta + (ma - l\beta)\, T.$$

By the ordinary transformation of co-ordinates we may get rid of the coefficients marked S. The equations then become

$$a = P_1' a + (n'\beta - m'\gamma)\, T,$$
$$b = P_2' \beta + (l'\gamma - n'a)\, T,$$
$$c = P_3' \gamma + (m'a - l'\beta)\, T,$$

where l', m', n' are the direction-cosines of the fixed line with reference to the new axes. If we make

$$a = \frac{dp}{dx}, \quad \beta = \frac{dp}{dy}, \quad \text{and} \quad \gamma = \frac{dp}{dz},$$

the equation of continuity

$$\frac{da}{dx} + \frac{db}{dy} + \frac{dc}{dz} = 0,$$

becomes

$$P_1' \frac{d^2 p}{dx^2} + P_2' \frac{d^2 p}{dy^2} + P_3' \frac{d^2 p}{dz^2} = 0,$$

and if we make $$x = \sqrt{P_1'}\xi, \quad y = \sqrt{P_2'}\eta, \quad z = \sqrt{P_3'}\zeta,$$

then $$\frac{d^2 p}{d\xi^2} + \frac{d^2 p}{d\eta^2} + \frac{d^2 p}{d\zeta^2} = 0,$$

the ordinary equation of conduction.

It appears therefore that the distribution of pressures is not altered by the existence of the coefficient T. Professor Thomson has shewn how to conceive a substance in which this coefficient determines a property having reference to an axis, which unlike the axes of P_1, P_2, P_3 is *dipolar*.

For further information on the equations of conduction, see Professor Stokes *On the Conduction of Heat in Crystals* (*Cambridge and Dublin Math. Journ.*), and Professor Thomson *On the Dynamical Theory of Heat*, Part v. (*Transactions of Royal Society of Edinburgh*, Vol. xxi. Part i.).

It is evident that all that has been proved in (14), (15), (16), (17), with respect to the superposition of different distributions of pressure, and there being only one distribution of pressures corresponding to a given distribution of sources, will be true also in the case in which the resistance varies from point to point, and the resistance at the same point is different in different directions. For if we examine the proof we shall find it applicable to such cases as well as to that of a uniform medium.

(29) We now are prepared to prove certain general propositions which are true in the most general case of a medium whose resistance is different in different directions and varies from point to point.

We may by the method of (28), when the distribution of pressures is known, construct the surfaces of equal pressure, the tubes of fluid motion, and the sources and sinks. It is evident that since in each cell into which a unit tube is divided by the surfaces of equal pressure unity of fluid passes from pressure p to pressure $(p-1)$ in unit of time, unity of work is done by the fluid in each cell in overcoming resistance.

The number of cells in each unit tube is determined by the number of surfaces of equal pressure through which it passes. If the pressure at the beginning of the tube be p and at the end p', then the number of cells in it will be $p-p'$. Now if the tube had extended from the source to a place where the pressure is zero, the number of cells would have been p, and if the tube had come from the sink to zero, the number would have been p', and the true number is the difference of these.

Therefore if we find the pressure at a source S from which S tubes proceed to be p, Sp is the number of cells due to the source S; but if S' of the tubes terminate in a sink at a pressure p', then we must cut off $S'p'$ cells from the number previously obtained. Now if we denote the source of S tubes by S, the sink of S' tubes may be written $-S'$, sinks always being reckoned negative, and the general expression for the number of cells in the system will be $\Sigma (Sp)$.

(30) The same conclusion may be arrived at by observing that unity of work is done on each cell. Now in each source S, S units of fluid are expelled against a pressure p, so that the work done by the fluid in overcoming resistance is Sp. At each sink in which S' tubes terminate, S' units of fluid sink into nothing under pressure p'; the work done upon the fluid by

the pressure is therefore $S'p'$. The whole work done by the fluid may therefore be expressed by

$$W = \Sigma Sp - \Sigma S'p',$$

or more concisely, considering sinks as negative sources,

$$W = \Sigma(Sp).$$

(31) Let S represent the rate of production of a source in any medium,
and let p be the pressure at any given point due to that source. Then if we
superpose on this another equal source, every pressure will be doubled, and
thus by successive superposition we find that a source nS would produce a
pressure np, or more generally the pressure at any point due to a given
source varies as the rate of production of the source. This may be expressed
by the equation

$$p = RS,$$

where R is a coefficient depending on the nature of the medium and on the
positions of the source and the given point. In a uniform medium whose
resistance is measured by k,

$$p = \frac{kS}{4\pi r}, \quad \therefore R = \frac{k}{4\pi r},$$

R may be called the coefficient of resistance of the medium between the source
and the given point. By combining any number of sources we have generally

$$p = \Sigma(RS).$$

(32) In a uniform medium the pressure due to a source S

$$p = \frac{k}{4\pi} \frac{S}{r}.$$

At another source S' at a distance r we shall have

$$S'p = \frac{k}{4\pi} \frac{SS'}{r} = Sp',$$

if p' be the pressure at S due to S'. If therefore there be two systems of
sources $\Sigma(S)$ and $\Sigma(S')$, and if the pressures due to the first be p and to the
second p', then

$$\Sigma(S'p) = \Sigma(Sp').$$

For every term $S'p$ has a term Sp' equal to it.

(33) Suppose that in a uniform medium the motion of the fluid is everywhere parallel to one plane, then the surfaces of equal pressure will be perpendicular to this plane. If we take two parallel planes at a distance equal to k from each other, we can divide the space between these planes into unit tubes by means of cylindric surfaces perpendicular to the planes, and these together with the surfaces of equal pressure will divide the space into cells of which the length is equal to the breadth. For if h be the distance between consecutive surfaces of equal pressure and s the section of the unit tube, we have by (13) $s = kh$.

But s is the product of the breadth and depth; but the depth is k, therefore the breadth is h and equal to the length.

If two systems of plane curves cut each other at right angles so as to divide the plane into little areas of which the length and breadth are equal, then by taking another plane at distance k from the first and erecting cylindric surfaces on the plane curves as bases, a system of cells will be formed which will satisfy the conditions whether we suppose the fluid to run along the first set of cutting lines or the second *.

Application of the Idea of Lines of Force.

I have now to shew how the idea of lines of fluid motion as described above may be modified so as to be applicable to the sciences of statical electricity, permanent magnetism, magnetism of induction, and uniform galvanic currents, reserving the laws of electro-magnetism for special consideration.

I shall assume that the phenomena of statical electricity have been already explained by the mutual action of two opposite kinds of matter. If we consider one of these as positive electricity and the other as negative, then any two particles of electricity repel one another with a force which is measured by the product of the masses of the particles divided by the square of their distance.

Now we found in (18) that the velocity of our imaginary fluid due to a source S at a distance r varies inversely as r^2. Let us see what will be the effect of substituting such a source for every particle of positive electricity. The velocity due to each source would be proportional to the attraction due to the corresponding particle, and the resultant velocity due to all the sources would

* See *Cambridge and Dublin Mathematical Journal*, Vol. III. p. 286.

be proportional to the resultant attraction of all the particles. Now we may find the resultant pressure at any point by adding the pressures due to the given sources, and therefore we may find the resultant velocity in a given direction from the rate of decrease of pressure in that direction, and this will be proportional to the resultant attraction of the particles resolved in that direction.

Since the resultant attraction in the electrical problem is proportional to the decrease of pressure in the imaginary problem, and since we may select any values for the constants in the imaginary problem, we may assume that the resultant attraction in any direction is numerically equal to the decrease of pressure in that direction, or

$$X = -\frac{dp}{dx}.$$

By this assumption we find that if V be the potential,

$$dV = Xdx + Ydy + Zdz = -dp,$$

or since at an infinite distance $V = 0$ and $p = 0$, $V = -p$.

In the electrical problem we have

$$V = -\Sigma\left(\frac{dm}{r}\right).$$

In the fluid $p = \Sigma\left(\frac{k}{4\pi}\frac{S}{r}\right);$

$$\therefore \ S = \frac{4\pi}{k}dm.$$

If k be supposed very great, the amount of fluid produced by each source in order to keep up the pressures will be very small.

The potential of any system of electricity on itself will be

$$\Sigma\left(pdm\right) = \frac{k}{4\pi}, \quad \Sigma\left(pS\right) = \frac{k}{4\pi}\ W.$$

If $\Sigma\left(dm\right)$, $\Sigma\left(dm'\right)$ be two systems of electrical particles and p, p' the potentials due to them respectively, then by (32)

$$\Sigma\left(pdm'\right) = \frac{k}{4\pi}\Sigma\left(pS'\right) = \frac{k}{4\pi}\Sigma\left(p'S\right) = \Sigma\left(p'dm\right),$$

or the potential of the first system on the second is equal to that of the second system on the first.

So that in the ordinary electrical problems the analogy in fluid motion is of this kind :

$$V = -p,$$

$$X = -\frac{dp}{dx} = ku,$$

$$dm = \frac{k}{4\pi} S,$$

whole potential of a system $= -\Sigma V dm = \frac{k}{4\pi} W$, where W is the work done by the fluid in overcoming resistance.

The lines of forces are the unit tubes of fluid motion, and they may be estimated numerically by those tubes.

Theory of Dielectrics.

The electrical induction exercised on a body at a distance depends not only on the distribution of electricity in the inductric, and the form and position of the inducteous body, but on the nature of the interposed medium, or dielectric. Faraday* expresses this by the conception of one substance having a *greater inductive capacity*, or conducting the lines of inductive action more freely than another. If we suppose that in our analogy of a fluid in a resisting medium the resistance is different in different media, then by making the resistance less we obtain the analogue to a dielectric which more easily conducts Faraday's lines.

It is evident from (23) that in this case there will always be an apparent distribution of electricity on the surface of the dielectric, there being negative electricity where the lines enter and positive electricity where they emerge. In the case of the fluid there are no real sources on the surface, but we use them merely for purposes of calculation. In the dielectric there may be no real charge of electricity, but only an apparent electric action due to the surface.

If the dielectric had been of less conductivity than the surrounding medium, we should have had precisely opposite effects, namely, positive electricity where lines enter, and negative where they emerge.

* Series XI.

23

If the conduction of the dielectric is perfect or nearly so for the small quantities of electricity with which we have to do, then we have the case of (24). The dielectric is then considered as a conductor, its surface is a surface of equal potential, and the resultant attraction near the surface itself is perpendicular to it.

Theory of Permanent Magnets.

A magnet is conceived to be made up of elementary magnetized particles, each of which has its own north and south poles, the action of which upon other north and south poles is governed by laws mathematically identical with those of electricity. Hence the same application of the idea of lines of force can be made to this subject, and the same analogy of fluid motion can be employed to illustrate it.

But it may be useful to examine the way in which the polarity of the elements of a magnet may be represented by the unit cells in fluid motion. In each unit cell unity of fluid enters by one face and flows out by the opposite face, so that the first face becomes a unit sink and the second a unit source with respect to the rest of the fluid. It may therefore be compared to an elementary magnet, having an equal quantity of north and south magnetic matter distributed over two of its faces. If we now consider the cell as forming part of a system, the fluid flowing out of one cell will flow into the next, and so on, so that the source will be transferred from the end of the cell to the end of the unit tube. If all the unit tubes begin and end on the bounding surface, the sources and sinks will be distributed entirely on that surface, and in the case of a magnet which has what has been called a solenoidal or tubular distribution of magnetism, all the imaginary magnetic matter will be on the surface[*].

Theory of Paramagnetic and Diamagnetic Induction.

Faraday[†] has shewn that the effects of paramagnetic and diamagnetic bodies in the magnetic field may be explained by supposing paramagnetic bodies to

---

[*] See Professor Thomson *On the Mathematical Theory of Magnetism*, Chapters III. and V. *Phil. Trans.* 1851.

[†] *Experimental Researches* (3292).

conduct the lines of force better, and diamagnetic bodies worse, than the surrounding medium. By referring to (23) and (26), and supposing sources to represent north magnetic matter, and sinks south magnetic matter, then if a paramagnetic body be in the neighbourhood of a north pole, the lines of force on entering it will produce south magnetic matter, and on leaving it they will produce an equal amount of north magnetic matter. Since the quantities of magnetic matter on the whole are equal, but the southern matter is nearest to the north pole, the result will be attraction. If on the other hand the body be diamagnetic, or a worse conductor of lines of force than the surrounding medium, there will be an imaginary distribution of northern magnetic matter where the lines pass into the worse conductor, and of southern where they pass out, so that on the whole there will be repulsion.

We may obtain a more general law from the consideration that the potential of the whole system is proportional to the amount of work done by the fluid in overcoming resistance. The introduction of a second medium increases or diminishes the work done according as the resistance is greater or less than that of the first medium. The amount of this increase or diminution will vary as the square of the velocity of the fluid.

Now, by the theory of potentials, the moving force in any direction is measured by the rate of decrease of the potential of the system in passing along that direction, therefore when k', the resistance within the second medium, is greater than k, the resistance in the surrounding medium, there is a force tending from places where the resultant force v is greater to where it is less, so that a diamagnetic body moves from greater to less values of the resultant force*.

In paramagnetic bodies k' is less than k, so that the force is now from points of less to points of greater resultant magnetic force. Since these results depend only on the relative values of k and k', it is evident that by changing the surrounding medium, the behaviour of a body may be changed from paramagnetic to diamagnetic at pleasure.

It is evident that we should obtain the same mathematical results if we had supposed that the magnetic force had a power of exciting a polarity in bodies which is in the *same* direction as the lines in paramagnetic bodies, and

* *Experimental Researches* (2797), (2798).   See Thomson, *Cambridge and Dublin Mathematical Journal*, May, 1847.

in the *reverse* direction in diamagnetic bodies*. ˙ In fact we have not as yet come to any facts which would lead us to choose any one out of these three theories, that of lines of force, that of imaginary magnetic matter, and that of induced polarity. As the theory of lines of force admits of the most precise, and at the same time least theoretic statement, we shall allow it to stand for the present.

Theory of Magnecrystallic Induction.

The theory of Faraday[†] with respect to the behaviour of crystals in the magnetic field may be thus stated. In certain crystals and other substances the lines of magnetic force are conducted with different facility in different directions. The body when suspended in a uniform magnetic field will turn or tend to turn into such a position that the lines of force shall pass through it with least resistance. It is not difficult by means of the principles in (28) to express the laws of this kind of action, and even to reduce them in certain cases to numerical formulæ. The principles of induced polarity and of imaginary magnetic matter are here of little use; but the theory of lines of force is capable of the most perfect adaptation to this class of phenomena.

Theory of the Conduction of Current Electricity.

It is in the calculation of the laws of constant electric currents that the theory of fluid motion which we have laid down admits of the most direct application. In addition to the researches of Ohm on this subject, we have those of M. Kirchhoff, *Ann. de Chim.* XLI. 496, and of M. Quincke, XLVII. 203, on the Conduction of Electric Currents in Plates. According to the received opinions we have here a current of fluid moving uniformly in conducting circuits, which oppose a resistance to the current which has to be overcome by the application of an electro-motive force at some part of the circuit. On account of this resistance to the motion of the fluid the pressure must be different at different points in the circuit. This pressure, which is commonly called electrical tension,

---

* *Exp. Res.* (2429), (3320).   See Weber, Poggendorff, LXXXVII. p. 145.   Prof. Tyndall, *Phil. Trans.* 1856, p. 237.

† *Exp. Res.* (2836), &c.

is found to be physically identical with the *potential* in statical electricity, and thus we have the means of connecting the two sets of phenomena. If we knew what amount of electricity, measured statically, passes along that current which we assume as our unit of current, then the connexion of electricity of tension with current electricity would be completed*. This has as yet been done only approximately, but we know enough to be certain that the conducting powers of different substances differ only in degree, and that the difference between glass and metal is, that the resistance is a great but finite quantity in glass, and a small but finite quantity in metal. Thus the analogy between statical electricity and fluid motion turns out more perfect than we might have supposed, for there the induction goes on by conduction just as in current electricity, but the quantity conducted is insensible owing to the great resistance of the dielectrics†.

On Electro-motive Forces.

When a uniform current exists in a closed circuit it is evident that some other forces must act on the fluid besides the pressures. For if the current were due to difference of pressures, then it would flow from the point of greatest pressure in both directions to the point of least pressure, whereas in reality it circulates in one direction constantly. We must therefore admit the existence of certain forces capable of keeping up a constant current in a closed circuit. Of these the most remarkable is that which is produced by chemical action. A cell of a voltaic battery, or rather the surface of separation of the fluid of the cell and the zinc, is the seat of an electro-motive force which can maintain a current in opposition to the resistance of the circuit. If we adopt the usual convention in speaking of electric currents, the positive current is from the fluid through the platinum, the conducting circuit, and the zinc, back to the fluid again. If the electro-motive force act only in the surface of separation of the fluid and zinc, then the tension of electricity in the fluid must exceed that in the zinc by a quantity depending on the nature and length of the circuit and on the strength of the current in the conductor. In order to keep up this difference of pressure there must be an electro-motive force whose intensity is measured by that difference of pressure. If F be the electro-motive force, I the quantity of the current or the number of electrical

* See *Exp. Res.* (371).   † *Exp. Res.* Vol. III. p. 513.

units delivered in unit of time, and K a quantity depending on the length and resistance of the conducting circuit, then

$$F = IK = p - p',$$

where p is the electric tension in the fluid and p' in the zinc.

If the circuit be broken at any point, then since there is no current the tension of the part which remains attached to the platinum will be p, and that of the other will be p', $p - p'$ or F affords a measure of the intensity of the current. This distinction of quantity and intensity is very useful [*], but must be distinctly understood to mean nothing more than this :—The quantity of a current is the amount of electricity which it transmits in unit of time, and is measured by I the number of unit currents which it contains. The intensity of a current is its power of overcoming resistance, and is measured by F or IK, where K is the resistance of the whole circuit.

The same idea of quantity and intensity may be applied to the case of magnetism [†]. The quantity of magnetization in any section of a magnetic body is measured by the number of lines of magnetic force which pass through it. The intensity of magnetization in the section depends on the resisting power of the section, as well as on the number of lines which pass through it. If k be the resisting power of the material, and S the area of the section, and I the number of lines of force which pass through it, then the whole intensity throughout the section

$$= F = I \frac{k}{S}.$$

When magnetization is produced by the influence of other magnets only, we may put p for the magnetic tension at any point, then for the whole magnetic solenoid

$$F = I \int \frac{k}{S} dx = IK = p - p'.$$

When a solenoidal magnetized circuit returns into itself, the magnetization does not depend on difference of tensions only, but on some magnetizing force of which the intensity is F.

If i be the quantity of the magnetization at any point, or the number of lines of force passing through unit of area in the section of the solenoid, then

---

the total quantity of magnetization in the circuit is the number of lines which pass through any section, $I = \Sigma i\, dy\, dz$, where $dy\, dz$ is the element of the section, and the summation is performed over the whole section.

The intensity of magnetization at any point, or the force required to keep up the magnetization, is measured by $ki = f$, and the total intensity of magnetization in the circuit is measured by the sum of the local intensities all round the circuit,

$$F = \Sigma\, (f\, dx),$$

where dx is the element of length in the circuit, and the summation is extended round the entire circuit.

In the same circuit we have always $F = IK$, where K is the total resistance of the circuit, and depends on its form and the matter of which it is composed.

On the Action of closed Currents at a Distance.

The mathematical laws of the attractions and repulsions of conductors have been most ably investigated by Ampère, and his results have stood the test of subsequent experiments.

From the single assumption, that the action of an element of one current upon an element of another current is an attractive or repulsive force acting in the direction of the line joining the two elements, he has determined by the simplest experiments the mathematical form of the law of attraction, and has put this law into several most elegant and useful forms. We must recollect however that no experiments have been made on these elements of currents except under the form of closed currents either in rigid conductors or in fluids, and that the laws of closed currents can only be deduced from such experiments. Hence if Ampère's formulæ applied to closed currents give true results, their truth is not proved for *elements* of currents unless we assume that the action between two such elements must be along the line which joins them. Although this assumption is most warrantable and philosophical in the present state of science, it will be more conducive to freedom of investigation if we endeavour to do without it, and to assume the laws of closed currents as the ultimate datum of experiment.

Ampère has shewn that when currents are combined according to the law of the parallelogram of forces, the force due to the resultant current is the resultant of the forces due to the component currents, and that equal and opposite currents generate equal and opposite forces, and when combined neutralize each other.

He has also shewn that a closed circuit of any form has no tendency to turn a moveable circular conductor about a fixed axis through the centre of the circle perpendicular to its plane, and that therefore the forces in the case of a closed circuit render $Xdx + Ydy + Zdz$ a complete differential.

Finally, he has shewn that if there be two systems of circuits similar and similarly situated, the quantity of electrical current in corresponding conductors being the same, the resultant forces are equal, whatever be the absolute dimensions of the systems, which proves that the forces are, *cæteris paribus*, inversely as the square of the distance.

From these results it follows that the mutual action of two closed currents whose areas are very small is the same as that of two elementary magnetic bars magnetized perpendicularly to the plane of the currents.

The direction of magnetization of the equivalent magnet may be predicted by remembering that a current travelling round the earth from east to west as the sun appears to do, would be equivalent to that magnetization which the earth actually possesses, and therefore in the reverse direction to that of a magnetic needle when pointing freely.

If a number of closed unit currents in contact exist on a surface, then at all points in which two currents are in contact there will be two equal and opposite currents which will produce no effect, but all round the boundary of the surface occupied by the currents there will be a residual current not neutralized by any other; and therefore the result will be the same as that of a single unit current round the boundary of all the currents.

From this it appears that the external attractions of a shell uniformly magnetized perpendicular to its surface are the same as those due to a current round its edge, for each of the elementary currents in the former case has the same effect as an element of the magnetic shell.

If we examine the lines of magnetic force produced by a closed current, we shall find that they form closed curves passing round the current and *embracing* it, and that the total intensity of the magnetizing force all along the closed line of force depends on the quantity of the electric current only.

The number of unit lines* of magnetic force due to a closed current depends on the form as well as the quantity of the current, but the number of unit cells† in each complete line of force is measured simply by the number of unit currents which embrace it. The unit cells in this case are portions of space in which unit of magnetic quantity is produced by unity of magnetizing force. The length of a cell is therefore inversely as the intensity of the magnetizing force, and its section inversely as the quantity of magnetic induction at that point.

The whole number of cells due to a given current is therefore proportional to the strength of the current multiplied by the number of lines of force which pass through it. If by any change of the form of the conductors the number of cells can be increased, there will be a force tending to produce that change, so that there is always a force urging a conductor transverse to the lines of magnetic force, so as to cause more lines of force to pass through the closed circuit of which the conductor forms a part.

The number of cells due to two given currents is got by multiplying the number of lines of inductive magnetic action which pass through each by the quantity of the currents respectively. Now by (9) the number of lines which pass through the first current is the sum of its own lines and those of the second current which would pass through the first if the second current alone were in action. Hence the whole number of cells will be increased by any motion which causes more lines of force to pass through either circuit, and therefore the resultant force will tend to produce such a motion, and the work done by this force during the motion will be measured by the number of new cells produced. All the actions of closed conductors on each other may be deduced from this principle.

On Electric Currents produced by Induction.

Faraday has shewn‡ that when a conductor moves transversely to the lines of magnetic force, an electro-motive force arises in the conductor, tending to produce a current in it. If the conductor is closed, there is a continuous current, if open, tension is the result. If a closed conductor move transversely to the lines of magnetic induction, then, if the number of lines which pass

---

* *Exp. Res.* (3122). See Art. (6) of this paper.   † Art. (13).
‡ *Exp. Res.* (3077), &c.

through it does not change during the motion, the electro-motive forces in the circuit will be in equilibrium, and there will be no current. Hence the electro-motive forces depend on the number of lines which are cut by the conductor during the motion. If the motion be such that a greater number of lines pass through the circuit formed by the conductor after than before the motion, then the electro-motive force will be measured by the increase of the number of lines, and will generate a current the reverse of that which would have produced the additional lines. When the number of lines of inductive magnetic action through the circuit is increased, the induced current will tend to diminish the number of lines, and when the number is diminished the induced current will tend to increase them.

That this is the true expression for the law of induced currents is shewn from the fact that, in whatever way the number of lines of magnetic induction passing through the circuit be increased, the electro-motive effect is the same, whether the increase take place by the motion of the conductor itself, or of other conductors, or of magnets, or by the change of intensity of other currents, or by the magnetization or demagnetization of neighbouring magnetic bodies, or lastly by the change of intensity of the current itself.

In all these cases the electro-motive force depends on the *change* in the number of lines of inductive magnetic action which pass through the circuit*.

---

* The electro-magnetic forces, which tend to produce motion of the material conductor, must be carefully distinguished from the electro-motive forces, which tend to produce electric currents.

Let an electric current be passed through a mass of metal of any form. The distribution of the currents within the metal will be determined by the laws of conduction. Now let a constant electric current be passed through another conductor near the first. If the two currents are in the same direction the two conductors will be attracted towards each other, and would come nearer if not held in their positions. But though the material conductors are attracted, the currents (which are free to choose any course within the metal) will not alter their original distribution, or incline towards each other. For, since no change takes place in the system, there will be no electro-motive forces to modify the original distribution of currents.

In this case we have electro-magnetic forces acting on the material conductor, without any electro-motive forces tending to modify the current which it carries.

Let us take as another example the case of a linear conductor, not forming a closed circuit, and let it be made to traverse the lines of magnetic force, either by its own motion, or by changes in the magnetic field. An electro-motive force will act in the direction of the conductor, and, as it cannot produce a current, because there is no circuit, it will produce electric tension at the extremities. There will be no electro-magnetic attraction on the material conductor, for this attraction depends on the existence of the current within it, and this is prevented by the circuit not being closed.

Here then we have the opposite case of an electro-motive force acting on the electricity in the conductor, but no attraction on its material particles.

It is natural to suppose that a force of this kind, which depends on a change in the number of lines, is due to a change of state which is measured by the number of these lines. A closed conductor in a magnetic field may be supposed to be in a certain state arising from the magnetic action. As long as this state remains unchanged no effect takes place, but, when the state changes, electro-motive forces arise, depending as to their intensity and direction on this change of state. I cannot do better here than quote a passage from the first series of Faraday's *Experimental Researches*, Art. (60).

"While the wire is subject to either volta-electric or magno-electric induction it appears to be in a peculiar state, for it resists the formation of an electrical current in it; whereas, if in its common condition, such a current would be produced; and when left uninfluenced it has the power of originating a current, a power which the wire does not possess under ordinary circumstances. This electrical condition of matter has not hitherto been recognised, but it probably exerts a very important influence in many if not most of the phenomena produced by currents of electricity. For reasons which will immediately appear (7) I have, after advising with several learned friends, ventured to designate it as the *electro-tonic* state." Finding that all the phenomena could be otherwise explained without reference to the electro-tonic state, Faraday in his second series rejected it as not necessary; but in his recent researches[*] he seems still to think that there may be some physical truth in his conjecture about this new state of bodies.

The conjecture of a philosopher so familiar with nature may sometimes be more pregnant with truth than the best established experimental law discovered by empirical inquirers, and though not bound to admit it as a physical truth, we may accept it as a new idea by which our mathematical conceptions may be rendered clearer.

In this outline of Faraday's electrical theories, as they appear from a mathematical point of view, I can do no more than simply state the mathematical methods by which I believe that electrical phenomena can be best comprehended and reduced to calculation, and my aim has been to present the mathematical ideas to the mind in an embodied form, as systems of lines or surfaces, and not as mere symbols, which neither convey the same ideas, nor readily adapt themselves to the phenomena to be explained. The idea of the electro-tonic state, however, has not yet presented itself to my mind in such a

[*] (3172) (3269).

form that its nature and properties may be clearly explained without reference to mere symbols, and therefore I propose in the following investigation to use symbols freely, and to take for granted the ordinary mathematical operations. By a careful study of the laws of elastic solids and of the motions of viscous fluids, I hope to discover a method of forming a mechanical conception of this electro-tonic state adapted to general reasoning*.

PART II.

On Faraday's "Electro-tonic State."

When a conductor moves in the neighbourhood of a current of electricity, or of a magnet, or when a current or magnet near the conductor is moved, or altered in intensity, then a force acts on the conductor and produces electric tension, or a continuous current, according as the circuit is open or closed. This current is produced only by *changes* of the electric or magnetic phenomena surrounding the conductor, and as long as these are constant there is no observed effect on the conductor. Still the conductor is in different states when near a current or magnet, and when away from its influence, since the removal or destruction of the current or magnet occasions a current, which would not have existed if the magnet or current had not been previously in action.

—Considerations of this kind led Professor Faraday to connect with his discovery of the induction of electric currents the conception of a state into which all bodies are thrown by the presence of magnets and currents. This state does not manifest itself by any known phenomena as long as it is undisturbed, but any change in this state is indicated by a current or tendency towards a current. To this state he gave the name of the "Electro-tonic State," and although he afterwards succeeded in explaining the phenomena which suggested it by means of less hypothetical conceptions, he has on several occasions hinted at the probability that some phenomena might be discovered which would render the electro-tonic state an object of legitimate induction. These speculations, into which Faraday had been led by the study of laws which he has well established, and which he abandoned only for want of experi-

* See Prof. W. Thomson *On a Mechanical Representation of Electric, Magnetic and Galvanic Forces. Camb. and Dub. Math. Jour.* Jan. 1847.

mental data for the direct proof of the unknown state, have not, I think, been made the subject of mathematical investigation. Perhaps it may be thought that the quantitative determinations of the various phenomena are not sufficiently rigorous to be made the basis of a mathematical theory; Faraday, however, has not contented himself with simply stating the numerical results of his experiments and leaving the law to be discovered by calculation. Where he has perceived a law he has at once stated it, in terms as unambiguous as those of pure mathematics; and if the mathematician, receiving this as a physical truth, deduces from it other laws capable of being tested by experiment, he has merely assisted the physicist in arranging his own ideas, which is confessedly a necessary step in scientific induction.

In the following investigation, therefore, the laws established by Faraday will be assumed as true, and it will be shewn that by following out his speculations other and more general laws can be deduced from them. If it should then appear that these laws, originally devised to include one set of phenomena, may be generalized so as to extend to phenomena of a different class, these mathematical connexions may suggest to physicists the means of establishing physical connexions; and thus mere speculation may be turned to account in experimental science.

On Quantity and Intensity as Properties of Electric Currents.

It is found that certain effects of an electric current are equal at whatever part of the circuit they are estimated. The quantities of water or of any other electrolyte decomposed at two different sections of the same circuit, are always found to be equal or equivalent, however different the material and form of the circuit may be at the two sections. The magnetic effect of a conducting wire is also found to be independent of the form or material of the wire in the same circuit. There is therefore an electrical effect which is equal at every section of the circuit. If we conceive of the conductor as the channel along which a fluid is constrained to move, then the quantity of fluid transmitted by each section will be the same, and we may define the *quantity* of an electric current to be the quantity of electricity which passes across a complete section of the current in unit of time. We may for the present measure quantity of electricity by the quantity of water which it would decompose in unit of time.

In order to express mathematically the electrical currents in any conductor, we must have a definition, not only of the entire flow across a complete section, but also of the flow at a given point in a given direction.

DEF. The quantity of a current at a given point and in a given direction is measured, when uniform, by the quantity of electricity which flows across unit of area taken at that point perpendicular to the given direction, and when variable by the quantity which would flow across this area, supposing the flow uniformly the same as at the given point.

In the following investigation, the quantity of electric current at the point (xyz) estimated in the directions of the axes x, y, z respectively will be denoted by a_2, b_2, c_2.

The quantity of electricity which flows in unit of time through the elementary area dS

$$= dS\,(la_2 + mb_2 + nc_2),$$

where l, m, n are the direction-cosines of the normal to dS.

This flow of electricity at any point of a conductor is due to the electromotive forces which act at that point. These may be either external or internal.

External electro-motive forces arise either from the relative motion of currents and magnets, or from changes in their intensity, or from other causes acting at a distance.

Internal electro-motive forces arise principally from difference of electric tension at points of the conductor in the immediate neighbourhood of the point in question. The other causes are variations of chemical composition or of temperature in contiguous parts of the conductor.

Let p_2 represent the electric tension at any point, and X_2, Y_2, Z_2 the sums of the parts of all the electro-motive forces arising from other causes resolved parallel to the co-ordinate axes, then if a_2, β_2, γ_2 be the effective electro-motive forces

$$\left.\begin{aligned}
a_2 &= X_2 - \frac{dp_2}{dx} \\[1mm]
\beta_2 &= Y_2 - \frac{dp_2}{dy} \\[1mm]
\gamma_2 &= Z_2 - \frac{dp_2}{dz}
\end{aligned}\right\} \quad \dots\dots\dots\dots\dots\dots\dots\text{ (A).}$$

Now the quantity of the current depends on the electro-motive force and on the resistance of the medium. If the resistance of the medium be uniform in all directions and equal to k_2,

$$a_2 = k_2 a_2, \qquad \beta_2 = k_2 b_2, \qquad \gamma_2 = k_2 c_2 \dots\dots\dots\dots\dots\dots (B),$$

but if the resistance be different in different directions, the law will be more complicated.

These quantities a_2, β_2, γ_2 may be considered as representing the intensity of the electric action in the directions of x, y, z.

The intensity measured along an element $d\sigma$ of a curve is given by

$$\epsilon = l\alpha + m\beta + n\gamma,$$

where l, m, n are the direction-cosines of the tangent.

The integral $\int \epsilon d\sigma$ taken with respect to a given portion of a curve line, represents the total intensity along that line. If the curve is a closed one, it represents the total intensity of the electro-motive force in the closed curve.

Substituting the values of α, β, γ from equations (A)

$$\int \epsilon d\sigma = \int (Xdx + Ydy + Zdz) - p + C.$$

If therefore $(Xdx + Ydy + Zdz)$ is a complete differential, the value of $\int \epsilon d\sigma$ for a closed curve will vanish, and in all closed curves

$$\int \epsilon d\sigma = \int (Xdx + Ydy + Zdz),$$

the integration being effected along the curve, so that in a closed curve the total intensity of the effective electro-motive force is equal to the total intensity of the impressed electro-motive force.

The total *quantity* of conduction through any surface is expressed by

$$\int e dS,$$

where

$$e = la + mb + nc,$$

l, m, n being the direction-cosines of the normal,

$$\therefore \quad \int e dS = \int\int a\,dydz + \int\int b\,dzdx + \int\int c\,dxdy,$$

the integrations being effected over the given surface. When the surface is a closed one, then we may find by integration by parts

$$\int e dS = \int\int\int \left(\frac{da}{dx} + \frac{db}{dy} + \frac{dc}{dz} \right) dxdydz.$$

If we make

$$\frac{da}{dx} + \frac{db}{dy} + \frac{dc}{dz} = 4\pi\rho \dots\dots\dots\dots\dots\dots(C),$$

$$\int e dS = 4\pi \iiint \rho \, dx \, dy \, dz,$$

where the integration on the right side of the equation is effected over every part of space within the surface. In a large class of phenomena, including all cases of uniform currents, the quantity ρ disappears.

Magnetic Quantity and Intensity.

From his study of the lines of magnetic force, Faraday has been led to the conclusion that in the tubular surface* formed by a system of such lines, the quantity of magnetic induction across any section of the tube is constant, and that the alteration of the character of these lines in passing from one substance to another, is to be explained by a difference of *inductive capacity* in the two substances, which is analogous to conductive power in the theory of electric currents.

In the following investigation we shall have occasion to treat of magnetic quantity and intensity in connection with electric. In such cases the magnetic symbols will be distinguished by the suffix 1, and the electric by the suffix 2. The equations connecting a, b, c, k, α, β, γ, p, and ρ, are the same in form as those which we have just given. a, b, c are the symbols of magnetic induction with respect to quantity; k denotes the resistance to magnetic induction, and may be different in different directions; α, β, γ, are the effective magnetizing forces, connected with a, b, c, by equations (B); p is the magnetic tension or potential which will be afterwards explained; ρ denotes the density of *real magnetic matter* and is connected with a, b, c by equations (C). As all the details of magnetic calculations will be more intelligible after the exposition of the connexion of magnetism with electricity, it will be sufficient here to say that all the definitions of total quantity, with respect to a surface, the total intensity to a curve, apply to the case of magnetism as well as to that of electricity.

---

* *Exp. Res.* 3271, definition of "Sphondyloid."

Electro-magnetism.

Ampère has proved the following laws of the attractions and repulsions of electric currents :

I.   Equal and opposite currents generate equal and opposite forces.

II.   A crooked current is equivalent to a straight one, provided the two currents nearly coincide throughout their whole length.

III.   Equal currents traversing similar and similarly situated closed curves act with equal forces, whatever be the linear dimensions of the circuits.

IV.   A closed current exerts no force tending to turn a circular conductor about its centre.

It is to be observed, that the currents with which Ampère worked were constant and therefore re-entering. All his results are therefore deduced from experiments on closed currents, and his expressions for the mutual action of the elements of a current involve the assumption that this action is exerted in the direction of the line joining those elements. This assumption is no doubt warranted by the universal consent of men of science in treating of attractive forces considered as due to the mutual action of particles ; but at present we are proceeding on a different principle, and searching for the explanation of the phenomena, not in the currents alone, but also in the surrounding medium.

The first and second laws shew that currents are to be combined like velocities or forces.

The third law is the expression of a property of all attractions which may be conceived of as depending on the inverse square of the distance from a fixed system of points ; and the fourth shews that the electro-magnetic forces may always be reduced to the attractions and repulsions of imaginary matter properly distributed.

In fact, the action of a very small electric circuit on a point in its neighbourhood is identical with that of a small magnetic element on a point outside it. If we divide any given portion of a surface into elementary areas, and cause equal currents to flow in the same direction round all these little areas, the effect on a point not in the surface will be the same as that of a shell coinciding with the surface, and uniformly magnetized normal to its surface. But by the first law all the currents forming the little circuits will destroy

25

one another, and leave a single current running round the bounding line. So that the magnetic effect of a uniformly magnetized shell is equivalent to that of an electric current round the edge of the shell. If the direction of the current coincide with that of the apparent motion of the sun, then the direction of magnetization of the imaginary shell will be the same as that of the real magnetization of the earth*.

The total intensity of magnetizing force in a closed curve passing through and embracing the closed current is constant, and may therefore be made a measure of the quantity of the current. As this intensity is independent of the form of the closed curve and depends only on the quantity of the current which passes through it, we may consider the elementary case of the current which flows through the elementary area $dydz$.

Let the axis of x point towards the west, z towards the south, and y upwards. Let x, y, z be the coordinates of a point in the middle of the area $dydz$, then the total intensity measured round the four sides of the element is

$$+\left(\beta_1 + \frac{d\beta_1}{dz}\frac{dz}{2}\right)dy,$$

$$-\left(\gamma_1 + \frac{d\gamma_1}{dy}\frac{dy}{2}\right)dz,$$

$$-\left(\beta_1 - \frac{d\beta_1}{dz}\frac{dz}{2}\right)dy,$$

$$+\left(\gamma_1 - \frac{d\gamma_1}{dy}\frac{dy}{2}\right)dz,$$

$$\text{Total intensity} = \left(\frac{d\beta_1}{dz} - \frac{d\gamma_1}{dy}\right)dy\,dz.$$

The quantity of electricity conducted through the elementary area $dydz$ is $a_2 dydz$, and therefore if we define the measure of an electric current to be the total intensity of magnetizing force in a closed curve embracing it, we shall have

$$a_2 = \frac{d\beta_1}{dz} - \frac{d\gamma_1}{dy},$$

$$b_2 = \frac{d\gamma_1}{dx} - \frac{da_1}{dz},$$

$$c_2 = \frac{da_1}{dy} - \frac{d\beta_1}{dx}.$$

* See *Experimental Researches* (3265) for the relations between the electrical and magnetic circuit considered as *mutually embracing* curves.

These equations enable us to deduce the distribution of the currents of electricity whenever we know the values of α, β, γ, the magnetic intensities. If α, β, γ be exact differentials of a function of x, y, z with respect to x, y and z respectively, then the values of a_2, b_2, c_2 disappear; and we know that the magnetism is not produced by electric currents in that part of the field which we are investigating. It is due either to the presence of permanent magnetism within the field, or to magnetizing forces due to external causes.

We may observe that the above equations give by differentiation

$$\frac{da_2}{dx} + \frac{db_2}{dy} + \frac{dc_2}{dz} = 0,$$

which is the equation of continuity for closed currents. Our investigations are therefore for the present limited to closed currents; and we know little of the magnetic effects of any currents which are not closed.

Before entering on the calculation of these electric and magnetic states it may be advantageous to state certain general theorems, the truth of which may be established analytically.

THEOREM I.

The equation

$$\frac{d^2V}{dx^2} + \frac{d^2V}{dy^2} + \frac{d^2V}{dz^2} + 4\pi\rho = 0,$$

(where V and ρ are functions of x, y, z never infinite, and vanishing for all points at an infinite distance), can be satisfied by one, and only one, value of V. See Art. (17) above.

THEOREM II.

The value of V which will satisfy the above conditions is found by integrating the expression

$$\iiint \frac{\rho\,dx\,dy\,dz}{\left((x-x')^2 + (y-y')^2 + (z-z')^2\right)^{\frac{1}{2}}},$$

where the limits of x, y, z are such as to include every point of space where ρ is finite.

The proofs of these theorems may be found in any work on attractions or electricity, and in particular in Green's *Essay on the Application of Mathematics to Electricity*. See Arts. 18, 19 of this paper. See also Gauss, *on Attractions*, translated in Taylor's *Scientific Memoirs*.

THEOREM III.

Let U and V be two functions of x, y, z, then

$$\iiint U \left(\frac{d^2 V}{dx^2} + \frac{d^2 V}{dy^2} + \frac{d^2 V}{dz^2} \right) dxdydz = -\iiint \left(\frac{dU}{dx} \frac{dV}{dx} + \frac{dU}{dy} \frac{dV}{dy} + \frac{dU}{dz} \frac{dV}{dz} \right) dxdydz$$

$$= \iiint \left(\frac{d^2 U}{dx^2} + \frac{d^2 U}{dy^2} + \frac{d^2 U}{dz^2} \right) V dx\, dy\, dz\,;$$

where the integrations are supposed to extend over all the space in which U and V have values differing from 0.—(Green, p. 10.)

This theorem shews that if there be two attracting systems the actions between them are equal and opposite. And by making $U = V$ we find that the potential of a system on itself is proportional to the integral of the square of the resultant attraction through all space; a result deducible from Art. (30) since the volume of each cell is inversely as the square of the velocity (Arts. 12, 13), and therefore the number of cells in a given space is directly as the square of the velocity.

THEOREM IV.

Let a, β, γ, ρ be quantities finite through a certain space and vanishing in the space beyond, and let k be given for all parts of space as a continuous or discontinuous function of x, y, z, then the equation in p

$$\frac{d}{dx} \frac{1}{k} \left(a - \frac{dp}{dx} \right) + \frac{d}{dy} \frac{1}{k} \left(\beta - \frac{dp}{dy} \right) + \frac{d}{dz} \frac{1}{k} \left(\gamma - \frac{dp}{dz} \right) + 4\pi\rho = 0,$$

has one, and only one solution, in which p is always finite and vanishes at an infinite distance.

The proof of this theorem, by Prof. W. Thomson, may be found in the *Cambridge and Dublin Mathematical Journal*, Jan. 1848.

If a, β, γ be the electro-motive forces, p the electric tension, and k the coefficient of resistance, then the above equation is identical with the equation of continuity

$$\frac{da_2}{dx} + \frac{db_2}{dy} + \frac{dc_2}{dz} + 4\pi\rho = 0\,;$$

and the theorem shews that when the electro-motive forces and the rate of production of electricity at every part of space are given, the value of the electric tension is determinate.

Since the mathematical laws of magnetism are identical with those of electricity, as far as we now consider them, we may regard a, β, γ as magnetizing forces, p as *magnetic tension*, and ρ as *real magnetic density*, k being the coefficient of resistance to magnetic induction.

The proof of this theorem rests on the determination of the minimum value of

$$Q = \iiint \left\{ \frac{1}{k}\left(a - \frac{dp}{dx} - k\frac{dV}{dx}\right)^2 + \frac{1}{k}\left(\beta - \frac{dp}{dy} - k\frac{dV}{dy}\right)^2 + \frac{1}{k}\left(\gamma - \frac{dp}{dz} - k\frac{dV}{dz}\right)^2 \right\} dx\,dy\,dz\,;$$

where V is got from the equation

$$\frac{d^2V}{dx^2} + \frac{d^2V}{dy^2} + \frac{d^2V}{dz^2} + 4\pi\rho = 0,$$

and p has to be determined.

The meaning of this integral in electrical language may be thus brought out. If the presence of the media in which k has various values did not affect the distribution of forces, then the "quantity" resolved in x would be simply $\dfrac{dV}{dx}$ and the intensity $k\dfrac{dV}{dx}$. But the actual quantity and intensity are $\dfrac{1}{k}\left(a - \dfrac{dp}{dx}\right)$ and $a - \dfrac{dp}{dx}$, and the parts due to the distribution of media alone are therefore

$$\frac{1}{k}\left(a - \frac{dp}{dx}\right) - \frac{dV}{dx} \text{ and } a - \frac{dp}{dx} - k\frac{dV}{dx}\,.$$

Now the product of these represents the work done on account of this distribution of media, the distribution of sources being determined, and taking in the terms in y and z we get the expression Q for the total work done by that part of the whole effect at any point which is due to the distribution of conducting media, and not directly to the presence of the sources.

This quantity Q is rendered a minimum by one and only one value of p, namely, that which satisfies the original equation.

THEOREM V.

If a, b, c be three functions of x, y, z satisfying the equation

$$\frac{da}{dx} + \frac{db}{dy} + \frac{dc}{dz} = 0,$$

it is always possible to find three functions α, β, γ which shall satisfy the equations

$$\frac{d\beta}{dz} - \frac{d\gamma}{dy} = a,$$

$$\frac{d\gamma}{dx} - \frac{d\alpha}{dz} = b,$$

$$\frac{d\alpha}{dy} - \frac{d\beta}{dx} = c.$$

Let $A = \int c\,dy$, where the integration is to be performed upon c considered as a function of y, treating x and z as constants. Let $B = \int a\,dz$, $C = \int b\,dx$, $A' = \int b\,dz$, $B' = \int c\,dx$, $C' = \int a\,dy$, integrated in the same way.

Then

$$a = A - A' + \frac{d\psi}{dx},$$

$$\beta = B - B' + \frac{d\psi}{dy},$$

$$\gamma = C - C' + \frac{d\psi}{dz}$$

will satisfy the given equations; for

$$\frac{d\beta}{dz} - \frac{d\gamma}{dy} = \int \frac{da}{dy}\,dz - \int \frac{dc}{dz}\,dx - \int \frac{db}{dy}\,dx + \int \frac{da}{dy}\,dy,$$

and

$$0 = \int \frac{da}{dx}\,dx + \int \frac{db}{dy}\,dx + \int \frac{dc}{dz}\,dx;$$

$$\therefore \frac{d\beta}{dz} - \frac{d\gamma}{dy} = \int \frac{da}{dx}\,dx + \int \frac{da}{dy}\,dy + \int \frac{da}{dz}\,dz,$$

$$= a.$$

In the same way it may be shewn that the values of a, β, γ satisfy the other given equations. The function ψ may be considered at present as perfectly indeterminate.

The method here given is taken from Prof. W. Thomson's memoir on Magnetism (*Phil. Trans.* 1851, p. 283).

As we cannot perform the required integrations when a, b, c are discontinuous functions of x, y, z, the following method, which is perfectly general though more complicated, may indicate more clearly the truth of the proposition.

Let A, B, C be determined from the equations

$$\frac{d^2A}{dx^2} + \frac{d^2A}{dy^2} + \frac{d^2A}{dz^2} + a = 0,$$

$$\frac{d^2B}{dx^2} + \frac{d^2B}{dy^2} + \frac{d^2B}{dz^2} + b = 0,$$

$$\frac{d^2C}{dx^2} + \frac{d^2C}{dy^2} + \frac{d^2C}{dz^2} + c = 0,$$

by the methods of Theorems I. and II., so that A, B, C are never infinite, and vanish when x, y, or z is infinite.

Also let

$$a = \frac{dB}{dz} - \frac{dC}{dy} + \frac{d\psi}{dx},$$

$$\beta = \frac{dC}{dx} - \frac{dA}{dz} + \frac{d\psi}{dy},$$

$$\gamma = \frac{dA}{dy} - \frac{dB}{dx} + \frac{d\psi}{dz},$$

then

$$\frac{d\beta}{dz} - \frac{d\gamma}{dy} = \frac{d}{dx}\left(\frac{dA}{dx} + \frac{dB}{dy} + \frac{dC}{dz}\right) - \left(\frac{d^2A}{dx^2} + \frac{d^2A}{dy^2} + \frac{d^2A}{dz^2}\right)$$

$$= \frac{d}{dx}\left(\frac{dA}{dx} + \frac{dB}{dy} + \frac{dC}{dz}\right) + a.$$

If we find similar equations in y and z, and differentiate the first by x, the second by y, and the third by z, remembering the equation between a, b, c, we shall have

$$\left(\frac{d^2}{dx^2} + \frac{d^2}{dy^2} + \frac{d^2}{dz^2}\right)\left(\frac{dA}{dx} + \frac{dB}{dy} + \frac{dC}{dz}\right) = 0 ;$$

and since A, B, C are always finite and vanish at an infinite distance, the only solution of this equation is

$$\frac{dA}{dx} + \frac{dB}{dy} + \frac{dC}{dz} = 0,$$

and we have finally

$$\frac{d\beta}{dz} - \frac{d\gamma}{dy} = a,$$

with two similar equations, shewing that a, β, γ have been rightly determined.

The function ψ is to be determined from the condition

$$\frac{da}{dx} + \frac{d\beta}{dy} + \frac{d\gamma}{dz} = \left(\frac{d^2}{dx^2} + \frac{d^2}{dy^2} + \frac{d^2}{dz^2}\right)\psi :$$

if the left-hand side of this equation be always zero, ψ must be zero also.

THEOREM VI.

Let a, b, c be any three functions of x, y, z, it is possible to find three functions a, β, γ and a fourth V, so that

$$\frac{da}{dx} + \frac{d\beta}{dy} + \frac{d\gamma}{dz} = 0,$$

and

$$a = \frac{d\beta}{dz} - \frac{d\gamma}{dy} + \frac{dV}{dx},$$

$$b = \frac{d\gamma}{dx} - \frac{da}{dz} + \frac{dV}{dy},$$

$$c = \frac{da}{dy} - \frac{d\beta}{dx} + \frac{dV}{dz}.$$

Let

$$\frac{da}{dx} + \frac{db}{dy} + \frac{dc}{dz} = -4\pi\rho,$$

and let V be found from the equation

$$\frac{d^2V}{dx^2} + \frac{d^2V}{dy^2} + \frac{d^2V}{dz^2} = -4\pi\rho,$$

then

$$a' = a - \frac{dV}{dx},$$

$$b' = b - \frac{dV}{dy},$$

$$c' = c - \frac{dV}{dz},$$

satisfy the condition

$$\frac{da'}{dx} + \frac{db'}{dy} + \frac{dc'}{dz} = 0;$$

and therefore we can find three functions A, B, C, and from these α, β, γ, so as to satisfy the given equations.

Theorem VII.

The integral throughout infinity

$$Q = \iiint (a_1\alpha_1 + b_1\beta_1 + c_1\gamma_1)\, dx\, dy\, dz,$$

where $a_1 b_1 c_1$, $\alpha_1\beta_1\gamma_1$ are any functions whatsoever, is capable of transformation into

$$Q = + \iiint \{4\pi p \rho_1 - (\alpha_0 a_2 + \beta_0 b_2 + \gamma_0 c_2)\}\, dx\, dy\, dz,$$

in which the quantities are found from the equations

$$\frac{da_1}{dx} + \frac{db_1}{dy} + \frac{dc_1}{dz} + 4\pi\rho_1 = 0,$$

$$\frac{da_1}{dx} + \frac{d\beta_1}{dy} + \frac{d\gamma_1}{dz} + 4\pi\rho_1' = 0;$$

$a_0\beta_0\gamma_0 V$ are determined from $a_1 b_1 c_1$ by the last theorem, so that

$$a_1 = \frac{d\beta_0}{dz} - \frac{d\gamma_0}{dy} + \frac{dV}{dx};$$

$a_2 b_2 c_2$ are found from $a_1\beta_1\gamma_1$ by the equations

$$a_2 = \frac{d\beta_1}{dz} - \frac{d\gamma_1}{dy}\ \&\text{c.},$$

and p is found from the equation

$$\frac{d^2p}{dx^2} + \frac{d^2p}{dy^2} + \frac{d^2p}{dz^2} + 4\pi\rho_1' = 0.$$

For, if we put a_1 in the form

$$\frac{d\beta_0}{dz} - \frac{d\gamma_0}{dy} + \frac{dV}{dx},$$

and treat b_1 and c_1 similarly, then we have by integration by parts through infinity, remembering that all the functions vanish at the limits,

$$Q = -\iiint \left\{ V\left(\frac{da_1}{dx} + \frac{d\beta_1}{dy} + \frac{d\gamma_1}{dz}\right) + a_0\left(\frac{d\beta_1}{dz} - \frac{d\gamma_1}{dy}\right) + \beta_0\left(\frac{d\gamma_1}{dx} - \frac{da_1}{dz}\right) \right.$$
$$\left. + \gamma_0\left(\frac{da_1}{dy} - \frac{d\beta_1}{dx}\right) \right\} dx\, dy\, dz,$$

or $Q = +\iiint \{(4\pi V\rho') - (a_0 a_2 + \beta_0 b_2 + \gamma_0 c_2)\} dx\, dy\, dz,$

and by Theorem III.

$$\iiint V\rho'\, dx\, dy\, dz = \iiint p\rho\, dx\, dy\, dz,$$

so that finally

$$Q = \iiint \{4\pi p\rho - (a_0 a_2 + \beta_0 b_2 + \gamma_0 c_2)\} dx\, dy\, dz.$$

If $a_1 b_1 c_1$ represent the components of magnetic quantity, and $a_1 \beta_1 \gamma_1$ those of magnetic intensity, then ρ will represent the *real magnetic density*, and p the magnetic potential or tension. $a_2 b_2 c_2$ will be the components of quantity of electric currents, and $a_0 \beta_0 \gamma_0$ will be three functions deduced from $a_1 b_1 c_1$, which will be found to be the mathematical expression for Faraday's Electro-tonic state.

Let us now consider the bearing of these analytical theorems on the theory of magnetism. Whenever we deal with quantities relating to magnetism, we shall distinguish them by the suffix ($_1$). Thus $a_1 b_1 c_1$ are the components resolved in the directions of x, y, z of the quantity of magnetic induction acting through a given point, and $a_1 \beta_1 \gamma_1$ are the resolved intensities of magnetization at the same point, or, what is the same thing, the components of the force which would be exerted on a unit south pole of a magnet placed at that point without disturbing the distribution of magnetism.

The electric currents are found from the magnetic intensities by the equations

$$a_2 = \frac{d\beta_1}{dz} - \frac{d\gamma_1}{dy} \text{ &c.}$$

When there are no electric currents, then

$$a_1 dx + \beta_1 dy + \gamma_1 dz = dp_1,$$

a perfect differential of a function of x, y, z. On the principle of analogy we may call p_1 the magnetic tension.

The forces which act on a mass m of south magnetism at any point are

$$-m\frac{dp_1}{dx}, \quad -m\frac{dp_1}{dy}, \text{ and } -m\frac{dp_1}{dz},$$

in the direction of the axes, and therefore the whole work done during any displacement of a magnetic system is equal to the decrement of the integral

$$Q = \iiint \rho_1 p_1 \, dx\,dy\,dz$$

throughout the system.

Let us now call Q the *total potential of the system on itself*. The increase or decrease of Q will measure the work lost or gained by any displacement of any part of the system, and will therefore enable us to determine the forces acting on that part of the system.

By Theorem III. Q may be put under the form

$$Q = +\frac{1}{4\pi}\iiint (a_1 a_1 + b_1 \beta_1 + c_1 \gamma_1)\, dx\,dy\,dz,$$

in which $a_1 \beta_1 \gamma_1$ are the differential coefficients of p_1 with respect to x, y, z respectively.

If we now assume that this expression for Q is true whatever be the values of a_1, β_1, γ_1, we pass from the consideration of the magnetism of permanent magnets to that of the magnetic effects of electric currents, and we have then by Theorem VII.

$$Q = \iiint \left\{ p_1 \rho_1 - \frac{1}{4\pi}(a_0 a_2 + \beta_0 b_2 + \gamma_0 c_2) \right\} dx\,dy\,dz.$$

So that in the case of electric currents, the components of the currents have to be multiplied by the functions a_0, β_0, γ_0 respectively, and the summations of all such products throughout the system gives us the part of Q due to those currents.

We have now obtained in the functions a_0, β_0, γ_0 the means of avoiding the consideration of the quantity of magnetic induction which *passes through* the circuit. Instead of this artificial method we have the natural one of considering the current with reference to quantities existing in the same space with the current itself. To these I give the name of *Electro-tonic functions*, or *components of the Electro-tonic intensity*.

Let us now consider the conditions of the conduction of the electric currents within the medium during changes in the electro-tonic state. The method which we shall adopt is an application of that given by Helmholtz in his memoir on the Conservation of Force*.

Let there be some external source of electric currents which would generate in the conducting mass currents whose quantity is measured by a_2, b_2, c_2 and their intensity by α_2, β_2, γ_2.

Then the amount of work due to this cause in the time dt is

$$dt \iiint (a_2\alpha_2 + b_2\beta_2 + c_2\gamma_2)\, dx\, dy\, dz$$

in the form of resistance overcome, and

$$\frac{dt}{4\pi} \frac{d}{dt} \iiint (a_2\alpha_0 + b_2\beta_0 + c_2\gamma_0)\, dx\, dy\, dz$$

in the form of work done mechanically by the electro-magnetic action of these currents. If there be no external cause producing currents, then the quantity representing the whole work done by the external cause must vanish, and we have

$$dt \iiint (a_2\alpha_2 + b_2\beta_2 + c_2\gamma_2)\, dx\, dy\, dz + \frac{dt}{4\pi} \frac{d}{dt} \iiint (a_2\alpha_0 + b_2\beta_0 + c_2\gamma_0)\, dx\, dy\, dz,$$

where the integrals are taken through any arbitrary space. We must therefore have

$$a_2\alpha_2 + b_2\beta_2 + c_2\gamma_2 = \frac{1}{4\pi} \frac{d}{dt} (a_2\alpha_0 + b_2\beta_0 + c_2\gamma_0)$$

for every point of space; and it must be remembered that the variation of Q is supposed due to variations of α_0, β_0, γ_0, and not of a_2, b_2, c_2. We must therefore treat a_2, b_2, c_2 as constants, and the equation becomes

$$a_2 \left(\alpha_2 + \frac{1}{4\pi} \frac{d\alpha_0}{dt} \right) + b_2 \left(\beta_2 + \frac{1}{4\pi} \frac{d\beta_0}{dt} \right) + c_2 \left(\gamma_2 + \frac{1}{4\pi} \frac{d\gamma_0}{dt} \right) = 0.$$

In order that this equation may be independent of the values of a_2, b_2, c_2, each of these coefficients must $= 0$; and therefore we have the following expressions for the electro-motive forces due to the action of magnets and currents at a distance in terms of the electro-tonic functions,

$$\alpha_2 = -\frac{1}{4\pi} \frac{d\alpha_0}{dt}, \qquad \beta_2 = -\frac{1}{4\pi} \frac{d\beta_0}{dt}, \qquad \gamma_2 = -\frac{1}{4\pi} \frac{d\gamma_0}{dt}.$$

* Translated in Taylor's *New Scientific Memoirs*, Part II.

It appears from experiment that the expression $\dfrac{da_0}{dt}$ refers to the change of electro-tonic state of a *given particle of the conductor*, whether due to change in the electro-tonic functions themselves or to the motion of the particle.

If a_0 be expressed as a function of x, y, z and t, and if x, y, z be the co-ordinates of a moving particle, then the electro-motive force measured in the direction of x is

$$a_2 = -\frac{1}{4\pi}\left(\frac{da_0}{dx}\frac{dx}{dt} + \frac{da_0}{dy}\frac{dy}{dt} + \frac{da_0}{dz}\frac{dz}{dt} + \frac{da_0}{dt}\right).$$

The expressions for the electro-motive forces in y and z are similar. The distribution of currents due to these forces depends on the form and arrangement of the conducting media and on the resultant electric tension at any point.

The discussion of these functions would involve us in mathematical formulæ, of which this paper is already too full. It is only on account of their physical importance as the mathematical expression of one of Faraday's conjectures that I have been induced to exhibit them at all in their present form. By a more patient consideration of their relations, and with the help of those who are engaged in physical inquiries both in this subject and in others not obviously connected with it, I hope to exhibit the theory of the electro-tonic state in a form in which all its relations may be distinctly conceived without reference to analytical calculations.

Summary of the Theory of the Electro-tonic State.

We may conceive of the electro-tonic state at any point of space as a quantity determinate in magnitude and direction, and we may represent the electro-tonic condition of a portion of space by any mechanical system which has at every point some quantity, which may be a velocity, a displacement, or a force, whose direction and magnitude correspond to those of the supposed electro-tonic state. This representation involves no physical theory, it is only a kind of artificial notation. In analytical investigations we make use of the three components of the electro-tonic state, and call them electro-tonic functions. We take the resolved part of the electro-tonic intensity at every point of a closed curve, and find by integration what we may call the *entire electro-tonic intensity round the curve.*

PROP. I.   *If on any surface a closed curve be drawn, and if the surface within it be divided into small areas, then the entire intensity round the closed curve is equal to the sum of the intensities round each of the small areas, all estimated in the same direction.*

For, in going round the small areas, every boundary line between two of them is passed along twice in opposite directions, and the intensity gained in the one case is lost in the other.   Every effect of passing along the interior divisions is therefore neutralized, and the whole effect is that due to the exterior closed curve.

LAW I.   *The entire electro-tonic intensity round the boundary of an element of surface measures the quantity of magnetic induction which passes through that surface, or, in other words, the number of lines of magnetic force which pass through that surface.*

By PROP. I. it appears that what is true of elementary surfaces is true also of surfaces of finite magnitude, and therefore any two surfaces which are bounded by the same closed curve will have the same quantity of magnetic induction through them.

LAW II.   *The magnetic intensity at any point is connected with the quantity of magnetic induction by a set of linear equations, called the equations of conduction*.*

LAW III.   *The entire magnetic intensity round the boundary of any surface measures the quantity of electric current which passes through that surface.*

LAW IV.   *The quantity and intensity of electric currents are connected by a system of equations of conduction.*

By these four laws the magnetic and electric quantity and intensity may be deduced from the values of the electro-tonic functions.   I have not discussed the values of the units, as that will be better done with reference to actual experiments.   We come next to the attraction of conductors of currents, and to the induction of currents within conductors.

* See Art. (28).

LAW V. *The total electro-magnetic potential of a closed current is measured by the product of the quantity of the current multiplied by the entire electro-tonic intensity estimated in the same direction round the circuit.*

Any displacement of the conductors which would cause an increase in the potential will be assisted by a force measured by the rate of increase of the potential, so that the mechanical work done during the displacement will be measured by the increase of potential.

Although in certain cases a displacement in direction or alteration of intensity *of the current* might increase the potential, such an alteration would not itself produce work, and there will be no tendency towards this displacement, for alterations in the current are due to electro-motive force, not to electro-magnetic attractions, which can only act on the conductor.

LAW VI. *The electro-motive force on any element of a conductor is measured by the instantaneous rate of change of the electro-tonic intensity on that element, whether in magnitude or direction.*

The electro-motive force in a closed conductor is measured by the rate of change of the entire electro-tonic intensity round the circuit referred to unit of time. It is independent of the nature of the conductor, though the current produced varies inversely as the resistance ; and it is the same in whatever way the change of electro-tonic intensity has been produced, whether by motion of the conductor or by alterations in the external circumstances.

In these six laws I have endeavoured to express the idea which I believe to be the mathematical foundation of the modes of thought indicated in the *Experimental Researches*. I do not think that it contains even the shadow of a true physical theory ; in fact, its chief merit as a temporary instrument of research is that it does not, even in appearance, *account for* anything.

There exists however a professedly physical theory of electro-dynamics, which is so elegant, so mathematical, and so entirely different from anything in this paper, that I must state its axioms, at the risk of repeating what ought to be well known. It is contained in M. W. Weber's *Electro-dynamic Measurements*, and may be found in the Transactions of the Leibnitz Society, and of the Royal Society of Sciences of Saxony*. The assumptions are,

* When this was written, I was not aware that part of M. Weber's Memoir is translated in Taylor's *Scientific Memoirs*, Vol. v. Art. XIV. The value of his researches, both experimental and theoretical, renders the study of his theory necessary to every electrician.

(1) That two particles of electricity when in motion do not repel each other with the same force as when at rest, but that the force is altered by a quantity depending on the relative motion of the two particles, so that the expression for the repulsion at distance r is

$$\frac{ee'}{r^2}\left(1 + a\left|\frac{\overline{dr}}{dt}\right|^2 + br\frac{d^2r}{dt^2}\right).$$

(2) That when electricity is moving in a conductor, the velocity of the positive fluid *relatively to the matter of the conductor* is equal and opposite to that of the negative fluid.

(3) The total action of one conducting element on another is the resultant of the mutual actions of the masses of electricity of both kinds which are in each.

(4) The electro-motive force at any point is the difference of the forces acting on the positive and negative fluids.

From these axioms are deducible Ampère's laws of the attraction of conductors, and those of Neumann and others, for the induction of currents. Here then is a really physical theory, satisfying the required conditions better perhaps than any yet invented, and put forth by a philosopher whose experimental researches form an ample foundation for his mathematical investigations. What is the use then of imagining an electro-tonic state of which we have no distinctly physical conception, instead of a formula of attraction which we can readily understand? I would answer, that it is a good thing to have two ways of looking at a subject, and to admit that there *are* two ways of looking at it. Besides, I do not think that we have any right at present to understand the action of electricity, and I hold that the chief merit of a temporary theory is, that it shall guide experiment, without impeding the progress of the true theory when it appears. There are also objections to making any ultimate forces in nature depend on the velocity of the bodies between which they act. If the forces in nature are to be reduced to forces acting between particles, the principle of the Conservation of Force requires that these forces should be in the line joining the particles and functions of the distance only. The experiments of M. Weber on the reverse polarity of diamagnetics, which have been recently repeated by Professor Tyndall, establish a fact which is equally a consequence of M. Weber's theory of electricity and of the theory of lines of force.

With respect to the history of the present theory, I may state that the recognition of certain mathematical functions as expressing the "electro-tonic state" of Faraday, and the use of them in determining electro-dynamic potentials and electro-motive forces is, as far as I am aware, original; but the distinct conception of the possibility of the mathematical expressions arose in my mind from the perusal of Prof. W. Thomson's papers "On a Mechanical Representation of Electric, Magnetic and Galvanic Forces," *Cambridge and Dublin Mathematical Journal*, January, 1847, and his "Mathematical Theory of Magnetism," *Philosophical Transactions*, Part I. 1851, Art. 78, &c. As an instance of the help which may be derived from other physical investigations, I may state that after I had investigated the Theorems of this paper Professor Stokes pointed out to me the use which he had made of similar expressions in his "Dynamical Theory of Diffraction," Section 1, *Cambridge Transactions*, Vol. IX. Part 1. Whether the theory of these functions, considered with reference to electricity, may lead to new mathematical ideas to be employed in physical research, remains to be seen. I propose in the rest of this paper to discuss a few electrical and magnetic problems with reference to spheres. These are intended merely as concrete examples of the methods of which the theory has been given; I reserve the detailed investigation of cases chosen with special reference to experiment till I have the means of testing their results.

EXAMPLES.

I. *Theory of Electrical Images.*

The method of Electrical Images, due to Prof. W. Thomson[*], by which the theory of spherical conductors has been reduced to great geometrical simplicity, becomes even more simple when we see its connexion with the methods of this paper. We have seen that the pressure at any point in a uniform medium, due to a spherical shell (radius $= a$) giving out fluid at the rate of $4\pi P a^2$ units in unit of time, is $kP \dfrac{a^2}{r}$ outside the shell, and kPa inside it, where r is the distance of the point from the centre of the shell.

[*] See a series of papers "On the Mathematical Theory of Electricity," in the *Cambridge and Dublin Math. Jour.*, beginning March, 1848.

If there be two shells, one giving out fluid at a rate $4\pi Pa^2$, and the other absorbing at the rate of $4\pi P'a'^2$, then the expression for the pressure will be, outside the shells,

$$p = 4\pi P\,\frac{a^2}{r} - 4\pi P'\,\frac{a'^2}{r'},$$

where r and r' are the distances from the centres of the two shells. Equating this expression to zero we have, as the surface of no pressure, that for which

$$\frac{r'}{r} = \frac{P'a'^2}{Pa^2}.$$

Now the surface, for which the distances to two fixed points have a given ratio, is a sphere of which the centre O is in the line joining the centres of the shells CC' produced, so that

$$C'O = CC'\,\frac{\overline{P'a'^2}\,|^2}{\overline{Pa^2}\,|^2 - \overline{P'a'^2}\,|^2},$$

and its radius

$$= CC'\,\frac{Pa^2 \cdot P'a'^2}{\overline{Pa^2}\,|^2 - \overline{P'a'^2}\,|^2},$$

If at the centre of this sphere we place another source of the fluid, then the pressure due to this source must be added to that due to the other two; and since this additional pressure depends only on the distance from the centre, it will be constant at the surface of the sphere, where the pressure due to the two other sources is zero.

We have now the means of arranging a system of sources within a given sphere, so that when combined with a given system of sources outside the sphere, they shall produce a given constant pressure at the surface of the sphere.

Let a be the radius of the sphere, and p the given pressure, and let the given sources be at distances b_1, b_2, &c. from the centre, and let their rates of production be $4\pi P_1$, $4\pi P_2$, &c.

Then if at distances $\dfrac{a^2}{b_1}$, $\dfrac{a^2}{b_2}$, &c. (measured in the same direction as b_1, b_2, &c. from the centre) we place negative sources whose rates are

$$-4\pi P_1\,\frac{a}{b_1}, \quad -4\pi P_2\,\frac{a}{b_2},\ \&c.,$$

the pressure at the surface $r = a$ will be reduced to zero. Now placing a source $4\pi \dfrac{pa}{k}$ at the centre, the pressure at the surface will be uniform and equal to p.

The whole amount of fluid emitted by the surface $r = a$ may be found by adding the rates of production of the sources within it. The result is

$$4\pi a \left\{ \frac{p}{k} - \frac{P_1}{b_1} - \frac{P_2}{b_2} - \&\mathrm{c.} \right\}.$$

To apply this result to the case of a conducting sphere, let us suppose the external sources $4\pi P_1$, $4\pi P_2$ to be small electrified bodies, containing e_1, e_2 of positive electricity. Let us also suppose that the whole charge of the conducting sphere is $= E$ previous to the action of the external points. Then all that is required for the complete solution of the problem is, that the surface of the sphere shall be a surface of equal potential, and that the total charge of the surface shall be E.

If by any distribution of imaginary sources within the spherical surface we can effect this, the value of the corresponding potential outside the sphere is the true and only one. The potential inside the sphere must really be constant and equal to that at the surface.

We must therefore find the *images* of the external electrified points, that is, for every point at distance b from the centre we must find a point on the same radius at a distance $\dfrac{a^2}{b_1}$, and at that point we must place a quantity $= -e \dfrac{a}{b_1}$ of imaginary electricity.

At the centre we must put a quantity E' such that

$$E' = E + e_1 \frac{a}{b_1} + e_2 \frac{a}{b_2} + \&\mathrm{c.};$$

then if R be the distance from the centre, r_1, r_2, &c. the distances from the electrified points, and r'_1, r'_2, &c. the distances from their images at any point outside the sphere, the potential at that point will be

$$p = \frac{E'}{R} + e_1 \left(\frac{1}{r_1} - \frac{a}{b_1} \frac{1}{r'_1} \right) + e_2 \left(\frac{1}{r_2} - \frac{a}{b_2} \frac{1}{r'_2} \right) + \&\mathrm{c.}$$

$$= \frac{E}{R} + \frac{e_1}{b_1} \left(\frac{a}{R} + \frac{b_1}{r_1} - \frac{a}{r'_1} \right) + \frac{e_2}{b_2} \left(\frac{a}{R} + \frac{b_2}{r_2} - \frac{a}{r'_2} \right) + \&\mathrm{c.}$$

This is the value of the potential outside the sphere. At the surface we have

$$R = a \text{ and } \frac{b_1}{r_1} = \frac{a}{r'_1}, \qquad \frac{b_2}{r_2} = \frac{a}{r'_2}, \quad \&c.,$$

so that at the surface

$$p = \frac{E}{a} + \frac{e_1}{b_1} + \frac{e_2}{b_2} + \&c.,$$

and this must also be the value of p for any point within the sphere.

For the application of the principle of electrical images the reader is referred to Prof. Thomson's papers in the *Cambridge and Dublin Mathematical Journal*. The only case which we shall consider is that in which $\frac{e_1}{b_1^2} = I$, and b_1 is infinitely distant along the axis of x, and $E = 0$.

The value p outside the sphere becomes then

$$p = Ix \left(-\frac{a^3}{r^3} \right),$$

and inside $p = 0$.

II. *On the effect of a paramagnetic or diamagnetic sphere in a uniform field of magnetic force*[*].

The expression for the potential of a small magnet placed at the origin of co-ordinates in the direction of the axis of x is

$$l \frac{d}{dx} \left(\frac{m}{r} \right) = - lm \frac{x}{r^3} .$$

The effect of the sphere in disturbing the lines of force may be supposed as a first hypothesis to be similar to that of a small magnet at the origin, whose strength is to be determined. (We shall find this to be accurately true.)

---

[*] See Prof. Thomson, on the Theory of Magnetic Induction, *Phil. Mag.* March, 1851. The *inductive capacity* of the sphere, according to that paper, is the ratio of the *quantity* of magnetic induction (not the *intensity*) within the sphere to that without. It is therefore equal to $\frac{1}{I} B \frac{k'}{k} = \frac{3k'}{2k + k'}$, according to our notation.

Let the value of the potential undisturbed by the presence of the sphere be
$$p = Ix.$$

Let the sphere produce an additional potential, which for external points is
$$p' = A \frac{a^3}{r^3} x,$$

and let the potential within the sphere be
$$p_1 = Bx.$$

Let k' be the coefficient of resistance outside, and k inside the sphere, then the conditions to be fulfilled are, that the interior and exterior potentials should coincide at the surface, and that the induction through the surface should be the same whether deduced from the external or the internal potential. Putting $x = r \cos \theta$, we have for the external potential
$$P = \left(Ir + A \frac{a^3}{r^2} \right) \cos \theta,$$

and for the internal
$$p_1 = Br \cos \theta,$$

and these must be identical when $r = a$, or
$$I + A = B.$$

The induction through the surface in the external medium is
$$\frac{1}{k'} \frac{dp}{dr_{r=a}} = \frac{1}{k'} (I - 2A) \cos \theta,$$

and that through the interior surface is
$$\frac{1}{k} \frac{dp_1}{dr_{r=a}} = \frac{1}{k} B \cos \theta ;$$

$$\text{and } \therefore \frac{1}{k'} (I - 2A) = \frac{1}{k} B.$$

These equations give
$$A = \frac{k - k'}{2k + k'} I, \qquad B = \frac{3k}{2k + k'} I.$$

The effect outside the sphere is equal to that of a little magnet whose length is l and moment ml, provided
$$ml = \frac{k - k'}{2k + k'} a^3 I.$$

Suppose this uniform field to be that due to terrestrial magnetism, then, if k is less than k' as in paramagnetic bodies, the marked end of the equivalent magnet will be turned to the north. If k is greater than k' as in diamagnetic bodies, the unmarked end of the equivalent magnet would be turned to the north.

III. *Magnetic field of variable Intensity.*

Now suppose the intensity in the undisturbed magnetic field to vary in magnitude and direction from one point to another, and that its components in x, y, z are represented by a, β, γ, then, if as a first approximation we regard the intensity within the sphere as sensibly equal to that at the centre, the change of potential outside the sphere arising from the presence of the sphere, disturbing the lines of force, will be the same as that due to three small magnets at the centre, with their axes parallel to x, y, and z, and their moments equal to

$$\frac{k-k'}{2k+k'}\,a^3a, \qquad \frac{k-k'}{2k+k'}\,a^3\beta, \qquad \frac{k-k'}{2k+k'}\,a^3\gamma.$$

The actual distribution of potential within and without the sphere may be conceived as the result of a distribution of imaginary magnetic matter on the surface of the sphere; but since the external effect of this superficial magnetism is exactly the same as that of the three small magnets at the centre, the mechanical effect of external attractions will be the same as if the three magnets really existed.

Now let three small magnets whose lengths are l_1, l_2, l_3, and strengths m_1, m_2, m_3, exist at the point x, y, z with their axes parallel to the axes of x, y, z; then resolving the forces on the three magnets in the direction of X, we have

$$-X = m_1 \left\{ \begin{array}{c} a+\dfrac{da}{dx}\dfrac{l_1}{2} \\[2mm] -a+\dfrac{da}{dx}\dfrac{l_1}{2} \end{array} \right\} + m_2 \left\{ \begin{array}{c} a+\dfrac{da}{dy}\dfrac{l_2}{2} \\[2mm] -a+\dfrac{da}{dy}\dfrac{l_2}{2} \end{array} \right\} + m_3 \left\{ \begin{array}{c} a+\dfrac{da}{dz}\dfrac{l_3}{2} \\[2mm] -a+\dfrac{da}{dz}\dfrac{l_2}{2} \end{array} \right\}$$

$$= m_1 l_1 \frac{da}{dx} + m_2 l_2 \frac{da}{dy} + m_3 l_3 \frac{da}{dz}.$$

Substituting the values of the moments of the imaginary magnets

$$-X = \frac{k-k'}{2k+k'}\, a^3 \left(a\, \frac{da}{dx} + \beta\, \frac{d\beta}{dx} + \gamma\, \frac{d\gamma}{dx} \right) = \frac{k-k'}{2k+k'}\, \frac{a^3}{2}\, \frac{d}{dx}\, (a^2 + \beta^2 + \gamma^2).$$

The force impelling the sphere in the direction of x is therefore dependent on the variation of the square of the intensity or $(a^2 + \beta^2 + \gamma^2)$, as we move along the direction of x, and the same is true for y and z, so that the law is, that the force acting on diamagnetic spheres is from places of greater to places of less intensity of magnetic force, and that in similar distributions of magnetic force it varies as the mass of the sphere and the square of the intensity.

It is easy by means of Laplace's Coefficients to extend the approximation to the value of the potential as far as we please, and to calculate the attraction. For instance, if a north or south magnetic pole whose strength is M, be placed at a distance b from a diamagnetic sphere, radius a, the repulsion will be

$$R = M^2\,(k-k')\, \frac{a^3}{b^5} \left(\frac{2\,.\,1}{2k+k'} + \frac{3\,.\,2}{3k+2k'}\, \frac{a^2}{b^2} + \frac{4\,.\,3}{4k+3k'}\, \frac{a^4}{b^4} + \&c. \right).$$

When $\frac{a}{b}$ is small, the first term gives a sufficient approximation. The repulsion is then as the square of the strength of the pole, and the mass of the sphere directly and the fifth power of the distance inversely, considering the pole as a point.

IV. *Two Spheres in uniform field.*

Let two spheres of radius a be connected together so that their centres are kept at a distance b, and let them be suspended in a uniform magnetic field, then, although each sphere by itself would have been in equilibrium at any part of the field, the disturbance of the field will produce forces tending to make the balls set in a particular direction.

Let the centre of one of the spheres be taken as origin, then the undisturbed potential is

$$p = Ir \cos \theta,$$

and the potential due to the sphere is

$$p' = I\, \frac{k-k'}{2k+k'}\, \frac{a^3}{r^2} \cos \theta.$$

The whole potential is therefore equal to

$$I\left(r + \frac{k-k'}{2k+k'}\frac{a^3}{r^2}\right)\cos\theta = p,$$

$$\frac{dp}{dr} = I\left(1 - 2\frac{k-k'}{2k+k'}\frac{a^3}{r^3}\right)\cos\theta,$$

$$\frac{1}{r}\frac{dp}{d\theta} = -I\left(1 + \frac{k-k'}{2k+k'}\frac{a^3}{r^3}\right)\sin\theta, \qquad \frac{dp}{d\phi} = 0,$$

$$\therefore \ i^2 = \overline{\frac{dp}{dr}}\bigg|^2 + \frac{1}{r^2}\overline{\frac{dp}{d\theta}}\bigg|^2 + \frac{1}{r^2\sin^2\theta}\overline{\frac{dp}{d\phi}}\bigg|^2$$

$$= I^2\left\{1 + \frac{k-k'}{2k+k'}\frac{a^3}{r^3}\left(1 - 3\cos^2\theta\right) + \overline{\frac{k-k'}{2k+k'}}\bigg|^2\frac{a^6}{r^6}\left(1 + 3\cos^2\theta\right)\right\}.$$

This is the value of the square of the intensity at any point. The moment of the couple tending to turn the combination of balls in the direction of the original force

$$L = \tfrac{1}{2}\frac{d}{d\theta}i^2\left(\frac{k-k'}{2k+k'}a^3\right) \text{ when } r = b,$$

$$L = \tfrac{3}{2}I^2\,\overline{\frac{k-k'}{2k+k'}}\bigg|^2\frac{a^6}{b^3}\left(1 - \frac{k-k'}{2k+k'}\frac{a^3}{b^3}\right)\sin 2\theta.$$

This expression, which must be positive, since b is greater than a, gives the moment of a force tending to turn the line joining the centres of the spheres towards the original lines of force.

Whether the spheres are magnetic or diamagnetic they tend to set in the *axial* direction, and that without distinction of north and south. If, however, one sphere be magnetic and the other diamagnetic, the line of centres will set equatoreally. The magnitude of the force depends on the square of $(k - k')$, and is therefore quite insensible except in iron[*].

V.   *Two Spheres between the poles of a Magnet.*

Let us next take the case of the same balls placed not in a uniform field but between a north and a south pole, $\pm M$, distant $2c$ from each other in the direction of x.

[*] See Prof. Thomson in *Phil. Mag.* March, 1851.

The expression for the potential, the middle of the line joining the poles being the origin, is

$$p = M \left(\frac{1}{\sqrt{c^2 + r^2 - 2cr \cos \theta}} - \frac{1}{\sqrt{c^2 + r^2 + 2cr \cos \theta}} \right).$$

From this we find as the value of I^2,

$$I^2 = \frac{4M^2}{c^4} \left(1 - 3\frac{r^2}{c^2} + 9\frac{r^2}{c^2} \cos^2 \theta \right);$$

$$\therefore I \frac{dI}{d\theta} = -18 \frac{M^2}{c^6} r^2 \sin 2\theta,$$

and the moment to turn a pair of spheres (radius a, distance $2b$) in the direction in which θ is increased is

$$-36 \frac{k - k'}{2k + k'} \frac{M^2 a^3 b^2}{c^6} \sin 2\theta.$$

This force, which tends to turn the line of centres equatoreally for diamagnetic and axially for magnetic spheres, varies directly as the square of the strength of the magnet, the cube of the radius of the spheres and the square of the distance of their centres, and inversely as the sixth power of the distance of the poles of the magnet, considered as points. As long as these poles are near each other this action of the poles will be much stronger than the mutual action of the spheres, so that as a general rule we may say that elongated bodies set axially or equatoreally between the poles of a magnet according as they are magnetic or diamagnetic. If, instead of being placed between two poles very near to each other, they had been placed in a uniform field such as that of terrestrial magnetism or that produced by a spherical electro-magnet (see Ex. VIII.), an elongated body would set axially whether magnetic or diamagnetic.

In all these cases the phenomena depend on $k - k'$, so that the sphere conducts itself magnetically or diamagnetically according as it is more or less magnetic, or less or more diamagnetic than the medium in which it is placed.

VI. *On the Magnetic Phenomena of a Sphere cut from a substance whose coefficient of resistance is different in different directions.*

Let the axes of magnetic resistance be parallel throughout the sphere, and let them be taken for the axes of x, y, z. Let k_1, k_2, k_3, be the coefficients of resistance in these three directions, and let k' be that of the external medium,

28

and a the radius of the sphere. Let I be the undisturbed magnetic intensity of the field into which the sphere is introduced, and let its direction-cosines be l, m, n.

Let us now take the case of a homogeneous sphere whose coefficient is k_1 placed in a uniform magnetic field whose intensity is lI in the direction of x. The resultant potential outside the sphere would be

$$p' = lI \left(1 + \frac{k_1 - k'}{2k_1 + k'} \frac{a^3}{r^3} \right) x,$$

and for internal points

$$p_1 = lI \frac{3k_1}{2k_1 + k'} x.$$

So that in the interior of the sphere the magnetization is entirely in the direction of x. It is therefore quite independent of the coefficients of resistance in the directions of x and y, which may be changed from k_1 into k_2 and k_3 without disturbing this distribution of magnetism. We may therefore treat the sphere as homogeneous for each of the three components of I, but we must use a different coefficient for each. We find for external points

$$p' = I \left\{ lx + my + nz + \left(\frac{k_1 - k'}{2k_1 + k'} lx + \frac{k_2 - k'}{2k_2 + k'} my + \frac{k_3 - k'}{2k_3 + k'} nz \right) \frac{a^3}{r^3} \right\},$$

and for internal points

$$p_1 = I \left(\frac{3k_1}{2k_1 + k'} lx + \frac{3k_2}{2k_2 + k'} my + \frac{3k_3}{2k_3 + k'} nz \right).$$

The external effect is the same as that which would have been produced if the small magnet whose moments are

$$\frac{k_1 - k'}{2k_1 + k'} lIa^3, \qquad \frac{k_2 - k'}{2k_2 + k'} mIa^3, \qquad \frac{k_3 - k'}{2k_3 + k'} nIa^3,$$

had been placed at the origin with their directions coinciding with the axes of x, y, z. The effect of the original force I in turning the sphere about the axis of x may be found by taking the moments of the components of that force on these equivalent magnets. The moment of the force in the direction of y acting on the third magnet is

$$\frac{k_3 - k'}{2k_3 + k'} mnI^2 a^3,$$

and that of the force in z on the second magnet is

$$-\frac{k_2 - k'}{2k_2 + k'} mnI^2 a^3.$$

The whole couple about the axis of x is therefore

$$\frac{3k'\,(k_3-k_2)}{(2k_3+k')\,(2k_2+k')}\,mnI^2a^3,$$

tending to turn the sphere round from the axis of y towards that of z. Suppose the sphere to be suspended so that the axis of x is vertical, and let I be horizontal, then if θ be the angle which the axis of y makes with the direction of I, $m=\cos\theta$, $n=-\sin\theta$, and the expression for the moment becomes

$$\tfrac{3}{2}\,\frac{k'\,(k_2-k_3)}{(2k_2+k')\,(2k_3+k')}\,I^2a^3\sin 2\theta,$$

tending to increase θ. The axis of least resistance therefore sets axially, but with either end indifferently towards the north.

Since in all bodies, except iron, the values of k are nearly the same as in a vacuum, the coefficient of this quantity can be but little altered by changing the value of k' to k, the value in space. The expression then becomes

$$\tfrac{1}{6}\,\frac{k_2-k_3}{k}\,I^2a^3\sin 2\theta,$$

independent of the external medium*.

VII. *Permanent magnetism in a spherical shell.*

The case of a homogeneous shell of a diamagnetic or paramagnetic substance presents no difficulty. The intensity within the shell is less than what it would have been if the shell were away, whether the substance of the shell be diamagnetic or paramagnetic. When the resistance of the shell is infinite, and when it vanishes, the intensity within the shell is zero.

In the case of no resistance the entire effect of the shell on any point, internal or external, may be represented by supposing a superficial stratum of

---

* Taking the more general case of magnetic induction referred to in Art. (28), we find, in the expression for the moment of the magnetic forces, a constant term depending on T, besides those terms which depend on sines and cosines of θ. The result is, that in every complete revolution in the negative direction round the axis of T, a certain positive amount of work is gained; but, since no inexhaustible source of work can exist in nature, we must admit that $T=0$ in all substances, with respect to magnetic induction. This argument does not hold in the case of electric conduction, or in the case of a body through which heat or electricity is passing, for such states are maintained by the continual expenditure of work. See Prof. Thomson, *Phil. Mag.* March, 1851, p. 186.

magnetic matter spread over the outer surface, the density being given by the equation

$$\rho = 3I \cos \theta.$$

Suppose the shell now to be converted into a permanent magnet, so that the distribution of imaginary magnetic matter is invariable, then the external potential due to the shell will be

$$p' = -I \frac{a^3}{r^2} \cos \theta,$$

and the internal potential $\qquad p_1 = -Ir \cos \theta.$

Now let us investigate the effect of filling up the shell with some substance of which the resistance is k, the resistance in the external medium being k'. The thickness of the magnetized shell may be neglected. Let the magnetic moment of the permanent magnetism be Ia^3, and that of the imaginary superficial distribution due to the medium $k = Aa^3$. Then the potentials are

external $p' = (I + A) \dfrac{a^3}{r^2} \cos \theta,$ $\qquad$ internal $p_1 = (I + A) r \cos \theta.$

The distribution of real magnetism is the same before and after the introduction of the medium k, so that

$$\frac{1}{k'} I + \frac{2}{k'} I = \frac{1}{k} (I + A) + \frac{2}{k'} (I + A),$$

$$\text{or } A = \frac{k - k'}{2k + k'} I.$$

The external effect of the magnetized shell is increased or diminished according as k is greater or less than k'. It is therefore increased by filling up the shell with diamagnetic matter, and diminished by filling it with paramagnetic matter, such as iron.

VIII. *Electro-magnetic spherical shell.*

Let us take as an example of the magnetic effects of electric currents an electro-magnet in the form of a thin spherical shell. Let its radius be a, and its thickness t, and let its external effect be that of a magnet whose moment is Ia^3. Both within and without the shell the magnetic effect may be represented by a potential, but within the substance of the shell, where there are electric currents, the magnetic effects cannot be represented by a potential. Let p', p_1 be the external and internal potentials,

$$p' = I \frac{a^3}{r^2} \cos \theta, \qquad p_1 = Ar \cos \theta,$$

and since there is no permanent magnetism, $\dfrac{dp'}{dr} = \dfrac{dp_1}{dr}$, when $r = a$,

$$A = -2I.$$

If we draw any closed curve cutting the shell at the equator, and at some other point for which θ is known, then the total magnetic intensity round this curve will be $3Ia \cos \theta$, and as this is a measure of the total electric current which flows through it, the quantity of the current at any point may be found by differentiation. The quantity which flows through the element $td\theta$ is $-3Ia \sin \theta d\theta$, so that the quantity of the current referred to unit of area of section is

$$-3I \frac{a}{t} \sin \theta.$$

If the shell be composed of a wire coiled round the sphere so that the number of coils to the inch varies as the sine of θ, then the external effect will be nearly the same as if the shell had been made of a uniform conducting substance, and the currents had been distributed according to the law we have just given.

If a wire conducting a current of strength I_2 be wound round a sphere of radius a so that the distance between successive coils measured along the axis of x is $\dfrac{2a}{n}$, then there will be n coils altogether, and the value of I_1 for the resulting electro-magnet will be

$$I_1 = \frac{n}{6a} I_2.$$

The potentials, external and internal, will be

$$p' = I_2 \frac{n}{6} \frac{a^2}{r^2} \cos \theta, \qquad p_1 = -2I_2 \frac{n}{6} \frac{r}{a} \cos \theta.$$

The interior of the shell is therefore a uniform magnetic field.

IX. *Effect of the core of the electro-magnet.*

Now let us suppose a sphere of diamagnetic or paramagnetic matter introduced into the electro-magnetic coil. The result may be obtained as in the last case, and the potentials become

$$p' = I_2 \frac{n}{6} \frac{3k'}{2k+k'} \frac{a^2}{r^2} \cos \theta, \qquad p_1 = -2 I_2 \frac{n}{6} \frac{3k}{2k+k'} \frac{r}{a} \cos \theta.$$

The external effect is greater or less than before, according as k' is greater or less than k, that is, according as the interior of the sphere is magnetic or diamagnetic with respect to the external medium, and the internal effect is altered in the opposite direction, being greatest for a diamagnetic medium.

This investigation explains the effect of introducing an iron core into an electro-magnet. If the value of k for the core were to vanish altogether, the effect of the electro-magnet would be three times that which it has without the core. As k has always a finite value, the effect of the core is less than this.

In the interior of the electro-magnet we have a uniform field of magnetic force, the intensity of which may be increased by surrounding the coil with a shell of iron. If $k' = 0$, and the shell infinitely thick, the effect on internal points would be tripled.

The effect of the core is greater in the case of a cylindric magnet, and greatest of all when the core is a ring of soft iron.

X. *Electro-tonic functions in spherical electro-magnet.*

Let us now find the electro-tonic functions due to this electro-magnet.

They will be of the form

$$\alpha_0 = 0, \qquad \beta_0 = \omega z, \qquad \gamma_0 = - \omega y,$$

where ω is some function of r. Where there are no electric currents, we must have a_2, b_2, c_2 each $= 0$, and this implies

$$\frac{d}{dr} \left(3\omega + r \frac{d\omega}{dr} \right) = 0,$$

the solution of which is

$$\omega = C_1 + \frac{C_2}{r^3}.$$

Within the shell ω cannot become infinite; therefore $\omega = C_1$ is the solution, and outside a must vanish at an infinite distance, so that

$$\omega = \frac{C_2}{r^3}$$

is the solution outside. The magnetic quantity within the shell is found by last article to be

$$-2I_2 \frac{n}{6a} \frac{3}{2k+k'} = a_1 = \frac{d\beta_0}{dz} - \frac{d\gamma_0}{dy} = 2C_1;$$

therefore within the sphere

$$\omega_0 = -\frac{I_2 n}{2a} \frac{1}{3k+k'}.$$

Outside the sphere we must determine ω so as to coincide at the surface with the internal value. The external value is therefore

$$\omega = -\frac{I_2 n}{2a} \frac{1}{3k+k'} \frac{a^3}{r^3},$$

where the shell containing the currents is made up of n coils of wire, conducting a current of total quantity I_2.

Let another wire be coiled round the shell according to the same law, and let the total number of coils be n'; then the total electro-tonic intensity EI_2 round the second coil is found by integrating

$$EI_2 = \int_0^{2\pi} \omega a \sin \theta ds,$$

along the whole length of the wire. The equation of the wire is

$$\cos \theta = \frac{\phi}{n'\pi},$$

where n' is a large number; and therefore

$$ds = a \sin \theta d\phi,$$

$$= -an'\pi \sin^2 \theta d\theta,$$

$$\therefore EI_2 = \frac{4\pi}{3} \omega a^2 n' = -\frac{2\pi}{3} ann'I \frac{1}{3k+k'}.$$

E may be called the electro-tonic coefficient for the particular wire.

XI. *Spherical electro-magnetic Coil-Machine.*

We have now obtained the electro-tonic function which defines the action of the one coil on the other. The action of each coil on itself is found by putting n^2 or n'^2 for nn'. Let the first coil be connected with an apparatus producing a variable electro-motive force F. Let us find the effects on both wires, supposing their total resistances to be R and R', and the quantity of the currents I and I'.

Let N stand for $\dfrac{2\pi}{3}\dfrac{a}{(3k+k')}$, then the electro-motive force of the first wire on the second is

$$-Nnn'\frac{dI}{dt}.$$

That of the second on itself is

$$-Nn'^2\frac{dI'}{dt}.$$

The equation of the current in the second wire is therefore

$$-Nnn'\frac{dI}{dt}-Nn'^2\frac{dI'}{dt}=R'I' \quad\dots\dots\dots\dots\dots\dots\dots (1).$$

The equation of the current in the first wire is

$$-Nn^2\frac{dI}{dt}-Nnn'\frac{dI'}{dt}+F=RI\dots\dots\dots\dots\dots\dots\dots(2).$$

Eliminating the differential coefficients, we get

$$\frac{R}{n}I-\frac{R'}{n'}I'=\frac{F}{n},$$

$$\text{and} \quad N\left(\frac{n^2}{R}+\frac{n'^2}{R'}\right)\frac{dI}{dt}+I=\frac{F}{R}+N\frac{n'^2}{R'}\frac{dF}{dt}\dots\dots\dots\dots\dots\dots (3),$$

from which to find I and I'. For this purpose we require to know the value of F in terms of t.

Let us first take the case in which F is constant and I and I' initially $=0$. This is the case of an electro-magnetic coil-machine at the moment when the connexion is made with the galvanic trough.

Putting $\frac{1}{2}\tau$ for $N\left(\dfrac{n^2}{R}+\dfrac{n'^2}{R'}\right)$ we find

$$I = \frac{F}{R}\left(1-\epsilon^{-\frac{2t}{\tau}}\right),$$

$$I' = -F\,\frac{n'}{R'n}\,\epsilon^{-\frac{2t}{\tau}}.$$

The primary current increases very rapidly from 0 to $\dfrac{F}{R}$, and the secondary commences at $-\dfrac{F}{R'}\dfrac{n'}{n}$ and speedily vanishes, owing to the value of τ being generally very small.

The whole work done by either current in heating the wire or in any other kind of action is found from the expression

$$\int_0^\infty I^2 R\,dt.$$

The total quantity of current is

$$\int_0^\infty I\,dt.$$

For the secondary current we find

$$\int_0^\infty I'^2 R'\,dt = \frac{F^2 n'^2}{R'n^2}\frac{\tau}{4}, \qquad \int_0^\infty I'\,dt = \frac{Fn'}{R'n}\frac{\tau}{2}.$$

The work done and the quantity of the current are therefore the same as if a current of quantity $I' = \dfrac{Fn'}{2R'n}$ had passed through the wire for a time τ, where

$$\tau = 2N\left(\frac{n^2}{R}+\frac{n'^2}{R'}\right).$$

This method of considering a variable current of short duration is due to Weber, whose experimental methods render the determination of the equivalent current a matter of great precision.

Now let the electro-motive force F suddenly cease while the current in the primary wire is I_0 and in the secondary $= 0$. Then we shall have for the subsequent time

$$I = I_0\,\epsilon^{-\frac{2t}{\tau}}, \qquad I' = \frac{I_0}{R'}\,\frac{Rn'}{n}\,\epsilon^{-\frac{2t}{\tau}}.$$

The equivalent currents are $\frac{1}{2}I_0$ and $\frac{1}{2}I_0 \dfrac{R}{R'} \dfrac{n'}{n}$, and their duration is τ.

When the communication with the source of the current is cut off, there will be a change of R. This will produce a change in the value of τ, so that if R be suddenly increased, the strength of the secondary current will be increased, and its duration diminished. This is the case in the ordinary coil-machines. The quantity N depends on the form of the machine, and may be determined by experiment for a machine of any shape.

XII. *Spherical shell revolving in magnetic field.*

Let us next take the case of a revolving shell of conducting matter under the influence of a uniform field of magnetic force. The phenomena are explained by Faraday in his *Experimental Researches*, Series II., and references are there given to previous experiments.

Let the axis of z be the axis of revolution, and let the angular velocity be ω. Let the magnetism of the field be represented in quantity by I, inclined at an angle θ to the direction of z, in the plane of zx.

Let R be the radius of the spherical shell, and T the thickness. Let the quantities a_0, β_0, γ_0, be the electro-tonic functions at any point of space; a_1, b_1, c_1, a_1, β_1, γ_1 symbols of magnetic quantity and intensity; a_2, b_2, c_2, a_2, β_2, γ_2 of electric quantity and intensity. Let p_2 be the electric tension at any point,

$$
\left.
\begin{aligned}
a_2 &= \frac{dp_2}{dx} + k a_2 \\[4pt]
\beta_2 &= \frac{dp_2}{dy} + k b_2 \\[4pt]
\gamma_2 &= \frac{dp_2}{dz} + k c_2
\end{aligned}
\right\} \dots\dots\dots\dots\dots\dots\dots (1),
$$

$$
\frac{da_2}{dx} + \frac{db_2}{dy} + \frac{dc_2}{dz} = 0 \dots\dots\dots\dots\dots\dots\dots (2);
$$

$$
\therefore \frac{da_2}{dx} + \frac{d\beta_2}{dy} + \frac{d\gamma_2}{dz} = \nabla^2 p.
$$

The expressions for a_0, β_0, γ_0 due to the magnetism of the field are

$$a_0 = A_0 + \frac{I}{2} \, y \cos \theta,$$

$$\beta_0 = B_0 + \frac{I}{2} \, (z \sin \theta - x \cos \theta),$$

$$\gamma_0 = C_0 - \frac{I}{2} \, y \sin \theta,$$

A_0, B_0, C_0 being constants; and the velocities of the particles of the revolving sphere are

$$\frac{dx}{dt} = -\omega y, \qquad \frac{dy}{dt} = \omega x, \qquad \frac{dz}{dt} = 0.$$

We have therefore for the electro-motive forces

$$a_2 = -\frac{1}{4\pi} \frac{da_0}{dt} = -\frac{1}{4\pi} \frac{I}{2} \cos \theta \omega x,$$

$$\beta_2 = -\frac{1}{4\pi} \frac{d\beta_0}{dt} = -\frac{1}{4\pi} \frac{I}{2} \cos \theta \omega y,$$

$$\gamma_2 = -\frac{1}{4\pi} \frac{d\gamma_0}{dt} = \frac{1}{4\pi} \frac{I}{2} \sin \theta \omega x.$$

Returning to equations (1), we get

$$k\left(\frac{db_2}{dz} - \frac{dc_2}{dy}\right) = \frac{d\beta_2}{dz} - \frac{d\gamma_2}{dy} = 0,$$

$$k\left(\frac{dc_2}{dx} - \frac{da_2}{dz}\right) = \frac{d\gamma_2}{dx} - \frac{da_2}{dz} = \frac{1}{4\pi} \frac{I}{2} \sin \theta \omega,$$

$$k\left(\frac{da_2}{dy} - \frac{db_2}{dx}\right) = \frac{da_2}{dy} - \frac{d\beta_2}{dx} = 0.$$

From which with equation (2) we find

$$a_2 = -\frac{1}{k} \frac{1}{4\pi} \frac{I}{4} \sin \theta \omega z,$$

$$b_2 = 0,$$

$$c_2 = \frac{1}{k} \frac{1}{4\pi} \frac{I}{4} \sin \theta \omega x,$$

$$p_2 = -\frac{1}{16\pi} \, I\omega \, \{(x^2 + y^2) \cos \theta - xz \sin \theta\}.$$

These expressions would determine completely the motion of electricity in a revolving sphere if we neglect the action of these currents on themselves. They express a system of circular currents about the axis of y, the quantity of current at any point being proportional to the distance from that axis. The external magnetic effect will be that of a small magnet whose moment is $\dfrac{TR^3}{48\pi k}\ \omega I \sin\theta$, with its direction along the axis of y, so that the magnetism of the field would tend to turn it back to the axis of x *.

The existence of these currents will of course alter the distribution of the electro-tonic functions, and so they will react on themselves. Let the final result of this action be a system of currents about an axis in the plane of xy inclined to the axis of x at an angle ϕ and producing an external effect equal to that of a magnet whose moment is $I'R^3$.

The magnetic inductive components within the shell are

$$I_1 \sin\theta - 2I' \cos\phi \quad \text{in } x,$$
$$- 2I' \sin\phi \quad \text{in } y,$$
$$I_1 \cos\theta \qquad\qquad \text{in } z.$$

Each of these would produce its own system of currents when the sphere is in motion, and these would give rise to new distributions of magnetism, which, when the velocity is uniform, must be the same as the original distribution,

$$(I_1 \sin\theta - 2I' \cos\phi) \text{ in } x \text{ produces } 2\,\frac{T}{48\pi k}\,\omega\,(I_1 \sin\theta - 2I' \cos\phi) \text{ in } y,$$

$$(- 2I' \sin\phi) \text{ in } y \text{ produces } 2\,\frac{T}{48\pi k}\,\omega\,(2I' \sin\phi) \text{ in } x;$$

$I_1 \cos\theta$ in z produces no currents.

We must therefore have the following equations, since the state of the shell is the same at every instant,

$$I_1 \sin\theta - 2I' \cos\phi = I_1 \sin\theta + \frac{T}{24\pi k}\,\omega 2I' \sin\phi$$

$$- 2I' \sin\phi = \frac{T}{24\pi k}\,\omega\,(I_1 \sin\theta - 2I' \cos\phi),$$

---

* The expression for p_z indicates a variable electric tension in the shell, so that currents might be collected by wires touching it at the equator and poles.

whence
$$\cot \phi = -\frac{TR^3}{24\pi k}\,\omega, \quad I' = \tfrac{1}{2}\,\frac{\dfrac{T}{4\pi k}}{\sqrt{1 + \left(\dfrac{T}{4\pi k}\,\omega\right)^2}}\,I_1 \sin\theta.$$

To understand the meaning of these expressions let us take a particular case.

Let the axis of the revolving shell be vertical, and let the revolution be from north to west. Let I be the total intensity of the terrestrial magnetism, and let the dip be θ, then $I\cos\theta$ is the horizontal component in the direction of magnetic north.

The result of the rotation is to produce currents in the shell about an axis inclined at a small angle $= \tan^{-1}\dfrac{T}{24\pi k}\,\omega$ to the south of magnetic west, and the external effect of these currents is the same as that of a magnet whose moment is

$$\tfrac{1}{2}\,\frac{T\omega}{\sqrt{\overline{24\pi k}\,|^2 + T^2\omega^2}}\,R^3 I \cos\theta.$$

The moment of the couple due to terrestrial magnetism tending to stop the rotation is

$$\frac{24\pi k}{2}\,\frac{T\omega}{\overline{24\pi k}\,|^2 + T^2\omega^2}\,R^3 I^2 \cos^2\theta,$$

and the loss of work due to this in unit of time is

$$\frac{24\pi k}{2}\,\frac{T\omega^2}{\overline{24\pi k}\,|^2 + T^2\omega^2}\,R^3 I^2 \cos^2\theta.$$

This loss of work is made up by an evolution of heat in the substance of the shell, as is proved by a recent experiment of M. Foucault (see *Comptes Rendus*, XLI. p. 450).

[From the *Transactions of the Royal Scottish Society of Arts*, Vol. IV. Part IV.]

IX. *Description of a New Form of the Platometer, an Instrument for measuring the Areas of Plane Figures drawn on Paper*.*

1. THE measurement of the area of a plane figure on a map or plan is an operation so frequently occurring in practice, that any method by which it may be easily and quickly performed is deserving of attention. A very able exposition of the principle of such instruments will be found in the article on Planimeters in the Reports of the Juries of the Great Exhibition, 1851.

2. In considering the principle of instruments of this kind, it will be most convenient to suppose the area of the figure measured by an imaginary straight line, which, by moving parallel to itself, and at the same time altering in length to suit the form of the area, accurately sweeps it out.

Let AZ be a fixed vertical line, $APQZ$ the boundary of the area, and let a variable horizontal line move parallel to itself from A to Z, so as to have its extremities, P, M, in the curve and in the fixed straight line. Now, suppose the horizontal line (which we shall call the generating line) to move from the position PM to QN, MN being some small quantity, say one inch for distinctness. During this movement, the generating line will have swept out the narrow strip of the surface, $PMNQ$, which exceeds the portion $PMNp$ by the small triangle PQp.

But since MN, the breadth of the strip, is one inch, the strip will contain as many square inches as PM is inches long; so that, when the generating line descends one inch, it sweeps out a number of square inches equal to the number of linear inches in its length.

Therefore, if we have a machine with an index of any kind, which, while the generating line moves one inch downwards, moves forward as many degrees as the generating line is inches long, and if the generating line be alternately moved an inch and altered in length, the index will mark the number of square inches swept over during the whole operation. By the ordinary method of limits, it may be shown that, if these changes be made continuous instead of sudden, the index will still measure the area of the curve traced by the extremity of the generating line.

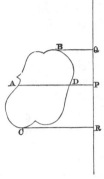

3. When the area is bounded by a closed curve, as $ABDC$, then to determine the area we must carry the tracing point from some point A of the curve, completely round the circumference to A again. Then, while the tracing point moves from A to C, the index will go forward and measure the number of square inches in $ACRP$, and, while it moves from C to D, the index will measure backwards the square inches in $CRPD$, so that it will now indicate the square inches in ACD. Similarly, during the other part of the motion from D to B, and from B to D, the part DBA will be measured; so that when the tracing point returns to D, the instrument will have measured the area $ACDB$. It is evident that the whole area will appear positive or negative according as the tracing point is carried round in the direction $ACDB$ or $ABDC$.

4. We have next to consider the various methods of communicating the required motion to the index. The first is by means of two discs, the first having a flat horizontal rough surface, turning on a vertical axis, OQ, and the second vertical, with its circumference resting on the flat surface of the first at P, so as to be driven round by the motion of the first disc. The velocity of the second disc will depend on OP, the distance of the point of contact from the centre of the first disc; so that if OP be

made always equal to the generating line, the conditions of the instrument will be fulfilled.

This is accomplished by causing the index-disc to slip along the radius of the horizontal disc; so that in working the instrument, the motion of the index-disc is compounded of a rolling motion due to the rotation of the first disc, and a slipping motion due to the variation of the generating line.

5. In the instrument presented by Mr Sang to the Society, the first disc is replaced by a cone, and the action of the instrument corresponds to a mathematical valuation of the area by the use of oblique co-ordinates. As he has himself explained it very completely, it will be enough here to say, that the index-wheel has still a motion of slipping as well as of rolling.

6. Now, suppose a wheel rolling on a surface, and pressing on it with a weight of a pound; then suppose the coefficient of friction to be $\frac{1}{8}$, it will require a force of 2 oz. at least to produce slipping at all, so that even if the resistance of the axis, &c., amounted to 1 oz., the rolling would be perfect. But if the wheel were forcibly pulled sideways, so as to slide along in the direction of the axis, then, if the friction of the axis, &c., opposed no resistance to the turning of the wheel, the rotation would still be that due to the forward motion; but if there were any resistance, however small, it would produce its effect in diminishing the amount of rotation.

The case is that of a mass resting on a rough surface, which requires a great force to produce the slightest motion; but when some other force acts on it and keeps it in motion, the very smallest force is sufficient to alter that motion in direction.

7. This effect of the combination of slipping and rolling has not escaped the observation of Mr Sang, who has both measured its amount, and shown how to eliminate its effect. In the improved instrument as constructed by him, I believe that the greatest error introduced in this way does not equal the ordinary errors of measurement by the old process of triangulation. This accuracy, however, is a proof of the excellence of the workmanship, and the smoothness of the action of the instrument; for if any considerable resistance had to be overcome, it would display itself in the results.

8. Having seen and admired these instruments at the Great Exhibition in 1851, and being convinced that the combination of slipping and rolling was a drawback on the perfection of the instrument, I began to search for some arrangement by which the motion should be that of perfect rolling in every

motion of which the instrument is capable. The forms of the rolling parts which I considered were—

1. Two equal spheres.
2. Two spheres, the diameters being as 1 to 2.
3. A cone and cylinder, axes at right angles.

Of these, the first combination only suited my purpose. I devised several modes of mounting the spheres so as to make the principle available. That which I adopted is borrowed, as to many details, from the instruments already constructed, so that the originality of the device may be reduced to this principle—The abolition of slipping by the use of two equal spheres.

9. The instrument (Fig. 1) is mounted on a frame, which rolls on the two connected wheels, *MM*, and is thus constrained to travel up and down the paper, moving parallel to itself.

CH is a horizontal axis, passing through two supports attached to the frame, and carrying the wheel *K* and the hemisphere *LAP*. The wheel *K* rolls on the plane on which the instrument travels, and communicates its motion to the hemisphere, which therefore revolves about the axis *AH* with a velocity proportional to that with which the instrument moves backwards or forwards.

FCO is a framework (better seen in the other figures) capable of revolving about a vertical axis, *Cc*, being joined at *C* and *c* to the frame of the instrument. The parts *CF* and *CO* are at right angles to each other and horizontal. The part *CO* carries with it a ring, *SOS*, which turns about a vertical axis *Oo*. This ring supports the index-sphere *Bb* by the extremities of its axis *Ss*, just as the meridian circle carries a terrestrial globe. By this arrangement, it will be seen that the axis of the sphere is kept always horizontal, while its centre moves so as to be always at a constant distance from that of the hemisphere. This distance must be adjusted so that the spheres may always remain in contact, and the pressure at the point of contact may be regulated by means of springs or compresses at *O* and *o* acting in the direction *OC*, *oc*. In this way the rotation of the hemisphere is made to drive the index-sphere.

10. Now, let us consider the working of the instrument. Suppose the arm *CE* placed so as to coincide with *CD*, then *O*, the centre of the index-sphere will be in the prolongation of the axis *HA*. Suppose also that, when in this position, the equator *bB* of the index-sphere is in contact with the pole *A* of the hemisphere. Now, let the arch be turned into the position *CE* as in the

figure, then the rest of the framework will be turned through an equal angle, and the index-sphere will roll on the hemisphere till it come into the position represented in the figure. Then, if there be no slipping, the arc $AP = BP$, and the angle $ACP = BOP$.

Next, let the instrument be moved backwards or forwards, so as to turn the wheel Kk and the hemisphere Ll, then the index-sphere will be turned about its axis Ss by the action of the hemisphere, but the ratio of their velocities will depend on their relative positions. If we draw PQ, PR, perpendiculars from the point of contact on the two axes, then the angular motion of the index-sphere will be to that of the hemisphere, as PQ is to PR; that is, as PQ is to QC, by the equal triangles POQ, PQC; that is, as ED is to DC, by the similar triangles CQP, CDE.

Therefore the ratio of the angular velocities is as ED to DC, but since DC is constant, this ratio varies as ED. We have now only to contrive some way of making ED act as the generating line, and the machine is complete (see art. 2).

11. The arm CF is moved in the following manner :—Tt is a rectangular metal beam, fixed to the frame of the instrument, and parallel to the axis AH. eEe is a little carriage which rolls along it, having two rollers on one side and one on the other, which is pressed against the beam by a spring. This carriage carries a vertical pin, E, turning in its socket, and having a collar above, through which the arm CF works smoothly. The tracing point G is attached to the carriage by a jointed frame eGe, which is so arranged that the point may not bear too heavily on the paper.

12. When the machine is in action, the tracing point is placed on a point in the boundary of the figure, and made to move round it always in one direction till it arrives at the same point again. The up-and-down motion of the tracing point moves the whole instrument over the paper, turns the wheel K, the hemisphere Ll, and the index-sphere Bb; while the lateral motion of the tracing point moves the carriage E on the beam Tt, and so works the arm CF and the framework CO; and so changes the relative velocities of the two spheres, as has been explained.

13. In this way the instrument works by a perfect rolling motion, in whatever direction the tracing point is moved; but since the accuracy of the result depends on the equality of the arcs AP and BP, and since the smallest error

of adjustment would, in the course of time, produce a considerable deviation from this equality, some contrivance is necessary to secure it. For this purpose a wheel is fixed on the same axis with the ring SOs, and another of the same size is fixed to the frame of the instrument, with its centre coinciding with the vertical axis through C. These wheels are connected by two pieces of watch-spring, which are arranged so as to apply closely to the edges of the wheels. The first is firmly attached to the nearer side of the fixed wheel, and to the farther side of the moveable wheel, and the second to the farther side of the fixed wheel, and the nearer side of the moveable wheel, crossing beneath the first steel band. In this way the spheres are maintained in their proper relative position; but since no instrument can be perfect, the wheels, by preventing derangement, must cause some slight slipping, depending on the errors of workmanship. This, however, does not ruin the pretensions of the instrument, for it may be shown that the error introduced by slipping depends on the distance through which the lateral slipping takes place; and since in this case it must be very small compared with its necessarily large amount in the other instruments, the error introduced by it must be diminished in the same proportion.

14. I have shewn how the rotation of the index-sphere is proportional to the area of the figure traced by the tracing point. This rotation must be measured by means of a graduated circle attached to the sphere, and read off by means of a vernier. The result, as measured in degrees, may be interpreted in the following manner:—

Suppose the instrument to be placed with the arm CF coinciding with CD, the equator Bb of the index-sphere touching the pole A of the hemisphere, and the index of the vernier at zero: then let these four operations be performed:—

(1) Let the tracing point be moved to the right till $DE = DC$, and therefore DCE, ACP, and $POB = 45°$.

(2) Let the instrument be rolled upwards till the wheel K has made a complete revolution, carrying the hemisphere with it; then, on account of the equality of the angles SOP, PCA, the index-sphere will also make a complete revolution.

(3) Let the arm CF be brought back again till F coincides with D.

(4) Let the instrument be rolled back again through a complete revolution of the wheel K. The index-sphere will not rotate, because the point of contact is at the pole of the hemisphere.

The tracing point has now traversed the boundary of a rectangle, whose length is the circumference of the wheel K, and its breadth is equal to CD; and during this operation, the index-sphere has made a complete revolution. $360°$ on the sphere, therefore, correspond to an area equal to the rectangle contained by the circumference of the wheel and the distance CD. The size of the wheel K being known, different values may be given to CD, so as to make the instrument measure according to any required scale. This may be done, either by shifting the position of the beam Tt, or by having several sockets in the carriage E for the pin which directs the arm to work in.

15. If I have been too prolix in describing the action of an instrument which has never been constructed, it is because I have myself derived great satisfaction from following out the mechanical consequences of the mathematical theorem on which the truth of this method depends. Among the other forms of apparatus by which the action of the two spheres may be rendered available, is one which might be found practicable in cases to which that here given would not apply. In this instrument (Fig. 4) the areas are swept out by a radius-vector of variable length, turning round a fixed point in the plane. The area is thus swept out with a velocity varying as the angular velocity of the radius-vector and the square of its length conjointly, and the construction of the machine is adapted to the case as follows:—

The hemisphere is *fixed* on the top of a vertical pillar, about which the rest of the instrument turns. The index-sphere is supported as before by a ring and framework. This framework turns about the vertical pillar along with the tracing point, but has also a motion in a vertical plane, which is communicated to it by a curved slide connected with the tracing point, and which, by means of a prolonged arm, moves the framework as the tracing point is moved to and from the pillar.

The form of the curved slide is such, that the tangent of the angle of inclination of the line joining the centres of the spheres with the vertical is proportional to the square of the distance of the tracing point from the vertical axis of the instrument. The curve which fulfils this condition is an hyperbola, one of whose asymptotes is vertical, and passes through the tracing point, and the other horizontal through the centre of the hemisphere.

The other parts of this instrument are identical with those belonging to that already described.

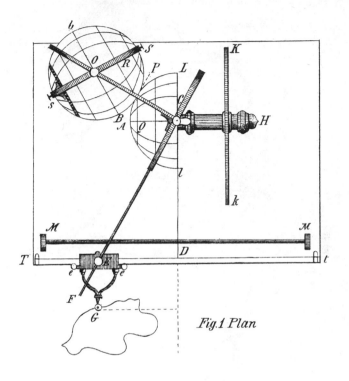

Fig.1 Plan

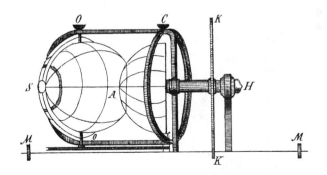

Fig 2 Front Elevation

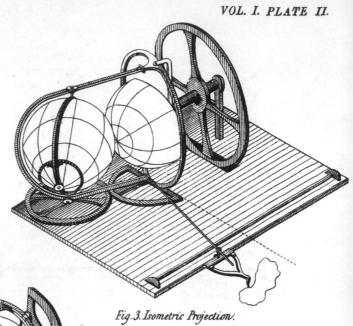

Fig. 3. *Isometric Projection.*

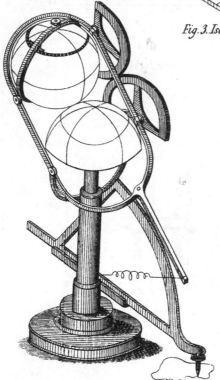

Fig. 4.

When the tracing point is made to traverse the boundary of a plane figure, there is a continued rotation of the radius-vector combined with a change of length. The rotation causes the index-sphere to roll on the fixed hemisphere, while the length of the radius-vector determines the *rate* of its motion about its axis, so that its whole motion measures the area swept out by the radius-vector during the motion of the tracing point.

The areas measured by this instrument may either lie on one side of the pillar, or they may extend all round it. In either case the action of the instrument is the same as in the ordinary case. In this form of the instrument we have the advantages of a fixed stand, and a simple motion of the tracing point; but there seem to be difficulties in the way of supporting the spheres and arranging the slide; and even then the instrument would require a tall pillar, in order to take in a large area.

16. It will be observed that I have said little or nothing about the practical details of these instruments. Many useful hints will be found in the large work on Platometers, by Professor T. Gonnellu, who has given us an account of the difficulties, as well as the results, of the construction of his most elaborate instrument. He has also given some very interesting investigations into the errors produced by various irregularities of construction, although, as far as I am aware, he has not even suspected the error which the sliding of the index-wheel over the disc must necessarily introduce. With respect to this, and other points relating to the working of the instrument, the memoir of Mr Sang, in the *Transactions* of this Society, is the most complete that I have met with. It may, however, be as well to state, that at the time when I devised the improvements here suggested, I had not seen that paper, though I had seen the instrument standing at rest in the Crystal Palace.

EDINBURGH, 30th *January*, 1855.

NOTE.—Since the design of the above instrument was submitted to the Society of Arts, I have met with a description of an instrument combining simplicity of construction with the power of adaptation to designs of any size, and at the same time more portable than any other instrument of the kind. Although it does not act by perfect rolling, and therefore belongs to a different class of instruments from that described in this paper, I think that its simplicity, and the beauty of the principle on which it acts, render it worth the attention of engineers and mechanists, whether practical or theoretical. A full account of this instrument is to be found in Moigno's " Cosmos," 5th year, Vol. VIII., Part VIII., p. 213, published 20th February 1856. *Description et Théorie du planimètre polaire, inventé par J. Amsler, de Schaffouse en Suisse.*

CAMBRIDGE, 30th *April*, 1856.

[From the *Cambridge Philosophical Society Proceedings*, Vol. I. pp. 173—175.]

X.   *On the Elementary Theory of Optical Instruments.*

THE object of this communication was to shew how the magnitude and position of the image of any object seen through an optical instrument could be ascertained without knowing the construction of the instrument, by means of data derived from two experiments on the instrument. Optical questions are generally treated of with respect to the pencils of rays which pass through the instrument. A pencil is a collection of rays which have passed through one point, and may again do so, by some optical contrivance. Now if we suppose all the points of a plane luminous, each will give out a pencil of rays, and that collection of pencils which passes through the instrument may be treated as a *beam* of light. In a pencil only one ray passes through any point of space, unless that point be the focus. In a beam an infinite number of rays, corresponding each to some point in the luminous plane, passes through any point; and we may, if we choose, treat this collection of rays as a pencil proceeding from that point. Hence the same beam of light may be decomposed into pencils in an infinite variety of ways; and yet, since we regard it as the same collection of rays, we may study its properties as a beam independently of the particular way in which we conceive it analysed into pencils.

Now in any instrument the incident and emergent beams are composed of the same light, and therefore every ray in the incident beam has a corresponding ray in the emergent beam. We do not know their path within the instrument, but before incidence and after emergence they are straight lines, and therefore any two points serve to determine the direction of each.

Let us suppose the instrument such that it forms an accurate image of a plane object in a given position. Then every ray which passes through a given point of the object before incidence passes through the corresponding point of the image after emergence, and this determines one point of the emergent ray. If at any other distance from the instrument a plane object has an accurate image, then there will be two other corresponding points given in the incident and emergent rays. Hence if we know the points in which an incident ray meets the planes of the two objects, we may find the incident ray by joining the points of the two images corresponding to them.

It was then shewn, that if the image of a plane object be distinct, flat, and similar to the object for two different distances of the object, the image of any other plane object perpendicular to the axis will be distinct, flat and similar to the object.

When the object is at an infinite distance, the plane of its image is the *principal focal plane*, and the point where it cuts the axis is the *principal focus*. The line joining any point in the object to the corresponding point of the image cuts the axis at a fixed point called the *focal centre*. The distance of the principal focus from the focal centre is called the *principal focal length*, or simply the *focal length*.

There are two principal foci, etc., formed by incident parallel rays passing in opposite directions through the instrument. If we suppose light always to pass in the same direction through the instrument, then the focus of incident rays when the emergent rays are parallel is the *first* principal focus, and the focus of emergent rays when the incident rays are parallel is the *second* principal focus.

Corresponding to these we have first and second focal centres and focal lengths.

Now let Q_1 be the focus of incident rays, P_1 the foot of the perpendicular from Q_1 on the axis, Q_2 the focus of emergent rays, P_2 the foot of the corresponding perpendicular, $F_1 F_2$ the first and second principal foci, $A_1 A_2$ the first and second focal centres, then

$$\frac{P_1 F_1}{A_1 F_1} = \frac{P_1 Q_1}{P_2 Q_2} = \frac{F_2 P_2}{F_2 A_2},$$

lines being positive when measured in the direction of the light. Therefore the position and magnitude of the image of any object is found by a simple proportion.

In one important class of instruments there are no principal foci or focal centres. A telescope in which parallel rays emerge parallel is an instance. In such instruments, if m be the angular magnifying power, the linear dimensions of the image are $\dfrac{1}{m}$ of the object, and the distance of the image of the object from the image of the object-glass is $\dfrac{1}{m^2}$ of the distance of the object from the object-glass. Rules were then laid down for the composition of instruments, and suggestions for the adaptation of this method to second approximations, and the method itself was considered with reference to the labours of Cotes, Smith, Euler, Lagrange, and Gauss on the same subject.

[From the *Report of the British Association*, 1856.]

XI. *On a Method of Drawing the Theoretical Forms of Faraday's Lines of
Force without Calculation.*

THE method applies more particularly to those cases in which the lines
are entirely parallel to one plane, such as the lines of electric currents in a
thin plate, or those round a system of parallel electric currents. In such cases,
if we know the forms of the lines of force in any two cases, we may combine
them by simple addition of the functions on which the equations of the lines
depend. Thus the system of lines in a uniform magnetic field is a series of
parallel straight lines at equal intervals, and that for an infinite straight electric
current perpendicular to the paper is a series of concentric circles whose radii
are in geometric progression. Having drawn these two sets of lines on two
separate sheets of paper, and laid a third piece above, draw a third set of lines
through the intersections of the first and second sets. This will be the system
of lines in a uniform field disturbed by an electric current. The most interesting
cases are those of uniform fields disturbed by a small magnet. If we draw a
circle of any diameter with the magnet for centre, and join those points in which
the circle cuts the lines of force, the straight lines so drawn will be parallel and
equidistant; and it is easily shown that they represent the actual lines of
force in a paramagnetic, diamagnetic, or crystallized body, according to the
nature of the original lines, the size of the circle, &c. No one can study
Faraday's researches without wishing to see the forms of the lines of force.
This method, therefore, by which they may be easily drawn, is recommended
to the notice of electrical students.

[From the *Report of the British Association*, 1856.]

XII. *On the Unequal Sensibility of the Foramen Centrale to Light of different Colours.*

WHEN observing the spectrum formed by looking at a long vertical slit through a simple prism, I noticed an elongated dark spot running up and down in the blue, and following the motion of the eye as it moved *up and down* the spectrum, but refusing to pass out of the blue into the other colours. It was plain that the spot belonged both to the eye and to the blue part of the spectrum. The result to which I have come is, that the appearance is due to the yellow spot on the retina, commonly called the *Foramen Centrale* of Soemmering. The most convenient method of observing the spot is by presenting to the eye in not too rapid succession, blue and yellow glasses, or, still better, allowing blue and yellow papers to revolve slowly before the eye. In this way the spot is seen in the blue. It fades rapidly, but is renewed every time the yellow comes in to relieve the effect of the blue. By using a Nicol's prism along with this apparatus, the brushes of Haidinger are well seen in connexion with the spot, and the fact of the brushes being the spot analysed by polarized light becomes evident. If we look steadily at an object behind a series of bright bars which move in front of it, we shall see a curious bending of the bars as they come up to the place of the yellow spot. The part which comes over the spot seems to start in advance of the rest of the bar, and this would seem to indicate a greater rapidity of sensation at the yellow spot than in the surrounding retina. But I find the experiment difficult, and I hope for better results from more accurate observers.

[From the *Report of the British Association,* 1856.]

XIII. *On the Theory of Compound Colours with reference to Mixtures of Blue and Yellow Light.*

WHEN we mix together blue and yellow paint, we obtain green paint. This fact is well known to all who have handled colours; and it is universally admitted that blue and yellow make green. Red, yellow, and blue, being the primary colours among painters, green is regarded as a secondary colour, arising from the mixture of blue and yellow. Newton, however, found that the green of the spectrum was not the same thing as the mixture of two colours of the spectrum, for such a mixture could be separated by the prism, while the green of the spectrum resisted further decomposition. But still it was believed that yellow and blue would make a green, though not that of the spectrum. As far as I am aware, the first experiment on the subject is that of M. Plateau, who, before 1819, made a disc with alternate sectors of prussian blue and gamboge, and observed that, when spinning, the resultant tint was not green, but a neutral gray, inclining sometimes to yellow or blue, but never to green. Prof. J. D. Forbes of Edinburgh made similar experiments in 1849, with the same result. Prof. Helmholtz of Königsberg, to whom we owe the most complete investigation on visible colour, has given the true explanation of this phænomenon. The result of mixing two coloured powders is not by any means the same as mixing the beams of light which flow from each separately. In the latter case we receive all the light which comes either from the one powder or the other. In the former, much of the light coming from one powder falls on particles of the other, and we receive only that portion which has escaped absorption by one or other. Thus the light coming from a mixture of blue and yellow powder, consists partly of light coming directly from blue particles or yellow particles, and partly of light acted on by both blue and yellow particles. This latter light is green, since the blue stops the red, yellow, and orange, and the yellow stops the blue and violet. I have made experiments on the mixture of blue and yellow *light*—by rapid rotation, by combined reflexion and transmission, by viewing them out of focus, in stripes, at a great distance, by throwing the colours of the spectrum on a screen, and by receiving them into the eye directly ; and I have arranged a portable apparatus by which any one may see the result of this or any other mixture of the colours of the spectrum. In all these cases blue and yellow do *not* make green. I have also made experiments on the mixture of coloured powders. Those which I used principally were " mineral blue" (from copper) and "chrome-yellow." Other blue and yellow pigments gave curious results, but it was more difficult to make the mixtures, and the greens were less uniform in tint. The mixtures of these colours were made by weight, and were painted on discs of paper, which were afterwards treated in the manner described in my paper " On Colour as perceived by the Eye," in the *Transactions of the Royal Society of Edinburgh*, Vol. XXI. Part 2. The visible effect of the colour is estimated in terms of the standard-coloured papers :—vermilion (V), ultramarine (U), and emerald-green (E). The accuracy of the results, and their significance, can be best understood by referring to the paper before mentioned. I shall denote mineral blue by B, and chrome-yellow by Y ; and $B_3 Y_5$ means a mixture of three parts blue and five parts yellow.

Given Colour.		Standard Colours.			Coefficient
		V.	U.	E.	of brightness.
B_8	, 100 =	2	36	7	 45
$B_7 \, Y_1$, 100 =		1	18	17	 37
$B_6 \, Y_2$, 100 =		4	11	34	 49
$B_5 \, Y_3$, 100 =		9	5	40	 54
$B_4 \, Y_4$, 100 =		15	1	40	 56
$B_3 \, Y_5$, 100 =		22	− 2	44	 64
$B_2 \, Y_6$, 100 =		35	−10	51	 76
$B_1 \, Y_7$, 100 =		64	−19	64	 109
Y_8 , 100 =		180	−27	124	 277

The columns V, U, E give the proportions of the standard colours which are equivalent. to 100 of the given colour; and the sum of V, U, E gives a co-efficient, which gives a general idea of the brightness. It will be seen that the first admixture of yellow *diminishes* the brightness of the blue. The negative values of U indicate that a mixture of V, U, and E cannot be made equivalent to the given colour. The experiments from which these results were taken had the negative values transferred to the other side of the equation. They were all made by means of the colour-top, and were verified by repetition at different times. It may be necessary to remark, in conclusion, with reference to the mode of registering visible colours in terms of three arbitrary standard colours, that it proceeds upon that theory of three primary elements in the sensation of colour, which treats the investigation of the laws of visible colour as a branch of human physiology, incapable of being deduced from the laws of light itself, as set forth in physical optics. It takes advantage of the methods of optics to study vision itself; and its appeal is not to physical principles, but to our consciousness of our own sensations.

[From the *Report of the British Association*, 1856.]

XIV. *On an Instrument to illustrate Poinsôt's Theory of Rotation.*

In studying the rotation of a solid body according to Poinsôt's method, we have to consider the successive positions of the instantaneous axis of rotation with reference both to directions fixed in space and axes assumed in the moving body. The paths traced out by the pole of this axis on the *invariable plane* and on the *central ellipsoid* form interesting subjects of mathematical investigation. But when we attempt to follow with our eye the motion of a rotating body, we find it difficult to determine through what point of the *body* the instantaneous axis passes at any time,—and to determine its path must be still more difficult. I have endeavoured to render visible the path of the instantaneous axis, and to vary the circumstances of motion, by means of a top of the same kind as that used by Mr Elliot, to illustrate precession*. The body of the instrument is a hollow cone of wood, rising from a ring, 7 inches in diameter and 1 inch thick. An iron axis, 8 inches long, screws into the vertex of the cone. The lower extremity has a point of hard steel, which rests in an agate cup, and forms the support of the instrument. An iron nut, three ounces in weight, is made to screw on the axis, and to be fixed at any point; and in the wooden ring are screwed four bolts, of three ounces, working horizontally, and four bolts, of one ounce, working vertically. On the upper part of the axis is placed a disc of card, on which are drawn four concentric rings. Each ring is divided into four quadrants, which are coloured red, yellow, green, and blue. The spaces between the rings are white. When the top is in motion, it is easy to see in which quadrant the instantaneous axis is at any moment and the distance between it and the axis of the instrument; and we observe,—1st. That the instantaneous axis travels in a closed curve, and returns to its original position in the body. 2ndly.

* *Transactions of the Royal Scottish Society of Arts*, 1855.

That by working the vertical bolts, we can make the axis of the instrument the centre of this closed curve. It will then be one of the principal axes of inertia.   3rdly. That, by working the nut on the axis, we can make the order of colours either red, yellow, green, blue, or the reverse. When the order of colours is in the *same* direction as the rotation, it indicates that the axis of the instrument is that of *greatest* moment of inertia.   4thly. That if we screw the two pairs of opposite horizontal bolts to different distances from the axis, the path of the instantaneous pole will no longer be equidistant from the axis, but will describe an ellipse, whose longer axis is in the direction of the *mean axis* of the instrument.   5thly. That if we now make one of the two horizontal axes less and the other greater than the vertical axis, the instantaneous pole will separate from the axis of the instrument, and the axis will incline more and more till the spinning can no longer go on, on account of the obliquity.   It is easy to see that, by attending to the laws of motion, we may produce any of the above effects at pleasure, and illustrate many different propositions by means of the same instrument.

[From the *Transactions of the Royal Society of Edinburgh*, Vol. XXI. Part IV.]

XV. *On a Dynamical Top, for exhibiting the phenomena of the motion of a system of invariable form about a fixed point, with some suggestions as to the Earth's motion.*

(Read 20th April, 1857.)

To those who study the progress of exact science, the common spinning-top is a symbol of the labours and the perplexities of men who had successfully threaded the mazes of the planetary motions. The mathematicians of the last age, searching through nature for problems worthy of their analysis, found in this toy of their youth, ample occupation for their highest mathematical powers.

No illustration of astronomical precession can be devised more perfect than that presented by a properly balanced top, but yet the motion of rotation has intricacies far exceeding those of the theory of precession.

Accordingly, we find Euler and D'Alembert devoting their talent and their patience to the establishment of the laws of the rotation of solid bodies. Lagrange has incorporated his own analysis of the problem with his general treatment of mechanics, and since his time M. Poinsôt has brought the subject under the power of a more searching analysis than that of the calculus, in which ideas take the place of symbols, and intelligible propositions supersede equations.

In the practical department of the subject, we must notice the rotatory machine of Bohnenberger, and the nautical top of Troughton. In the first of these instruments we have the model of the Gyroscope, by which Foucault has been able to render visible the effects of the earth's rotation. The beautiful experiments by which Mr J. Elliot has made the ideas of precession so familiar to us are performed with a top, similar in some respects to Troughton's, though not borrowed from his.

The top which I have the honour to spin before the Society, differs from that of Mr Elliot in having more adjustments, and in being designed to exhibit far more complicated phenomena.

The arrangement of these adjustments, so as to produce the desired effects, depends on the mathematical theory of rotation. The method of exhibiting the motion of the axis of rotation, by means of a coloured disc, is essential to the success of these adjustments. This optical contrivance for rendering visible the nature of the rapid motion of the top, and the practical methods of applying the theory of rotation to such an instrument as the one before us, are the grounds on which I bring my instrument and experiments before the Society as my own.

I propose, therefore, in the first place, to give a brief outline of such parts of the theory of rotation as are necessary for the explanation of the phenomena of the top.

I shall then describe the instrument with its adjustments, and the effect of each, the mode of observing of the coloured disc when the top is in motion, and the use of the top in illustrating the mathematical theory, with the method of making the different experiments.

Lastly, I shall attempt to explain the nature of a possible variation in the earth's axis due to its figure. This variation, if it exists, must cause a periodic inequality in the latitude of every place on the earth's surface, going through its period in about eleven months. The amount of variation must be very small, but its character gives it importance, and the necessary observations are already made, and only require reduction.

On the Theory of Rotation.

The theory of the rotation of a rigid system is strictly deduced from the elementary laws of motion, but the complexity of the motion of the particles of a body freely rotating renders the subject so intricate, that it has never been thoroughly understood by any but the most expert mathematicians. Many who have mastered the lunar theory have come to erroneous conclusions on this subject; and even Newton has chosen to deduce the disturbance of the earth's axis from his theory of the motion of the nodes of a free orbit, rather than attack the problem of the rotation of a solid body.

The method by which M. Poinsôt has rendered the theory more manageable, is by the liberal introduction of "appropriate ideas," chiefly of a geometrical character, most of which had been rendered familiar to mathematicians by the writings of Monge, but which then first became illustrations of this branch of dynamics. If any further progress is to be made in simplifying and arranging the theory, it must be by the method which Poinsôt has repeatedly pointed out as the only one which can lead to a true knowledge of the subject,—that of proceeding from one distinct idea to another, instead of trusting to symbols and equations.

An important contribution to our stock of appropriate ideas and methods has lately been made by Mr R. B. Hayward, in a paper, "On a Direct Method of estimating Velocities, Accelerations, and all similar quantities, with respect to axes, moveable in any manner in Space." (*Trans. Cambridge Phil. Soc.* Vol. x. Part I.)

* In this communication I intend to confine myself to that part of the subject which the top is intended to illustrate, namely, the alteration of the position of the axis in a body rotating freely about its centre of gravity. I shall, therefore, deduce the theory as briefly as possible, from two considerations only,—the permanence of the original *angular momentum* in direction and magnitude, and the permanence of the original *vis viva*.

* The mathematical difficulties of the theory of rotation arise chiefly from the want of geometrical illustrations and sensible images, by which we might fix the results of analysis in our minds.

It is easy to understand the motion of a body revolving about a fixed axle. Every point in the body describes a circle about the axis, and returns to its original position after each complete revolution. But if the axle itself be in motion, the paths of the different points of the body will no longer be circular or re-entrant. Even the velocity of rotation about the axis requires a careful definition, and the proposition that, in all motion about a fixed point, there is always one line of particles forming an instantaneous axis, is usually given in the form of a very repulsive mass of calculation. Most of these difficulties may be got rid of by devoting a little attention to the mechanics and geometry of the problem before entering on the discussion of the equations.

Mr Hayward, in his paper already referred to, has made great use of the mechanical conception of Angular Momentum.

---

* 7th May, 1857. The paragraphs marked thus have been rewritten since the paper was read.

DEFINITION.—*The Angular Momentum of a particle about an axis is measured by the product of the mass of the particle, its velocity resolved in the normal plane, and the perpendicular from the axis on the direction of motion.*

* The angular momentum of any system about an axis is the algebraical sum of the angular momenta of its parts.

As the *rate of change* of the *linear momentum* of a particle measures the *moving force* which acts on it, so the *rate of change* of *angular momentum* measures the *moment* of that force about an axis.

All actions between the parts of a system, being pairs of equal and opposite forces, produce equal and opposite changes in the angular momentum of those parts. Hence the whole angular momentum of the system is not affected by these actions and re-actions.

* When a system of invariable form revolves about an axis, the angular velocity of every part is the same, and the angular momentum about the axis is the product of the *angular velocity* and the *moment of inertia* about that axis.

* It is only in particular cases, however, that the *whole* angular momentum can be estimated in this way. In general, the axis of angular momentum differs from the axis of rotation, so that there will be a residual angular momentum about an axis perpendicular to that of rotation, unless that axis has one of three positions, called the principal axes of the body.

By referring everything to these three axes, the theory is greatly simplified. The moment of inertia about one of these axes is greater than that about any other axis through the same point, and that about one of the others is a minimum. These two are at right angles, and the third axis is perpendicular to their plane, and is called the mean axis.

* Let A, B, C be the moments of inertia about the principal axes through the centre of gravity, taken in order of magnitude, and let ω_1 ω_2 ω_3 be the angular velocities about them, then the angular momenta will be $A\omega_1$, $B\omega_2$ and $C\omega_3$.

Angular momenta may be compounded like forces or velocities, by the law of the "parallelogram," and since these three are at right angles to each other, their resultant is

$$\sqrt{A^2\omega_1{}^2 + B^2\omega_2{}^2 + C^2\omega_3{}^2} = H \dots\dots\dots\dots\dots\dots(1),$$

and this must be constant, both in magnitude and direction in space, since no external forces act on the body.

We shall call this axis of angular momentum the *invariable axis*. It is perpendicular to what has been called the invariable plane. Poinsôt calls it the axis of the couple of impulsion. The *direction-cosines* of this axis in the body are,

$$l = \frac{A\omega_1}{H}, \qquad m = \frac{B\omega_2}{H}, \qquad n = \frac{C\omega_3}{H}.$$

Since l, m and n vary during the motion, we need some additional condition to determine the relation between them. We find this in the property of the *vis viva* of a system of invariable form in which there is no friction. The *vis viva* of such a system must be constant. We express this in the equation

$$A\omega_1^2 + B\omega_2^2 + C\omega_3^2 = V \quad\dots\dots\dots\dots\dots\dots\dots(2).$$

Substituting the values of ω_1, ω_2, ω_3 in terms of l, m, n,

$$\frac{l^2}{A} + \frac{m^2}{B} + \frac{n^2}{C} = \frac{V}{H^2}.$$

Let $\dfrac{1}{A} = a^2$, $\qquad \dfrac{1}{B} = b^2$, $\qquad \dfrac{1}{C} = c^2$, $\qquad \dfrac{V}{H^2} = e^2$,

and this equation becomes

$$a^2 l^2 + b^2 m^2 + c^2 n^2 = e^2 \quad\dots\dots\dots\dots\dots\dots\dots(3),$$

and the equation to the cone, described by the invariable axis within the body, is

$$(a^2 - e^2) x^2 + (b^2 - e^2) y^2 + (c^2 - e^2) z^2 = 0 \quad\dots\dots\dots\dots\dots(4).$$

The intersections of this cone with planes perpendicular to the principal axes are found by putting x, y, or z, constant in this equation. By giving e various values, all the different paths of the pole of the invariable axis, corresponding to different initial circumstances, may be traced.

*In the figures, I have supposed $a^2 = 100$, $b^2 = 107$, and $c^2 = 110$. The first figure represents a section of the various cones by a plane perpendicular to the axis of x, which is that of greatest moment of inertia. These sections are ellipses having their major axis parallel to the axis of b. The value of e^2 corresponding to each of these curves is indicated by figures beside the curve. The ellipticity increases with the size of the ellipse, so that the section corresponding to $e^2 = 107$ would be two parallel straight lines (beyond the bounds of the figure), after which the sections would be hyperbolas.

*The second figure represents the sections made by a plane, perpendicular to the *mean* axis. They are all hyperbolas, except when $e^2 = 107$, when the section is two intersecting straight lines.

The third figure shows the sections perpendicular to the axis of least moment of inertia. From $e^2 = 110$ to $e^2 = 107$ the sections are ellipses, $e^2 = 107$ gives two parallel straight lines, and beyond these the curves are hyperbolas.

*The fourth and fifth figures show the sections of the series of cones made by a cube and a sphere respectively. The use of these figures is to exhibit the connexion between the different curves described about the three principal axes by the invariable axis during the motion of the body.

*We have next to compare the velocity of the invariable axis with respect to the body, with that of the body itself round one of the principal axes. Since the invariable axis is fixed in space, its motion relative to the body must be equal and opposite to that of the portion of the body through which it passes. Now the angular velocity of a portion of the body whose direction-cosines are l, m, n, about the axis of x is

$$\frac{\omega_1}{1 - l^2} - \frac{l}{1 - l^2}(l\omega_1 + m\omega_2 + n\omega_3).$$

Substituting the values of ω_1, ω_2, ω_3, in terms of l, m, n, and taking account of equation (3), this expression becomes

$$H\frac{(a^2 - e^2)}{1 - l^2}\, l.$$

Changing the sign and putting $l = \dfrac{\omega_1}{a^2 H}$ we have the angular velocity of the invariable axis about that of x

$$= \frac{\omega_1}{1 - l^2}\frac{e^2 - a^2}{a^2},$$

always positive about the axis of greatest moment, negative about that of least moment, and positive or negative about the mean axis according to the value of e^2. The direction of the motion in every case is represented by the arrows in the figures. The arrows on the outside of each figure indicate the direction of rotation of the body.

*If we attend to the curve described by the pole of the invariable axis on the sphere in fig. 5, we shall see that the areas described by that point, if projected on the plane of yz, are swept out at the rate

$$\omega_1 \frac{e^2 - a^2}{a^2}.$$

Now the semi-axes of the projection of the spherical ellipse described by the pole are

$$\sqrt{\frac{e^2 - a^2}{b^2 - a^2}} \text{ and } \sqrt{\frac{e^2 - a^2}{c^2 - a^2}}.$$

Dividing the area of this ellipse by the area described during one revolution of the body, we find the number of revolutions of the body during the description of the ellipse—

$$= \frac{a^2}{\sqrt{b^2 - a^2}\sqrt{c^2 - a^2}}.$$

The projections of the spherical ellipses upon the plane of yz are all similar ellipses, and described in the same number of revolutions; and in each ellipse so projected, the area described in any time is proportional to the number of revolutions of the body about the axis of x, so that if we measure time by revolutions of the body, the motion of the projection of the pole of the invariable axis is identical with that of a body acted on by an attractive central force varying directly as the distance. In the case of the hyperbolas in the plane of the greatest and least axis, this force must be supposed repulsive. The dots in the figures 1, 2, 3, are intended to indicate roughly the progress made by the invariable axis during each revolution of the body about the axis of x, y and z respectively. It must be remembered that the rotation about these axes varies with their inclination to the invariable axis, so that the angular velocity diminishes as the inclination increases, and therefore the areas in the ellipses above mentioned are not described with uniform velocity in absolute time, but are less rapidly swept out at the extremities of the major axis than at those of the minor.

*When two of the axes have equal moments of inertia, or $b = c$, then the angular velocity ω_1 is constant, and the path of the invariable axis is circular, the number of revolutions of the body during one circuit of the invariable axis, being

$$\frac{a^2}{b^2 - a^2}.$$

The motion is in the same direction as that of rotation, or in the opposite direction, according as the axis of x is that of greatest or of least moment of inertia.

*Both in this case, and in that in which the three axes are unequal, the motion of the invariable axis in the body may be rendered very slow by diminishing the difference of the moments of inertia. The angular velocity of the axis of x about the invariable axis in space is

$$\omega_1 \frac{e^2 - a^2 l^2}{a^2 (1 - l^2)},$$

which is greater or less than ω_1, as e^2 is greater or less than a^2, and, when these quantities are nearly equal, is very nearly the same as ω_1 itself. This quantity indicates the rate of revolution of the axle of the top about its mean position, and is very easily observed.

*The *instantaneous axis* is not so easily observed. It revolves round the invariable axis in the same time with the axis of x, at a distance which is very small in the case when a, b, c, are nearly equal. From its rapid angular motion in space, and its near coincidence with the invariable axis, there is no advantage in studying its motion in the top.

*By making the moments of inertia very unequal, and in definite proportion to each other, and by drawing a few strong lines as diameters of the disc, the combination of motions will produce an appearance of epicycloids, which are the result of the continued intersection of the successive positions of these lines, and the cusps of the epicycloids lie in the curve in which the instantaneous axis travels. Some of the figures produced in this way are very pleasing.

In order to illustrate the theory of rotation experimentally, we must have a body balanced on its centre of gravity, and capable of having its principal axes and moments of inertia altered in form and position within certain limits. We must be able to make the axle of the instrument the greatest, least, or mean principal axis, or to make it not a principal axis at all, and we must be able to *see* the position of the invariable axis of rotation at any time. There must be three adjustments to regulate the position of the centre of gravity, three for the magnitudes of the moments of inertia, and three for the directions of the principal axes, nine independent adjustments, which may be distributed as we please among the screws of the instrument.

The form of the body of the instrument which I have found most suitable is that of a bell (p. 262, fig. 6). C is a hollow cone of brass, R is a heavy ring cast in the same piece. Six screws, with heavy heads, x, y, z, x', y', z', work horizontally in the ring, and three similar screws, l, m, n, work vertically through the ring at equal intervals. AS is the axle of the instrument, SS is a brass screw working in the upper part of the cone C, and capable of being firmly clamped by means of the nut c. B is a cylindrical brass bob, which may be screwed up or down the axis, and fixed in its place by the nut b.

The lower extremity of the axle is a fine steel point, finished without emery, and afterwards hardened. It runs in a little agate cup set in the top of the pillar P. If any emery had been embedded in the steel, the cup would soon be worn out. The upper end of the axle has also a steel point by which it may be kept steady while spinning.

When the instrument is in use, a coloured disc is attached to the upper end of the axle.

It will be seen that there are eleven adjustments, nine screws in the brass ring, the axle screwing in the cone, and the bob screwing on the axle. The advantage of the last two adjustments is, that by them large alterations can be made, which are not possible by means of the small screws.

The first thing to be done with the instrument is, to make the steel point at the end of the axle coincide with the centre of gravity of the whole. This is done roughly by screwing the axle to the right place nearly, and then balancing the instrument on its point, and screwing the bob and the horizontal screws till the instrument will remain balanced in any position in which it is placed.

When this adjustment is carefully made, the rotation of the top has no tendency to shake the steel point in the agate cup, however irregular the motion may appear to be.

The next thing to be done, is to make one of the principal axes of the central ellipsoid coincide with the axle of the top.

To effect this, we must begin by spinning the top gently about its axle, steadying the upper part with the finger at first. If the axle is already a principal axis the top will continue to revolve about its axle when the finger is removed. If it is not, we observe that the top begins to spin about some other axis, and the axle moves away from the centre of motion and then back to it again, and so on, alternately widening its circles and contracting them.

It is impossible to observe this motion successfully, without the aid of the coloured disc placed near the upper end of the axis. This disc is divided into sectors, and strongly coloured, so that each sector may be recognised by its colour when in rapid motion. If the axis about which the top is really revolving, falls within this disc, its position may be ascertained by the colour of the spot at the centre of motion. If the central spot appears red, we know that the invariable axis at that instant passes through the red part of the disc.

In this way we can trace the motion of the invariable axis in the revolving body, and we find that the path which it describes upon the disc may be a circle, an ellipse, an hyperbola, or a straight line, according to the arrangement of the instrument.

In the case in which the invariable axis coincides at first with the axle of the top, and returns to it after separating from it for a time, its true path is a circle or an ellipse having the axle in its *circumference*. The true principal axis is at the *centre* of the closed curve. It must be made to coincide with the axle by adjusting the vertical screws *l*, *m*, *n*.

Suppose that the colour of the centre of motion, when farthest from the axle, indicated that the axis of rotation passed through the sector *L*, then the principal axis must also lie in that sector at half the distance from the axle.

If this principal axis be that of *greatest* moment of inertia, we must *raise* the screw *l* in order to bring it nearer the axle *A*. If it be the axis of least moment we must *lower* the screw *l*. In this way we may make the principal axis coincide with the axle. Let us suppose that the principal axis is that of greatest moment of inertia, and that we have made it coincide with the axle of the instrument. Let us also suppose that the moments of inertia about the other axes are equal, and very little less than that about the axle. Let the top be spun about the axle and then receive a disturbance which causes it to spin about some other axis. The instantaneous axis will not remain at rest either in space or in the body. In space it will describe a right cone, completing a revolution in somewhat less than the time of revolution of the top. In the body it will describe another cone of larger angle in a period which is longer as the difference of axes of the body is smaller. The invariable axis will be fixed in space, and describe a cone in the body.

The relation of the different motions may be understood from the following illustration. Take a hoop and make it revolve about a stick which remains at rest and touches the inside of the hoop. The section of the stick represents the path of the instantaneous axis in space, the hoop that of the same axis in the body, and the axis of the stick the invariable axis. The point of contact represents the pole of the instantaneous axis itself, travelling many times round the stick before it gets once round the hoop. It is easy to see that the direction in which the instantaneous axis travels round the hoop, is in this case the same as that in which the hoop moves round the stick, so that if the top be spinning in the direction L, M, N, the colours will appear in the same order.

By screwing the bob B up the axle, the difference of the axes of inertia may be diminished, and the time of a complete revolution of the invariable axis in the body increased. By observing the number of revolutions of the top in a complete cycle of colours of the invariable axis, we may determine the ratio of the moments of inertia.

By screwing the bob up farther, we may make the axle the principal axis of *least* moment of inertia.

The motion of the instantaneous axis will then be that of the point of contact of the stick with the *outside* of the hoop rolling on it. The order of colours will be N, M, L, if the top be spinning in the direction L, M, N, and the more the bob is screwed up, the more rapidly will the colours change, till it ceases to be possible to make the observations correctly.

In calculating the dimensions of the parts of the instrument, it is necessary to provide for the exhibition of the instrument with its axle either the greatest or the least axis of inertia. The dimensions and weights of the parts of the top which I have found most suitable, are given in a note at the end of this paper.

Now let us make the axes of inertia in the plane of the ring unequal. We may do this by screwing the balance screws x and x^1 farther from the axle without altering the centre of gravity.

Let us suppose the bob B screwed up so as to make the axle the axis of least inertia. Then the mean axis is parallel to xx^1, and the greatest is at right angles to xx^1 in the horizontal plane. The path of the invariable axis on the disc is no longer a circle but an ellipse, concentric with the disc, and having its major axis parallel to the mean axis xx^1.

The smaller the difference between the moment of inertia about the axle and about the mean axis, the more eccentric the ellipse will be; and if, by screwing the bob down, the axle be made the mean axis, the path of the invariable axis will be no longer a closed curve, but an hyperbola, so that it will depart altogether from the neighbourhood of the axle. When the top is in this condition it must be spun gently, for it is very difficult to manage it when its motion gets more and more eccentric.

When the bob is screwed still farther down, the axle becomes the axis of greatest inertia, and xx^1 the least. The major axis of the ellipse described by the invariable axis will now be perpendicular to xx^1, and the farther the bob is screwed down, the eccentricity of the ellipse will diminish, and the velocity with which it is described will increase.

I have now described all the phenomena presented by a body revolving freely on its centre of gravity. If we wish to trace the motion of the invariable axis by means of the coloured sectors, we must make its motion very slow compared with that of the top. It is necessary, therefore, to make the moments of inertia about the principal axes very nearly equal, and in this case a very small change in the position of any part of the top will greatly derange the *position* of the principal axis. So that when the top is well adjusted, a single turn of one of the screws of the ring is sufficient to make the axle no longer a principal axis, and to set the true axis at a considerable inclination to the axle of the top.

All the adjustments must therefore be most carefully arranged, or we may have the whole apparatus deranged by some eccentricity of spinning. The method of making the principal axis coincide with the axle must be studied and practised, or the first attempt at spinning rapidly may end in the destruction of the top, if not of the table on which it is spun.

On the Earth's Motion.

We must remember that these motions of a body about its centre of gravity, are *not* illustrations of the theory of the precession of the Equinoxes. Precession can be illustrated by the apparatus, but we must arrange it so that the force of gravity acts the part of the attraction of the sun and moon in producing a force tending to alter the axis of rotation. This is easily done by bringing the centre of gravity of the whole a little below the point on which it spins. The theory of such motions is far more easily comprehended than that which we have been investigating.

But the earth is a body whose principal axes are unequal, and from the phenomena of precession we can determine the ratio of the polar and equatorial axes of the "central ellipsoid;" and supposing the earth to have been set in motion about any axis except the principal axis, or to have had its original axis disturbed in any way, its subsequent motion would be that of the top when the bob is a little below the critical position.

The axis of angular momentum would have an invariable position in space, and would travel with respect to the earth round the axis of figure with a velocity $= \omega \dfrac{C-A}{A}$ where ω is the sidereal angular velocity of the earth. The apparent pole of the earth would travel (with respect to the earth) from west to east round the true pole, completing its circuit in $\dfrac{A}{C-A}$ sidereal days, which appears to be about 325·6 solar days.

The instantaneous axis would revolve about this axis in space in about a day, and would always be in a plane with the true axis of the earth and the axis of angular momentum. The effect of such a motion on the apparent position of a star would be, that its zenith distance would be increased and diminished during a period of 325·6 days. This alteration of zenith distance is the same above and below the pole, so that the polar distance of the star is unaltered. In fact the method of finding the pole of the heavens by observations of stars, gives the pole of the *invariable axis*, which is altered only by external forces, such as those of the sun and moon.

There is therefore no change in the apparent polar distance of stars due to this cause. It is the latitude which varies. The magnitude of this variation cannot be determined by theory. The periodic time of the variation may be found approximately from the known dynamical properties of the earth. The epoch of maximum latitude cannot be found except by observation, but it must be later in proportion to the east longitude of the observatory.

In order to determine the existence of such a variation of latitude, I have examined the observations of *Polaris* with the Greenwich Transit Circle in the years 1851-2-3-4. The observations of the upper transit during each month were collected, and the mean of each month found. The same was done for the lower transits. The difference of zenith distance of upper and lower transit is twice the polar distance of Polaris, and half the sum gives the co-latitude of Greenwich.

In this way I found the apparent co-latitude of Greenwich for each month of the four years specified.

There appeared a very slight indication of a maximum belonging to the set of months,

March, 51.   Feb. 52.   Dec. 52.   Nov. 53.   Sept. 54.

This result, however, is to be regarded as very doubtful, as there did not appear to be evidence for any variation exceeding half a second of space, and more observations would be required to establish the existence of so small a variation at all.

I therefore conclude that the earth has been for a long time revolving about an axis very near to the axis of figure, if not coinciding with it. The cause of this near coincidence is either the original softness of the earth, or the present fluidity of its interior. The axes of the earth are so nearly equal, that a considerable elevation of a tract of country might produce a deviation of the principal axis within the limits of observation, and the only cause which would restore the uniform motion, would be the action of a fluid which would gradually diminish the oscillations of latitude. The permanence of latitude essentially depends on the inequality of the earth's axes, for if they had been all equal, any alteration of the crust of the earth would have produced new principal axes, and the axis of rotation would travel about those axes, altering the latitudes of all places, and yet not in the least altering the position of the axis of rotation among the stars.

Perhaps by a more extensive search and analysis of the observations of different observatories, the nature of the periodic variation of latitude, if it exist, may be determined. I am not aware of any calculations having been made to prove its non-existence, although, on dynamical grounds, we have every reason to look for some very small variation having the periodic time of 325·6 days nearly, a period which is clearly distinguished from any other astronomical cycle, and therefore easily recognised.

NOTE.

Dimensions and Weights of the parts of the Dynamical Top.

I. Body of the top—

Mean diameter of ring, 4 inches.

Section of ring, $\frac{1}{2}$ inch square.

The conical portion rises from the upper and inner edge of the ring, a height of $1\frac{1}{2}$ inches from the base.

The whole body of the top weighs . . . . 1 lb. 7 oz.

Each of the nine adjusting screws has its screw 1 inch long, and the screw and head together weigh 1 ounce. The whole weigh . . 9 „

II. Axle, &c.—

Length of axle 5 inches, of which $\frac{1}{2}$ inch at the bottom is occupied by the steel point, $3\frac{1}{2}$ inches are brass with a good screw turned on it, and the remaining inch is of steel, with a sharp point at the top. The whole weighs . . . . 1$\frac{1}{2}$ „

The bob B has a diameter of 1·4 inches, and a thickness of ·4. It weighs 2$\frac{3}{4}$ „

The nuts b and c, for clamping the bob and the body of the top on the axle, each weigh $\frac{1}{2}$ oz. . . . . 1 „

Weight of whole top   2 lb. 5$\frac{1}{4}$ oz.

The best arrangement, for general observations, is to have the disc of card divided into four quadrants, coloured with vermilion, chrome yellow, emerald green, and ultramarine. These are bright colours, and, if the vermilion is good, they combine into a grayish tint when the revolution is about the axle, and burst into brilliant colours when the axis is disturbed. It is useful to have some concentric circles, drawn with ink, over the colours and about 12 radii drawn in strong pencil lines. It is easy to distinguish the ink from the pencil lines, as they cross the invariable axis, by their want of lustre. In this way the path of the invariable axis may be identified with great accuracy, and compared with theory.

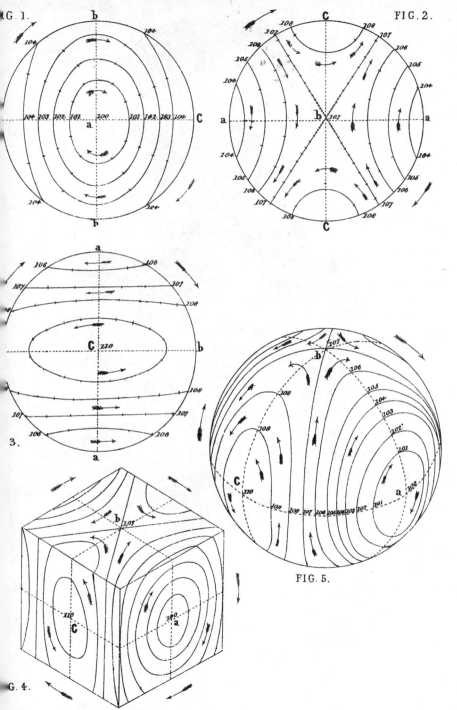

VOL. I. PLATE III.

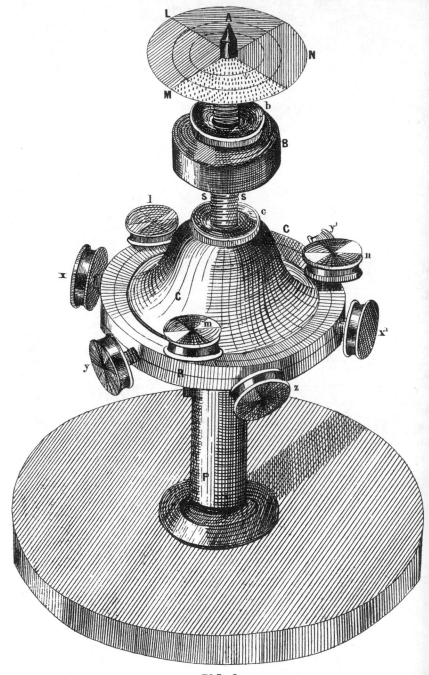

FIG. 6.

[From the *Philosophical Magazine*, Vol. XIV.]

XVI. *Account of Experiments on the Perception of Colour.*

To the Editors of the Philosophical Magazine and Journal.

GENTLEMEN,

THE experiments which I intend to describe were undertaken in order to render more perfect the quantitative proof of the theory of three primary colours. According to that theory, every sensation of colour in a perfect human eye is distinguished by three, and only three, elementary qualities, so that in mathematical language the quality of a colour may be expressed as a function of three independent variables. There is very little evidence at present for deciding the precise tints of the true primaries. I have ascertained that a certain red is the sensation wanting in colour-blind eyes, but the mathematical theory relates to the number, not to the nature of the primaries. If, with Sir David Brewster, we assume red, blue, and yellow to be the primary colours, this amounts to saying that every conceivable tint may be produced by adding together so much red, so much yellow, and so much blue. This is perhaps the best method of forming a provisional notion of the theory. It is evident that if any colour could be found which could not be accurately defined as so much of each of the three primaries, the theory would fall to the ground. Besides this, the truth of the theory requires that every mathematical consequence of assuming every colour to be the result of mixture of three primaries should also be true.

I have made experiments on upwards of 100 different artificial colours, consisting of the pigments used in the arts, and their mechanical mixtures. These experiments were made primarily to trace the effects of mechanical mixture on various coloured powders; but they also afford evidence of the truth of the theory, that all these various colours can be referred to three primaries. The following experiments relate to the combinations of six well-defined colours only, and I shall describe them the more minutely, as I hope to induce those who have good eyes to subject them to the same trial of skill in distinguishing tints.

The method of performing the experiments is described in the Transactions of the Royal Society of Edinburgh, Vol. XXI. Part 2. The colour-top or teetotum which I used may be had of Mr J. M. Bryson, Edinburgh, or it may be easily extemporized. Any rotatory apparatus which will keep a disc revolving steadily and rapidly in a good light, without noise or disturbance, and can be easily stopped and shifted, will do as well as the contrivance of the spinning-top.

The essential part of the experiment consists in placing several discs of coloured paper of the same size, and slit along a radius, over one another, so that a portion of each is seen, the rest being covered by the other discs. By sliding the discs over each other the proportion of each colour may be varied, and by means of divisions on a circle on which the discs lie, the proportion of each colour may be read off. My circle was divided into 100 parts.

On the top of this set of discs is placed a smaller set of concentric discs, so that when the whole is in motion round the centre, the colour resulting from the mixture of colours of the small discs is seen in the middle of that arising from the larger discs. It is the object of the experimenter to shift the colours till the outer and inner tints appear exactly the same, and then to read off the proportions.

It is easy to deduce from the theory of three primary colours what must be the number of discs exposed at one time, and how much of each colour must appear.

Every colour placed on either circle consists of a certain proportion of each of the primaries, and in order that the outer and inner circles may have precisely the same resultant colour in every respect, there must be the same amount of each of the primary colours in the outer and inner circles. Thus we have as many conditions to fulfil as there are primary colours; and besides these we have two more, because the whole number of divisions in either the outer or the inner circle is 100, so that if there are three primary colours there will be five conditions to fulfil, and this will require five discs to be disposable, and these must be arranged so that three are matched against two, or four against one.

If we take six different colours, we may leave out any one of the six, and so form six different combinations of five colours. It is plain that these six combinations must be equivalent to two equations only, if the theory of three primaries be true.

The method which I have found most convenient for registering the result of an experiment, after an identity of tint has been obtained in the inner and outer circles, is the following :—

Write down the names or symbols of the coloured discs each at the top of a column, and underneath write the number of degrees of that colour observed, calling it + when the colour is in the outer circle, and — when it is in the inner circle; then equate the whole to zero. In this way the account of each colour is kept in a separate column, and the equations obtained are easily combined and reduced, without danger of confounding the colours of which the quantities have been measured. The following experiments were made between the 3rd and 11th of September, 1856, about noon of each day, in a room fronting the north, without curtains or any bright-coloured object near the window. The same combination was never made twice in one day, and no thought was bestowed upon the experiments except at the time of observation. Of course the gradation was never consulted, nor former experiments referred to, till each combination of colours had been fixed by the eye alone; and no reduction was attempted till all the experiments were concluded.

The coloured discs were cut from paper painted of the following colours :— Vermilion, Ultramarine, Emerald-green, Snow-white, Ivory-black, and Pale Chrome-yellow. They are denoted by the letters V, U, G, W, B, Y respectively. These colours were chosen, because each is well distinguished from the rest, so that a small change of its intensity in any combination can be observed. Two discs of each colour were prepared, so that in each combination the colours might occasionally be transposed from the outer circle to the inner.

The first equation was formed by leaving out vermilion. The remaining colours are Ultramarine-blue, Emerald-green, White, Black, and Yellow. We might suppose, that by mixing the blue and yellow in proper proportions, we should get a green of the same hue as the emerald-green, but not so intense, so that in order to match it we should have to mix the green with white to dilute it, and with black to make it darker. But it is not in this way that we have to arrange the colours, for our blue and yellow produce a pinkish tint, and never a green, so that we must add *green* to the combination of blue and yellow, to produce a neutral tint, identical with a mixture of white and black.

Blue, green, and yellow must therefore be combined on the large discs, and stand on one side of the equation, and black and white, on the small discs, must stand on the other side. In order to facilitate calculations, the colours are always put down in the same order; but those belonging to the small discs are marked negative. Thus, instead of writing

$$54U + 14G + 32Y = 32W + 68B,$$

we write $$+ 54U + 14G - 32W - 68B + 32Y = 0.$$

The sum of all the positive terms of such an equation is 100, being the whole number of divisions in the circle. The sum of the negative terms is also 100.

The second equation consists of all the colours except blue; and in this way we obtain six different combinations of five colours.

Each of these combinations was formed by the unassisted judgment of my eye, on six different occasions, so that there are thirty-six independent observations of equations between five colours.

Table I. gives the actual observations, with their dates.

Table II. gives the result of summing together each group of six equations.

Each equation in Table II. has the sums of its positive and negative coefficients each equal to 600.

Having obtained a number of observations of each combination of colours, we have next to test the consistency of these results, since theoretically two equations are sufficient to determine all the relations among six colours. We must therefore, in the first place, determine the comparative accuracy of the different sets of observations. Table III. gives the averages of the errors of each of the six groups of observations. It appears that the combination IV. is the least accurately observed, and that VI. is the best.

Table IV. gives the averages of the errors in the observation of each colour in the whole series of experiments. This Table was computed in order to detect any tendency to colour-blindness in my own eyes, which might be less accurate in discriminating red and green, than in detecting variations of other colours. It appears, however, that my observations of red and green were more accurate than those of blue or yellow. White is the most easily observed, from the brilliancy of the colour, and black is liable to the greatest mistakes. I would recommend this method of examining a series of experiments as a means of detecting partial colour-blindness, by the different accuracy in observing different colours. The next operation is to combine all the equations according to their values. Each was first multiplied by a coefficient proportional to its accuracy, and to the coefficient of white in that equation. The result of adding all the equations so found is given in equation (W).

Equation (Y) is the result of similar operations with reference to the yellow on each equation.

We have now two equations from which to deduce six new equations, by eliminating each of the six colours in succession. We must first combine the equations, so as to get rid of one of the colours, and then we must divide by the sum of the positive or negative coefficients, so as to reduce the equations to the form of the observed equations. The results of these operations are given in Table V., along with the means of each group of six observations. It will be seen that the differences between the results of calculation from two equations and the six independent observed equations are very small. The errors in red and green are here again somewhat less than in blue and yellow, so that there is certainly no tendency to mistake red and green more than other colours. The average difference between the observed mean value of a colour and the calculated value is ·77 of a degree. The average error of an observation in any group from the mean of that group was ·92. No observation was attempted to be registered nearer than one degree of the top, or $\frac{1}{100}$ of a circle; so that this set of observations agrees with the theory of three primary colours quite as far as the observations can warrant us in our calculations; and I think that the human eye has seldom been subjected to so severe a test of its power of distinguishing colours. My eyes are by no means so accurate in this respect as many eyes I have examined, but a little practice produces great improvement even in inaccurate observers.

I have laid down, according to Newton's method, the relative positions of the five positive colours with which I worked. It will be seen that W lies within the triangle V U G, and Y outside that triangle.

The first combination, Equation I., consisted of blue, yellow, and green, taken in such proportions that their centre of gravity falls at W.

In Equation II. a mixture of red and green, represented in the diagram by the point 2, is seen to be equivalent to a mixture of white and yellow, also represented by 2, which is a pale yellow tint.

Equation III. is between a mixture of blue and yellow and another of white and red. The resulting tint is at the intersection of YU and WV; that is, at the point 3, which represents a pale pink grey.

Equation IV. is between VG and UY, that is, at 4, a dirty yellow.

Equation V. is between a mixture of white, red, and green, and a mixture of blue and yellow at the point 5, a pale dirty yellow.

Equation VI. has W. for its resulting tint.

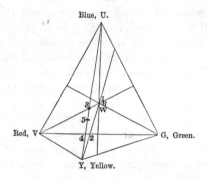

Of all the resulting tints, that of Equation IV. is the furthest from white; and we find that the observations of this equation are affected with the greatest errors. Hence the importance of reducing the resultant tint to as nearly a neutral colour as possible.

It is hardly necessary for me to observe, that the whole of the numerical results which I have given apply only to the coloured papers which I used, and to them only when illuminated by daylight from the north at mid-day in September, latitude 55°. In the evening, or in winter, or by candlelight, the results are very different. I believe, however, that the results would differ far less if observed by different persons, than if observed under different lights; for the apparatus of vision is wonderfully similar in different eyes, and even in colour-blind eyes the system of perception is not different, but defective.

TABLE I.—The observations arranged in groups.

Equation I.	V=0.	+U.	+G.	−W.	−B.	+Y.	Equation IV.	−V.	+U.	−G.	W=0.	+B.	+Y.
1856, Sept. 3.	0	54	12	34	66	34	1856, Sept. 3.	62	15	38	0	53	32
4.	0	58	14	31	69	28	4.	63	17	37	0	46	37
5.	0	55	12	32	68	33	5.	64	16	36	0	50	34
6.	0	54	14	32	68	32	6.	62	19	38	0	46	35
8.	0	54	14	32	68	32	8.	62	19	38	0	47	34
9.	0	53	15	32	68	32	9.	63	17	37	0	49	34

Equation II.	−V.	U=0.	−G.	+W.	+B.	+Y.	Equation V.	+V.	−U.	+G.	+W.	B=0.	−Y.
Sept. 3.	59	0	41	9	71	20	Sept. 3.	56	47	28	16	0	53
4.	61	0	39	9	68	23	4.	57	50	25	18	0	50
5.	61	0	39	9	67	24	5.	56	49	24	20	0	51
6.	59	0	41	10	66	24	6.	55	47	27	18	0	53
8.	60	0	40	9	69	22	8.	54	49	26	20	0	51
9.	61	0	39	9	68	23	11.	56	50	27	17	0	50

Equation III.	+V.	−U.	G=0.	+W.	+B.	−Y.	Equation VI.	+V.	+U.	+G.	−W.	−B.	Y=0.
Sept. 3.	20	56	0	28	52	44	Sept. 3.	38	27	35	24	76	0
4.	23	58	0	30	47	42	4.	39	27	34	24	76	0
5.	24	56	0	29	47	44	5.	40	26	34	24	76	0
6.	20	56	0	31	49	44	6.	38	28	34	24	76	0
8.	21	57	0	29	50	43	8.	39	28	33	24	76	0
9.	21	58	0	29	50	42	11.	39	27	34	23	77	0

TABLE II.—The sums of the observed equations.

	V.	U.	G.	W.	B.	Y.
Equation I.	0	+ 328	+ 81	− 193	− 407	+ 191
... II.	− 361	0	− 239	+ 55	+ 409	+ 136
... III.	+ 129	− 341	0	+ 176	+ 295	− 259
... IV.	− 376	+ 103	− 224	0	+ 291	+ 206
... V.	+ 334	− 292	+ 157	+ 109	0	− 308
... VI.	+ 233	+ 163	+ 204	− 143	− 457	0

TABLE III.—The averages of the errors of the several equations from the means expressed in $\frac{1}{100}$ parts of a circle.

Equations.	I.	II.	III.	IV.	V.	VI.
Errors.	·94	·85	1·05	1·17	1·08	·40

TABLE IV.—The averages of the errors of the several colours from the means in $\frac{1}{100}$ parts of a circle.

Colours.	V.	U.	G.	W.	B.	Y.
Errors.	·83	·99	·80	·61	1·15	1·09

Average error on the whole ·92.

The equations from which the reduced results were obtained were calculated as follow :—

Equation for $(W) = (II) + 2\,(III) + (V) − 2\,(I) − 4\,(VI)$.
Equation for $(Y) = 2\,(I) + 2\,(II) − 3\,(III) + 2\,(IV) − 3\,(V)$.

These operations being performed, gave

	V.	U.	G.	W.	B.	Y.
(W)	+ 701	+ 2282	+ 1060	− 1474	− 3641	+ 1072 = 0.
(Y)	+ 2863	− 2761	+ 1235	+ 1131	+ 299	− 2767 = 0.

From these were obtained the following results by elimination :—

TABLE V.

Equation							
I.	From (W) and (Y)	0	− 54·1	− 13·9	+ 32·0	+ 68·0	− 32·0
	From observation	0	− 54·7	− 13·5	+ 32·1	+ 67·9	− 31·8
II.	From (W) and (Y)	− 59·6	0	− 40·4	+ 10·4	+ 66·0	+ 23·6
	From observation	− 60·2	0	− 39·8	+ 9·2	+ 68·2	+ 22·6
III.	From (W) and (Y)	− 21·7	+ 57·4	0	− 30·2	− 48·1	+ 42·6
	From observation	− 21·5	+ 56·8	0	− 29·3	− 49·2	+ 43·2
IV.	From (W) and (Y)	− 62·4	+ 18·6	− 37·6	0	+ 45·7	+ 35·7
	From observation	− 62·7	+ 17·2	− 37·3	0	+ 48·5	+ 34·3
V.	From (W) and (Y)	+ 55·6	− 49·0	+ 25·2	+ 19·2	0	− 51·0
	From observation	+ 55·7	− 48·7	+ 26·1	+ 18·2	0	− 51·3
VI.	From (W) and (Y)	− 39·7	− 26·6	− 33·7	+ 22·7	+ 77·3	0
	From observation	− 38·8	− 27·2	− 34·0	+ 28·3	+ 76·2	0

JAMES CLERK MAXWELL.

GLENLAIR, *June* 13, 1857.

[From *The Quarterly Journal of Pure and Applied Mathematics*, Vol. II.]

XVII. *On the General Laws of Optical Instruments.*

THE optical effects of compound instruments have been generally deduced from those of the elementary parts of which they are composed. The formulæ given in most works on Optics for calculating the effect of each spherical surface are simple enough, but, when we attempt to carry on our calculations from one of these surfaces to the next, we arrive at fractional expressions so complicated as to make the subsequent steps very troublesome.

Euler (Acad. R. de Berlin, 1757, 1761. Acad. R. de Paris, 1765) has attacked these expressions, but his investigations are not easy reading. Lagrange (Acad. Berlin, 1778, 1803) has reduced the case to the theory of continued fractions and so obtained general laws.

Gauss (*Dioptrische Untersuchungen*, Göttingen, 1841) has treated the subject with that combination of analytical skill with practical ability which he displays elsewhere, and has made use of the properties of principal foci and principal planes. An account of these researches is given by Prof. Miller in the third volume of Taylor's *Scientific Memoirs*. It is also given entire in French by M. Bravais in *Liouville's Journal* for 1856, with additions by the translator.

The method of Gauss has been followed by Prof. Listing in his *Treatise on the Dioptrics of the Eye* (in Wagner's *Handworterbuch der Physiologie*) from whom I copy these references, and by Prof. Helmholtz in his *Treatise on Physiological Optics* (in Karsten's *Cyclopadie*).

The earliest general investigations are those of Cotes, given in Smith's *Optics*, II. 76 (1738). The method there is geometrical, and perfectly general, but proceeding from the elementary cases to the more complex by the method of mathematical induction. Some of his modes of expression, as for instance his measure of "apparent distance," have never come into use, although his results may easily be expressed more intelligibly ; and indeed the whole fabric of

Geometrical Optics, as conceived by Cotes and laboured by Smith, has fallen into neglect, except among the writers before named. Smith tells us that it was with reference to these optical theorems that Newton said "If Mr Cotes had lived we might have known something."

The investigations which I now offer are intended to show how simple and how general the theory of instruments may be rendered, by considering the optical effects of the entire instrument, without examining the mechanism by which those effects are obtained. I have thus established a theory of "perfect instruments," geometrically complete in itself, although I have also shown, that no instrument depending on refraction and reflexion, (except the plane mirror) can be optically perfect. The first part of this theory was communicated to the Philosophical Society of Cambridge, 28th April, 1856, and an abstract will be found in the *Philosophical Magazine*, November, 1856. Propositions VIII. and IX. are now added. I am not aware that the last has been proved before.

In the following propositions I propose to establish certain rules for determining, from simple data, the path of a ray of light after passing through any optical instrument, the position of the conjugate focus of a luminous point, and the magnitude of the image of a given object. The method which I shall use does not require a knowledge of the internal construction of the instrument and derives all its data from two simple experiments.

There are certain defects incident to optical instruments from which, in the elementary theory, we suppose them to be free. A perfect instrument must fulfil three conditions :

I. Every ray of the pencil, proceeding from a single point of the object, must, after passing through the instrument, converge to, or diverge from, a single point of the image. The corresponding defect, when the emergent rays have not a common focus, has been appropriately called (by Dr Whewell) *Astigmatism*.

II. If the object is a plane surface, perpendicular to the axis of the instrument, the image of any point of it must also lie in a plane perpendicular to the axis. When the points of the image lie in a curved surface, it is said to have the defect of *curvature*.

III. The image of an object on this plane must be similar to the object, whether its linear dimensions be altered or not; when the image is not similar to the object, it is said to be *distorted*.

An image free from these three defects is said to be *perfect*.

In Fig. 1, p. 285, let $A_1a_1\alpha_1$ represent a plane object perpendicular to the axis of an instrument represented by I., then if the instrument is perfect, as regards an object at that distance, an image $A_2a_2\alpha_2$ will be formed by the emergent rays, which will have the following properties:

I.   Every ray, which passes through a point a_1 of the object, will pass through the corresponding point a_2 of the image.

II.   Every point of the image will lie in a plane perpendicular to the axis.

III.   The figure $A_2a_2\alpha_2$ will be similar and similarly situated to the figure $A_1a_1\alpha_1$.

Now let us assume that the instrument is also perfect as regards an object in the plane $B_1b_1\beta_1$ perpendicular to the axis through B_1, and that the image of such an object is in the plane $B_2b_2\beta_2$ and similar to the object, and we shall be able to prove the following proposition:

Prop. I.   If an instrument give a perfect image of a plane object at two different distances from the instrument, *all* incident rays having a common focus will have a common focus after emergence.

Let P_1 be the focus of incident rays.   Let $P_1a_1b_1$ be any incident ray. Then, since every ray which passes through a_1 passes through a_2, its image after emergence, and since every ray which passes through b_1 passes through b_2, the direction of the ray $P_1a_1b_1$ after emergence must be a_2b_2.

Similarly, since a_2 and β_2 are the images of a_1 and β_1, if $P_1a_1\beta_1$ be any other ray, its direction after emergence will be $a_2\beta_2$.

Join a_1a_1, $b_1\beta_1$, a_2a_2, $b_2\beta_2$; then, since the parallel planes $A_1a_1\alpha_1$ and $B_1b_1\beta_1$ are cut by the plane of the two rays through P_1, the intersections a_1a_1 and $b_1\beta_1$ are parallel.

Also, their images, being similarly situated, are parallel to them, therefore a_2a_2 is parallel to $b_2\beta_2$, and the lines a_2b_2 and $a_2\beta_2$ are in the same plane, and therefore either meet in a point P_2 or are parallel.

Now take a third ray through P_1, not in the plane of the two former. After emergence it must either cut both, or be parallel to them.   If it cuts both it must pass through the point P_2, and then every other ray must pass through P_2, for no line can intersect three lines, not in one plane, without passing through their point of intersection.   If not, then all the emergent rays are parallel, which is a particular case of a perfect pencil. So that for every position of the focus of incident rays, the emergent pencil is free from *astigmatism*.

PROP. II. In an instrument, perfect at two different distances, the image of any plane object perpendicular to the axis will be free from the defects of curvature and distortion.

Through the point P_1 of the object draw any line P_1Q_1 in the plane of the object, and through P_1Q_1 draw a plane cutting the planes A_1, B_1 in the lines a_1a_1, $b_1\beta_1$. These lines will be parallel to P_1Q_1 and to each other, wherefore also their images, a_2a_2, $b_2\beta_2$, will be parallel to P_1Q_1 and to each other, and therefore in one plane.

Now suppose another plane drawn through P_1Q_1 cutting the planes A_1 and B_1 in two other lines parallel to P_1Q_1. These will have parallel images in the planes A_2 and B_2, and the intersection of the planes passing through the two pairs of images will define the line P_2Q_2 which will be parallel to them, and therefore to P_1Q_1, and will be the *image* of P_1Q_1. Therefore P_2Q_2, the image of P_1Q_1 is parallel to it, and therefore in a plane perpendicular to the axis. Now if all corresponding lines in any two figures be parallel, however the lines be drawn, the figures are similar, and similarly situated.

From these two propositions it follows that an instrument giving a perfect image at two different distances will give a perfect image at all distances. We have now only to determine the simplest method of finding the position and magnitude of the image, remembering that wherever two rays of a pencil intersect, all other rays of the pencil must meet, and that all parts of a plane object have their images in the same plane, and equally magnified or diminished.

PROP. III. A ray is incident on a perfect instrument parallel to the axis, to find its direction after emergence.

Let a_1b_1 (fig. 2) be the incident ray, A_1a_1 one of the planes at which an object has been ascertained to have a perfect image. A_2a_2 that image, similar to A_1a_1 but in magnitude such that $A_2a_2 = xA_1a_1$.

Similarly let B_2b_2 be the image of B_1b_1, and let $B_2b_2 = yB_1b_1$. Also let $A_1B_1 = c_1$ and $A_2B_2 = c_2$.

Then since a_2 and b_2 are the images of a_1 and b_1, the line $F_2a_2b_2$ will be the direction of the ray after emergence, cutting the axis in F_2, (unless $x = y$, when a_2b_2 becomes parallel to the axis). The point F_2 may be found, by remembering that $A_1a_1 = B_1b_1$, $A_2a_2 = xA_1a_1$, $B_2b_2 = yB_1b_1$. We find—

$$A_2F_2 = c_2 \frac{x}{y-x}.$$

Let g_2 be the point at which the emergent ray is at the same distance from the axis as the incident ray, draw g_2G_2 perpendicular to the axis, then we have

$$F_2G_2 = \frac{c_2}{y-x}.$$

Similarly, if $a_1\beta_1F_1$ be a ray, which, after emergence, becomes parallel to the axis; and g_1G_1 a line perpendicular to the axis, equal to the distance of the parallel emergent ray, then

$$A_1F_1 = c_1 \frac{y}{x-y}, \qquad F_1G_1 = \frac{c_1xy}{x-y}.$$

Definitions.

I. The point F_1, the focus of incident rays when the emergent rays are parallel to the axis, is called the *first principal focus* of the instrument.

II. The plane G_1g_1 at which incident rays through F_1 are at the same distance from the axis as they are after emergence, is called the *first principal plane* of the instrument. F_1G_1 is called the *first focal length*.

III. The point F_2, the focus of emergent rays when the incident rays are parallel, is called the *second principal focus*.

IV. The plane G_2g_2, at which the emergent rays are at the same distance from the axis, as before incidence, is called the *second principal plane*, and F_2G_2 is called the *second focal length*.

When $x = y$, the ray is parallel to the axis, both at incidence and emergence, and there are no such points as F and G. The instrument is then called a *telescope*. $x (=y)$ is called the *linear magnifying power* and is denoted by l, and the ratio $\frac{c_2}{c_1}$ is denoted by n, and may be called the *elongation*.

In the more general case, in which x and y are different, the principal foci and principal planes afford the readiest means of finding the position of images.

Prop. IV. Given the principal foci and principal planes of an instrument, to find the relations of the foci of the incident and emergent pencils.

Let F_1, F_2 (fig. 3) be the principal foci, G_1, G_2 the principal planes, Q_1 the focus of incident light, Q_1P_1 perpendicular to the axis.

Through Q_1 draw the ray $Q_1g_1F_1$. Since this ray passes through F_1 it emerges parallel to the axis, and at a distance from it equal to G_1g_1. Its direction after emergence is therefore Q_2g_2 where $G_2g_2 = G_1g_1$. Through Q_1 draw $Q_1\gamma_1$ parallel to the axis. The corresponding emergent ray will pass through F_2, and will cut the second principal plane at a distance $G_2\gamma_2 = G_1\gamma_1$, so that $F_2\gamma_2$ is the direction of this ray after emergence.

Since both rays pass through the focus of the emergent pencil, Q_2, the point of intersection, is that focus. Draw Q_2P_2 perpendicular to the axis. Then $P_1Q_1 = G_1\gamma_1 = G_2\gamma_2$, and $G_1g_1 = G_2g_2 = P_2Q_2$. By similar triangles $F_1P_1Q_1$ and $F_1G_1g_1$

$$P_1F_1 \,:\, F_1G_1 \,::\, P_1Q_1 \,:\, (G_1g_1 =)\, P_2Q_2.$$

And by similar triangles $F_2P_2Q_2$ and $F_2G_2\gamma_2$

$$P_1Q_1\,(= G_2\gamma_2) \,:\, P_2Q_2 \,::\, G_2F_2 \,:\, F_2P_2.$$

We may put these relations into the concise form

$$\frac{P_1F_1}{F_1G_1} = \frac{P_1Q_1}{P_2Q_2} = \frac{G_2F_2}{F_2P_2},$$

and the values of F_2P_2 and P_2Q_2 are

$$F_2P_2 = \frac{F_1G_1 \cdot G_2F_2}{P_1F_1} \text{ and } P_2Q_2 = \frac{F_1G_1}{P_1F_1}\, P_1Q_1.$$

These expressions give the distance of the image from F_2 measured along the axis, and also the perpendicular distance from the axis, so that they serve to determine completely the position of the image of any point, when the principal foci and principal planes are known.

Prop. V. To find the focus of emergent rays, when the instrument is a *telescope*.

Let Q_1 (fig. 4) be the focus of incident rays, and let $Q_1a_1b_1$ be a ray parallel to the axis; then, since the instrument is telescopic, the emergent ray $Q_2a_2b_2$ will be parallel to the axis, and $Q_2P_2 = l \cdot Q_1P_1$.

Let $Q_1 a_1 B_1$ be a ray through B_1, the emergent ray will be $Q_2 a_2 B_2$, and $A_2 a_2 = l \cdot A_1 a_1$.

Now
$$\frac{P_2 B_2}{A_2 B_2} = \frac{P_2 Q_2}{A_2 a_2} = \frac{l \cdot P_1 Q_1}{l \cdot A_1 a_1} = \frac{P_1 Q_1}{A_1 a_1} = \frac{P_1 B_1}{A_1 B_1},$$

so that
$$\frac{P_2 B_2}{P_1 B_1} = \frac{A_2 B_2}{A_1 B_1} = n, \text{ a constant ratio.}$$

Cor. If a point C be taken on the axis of the instrument so that

$$CB_2 = \frac{A_2 B_2}{A_1 B_1 - A_2 B_2} B_1 B_2 = \frac{n}{1-n} B_1 B_2,$$

then
$$CP_2 = n \cdot CP_1.$$

Def. The point C is called the *centre* of the telescope.

It appears, therefore, that the image of an object in a telescope has its dimensions perpendicular to the axis equal to l times the corresponding dimensions of the object, and the distance of any part from the plane through C equal to n times the distance of the corresponding part of the object. Of course all longitudinal distances among objects must be multiplied by n to obtain those of their images, and the tangent of the angular magnitude of an object as seen from a given point in the axis must be multiplied by $\frac{l}{n}$ to obtain that of the image of the object as seen from the image of the given point. The quantity $\frac{l}{n}$ is therefore called the *angular magnifying power*, and is denoted by m.

Prop. VI. To find the principal foci and principal planes of a combination of two instruments having a common axis.

Let 1, I' (fig. 5) be the two instruments, $G_1 F_1 F_2 G_2$ the principal foci and planes of the first, $G_1' F_1' F_2' G_2'$ those of the second, $\Gamma_1 \phi_1 \phi_2 \Gamma_2$ those of the combination. Let the ray $g_1 g_2 g_1' g_2'$ pass through both instruments, and let it be parallel to the axis before entering the first instrument. It will therefore pass through F_2 the second principal focus of the first instrument, and through g_2 so that $G_2 g_2 = G_1 g_1$.

On emergence from the second instrument it will pass through ϕ_2 the focus conjugate to F_2, and through g_2' in the second principal plane, so that

$G_2'g_2' = G_1'g_1'.$ ϕ_2 is by definition the second principal focus of the combination of instruments, and if $\Gamma_2\gamma_2$ be the second principal plane, then $\Gamma_2\gamma_2 = G_1g_1.$

We have now to find the positions of ϕ_2 and Γ_2.

By Prop. IV., we have

$$F_2'\phi_2 = \frac{F_1'G_1' \cdot G_2'F_2'}{F_2F_1'} .$$

Or, the distance of the principal focus of the combination, from that of the second instrument, is equal to the product of the focal lengths of the second instrument, divided by the distance of the second principal focus of the first instrument from the first of the second.   From this we get

$$G_2'F_2' - F_2'\phi_2 = \frac{G_2'F_2' \left(F_2F_1' - F_1'G_1' \right)}{F_2F_1'} ,$$

or

$$G_2'\phi_2 = \frac{G_2'F_2' \cdot G_1'F_2}{F_2F_1'} .$$

Now, by the pairs of similar triangles $\phi G_2'g_2'$, $\phi\Gamma_2\gamma_2$ and $F_2G_1'g_1'$, $F_2G_2g_2$,

$$\frac{\Gamma_2\phi_2}{G_2'\phi_2} = \frac{\Gamma_2\gamma_2}{G_2'g_2} = \frac{G_2g_2}{G_1'g_1'} = \frac{F_2G_2}{G_1'F_2} .$$

Multiplying the two sides of the former equation respectively by the first and last of these equal quantities, we get

$$\Gamma_2\phi_2 = \frac{G_2F_2 \cdot G_2'F_2'}{F_2F_1'} .$$

Or, the second focal distance of a combination is the product of the second focal lengths of its two components, divided by the distance of their consecutive principal foci.

If we call the focal distances of the first instrument f_1 and f_2, those of the second f_1' and f_2', and those of the combination $\bar{f}_1$, $\bar{f}_2$, and put $F_2F_1' = d$, then the positions of the principal foci are found from the values

$$\phi_1F_1 = \frac{f_1f_2}{d} , \qquad F_2'\phi_2 = \frac{f_1'f_2'}{d} ,$$

and the focal lengths of the combination from

$$\bar{f}_1 = \frac{f_1f_1'}{d} , \qquad \bar{f}_2 = \frac{f_2f_2'}{d} .$$

When $d = 0$, all these values become infinite, and the compound instrument becomes a telescope.

PROP. VII. To find the linear magnifying power, the elongation, and the centre of the instrument, when the combination becomes a telescope.

Here (fig. 6) the second principal focus of the first instrument coincides at F with the first of the second. (In the figure, the focal distances of both instruments are taken in the opposite direction from that formerly assumed. They are therefore to be regarded as *negative*.)

In the first place, F_2' is conjugate to F_1, for a pencil whose focus before incidence is F_1 will be parallel to the axis between the instruments, and will converge to F_2' after emergence.

Also if $G_1 g_1$ be an object in the first principal plane, $G_2 g_2$ will be its first image, equal to itself, and if Hh be its final image

$$F_2'H = \frac{FG_1' \cdot G_2'F_2'}{G_2 F} = \frac{f_1' f_2'}{f_2},$$

$$Hh = \frac{FG_1'}{G_2 F} G_2 g_2 = -\frac{f_1'}{f_2} G_1 g_1.$$

Now the linear magnifying power is $\dfrac{Hh}{G_1 g_1}$, and the elongation is $\dfrac{F_2'H}{F_1 G_1}$, because F_2' and H are the images of F_1 and G_1 respectively; therefore

$$l = -\frac{f_1'}{f_2}, \quad \text{and} \quad n = \frac{f_1' f_2'}{f_1 f_2}.$$

The angular magnifying power $= m = \dfrac{l}{n} = -\dfrac{f_1}{f_2'}$.

The centre of the telescope is at the point C, such that

$$F_2'C = \frac{n}{1-n} F_1 F_2'.$$

When n becomes 1 the telescope has no centre. The effect of the instrument is then simply to alter the position of an object by a certain distance measured along the axis, as in the case of refraction through a plate of glass bounded by parallel planes. In certain cases this constant distance itself disappears, as in the case of a combination of three convex lenses of which the focal lengths are

4, 1, 4 and the distances 4 and 4. This combination simply inverts every object without altering its magnitude or distance along the axis.

The preceding theory of perfect instruments is quite independent of the mode in which the course of the rays is changed within the instrument, as we are supposed to know only that the path of every ray is straight before it enters, and after it emerges from the instrument. We have now to consider, how far these results can be applied to actual instruments, in which the course of the rays is changed by reflexion or refraction. We know that such instruments may be made so as to fulfil approximately the conditions of a perfect instrument, but that absolute perfection has not yet been obtained. Let us inquire whether any additional general law of optical instruments can be deduced from the laws of reflexion and refraction, and whether the imperfection of instruments is necessary or removeable.

The following theorem is a necessary consequence of the known laws of reflexion and refraction, whatever theory we adopt.

If we multiply the length of the parts of a ray which are in different media by the indices of refraction of those media, and call the sum of these products the *reduced path* of the ray, then:

I. The extremities of all rays from a given origin, which have the same reduced path, lie in a surface normal to those rays.

II. When a pencil of rays is brought to a focus, the reduced path from the origin to the focus is the same for every ray of the pencil.

In the undulatory theory, the "reduced path" of a ray is the distance through which light would travel in space, during the time which the ray takes to traverse the various media, and the surface of equal "reduced paths" is the wave-surface. In *extraordinary* refraction the wave-surface is not always normal to the ray, but the other parts of the proposition are true in this and all other cases.

From this general theorem in optics we may deduce the following propositions, true for all instruments depending on refraction and reflexion.

PROP. VIII. In any optical instrument depending on refraction or reflexion, if a_1a_1, $b_1\beta_1$ (fig. 7) be two objects and a_2a_2, $b_2\beta_2$ their images, A_1B_1 the distance of the objects, A_2B_2 that of the images, μ_1 the index of refraction of the medium in which the objects are, μ_2 that of the medium in which the images are, then

$$\mu_1 \frac{a_1 a_1 \times b_1 \beta_1}{A_1 B_1} = \mu_2 \frac{a_2 a_2 \times b_2 \beta_2}{A_2 B_2},$$

approximately, when the objects are small.

Since a_2 is the image of a_1, the reduced path of the ray $a_1 b_1 a_2$ will be equal to that of $a_1 \beta_1 a_2$, and the reduced paths of the rays $a_1 \beta_1 a_2$ and $a_1 b_1 a_2$ will be equal.

Also because $b_1 \beta_1$ and $b_2 \beta_2$ are conjugate foci, the reduced paths of the rays $b_1 a_2 b_2$ and $b_1 a_2 b_2$, and of $\beta_1 a_2 \beta_2$ and $\beta_1 a_2 \beta_2$ will be equal. So that the reduced paths

$$a_1 b_1 + b_1 a_2 = a_1 \beta_1 + \beta_1 a_2$$
$$a_1 \beta_1 + \beta_1 a_2 = a_1 b_1 + b_1 a_2$$
$$b_1 a_2 + a_2 b_2 = b_1 a_2 + a_2 b_2$$
$$\beta_1 a_2 + a_2 \beta_2 = \beta_1 a_2 + a_2 \beta_2$$

$$\therefore \; a_1 b_1 + a_1 \beta_1 + a_2 b_2 + a_2 \beta_2 = a_1 \beta_1 + a_1 b_1 + a_2 b_2 + a_2 \beta_2,$$

these being still the *reduced paths* of the rays, that is, the length of each ray multiplied by the index of refraction of the medium.

If the figure is symmetrical about the axis, we may write the equation

$$\mu_1 (a_1 \beta_1 - a_1 b_1) = \mu_2 (a_2 \beta_2 - a_2 b_2),$$

where $a_1 \beta_1$, &c. are now the *actual lengths* of the rays so named.

Now
$$\overline{a_1 \beta_1}^2 = \overline{A_1 B_1}^2 + \tfrac{1}{4} (a_1 a_1 + b_1 \beta_1)^2,$$

$$\overline{a_1 b_1}^2 = \overline{A_1 B_1}^2 + \tfrac{1}{4} (a_1 a_1 - b_1 \beta_1)^2,$$

so that
$$\overline{a_1 \beta_1}^2 - \overline{a_1 b_1}^2 = a_1 a_1 \times b_1 \beta_1,$$

and
$$\mu_1 (a_1 \beta_1 - a_1 b_1) = \mu_1 \frac{a_1 a_1 \times b_1 \beta_1}{a_1 \beta_1 + a_1 b_1}.$$

Similarly
$$\mu_2 (a_2 \beta_2 - a_2 b_2) = \mu_2 \frac{a_2 a_2 \times b_2 \beta_2}{a_2 \beta_2 + a_2 b_2}.$$

So that the equation
$$\mu_1 \frac{a_1 a_1 \times b_1 \beta_1}{a_1 \beta_1 + a_1 b_1} = \mu_2 \frac{a_2 a_2 \times b_2 \beta_2}{a_2 \beta_2 + a_2 b_2},$$

is true accurately, and since when the objects are small, the denominators are nearly $2A_1B_1$ and $2A_2B_2$, the proposition is proved approximately true.

Using the expressions of Prop. III., this equation becomes

$$\mu_1 \frac{1}{c_1} = \mu_2 \frac{xy}{c_2}.$$

Now by Prop. III., when x and y are different, the focal lengths f_1 and f_2 are

$$f_1 = c_1 \frac{xy}{x-y}, \qquad f_2 = c_2 \frac{1}{y-x};$$

therefore $\dfrac{f_1}{f_2} = \dfrac{c_1 xy}{c_2} = \dfrac{\mu_1}{\mu_2}$ by the present theorem.

So that in any instrument, not a telescope, the focal lengths are directly as the indices of refraction of the media to which they belong. If, as in most cases, these media are the same, then the two focal distances are *equal*.

When $x = y$, the instrument becomes a telescope, and we have, by Prop. V., $l = x$, and $n = \dfrac{c_2}{c_1}$; and therefore by this theorem

$$\frac{\mu_1}{\mu_2} = \frac{l^2}{n}.$$

We may find l experimentally by measuring the actual diameter of the image of a known near object, such as the aperture of the object glass. If O be the diameter of the aperture and o that of the circle of light at the eye-hole (which is its image), then

$$l = \frac{o}{O}.$$

From this we find the elongation and the angular magnifying power

$$n = \frac{\mu_2}{\mu_1} l^2, \text{ and } m = \frac{\mu_1}{\mu_2} \frac{1}{l}.$$

When $\mu_1 = \mu_2$, as in ordinary cases, $m = \dfrac{1}{l} = \dfrac{O}{o}$, which is Gauss' rule for determining the magnifying power of a telescope.

PROP. IX. It is impossible, by means of any combination of reflexions and refractions, to produce a *perfect* image of an object at two different distances, unless the instrument be a telescope, and

$$l = n = \frac{\mu_1}{\mu_2}, \qquad m = 1.$$

It appears from the investigation of Prop. VIII. that the results there obtained, if true when the objects are very small, will be incorrect when the objects are large, unless

$$a_1\beta_1 + a_1b_1 \ : \ a_2\beta_2 + a_2b_2 \ :: \ A_1B_1 \ : \ A_2B_2,$$

and it is easy to prove that this cannot be, unless all the lines in the one figure are proportional to the corresponding lines in the other.

In this way we might show that we cannot in general have an astigmatic, plane, undistorted image of a plane object. But we can prove that we cannot get perfectly focussed images of an object in two positions, even at the expense of curvature and distortion.

We shall first prove that if two objects have perfect images, the reduced path of the ray joining any given points of the two objects is equal to that of the ray joining the corresponding points of the images.

Let a_2 (fig. 8) be the perfect image of a_1 and β_2 of β_1. Let

$$A_1a_1 = a_1, \quad B_1\beta_1 = b_1, \quad A_2a_2 = a_2, \quad B_2\beta_2 = b_2, \quad A_1B_1 = c_1, \quad A_2B_2 = c_2.$$

Draw a_1D_1 parallel to the axis to meet the plane B_1, and a_2D_2 to the plane of B_2.

Since everything is symmetrical about the axis of the instrument we shall have the angles $D_1B_1\beta_1 = D_2B_2\beta_2 = \theta$, then in either figure, omitting the suffixes,

$$\overline{a\beta^2} = \overline{aD^2} + \overline{D\beta^2}$$

$$= c^2 + a^2 + b^2 - 2ab\cos\theta.$$

It has been shown in Prop. VIII. that the difference of the reduced paths of the rays a_1b_1, $a_1\beta_1$ in the object must be equal to the difference of the reduced paths of a_2b_2, $a_2\beta_2$ in the image. Therefore, since we may assume any value for θ

$$\mu_1\sqrt{(a_1^2 + b_1^2 + c_1^2 - 2a_1b_1\cos\theta)} - \mu_2\sqrt{(a_2^2 + b_2^2 + c_2^2 - 2a_2b_2\cos\theta)}$$

is constant for all values of θ. This can be only when

$$\mu_1 \sqrt{(a_1^2 + b_1^2 + c_1^2)} = \mu_2 \sqrt{(a_2^2 + b_2^2 + c_2^2)},$$

and
$$\mu_1 \sqrt{(a_1 b_1)} \qquad = \mu_2 \sqrt{(a_2 b_2)},$$

which shows that the constant must vanish, and that the lengths of lines joining corresponding points of the objects and of the images must be inversely as the indices of refraction before incidence and after emergence.

Next let ABC, DEF (fig. 9) represent three points in the one object and three points in the other object, the figure being drawn to a scale so that all the lines in the figure are the actual lines multiplied by μ_1. The lines of the figure represent the reduced paths of the rays between the corresponding points of the objects.

Now it may be shown that the form of this figure cannot be altered without altering the length of one or more of the nine lines joining the points ABC to DEF. Therefore since the reduced paths of the rays in the image are equal to those in the object, the figure must represent the image on a scale of μ_2 to 1, and therefore the instrument must magnify every part of the object alike and elongate the distances parallel to the axis in the same proportion. It is therefore a telescope, and $m = 1$.

If $\mu_1 = \mu_2$, the image is exactly equal to the object, which is the case in reflexion in a plane mirror, which we know to be a perfect instrument for all distances.

The only case in which by refraction at a single surface we can get a perfect image of more than one point of the object, is when the refracting surface is a sphere, radius r, index μ, and when the two objects are spherical surfaces, concentric with the sphere, their radii being $\dfrac{r}{\mu}$, and r; and the two images also concentric spheres, radii μr, and r.

In this latter case the image is perfect, only at these particular distances and not generally.

I am not aware of any other case in which a perfect image of an object can be formed, the rays being straight before they enter, and after they emerge from the instrument. The only case in which perfect astigmatism for all pencils has hitherto been proved to exist, was suggested to me by the consideration

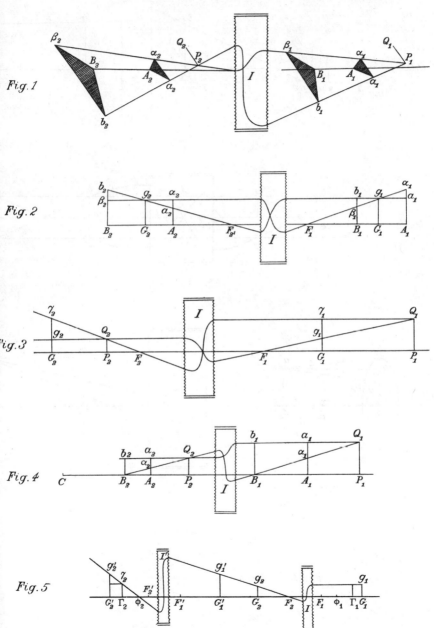

Fig. 1

Fig. 2

Fig. 3

Fig. 4

Fig. 5

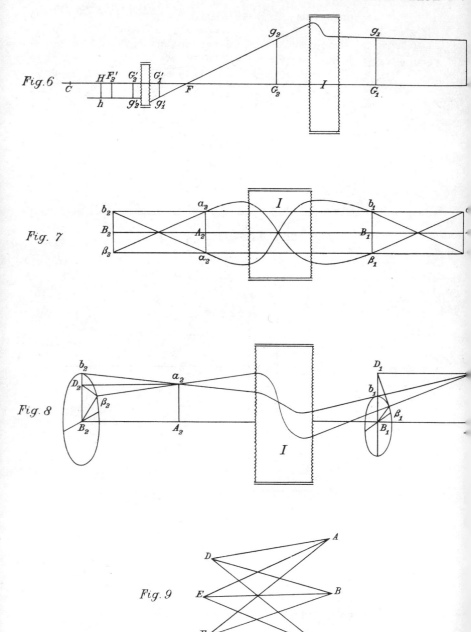

of the structure of the crystalline lens in fish, and was published in one of the problem-papers of the *Cambridge and Dublin Mathematical Journal*. My own method of treating that problem is to be found in that *Journal*, for February, 1854. The case is that of a medium whose index of refraction varies with the distance from a centre, so that if μ_0 be its value at the centre, a a given line, and r the distance of any point where the index is μ, then

$$\mu = \mu_0 \frac{a^2}{a^2 + r^2}.$$

The path of every ray within this medium is a circle in a plane passing through the centre of the medium.

Every ray from a point in the medium, distant b from the centre, will converge to a point on the opposite side of the centre and distant from it $\dfrac{a^2}{b}$.

It will be observed that both the object and the image are included in the variable medium, otherwise the images would not be perfect. This case therefore forms no exception to the result of Prop. IX., in which the object and image are supposed to be outside the instrument.

Aberdeen, 12th Jan., 1858.

[From the *Proceedings of the Royal Society of Edinburgh*, Vol. IV.]

XVIII. *On Theories of the Constitution of Saturn's Rings.*

THE planet Saturn is surrounded by several concentric flattened rings, which appear to be quite free from any connection with each other, or with the planet, except that due to gravitation.

The exterior diameter of the whole system of rings is estimated at about 176,000 miles, the breadth from outer to inner edge of the entire system, 36,000 miles, and the thickness not more than 100 miles.

It is evident that a system of this kind, so broad and so thin, must depend for its stability upon the dynamical equilibrium between the motions of each part of the system, and the attractions which act on it, and that the cohesion of the parts of so large a body can have no effect whatever on its motions, though it were made of the most rigid material known on earth. It is therefore necessary, in order to satisfy the demands of physical astronomy, to explain how a material system, presenting the appearance of Saturn's Rings, can be maintained in permanent motion consistently with the laws of gravitation. The principal hypotheses which present themselves are these—

    I. The rings are solid bodies, regular or irregular.

    II. The rings are fluid bodies, liquid or gaseous.

    III. The rings are composed of loose materials.

The results of mathematical investigation applied to the first case are,—

1st. That a uniform ring cannot have a permanent motion.

2nd. That it is possible, by loading one side of the ring, to produce stability of motion, but that this loading must be very great compared with the whole mass of the rest of the ring, being as 82 to 18.

3rd. That this loading must not only be very great, but very nicely adjusted; because, if it were less than ·81, or more than ·83 of the whole, the motion would be unstable.

The mode in which such a system would be destroyed would be by the collision between the planet and the inside of the ring.

And it is evident that as no loading so enormous in comparison with the ring actually exists, we are forced to consider the rings as fluid, or at least not solid; and we find that, in the case of a fluid ring, waves would be generated, which would break it up into portions, the number of which would depend on the mass of Saturn directly, and on that of the ring inversely.

It appears, therefore, that the only constitution possible for such a ring is a series of disconnected masses, which may be fluid or solid, and need not be equal. The complicated internal motions of such a ring have been investigated, and found to consist of four series of waves, which, when combined together, will reproduce any form of original disturbance with all its consequences. The motion of one of these waves was exhibited to the Society by means of a small mechanical model made by Ramage of Aberdeen.

This theory of the rings, being indicated by the mechanical theory as the only one consistent with permanent motion, is further confirmed by recent observations on the inner obscure ring of Saturn. The limb of the planet is seen through the substance of this ring, not refracted, as it would be through a gas or fluid, but in its true position, as would be the case if the light passed through interstices between the separate particles composing the ring.

As the whole investigations are shortly to be published in a separate form, the mathematical methods employed were not laid before the Society.

XIX. *On the Stability of the motion of Saturn's Rings.*

[An Essay, which obtained the Adams Prize for the year 1856, in the University of Cambridge.]

ADVERTISEMENT.

THE Subject of the Prize was announced in the following terms :—

> The University having accepted a fund, raised by several members of St John's College, for the purpose of founding a Prize to be called the ADAMS PRIZE, for the best Essay on some subject of Pure Mathematics, Astronomy, or other branch of Natural Philosophy, the Prize to be given once in two years, and to be *open to the competition of all persons who have at any time been admitted to a degree in this University :—*

The Examiners give Notice, that the following is the subject for the Prize to be adjudged in 1857 :—

The Motions of Saturn's Rings.

*** The problem may be treated on the supposition that the system of Rings is exactly or very approximately concentric with Saturn and symmetrically disposed about the plane of his Equator, and different hypotheses may be made respecting the physical constitution of the Rings. It may be supposed (1) that they are rigid : (2) that they are fluid, or in part aeriform : (3) that they consist of masses of matter not mutually coherent. The question will be considered to be answered by ascertaining on these hypotheses severally, whether the conditions of mechanical stability are satisfied by the mutual attractions and motions of the Planet and the Rings.

It is desirable that an attempt should also be made to determine on which of the above hypotheses the appearances both of the bright Rings and the recently discovered dark Ring may be most satisfactorily explained; and to indicate any causes to which a change of form, such as is supposed from a comparison of modern with the earlier observations to have taken place, may be attributed.

E. GUEST, *Vice-Chancellor.*
J. CHALLIS.
S. PARKINSON.
W. THOMSON.

March 23, 1855.

CONTENTS.

PART I.

ON THE MOTION OF A RIGID BODY OF ANY FORM ABOUT
A SPHERE.

PART II.

ON THE MOTION OF A RING, THE PARTS OF WHICH ARE NOT
RIGIDLY CONNECTED.

THERE are some questions in Astronomy, to which we are attracted rather on account of their peculiarity, as the possible illustration of some unknown principle, than from any direct advantage which their solution would afford to mankind. The theory of the Moon's inequalities, though in its first stages it presents theorems interesting to all students of mechanics, has been pursued into such intricacies of calculation as can be followed up only by those who make the improvement of the Lunar Tables the object of their lives. The value of the labours of these men is recognised by all who are aware of the importance of such tables in Practical Astronomy and Navigation. The methods by which the results are obtained are admitted to be sound, and we leave to professional astronomers the labour and the merit of developing them.

The questions which are suggested by the appearance of Saturn's Rings cannot, in the present state of Astronomy, call forth so great an amount of labour among mathematicians. I am not aware that any practical use has been made of Saturn's Rings, either in Astronomy or in Navigation. They are too distant, and too insignificant in mass, to produce any appreciable effect on the motion of other parts of the Solar system; and for this very reason it is diffi- cult to determine those elements of their motion which we obtain so accurately in the case of bodies of greater mechanical importance.

But when we contemplate the Rings from a purely scientific point of view, they become the most remarkable bodies in the heavens, except, perhaps, those still less *useful* bodies—the spiral nebulæ. When we have actually seen that great arch swung over the equator of the planet without any visible connexion, we cannot bring our minds to rest. We cannot simply admit that such is the case, and describe it as one of the observed facts in nature, not admitting or requiring explanation. We must either explain its motion on the principles of mechanics, or admit that, in the Saturnian realms, there can be motion regu- lated by laws which we are unable to explain.

The arrangement of the rings is represented in the figure (1) on a scale of one inch to a hundred thousand miles. *S* is a section of Saturn through his equator, *A*, *B* and *C* are the three rings. *A* and *B* have been known for 200 years. They were mistaken by Galileo for protuberances on the planet itself, or perhaps satellites. Huyghens discovered that what he saw was a thin flat ring not touching the planet, and Ball discovered the division between *A* and *B*. Other divisions have been observed splitting these again into concentric rings, but these have not continued visible, the only well-established division being one in the middle of *A*. The third ring *C* was first detected by Mr Bond, at Cambridge U.S. on November 15, 1850; Mr Dawes, not aware of Mr Bond's discovery, observed it on November 29th, and Mr Lassel a few days later. It gives little light compared with the other rings, and is seen where it crosses the planet as an obscure belt, but it is so transparent that the limb of the planet is visible through it, and this without distortion, shewing that the rays of light have not passed through a transparent substance, but between the scattered particles of a discontinuous stream.

It is difficult to estimate the thickness of the system; according to the best estimates it is not more than 100 miles, the diameter of A being 176,418 miles; so that on the scale of our figure the thickness would be one thousandth of an inch.

Such is the scale on which this magnificent system of concentric rings is constructed; we have next to account for their continued existence, and to reconcile it with the known laws of motion and gravitation, so that by rejecting every hypothesis which leads to conclusions at variance with the facts, we may learn more of the nature of these distant bodies than the telescope can yet ascertain. We must account for the rings remaining suspended above the planet, concentric with Saturn and in his equatoreal plane; for the flattened figure of the section of each ring, for the transparency of the inner ring, and for the gradual approach of the inner edge of the ring to the body of Saturn as deduced from all the recorded observations by M. Otto Struvé (*Sur les dimensions des Anneaux de Saturne*—Recueil de Mémoires Astronomiques, Poulkowa, 15 Nov. 1851). For an account of the general appearance of the rings as seen from the planet, see Lardner on the Uranography of Saturn, *Mem. of the Astronomical Society*, 1853. See also the article "Saturn" in Nichol's *Cyclopædia of the Physical Sciences.*

Our curiosity with respect to these questions is rather stimulated than appeased by the investigations of Laplace. That great mathematician, though occupied with many questions which more imperiously demanded his attention, has devoted several chapters in various parts of his great work, to points connected with the Saturnian System.

He has investigated the law of attraction of a ring of small section on a point very near it (*Méc. Cél.* Liv. III. Chap. VI.), and from this he deduces the equation from which the ratio of the breadth to the thickness of each ring is to be found,

$$e = \frac{R^3}{3a^3}\frac{\rho}{\rho'} = \frac{\lambda(\lambda-1)}{(\lambda+1)(3\lambda^2+1)},$$

where R is the radius of Saturn, and ρ his density; a the radius of the ring, and ρ' its density; and λ the ratio of the breadth of the ring to its thickness. The equation for determining λ when e is given has one negative root which must be rejected, and two roots which are positive while $e < 0\cdot0543$, and impossible when e has a greater value. At the critical value of e, $\lambda = 2\cdot594$ nearly.

The fact that λ is impossible when e is above this value, shews that the ring cannot hold together if the ratio of the density of the planet to that of the ring exceeds a certain value. This value is estimated by Laplace at $1\cdot3$, assuming $a = 2R$.

We may easily follow the physical interpretation of this result, if we observe that the forces which act on the ring may be reduced to—

(1) The attraction of Saturn, varying inversely as the square of the distance from his centre.

(2) The centrifugal force of the particles of the ring, acting outwards, and varying directly as the distance from Saturn's polar axis.

(3) The attraction of the ring itself, depending on its form and density, and directed, roughly speaking, towards the centre of its section.

The first of these forces must balance the second somewhere near the mean distance of the ring. Beyond this distance their resultant will be outwards, within this distance it will act inwards.

If the attraction of the ring itself is not sufficient to balance these residual forces, the outer and inner portions of the ring will tend to separate, and the ring will be split up; and it appears from Laplace's result that this will be the case if the density of the ring is less than $\frac{1\,0}{1\,3}$ of that of the planet.

This condition applies to all rings whether broad or narrow, of which the parts are separable, and of which the outer and inner parts revolve with the same angular velocity.

Laplace has also shewn (Liv. v. Chap. iii.), that on account of the oblateness of the figure of Saturn, the planes of the rings will follow that of Saturn's equator through every change of its position due to the disturbing action of other heavenly bodies.

Besides this, he proves most distinctly (Liv. iii. Chap. vi.), that a solid uniform ring cannot possibly revolve about a central body in a permanent manner, for the slightest displacement of the centre of the ring from the centre of the planet would originate a motion which would never be checked, and would inevitably precipitate the ring upon the planet, not necessarily by breaking the ring, but by the inside of the ring falling on the equator of the planet.

He therefore infers that the rings are irregular solids, whose centres of gravity do not coincide with their centres of figure. We may draw the conclusion more formally as follows, "If the rings were solid and uniform, their motion would be unstable, and they would be destroyed. But they are not destroyed, and their motion is stable; therefore they are either not uniform or not solid."

I have not discovered * either in the works of Laplace or in those of more recent mathematicians, any investigation of the motion of a ring either not uniform or not solid. So that in the present state of mechanical science, we do not know whether an irregular solid ring, or a fluid or disconnected ring, can revolve permanently about a central body; and the Saturnian system still remains an unregarded witness in heaven to some necessary, but as yet unknown, development of the laws of the universe.

We know, since it has been demonstrated by Laplace, that a uniform solid ring cannot revolve permanently about a planet. We propose in this Essay to determine the amount and nature of the irregularity which would be required to make a permanent rotation possible. We shall find that the stability of the motion of the ring would be ensured by loading the ring at one point with a

---

* Since this was written, Prof. Challis has pointed out to me three important papers in Gould's *Astronomical Journal*:—Mr G. P. Bond *on the Rings of Saturn* (May 1851) and Prof. B. Pierce of Harvard University *on the Constitution of Saturn's Rings* (June 1851), and *on the Adams' Prize Problem* for 1856 (Sept. 1855). These American mathematicians have both considered the conditions of statical equilibrium of a transverse section of a ring, and have come to the conclusion that the rings, if they move each as a whole, must be very narrow compared with the observed rings, so that in reality there must be a great number of them, each revolving with its own velocity. They have also entered on the question of the fluidity of the rings, and Prof. Pierce has made an investigation as to the permanence of the motion of an irregular solid ring and of a fluid ring. The paper in which these questions are treated at large has not (so far as I am aware) been published, and the references to it in Gould's Journal are intended to give rather a popular account of the results, than an accurate outline of the methods employed. In treating of the attractions of an irregular ring, he makes admirable use of the theory of potentials, but his published investigation of the motion of such a body contains some oversights which are due perhaps rather to the imperfections of popular language than to any thing in the mathematical theory. The only part of the theory of a fluid ring which he has yet given an account of, is that in which he considers the form of the ring at any instant as an ellipse; corresponding to the case where $n = \omega$, and $m = 1$. As I had only a limited time for reading these papers, and as I could not ascertain the methods used in the original investigations, I am unable at present to state how far the results of this essay agree with or differ from those obtained by Prof. Pierce.

heavy satellite about $4\frac{1}{2}$ times the weight of the ring, but this load, besides being inconsistent with the observed appearance of the rings, must be far too artificially adjusted to agree with the natural arrangements observed elsewhere, for a very small error in excess or defect would render the ring again unstable.

We are therefore constrained to abandon the theory of a solid ring, and to consider the case of a ring, the parts of which are not rigidly connected, as in the case of a ring of independent satellites, or a fluid ring.

There is now no danger of the whole ring or any part of it being precipitated on the body of the planet. Every particle of the ring is now to be regarded as a satellite of Saturn, disturbed by the attraction of a ring of satellites at the same mean distance from the planet, each of which however is subject to slight displacements. The mutual action of the parts of the ring will be so small compared with the attraction of the planet, that no part of the ring can ever cease to move round Saturn as a satellite.

But the question now before us is altogether different from that relating to the solid ring. We have now to take account of variations in the form and arrangement of the parts of the ring, as well as its motion as a whole, and we have as yet no security that these variations may not accumulate till the ring entirely loses its original form, and collapses into one or more satellites, circulating round Saturn. In fact such a result is one of the leading doctrines of the "nebular theory" of the formation of planetary systems: and we are familiar with the actual breaking up of fluid rings under the action of "capillary" force, in the beautiful experiments of M. Plateau.

In this essay I have shewn that such a destructive tendency actually exists, but that by the revolution of the ring it is converted into the condition of dynamical stability. As the scientific interest of Saturn's Rings depends at present mainly on this question of their stability, I have considered their motion rather as an illustration of general principles, than as a subject for elaborate calculation, and therefore I have confined myself to those parts of the subject which bear upon the question of the permanence of a given form of motion.

There is a very general and very important problem in Dynamics, the solution of which would contain all the results of this Essay and a great deal more. It is this—

"Having found a particular solution of the equations of motion of any material system, to determine whether a slight disturbance of the motion indicated by the solution would cause a small periodic variation, or a total derangement of the motion."

The question may be made to depend upon the conditions of a maximum or a minimum of a function of many variables, but the theory of the tests for distinguishing maxima from minima by the Calculus of Variations becomes so intricate when applied to functions of several variables, that I think it doubtful whether the physical or the abstract problem will be first solved.

PART I.

ON THE MOTION OF A RIGID BODY OF ANY FORM ABOUT A SPHERE.

WE confine our attention for the present to the motion in the plane of reference, as the interest of our problem belongs to the character of this motion, and not to the librations, if any, from this plane.

Let S (Fig. 2) be the centre of gravity of the sphere, which we may call Saturn, and R that of the rigid body, which we may call the Ring. Join RS, and divide it in G so that

$$SG : GR :: R : S,$$

R and S being the masses of the Ring and Saturn respectively.

Then G will be the centre of gravity of the system, and its position will be unaffected by any mutual action between the parts of the system. Assume G as the point to which the motions of the system are to be referred. Draw GA in a direction fixed in space.

Let $AGR = \theta$, and $SR = r$,

then $GR = \dfrac{S}{S+R} r$, and $GS = \dfrac{R}{S+R} r$,

so that the positions of S and R are now determined.

Let BRB' be a straight line through R, *fixed with respect to the substance of the ring*, and let $BRK = \phi$.

This determines the angular position of the ring, so that from the values of r, θ, and ϕ the configuration of the system may be deduced, as far as relates to the plane of reference.

We have next to determine the forces which act between the ring and the sphere, and this we shall do by means of the *potential function* due to the ring, which we shall call V.

The value of V for any point of space S, depends on its position relatively to the ring, and it is found from the equation

$$V = \Sigma \left(\frac{dm}{r'} \right),$$

where dm is an element of the mass of the ring, and r' is the distance of that element from the given point, and the summation is extended over every element of mass belonging to the ring. V will then depend entirely upon the position of the point S relatively to the ring, and may be expressed as a function of r, the distance of S from R, the centre of gravity of the ring, and ϕ, the angle which the line SR makes with the line RB, fixed in the ring.

A particle P, placed at S, will, by the theory of potentials, experience a moving force $P \dfrac{dV}{dr}$ in the direction which tends to increase r, and $P \dfrac{1}{r} \dfrac{dV}{d\phi}$ in a tangential direction, tending to increase ϕ.

Now we know that the attraction of a sphere is the same as that of a particle of equal mass placed at its centre. The forces acting between the sphere and the ring are therefore $S \dfrac{dV}{dr}$ tending to increase r, and a tangential force $S \dfrac{1}{r} \dfrac{dV}{d\phi}$, applied at S tending to increase ϕ. In estimating the effect of this latter force on the ring, we must resolve it into a tangential force $S \dfrac{1}{r} \dfrac{dV}{d\phi}$ acting at R, and a couple $S \dfrac{dV}{d\phi}$ tending to increase ϕ.

We are now able to form the equations of motion for the planet and the ring.

For the planet

$$S \frac{d}{dt} \left\{ \left(\frac{Rr}{S+R} \right)^2 \frac{d\theta}{dt} \right\} = - \frac{R}{S+R} \, S \frac{dV}{d\phi} \quad \text{.................(1),}$$

$$S \frac{d^2}{dt^2} \left(\frac{Rr}{S+R} \right) - S \frac{Rr}{S+R} \left(\frac{d\theta}{dt} \right)^2 = S \frac{dV}{dr} \quad \text{.....................(2).}$$

For the centre of gravity of the ring,

$$R \frac{d}{dt} \left\{ \left(\frac{Sr}{S+R} \right)^2 \frac{d\theta}{dt} \right\} = - \frac{S}{S+R} \, S \frac{dV}{d\phi} \quad \text{.................(3),}$$

$$R \frac{d^2}{dt^2} \left(\frac{Sr}{S+R} \right) - R \frac{Sr}{S+R} \left(\frac{d\theta}{dt} \right)^2 = S \frac{dV}{dr} \quad \text{.................(4).}$$

For the rotation of the ring about its centre of gravity,

$$Rk^2 \frac{d^2}{dt^2} (\theta + \phi) = S \frac{dV}{d\phi} \quad \text{.............................(5),}$$

where k is the radius of gyration of the ring about its centre of gravity.

Equation (3) and (4) are necessarily identical with (1) and (2), and shew that the orbit of the centre of gravity of the ring must be similar to that of the Planet. Equations (1) and (3) are equations of areas, (2) and (4) are those of the radius vector.

Equations (3), (4) and (5) may be thus written,

$$R \left\{ 2r \frac{dr}{dt} \frac{d\theta}{dt} + r^2 \frac{d^2\theta}{dt^2} \right\} + (R+S) \frac{dV}{d\phi} = 0 \quad \text{....................(6),}$$

$$R \left\{ \frac{d^2r}{dt^2} - r \left(\frac{d\theta}{dt} \right)^2 \right\} - (R+S) \frac{dV}{dr} \quad = 0 \quad \text{....................(7),}$$

$$Rk^2 \left(\frac{d^2\theta}{dt^2} + \frac{d^2\phi}{dt^2} \right) - S \frac{dV}{d\phi} \quad = 0 \quad \text{....................(8).}$$

These are the necessary and sufficient data for determining the motion of the ring, the initial circumstances being given.

PROB. I.   To find the conditions under which a uniform motion of the ring is possible.

By a uniform motion is here meant a motion of uniform rotation, during which the position of the centre of the Planet with respect to the ring does not change.

In this case r and ϕ are constant, and therefore V and its differential coefficients are given. Equation (7) becomes,

$$Rr \left(\frac{d\theta}{dt}\right)^2 + (R+S)\frac{dV}{dr} = 0,$$

which shews that the angular velocity is constant, and that

$$\left(\frac{d\theta}{dt}\right)^2 = -\frac{R+S}{Rr}\frac{dV}{dr} = \omega^2, \text{ say} \quad \ldots\ldots\ldots\ldots\ldots\ldots (9).$$

Hence, $\frac{d^2\theta}{dt^2} = 0$, and therefore by equation (8),

$$\frac{dV}{d\phi} = 0 \ldots\ldots\ldots\ldots\ldots\ldots\ldots\ldots\ldots\ldots\ldots\ldots\ldots(10).$$

Equations (9) and (10) are the conditions under which the uniform motion is possible, and if they were exactly fulfilled, the uniform motion would go on for ever if not disturbed. But it does not follow that if these conditions were *nearly* fulfilled, or that if when accurately adjusted, the motion were *slightly* disturbed, the motion would go on for ever *nearly* uniform. The effect of the disturbance might be either to produce a periodic variation in the elements of the motion, the amplitude of the variation being small, or to produce a displacement which would increase indefinitely, and derange the system altogether. In the one case the motion would be *dynamically stable*, and in the other it would be *dynamically unstable*. The investigation of these displacements while still very small will form the next subject of inquiry.

PROB. II.   To find the equations of the motion when slightly disturbed.

Let $r = r_0$, $\theta = \omega t$ and $\phi = \phi_0$ in the case of uniform motion, and let

$$r = r_0 + r_1,$$
$$\theta = \omega t + \theta_1,$$
$$\phi = \phi_0 + \phi_1,$$

when the motion is slightly disturbed, where r_1, θ_1, and ϕ_1 are to be treated as small quantities of the first order, and their powers and products are to be neglected. We may expand $\frac{dV}{dr}$ and $\frac{dV}{d\phi}$ by Taylor's Theorem,

$$\frac{dV}{dr} = \frac{dV}{dr} + \frac{d^2V}{dr^2}\ r_1 + \frac{d^2V}{drd\phi}\ \phi_1,$$

$$\frac{dV}{d\phi} = \frac{dV}{d\phi} + \frac{d^2V}{drd\phi}\ r_1 + \frac{d^2V}{d\phi^2}\ \phi_1,$$

where the values of the differential coefficients on the right-hand side of the equations are those in which r_0 stands for r, and ϕ_0 for ϕ.

Calling
$$\frac{d^2V}{dr^2} = L, \quad \frac{d^2V}{dr\,d\phi} = M, \quad \frac{d^2V}{d\phi^2} = N,$$

and taking account of equations (9) and (10), we may write these equations,

$$\frac{dV}{dr} = -\frac{Rr_0}{R+S}\omega^2 + Lr_1 + M\phi_1,$$

$$\frac{dV}{d\phi} = Mr_1 + N\phi_1.$$

Substituting these values in equations (6), (7), (8), and retaining all small quantities of the first order while omitting their powers and products, we have the following system of linear equations in r_1, θ_1, and ϕ_1,

$$R\left(2r_0\omega\frac{dr_1}{dt} + r_0^2\frac{d^2\theta_1}{dt^2}\right) + (R+S)\,(Mr_1 + N\phi_1) \quad = 0 \,\ldots\ldots\ldots(11),$$

$$R\left(\frac{d^2r_1}{dt^2} - \omega^2r_1 - 2r_0\omega\frac{d\theta_1}{dt}\right) - (R+S)\,(Lr_1 + M\phi_1) = 0 \,\ldots\ldots\ldots(12),$$

$$Rk^2\left(\frac{d^2\theta_1}{dt^2} + \frac{d\phi_1}{dt^2}\right) - S\,(Mr_1 + N\phi_1) \qquad = 0 \,\ldots\ldots\ldots(13).$$

PROB. III. To reduce the three simultaneous equations of motion to the form of a single linear equation.

Let us write n instead of the symbol $\dfrac{d}{dt}$, then arranging the equations in terms of r_1, θ_1, and ϕ_1, they may be written:

$$\{2R_0\omega n + (R+S)\,M\}\,r_1 + (Rr_0^2n^2)\,\theta_1 + (R+S)\,N\phi_1 \qquad = 0 \,\ldots\ldots(14),$$

$$\{Rn^2 - R\omega^2 - (R+S)\,L\}\,r_1 - (2Rr_0\omega n)\,\theta_1 - (R+S)\,M\phi_1 = 0 \,\ldots\ldots(15),$$

$$-(SM)\,r_1 + (Rk^2n^2)\,\theta_1 + (Rk^2n^2 - SN)\,\phi_1 \qquad = 0 \,\ldots\ldots(16).$$

Here we have three equations to determine three quantities r_1, θ_1, ϕ_1; but it is evident that only a relation can be determined between them, and that in the process for finding their absolute values, the three quantities will vanish together, and leave the following relation among the coefficients,

$$\left.\begin{aligned}
&-\{2Rr_0\omega n+(R+S)\,M\}\,\{2Rr_0\omega n\}\,\{Rk^2n^2-SN\}\\
&+\{Rn^2-R\omega^2-(R+S)\,L\}\,\{Rk^2n^2\}\,\{(R+S)\,N\}\\
&+(SM)\,(Rr_0^2n^2)\,(R+S)\,M-(SM)\,(2Rr_0\omega n)\,(R+S)\,N\\
&+\{2Rr_0\omega n+(R+S)\,M\}\,\{Rk^2n^2\}\,\{(R+S)\,M\}\\
&-\{Rn^2-R\omega^2-(R+S)\}\,\{Rr_0^2n^2\}\,\{Rk^2n^2-SN\}
\end{aligned}\right\}=0\ \dots\dots(17).$$

By multiplying up, and arranging by powers of n and dividing by Rn^2, this equation becomes

$$An^4+Bn^2+C=0\ \dots\dots\dots\dots\dots\dots\dots\dots(18),$$

where

$$\left.\begin{aligned}
A&=R^2r_0^2k^2,\\
B&=3R^2r_0^2k^2\omega^2-R\,(R+S)\,Lr_0^2k^2-R\,\{(R+S)\,k^2+Sr^2\}\,N\\
C&=R\,\{(R+S)\,k^2-3Sr_0^2\}\,\omega^2+(R+S)\,\{(R+S)\,k^2+Sr_0^2\}\,(LN-M^2)
\end{aligned}\right\}\ \dots\dots(19).$$

Here we have a biquadratic equation in n which may be treated as a quadratic in n^2, it being remembered that n stands for the operation $\dfrac{d}{dt}$.

Prob. IV. To determine whether the motion of the ring is stable or unstable, by means of the relations of the coefficients A, B, C.

The equations to determine the forms of r_1, θ_1, and ϕ_1 are all of the form

$$A\,\frac{d^4u}{dt^4}+B\,\frac{d^2u}{dt^2}+Cu=0\ \dots\dots\dots\dots\dots\dots(20),$$

and if n be one of the four roots of equation (18), then

$$u=De^{nt}$$

will be one of the four terms of the solution, and the values of r_1, θ_1, and ϕ_1 will differ only in the values of the coefficient D.

Let us inquire into the nature of the solution in different cases.

(1) If n be positive, this term would indicate a displacement which must increase indefinitely, so as to destroy the arrangement of the system.

(2) If n be negative, the disturbance which it belongs to would gradually die away.

(3) If n be a pure impossible quantity, of the form $\pm a\sqrt{-1}$, then there will be a term in the solution of the form $D\cos(at+a)$, and this would indicate a periodic variation, whose amplitude is D, and period $\dfrac{2\pi}{a}$.

(4) If n be of the form $b \pm \sqrt{-1}a$, the first term being positive and the second impossible, there will be a term in the solution of the form

$$D\epsilon^{bt} \cos (at + a),$$

which indicates a periodic disturbance, whose amplitude continually increases till it disarranges the system.

(5) If n be of the form $-b \pm \sqrt{-1}a$, a negative quantity and an impossible one, the corresponding term of the solution is

$$D\epsilon^{-bt} \cos (at + a),$$

which indicates a periodic disturbance whose amplitude is constantly diminishing.

It is manifest that the first and fourth cases are inconsistent with the permanent motion of the system. Now since equation (18) contains only even powers of n, it must have pairs of equal and opposite roots, so that every root coming under the second or fifth cases, implies the existence of another root belonging to the first or fourth. If such a root exists, some disturbance may occur to produce the kind of derangement corresponding to it, so that the system is not safe unless roots of the first and fourth kinds are altogether excluded. This cannot be done without excluding those of the second and fifth kinds, so that, to insure stability, all the four roots must be of the third kind, that is, pure impossible quantities.

That this may be the case, both values of n^2 must be real and negative, and the conditions of this are—

1st. That A, B, and C should be of the same sign,

2ndly. That $B^2 > 4AC$.

When these conditions are fulfilled, the disturbances will be periodic and consistent with stability. When they are not both fulfilled, a small disturbance may produce total derangement of the system.

PROB. V. To find the centre of gravity, the radius of gyration, and the variations of the potential near the centre of a circular ring of small but variable section.

Let a be the radius of the ring, and let θ be the angle subtended at the centre between the radius through the centre of gravity and the line through a given point in the ring. Then if μ be the mass of unit of length of the ring near the given point, μ will be a periodic function of θ, and may there-fore be expanded by Fourier's theorem in the series,

$$\mu = \frac{R}{2\pi a} \left\{ 1 + 2f \cos \theta + \tfrac{2}{3}g \cos 2\theta + \tfrac{2}{3}h \sin 2\theta + 2i \cos (3\theta + a) + \&c. \right\} \dots (21),$$

where f, g, h, &c. are arbitrary coefficients, and R is the mass of the ring.

(1) The moment of the ring about the diameter perpendicular to the prime radius is

$$R r_0 = \int_0^{2\pi} \mu a^2 \cos \theta d\theta = R a f,$$

therefore the distance of the centre of gravity from the centre of the ring,

$$r_0 = a f.$$

(2) The radius of gyration of the ring about its centre in its own plane is evidently the radius of the ring $= a$, but if k be that about the centre of gravity, we have

$$k^2 + r_0^2 = a^2 ;$$
$$\therefore \ k^2 = a^2 (1 - f^2).$$

(3) The potential at any point is found by dividing the mass of each element by its distance from the given point, and integrating over the whole mass.

Let the given point be near the centre of the ring, and let its position be defined by the co-ordinates r' and ψ, of which r' is small compared with a.

The distance (ρ) between this point and a point in the ring is

$$\frac{1}{\rho} = \frac{1}{a} \left\{ 1 + \frac{r'}{a} \cos (\psi - \theta) + \tfrac{1}{4} \left(\frac{r'}{a} \right)^2 + \tfrac{3}{4} \left(\frac{r'}{a} \right)^2 \cos 2 (\psi - \theta) + \&c. \right\}.$$

The other terms contain powers of $\dfrac{r'}{a}$ higher than the second.

We have now to determine the value of the integral,

$$V = \int_0^{2\pi} \frac{\mu}{\rho} a d\theta ;$$

and in multiplying the terms of (μ) by those of $\left(\dfrac{1}{\rho} \right)$, we need retain only those which contain constant quantities, for all those which contain sines or cosines of multiples of $(\psi - \theta)$ will vanish when integrated between the limits. In this way we find

$$V = \frac{R}{a} \left\{ 1 + f \frac{r'}{a} \cos \psi + \tfrac{1}{4} \frac{r'^2}{a^2} (1 + g \cos 2\psi + h \sin 2\psi) \right\} \dots\dots\dots (22).$$

The other terms containing higher powers of $\dfrac{r'}{a}$.

In order to express V in terms of r_1 and ϕ_1, as we have assumed in the former investigation, we must put

$$r' \cos \psi = -r_1 + \tfrac{1}{2} r_0 \phi_1^2,$$
$$r' \sin \psi = -r_0 \phi_1,$$
$$V = \frac{R}{a} \left\{ 1 - f \frac{r_1}{a} + \tfrac{1}{4} \frac{r_1^2}{a^2} (1+g) + \tfrac{1}{2} \frac{h}{a} f r_1 \phi_1 + \tfrac{1}{4} f^2 \phi_1^2 (3-g) \right\} \dots\dots\dots\dots (23).$$

From which we find $\left(\dfrac{dV}{dr} \right)_0 = -\dfrac{R}{a^2} f$,

$$\left. \begin{array}{l} \left(\dfrac{d^2 V}{dr^2} \right)_0 = L = \dfrac{R}{2a^3} (1+g) \\[2mm] \left(\dfrac{d^2 V}{dr\,d\phi} \right)_0 = M = \dfrac{R}{2a^2} fh \\[2mm] \left(\dfrac{d^2 V}{d\phi^2} \right)_0 = N = \dfrac{R}{2a} f^2 (3-g) \end{array} \right\} \dots\dots\dots\dots\dots\dots (24).$$

These results may be confirmed by the following considerations applicable to any circular ring, and not involving any expansion or integration. Let af be the distance of the centre of gravity from the centre of the ring, and let the ring revolve about its centre with velocity ω. Then the force necessary to keep the ring in that orbit will be $-Raf\omega^2$.

But let S be a mass fixed at the centre of the ring, then if

$$\omega^2 = \frac{S}{a^3},$$

every portion of the ring will be separately retained in its orbit by the attraction of S, so that the whole ring will be retained in its orbit. The resultant attraction must therefore pass through the centre of gravity, and be

$$-Raf\omega^2 = -RS \frac{f}{a^2};$$

therefore

$$\frac{dV}{dr} = -R \frac{f}{a^2}.$$

The equation
$$\frac{d^2V}{dx^2} + \frac{d^2V}{dy^2} + \frac{d^2V}{dz^2} + 4\pi\rho = 0$$

is true for any system of matter attracting according to the law of gravitation. If we bear in mind that the expression is identical in form with that which measures the total efflux of fluid from a differential element of volume, where $\frac{dV}{dx}$, $\frac{dV}{dy}$, $\frac{dV}{dz}$ are the rates at which the fluid passes through its sides, we may easily form the equation for any other case. Now let the position of a point in space be determined by the co-ordinates r, ϕ and z, where z is measured perpendicularly to the plane of the angle ϕ. Then by choosing the directions of the axes x, y, z, so as to coincide with those of the radius vector r, the perpendicular to it in the plane of ϕ, and the normal, we shall have

$$dx = dr, \qquad dy = rd\phi, \qquad dz = dz,$$

$$\frac{dV}{dx} = \frac{dV}{dr}, \quad \frac{dV}{dy} = \frac{1}{r}\frac{dV}{d\phi}, \quad \frac{dV}{dz} = \frac{dV}{dz}.$$

The quantities of fluid passing through an element of area in each direction are

$$\frac{dV}{dr}\, rd\phi dz, \quad \frac{dV}{d\phi}\frac{1}{r}drdz, \quad \frac{dV}{dz}\, rd\phi dr,$$

so that the expression for the whole efflux is

$$\frac{1}{r}\frac{dV}{dr} + \frac{d^2V}{dr^2} + \frac{1}{r^2}\frac{d^2V}{d\phi^2} + \frac{d^2V}{dz^2} \quad\dots\dots\dots\dots\dots\dots (25),$$

which is necessarily equivalent to the former expression.

Now at the centre of the ring $\frac{d^2V}{dz^2}$ may be found by considering the attraction on a point just above the centre at a distance z,

$$\frac{dV}{dz} = -R\frac{z}{(a^2+z^2)^{\frac{3}{2}}},$$

$$\frac{d^2V}{dz^2} = -\frac{R}{a^3}, \text{ when } z = 0.$$

Also we know $\qquad \dfrac{1}{r}\dfrac{dV}{dr} = -\dfrac{R}{a^3}$, and $r = af$,

so that in any circular ring $\qquad \dfrac{d^2V}{dr^2} + \dfrac{1}{a^2f^2}\dfrac{d^2V}{d\phi^2} = 2\dfrac{R}{a^3} \quad\dots\dots\dots\dots\dots\dots (26),$

an equation satisfied by the former values of L and N.

By referring to the original expression for the variable section of the ring, it appears that the effect of the coefficient f is to make the ring thicker on one side and thinner on the other in a uniformly graduated manner. The effect of g is to thicken the ring at two opposite sides, and diminish its section in the parts between. The coefficient h indicates an inequality of the same kind, only not symmetrically disposed about the diameter through the centre of gravity.

Other terms indicating inequalities recurring three or more times in the circumference of the ring, have no effect on the values of L, M and N. There is one remarkable case, however, in which the irregularity consists of a single heavy particle placed at a point on the circumference of the ring.

Let P be the mass of the particle, and Q that of the uniform ring on which it is fixed, then $R = P + Q$,

$$f = \frac{P}{R},$$

$$L = 2\,\frac{P}{a^3} + \frac{Q}{2a^3} = \frac{P+Q}{2a^3}\left(1 + 3\,\frac{P}{R}\right) = \frac{R}{2a^3}(1 + g);$$

$$\therefore\ g = \frac{3P}{R} = 3f \dots\dots\dots\dots\dots\dots\dots\dots(27).$$

PROB. VI. To determine the conditions of stability of the motion in terms of the coefficients f, g, h, which indicate the distribution of mass in the ring.

The quantities which enter into the differential equation of motion (18) are R, S, k^2, r_0, ω^2, L, M, N. We must observe that S is very large compared with R, and therefore we neglect R in those terms in which it is added to S, and we put

$$S = a^3\omega^2,$$

$$k^2 = a^2(1 - f^2),$$

$$r_0 = af,$$

$$L = \frac{R}{2a^3}(1 + g),$$

$$M = \frac{R}{2a^2}fh,$$

$$N = \frac{R}{2a}f^2(3 - g).$$

Substituting these values in equation (18) and dividing by $R^2 a' f^2$, we obtain

$$(1-f^2)\, n^4 + \left(1 - \tfrac{5}{2} f^2 + \tfrac{1}{2} f^2 g\right) n^2 \omega^2 + \left(\tfrac{9}{4} - 6f^2 - \tfrac{1}{4} g^2 - \tfrac{1}{4} h^2 + 2f^2 g\right) \omega^4 = 0 \ldots\ldots(28).$$

The condition of stability is that this equation shall give both values of n^2 negative, and this renders it necessary that all the coefficients should have the same sign, and that the square of the second should exceed four times the product of the first and third.

(1) Now if we suppose the ring to be uniform, f, g and h disappear, and the equation becomes

$$n^4 + n^2 \omega^2 + \tfrac{9}{4} = 0 \ldots\ldots\ldots\ldots\ldots\ldots\ldots\ldots\ldots\ldots\ldots (29),$$

which gives impossible values to n^2 and indicates the instability of a uniform ring.

(2) If we make g and $h = 0$, we have the case of a ring thicker at one side than the other, and varying in section according to the simple law of sines. We must remember, however, that f must be less than $\tfrac{1}{2}$, in order that the section of the ring at the thinnest part may be real. The equation becomes

$$(1-f^2)\, n^4 + \left(1 - \tfrac{5}{2} f^2\right) n^2 \omega^2 + \left(\tfrac{9}{4} - 6f^2\right) \omega^4 = 0 \ldots\ldots\ldots\ldots\ldots(30).$$

The condition that the third term should be positive gives

$$f^2 < \cdot 375.$$

The condition that n^2 should be real gives

$$71 f^4 - 112 f^2 + 32 \text{ negative,}$$

which requires f^2 to be between $\cdot 37445$ and $1 \cdot 2$.

The condition of stability is therefore that f^2 should lie between

$$\cdot 37445 \text{ and } \cdot 375,$$

but the construction of the ring on this principle requires that f^2 should be less than $\cdot 25$, so that it is impossible to reconcile this form of the ring with the conditions of stability.

(3) Let us next take the case of a uniform ring, loaded with a heavy particle at a point of its circumference. We have then $g = 3f$, $h = 0$, and the equation becomes

$$(1-f^2)\, n^4 + \left(1 - \tfrac{5}{2} f^2 + \tfrac{3}{2} f^3\right) n^2 \omega^2 + \left(\tfrac{9}{4} - \tfrac{33}{4} f^2 + 6f^3\right) \omega^4 = 0 \ldots\ldots\ldots\ldots (31).$$

Dividing each term by $1-f$, we get

$$(1+f)\, n^4 + (1+f-\tfrac{3}{2}f^2)\, n^2\omega^2 + \tfrac{3}{4}\{3\,(1+f)-8f^2\}\,\omega^4 = 0 \ldots\ldots\ldots\ldots(32).$$

The first condition gives f less than $\cdot 8279$.

The second condition gives f greater than $\cdot 815865$.

Let us assume as a particular case between these limits $f = \cdot 82$, which makes the ratio of the mass of the particle to that of the ring as 82 to 18, then the equation becomes

$$1\cdot 82\, n^4 + \cdot 8114\, n^2\omega^2 + \cdot 9696\omega^4 = 0 \ldots\ldots\ldots\ldots\ldots (33),$$

which gives $\qquad \sqrt{-1}\, n = \pm\, \cdot 5916\omega \text{ or } \pm\, \cdot 3076\omega.$

These values of n indicate variations of r_1, θ_1, and ϕ_1, which are compounded of two simple periodic inequalities, the period of the one being $1\cdot 69$ revolutions, and that of the other $3\cdot 251$ revolutions of the ring. The relations between the phases and amplitudes of these inequalities must be deduced from equations (14), (15), (16), in order that the character of the motion may be completely determined.

Equations (14), (15), (16) may be written as follows:

$$(4n\omega + h\omega^2)\, \frac{r_1}{a} + 2fn^2\theta_1 + f(3-g)\, \omega^2\phi_1 = 0 \ldots\ldots\ldots\ldots (34),$$

$$\{n^2 - \tfrac{1}{2}\omega^2\,(3+g)\}\, \frac{r_1}{a} - 2f\omega n\theta_1 - \tfrac{1}{2}fh\omega^2\phi_1 = 0 \ldots\ldots\ldots\ldots (35),$$

$$-fh\omega^2\, \frac{r_1}{a} + 2\,(1-f^2)\, n^2\theta_1 + \{2\,(1-f^2)\, n^2 - f^2\,(3-g)\, \omega^2\}\,\phi_1 = 0 \ldots\ldots (36).$$

By eliminating one of the variables between any two of these equations, we may determine the relation between the two remaining variables. Assuming one of these to be a periodic function of t of the form $A\cos\nu t$, and remembering that n stands for the operation $\dfrac{d}{dt}$, we may find the form of the other.

Thus, eliminating θ_1 between the first and second equations,

$$\{n^3 + \tfrac{1}{2}n\omega^2\,(5-g) + h\omega^3\}\, \frac{r_1}{a} + f\omega^2\{(3-g)\,\omega - \tfrac{1}{2}hn\}\,\phi_1 = 0 \ldots\ldots\ldots\ldots (37).$$

Assuming $\qquad \dfrac{r_1}{a} = A \sin \nu t$, and $\phi_1 = Q \cos(\nu t - \beta)$,

$$\{-\nu^3 + \tfrac{1}{2}\nu\omega^2(5-g)\} A \cos \nu t + h\omega^3 A \sin \nu t + f\omega^3(3-g)Q\cos(\nu t-\beta) + \tfrac{1}{2}fh\omega^2\nu Q \sin(\nu t - \beta).$$

Equating νt to 0, and to $\dfrac{\pi}{2}$, we get the equations

$$\{\nu^3 - \tfrac{1}{2}\nu\omega^2(5-g)\} A = f\omega^2 Q\{(3-g)\omega \cos\beta - \tfrac{1}{2}h\nu \sin\beta\},$$

$$-h\omega^3 A = f\omega^2 Q\{(3-g)\omega \sin\beta + \tfrac{1}{2}h\nu \cos\beta\},$$

from which to determine Q and β.

In all cases in which the mass is disposed symmetrically about the diameter through the centre of gravity, $h = 0$ and the equations may be greatly simplified.

Let $\theta_1 = P \cos(\nu t - \alpha)$, then the second equation becomes

$$\{\nu^2 + \tfrac{1}{2}\omega^2(3+g)\} A \sin \nu t = 2Pf\omega\nu \sin(\nu t - \alpha),$$

whence $\qquad\qquad \alpha = 0, \quad P = \dfrac{\nu^2 + \tfrac{1}{2}\omega^2(3+g)}{2f\omega\nu} A \quad \dotfill (38).$

The first equation becomes

$$4A\omega\nu \cos \nu t - 2Pf\nu^2 \cos \nu t + Qf(3-g)\omega^2 \cos(\nu t - \beta) = 0,$$

whence $\qquad\qquad \beta = 0, \quad Q = \dfrac{\nu^3 - \tfrac{1}{2}\omega^2\nu(5-g)}{f(3-g)\omega^3} A \quad \dotfill (39).$

In the numerical example in which a heavy particle was fixed to the circumference of the ring, we have, when $f = \cdot 82$,

$$\dfrac{\nu}{\omega} = \begin{cases} \cdot 5916 \\ \cdot 3076 \end{cases}, \quad \dfrac{P}{A} = \begin{cases} 3\cdot 21 \\ 5\cdot 72 \end{cases}, \quad \dfrac{Q}{A} = \begin{cases} -1\cdot 229 \\ -\ \cdot 797 \end{cases},$$

so that if we put $\omega t = \theta_0 =$ the mean anomaly,

$$\dfrac{r_1}{a} = A \sin(\cdot 5916\,\theta_0 - \alpha) + B \sin(\cdot 3076\,\theta_0 - \beta) \quad \dotfill (40),$$

$$\theta_1 = 3\cdot 21 A \cos(\cdot 5916\,\theta_0 - \alpha) + 5\cdot 72 B \cos(\cdot 3076\,\theta_0 - \beta) \dotfill (41),$$

$$\phi_1 = -1\cdot 229 A \cos(\cdot 5916\,\theta_0 - \alpha) - 5\cdot 797 B \cos(\cdot 3076\,\theta_0 - \beta) \ \dots (42).$$

These three equations serve to determine r_1, θ_1 and ϕ_1 when the original motion is given. They contain four arbitrary constants A, B, α, β. Now since the original values r_1, θ_1, ϕ_1, and also their first differential coefficients with respect to t, are arbitrary, it would appear that six arbitrary constants ought to enter into the equation. The reason why they do not is that we assume r_0 and θ_0 as the *mean values* of r and θ in the *actual motion*. These quantities therefore depend on the original circumstances, and the two additional arbitrary constants enter into the values of r_0 and θ_0. In the analytical treatment of the problem the differential equation in n was originally of the sixth degree with a solution $n^2 = 0$, which implies the possibility of terms in the solution of the form $Ct + D$.

The existence of such terms depends on the previous equations, and we find that a term of this form may enter into the value of θ, and that r_1 may contain a constant term, but that in both cases these additions will be absorbed into the values of θ_0 and r_0.

PART II.

ON THE MOTION OF A RING, THE PARTS OF WHICH ARE NOT RIGIDLY CONNECTED.

1. In the case of the Ring of invariable form, we took advantage of the principle that the mutual actions of the parts of any system form at all times a system of forces in equilibrium, and we took no account of the attraction between one part of the ring and any other part, since no motion could result from this kind of action. But when we regard the different parts of the ring as capable of independent motion, we must take account of the attraction on each portion of the ring as affected by the irregularities of the other parts, and therefore we must begin by investigating the statical part of the problem in order to determine the forces that act on any portion of the ring, as depending on the instantaneous condition of the rest of the ring.

In order to bring the problem within the reach of our mathematical methods, we limit it to the case in which the ring is *nearly* circular and uniform, and has a transverse section very small compared with the radius of the ring. By analysing the difficulties of the theory of a linear ring, we shall be better able to appreciate those which occur in the theory of the actual rings.

The ring which we consider is therefore small in section, and very nearly circular and uniform, and revolving with nearly uniform velocity. The variations from circular form, uniform section, and uniform velocity must be expressed by a proper notation.

2.   To express the position of an element of a variable ring at a given time in terms of the original position of the element in the ring.

Let S (fig. 3) be the central body, and SA a direction fixed in space.

Let SB be a radius, revolving with the mean angular velocity ω of the ring, so that $ASB = \omega t$.

Let π be an element of the ring in its actual position, and let P be the position it would have had if it had moved uniformly with the mean velocity ω and had not been displaced, then BSP is a constant angle $= s$, and the value of s enables us to identify any element of the ring.

The element may be removed from its mean position P in three different ways.

(1)   By change of distance from S by a quantity $p\pi = \rho$.

(2)   By change of angular position through a space $Pp = \sigma$.

(3)   By displacement perpendicular to the plane of the paper by a quantity ζ.

ρ, σ and ζ are all functions of s and t.   If we could calculate the attractions on any element as depending on the form of these functions, we might determine the motion of the ring for any given original disturbance. We cannot, however, make any calculations of this kind without knowing the form of the functions, and therefore we must adopt the following method of separating the original disturbance into others of simpler form, first given in Fourier's *Traité de Chaleur.*

3.   Let U be a function of s, it is required to express U in a series of sines and cosines of multiples of s between the values $s = 0$ and $s = 2\pi$.

Assume $U = A_1 \cos s + A_2 \cos 2s + \&c. + A_m \cos ms + A_n \cos ns$

$+ B_1 \sin s + B_2 \cos 2s + \&c. + B_m \sin ms + B_n \sin ns.$

Multiply by $\cos ms\, ds$ and integrate, then all terms of the form

$$\int \cos ms \cos ns\, ds \quad \text{and} \quad \int \cos ms \sin ns\, ds$$

will vanish, if we integrate from $s=0$ to $s=2\pi$, and there remains

$$\int_0^{2\pi} U \cos ms\, ds = \pi A_m, \qquad \int_0^{2\pi} U \sin ms\, ds = \pi B_m.$$

If we can determine the values of these integrals in the given case, we can find the proper coefficients A_m, B_m, &c., and the series will then represent the values of U from $s=0$ to $s=2\pi$, whether those values be continuous or discontinuous, and when none of those values are infinite the series will be convergent.

In this way we may separate the most complex disturbances of a ring into parts whose form is that of a circular function of s or its multiples. Each of these partial disturbances may be investigated separately, and its effect on the attractions of the ring ascertained either accurately or approximately.

4. To find the magnitude and direction of the attraction between two elements of a disturbed ring.

Let P and Q (fig. 4) be the two elements, and let their original positions be denoted by s_1 and s_2, the values of the arcs BP, BQ before displacement. The displacement consists in the angle BSP being increased by σ_1 and BSQ by σ_2, while the distance of P from the centre is increased by ρ_1 and that of Q by ρ_2. We have to determine the effect of these displacements on the distance PQ and the angle SPQ.

Let the radius of the ring be unity, and $s_2 - s_1 = 2\theta$, then the original value of PQ will be $2 \sin \theta$, and the increase due to displacement

$$= (\rho_2 + \rho_1) \sin \theta + (\sigma_2 - \sigma_1) \cos \theta.$$

We may write the complete value of PQ thus,

$$PQ = 2 \sin \theta \left\{ 1 + \tfrac{1}{2}(\rho_2 + \rho_1) + \tfrac{1}{2}(\sigma_2 - \sigma_1) \cot \theta \right\} \quad \dots\dots\dots\dots (1).$$

The original value of the angle SPQ was $\dfrac{\pi}{2} - \theta$, and the increase due to displacement is $\qquad \tfrac{1}{2}(\rho_2 - \rho_1) \cot \theta - \tfrac{1}{2}(\sigma_2 - \sigma_1),$

so that we may write the values of $\sin SPQ$ and $\cos SPQ$,

$$\sin SPQ = \cos\theta\left\{1 + \tfrac{1}{2}\left(\rho_2 - \rho_1\right) - \tfrac{1}{2}\left(\sigma_2 - \sigma_1\right)\tan\theta\right\} \quad\dots\dots\dots\dots (2),$$

$$\cos SPQ = \sin\theta\left\{1 - \tfrac{1}{2}\left(\rho_2 - \rho_1\right)\cot^2\theta + \tfrac{1}{2}\left(\sigma_2 - \sigma_1\right)\cot\theta\right\} \quad\dots\dots (3).$$

If we assume the masses of P and Q each equal to $\dfrac{1}{\mu}R$, where R is the mass of the ring, and μ the number of satellites of which it is composed, the accelerating effect of the radial force on P is

$$\frac{1}{\mu}R\frac{\cos SPQ}{PQ^2} = \frac{1}{\mu}\frac{R}{4\sin\theta}\left\{1 - \left(\rho_2 + \rho_1\right) - \tfrac{1}{2}\left(\rho_2 - \rho_1\right)\cot^2\theta - \tfrac{1}{2}\left(\sigma_2 - \sigma_1\right)\cot\theta\right\}\dots(4),$$

and the tangential force

$$\frac{1}{\mu}R\frac{\sin SPQ}{PQ^2} = \frac{1}{\mu}\frac{R\cos\theta}{4\sin^2\theta}\left\{1 - \tfrac{1}{2}\rho_2 - \tfrac{3}{2}\rho_1 - \left(\sigma_2 - \sigma_1\right)\left(\cot\theta + \tfrac{1}{2}\tan\theta\right)\right\}\dots\dots(5).$$

The normal force is $\dfrac{1}{\mu}R\dfrac{\zeta_2 - \zeta_1}{8\sin^3\theta}$.

5. Let us substitute for ρ, σ and ζ their values expressed in a series of sines and cosines of multiples of s, the terms involving ms being

$$\rho_1 = A\cos\left(ms + \alpha\right), \qquad \rho_2 = A\cos\left(ms + \alpha + 2\theta\right),$$

$$\sigma_1 = B\sin\left(ms + \beta\right), \qquad \sigma_2 = B\sin\left(ms + \beta + 2\theta\right),$$

$$\zeta_1 = C\cos\left(ms + \gamma\right), \qquad \zeta_2 = C\cos\left(ms + \gamma + 2\theta\right).$$

The radial force now becomes

$$\frac{1}{\mu}\frac{R}{4\sin\theta}\left\{\begin{array}{l}1 - A\cos\left(ms + \alpha\right)\left(1 + \cos 2m\theta\right) + A\sin\left(ms + \alpha\right)\sin 2m\theta \\[4pt] + \tfrac{1}{2}A\cos\left(ms + \alpha\right)\left(1 - \cos 2m\theta\right)\cot^2\theta - \tfrac{1}{2}A\sin\left(ms + \alpha\right)\sin 2m\theta\cot^2\theta \\[4pt] + \tfrac{1}{2}B\sin\left(ms + \beta\right)\left(1 - \cos 2m\theta\right)\cot\theta - \tfrac{1}{2}B\cos\left(ms + \beta\right)\sin 2m\theta\cot\theta\end{array}\right\} \quad (6).$$

The radial component of the attraction of a corresponding particle on the other side of P may be found by changing the sign of θ. Adding the two together, we have for the effect of the pair

$$\frac{1}{\mu}\frac{R}{2\sin\theta}\left\{1 - A\cos\left(ms + \alpha\right)\left(2\cos^2 m\theta - \sin^2 m\theta\cot^2\theta\right)\right.$$

$$\left. - B\cos\left(ms + \beta\right)\tfrac{1}{2}\sin 2m\theta\cot\theta\right\} \quad\dots\dots\dots\dots (7).$$

Let us put
$$L = \Sigma \left(\tfrac{1}{2} \frac{\sin^2 m\theta \cos^2 \theta}{\sin^3 \theta} - \frac{\cos^2 m\theta}{\sin \theta} \right)$$
$$M = \Sigma \left(\frac{\sin 2m\theta \cos \theta}{4 \sin^2 \theta} \right)$$
$$N = \Sigma \left(\frac{\sin^2 m\theta \cos^2 \theta}{\sin^3 \theta} + \tfrac{1}{2} \frac{\sin^2 m\theta}{\sin \theta} \right) \quad \Bigg\} \quad \ldots\ldots\ldots\ldots\ldots\ldots (8)^*,$$
$$J = \Sigma \left(\frac{\sin^2 m\theta}{2 \sin^3 \theta} \right)$$
$$K = \Sigma \left(\frac{1}{2 \sin \theta} \right)$$

where the summation extends to all the satellites on the same side of P, that is, every value of θ of the form $\frac{x}{\mu} \pi$, where x is a whole number less than $\frac{\mu}{2}$.

The radial force may now be written

$$P = \frac{1}{\mu} R \{ K + LA \cos (ms + a) - MB \cos (ms + \beta) \} \ldots\ldots\ldots\ldots (9).$$

* The following values of several quantities which enter into these investigations are calculated for a ring of 36 satellites.

$$K = 24 \cdot 5.$$

	$\Sigma \frac{\sin^2 m\theta \cos^2 \theta}{\sin^3 \theta}$	$\Sigma \frac{\cos^2 m\theta}{\sin \theta}$	L	M	N
$m = 0$	0	43	-43	0	0
$m = 1$	32	32	-16	16	37
$m = 2$	107	28	26	25	115
$m = 3$	212	25	81	28	221
$m = 4$	401	24	177	32	411
$m = 9$	975	20	468	30	986
$m = 18$	1569	18	767	0	1582

When μ is very great,

$$\left. \frac{\pi}{\mu} \right|^3 L = \cdot 5259 \text{ when } m = \frac{\mu}{2},$$

$$= \cdot 4342 \quad ,, \quad m = \frac{\mu}{3},$$

$$= \cdot 3287 \quad ,, \quad m = \frac{\mu}{4}.$$

The tangential force may be calculated in the same way, it is

$$T = \frac{1}{\mu} R \{MA \sin (ms + \alpha) + NB \sin (ms + \beta)\} \dots\dots\dots\dots (10).$$

The normal force is

$$Z = -\frac{1}{\mu} RJC \cos (ms + \gamma) \dots\dots\dots\dots\dots (11).$$

6. We have found the expressions for the forces which act upon each member of a system of equal satellites which originally formed a uniform ring, but are now affected with displacements depending on circular functions. If these displacements can be propagated round the ring in the form of waves with the velocity $\frac{m}{n}$, the quantities α, β, and γ will depend on t, and the complete expressions will be

$$\left.\begin{array}{l} \rho = A \cos (ms + nt + \alpha) \\ \sigma = B \sin (ms + nt + \beta) \\ \zeta = C \cos (ms + n't + \gamma) \end{array}\right\} \dots\dots\dots\dots\dots\dots(12).$$

Let us find in what cases expressions such as these will be true, and what will be the result when they are not true.

Let the position of a satellite at any time be determined by the values of r, ϕ, and ζ, where r is the radius vector reduced to the plane of reference, ϕ the angle of position measured on that plane, and ζ the distance from it. The equations of motion will be

$$\left.\begin{array}{c} r \left(\dfrac{d\phi}{dt}\right)^2 - \dfrac{d^2r}{dt^2} = S \dfrac{1}{r^2} + P \\[2mm] 2 \dfrac{dr}{dt} \dfrac{d\phi}{dt} + r \dfrac{d^2\phi}{dt^2} = T \\[2mm] \dfrac{d^2\zeta}{dt^2} = -S \dfrac{\zeta}{r^3} + Z \end{array}\right\} \dots\dots\dots\dots(13).$$

If we substitute the value of ζ in the third equation and remember that r is nearly $=1$, we find

$$n'^2 = S + \frac{1}{\mu} RJ \dots\dots\dots\dots\dots (14).$$

As this expression is necessarily positive, the value of n' is always real, and the disturbances normal to the plane of the ring can always be propagated as waves, and therefore can never be the cause of instability. We therefore confine our attention to the motion in the plane of the ring as deduced from the two former equations.

Putting $r = 1 + \rho$ and $\phi = \omega t + s + \sigma$, and omitting powers and products of ρ, σ and their differential coefficients,

$$\left. \begin{array}{l} \omega^2 + \omega^2 \rho + 2\omega \dfrac{d\sigma}{dt} - \dfrac{d^2\rho}{dt^2} = S - 2S\rho + P \\[2mm] 2\omega \dfrac{d\rho}{dt} + \dfrac{d^2\sigma}{dt^2} = T \end{array} \right\} \quad \dots\dots\dots\dots (15).$$

Substituting the values of ρ and σ as given above, these equations become

$$\omega^2 - S - \frac{1}{\mu} RK + \left(\omega^2 + 2S - \frac{1}{\mu} RL + n^2\right) A \cos (ms + nt + a)$$

$$+ \left(2\omega n + \frac{1}{\mu} RM\right) B \cos (ms + nt + \beta) = 0 \dots\dots\dots\dots (16),$$

$$\left(2\omega n + \frac{1}{\mu} RM\right) A \sin (ms + nt + a) + \left(n^2 + \frac{1}{\mu} RN\right) B \sin (ms + nt + \beta) = 0 \dots (17).$$

Putting for $(ms + nt)$ any two different values, we find from the second equation (17)

$$a = \beta \dots\dots\dots\dots\dots\dots\dots\dots (18),$$

and

$$\left(2\omega n + \frac{1}{\mu} RM\right) A + \left(n^2 + \frac{1}{\mu} RN\right) B = 0 \dots\dots\dots\dots (19),$$

and from the first (16)

$$\left(\omega^2 + 2S - \frac{1}{\mu} RL + n^2\right) A + \left(2\omega n + \frac{1}{\mu} RM\right) B = 0 \dots\dots (20),$$

and

$$\omega^2 - S - \frac{1}{\mu} RK = 0 \dots\dots\dots\dots\dots\dots (21).$$

Eliminating A and B from these equations, we get

$$n^4 - \left\{3\omega^2 - 2S + \frac{1}{\mu} R (L - N)\right\} n^2$$

$$- 4\omega \frac{1}{\mu} RMn + \left(\omega^2 + 2S - \frac{1}{\mu} RL\right) \frac{1}{\mu} RN - \frac{1}{\mu^2} R^2 M^2 = 0 \dots\dots\dots\dots (22),$$

a biquadratic equation to determine n.

For every *real* value of n there are terms in the expressions for ρ and σ of the form

$$A \cos (ms + nt + a).$$

For every *pure impossible* root of the form $\pm\sqrt{-1}n'$ there are terms of the forms

$$A\epsilon^{\pm n't} \cos(ms + a).$$

Although the negative exponential coefficient indicates a continually diminishing displacement which is consistent with stability, the positive value which necessarily accompanies it indicates a continually increasing disturbance, which would completely derange the system in course of time.

For every mixed root of the form $\pm\sqrt{-1}n' + n$, there are terms of the form

$$A\epsilon^{\pm n't} \cos(ms + nt + a).$$

If we take the positive exponential, we have a series of m waves travelling with velocity $\dfrac{n}{m}$ and increasing in amplitude with the coefficient $\epsilon^{+n't}$. The negative exponential gives us a series of m waves gradually dying away, but the negative exponential cannot exist without the possibility of the positive one having a finite coefficient, so that it is necessary for the stability of the motion that the four values of n be all real, and none of them either impossible quantities or the sums of possible and impossible quantities.

We have therefore to determine the relations among the quantities K, L, M, N, R, S, that the equation

$$n^4 - \left\{S + \frac{1}{\mu} R (3K + L - N)\right\} n^2$$

$$- 4\omega \frac{1}{\mu} RMn + \left\{3S + \frac{1}{\mu} R (K - L)\right\} \frac{1}{\mu} RN - \frac{1}{\mu^2} R^2 M^2 = U = 0$$

may have four real roots.

7. In the first place, U is positive, when n is a large enough quantity, whether positive or negative.

It is also positive when $n = 0$, provided S be large, as it must be, compared with $\dfrac{1}{\mu} RL$, $\dfrac{1}{\mu} RM$ and $\dfrac{1}{\mu} RN$.

If we can now find a positive and a negative value of n for which U is negative, there must be four real values of n for which $U = 0$, and the four roots will be real.

Now if we put $n = \pm \sqrt{\tfrac{1}{2}} \sqrt{S}$,

$$U = -\tfrac{1}{4}S^2 + \tfrac{1}{2}\frac{1}{\mu} R \left(7N \pm 4\sqrt{2}M - L - 3K\right) S + \frac{1}{\mu^2} R^2 (KN - LN - M^2),$$

which is negative if S be large compared to R.

So that a ring of satellites can always be rendered stable by increasing the mass of the central body and the angular velocity of the ring.

The values of L, M, and N depend on m, the number of undulations in the ring. When $m = \frac{\mu}{2}$, the values of L and N will be at their maximum and $M = 0$. If we determine the relation between S and R in this case so that the system may be stable, the stability of the system for every other displacement will be secured.

8.   To find the mass which must be given to the central body in order that a ring of satellites may permanently revolve round it.

We have seen that when the attraction of the central body is sufficiently great compared with the forces arising from the mutual action of the satellites, a permanent ring is possible. Now the forces between the satellites depend on the manner in which the displacement of each satellite takes place. The conception of a perfectly arbitrary displacement of all the satellites may be rendered manageable by separating it into a number of partial displacements depending on periodic functions. The motions arising from these small displacements will take place independently, so that we have to consider only one at a time.

Of all these displacements, that which produces the greatest disturbing forces is that in which consecutive satellites are oppositely displaced, that is, when $m = \frac{\mu}{2}$, for then the nearest satellites are displaced so as to increase as much as possible the effects of the displacement of the satellite between them. If we make μ a large quantity, we shall have

$$\Sigma \frac{\sin^2 m\theta \cos^2 \theta}{\sin^3 \theta} = \frac{\mu^3}{\pi^3}\left(1 + 3^{-3} + 5^{-3} + \&c.\right) = \frac{\mu^3}{\pi^3}\left(1 \cdot 0518\right),$$

$$L = \frac{\mu^3}{\pi^3} \cdot 5259, \qquad M = 0, \qquad N = 2L, \qquad K \text{ very small.}$$

Let $\dfrac{1}{\mu} RL = x$, then the equation of motion will be

$$n^4 - (S-x) n^2 + 2x (3S-x) = U = 0 \ \dots\dots\dots\dots\dots\dots\dots (23).$$

The conditions of this equation having real roots are

$$S > x \ \dots\dots\dots\dots\dots\dots\dots\dots\dots\dots\dots\dots\dots\dots\dots(24),$$

$$(S-x)^2 > 8x (3S-x) \ \dots\dots\dots\dots\dots\dots\dots\dots\dots(25).$$

The last condition gives the equation

$$S^2 - 26Sx + 9x^2 > 0,$$

whence $\qquad\qquad S > 26\cdot642x, \ \text{ or } \ S < 0\cdot351x \ \dots\dots\dots\dots\dots\dots (26).$

The last solution is inadmissible because S must be greater than x, so that the true condition is $\qquad S > 25\cdot649x,$

$$> 25\cdot649 \frac{1}{\mu} R \frac{\mu^3}{\pi^3} \cdot5259,$$

$$S > \cdot4352\mu^2R \ \dots\dots\dots\dots\dots\dots\dots\dots\dots\dots\dots\dots (27).$$

So that if there were 100 satellites in the ring, then

$$S > 4352 \, R$$

is the condition which must be fulfilled in order that the motion arising from every conceivable displacement may be periodic.

If this condition be not fulfilled, and if S be not sufficient to render the motion perfectly stable, then although the motion depending upon long undulations may remain stable, the short undulations will increase in amplitude till some of the neighbouring satellites are brought into collision.

9. To determine the nature of the motion when the system of satellites is of small mass compared with the central body.

The equation for the determination of n is

$$U = n^4 - \left\{\omega^2 + \frac{1}{\mu} R (2K+L-N)\right\} n^2 - 4\omega \frac{1}{\mu} RMn$$

$$+ \left\{3\omega^2 - \frac{1}{\mu} R (2K+L)\right\}\frac{1}{\mu} RN - \frac{1}{\mu^2} R^2M^2 = 0 \ \dots\dots\dots (28).$$

When R is very small we may approximate to the values of n by assuming that two of them are nearly $\pm \omega$, and that the other two are small.

If we put $n = \pm \omega$,

$$U = -\frac{1}{\mu} R (2K + L \pm 4M - 4N)\omega^2 + \&c.,$$

$$\frac{dU}{dn} = \pm 2\omega^3 + \&c.$$

Therefore the corrected values of n are

$$n = \pm \{\omega + \frac{1}{2\mu\omega} R (2K + L - 4N)\} + \frac{2}{\mu\omega} RM \dots\dots\dots\dots (29).$$

The small values of n are nearly $\pm \sqrt{3\frac{1}{\mu} RN}$: correcting them in the same way, we find the approximate values

$$n = \pm \sqrt{3\frac{1}{\mu}RN} - 2\frac{1}{\mu\omega} RM \dots\dots\dots\dots\dots (30).$$

The four values of n are therefore

$$\left.\begin{aligned}
n_1 &= -\omega - \frac{1}{2\mu\omega} R(2K + L - 4M - 4N) \\
n_2 &= -\sqrt{3\frac{1}{\mu} RN} - \frac{2}{\mu\omega} RM \\
n_3 &= +\sqrt{3\frac{1}{\mu} RN} - \frac{2}{\mu\omega} RM \\
n_4 &= +\omega + \frac{1}{2\mu\omega} R(2K + L + 4M - 4N)
\end{aligned}\right\} \dots\dots\dots\dots (31),$$

and the complete expression for ρ, so far as it depends on terms containing ms, is therefore
$$\rho = A_1 \cos (ms + n_1 t + a_1) + A_2 \cos (ms + n_2 t + a_2)$$
$$+ A_3 \cos (ms + n_3 t + a_3) + A_4 \cos (ms + n_4 t + a_4) \dots\dots\dots\dots (32),$$

and there will be other systems, of four terms each, for every value of m in the expansion of the original disturbance.

We are now able to determine the value of σ from equations (12), (20), by putting $\beta = a$, and

$$B = -\frac{2\omega n + \frac{1}{\mu} RM}{n^2 + \frac{1}{\mu} RN} A \dots\dots\dots\dots\dots (33).$$

So that for every term of ρ of the form

$$\rho = A \cos (ms + nt + a) \quad \dots\dots\dots\dots\dots\dots\dots (34),$$

there is a corresponding term in σ,

$$\sigma = -\frac{2\omega n + \dfrac{1}{\mu} RM}{n^2 + \dfrac{1}{\mu} RN} A \sin (ms + nt + a) \quad \dots\dots\dots\dots\dots (35).$$

10. Let us now fix our attention on the motion of a single satellite, and determine its motion by tracing the changes of ρ and σ while t varies and s is constant, and equal to the value of s corresponding to the satellite in question.

We must recollect that ρ and σ are measured outwards and forwards from an imaginary point revolving at distance 1 and velocity ω, so that the motions we consider are not the absolute motions of the satellite, but its motions relative to a point fixed in a revolving plane. This being understood, we may describe the motion as elliptic, the major axis being in the tangential direction, and the ratio of the axes being nearly $2\dfrac{\omega}{n}$, which is nearly 2 for n_1 and n_4 and is very large for n_2 and n_3.

The time of revolution is $\dfrac{2\pi}{n}$, or if we take a revolution of the ring as the unit of time, the time of a revolution of the satellite about its mean position is $\dfrac{\omega}{n}$.

The *direction* of revolution of the satellite about its mean position is in every case opposite to that of the motion of the ring.

11. The absolute motion of a satellite may be found from its motion relative to the ring by writing

$$r = 1 + \rho = 1 + A \cos (ms + nt + a),$$

$$\theta = \omega t + s + \sigma = \omega t + s - 2\frac{\omega}{n} A \sin (ms + nt + a).$$

When n is nearly equal to $\pm \omega$, the motion of each satellite in space is nearly elliptic. The eccentricity is A, the longitude at epoch s, and the longitude when at the greatest distance from Saturn is for the negative value n_1

$$- \frac{1}{\mu\omega} R \left(2K + L - 4M - 4N \right) t + (m+1) s + a,$$

and for the positive value n_4

$$- \frac{1}{\mu\omega} R \left(2K + L + 4M - 4N \right) t - (m+1) s - a.$$

We must recollect that in all cases the quantity within brackets is negative, so that the major axis of the ellipse travels forwards in both cases. The chief difference between the two cases lies in the arrangement of the major axes of the ellipses of the different satellites. In the first case as we pass from one satellite to the next in front the axes of the two ellipses lie in the same order. In the second case the particle in front has its major axis behind that of the other. In the cases in which n is small the radius vector of each satellite increases and diminishes during a periodic time of several revolutions. This gives rise to an inequality, in which the tangential displacement far exceeds the radial, as in the case of the *annual equation* of the Moon.

12. Let us next examine the condition of the ring of satellites at a given instant. We must therefore fix on a particular value of t and trace the changes of ρ and σ for different values of s.

From the expression for ρ we learn that the satellites form a wavy line, which is furthest from the centre when $(ms + nt + a)$ is a multiple of 2π, and nearest to the centre for intermediate values.

From the expression for σ we learn that the satellites are sometimes in advance and sometimes in the rear of their mean position, so that there are places where the satellites are crowded together, and others where they are drawn asunder. When n is positive, B is of the opposite sign to A, and the crowding of the satellites takes place when they are furthest from the centre. When n is negative, the satellites are separated most when furthest from the centre, and crowded together when they approach it.

The form of the ring at any instant is therefore that of a string of beads forming a re-entering curve, nearly circular, but with a small variation of distance from the centre recurring m times, and forming m regular waves of transverse displacement at equal intervals round the circle. Besides these, there are waves of condensation and rarefaction, the effect of longitudinal displacement. When n is positive the points of greatest distance from the centre are points of greatest condensation, and when n is negative they are points of greatest rarefaction.

13. We have next to determine the velocity with which these waves of disturbance are propagated round the ring. We fixed our attention on a particular satellite by making s constant, and on a particular instant by making t constant, and thus we determined the motion of a satellite and the form of the ring. We must now fix our attention on a *phase* of the motion, and this we do by making ρ or σ constant. This implies

$$ms + nt + a = \text{constant,}$$

$$\frac{ds}{dt} = -\frac{n}{m}.$$

So that the particular phase of the disturbance travels round the ring with an angular velocity $= -\dfrac{n}{m}$ relative to the ring itself. Now the ring is revolving in space with the velocity ω, so that the angular velocity of the wave in space is

$$\varpi = \omega - \frac{n}{m} \quad\quad\quad\quad\quad\quad\quad\quad\quad\quad\quad\quad(36).$$

Thus each satellite moves in an ellipse, while the general aspect of the ring is that of a curve of m waves revolving with velocity ϖ. This, however, is only the part of the whole motion, which depends on a single term of the solution. In order to understand the general solution we must shew how to determine the whole motion from the state of the ring at a given instant.

14. *Given the position and motion of every satellite at any one time, to calculate the position and motion of every satellite at any other time, provided that the condition of stability is fulfilled.*

The position of any satellite may be denoted by the values of ρ and σ for that satellite, and its velocity and direction of motion are then indicated by the values of $\dfrac{d\rho}{dt}$ and $\dfrac{d\sigma}{dt}$ at the given instant.

These four quantities may have for each satellite any four arbitrary values, as the position and motion of each satellite are independent of the rest, at the beginning of the motion.

Each of these quantities is therefore a perfectly arbitrary function of s, the mean angular position of the satellite in the ring.

But any function of s from $s = 0$ to $s = 2\pi$, however arbitrary or discontinuous, can be expanded in a series of terms of the form $A \cos (s + a) + A' \cos (2s + a') + \&c.$ See § 3.

Let each of the four quantities ρ, $\dfrac{d\rho}{dt}$, σ, $\dfrac{d\sigma}{dt}$ be expressed in terms of such a series, and let the terms in each involving ms be

$$\rho = E \cos (ms + e) \dotfill (37),$$

$$\frac{d\rho}{dt} = F \cos (ms + f) \dotfill (38),$$

$$\sigma = G \cos (ms + g) \dotfill (39),$$

$$\frac{d\sigma}{dt} = H \cos (ms + h) \dotfill (40).$$

These are the parts of the values of each of the four quantities which are capable of being expressed in the form of periodic functions of ms. It is evident that the eight quantities E, F, G, H, e, f, g, h, are all independent and arbitrary.

The next operation is to find the values of L, M, N, belonging to disturbances in the ring whose index is m [see equation (8)], to introduce these values into equation (28), and to determine the four values of n, (n_1, n_2, n_3, n_4).

This being done, the expression for ρ is that given in equation (32), which contains eight arbitrary quantities $(A_1, A_2, A_3, A_4, a_1, a_2, a_3, a_4)$.

Giving t its original value in this expression, and equating it to $E \cos (ms + e)$, we get an equation which is equivalent to two. For, putting $ms = 0$, we have

$$A_1 \cos a_1 + A_2 \cos a_2 + A_3 \cos a_3 + A_4 \cos a_4 = E \cos e \dotfill (41).$$

And putting $ms = \dfrac{\pi}{2}$, we have another equation

$$A_1 \sin a_1 + A_2 \sin a_2 + A_3 \sin a_3 + A_4 \sin a_4 = E \sin e \dotfill (42).$$

Differentiating (32) with respect to t, we get two other equations

$$-A_1 n_1 \sin a - \&c. = F \cos f \dots\dots\dots\dots\dots\dots\dots (43),$$

$$A_1 n_1 \cos a + \&c. = F \sin f \dots\dots\dots\dots\dots\dots (44).$$

Bearing in mind that B_1, B_2, &c. are connected with A_1, A_2, &c. by equation (33), and that B is therefore proportional to A, we may write $B = A\beta$, where

$$\beta = - \frac{2\omega n + \dfrac{1}{\mu} RM}{n^2 + \dfrac{1}{\mu} RN},$$

β being thus a function of n and a known quantity.

The value of σ then becomes at the epoch

$$\sigma = A_1 \beta_1 \sin (ms + a_1) + \&c. = G \cos (ms + g),$$

from which we obtain the two equations

$$A_1 \beta_1 \sin a_1 + \&c. = G \cos g \dots\dots\dots\dots\dots\dots\dots (45),$$

$$A_1 \beta_1 \cos a_1 + \&c. = - G \sin g \dots\dots\dots\dots\dots\dots\dots (46).$$

Differentiating with respect to t, we get the remaining equations

$$A_1 \beta_1 n_1 \cos a_1 + \&c. = H \cos h \dots\dots\dots\dots\dots\dots (47),$$

$$A_1 \beta_1 n_1 \sin a_1 + \&c. = H \sin h \dots\dots\dots\dots\dots\dots\dots (48).$$

We have thus found eight equations to determine the eight quantities A_1, &c. and a_1, &c. To solve them, we may take the four in which $A_1 \cos a_1$, &c. occur, and treat them as simple equations, so as to find $A_1 \cos a_1$, &c. Then taking those in which $A_1 \sin a_1$, &c. occur, and determining the values of those quantities, we can easily deduce the value of A_1 and a_1, &c. from these.

We now know the amplitude and phase of each of the four waves whose index is m. All other systems of waves belonging to any other index must be treated in the same way, and since the original disturbance, however arbitrary, can be broken up into periodic functions of the form of equations (37—40), our solution is perfectly general, and applicable to every possible disturbance of a ring fulfilling the condition of stability (27).

15.   We come next to consider the effect of an external disturbing force, due either to the irregularities of the planet, the attraction of satellites, or the motion of waves in other rings.

All disturbing forces of this kind may be expressed in series of which the general term is

$$A \cos (vt + ms + a),$$

where v is an angular velocity and m a whole number.

Let $P \cos (ms + vt + p)$ be the central part of the force, acting inwards, and $Q \sin (ms + vt + q)$ the tangential part, acting forwards. Let $\rho = A \cos (ms + vt + a)$ and $\sigma = B \sin (ms + vt + \beta)$, be the terms of ρ and σ which depend on the external disturbing force. These will simply be added to the terms depending on the original disturbance which we have already investigated, so that the complete expressions for ρ and σ will be as general as before. In consequence of the additional forces and displacements, we must add to equations (16) and (17), respectively, the following terms:

$$\left\{3\omega^2 - \frac{1}{\mu} R \left(2K + L\right) + v^2\right\} A \cos (ms + vt + a)$$

$$+ \left(2\omega v + \frac{1}{\mu} RM\right) B \cos (ms + vt + \beta) - P \cos (ms + vt + p) = 0 \ldots\ldots(49).$$

$$\left(2\omega v + \frac{1}{\mu} RM\right) A \sin (ms + vt + a)$$

$$+ \left(v^2 + \frac{1}{\mu} RN\right) B \sin (ms + vt + \beta) + Q \sin (ms + vt + q) = 0 \ldots\ldots\ldots(50).$$

Making $ms + vt = 0$ in the first equation and $\frac{\pi}{2}$ in the second,

$$\left\{3\omega^2 - \frac{1}{\mu} R \left(2K + L\right) + v^2\right\} A \cos a + \left(2\omega v + \frac{1}{\mu} RM\right) B \cos \beta - P \cos p = 0 \ldots\ldots(51).$$

$$\left(2\omega v + \frac{1}{\mu} RM\right) A \cos a + \left(v^2 + \frac{1}{\mu} RN\right) B \cos \beta + Q \cos q = 0 \ldots\ldots(52).$$

Then if we put

$$U' = v^4 - \left\{\omega^2 + \frac{1}{\mu} R \left(2K + L - N\right)\right\} v^2 - 4 \frac{\omega}{\mu} RMv$$

$$+ \left\{3\omega^2 - \frac{1}{\mu} R \left(2K + L\right)\right\} \frac{1}{\mu} RN - \frac{1}{\mu^2} R^2M^2 \ldots\ldots\ldots(53),$$

we shall find the value of $A \cos a$ and $B \cos \beta$;

$$A \cos a = \frac{v^2 + \frac{1}{\mu} RN}{U'} P \cos p + \frac{2\omega v + \frac{1}{\mu} RM}{U'} Q \cos q \dots\dots\dots (54).$$

$$B \cos \beta = -\frac{2\omega v + \frac{1}{\mu} RM}{U'} P \cos p - \frac{v^2 + 3\omega^2 - \frac{1}{\mu} R(K+L)}{U'} Q \cos q \dots\dots (55).$$

Substituting sines for cosines in equations (51), (52), we may find the values of $A \sin a$ and $B \sin \beta$.

Now U' is precisely the same function of v that U is of n, so that if v coincides with one of the four values of n, U' will vanish, the coefficients A and B will become infinite, and the ring will be destroyed. The disturbing force is supposed to arise from a revolving body, or an undulation of any kind which has an angular velocity $-\dfrac{v}{m}$ relatively to the ring, and therefore an absolute angular velocity $= \omega - \dfrac{v}{m}$.

If then the absolute angular velocity of the disturbing body is exactly or nearly equal to the absolute angular velocity of any of the free waves of the ring, that wave will increase till the ring be destroyed.

The velocities of the free waves are nearly

$$\omega \left(1 + \frac{1}{m}\right), \ \ \omega + \frac{1}{m}\sqrt{3\frac{1}{\mu}RN}, \ \ \omega - \frac{1}{m}\sqrt{3\frac{1}{\mu}RN}, \ \text{ and } \ \omega \left(1 - \frac{1}{m}\right)\dots\dots (56).$$

When the angular velocity of the disturbing body is greater than that of the first wave, between those of the second and third, or less than that of the fourth, U' is positive. When it is between the first and second, or between the third and fourth, U' is negative.

Let us now simplify our conception of the disturbance by attending to the central force only, and let us put $p = 0$, so that P is a maximum when $ms + vt$ is a multiple of 2π. We find in this case $a = 0$, and $\beta = 0$. Also

$$A = \frac{v^2 + \frac{1}{\mu}RN}{U'} P \dots\dots\dots\dots\dots\dots\dots (57),$$

$$B = -\frac{2\omega v + \frac{1}{\mu}RM}{U'} P \dots\dots\dots\dots\dots\dots (58).$$

When U' is positive, A will be of the same sign as P, that is, the parts of the ring will be furthest from the centre where the disturbing force towards the centre is greatest. When U' is negative, the contrary will be the case.

When v is positive, B will be of the opposite sign to A, and the parts of the ring furthest from the centre will be most crowded. When v is negative, the contrary will be the case.

Let us now attend only to the tangential force, and let us put $q = 0$. We find in this case also $a = 0$, $\beta = 0$,

$$A = \frac{2\omega v + \frac{1}{\mu} RM}{U'} Q \dots\dots\dots\dots\dots\dots\dots\dots\dots (59),$$

$$B = - \frac{v^2 + 3\omega^2 - \frac{1}{\mu} R(K+L)}{U'} Q \dots\dots\dots\dots\dots (60).$$

The tangential displacement is here in the same or in the opposite direction to the tangential force, according as U' is negative or positive. The crowding of satellites is at the points farthest from or nearest to Saturn according as v is positive or negative.

16. The effect of any disturbing force is to be determined in the following manner. The disturbing force, whether radial or tangential, acting on the ring may be conceived to vary from one satellite to another, and to be different at different times. It is therefore a perfectly arbitrary function of s and t.

Let Fourier's method be applied to the general disturbing force so as to divide it up into terms depending on periodic functions of s, so that each term is of the form $F(t) \cos(ms + a)$, where the function of t is still perfectly arbitrary.

But it appears from the general theory of the permanent motions of the heavenly bodies that they may all be expressed by periodic functions of t arranged in series. Let vt be the argument of one of these terms, then the corresponding term of the disturbance will be of the form

$$P \cos(ms + vt + a).$$

This term of the disturbing force indicates an alternately positive and negative action, disposed in m waves round the ring, completing its period relatively to each particle in the time $\dfrac{2\pi}{v}$, and travelling as a wave among the particles with an angular velocity $-\dfrac{v}{m}$, the angular velocity relative to fixed space being of course $\omega - \dfrac{v}{m}$. The whole disturbing force may be split up into terms of this kind.

17. Each of these elementary disturbances will produce its own wave in the ring, independent of those which belong to the ring itself. This new wave, due to external disturbance, and following different laws from the natural waves of the ring, is called the *forced wave*. The angular velocity of the forced wave is the same as that of the disturbing force, and its maxima and minima coincide with those of the force, but the extent of the disturbance and its direction depend on the comparative velocities of the forced wave and the four natural waves.

When the velocity of the forced wave lies between the velocities of the two middle free waves, or is greater than that of the swiftest, or less than that of the slowest, then the radial displacement due to a radial disturbing force is in the same direction as the force, but the tangential displacement due to a tangential disturbing force is in the opposite direction to the force.

The radial force therefore in this case produces a *positive forced wave*, and the tangential force a *negative forced wave*.

When the velocity of the forced wave is either between the velocities of the first and second free waves, or between those of the third and fourth, then the radial disturbance produces a forced wave in the contrary direction to that in which it acts, or a negative wave, and the tangential force produces a positive wave.

The coefficient of the forced wave changes sign whenever its velocity passes through the value of any of the velocities of the free waves, but it does so by becoming infinite, and not by vanishing, so that when the angular velocity very nearly coincides with that of a free wave, the forced wave becomes very great, and if the velocity of the disturbing force were made exactly equal to that of a free wave, the coefficient of the forced wave would become infinite. In such a case we should have to readjust our approximations, and to find whether such a coincidence might involve a physical impossibility.

The forced wave which we have just investigated is that which would main-tain itself in the ring, supposing that it had been set agoing at the commence-ment of the motion. It is in fact the form of dynamical equilibrium of the ring under the influence of the given forces. In order to find the actual motion of the ring we must combine this forced wave with all the free waves, which go on independently of it, and in this way the solution of the problem becomes perfectly complete, and we can determine the whole motion under any given initial circumstances, as we did in the case where no disturbing force acted.

For instance, if the ring were perfectly uniform and circular at the instant when the disturbing force began to act, we should have to combine with the constant forced wave a system of four free waves so disposed, that at the given epoch, the displacements due to them should exactly neutralize those due to the forced wave. By the combined effect of these four free waves and the forced one the whole motion of the ring would be accounted for, beginning from its undisturbed state.

The disturbances which are of most importance in the theory of Saturn's rings are those which are produced in one ring by the action of attractive forces arising from waves belonging to another ring.

The effect of this kind of action is to produce in each ring, besides its own four free waves, four forced waves corresponding to the free waves of the other ring. There will thus be eight waves in each ring, and the corresponding waves in the two rings will act and react on each other, so that, strictly speak-ing, every one of the waves will be in some measure a forced wave, although the system of eight waves will be the free motion of the two rings taken together. The theory of the mutual disturbance and combined motion of two concentric rings of satellites requires special consideration.

18. On the motion of a ring of satellites when the conditions of stability are not fulfilled.

We have hitherto been occupied with the case of a ring of satellites, the stability of which was ensured by the smallness of mass of the satellites com-pared with that of the central body. We have seen that the statically unstable condition of each satellite between its two immediate neighbours may be com-pensated by the dynamical effect of its revolution round the planet, and a planet of sufficient mass can not only direct the motion of such satellites round its own body, but can likewise exercise an influence over their relations to each other, so as to overrule their natural tendency to crowd together, and distribute and preserve them in the form of a ring.

We have traced the motion of each satellite, the general shape of the disturbed ring, and the motion of the various waves of disturbance round the ring, and determined the laws both of the natural or free waves of the ring, and of the forced waves, due to extraneous disturbing forces.

We have now to consider the cases in which such a permanent motion of the ring is impossible, and to determine the mode in which a ring, originally regular, will break up, in the different cases of instability.

The equation from which we deduce the conditions of stability is—

$$U = n^4 - \left\{ \omega^2 + \frac{1}{\mu} R \left(2K + L - N\right) \right\} n^2 - 4\omega \frac{1}{\mu} RMn$$

$$+ \left\{ 3\omega^2 - \frac{1}{\mu} R \left(2K + L\right) \right\} \frac{1}{\mu} RN - \frac{1}{\mu^2} R^2 M^2 = 0.$$

The quantity, which, in the critical cases, determines the nature of the roots of this equation, is N. The quantity M in the third term is always small compared with L and N when m is large, that is, in the case of the dangerous short waves. We may therefore begin our study of the critical cases by leaving out the third term. The equation then becomes a quadratic in n^2, and in order that all the values of n may be real, both values of n^2 must be real and positive.

The condition of the values of n^2 being real is

$$\omega^4 + \omega^2 \frac{1}{\mu} R \left(4K + 2L - 14N\right) + \frac{1}{\mu^2} R^2 \left(2K + L + N\right)^2 > 0 \ldots\ldots\ldots(61),$$

which shews that ω^2 must either be about 14 times at least smaller, or about 14 times at least greater, than quantities like $\frac{1}{\mu} RN$.

That both values of n^2 may be positive, we must have

$$\left.\begin{array}{c} \omega^2 + \frac{1}{\mu} R \left(2K + L - N\right) > 0 \\[2mm] \left\{ 3\omega^2 - \frac{1}{\mu} R \left(2K + L\right) \right\} \frac{1}{\mu} RN > 0 \end{array}\right\} \ldots\ldots\ldots\ldots\ldots (62).$$

We must therefore take the larger value of ω^2, and also add the condition that N be positive.

We may therefore state roughly, that, to ensure stability, $\dfrac{RN}{\mu}$, the coefficient of tangential attraction, must lie between zero and $\tfrac{1}{14}\omega^2$. If the quantity be negative, the two *small* values of n will become *pure impossible* quantities. If it exceed $\tfrac{1}{14}\omega^2$, *all* the values of n will take the form of mixed impossible quantities.

If we write x for $\dfrac{1}{\mu} RN$, and omit the other disturbing forces, the equation becomes

$$U = n^4 - (\omega^2 - x) n^2 + 3\omega^2 x = 0 \quad\text{.........................} (63),$$

whence

$$n^2 = \tfrac{1}{2} (\omega^2 - x) \pm \tfrac{1}{2} \sqrt{\omega^4 - 14\omega^2 x + x^2} \quad\text{..................} (64).$$

If x be small, two of the values of n are nearly $\pm \omega$, and the others are small quantities, real when x is positive and impossible when x is negative.

If x be greater than $(7 - \sqrt{48})\,\omega^2$, or $\dfrac{\omega^2}{14}$ nearly, the term under the radical becomes negative, and the value of n becomes

$$n = \pm \tfrac{1}{2} \sqrt{\sqrt{12\omega^2 x} + \omega^2 - x} \pm \tfrac{1}{2} \sqrt{-1} \sqrt{\sqrt{12\omega^2 x} - \omega^2 + x} \quad\text{.........} (65),$$

where one of the terms is a real quantity, and the other impossible. Every solution may be put under the form

$$n = p \pm \sqrt{-1}\, q \quad\text{.................................} (66),$$

where $q = 0$ for the case of stability, $p = 0$ for the pure impossible roots, and p and q finite for the mixed roots.

Let us now adopt this general solution of the equation for n, and determine its mechanical significance by substituting for the impossible circular functions their equivalent real exponential functions.

Substituting the general value of n in equations (34), (35),

$$\rho = A\left[\cos\{ms + (p + \sqrt{-1}q)\,t + a\} + \cos\{ms + (p - \sqrt{-1}q)\,t + a\}\right] \dots (67),$$

$$\left.\begin{aligned}
\sigma = &-A\, \frac{2\omega\,(p + \sqrt{-1}q)}{(p + \sqrt{-1}q)^2 + x} \sin\{ms + (p + \sqrt{-1}q)\,t + a\} \\
&-A\, \frac{2\omega\,(p - \sqrt{-1}q)}{(p - \sqrt{-1}q)^2 + x} \sin\{ms + (p - \sqrt{-1}q)\,t + a\}
\end{aligned}\right\} \quad\text{......} (68).$$

Introducing the exponential notation, these values become

$$\rho = A \left(\epsilon^{qt} + \epsilon^{-qt}\right) \cos \left(ms + pt + a\right) \quad\quad\quad\quad (69),$$

$$\sigma = -\frac{2\omega A}{\left(p^2 + q^2\right)^2 + 2\left(p^2 - q^2\right)x + x^2} \left\{ \begin{array}{l} p\left(p^2 + q^2 + x\right)\left(\epsilon^{qt} + \epsilon^{-qt}\right)\sin\left(ms + pt + a\right) \\ + q\left(p^2 + q^2 - x\right)\left(\epsilon^{qt} - \epsilon^{-qt}\right)\cos\left(ms + pt + a\right) \end{array} \right\} \, ...(70).$$

We have now obtained a solution free from impossible quantities, and applicable to every case.

When $q = 0$, the case becomes that of real roots, which we have already discussed. When $p = 0$, we have the case of pure impossible roots arising from the negative values of n^2. The solutions corresponding to these roots are

$$\rho = A \left(\epsilon^{qt} + \epsilon^{-qt}\right) \cos \left(ms + a\right) \quad\quad\quad\quad (71).$$

$$\sigma = -\frac{2\omega q A}{q^2 - x} \left(\epsilon^{qt} - \epsilon^{-qt}\right) \cos \left(ms + a\right) \quad\quad\quad\quad (72).$$

The part of the coefficient depending on ϵ^{-qt} diminishes indefinitely as the time increases, and produces no marked effect. The other part, depending on ϵ^{qt}, increases in a geometrical proportion as the time increases arithmetically, and so breaks up the ring. In the case of x being a small negative quantity, q^2 is nearly $3x$, so that the coefficient of σ becomes

$$-3\frac{\omega}{q}A.$$

It appears therefore that the motion of each particle is either outwards and backwards or inwards and forwards, but that the tangential part of the motion greatly exceeds the normal part.

It may seem paradoxical that a tangential force, acting *towards* a position of equilibrium, should produce instability, while a small tangential force *from* that position ensures stability, but it is easy to trace the destructive tendency of this apparently conservative force.

Suppose a particle slightly in front of a crowded part of the ring, then if x is negative there will be a tangential force pushing it forwards, and this force will cause its distance from the planet to increase, its angular velocity to diminish, and the particle itself to fall back on the crowded part, thereby increasing the irregularity of the ring, till the whole ring is broken up. In the same way it may be shewn that a particle *behind* a crowded part will be pushed into it. The only force which could preserve the ring from the effect of this action, is one which would prevent the particle from receding from the planet under the influence of the tangential force, or at least prevent the diminution of angular velocity. The transversal force of attraction of the ring is of this kind, and acts in the right direction, but it can never be of sufficient magnitude to have the required effect. In fact the thing to be done is to render the last term of the equation in n^2 positive when N is negative, which requires

$$\frac{1}{\mu} R \left(2K + L\right) > 3\omega^2,$$

and this condition is quite inconsistent with any constitution of the ring which fulfils the other condition of stability which we shall arrive at presently.

We may observe that the waves belonging to the two real values of n, $\pm \omega$, must be conceived to be travelling round the ring during the whole time of its breaking up, and conducting themselves like ordinary waves, till the excessive irregularities of the ring become inconsistent with their uniform propagation.

The irregularities which depend on the exponential solutions do not travel round the ring by propagation among the satellites, but remain among the same satellites which first began to move irregularly.

We have seen the fate of the ring when x is negative. When x is small we have two small and two large values of n, which indicate regular waves, as we have already shewn. As x increases, the small values of n increase, and the large values diminish, till they meet and form a pair of positive and a pair of negative equal roots, having values nearly $\pm \cdot 68\omega$. When x becomes greater than about $\frac{1}{14}\omega^2$, then all the values of n become impossible, of the form $p + \sqrt{-1}q$, q being small when x first begins to exceed its limits, and p being nearly $\pm \cdot 68\omega$.

The values of ρ and σ indicate periodic inequalities having the period $\frac{2\pi}{p}$, but increasing in amplitude at a rate depending on the exponential ϵ^{qt}. At the beginning of the motion the oscillations of the particles are in ellipses as in the case of stability, having the ratio of the axes about 1 in the normal direction to 3 in the tangential direction. As the motion continues, these ellipses increase in magnitude, and another motion depending on the second term of σ is combined with the former, so as to increase the ellipticity of the oscillations and to turn the major axis into an inclined position, so that its fore end points a little inwards, and its hinder end a little outwards. The oscillations of each particle round its mean position are therefore in ellipses, of which both axes increase continually while the eccentricity increases, and the major axis becomes slightly inclined to the tangent, and this goes on till the ring is destroyed. In the mean time the irregularities of the ring do not remain among the same set of particles as in the former case, but travel round the ring with a relative angular velocity $-\dfrac{p}{m}$. Of these waves there are four, two travelling forwards among the satellites, and two travelling backwards. One of each of these pairs depends on a negative value of q, and consists of a wave whose amplitude continually decreases. The other depends on a positive value of q, and is the destructive wave whose character we have just described.

19. We have taken the case of a ring composed of equal satellites, as that with which we may compare other cases in which the ring is constructed of loose materials differently arranged.

In the first place let us consider what will be the conditions of a ring composed of satellites of unequal mass. We shall find that the motion is of the same kind as when the satellites are equal.

For by arranging the satellites so that the smaller satellites are closer together than the larger ones, we may form a ring which will revolve uniformly about Saturn, the resultant force on each satellite being just sufficient to keep it in its orbit.

To determine the stability of this kind of motion, we must calculate the disturbing forces due to any given displacement of the ring. This calculation will be more complicated than in the former case, but will lead to results of the same general character. Placing these forces in the equations of motion, we shall find a solution of the same general character as in the former case, only instead of regular waves of displacement travelling round the ring, each wave will be split and reflected when it comes to irregularities in the chain of satellites. But if the condition of stability for every kind of wave be fulfilled, the motion of each satellite will consist of small oscillations about its position of dynamical equilibrium, and thus, on the whole, the ring will of itself assume the arrangement necessary for the continuance of its motion, if it be originally in a state not very different from that of equilibrium.

20. We now pass to the case of a ring of an entirely different construction. It is possible to conceive of a quantity of matter, either solid or liquid, not collected into a continuous mass, but scattered thinly over a great extent of space, and having its motion regulated by the gravitation of its parts to each other, or towards some dominant body. A shower of rain, hail, or cinders is a familiar illustration of a number of unconnected particles in motion; the visible stars, the milky way, and the resolved nebulæ, give us instances of a similar scattering of bodies on a larger scale. In the terrestrial instances we see the motion plainly, but it is governed by the attraction of the earth, and retarded by the resistance of the air, so that the mutual attraction of the parts is completely masked. In the celestial cases the distances are so enormous, and the time during which they have been observed so short, that we can perceive no motion at all. Still we are perfectly able to conceive of a collection of particles of small size compared with the distances between them, acting upon one another only by the attraction of gravitation, and revolving round a central body. The average density of such a system may be smaller than that of the rarest gas, while the particles themselves may be of great density; and the appearance from a distance will be that of a cloud of vapour, with this difference, that as the space between the particles is empty, the rays of light will pass through the system without being refracted, as they would have been if the system had been gaseous.

Such a system will have an *average density* which may be greater in some places than others. The resultant attraction will be towards places of greater average density, and thus the density of those places will be increased so as to increase the irregularities of density. The system will therefore be statically unstable, and nothing but motion of some kind can prevent the particles from forming agglomerations, and these uniting, till all are reduced to one solid mass.

We have already seen how dynamical stability can exist where there is statical instability in the case of a row of particles revolving round a central body. Let us now conceive a cloud of particles forming a ring of nearly uniform density revolving about a central body. There will be a primary effect of inequalities in density tending to draw particles towards the denser parts of the ring, and this will elicit a secondary effect, due to the motion of revolution, tending in the contrary direction, so as to restore the rings to uniformity. The relative magnitude of these two opposing forces determines the destruction or preservation of the ring.

To calculate these effects we must begin with the statical problem:—To determine the forces arising from the given displacements of the ring.

The longitudinal force arising from longitudinal displacements is that which has most effect in determining the stability of the ring. In order to estimate its limiting value we shall solve a problem of a simpler form.

21. An infinite mass, originally of uniform density k, has its particles displaced by a quantity ξ parallel to the axis of x, so that $\xi = A \cos mx$, to determine the attraction on each particle due to this displacement.

The density at any point will differ from the original density by a quantity k', so that

$$(k + k')\,(dx + d\xi) = k\,dx \dots\dots\dots\dots\dots\dots (73),$$

$$k' = -k\frac{d\xi}{dx} = Akm \sin mx \dots\dots\dots\dots\dots\dots (74).$$

The potential at any point will be $V + V'$, where V is the original potential, and V' depends on the displacement only, so that

$$\frac{d^2V'}{dx^2} + \frac{d^2V'}{dy^2} + \frac{d^2V'}{dz^2} + 4\pi k' = 0 \dots\dots\dots\dots\dots (75).$$

Now V' is a function of x only, and therefore,

$$V' = 4\pi A k \frac{1}{m} \sin mx \dots\dots\dots\dots\dots\dots (76),$$

and the longitudinal force is found by differentiating V' with respect to x.

$$X = \frac{dV'}{dx} = 4\pi kA \cos mx = 4\pi k\xi \dots\dots\dots\dots\dots (77).$$

Now let us suppose this mass not of infinite extent, but of finite section parallel to the plane of yz. This change amounts to cutting off all portions of the mass beyond a certain boundary. Now the effect of the portion so cut off upon the longitudinal force depends on the value of m. When m is large, so that the wave-length is small, the effect of the external portion is insensible, so that the longitudinal force due to short waves is not diminished by cutting off a great portion of the mass.

22. Applying this result to the case of a ring, and putting s for x, and σ for ξ we have

$$\sigma = A \cos ms, \text{ and } T = 4\pi k A \cos ms,$$

so that

$$\frac{1}{\mu} RN = 4\pi k,$$

when m is very large, and this is the greatest value of N.

The value of L has little effect on the condition of stability. If L and M are both neglected, that condition is

$$\omega^2 > 27\cdot856 \ (2\pi k) \dots\dots\dots\dots\dots\dots\dots (78),$$

and if L be as much as $\frac{1}{2}N$, then

$$\omega^2 > 25\cdot649 \ (2\pi k) \dots\dots\dots\dots\dots\dots\dots(79),$$

so that it is not important whether we calculate the value of L or not.

The condition of stability is, that the average density must not exceed a certain value. Let us ascertain the relation between the maximum density of the ring and that of the planet.

Let b be the radius of the planet, that of the ring being unity, then the mass of Saturn is $\frac{4}{3}\pi b^3 k' = \omega^2$ if k' be the density of the planet. If we assume that the radius of the ring is twice that of the planet, as Laplace has done, then $b = \frac{1}{2}$ and

$$\frac{k'}{k} = 334\cdot2 \text{ to } 307\cdot7 \dots\dots\dots\dots\dots\dots\dots (80),$$

so that the density of the ring cannot exceed $\frac{1}{300}$ of that of the planet. Now Laplace has shewn that if the outer and inner parts of the ring have the same angular velocity, the ring will not hold together if the ratio of the density of the planet to that of the ring exceeds $1\cdot3$, so that in the first place, our ring cannot have uniform angular velocity, and in the second place, Laplace's ring cannot preserve its form, if it is composed of loose materials acting on each other only by the attraction of gravitation, and moving with the same angular velocity throughout.

23. On the forces arising from inequalities of thickness in a thin stratum of fluid of indefinite extent.

The forces which act on any portion of a continuous fluid are of two kinds, the pressures of contiguous portions of fluid, and the attractions of all portions of the fluid whether near or distant. In the case of a thin stratum of fluid, not acted on by any external forces, the pressures are due mainly to the component of the attraction which is perpendicular to the plane of the stratum. It is easy to shew that a fluid acted on by such a force will tend to assume a position of equilibrium, in which its free surface is plane ; and that any irregularities will tend to equalise themselves, so that the plane surface will be one of stable equilibrium.

It is also evident, that if we consider only that part of the attraction which is parallel to the plane of the stratum, we shall find it always directed towards the thicker parts, so that the effect of this force is to draw the fluid from thinner to thicker parts, and so to increase irregularities and destroy equilibrium.

The normal attraction therefore tends to preserve the stability of equilibrium, while the tangential attraction tends to render equilibrium unstable.

According to the nature of the irregularities one or other of these forces will prevail, so that if the extent of the irregularities is small, the normal forces will ensure stability, while, if the inequalities cover much space, the tangential forces will render equilibrium unstable, and break up the stratum into beads.

To fix our ideas, let us conceive the irregularities of the stratum split up into the form of a number of systems of waves superposed on one another, then, by what we have just said, it appears, that very short waves will disappear of themselves, and be consistent with stability, while very long waves will tend to increase in height, and will destroy the form of the stratum.

In order to determine the law according to which these opposite effects take place, we must subject the case to mathematical investigation.

Let us suppose the fluid incompressible, and of the density k; and let it be originally contained between two parallel planes, at distances $+c$ and $-c$ from that of (xy), and extending to infinity. Let us next conceive a series of imaginary planes, parallel to the plane of (yz), to be plunged into the fluid stratum at infinitesimal distances from one another, so as to divide the fluid into imaginary slices perpendicular to the plane of the stratum.

Next let these planes be displaced parallel to the axis of x according to this law—that if x be the original distance of the plane from the origin, and ξ its displacement in the direction of x,

$$\xi = A \cos mx \quad\text{................................... (81).}$$

According to this law of displacement, certain alterations will take place in the distances between consecutive planes; but since the fluid is incompressible, and of indefinite extent in the direction of y, the change of dimension must occur in the direction of z. The original thickness of the stratum was $2c$. Let its thickness at any point after displacement be $2c + 2\zeta$, then we must have

$$(2c + 2\zeta)\left(1 + \frac{d\xi}{dx}\right) = 2c \dots\dots\dots\dots\dots\dots (82),$$

or
$$\zeta = -c\,\frac{d\xi}{dx} = cmA \sin mx \dots\dots\dots\dots\dots\dots (83).$$

Let us assume that the increase of thickness 2ζ is due to an increase of ζ at each surface; this is necessary for the equilibrium of the fluid between the imaginary planes.

We have now produced artificially, by means of these planes, a system of waves of longitudinal displacement whose length is $\frac{2\pi}{m}$ and amplitude A; and we have found that this has produced a system of waves of normal displacement on each surface, having the same length, with a height $= cmA$.

In order to determine the forces arising from these displacements, we must, in the first place, determine the potential function at any point of space, and this depends partly on the state of the fluid before displacement, and partly on the displacement itself. We have, in all cases—

$$\frac{d^2V}{dx^2} + \frac{d^2V}{dy^2} + \frac{d^2V}{dz^2} = -4\pi\rho \dots\dots\dots\dots\dots\dots (84).$$

Within the fluid, $\rho = k$; beyond it, $\rho = 0$.

Before displacement, the equation is reduced to

$$\frac{d^2V}{dz^2} = -4\pi\rho \dots\dots\dots\dots\dots\dots\dots (85).$$

Instead of assuming $V = 0$ at infinity, we shall assume $V = 0$ at the origin, and since in this case all is symmetrical, we have

within the fluid
$$V_1 = -2\pi kz^2; \quad \frac{dV_1}{dz} = -4\pi kz$$

at the bounding planes
$$V = -2\pi kc^2; \quad \frac{dV}{dz} = \mp 4\pi kc \quad \left.\vphantom{\begin{matrix}1\\1\\1\end{matrix}}\right\} \dots\dots\dots\dots (86);$$

beyond them
$$V_2 = 2\pi kc\,(\mp 2z \pm c); \quad \frac{dV}{dz} = \mp 4\pi kc$$

the upper sign being understood to refer to the boundary at distance $+c$, and the lower to the boundary at distance $-c$ from the origin.

Having ascertained the potential of the undisturbed stratum, we find that of the disturbance by calculating the effect of a stratum of density k and thickness ζ, spread over each surface according to the law of thickness already found. By supposing the coefficient A small enough, (as we may do in calculating the displacements on which stability depends), we may diminish the absolute thickness indefinitely, and reduce the case to that of a mere "superficial density," such as is treated of in the theory of electricity. We have here, too, to regard some parts as of *negative* density; but we must recollect that we are dealing with the *difference* between a disturbed and an undisturbed system, which may be positive or negative, though no real mass can be negative.

Let us for an instant conceive only one of these surfaces to exist, and let us transfer the origin to it. Then the law of thickness is

$$\zeta = mcA \sin mx \dots\dots\dots\dots (83),$$

and we know that the normal component of attraction at the surface is the same as if the thickness had been uniform throughout, so that

$$\frac{dV}{dz} = -2\pi k\zeta,$$

on the positive side of the surface.

Also, the solution of the equation

$$\frac{d^2V}{dx^2} + \frac{d^2V}{dz^2} = 0,$$

consists of a series of terms of the form $C\epsilon^{iz} \sin ix$.

Of these the only one with which we have to do is that in which $i = -m$. Applying the condition as to the normal force at the surface, we get

$$V = 2\pi kc\epsilon^{-mz}A \sin mx \dots\dots\dots\dots (87),$$

for the potential on the positive side of the surface, and

$$V = 2\pi kc\epsilon^{mz}A \sin mx \dots\dots\dots\dots(88),$$

on the negative side.

Calculating the potentials of a pair of such surfaces at distances $+c$ and $-c$ from the plane of xy, and calling V' the sum of their potentials, we have for the space between these planes

$$V_1' = 2\pi kcA \sin mx\epsilon^{-mc}\left(\epsilon^{mz} + \epsilon^{-mz}\right)$$

beyond them

$$V_2' = 2\pi kcA \sin mx\epsilon^{\mp mz}\left(\epsilon^{mc} + \epsilon^{-mc}\right)$$

.... (89);

the upper or lower sign of the index being taken according as z is positive or negative.

These potentials must be added to those formerly obtained, to get the potential at any point after displacement.

We have next to calculate the pressure of the fluid at any point, on the supposition that the imaginary planes protect each slice of the fluid from the pressure of the adjacent slices, so that it is in equilibrium under the action of the forces of attraction, and the pressure of these planes on each side. Now in a fluid of density k, in equilibrium under forces whose potential is V, we have always—

$$\frac{dp}{dV} = k ;$$

so that if we know that the value of p is p_0 where that of V is V_0, then at any other point

$$p = p_0 + k\left(V - V_0\right).$$

Now, at the free surface of the fluid, $p = 0$, and the distance from the free surface of the disturbed fluid to the plane of the original surface is ζ, a small quantity. The attraction which acts on this stratum of fluid is, in the first place, that of the undisturbed stratum, and this is equal to $4\pi kc$, towards that stratum. The pressure due to this cause at the level of the original surface will be $4\pi k^2 c\zeta$, and the pressure arising from the attractive forces due to the displacements upon this thin layer of fluid, will be small quantities of the second order, which we neglect. We thus find the pressure when $z = c$ to be,

$$p_0 = 4\pi k^2 c^2 mA \sin mx.$$

The potential of the undisturbed mass when $z = c$ is

$$V_0 = -2\pi kc^2,$$

and the potential of the disturbance itself for the same value of z, is

$$V_0' = 2\pi kcA \sin mx\left(1 + \epsilon^{-2mc}\right).$$

So that we find the general value of p at any other point to be

$$p = 2\pi k^2 (c^2 - z^2) + 2\pi k^2 cA \sin mx \{2cm - 1 - \epsilon^{-2mc} + \epsilon^{mc} (\epsilon^{mz} + \epsilon^{-mz})\} \dots (90).$$

This expression gives the pressure of the fluid at any point, as depending on the state of constraint produced by the displacement of the imaginary planes. The accelerating effect of these pressures on any particle, if it were allowed to move parallel to x, instead of being confined by the planes, would be

$$= \frac{1}{k} \frac{dp}{dx}.$$

The accelerating effect of the attractions in the same direction is

$$\frac{dV}{dx},$$

so that the whole acceleration parallel to x is

$$X = -2\pi kmcA \cos mx (2mc - \epsilon^{-2mc} - 1) \dots (91).$$

It is to be observed, that this quantity is independent of z, so that every particle in the slice, by the combined effect of pressure and attraction, is urged with the same force, and, if the imaginary planes were removed, each slice would move parallel to itself without distortion, as long as the absolute displacements remained small. We have now to consider the direction of the resultant force X, and its changes of magnitude.

We must remember that the original displacement is $A \cos mx$, if therefore $(2mc - \epsilon^{-2mc} - 1)$ be positive, X will be opposed to the displacement, and the equilibrium will be stable, whereas if that quantity be negative, X will act along with the displacement and increase it, and so constitute an unstable condition.

It may be seen that large values of mc give positive results and small ones negative. The sign changes when

$$2mc = 1 \cdot 147 \dots (92),$$

which corresponds to a wave-length

$$\lambda = 2c \frac{2\pi}{1 \cdot 147} = 2c (5 \cdot 471) \dots (93).$$

The length of the complete wave in the critical case is $5 \cdot 471$ times the thickness of the stratum. Waves shorter than this are stable, longer waves are unstable.

The quantity $\qquad 2mc\left(2mc - \epsilon^{-2mc} - 1\right)$,

has a minimum when $\qquad 2mc = \cdot607$ ....(94),

and the wave-length is $10\cdot353$ times the thickness of the stratum.

In this case $\qquad 2mc\left(2mc - \epsilon^{-2mc} - 1\right) = -\cdot509$ ....(95),

and $\qquad X = \cdot509\pi kA \cos mx$ ....(96).

24. Let us now conceive that the stratum of fluid, instead of being infinite in extent, is limited in breadth to about 100 times the thickness. The pressures and attractions will not be much altered by this removal of a distant part of the stratum. Let us also suppose that this thin but broad strip is bent round in its own plane into a circular ring whose radius is more than ten times the breadth of the strip, and that the waves, instead of being exactly parallel to each other, have their ridges in the direction of radii of the ring. We shall then have transformed our stratum into one of Saturn's Rings, if we suppose those rings to be liquid, and that a considerable breadth of the ring has the same angular velocity.

Let us now investigate the conditions of stability by putting

$$x = -2\pi kmc\left(2mc - \epsilon^{-2mc} - 1\right)$$

into the equation for n. We know that x must lie between 0 and $\dfrac{\omega^2}{13\cdot9}$ to ensure stability. Now the greatest value of x in the fluid stratum is $\cdot509\pi k$. Taking Laplace's ratio of the diameter of the ring to that of the planet, this gives $42\cdot5$ as the minimum value of the density of the planet divided by that of the fluid of the ring.

Now Laplace has shewn that any value of this ratio greater than $1\cdot3$ is inconsistent with the rotation of any considerable breadth of the fluid at the same angular velocity, so that our hypothesis of a broad ring with uniform velocity is untenable.

But the stability of such a ring is impossible for another reason, namely, that for waves in which $2mc > 1\cdot147$, x is negative, and the ring will be destroyed by these short waves in the manner described at page (333).

When the fluid ring is treated, not as a broad strip, but as a filament of circular or elliptic section, the mathematical difficulties are very much increased, but it may be shown that in this case also there will be a maximum value of x, which will require the density of the planet to be several times that of the ring, and that in all cases short waves will give rise to negative values of x, inconsistent with the stability of the ring.

It appears, therefore, that a ring composed of a continuous liquid mass cannot revolve about a central body without being broken up, but that the parts of such a broken ring may, under certain conditions, form a permanent ring of satellites.

On the Mutual Perturbations of Two Rings.

25. We shall assume that the difference of the mean radii of the rings is small compared with the radii themselves, but large compared with the distance of consecutive satellites of the same ring. We shall also assume that each ring separately satisfies the conditions of stability.

We have seen that the effect of a disturbing force on a ring is to produce a series of waves whose number and period correspond with those of the disturbing force which produces them, so that we have only to calculate the coefficient belonging to the wave from that of the disturbing force.

Hence in investigating the simultaneous motions of two rings, we may assume that the mutually disturbing waves travel with the same *absolute* angular velocity, and that a maximum in one corresponds either to a maximum or a minimum of the other, according as the coefficients have the same or opposite signs.

Since the motions of the particles of each ring are affected by the disturbance of the other ring, as well as of that to which they belong, the equations of motion of the two rings will be involved in each other, and the final equation for determining the wave-velocity will have eight roots instead of four. But as each of the rings has four *free* waves, we may suppose these to originate *forced* waves in the other ring, so that we may consider the eight waves of each ring as consisting of four free waves and four forced ones.

In strictness, however, the wave-velocity of the "free" waves will be affected by the existence of the forced waves which they produce in the other ring, so that none of the waves are really "free" in either ring independently, though the whole motion of the system of two rings as a whole is free.

We shall find, however, that it is best to consider the waves first as free, and then to determine the reaction of the other ring upon them, which is such as to alter the wave-velocity of both, as we shall see.

The forces due to the second ring may be separated into three parts.

1st. The constant attraction when both rings are at rest.

2nd. The variation of the attraction on the first ring, due to its own disturbances.

3rd. The variation of the attraction due to the disturbances of the second ring.

The first of these affects only the angular velocity. The second affects the waves of each ring independently, and the mutual action of the waves depends entirely on the third class of forces.

26. *To determine the attractions between two rings.*

Let R and a be the mass and radius of the exterior ring, R' and a' those of the interior, and let all quantities belonging to the interior ring be marked with accented letters. (Fig. 5.)

1st. *Attraction between the rings when at rest.*

Since the rings are at a distance small compared with their radii, we may calculate the attraction on a particle of the first ring as if the second were an infinite straight line at distance $a' - a$ from the first.

The mass of unit of length of the second ring is $\dfrac{R'}{2\pi a'}$, and the accelerating effect of the attraction of such a filament on an element of the first ring is

$$\frac{R'}{\pi a'\,(a - a')} \text{ inwards } \dots\dots\dots\dots\dots\dots(97).$$

The attraction of the first ring on the second may be found by transposing accented and unaccented letters.

In consequence of these forces, the outer ring will revolve faster, and the inner ring slower than would otherwise be the case. These forces enter into the *constant terms* of the equations of motion, and may be included in the value of K.

2nd. *Variation due to disturbance of first ring.*

If we put $a(1+\rho)$ for a in the last expression, we get the attraction when the first ring is displaced. The part depending on ρ is

$$-\frac{R'a}{\pi a'(a-a')^2}\,\rho\ \text{inwards}\ \dots\dots\dots\dots\dots\dots(98).$$

This is the only variation of force arising from the displacement of the first ring. It affects the value of L in the equations of motion.

3rd. *Variation due to waves in the second ring.*

On account of the waves, the second ring varies in distance from the first, and also in mass of unit of length, and each of these alterations produces variations both in the radial and tangential force, so that there are four things to be calculated:

1st.   Radial force due to radial displacement.

2nd.   Radial force due to tangential displacement.

3rd.   Tangential force due to radial displacement.

4th.   Tangential force due to tangential displacement.

1st.   Put $a'(1+\rho')$ for a', and we get the term in ρ'

$$\frac{R'}{\pi a'}\,\frac{(2a'-a)}{(a'-a)^2}\,\rho'\ \text{inwards}=\lambda'\rho',\ \text{say}\ \dots\dots\dots\dots(99).$$

2nd. By the tangential displacement of the second ring the section is reduced in the proportion of 1 to $1-\dfrac{d\sigma'}{ds'}$, and therefore there is an alteration of the radial force equal to

$$-\frac{R'}{\pi a'(a-a')}\,\frac{d\sigma'}{ds'}\ \text{inwards}=-\mu'\frac{d\sigma'}{ds'}\ \text{say}\ \dots\dots\dots\dots(100).$$

3rd. By the radial displacement of the second ring the direction of the filament near the part in question is altered, so that the attraction is no longer radial but forwards, and the tangential part of the force is

$$\frac{R'}{\pi a'(a-a')}\,\frac{d\rho'}{ds'}=+\mu'\frac{d\rho'}{ds'}\ \text{forwards}\ \dots\dots\dots\dots(101).$$

4th. By the tangential displacement of the second ring a tangential force arises, depending on the relation between the length of the waves and the distance between the rings.

If we make $m \dfrac{a-a'}{a'} = p$, and $m \displaystyle\int_{-\infty}^{+\infty} \dfrac{x \sin px}{(1+x^2)^{\frac{3}{2}}} dx = \Pi$,

the tangential force is $\dfrac{R'}{\pi a' (a-a')^2} \Pi \sigma' = \nu' \sigma'$ .... (102).

We may now write down the values of λ, μ, and ν by transposing accented and unaccented letters.

$$\lambda = \frac{R}{\pi a} \frac{(2a-a')}{(a-a')^2}; \ \mu = \frac{R}{\pi a (a'-a)}; \ \nu = \frac{R}{\pi a' (a-a')^2} \Pi \ \text{.........} \ (103).$$

Comparing these values with those of λ', μ', and ν', it will be seen that the following relations are approximately true when a is nearly equal to a':

$$\frac{\lambda'}{\lambda} = -\frac{\mu'}{\mu} = \frac{\nu'}{\nu} = \frac{R'a}{Ra'} \ \text{............................} \ (104).$$

27. To form the equations of motion.

*The original equations were

$$\omega^2 + \omega^2 \rho + 2\omega \frac{d\sigma}{dt} - \frac{d^2\rho}{dt^2} = P = S + K - (2S - L) A\rho - MB\rho + \lambda'\rho' - \mu' \frac{d\sigma'}{ds'},$$

$$2\omega \frac{d\rho}{dt} + \frac{d^2\sigma}{dt^2} = Q = MA\sigma + NB\sigma + \mu' \frac{d\rho'}{ds'} + \nu'\sigma'.$$

Putting $\qquad \rho = A \cos (ms+nt), \quad \sigma = B \sin (ms+nt),$

$\qquad\qquad\qquad \rho' = A' \cos (ms+nt), \quad \sigma' = B' \sin (ms+nt),$

then $\qquad\qquad\qquad\qquad \omega^2 = S + K$

$$\left. \begin{array}{l} (\omega^2 + 2S + n^2 - L) A + (2\omega n + M) B - \lambda'A' + \mu'mB' = 0 \\ (2\omega n + M) A + (n^2 + N) B - \mu'mA' + \nu'B' = 0 \end{array} \right\} \text{.........} (105).$$

The corresponding equations for the second ring may be found by transposing accented and unaccented letters. We should then have four equations to determine the ratios of A, B, A', B', and a resultant equation of the eighth degree to determine n. But we may make use of a more convenient method, since λ', μ', and ν' are small. Eliminating B we find

$$\left. \begin{array}{l} An^4 - A (\omega^2 + 2K + L - N) n^2 - 4A\omega Mn + AN (3\omega^2) \\ (-\lambda'A' + \mu'mB') n^2 + (\mu'mA' - \nu'B') 2\omega n \end{array} \right\} = 0 \ \text{..........} (106).$$

---

* [The analysis in this article is somewhat unsatisfactory, the equations of motion employed being those which were applicable in the case of a ring of radius unity. ED.]

Putting $\qquad B = \beta A, \quad A' = xA, \quad B' = \beta' A' = \beta' x A,$

we have
$$\left. \begin{array}{l} n^4 - \{\omega^2(+2K) + L - N\}\, n^2 - 4\omega Mn + 3\omega^2 N \\ + (-\lambda' + \mu' m \beta')\, n^2 x + (\mu' m - \nu' \beta')\, 2\omega n x \end{array} \right\} = U = 0 \dots (107).$$

$$\frac{dU}{dn} = 4n^3 - 2\omega^2 n + \&c. \dots (108),$$

$$\frac{dU}{dx} = -\lambda' n^2 + \mu' m \beta' n^2 + 2\mu' m \omega n - 2\nu' \beta' \omega n \dots (109),$$

whence
$$\frac{dn}{dx} = \frac{\lambda' n - \mu' m \beta' n - 2\mu' m \omega + 2\nu' \beta' \omega}{4n^2 - 2\omega^2} \dots (110).$$

28. If we were to solve the equation for n, leaving out the terms involving x, we should find the wave-velocities of the four free waves of the first ring, supposing the second ring to be prevented from being disturbed. But in reality the waves in the first ring produce a disturbance in the second, and these in turn react upon the first ring, so that the wave-velocity is somewhat different from that which it would be in the supposed case. Now if x be the ratio of the radial amplitude of displacement in the second ring to that in the first, and if $\bar{n}$ be a value of n supposing $x = 0$, then by Maclaurin's theorem,

$$n = +\bar{n} + \frac{dn}{dx}\, x \dots (111).$$

The wave-velocity relative to the ring is $-\dfrac{n}{m}$, and the absolute angular velocity of the wave in space is

$$\varpi = \omega - \frac{n}{m} = \omega - \frac{\bar{n}}{m} - \frac{1}{m}\frac{dn}{dx}\, x \dots (112),$$

$$= +p - qx \dots (113),$$

where $p = \omega - \dfrac{\bar{n}}{m}$, and $q = \dfrac{1}{m}\dfrac{dn}{dx}$.

Similarly in the second ring we should have

$$\varpi' = p' - q'\,\frac{1}{x} \dots (114) ;$$

and since the corresponding waves in the two rings must have the same absolute angular velocity,

$$\varpi = \varpi', \quad \text{or} \quad p - qx = p' - q'\,\frac{1}{x} \dots (115).$$

This is a quadratic equation in x, the roots of which are real when

$$(p-p')^2 + 4qq'$$

is positive. When this condition is not fulfilled, the roots are impossible, and the general solution of the equations of motion will contain exponential factors, indicating destructive oscillations in the rings.

Since q and q' are small quantities, the solution is always real whenever p and p' are considerably different. The absolute angular velocities of the two pairs of reacting waves, are then nearly

$$p + \frac{qq'}{p-p'}, \text{ and } p' - \frac{qq'}{p-p'},$$

instead of p and p', as they would have been if there had been no reaction of the forced wave upon the free wave which produces it.

When p and p' are equal or nearly equal, the character of the solution will depend on the sign of qq'. We must therefore determine the signs of q and q' in such cases.

Putting $\beta' = \frac{2\omega'}{n'}$, we may write the values of q and q'

$$\left. \begin{array}{l} q = \dfrac{n}{m} \cdot \dfrac{\lambda' + 2\mu'm \left(\dfrac{\omega'}{n'} - \dfrac{\omega}{n} \right) - 4\nu' \dfrac{\omega'}{n'} \dfrac{\omega}{n}}{4n^2 - 2\omega^3} \\[4mm] q' = \dfrac{n'}{m'} \cdot \dfrac{\lambda + 2\mu m \left(\dfrac{\omega}{n} - \dfrac{\omega'}{n'} \right) - 4\nu \dfrac{\omega'}{n'} \dfrac{\omega}{n}}{4n'^2 - 2\omega'^2} \end{array} \right\} \quad \ldots\ldots\ldots\ldots\ldots (116).$$

Referring to the values of the disturbing forces, we find that

$$\frac{\lambda'}{\lambda} = -\frac{\mu'}{\mu} = \frac{\nu'}{\nu} = \frac{R'a}{Ra'}.$$

Hence

$$\frac{q}{q'} = \frac{n}{n'} \frac{4n'^2 - 2\omega'^2}{4n^2 - 2\omega^2} \cdot \frac{R'a}{Ra'} \quad \ldots\ldots\ldots\ldots\ldots\ldots\ldots (117).$$

Since qq' is of the same sign as $\dfrac{q}{q'}$, we have only to determine whether $2n - \dfrac{\omega^2}{n}$, and $2n' - \dfrac{\omega'^2}{n}$, are of the same or of different signs. If these quantities are of the same sign, qq' is positive, if of different signs, qq' is negative.

Now there are four values of n, which give four corresponding values of $2n - \dfrac{\omega^2}{n}$:

$$n_1 = -\omega + \&c., \qquad 2n_1 - \dfrac{\omega^2}{n_1} \text{ is negative,}$$

$$n_2 = -\text{a small quantity}, \ 2n_2 - \dfrac{\omega^2}{n_2} \text{ is positive,}$$

$$n_3 = +\text{a small quantity}, \ 2n_3 - \dfrac{\omega^2}{n_3} \text{ is negative,}$$

$$n_4 = \omega - \&c., \qquad 2n_4 - \dfrac{\omega^2}{n_4} \text{ is positive.}$$

The quantity with which we have to do is therefore positive for the even orders of waves and negative for the odd ones, and the corresponding quantity in the other ring obeys the same law. Hence when the waves which act upon each other are either both of even or both of odd names, qq' will be positive, but when one belongs to an even series, and the other to an odd series, qq' is negative.

29. The values of p and p' are, roughly,

$$\left. \begin{array}{l} p_1 = \omega + \dfrac{\omega}{m} - \&c., \ p_2 = \omega + \&c., \ p_3 = \omega - \&c., \ p_4 = \omega - \dfrac{\omega}{m} + \&c. \\[2mm] p_1' = \omega' + \dfrac{\omega'}{m} - \&c., \ p_2' = \omega' + \&c., \ p_3' = \omega' - \&c., \ p_4' = \omega' - \dfrac{\omega'}{m} + \&c. \end{array} \right\} \ \ \dots\dots\dots (118).$$

ω' is greater than ω, so that p_1' is the greatest, and p_4 the least of these values, and of those of the same order, the accented is greater than the unaccented. The following cases of equality are therefore possible under suitable circumstances :

$$\begin{array}{ll} p_1 = p_3', & p_1 = p_2', \\ p_2 = p_4', & p_1 = p_4', \\ p_4 = p_4' \ (\text{when } m = 1), & p_2 = p_3', \\ & p_3 = p_4', \end{array}$$

In the cases in the first column qq' will be positive, in those in the second column qq' will be negative.

30. Now each of the four values of p is a function of m, the number of undulations in the ring, and of a the radius of the ring, varying nearly as $a^{-\frac{3}{2}}$. Hence m being given, we may alter the radius of the ring till any one of the four values of p becomes equal to a given quantity, say a given value of p', so that if an indefinite number of rings coexisted, so as to form a sheet of rings, it would be always possible to discover instances of the equality of p and p' among them. If such a case of equality belongs to the first column given above, two constant waves will arise in both rings, one travelling a little faster, and the other a little slower than the free waves. If the case belongs to the second column, two waves will also arise in each ring, but the one pair will gradually die away, and the other pair will increase in amplitude indefinitely, the one wave strengthening the other till at last both rings are thrown into confusion.

The only way in which such an occurrence can be avoided is by placing the rings at such a distance that no value of m shall give coincident values of p and p'. For instance, if $\omega' > 2\omega$, but $\omega' < 3\omega$, no such coincidence is possible. For p_1 is always less than p_2', it is greater than p_4 when $m = 1$ or 2, and less than p_4 when m is 3 or a greater number. There are of course an infinite number of ways in which this noncoincidence might be secured, but it is plain that if a number of concentric rings were placed at small intervals from each other, such coincidences must occur accurately or approximately between some pairs of rings, and if the value of $(p-p')^2$ is brought lower than $-4qq'$, there will be destructive interference.

This investigation is applicable to any number of concentric rings, for, by the principle of superposition of small displacements, the reciprocal actions of any pair of rings are independent of all the rest.

31. *On the effect of long-continued disturbances on a system of rings.*

The result of our previous investigations has been to point out several ways in which disturbances may accumulate till collisions of the different particles of the rings take place. After such a collision the particles will still continue to revolve about the planet, but there will be a loss of energy in the system during the collision which can never be restored. Such collisions however will not affect what is called the Angular Momentum of the system about the planet, which will therefore remain constant.

Let M be the mass of the system of rings, and δm that of one ring whose radius is r, and angular velocity $\omega = S^{\frac{1}{2}} r^{-\frac{3}{2}}$. The angular momentum of the ring is

$$\omega r^2 \delta m = S^{\frac{1}{2}} r^{\frac{1}{2}} \delta m,$$

half its *vis viva* is $\qquad \frac{1}{2}\omega^2 r^2 \delta m = \frac{1}{2} S r^{-1} \delta m.$

The potential energy due to Saturn's attraction on the ring is

$$- S r^{-1} \delta m.$$

The angular momentum of the whole system is invariable, and is

$$S^{\frac{1}{2}} \Sigma \left(r^{\frac{1}{2}} \delta m \right) = A \quad \dots\dots\dots\dots\dots\dots\dots\dots \text{(119)}.$$

The whole energy of the system is the sum of half the *vis viva* and the potential energy, and is

$$-\tfrac{1}{2} S \Sigma \left(r^{-1} \delta m \right) = E \quad \dots\dots\dots\dots\dots\dots\dots \text{(120)}.$$

A is invariable, while E necessarily diminishes. We shall find that as E diminishes, the distribution of the rings must be altered, some of the outer rings moving outwards, while the inner rings move inwards, so as either to spread out the whole system more, both on the outer and on the inner edge of the system, or, without affecting the extreme rings, to diminish the density or number of the rings at the mean distance, and increase it at or near the inner and outer edges.

Let us put $x = r^{\frac{1}{2}}$, then $A = S^{\frac{1}{2}} \Sigma \left(x\, dm \right)$ is constant.

Now let $\qquad\qquad\qquad x_1 = \dfrac{\Sigma \left(x\, dm \right)}{\Sigma \left(dm \right)},$

and $\qquad\qquad\qquad x = x_1 + x',$

then we may write

$$-\frac{2E}{S} = \Sigma \left(r^{-1} \delta m \right) = \Sigma \left(x^{-2}\, dm \right),$$

$$= \Sigma dm \left(x_1^{-2} - 2\, \frac{x'}{x_1^{3}} + 3\, \frac{x'^{2}}{x_1^{4}} - \&\text{c.} \right),$$

$$= \frac{1}{x_1^{2}} \Sigma \left(dm \right) - \frac{2}{x_1^{3}} \Sigma \left(x'\, dm \right) + \frac{3}{x_1^{4}} \Sigma \left(x'^{2} \delta m \right) - \&\text{c.} \dots\dots (121).$$

Now $\Sigma\,(dm) = M$ a constant, $\Sigma\,(x'dm) = 0$, and $\Sigma\,(x'^2\delta m)$ is a quantity which increases when the rings are spread out from the mean distance either way, x' being subject only to the restriction $\Sigma\,(x'dm) = 0$. But $\Sigma\,(x'^2dm)$ may increase without the extreme values of x' being increased, provided some other values be increased.

32. In fact, if we consider the very innermost particle as moving in an ellipse, and at the further apse of its orbit encountering another particle belonging to a larger orbit, we know that the second particle, when at the same distance from the planet, moves the faster. The result is, that the interior satellite will receive a forward impulse at its further apse, and will move in a larger and less eccentric orbit than before. In the same way one of the outermost particles may receive a backward impulse at its nearer apse, and so be made to move in a smaller and less eccentric orbit than before. When we come to deal with collisions among bodies of unknown number, size, and shape, we can no longer trace the mathematical laws of their motion with any distinctness. All we can now do is to collect the results of our investigations and to make the best use we can of them in forming an opinion as to the constitution of the actual rings of Saturn which are still in existence and apparently in steady motion, whatever catastrophes may be indicated by the various theories we have attempted.

33. *To find the Loss of Energy due to internal friction in a broad Fluid Ring, the parts of which revolve about the Planet, each with the velocity of a satellite at the same distance.*

Conceive a fluid, the particles of which move parallel to the axis of x with a velocity u, u being a function of z, then there will be a tangential pressure on a plane parallel to xy

$$= \mu\,\frac{du}{dz} \text{ on unit of area}$$

due to the relative sliding of the parts of the fluid over each other.

In the case of the ring we have

$$\omega = S^{\frac{1}{2}}\,r^{-\frac{3}{2}}.$$

The absolute velocity of any particle is ωr. That of a particle at distance $(r+\delta r)$ is

$$\omega r + \frac{d}{dr}\,(\omega r)\,\delta r.$$

If the angular velocity had been uniform, there would have been no sliding, and the velocity would have been

$$\omega r + \omega \delta r.$$

The sliding is therefore

$$r \frac{d\omega}{dr} \delta r,$$

and the friction on unit of area perpendicular to r is $\mu r \dfrac{d\omega}{dr}$.

The loss of Energy, per unit of area, is the product of the sliding by the friction,

or, $$\mu r^2 \overline{\frac{d\omega}{dr}}\Big|^2 \delta r \text{ in unit of time.}$$

The loss of Energy in a part of the Ring whose radius is r, breadth δr, and thickness c, is

$$2\pi r^3 c\mu \overline{\frac{d\omega}{dr}}\Big|^2 \delta r.$$

In the case before us it is $$\tfrac{9}{2}\pi\mu Scr^{-2}\,\delta r.$$

If the thickness of the ring is uniform between $r = a$ and $r = b$, the whole loss of Energy is

$$\tfrac{9}{2}\pi\mu Sc\left(\frac{1}{b} - \frac{1}{a}\right),$$

in unit of time.

Now half the *vis viva* of an elementary ring is

$$\pi\rho cr\delta r\; r^2\omega^2 = \pi\rho cS\delta r,$$

and this between the limits $r = a$ and $r = b$ gives

$$\pi\rho cS\,(a - b).$$

The potential due to the attraction of S is twice this quantity with the sign changed, so that

$$E = -\pi\rho cS\,(a - b),$$

and $$\frac{dE}{dt} = \tfrac{9}{2}\pi\mu S\left(\frac{1}{b} - \frac{1}{a}\right),$$

$$\frac{1}{E}\frac{dE}{dt} = -\tfrac{9}{2}\frac{\mu}{\rho}\frac{1}{ab}.$$

Now Professor Stokes finds $\sqrt{\dfrac{\mu}{\rho}} = 0\cdot0564$ for water,

and $= 0\cdot116$ for air,

taking the unit of space one English inch, and the unit of time one second. We may take $a = 88,209$ miles, and $b = 77,636$ for the ring A; and $a = 75,845$, and $b = 58,660$ for the ring B. We may also take one year as the unit of time. The quantity representing the ratio of the loss of energy in a year to the whole energy is

$$\frac{1}{E}\frac{dE}{dt} = \frac{1}{60,880,000,000,000} \text{ for the ring } A,$$

$$\text{and } \frac{1}{39,540,000,000,000} \text{ for the ring } B,$$

showing that the effect of internal friction in a ring of water moving with steady motion is inappreciably small. It cannot be from this cause therefore that any decay can take place in the motion of the ring, provided that no waves arise to disturb the motion.

Recapitulation of the Theory of the Motion of a Rigid Ring.

The position of the ring relative to Saturn at any given instant is defined by three variable quantities.

1st. The distance between the centre of gravity of Saturn and the centre of gravity of the ring. This distance we denote by r.

2nd. The angle which the line r makes with a fixed line in the plane of the motion of the ring. This angle is called θ.

3rd. The angle between the line r and a line fixed with respect to the ring so that it coincides with r when the ring is in its mean position. This is the angle ϕ.

The values of these three quantities determine the position of the ring so far as its motion in its own plane is concerned. They may be referred to as the *radius vector, longitude,* and *angle of libration* of the ring.

The forces which act between the ring and the planet depend entirely upon their relative positions. The method adopted above consists in determining the *potential* (V) of the ring at the centre of the planet in terms of r and ϕ. Then the *work done* by any displacement of the system is measured by the change of VS during that displacement. The attraction between the centre of gravity of the Ring and that of the planet is $-S\dfrac{dV}{dr}$, and the moment of the couple tending to turn the ring about its centre of gravity is $S\dfrac{dV}{d\phi}$.

It is proved in Problem V, that if a be the radius of a circular ring, $r_0 = af$ the distance of its centre of gravity from the centre of the circle, and R the mass of the ring, then, at the centre of the ring, $\dfrac{dV}{dr} = -\dfrac{R}{a^2}f$, $\dfrac{dV}{d\phi} = 0$.

It also appears that $\dfrac{d^2V}{dr^2} = \tfrac{1}{2}\dfrac{R}{a^3}(1+g)$, which is positive when $g > -1$, and that $\dfrac{d^2V}{d\phi^2} = \tfrac{1}{2}\dfrac{R}{a}f^2(3-g)$, which is positive when $g < 3$.

If $\dfrac{d^2V}{dr^2}$ is positive, then the attraction between the centres decreases as the distance increases, so that, if the two centres were kept at rest at a given distance by a constant force, the equilibrium would be unstable. If $\dfrac{d^2V}{d\phi^2}$ is positive, then the forces tend to increase the angle of libration, in whichever direction the libration takes place, so that if the ring were fixed by an axis through its centre of gravity, its equilibrium round that axis would be unstable.

In the case of the uniform ring with a heavy particle on its circumference whose weight $= \cdot82$ of the whole, the direction of the whole attractive force of the ring near the centre will pass through a point lying in the same radius as the centre of gravity, but at a distance from the centre $= \tfrac{2}{3}a$. (Fig. 6.)

If we call this point O, the line SO will indicate the direction and position of the force acting on the ring, which we may call F.

It is evident that the force F, acting on the ring in the line OS, will tend to turn it round its centre of gravity R and to increase the angle of libration KRO. The direct action of this force can never reduce the angle of libration to zero again. To understand the indirect action of the force, we must recollect that the centre of gravity (R) of the ring is revolving about Saturn in the direction of the arrows, and that the ring is revolving about its centre of gravity

with nearly the same velocity. If the angular velocity of the centre of gravity
about Saturn were always equal to the rotatory velocity of the ring, there
would be no libration.

Now suppose that the angle of rotation of the ring is in advance of the
longitude of its centre of gravity, so that the line RO has got in advance of
SRK by the angle of libration KRO. The attraction between the planet and
the ring is a force F acting in SO. We resolve this force into a couple, whose
moment is $F \cdot RN$, and a force F acting through R the centre of gravity of the
ring.

The couple affects the rotation of the ring, but not the position of its centre
of gravity, and the force RF acts on the centre of gravity without affecting the
rotation.

Now the couple, in the case represented in the figure, acts in the positive
direction, so as to *increase* the angular velocity of the ring, which was already
greater than the velocity of revolution of R about S, so that the angle of
libration would increase, and never be reduced to zero.

The force RF does not act in the direction of S, but behind it, so that it
becomes a retarding force acting upon the centre of gravity of the ring. Now
the effect of a retarding force is to cause the distance of the revolving body to
decrease and the angular velocity to increase, so that a retarding force increases
the angular velocity of R about S.

The effect of the attraction along SO in the case of the figure is, first, to
increase the rate of rotation of the ring round R, and secondly, to increase the
angular velocity of R about S. If the second effect is greater than the first,
then, although the line RO increases its angular velocity, SR will increase its
angular velocity more, and will overtake RO, and restore the ring to its original
position, so that SRO will be made a straight line as at first. If this accelerating effect is not greater than the acceleration of rotation about R due to the
couple, then no compensation will take place, and the motion will be essentially
unstable.

If in the figure we had drawn ϕ negative instead of positive, then the
couple would have been negative, the tangential force on R accelerative, r would
have increased, and in the cases of stability the retardation of θ would be greater
than that of $(\theta + \phi)$, and the normal position would be restored, as before.

The object of the investigation is to find the conditions under which this compensation is possible.

It is evident that when SRO becomes straight, there is still a difference of angular velocities between the rotation of the ring and the revolution of the centre of gravity, so that there will be an oscillation on the other side, and the motion will proceed by alternate oscillations without limit.

If we begin with r at its mean value, and ϕ negative, then the rotation of the ring will be retarded, r will be increased, the revolution of r will be more retarded, and thus ϕ will be reduced to zero. The next part of the motion will reduce r to its mean value, and bring ϕ to its greatest positive value. Then r will diminish to its least value, and ϕ will vanish. Lastly r will return to the mean value, and ϕ to the greatest negative value.

It appears from the calculations, that there are, in general, two different ways in which this kind of motion may take place, and that these may have different periods, phases, and amplitudes. The mental exertion required in following out the results of a combined motion of this kind, with all the variations of force and velocity during a complete cycle, would be very great in proportion to the additional knowledge we should derive from the exercise.

The result of this theory of a rigid ring shows not only that a perfectly uniform ring cannot revolve permanently about the planet, but that the irregularity of a permanently revolving ring must be a very observable quantity, the distance between the centre of the ring and the centre of gravity being between ·8158 and ·8279 of the radius. As there is no appearance about the rings justifying a belief in so great an irregularity, the theory of the solidity of the rings becomes very improbable.

When we come to consider the additional difficulty of the tendency of the fluid or loose parts of the ring to accumulate at the thicker parts, and thus to destroy that nice adjustment of the load on which stability depends, we have another powerful argument against solidity.

And when we consider the immense size of the rings, and their comparative thinness, the absurdity of treating them as rigid bodies becomes self-evident. An iron ring of such a size would be not only plastic but semifluid under the forces which it would experience, and we have no reason to believe these rings to be artificially strengthened with any material unknown on this earth.

Recapitulation of the Theory of a Ring of equal Satellites.

In attempting to conceive of the disturbed motion of a ring of unconnected satellites, we have, in the first place, to devise a method of identifying each satellite at any given time, and in the second place, to express the motion of every satellite under the same general formula, in order that the mathematical methods may embrace the whole system of bodies at once.

By conceiving the ring of satellites arranged regularly in a circle, we may easily identify any satellite, by stating the angular distance between it and a known satellite when so arranged. If the motion of the ring were undisturbed, this angle would remain unchanged during the motion, but, in reality, the satellite has its position altered in three ways: 1st, it may be further from or nearer to Saturn; 2ndly, it may be in advance or in the rear of the position it would have had if undisturbed; 3rdly, it may be on one side or other of the mean plane of the ring. Each of these displacements may vary in any way whatever as we pass from one satellite to another, so that it is impossible to assign beforehand the place of any satellite by knowing the places of the rest. § 2.

The formula, therefore, by which we are enabled to predict the place of every satellite at any given time, must be such as to allow the initial position of every satellite to be independent of the rest, and must express all future positions of that satellite by inserting the corresponding value of the quantity denoting time, and those of every other satellite by inserting the value of the angular distance of the given satellite from the point of reference. The three displacements of the satellite will therefore be functions of two variables—the angular position of the satellite, and the time. When the time alone is made to vary, we trace the complete motion of a single satellite; and when the time is made constant, and the angle is made to vary, we trace the form of the ring at a given time.

It is evident that the form of this function, in so far as it indicates the state of the whole ring at a given instant, must be wholly arbitrary, for the form of the ring and its motion at starting are limited only by the condition that the irregularities must be small. We have, however, the means of breaking up any function, however complicated, into a series of simple functions, so that the value of the function between certain limits may be accurately expressed as the sum of a series of sines and cosines of multiples of the variable. This method, due to Fourier, is peculiarly applicable to the case of a ring returning into itself, for the value of Fourier's series is necessarily periodic. We now regard the form of the disturbed ring at any instant as the result of the superposition of a number of separate disturbances, each of which is of the nature of a series of equal waves regularly arranged round the ring. Each of these elementary disturbances is characterised by the number of undulations in it, by their amplitude, and by the position of the first maximum in the ring. § 3.

When we know the form of each elementary disturbance, we may calculate the attraction of the disturbed ring on any given particle in terms of the constants belonging to that disturbance, so that as the actual displacement is the resultant of the elementary displacements, the actual attraction will be the resultant of the corresponding elementary attractions, and therefore the actual motion will be the resultant of all the motions arising from the elementary disturbances. We have therefore only to investigate the elementary disturbances one by one, and having established the theory of these, we calculate the actual motion by combining the series of motions so obtained.

Assuming the motion of the satellites in one of the elementary disturbances to be that of oscillation about a mean position, and the whole motion to be that of a uniformly revolving series of undulations, we find our supposition to be correct, provided a certain biquadratic equation is satisfied by the quantity denoting the rate of oscillation. § 6.

When the four roots of this equation are all real, the motion of each satellite is compounded of four different oscillations of different amplitudes and periods, and the motion of the whole ring consists of four series of undulations, travelling round the ring with different velocities. When any of these roots are impossible, the motion is no longer oscillatory, but tends to the rapid destruction of the ring.

To determine whether the motion of the ring is permanent, we must assure ourselves that the four roots of this equation are real, whatever be the number of undulations in the ring; for if any one of the possible elementary disturbances should lead to destructive oscillations, that disturbance might sooner or later commence, and the ring would be destroyed.

Now the number of undulations in the ring may be any whole number from one up to half the number of satellites. The forces from which danger is to be apprehended are greatest when the number of undulations is greatest, and by taking that number equal to half the number of satellites, we find the condition of stability to be

$$S > .4352 \, \mu^2 R,$$

where S is the mass of the central body, R that of the ring, and μ the number of satellites of which it is composed. § 8. If the number of satellites be too great, destructive oscillations will commence, and finally some of the satellites will come into collision with each other and unite, so that the number of independent satellites will be reduced to that which the central body can retain and keep in discipline. When this has taken place, the satellites will not only be kept at the proper distance from the primary, but will be prevented by its preponderating mass from interfering with each other.

We next considered more carefully the case in which the mass of the ring is very small, so that the forces arising from the attraction of the ring are small compared with that due to the central body. In this case the values of the roots of the biquadratic are all real, and easily estimated. § 9.

If we consider the motion of any satellite about its mean position, as referred to axes fixed in the plane of the ring, we shall find that it describes an ellipse in the direction opposite to that of the revolution of the ring, the periodic time being to that of the ring as ω to n, and the tangential amplitude of oscillation being to the radial as 2ω to n. § 10.

The absolute motion of each satellite in space is nearly elliptic for the large values of n, the axis of the ellipse always advancing slowly in the direction of rotation. The path of a satellite corresponding to one of the small values of n is nearly circular, but the radius slowly increases and diminishes during a period of many revolutions. § 11.

The form of the ring at any instant is that of a re-entering curve, having m alternations of distance from the centre, symmetrically arranged, and m points of condensation, or crowding of the satellites, which coincide with the points of greatest distance when n is positive, and with the points nearest the centre when n is negative. § 12.

This system of undulations travels with an angular velocity $-\dfrac{n}{m}$ relative to the ring, and $\omega - \dfrac{n}{m}$ in space, so that during each oscillation of a satellite a complete wave passes over it. § 14.

To exhibit the movements of the satellites, I have made an arrangement by which 36 little ivory balls are made to go through the motions belonging to the first or fourth series of waves. (Figs. 7, 8.)

The instrument stands on a pillar A, in the upper part of which turns the cranked axle CC. On the parallel parts of this axle are placed two wheels, RR and TT, each of which has 36 holes at equal distances in a circle near its circumference. The two circles are connected by 36 small cranks of the form KK, the extremities of which turn in the corresponding holes of the two wheels. That axle of the crank K which passes through the hole in the wheel S is bored, so as to hold the end of the bent wire which carries the satellite S. This wire may be turned in the hole so as to place the bent part carrying the satellite at any angle with the crank. A pin P, which passes through the top of the pillar, serves to prevent the cranked axle from turning; and a pin Q, passing through the pillar horizontally, may be made to fix the wheel R, by inserting it in a hole in one of the spokes of that wheel. There is also a handle H, which is in one piece with the wheel T, and serves to turn the axle.

Now suppose the pin P taken out, so as to allow the cranked axle to turn, and the pin Q inserted in its hole, so as to prevent the wheel R from revolving; then if the crank C be turned by means of the handle H, the wheel T will have its centre carried round in a vertical circle, but will remain parallel to itself during the whole motion, so that every point in its plane will describe an equal circle, and all the cranks K will be made to revolve exactly as the large crank C does. Each satellite will therefore revolve in a small circular orbit, in the same time with the handle H, but the position of each satellite in that orbit may be arranged as we please, according as we turn the wire which supports it in the end of the crank.

In fig. 8, which gives a front view of the instrument, the satellites are so placed that each is turned 60° further round in its socket than the one behind it. As there are 36 satellites, this process will bring us back to our starting-point after six revolutions of the direction of the arm of the satellite; and therefore as we have gone round the ring once in the same direction, the arm of the satellite will have overtaken the radius of the ring five times.

Hence there will be five places where the satellites are beyond their mean distance from the centre of the ring, and five where they are within it, so that we have here a series of five undulations round the circumference of the ring. In this case the satellites are crowded together when nearest to the centre, so that the case is that of the *first* series of waves, when $m = 5$.

Now suppose the cranked axle C to be turned, and all the small cranks K to turn with it, as before explained, every satellite will then be carried round on its own arm in the same direction; but, since the direction of the arms of different satellites is different, their phases of revolution will preserve the same difference, and the system of satellites will still be arranged in five undulations, only the undulations will be propagated round the ring in the direction opposite to that of the revolution of the satellites.

To understand the motion better, let us conceive the centres of the orbits of the satellites to be arranged in a straight line instead of a circle, as in fig. 10. Each satellite is here represented in a different phase of its orbit, so that as we pass from one to another from left to right, we find the position of the satellite in its orbit altering in the direction opposite to that of the hands of a watch. The satellites all lie in a trochoidal curve, indicated by the line through them in the figure. Now conceive every satellite to move in its orbit through a certain angle in the direction of the arrows. The satellites will then lie in the dotted line, the form of which is the same as that of the former curve, only shifted in the direction of the large arrow. It appears, therefore, that as the satellites revolve, the undulation travels, so that any part of it reaches successively each satellite as it comes into the same phase of rotation. It therefore travels from those satellites which are most advanced in phase to those which are less so, and passes over a complete wave-length in the time of one revolution of a satellite.

Now if the satellites be arranged as in fig. 8, where each is more advanced in phase as we go round the ring in the direction of rotation, the wave will travel in the direction opposite to that of rotation, but if they are arranged as in fig. 12, where each satellite is less advanced in phase as we go round the ring, the wave will travel in the direction of rotation. Fig. 8 represents the *first* series of waves where $m = 5$, and fig. 12 represents the *fourth* series where $m = 7$. By arranging the satellites in their sockets before starting, we might make m equal to any whole number, from 1 to 18. If we chose any number above 18 the result would be the same as if we had taken a number as much below 18 and changed the arrangement from the first wave to the fourth.

In this way we can exhibit the motions of the satellites in the first and fourth waves. In reality they ought to move in ellipses, the major axes being twice the minor, whereas in the machine they move in circles: but the character of the motion is the same, though the form of the orbit is different.

We may now show these motions of the satellites among each other, combined with the motion of rotation of the whole ring. For this purpose we put in the pin P, so as to prevent the crank axle from turning, and take out the pin Q so as to allow the wheel R to turn. If we then turn the wheel T, all the small cranks will remain parallel to the fixed crank, and the wheel R will revolve at the same rate as T. The arm of each satellite will continue parallel to itself during the motion, so that the satellite will describe a circle whose centre is at a distance from the centre of R, equal to the arm of the satellite, and measured in the same direction. In our theory of real satellites, each moves in an ellipse, having the central body in its focus, but this motion in an eccentric circle is sufficiently near for illustration. The motion of the waves relative to the ring is the same as before. The waves of the first kind travel faster than the ring itself, and overtake the satellites, those of the fourth kind travel slower, and are overtaken by them.

In fig. 11 we have an exaggerated representation of a ring of twelve satellites affected by a wave of the fourth kind where $m = 2$. The satellites here lie in an ellipse at any given instant, and as each moves round in its circle about its mean position, the ellipse also moves round in the same direction with half their angular velocity. In the figure the dotted line represents the position of the ellipse when each satellite has moved forward into the position represented by a dot.

Fig. 13 represents a wave of the first kind where $m = 2$. The satellites at any instant lie in an epitrochoid, which, as the satellites revolve about their mean positions, revolves in the opposite direction with half their angular velocity, so that when the satellites come into the positions represented by the dots, the curve in which they lie turns round in the opposite direction and forms the dotted curve.

In fig. 9 we have the same case as in fig. 13, only that the absolute orbits of the satellites in space are given, instead of their orbits about their mean positions in the ring. Here each moves about the central body in an eccentric circle, which in strictness ought to be an ellipse not differing much from the circle.

As the satellites move in their orbits in the direction of the arrows, the curve which they form revolves in the same direction with a velocity $1\frac{1}{2}$ times that of the ring.

By considering these figures, and still more by watching the actual motion of the ivory balls in the model, we may form a distinct notion of the motions of the particles of a discontinuous ring, although the motions of the model are circular and not elliptic. The model, represented on a scale of one-third in figs. 7 and 8, was made in brass by Messrs. Smith and Ramage of Aberdeen.

We are now able to understand the mechanical principle, on account of which a massive central body is enabled to govern a numerous assemblage of satellites, and to space them out into a regular ring; while a smaller central body would allow disturbances to arise among the individual satellites, and collisions to take place.

When we calculated the attractions among the satellites composing the ring, we found that if any satellite be displaced tangentially, the resultant attraction will draw it away from its mean position, for the attraction of the satellites it approaches will increase, while that of those it recedes from will diminish, so that its equilibrium when in the mean position is unstable with respect to tangential displacements; and therefore, since every satellite of the ring is statically unstable between its neighbours, the slightest disturbance would tend to produce collisions among the satellites, and to break up the ring into groups of conglomerated satellites.

But if we consider the dynamics of the problem, we shall find that this effect need not necessarily take place, and that this very force which tends towards destruction may become the condition of the preservation of the ring. Suppose the whole ring to be revolving round a central body, and that one satellite gets in advance of its mean position. It will then be attracted forwards, its path will become less concave towards the attracting body, so that its distance from that body will increase. At this increased distance its angular velocity will be less, so that instead of overtaking those in front, it may by this means be made to fall back to its original position. Whether it does so or not must depend on the actual values of the attractive forces and on the angular velocity of the ring. When the angular velocity is great and the attractive forces small, the compensating process will go on vigorously, and the ring will be preserved. When the angular velocity is small and the attractive forces of the ring great, the dynamical effect will not compensate for the disturbing action of the forces and the ring will be destroyed.

If the satellite, instead of being displaced forwards, had been originally behind its mean position in the ring, the forces would have pulled it backwards, its path would have become more concave towards the centre, its distance from the centre would diminish, its angular velocity would increase, and it would gain upon the rest of the ring till it got in front of its mean position. This effect is of course dependent on the very same conditions as in the former case, and the actual effect on a disturbed satellite would be to make it describe an orbit about its mean position in the ring, so that if in advance of its mean position, it first recedes from the centre, then falls behind its mean position in the ring, then approaches the centre within the mean distance, then advances beyond its mean position, and, lastly, recedes from the centre till it reaches its starting-point, after which the process is repeated indefinitely, the orbit being always described in the direction opposite to that of the revolution of the ring.

We now understand what would happen to a disturbed satellite, if all the others were preserved from disturbance. But, since all the satellites are equally free, the motion of one will produce changes in the forces acting on the rest, and this will set them in motion, and this motion will be propagated from one satellite to another round the ring. Now propagated disturbances constitute waves, and all waves, however complicated, may be reduced to combinations of simple and regular waves; and therefore all the disturbances of the ring may be considered as the resultant of many series of waves, of different lengths, and travelling with different velocities. The investigation of the relation between the length and velocity of these waves forms the essential part of the problem, after which we have only to split up the original disturbance into its simple elements, to calculate the effect of each of these separately, and then to combine the results. The solution thus obtained will be perfectly general, and quite independent of the particular form of the ring, whether regular or irregular at starting. § 14.

We next investigated the effect upon the ring of an external disturbing force. Having split up the disturbing force into components of the same type with the waves of the ring (an operation which is always possible), we found that each term of the disturbing force generates a "forced wave" travelling with its own angular velocity. The magnitude of the forced wave depends not only on that of the disturbing force, but on the angular velocity with which the disturbance travels round the ring, being greater in proportion as this velocity more nearly coincides with that of one of the "free waves" of the ring. We also found that the displacement of the satellites was sometimes in the direction of the disturbing force, and sometimes in the opposite direction, according to the relative position of the forced wave among the four natural ones, producing in the one case positive, and in the other negative forced waves. In treating the problem generally, we must determine the forced waves belonging to every term of the disturbing force, and combine these with such a system of free waves as shall reproduce the initial state of the ring. The subsequent motion of the ring is that which would result from the free waves and forced waves together. The most important class of forced waves are those which are produced by waves in neighbouring rings. § 15.

We concluded the theory of a ring of satellites by tracing the process by which the ring would be destroyed if the conditions of stability were not fulfilled. We found two cases of instability, depending on the nature of the tangential force due to tangential displacement. If this force be in the direction opposite to the displacement, that is, if the parts of the ring are *statically stable*, the ring will be destroyed, the irregularities becoming larger and larger without being propagated round the ring. When the tangential force is in the direction of the tangential displacement, if it is below a certain value, the disturbances will be propagated round the ring without becoming larger, and we have the case of stability treated of at large. If the force exceed this value, the disturbances will still travel round the ring, but they will increase in amplitude continually till the ring falls into confusion. § 18.

We then proceeded to extend our method to the case of rings of different constitutions. The first case was that of a ring of satellites of unequal size. If the central body be of sufficient mass, such a ring will be spaced out, so that the larger satellites will be at wider intervals than the smaller ones, and the waves of disturbance will be propagated as before, except that there may be reflected waves when a wave reaches a part of the ring where there is a change in the average size of the satellites. § 19.

The next case was that of an annular cloud of meteoric stones, revolving uniformly about the planet. The *average density* of the space through which these small bodies are scattered will vary with every irregularity of the motion, and this variation of density will produce variations in the forces acting upon the other parts of the cloud, and so disturbances will be propagated in this ring, as in a ring of a finite number of satellites. The condition that such a ring should be free from destructive oscillations is, that the density of the planet should be more than three hundred times that of the ring. This would make the ring much rarer than common air, as regards its *average density*, though the density of the particles of which it is composed may be great. Comparing this result with Laplace's minimum density of a ring revolving as a whole, we find that such a ring cannot revolve as a whole, but that the inner parts must have a greater angular velocity than the outer parts. § 20.

We next took up the case of a flattened ring, composed of incompressible fluid, and moving with uniform angular velocity. The internal forces here arise partly from attraction and partly from fluid pressure. We began by taking the case of an infinite stratum of fluid affected by regular waves, and found the accurate values of the forces in this case. For long waves the resultant force is in the same direction as the displacement, reaching a maximum for waves whose length is about ten times the thickness of the stratum. For waves about five times as long as the stratum is thick there is no resultant force, and for shorter waves the force is in the opposite direction to the displacement. § 23.

Applying these results to the case of the ring, we find that it will be destroyed by the long waves unless the fluid is less than $\frac{1}{42}$ of the density of the planet, and that in all cases the short waves will break up the ring into small satellites.

Passing to the case of *narrow* rings, we should find a somewhat larger maximum density, but we should still find that very short waves produce forces in the direction opposite to the displacement, and that therefore, as already explained (page 333), these short undulations would increase in magnitude without being propagated along the ring, till they had broken up the fluid filament into drops. These drops may or may not fulfil the condition formerly given for the stability of a ring of equal satellites. If they fulfil it, they will move as a permanent ring. If they do not, short waves will arise and be propagated among the satellites, with ever increasing magnitude, till a sufficient number of drops have been brought into collision, so as to unite and form a smaller number of larger drops, which may be capable of revolving as a permanent ring.

We have already investigated the disturbances produced by an external force independent of the ring; but the special case of the mutual perturbations of two concentric rings is considerably more complex, because the existence of a double system of waves changes the character of both, and the waves produced react on those that produced them.

We determined the attraction of a ring upon a particle of a concentric ring, first, when both rings are in their undisturbed state; secondly, when the particle is disturbed; and, thirdly, when the attracting ring is disturbed by a series of waves. § 26.

We then formed the equations of motion of one of the rings, taking in the disturbing forces arising from the existence of a wave in the other ring, and found the small variation of the velocity of a wave in the first ring as dependent on the magnitude of the wave in the second ring, which travels with it. § 27.

The forced wave in the second ring must have the same absolute angular velocity as the free wave of the first which produces it, but this velocity of the free wave is slightly altered by the reaction of the forced wave upon it. We find that if a free wave of the first ring has an absolute angular velocity not very different from that of a free wave of the second ring, then if both free waves be of even orders (that is, of the second or fourth varieties of waves), or both of odd orders (that is, of the first or third), then the swifter of the two free waves has its velocity increased by the forced wave which it produces, and the slower free wave is rendered still slower by its forced wave; and even when the two free waves have the same angular velocity, their mutual action will make them both split into two, one wave in each ring travelling faster, and the other wave in each ring travelling slower, than the rate with which they would move if they had not acted on each other.

But if one of the free waves be of an even order and the other of an odd order, the swifter free wave will travel slower, and the slower free wave will travel swifter, on account of the reaction of their respective forced waves. If the two free waves have naturally a certain small difference of velocities, they will be made to travel together, but if the difference is less than this, they will again split into two pairs of waves, one pair continually increasing in magnitude without limit, and the other continually diminishing, so that one of the waves in each ring will increase in violence till it has thrown the ring into a state of confusion.

There are four cases in which this may happen. The first wave of the outer ring may conspire with the second or the fourth of the inner ring, the second of the outer with the third of the inner, or the third of the outer with the fourth of the inner. That two rings may revolve permanently, their distances must be arranged so that none of these conspiracies may arise between odd and even waves, whatever be the value of m. The number of conditions to be fulfilled is therefore very great, especially when the rings are near together and have nearly the same angular velocity, because then there are a greater number of dangerous values of m to be provided for.

In the case of a large number of concentric rings, the stability of each pair must be investigated separately, and if in the case of any two, whether consecutive rings or not, there are a pair of conspiring waves, those two rings will be agitated more and more, till waves of that kind are rendered impossible by the breaking up of those rings into some different arrangement. The presence of the other rings cannot prevent the mutual destruction of any pair which bear such relations to each other.

It appears, therefore, that in a system of many concentric rings there will be continually new cases of mutual interference between different pairs of rings. The forces which excite these disturbances being very small, they will be slow of growth, and it is possible that by the irregularities of each of the rings the waves may be so broken and confused (see § 19), as to be incapable of mounting up to the height at which they would begin to destroy the arrangement of the ring. In this way it may be conceived to be possible that the gradual disarrangement of the system may be retarded or indefinitely postponed.

But supposing that these waves mount up so as to produce collisions among the particles, then we may deduce the result upon the system from general dynamical principles. There will be a tendency among the exterior rings to remove further from the planet, and among the interior rings to approach the planet, and this either by the extreme interior and exterior rings diverging from each other, or by intermediate parts of the system moving away from the mean ring. If the interior rings are observed to approach the planet, while it is known that none of the other rings have expanded, then the cause of the change cannot be the mutual action of the parts of the system, but the resistance of some medium in which the rings revolve.   § 31.

There is another cause which would gradually act upon a broad fluid ring of which the parts revolve each with the angular velocity due to its distance from the planet, namely, the internal friction produced by the slipping of the concentric rings with different angular velocities.   It appears, however (§ 33), that the effect of fluid friction would be insensible if the motion were regular.

Let us now gather together the conclusions we have been able to draw from the mathematical theory of various kinds of conceivable rings.

We found that the stability of the motion of a solid ring depended on so delicate an adjustment, and at the same time so unsymmetrical a distribution of mass, that even if the exact condition were fulfilled, it could scarcely last long, and if it did, the immense preponderance of one side of the ring would be easily observed, contrary to experience.   These considerations, with others derived from the mechanical structure of so vast a body, compel us to abandon any theory of solid rings.

We next examined the motion of a ring of equal satellites, and found that if the mass of the planet is sufficient, any disturbances produced in the arrangement of the ring will be propagated round it in the form of waves, and will not introduce dangerous confusion. If the satellites are unequal, the propagation of the waves will no longer be regular, but disturbances of the ring will in this, as in the former case, produce only waves, and not growing confusion. Supposing the ring to consist, not of a single row of large satellites, but of a cloud of evenly distributed unconnected particles, we found that such a cloud must have a very small density in order to be permanent, and that this is inconsistent with its outer and inner parts moving with the same angular velocity. Supposing the ring to be fluid and continuous, we found that it will be necessarily broken up into small portions.

We conclude, therefore, that the rings must consist of disconnected particles ; these may be either solid or liquid, but they must be independent. The entire system of rings must therefore consist either of a series of many concentric rings, each moving with its own velocity, and having its own systems of waves, or else of a confused multitude of revolving particles, not arranged in rings, and continually coming into collision with each other.

Taking the first case, we found that in an indefinite number of possible cases the mutual perturbations of two rings, stable in themselves, might mount up in time to a destructive magnitude, and that such cases must continually occur in an extensive system like that of Saturn, the only retarding cause being the possible irregularity of the rings.

The result of long-continued disturbance was found to be the spreading out of the rings in breadth, the outer rings pressing outwards, while the inner rings press inwards.

The final result, therefore, of the mechanical theory is, that the only system of rings which can exist is one composed of an indefinite number of unconnected particles, revolving round the planet with different velocities according to their respective distances. These particles may be arranged in series of narrow rings, or they may move through each other irregularly. In the first case the destruction of the system will be very slow, in the second case it will be more rapid, but there may be a tendency towards an arrangement in narrow rings, which may retard the process.

We are not able to ascertain by observation the constitution of the two outer divisions of the system of rings, but the inner ring is certainly transparent, for the limb of Saturn has been observed through it. It is also certain, that though the space occupied by the ring is transparent, it is not through the material parts of it that Saturn was seen, for his limb was observed without distortion; which shows that there was no refraction, and therefore that the rays did not pass through a medium at all, but between the solid or liquid particles of which the ring is composed. Here then we have an optical argument in favour of the theory of independent particles as the material of the rings. The two outer rings may be of the same nature, but not so exceedingly rare that a ray of light can pass through their whole thickness without encountering one of the particles.

Finally, the two outer rings have been observed for 200 years, and it appears, from the careful analysis of all the observations by M. Struvé, that the second ring is broader than when first observed, and that its inner edge is nearer the planet than formerly. The inner ring also is suspected to be approaching the planet ever since its discovery in 1850. These appearances seem to indicate the same slow progress of the rings towards separation which we found to be the result of theory, and the remark, that the inner edge of the inner ring is most distinct, seems to indicate that the approach towards the planet is less rapid near the edge, as we had reason to conjecture. As to the apparent unchangeableness of the exterior diameter of the outer ring, we must remember that the outer rings are certainly far more dense than the inner one, and that a small change in the outer rings must balance a great change in the inner one. It is possible, however, that some of the observed changes may be due to the existence of a resisting medium. If the changes already suspected should be confirmed by repeated observations with the same instruments, it will be worth while to investigate more carefully whether Saturn's Rings are permanent or transitionary elements of the Solar System, and whether in that part of the heavens we see celestial immutability, or terrestrial corruption and generation, and the old order giving place to new before our own eyes.

APPENDIX.

On the Stability of the Steady Motion of a Rigid Body about a Fixed Centre of Force.
By Professor W. Thomson *(communicated in a letter).*

The body will be supposed to be symmetrical on the two sides of a certain plane containing the centre of force, and no motion except that of parts of the body parallel to the plane will be considered. Taking it as the plane of construction, let G (fig. 14) be the centre of gravity of the body, and O a point at which the resultant attraction of the body is in the line OG towards G. Then if the body be placed with O coinciding with the centre of force, and set in a state of rotation about that point as an axis, with an angular velocity equal to $\sqrt{\dfrac{fS}{aM}}$, (where f denotes the attraction of the body on a unit of matter at O, S the amount of matter in the central body, M the mass of the revolving body, and a the distance OG), it will continue, provided it be perfectly undisturbed, to revolve uniformly at this rate, and the attraction Sf on the moving body will be constantly balanced by the centrifugal force $\omega^2 aM$ of its motion.

Let us now suppose the motion to be slightly disturbed, and let it be required to investigate the consequences. Let X, S, Y, be rectangular axes of reference revolving uniformly with the angular velocity ω, round S, the fixed attracting point. Let $\bar{x}$, $\bar{y}$, be the co-ordinates of G with reference to these axes, and let XS, YS denote the components of the whole force of attraction of S on the rigid body. Then since this force is in the line through S, its moment round G is

$$SY\bar{x} - SX\bar{y};$$

the components of the forces on the moving body being reckoned as *positive* when they tend to *diminish* $\bar{x}$ and $\bar{y}$ respectively. Hence if k denote the radius of gyration of the body round G, and if ϕ denote the angle which OG makes with SX (*i.e.* the angle GOK), the equations of motion are,

$$M \left(\frac{d^2\bar{x}}{dt^2} - 2\omega \frac{d\bar{y}}{dt} - \omega^2\bar{x} \right) + SX = 0,$$

$$M \left(\frac{d^2\bar{y}}{dt^2} + 2\omega \frac{d\bar{x}}{dt} - \omega^2\bar{y} \right) + SY = 0,$$

$$Mk^2 \frac{d^2\phi}{dt^2} - S(Y\bar{x} - X\bar{y}) = 0.$$

In the first place we see that one integral of these equations is

$$M \left(\bar{x}\frac{d\bar{y}}{dt} - \bar{y}\frac{d\bar{x}}{dt} \right) + M\omega(\bar{x}^2 + \bar{y}^2) + Mk^2 \frac{d\phi}{dt} = H.$$

This is the "equation of angular momentum."

In considering whether the motion round S with velocity ω when O coincides with S is stable or unstable, we must find whether every possible motion with the same "angular momentum" round S is such that it will never bring O to more than an infinitely small distance from S: that is to say, we must find whether, for every possible solution in which $H = M(a^2 + k^2)\omega$, and for which the co-ordinates of O are infinitely small at one time, these co-ordinates remain infinitely small. Let these values at time t be denoted thus: $SN = \xi$, and $NO = \eta$; let OG be at first infinitely nearly parallel to OX, *i.e.* let ϕ be infinitely small (the full solution will tell us whether or not ϕ remains infinitely small); then, as long as ϕ is infinitely small, we have

$$\bar{x} = a + \xi, \quad \bar{y} = \eta + a\phi,$$

and the equations of motion have the forms

$$M \left\{ \frac{d^2\xi}{dt^2} - 2\omega \left(\frac{d\eta}{dt} + a\frac{d\phi}{dt} \right) - \omega^2(a + \xi) \right\} + SX = 0,$$

$$M \left\{ \frac{d^2\eta}{dt^2} + a\frac{d^2\phi}{dt^2} + 2\omega\frac{d\xi}{dt} - \omega^2(\eta + a\phi) \right\} + SY = 0,$$

and we may write the equation of angular momentum instead of the third equation,

$$M \left\{ (a + \xi)\left(\frac{d\eta}{dt} + a\frac{d\phi}{dt} \right) - (\eta + a\phi)\left(\frac{d\xi}{dt} \right) + \omega(a + \xi)^2 + \omega(\eta + a\phi)^2 + k^2\frac{d\phi}{dt} \right\} = H.$$

If now we suppose ξ and η to be infinitely small, the last of these equations becomes

$$(a^2 + k^2)\frac{d\phi}{dt} + 2\omega a\xi + a\frac{d\eta}{dt} = 0. \dots\dots\dots\dots\dots\dots\dots\dots(a).$$

If p and q denote the components parallel and perpendicular to OG of the attraction of the body on a unit of matter at S, we have

$$X = p \cos\phi - q \sin\phi = p, \text{ and } Y = p \sin\phi + q \cos\phi = p\phi + q,$$

since q and ϕ are each infinitely small; and if we put $V =$ potential at S, and

$$a = \frac{d^2 V}{d\xi^2}, \quad \beta = \frac{d^2 V}{d\eta^2}, \quad \gamma = \frac{d^2 V}{d\xi d\eta},$$

then

$$p = f - a\xi - \gamma\eta, \quad q = -\beta\eta - \gamma\xi,$$
$$X = f - a\xi - \gamma\eta, \quad Y = f\phi - \beta\eta - \gamma\xi.$$

If we make these substitutions for X and Y, and take into account that

$$f = \omega^2 a \frac{M}{S} \quad \dots\dots\dots\dots\dots\dots\dots\dots\dots\dots\dots\dots\dots\dots \text{ (b)},$$

the first and second equations of motion become

$$\frac{d^2\xi}{dt^2} - 2\omega \frac{d\eta}{dt} - \omega^2\xi - 2\omega a \frac{d\phi}{dt} - \frac{S}{M}(a\xi + \gamma\eta) = 0 \quad \dots\dots\dots\dots\dots\dots\dots \text{ (c)},$$

$$\frac{d^2\eta}{dt^2} + 2\omega \frac{d\xi}{dt} - \omega^2\eta + a \frac{d^2\phi}{dt^2} - \frac{S}{M}(\beta\eta + \gamma\xi) = 0 \quad \dots\dots\dots\dots\dots\dots\dots \text{ (d)}.$$

Combining equations (a), (c), and (d), by the same method as that adopted in the text, we find that the differential equation in ξ, η, or ϕ, is of the form

$$A \frac{d^4 u}{dt^4} + B \frac{d^2 u}{dt^2} + Cu = 0,$$

where $A = k^2,$

$$B = \omega^2 (2k^2 - a^2) - \frac{S}{M} \{k^2 a + (a^2 + k^2)\beta\},$$

$$C = \omega^4 (k^2 - 3a^2) + \omega^2 \frac{S}{M} \{(a^2 + k^2)(a + \beta) - 4a^2\beta\} + (a^2 + k^2) \frac{S^2}{M^2}(a\beta - \gamma).$$

In comparing this result with that obtained in the Essay, we must put

$$r_0 \text{ for } a,$$
$$R \text{ for } M,$$
$$R + S \text{ for } S,$$
$$L \text{ for } a,$$
$$N r_0^2 \text{ for } \beta,$$
$$M r_0 \text{ for } \gamma.$$

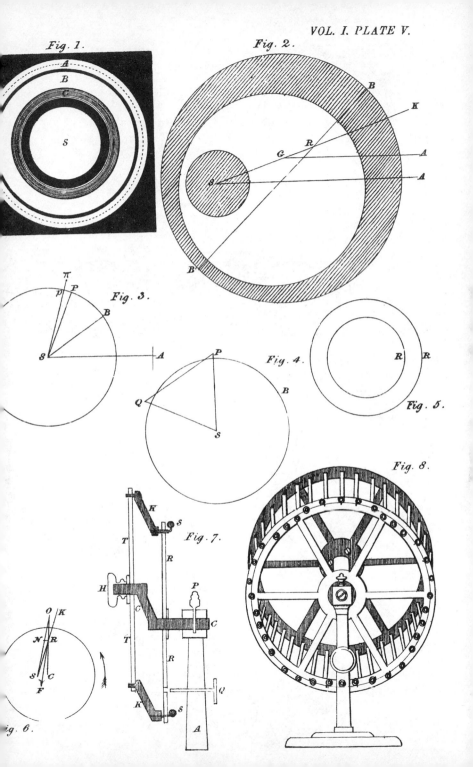

Fig. 1.

Fig. 2.

Fig. 3.

Fig. 4.

Fig. 5.

Fig. 6.

Fig. 7.

Fig. 8.

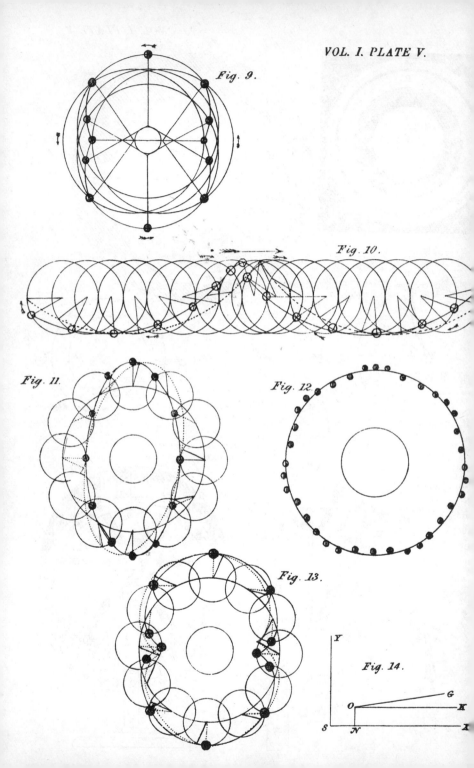

Fig. 9.

Fig. 10.

Fig. 11.

Fig. 12.

Fig. 13.

Fig. 14.

[From the *Philosophical Magazine* for January and July, 1860.]

XX. *Illustrations of the Dynamical Theory of Gases*[*].

PART I.

ON THE MOTIONS AND COLLISIONS OF PERFECTLY ELASTIC SPHERES.

So many of the properties of matter, especially when in the gaseous form, can be deduced from the hypothesis that their minute parts are in rapid motion, the velocity increasing with the temperature, that the precise nature of this motion becomes a subject of rational curiosity. Daniel Bernouilli, Herapath, Joule, Krönig, Clausius, &c. have shewn that the relations between pressure, temperature, and density in a perfect gas can be explained by supposing the particles to move with uniform velocity in straight lines, striking against the sides of the containing vessel and thus producing pressure. It is not necessary to suppose each particle to travel to any great distance in the same straight line; for the effect in producing pressure will be the same if the particles strike against each other; so that the straight line described may be very short. M. Clausius has determined the mean length of path in terms of the average distance of the particles, and the distance between the centres of two particles when collision takes place. We have at present no means of ascertaining either of these distances; but certain phenomena, such as the internal friction of gases, the conduction of heat through a gas, and the diffusion of one gas through another, seem to indicate the possibility of determining accurately the mean length of path which a particle describes between two successive collisions. In order to lay the foundation of such investigations on strict mechanical principles, I shall demonstrate the laws of motion of an indefinite number of small, hard, and perfectly elastic spheres acting on one another only during impact.

* Read at the Meeting of the British Association at Aberdeen, September 21, 1859.

If the properties of such a system of bodies are found to correspond to those of gases, an important physical analogy will be established, which may lead to more accurate knowledge of the properties of matter. If experiments on gases are inconsistent with the hypothesis of these propositions, then our theory, though consistent with itself, is proved to be incapable of explaining the phenomena of gases. In either case it is necessary to follow out the consequences of the hypothesis.

Instead of saying that the particles are hard, spherical, and elastic, we may if we please say that the particles are centres of force, of which the action is insensible except at a certain small distance, when it suddenly appears as a repulsive force of very great intensity. It is evident that either assumption will lead to the same results. For the sake of avoiding the repetition of a long phrase about these repulsive forces, I shall proceed upon the assumption of perfectly elastic spherical bodies. If we suppose those aggregate molecules which move together to have a bounding surface which is not spherical, then the rotatory motion of the system will store up a certain proportion of the whole *vis viva*, as has been shewn by Clausius, and in this way we may account for the value of the specific heat being greater than on the more simple hypothesis.

On the Motion and Collision of Perfectly Elastic Spheres.

Prop. I. Two spheres moving in opposite directions with velocities inversely as their masses strike one another; to determine their motions after impact.

Let P and Q be the position of the centres at impact; AP, BQ the directions and magnitudes of the velocities before impact; Pa, Qb the same after impact; then, resolving the velocities parallel and perpendicular to PQ the line of centres, we find that the velocities parallel to the line of centres are exactly reversed, while those perpendicular to that line are unchanged. Compounding these velocities again, we find that the velocity of each ball is the same before and after impact, and that the directions before and after impact lie in the same plane with the line of centres, and make equal angles with it.

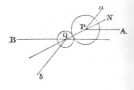

Prop. II.   To find the probability of the direction of the velocity after impact lying between given limits.

In order that a collision may take place, the line of motion of one of the balls must pass the centre of the other at a distance less than the sum of their radii; that is, it must pass through a circle whose centre is that of the other ball, and radius (s) the sum of the radii of the balls.   Within this circle every position is equally probable, and therefore the probability of the distance from the centre being between r and $r + dr$ is

$$\frac{2r\,dr}{s^2}.$$

Now let ϕ be the angle APa between the original direction and the direction after impact, then $APN = \frac{1}{2}\phi$, and $r = s \sin \frac{1}{2}\phi$, and the probability becomes

$$\tfrac{1}{2} \sin \phi\, d\phi.$$

The area of a spherical zone between the angles of polar distance ϕ and $\phi + d\phi$ is

$$2\pi \sin \phi\, d\phi;$$

therefore if ω be any small area on the surface of a sphere, radius unity, the probability of the direction of rebound passing through this area is

$$\frac{\omega}{4\pi};$$

so that the probability is independent of ϕ, that is, all directions of rebound are equally likely.

Prop. III.   Given the direction and magnitude of the velocities of two spheres before impact, and the line of centres at impact; to find the velocities after impact.

Let OA, OB represent the velocities before impact, so that if there had been no action between the bodies they would have been at A and B at the end of a second.   Join AB, and let G be their centre of gravity, the position of which is not affected by their mutual action.   Draw GN parallel to the line of centres at impact (not necessarily in the plane AOB).   Draw aGb in the plane AGN, making $NGa = NGA$, and $Ga = GA$ and $Gb = GB$; then by

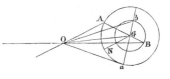

Prop. I. Ga and Gb will be the velocities relative to G; and compounding these with OG, we have Oa and Ob for the true velocities after impact.

By Prop. II. all directions of the line aGb are equally probable. It appears therefore that the velocity after impact is compounded of the velocity of the centre of gravity, and of a velocity equal to the velocity of the sphere relative to the centre of gravity, which may with equal probability be in any direction whatever.

If a great many equal spherical particles were in motion in a perfectly elastic vessel, collisions would take place among the particles, and their velocities would be altered at every collision; so that after a certain time the *vis viva* will be divided among the particles according to some regular law, the average number of particles whose velocity lies between certain limits being ascertainable though the velocity of each particle changes at every collision.

Prop. IV. To find the average number of particles whose velocities lie between given limits, after a great number of collisions among a great number of equal particles.

Let N be the whole number of particles. Let x, y, z be the components of the velocity of each particle in three rectangular directions, and let the number of particles for which x lies between x and $x + dx$, be $Nf(x)dx$, where $f(x)$ is a function of x to be determined.

The number of particles for which y lies between y and $y + dy$ will be $Nf(y)dy$; and the number for which z lies between z and $z + dz$ will be $Nf(z)dz$, where f always stands for the same function.

Now the existence of the velocity x does not in any way affect that of the velocities y or z, since these are all at right angles to each other and independent, so that the number of particles whose velocity lies between x and $x + dx$, and also between y and $y + dy$, and also between z and $z + dz$, is

$$Nf(x)f(y)f(z)\,dx\,dy\,dz.$$

If we suppose the N particles to start from the origin at the same instant, then this will be the number in the element of volume $(dx\,dy\,dz)$ after unit of time, and the number referred to unit of volume will be

$$Nf(x)f(y)f(z).$$

But the directions of the coordinates are perfectly arbitrary, and therefore this number must depend on the distance from the origin alone, that is

$$f(x)f(y)f(z) = \phi(x^2 + y^2 + z^2).$$

Solving this functional equation, we find

$$f(x) = Ce^{Ax^2}, \qquad \phi(r^2) = C^3 e^{Ar^2}.$$

If we make A positive, the number of particles will increase with the velocity, and we should find the whole number of particles infinite. We therefore make A negative and equal to $-\dfrac{1}{a^2}$, so that the number between x and $x + dx$ is

$$NCe^{-\frac{x^2}{a^2}} dx.$$

Integrating from $x = -\infty$ to $x = +\infty$, we find the whole number of particles,

$$NC\sqrt{\pi}a = N, \quad \therefore \ C = \frac{1}{a\sqrt{\pi}},$$

$f(x)$ is therefore

$$\frac{1}{a\sqrt{\pi}} e^{-\frac{x^2}{a^2}}.$$

Whence we may draw the following conclusions :—

1st. The number of particles whose velocity, resolved in a certain direction, lies between x and $x + dx$ is

$$N \frac{1}{a\sqrt{\pi}} e^{-\frac{x^2}{a^2}} dx \dots\dots\dots\dots\dots\dots\dots\dots (1).$$

2nd. The number whose actual velocity lies between v and $v + dv$ is

$$N \frac{4}{a^3\sqrt{\pi}} v^2 e^{-\frac{v^2}{a^2}} dv \dots\dots\dots\dots\dots\dots\dots\dots(2).$$

3rd. To find the mean value of v, add the velocities of all the particles together and divide by the number of particles; the result is

$$\text{mean velocity} = \frac{2a}{\sqrt{\pi}} \dots\dots\dots\dots\dots\dots\dots\dots\dots(3).$$

4th. To find the mean value of v^2, add all the values together and divide by N,

$$\text{mean value of } v^2 = \tfrac{3}{2}a^2 \dots\dots\dots\dots\dots\dots\dots\dots(4).$$

This is greater than the square of the mean velocity, as it ought to be.

It appears from this proposition that the velocities are distributed among the particles according to the same law as the errors are distributed among the observations in the theory of the "method of least squares." The velocities range from 0 to ∞, but the number of those having great velocities is comparatively small. In addition to these velocities, which are in all directions equally, there may be a general motion of translation of the entire system of particles which must be compounded with the motion of the particles relatively to one another. We may call the one the motion of translation, and the other the motion of agitation.

PROP. V. Two systems of particles move each according to the law stated in Prop. IV.; to find the number of pairs of particles, one of each system, whose relative velocity lies between given limits.

Let there be N particles of the first system, and N' of the second, then NN' is the whole number of such pairs. Let us consider the velocities in the direction of x only; then by Prop. IV. the number of the first kind, whose velocities are between x and $x + dx$, is

$$N \frac{1}{\alpha \sqrt{\pi}} e^{-\frac{x^2}{\alpha^2}} dx.$$

The number of the second kind, whose velocity is between $x + y$ and $x + y + dy$, is

$$N' \frac{1}{\beta \sqrt{\pi}} e^{-\frac{(x+y)^2}{\beta^2}} dy,$$

where β is the value of α for the second system.

The number of pairs which fulfil both conditions is

$$NN' \frac{1}{\alpha\beta\pi} e^{-\left(\frac{x^2}{\alpha^2} + \frac{(x+y)^2}{\beta^2}\right)} dx\, dy.$$

Now x may have any value from $-\infty$ to $+\infty$ consistently with the difference of velocities being between y and $y + dy$; therefore integrating between these limits, we find

$$NN' \frac{1}{\sqrt{\alpha^2 + \beta^2}\sqrt{\pi}} e^{-\frac{y^2}{\alpha^2 + \beta^2}} dy \dots\dots\dots\dots\dots\dots (5)$$

for the whole number of pairs whose difference of velocity lies between y and $y + dy$.

This expression, which is of the same form with (1) if we put NN' for N, $a^2 + \beta^2$ for a^2, and y for x, shews that the distribution of relative velocities is regulated by the same law as that of the velocities themselves, and that the mean relative velocity is the square root of the sum of the squares of the mean velocities of the two systems.

Since the direction of motion of every particle in one of the systems may be reversed without changing the distribution of velocities, it follows that the velocities compounded of the velocities of two particles, one in each system, are distributed according to the same formula (5) as the relative velocities.

PROP. VI. Two systems of particles move in the same vessel; to prove that the mean *vis viva* of each particle will become the same in the two systems.

Let P be the mass of each particle of the first system, Q that of each particle of the second. Let p, q be the mean veloci-ties in the two systems before impact, and let p', q' be the mean velocities after one impact. Let $OA = p$ and $OB = q$, and let AOB be a right angle; then, by Prop. V., AB will be the mean relative velocity, OG will be the mean velocity of the centre of gravity; and drawing aGb at right angles to OG, and making $aG = AG$ and $bG = BG$, then Oa will be the mean velocity of P after

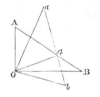

impact, compounded of OG and Ga, and Ob will be that of Q after impact.

Now $$AB = \sqrt{p^2 + q^2}, \quad AG = \frac{Q}{P+Q}\sqrt{p^2 + q^2}, \quad BG = \frac{P}{P+Q}\sqrt{p^2 + q^2},$$

$$OG = \frac{\sqrt{P^2 p^2 + Q^2 q^2}}{P+Q},$$

therefore $$p' = Oa = \frac{\sqrt{Q^2 (p^2 + q^2) + P^2 p^2 + Q^2 q^2}}{P+Q},$$

and $$q' = Ob = \frac{\sqrt{P^2 (p^2 + q^2) + P^2 p^2 + Q^2 q^2}}{P+Q},$$

and $$Pp'^2 - Qq'^2 = \left(\frac{P-Q}{P+Q}\right)^2 (Pp^2 - Qq^2) \dots\dots\dots\dots\dots\dots (6).$$

It appears therefore that the quantity $Pp^2 - Qq^2$ is diminished at every impact in the same ratio, so that after many impacts it will vanish, and then

$$Pp^2 = Qq^2.$$

Now the mean *vis viva* is $\frac{3}{2}Pa^2 = \frac{3\pi}{8}Pp^2$ for P, and $\frac{3\pi}{8}Qq^2$ for Q; and it is manifest that these quantities will be equal when $Pp^2 = Qq^2$.

If any number of different kinds of particles, having masses P, Q, R and velocities p, q, r respectively, move in the same vessel, then after many impacts

$$Pp^2 = Qq^2 = Rr^2, \text{ &c. } \dots\dots\dots\dots\dots\dots\dots(7).$$

PROP. VII. A particle moves with velocity r relatively to a number of particles of which there are N in unit of volume; to find the number of these which it approaches within a distance s in unit of time.

If we describe a tubular surface of which the axis is the path of the particle, and the radius the distance s, the content of this surface generated in unit of time will be $\pi r s^2$, and the number of particles included in it will be

$$N\pi r s^2 \dots\dots\dots\dots\dots\dots\dots\dots\dots\dots\dots\dots\dots(8),$$

which is the number of particles to which the moving particle approaches within a distance s.

PROP. VIII. A particle moves with velocity v in a system moving according to the law of Prop. IV.; to find the number of particles which have a velocity relative to the moving particle between r and $r + dr$.

Let u be the actual velocity of a particle of the system, v that of the original particle, and r their relative velocity, and θ the angle between v and r, then

$$u^2 = v^2 + r^2 - 2vr \cos \theta.$$

If we suppose, as in Prop. IV., all the particles to start from the origin at once, then after unit of time the "density" or number of particles to unit of volume at distance u will be

$$N \frac{1}{\alpha^3 \pi^{\frac{3}{2}}} e^{-\frac{u^2}{\alpha^2}}.$$

From this we have to deduce the number of particles in a shell whose centre is at distance v, radius $= r$, and thickness $= dr$,

$$N \frac{1}{a\sqrt{\pi}} \frac{r}{v} \left\{ e^{-\frac{(r-v)^2}{a^2}} - e^{-\frac{(r+v)^2}{a^2}} \right\} dr \dots\dots\dots\dots\dots\dots (9),$$

which is the number required.

Cor. It is evident that if we integrate this expression from $r = 0$ to $r = \infty$, we ought to get the whole number of particles $= N$, whence the following mathematical result,

$$\int_0^\infty dx \cdot x \left(e^{-\frac{(x-a)^2}{a^2}} - e^{-\frac{(x+a)^2}{a^2}} \right) = \sqrt{\pi} a a \dots\dots\dots\dots\dots\dots (10).$$

Prop. IX. Two sets of particles move as in Prop. V.; to find the number of pairs which approach within a distance s in unit of time.

The number of the second kind which have a velocity between v and $v + dv$ is

$$N' \frac{4}{\beta^3 \sqrt{\pi}} v^2 e^{-\frac{v^2}{\beta^2}} dv = n'.$$

The number of the first kind whose velocity relative to these is between r and $r + dr$ is

$$N \frac{1}{a\sqrt{\pi}} \frac{r}{v} \left(e^{-\frac{(r-v)^2}{a^2}} - e^{-\frac{(r+v)^2}{a^2}} \right) dr = n,$$

and the number of pairs which approach within distance s in unit of time is

$$nn'\pi r s^2,$$

$$= NN' \frac{4}{a\beta^3} s^2 r^2 v e^{-\frac{v^2}{\beta}} \left\{ e^{-\frac{(v-r)^2}{a^2}} - e^{-\frac{(v+r)^2}{a^2}} \right\} dr \, dv.$$

By the last proposition we are able to integrate with respect to v, and get

$$NN' \frac{4\sqrt{\pi}}{(a^2+\beta^2)^{\frac{3}{2}}} s^2 r^3 e^{-\frac{r^2}{a^2+\beta^2}} dr.$$

Integrating this again from $r = 0$ to $r = \infty$,

$$2NN' \sqrt{\pi} \sqrt{a^2+\beta^2} s^2 \dots\dots\dots\dots\dots\dots\dots (11)$$

is the number of collisions in unit of time which take place in unit of volume between particles of different kinds, s being the distance of centres at collision.

The number of collisions between two particles of the first kind, s_1 being the striking distance, is

$$2N^2 \sqrt{\pi} \sqrt{2a^2 s_1^2} ;$$

and for the second system it is

$$2N'^2 \sqrt{\pi} \sqrt{2\beta^2 s_2^2}.$$

The mean velocities in the two systems are $\dfrac{2a}{\sqrt{\pi}}$ and $\dfrac{2\beta}{\sqrt{\pi}}$; so that if l_1 and l_2 be the mean distances travelled by particles of the first and second systems between each collision, then

$$\frac{1}{l_1} = \pi N_1 \sqrt{2} s_1^2 + \pi N_2 \frac{\sqrt{a^2 + \beta^2}}{a} s^2,$$

$$\frac{1}{l_2} = \pi N_1 \frac{\sqrt{a^2 + \beta^2}}{\beta} s^2 + \pi N_2 \sqrt{2} s_2^2.$$

PROP. X. To find the probability of a particle reaching a given distance before striking any other.

Let us suppose that the probability of a particle being stopped while passing through a distance dx, is $a\,dx$; that is, if N particles arrived at a distance x, $Na\,dx$ of them would be stopped before getting to a distance $x + dx$. Putting this mathematically,

$$\frac{dN}{dx} = -Na, \text{ or } N = Ce^{-ax}.$$

Putting $N = 1$ when $x = 0$, we find e^{-ax} for the probability of a particle not striking another before it reaches a distance x.

The *mean distance* travelled by each particle before striking is $\dfrac{1}{a} = l$. The probability of a particle reaching a distance $= nl$ without being struck is e^{-n}. (See a paper by M. Clausius, *Philosophical Magazine*, February 1859.)

If all the particles are at rest but one, then the value of a is

$$a = \pi s^2 N,$$

where s is the distance between the centres at collision, and N is the number of particles in unit of volume. If v be the velocity of the moving particle relatively to the rest, then the number of collisions in unit of time will be

$$v \pi s^2 N ;$$

and if v_1 be the actual velocity, then the number will be v_1a; therefore

$$a = \frac{v}{v_1}\,\pi s^2 N,$$

where v_1 is the actual velocity of the striking particle, and v its velocity relatively to those it strikes. If v_2 be the actual velocity of the other particles, then $v = \sqrt{v_1^2 + v_2^2}$. If $v_1 = v_2$, then $v = \sqrt{2}v_1$, and

$$a = \sqrt{2}\pi s^2 N.$$

Note*. M. Clausius makes $a = \frac{4}{3}\pi s^2 N$.

PROP. XI. In a mixture of particles of two different kinds, to find the mean path of each particle.

Let there be N_1 of the first, and N_2 of the second in unit of volume. Let s_1 be the distance of centres for a collision between two particles of the first set, s_2 for the second set, and s' for collision between one of each kind. Let v_1 and v_2 be the coefficients of velocity, M_1, M_2 the mass of each particle.

The probability of a particle M_1 not being struck till after reaching a distance x_1 by another particle of the same kind is

$$e^{-\sqrt{2}\pi s_1^2 N_1 x}.$$

* [In the *Philosophical Magazine* of 1860, Vol. I. pp. 434—6 Clausius explains the method by which he found his value of the mean relative velocity. It is briefly as follows: If u, v be the velocities of two particles their relative velocity is $\sqrt{u^2 + v^2 - 2uv\cos\theta}$ and the mean of this as regards direction only, all directions of v being equally probable, is shewn to be

$$v + \frac{1}{3}\frac{u^2}{v} \text{ when } u < v, \text{ and } u + \frac{1}{3}\frac{v^2}{u} \text{ when } u > v.$$

If $v = u$ these expressions coincide. Clausius in applying this result and putting u, v for the mean velocities assumes that the mean relative velocity is given by expressions of the same form, so that when the mean velocities are each equal to u the mean relative velocity would be $\frac{4}{3}u$. This step is, however, open to objection, and in fact if we take the expressions given above for the mean velocity, treating u and v as the velocities of two particles which may have any values between 0 and ∞, to calculate the mean relative velocity we should proceed as follows: Since the number of particles with velocities between u and $u + du$ is $N\,\dfrac{4}{a^3\sqrt{\pi}}\,u^2 e^{-\frac{u^2}{a^2}}\,du$, the mean relative velocity is

$$\frac{16}{a^3\beta^3\pi}\int_0^\infty\int_v^\infty u^2 v^2 e^{-\left(\frac{u^2}{a^2}+\frac{v^2}{\beta^2}\right)}\left(u + \frac{1}{3}\frac{v^2}{u}\right)du\,dv + \frac{16}{a^3\beta^3\pi}\int_0^\infty\int_0^v u^2 v^2 e^{-\left(\frac{u^2}{a^2}+\frac{v^2}{\beta^2}\right)}\left(v + \frac{1}{3}\frac{u^2}{v}\right)du\,dv.$$

This expression, when reduced, leads to $\dfrac{2}{\sqrt{\pi}}\sqrt{a^2 + \beta^2}$, which is the result in the text. Ed.]

The probability of not being struck by a particle of the other kind in the same distance is

$$e^{-\sqrt{1+\frac{v_2^2}{v_1^2}}\pi s'^2 N_2 x}$$

Therefore the probability of not being struck by any particle before reaching a distance x is

$$e^{-\pi\left(\sqrt{2}s_1^2 N_1 + \sqrt{1+\frac{v_2^2}{v_1^2}}s'^2 N_2\right)x};$$

and if l_1 be the *mean distance* for a particle of the first kind,

$$\frac{1}{l_1} = \sqrt{2}\pi s_1^2 N_1 + \pi\sqrt{1+\frac{v_2^2}{v_1^2}}\,s'^2 N_2 \dots\dots\dots\dots\dots (12).$$

Similarly, if l_2 be the mean distance for a particle of the second kind,

$$\frac{1}{l_2} = \sqrt{2}\pi s_2^2 N_2 + \pi\sqrt{1+\frac{v_1^2}{v_2^2}}\,s'^2 N_1 \dots\dots\dots\dots\dots(13).$$

The mean density of the particles of the first kind is $N_1 M_1 = \rho_1$, and that of the second $N_2 M_2 = \rho_2$. If we put

$$A = \sqrt{2}\,\frac{\pi s_1^2}{M_1},\quad B = \pi\sqrt{1+\frac{v_2^2}{v_1^2}}\frac{s'^2}{M_2},\quad C = \pi\sqrt{1+\frac{v_1^2}{v_2^2}}\frac{s'^2}{M_1},\quad D = \sqrt{2}\,\frac{\pi s_2^2}{M_2}\dots\dots(14),$$

$$\frac{1}{l_1} = A\rho_1 + B\rho_2,\quad \frac{1}{l_2} = C\rho_1 + D\rho_2\dots\dots\dots\dots\dots(15),$$

and

$$\frac{B}{C} = \frac{M_1 v_2}{M_2 v_1} = \frac{v_2^3}{v_1^3}\dots\dots\dots\dots\dots\dots\dots(16).$$

PROP. XII. To find the pressure on unit of area of the side of the vessel due to the impact of the particles upon it.

Let N = number of particles in unit of volume;

   M = mass of each particle;

   v = velocity of each particle;

   l = mean path of each particle;

then the number of particles in unit of area of a stratum dz thick is

$$N dz \dots\dots\dots\dots\dots\dots\dots (17).$$

The number of collisions of these particles in unit of time is

$$N dz\,\frac{v}{l}\dots\dots\dots\dots\dots\dots\dots(18).$$

The number of particles which after collision reach a distance between nl and $(n+dn)\, l$ is

$$N \frac{v}{l} e^{-n}\, dz\, dn \dots\dots\dots\dots\dots\dots (19).$$

The proportion of these which strike on unit of area at distance z is

$$\frac{nl - z}{2nl} \dots\dots\dots\dots\dots\dots\dots\dots\dots(20)\, ;$$

the mean velocity of these in the direction of z is

$$v\, \frac{nl + z}{2nl} \dots\dots\dots\dots\dots\dots\dots\dots (21).$$

Multiplying together (19), (20), and (21), and M, we find the momentum at impact

$$MN\, \frac{v^2}{4n^2 l^3}\, (n^2 l^2 - z^2)\, e^{-n}\, dz\, dn.$$

Integrating with respect to z from 0 to nl, we get

$$\tfrac{1}{6} MN v^2\, n e^{-n}\, dn.$$

Integrating with respect to n from 0 to ∞, we get

$$\tfrac{1}{6} MN v^2$$

for the momentum in the direction of z of the striking particles; for the momentum of the particles after impact is the same, but in the opposite direction; so that the whole pressure on unit of area is twice this quantity, or

$$p = \tfrac{1}{3} MN v^2.$$

This value of p is independent of l the length of path. In applying this result to the theory of gases, we put $MN = \rho$, and $v^2 = 3k$, and then

$$p = k\rho,$$

which is Boyle and Mariotte's law. By (4) we have

$$v^2 = \tfrac{3}{2} a^2, \quad \therefore\ a^2 = 2k \dots\dots\dots\dots\dots\dots (23).$$

We have seen that, on the hypothesis of elastic particles moving in straight lines, the pressure of a gas can be explained by the assumption that the square of the velocity is proportional directly to the absolute temperature, and inversely to the specific gravity of the gas at constant temperature, so that at the same pressure and temperature the value of NMv^2 is the same for all gases. But we found in Prop. VI. that when two sets of particles communicate agitation to one another, the value of Mv^2 is the same in each. From this it appears that N, the number of particles in unit of volume, is the same for all gases at the same pressure and temperature. This result agrees with the chemical law, that equal volumes of gases are chemically equivalent.

We have next to determine the value of l, the mean length of the path of a particle between consecutive collisions. The most direct method of doing this depends upon the fact, that when different strata of a gas slide upon one another with different velocities, they act upon one another with a tangential force tending to prevent this sliding, and similar in its results to the friction between two solid surfaces sliding over each other in the same way. The explanation of gaseous friction, according to our hypothesis, is, that particles having the mean velocity of translation belonging to one layer of the gas, pass out of it into another layer having a different velocity of translation; and by striking against the particles of the second layer, exert upon it a tangential force which constitutes the internal friction of the gas. The whole friction between two portions of gas separated by a plane surface, depends upon the total action between all the layers on the one side of that surface upon all the layers on the other side.

PROP. XIII. To find the internal friction in a system of moving particles.

Let the system be divided into layers parallel to the plane of xy, and let the motion of translation of each layer be u in the direction of x, and let $u = A + Bz$. We have to consider the mutual action between the layers on the positive and negative sides of the plane xy. Let us first determine the action between two layers dz and dz', at distances z and $-z'$ on opposite sides of this plane, each unit of area. The number of particles which, starting from dz in unit of time, reach a distance between nl and $(n+dn)\,l$ is by (19),

$$N \frac{v}{l} e^{-n}\, dz\, dn.$$

The number of these which have the ends of their paths in the layer dz' is

$$N \frac{v}{2nl^2} e^{-n}\, dz\, dz'\, dn.$$

The mean velocity in the direction of x which each of these has before impact is $A + Bz$, and after impact $A + Bz'$; and its mass is M, so that a mean momentum $= MB(z-z')$ is communicated by each particle. The whole action due to these collisions is therefore

$$NMB\frac{v}{2nl^2}(z-z')e^{-n}\,dz\,dz'\,dn.$$

We must first integrate with respect to z' between $z'=0$ and $z'=z-nl$; this gives

$$\tfrac{1}{2}NMB\frac{v}{2nl^2}(n^2l^2-z^2)e^{-n}\,dz\,dn$$

for the action between the layer dz and all the layers below the plane xy. Then integrate from $z=0$ to $z=nl$,

$$\tfrac{1}{6}MNBlvn^2e^{-n}\,dn.$$

Integrate from $n=0$ to $n=\infty$, and we find the whole friction between unit of area above and below the plane to be

$$F=\tfrac{1}{3}MNlvB=\tfrac{1}{3}\rho lv\frac{du}{dz}=\mu\frac{du}{dz},$$

where μ is the ordinary coefficient of internal friction,

$$\mu=\tfrac{1}{3}\rho lv=\frac{1}{3\sqrt{2}}\frac{Mv}{\pi s^2}\ \dots\dots\dots\dots\dots\dots\dots\ (24),$$

where ρ is the density, l the mean length of path of a particle, and v the mean velocity $v=\dfrac{2a}{\sqrt{\pi}}=2\sqrt{\dfrac{2k}{\pi}}$,

$$l=\tfrac{3}{2}\frac{\mu}{\rho}\sqrt{\frac{\pi}{2k}}\ \dots\dots\dots\dots\dots\dots\dots\dots\dots\ (25).$$

Now Professor Stokes finds by experiments on air,

$$\sqrt{\frac{\mu}{\rho}}=\cdot116.$$

If we suppose $\sqrt{k}=930$ feet per second for air at $60°$, and therefore the mean velocity $v=1505$ feet per second, then the value of l, the mean distance travelled over by a particle between consecutive collisions, $-\frac{1}{447000}$th of an inch, and each particle makes 8,077,200,000 collisions per second.

A remarkable result here presented to us in equation (24), is that if this explanation of gaseous friction be true, the coefficient of friction is independent of the density. Such a consequence of a mathematical theory is very startling, and the only experiment I have met with on the subject does not seem to confirm it. We must next compare our theory with what is known of the diffusion of gases, and the conduction of heat through a gas.

PART II.

*ON THE PROCESS OF DIFFUSION OF TWO OR MORE KINDS OF MOVING PARTICLES AMONG ONE ANOTHER.

We have shewn, in the first part of this paper, that the motions of a system of many small elastic particles are of two kinds : one, a general motion of translation of the whole system, which may be called the motion in mass; and the other a motion of agitation, or molecular motion, in virtue of which velocities in all directions are distributed among the particles according to a certain law. In the cases we are considering, the collisions are so frequent that the law of distribution of the molecular velocities, if disturbed in any way, will be re-established in an inappreciably short time; so that the motion will always consist of this definite motion of agitation, combined with the general motion of translation.

When two gases are in communication, streams of the two gases might run freely in opposite directions, if it were not for the collisions which take place between the particles. The rate at which they actually interpenetrate each other must be investigated. The diffusion is due partly to the spreading of the particles by the molecular agitation, and partly to the actual motion of the two opposite currents in mass, produced by the pressure behind, and resisted

---

* [The methods and results of this paper have been criticised by Clausius in a memoir published in Poggendorff's *Annalen*, Vol. CXV., and in the *Philosophical Magazine*, Vol. XXIII. His main objection is that the various circumstances of the strata, discussed in the paper, have not been sufficiently represented in the equations. In particular, if there be a series of strata at different temperatures perpendicular to the axis of x, then the proportion of molecules whose directions form with the axis of x angles whose cosines lie between μ and $\mu + d\mu$ is not $\frac{1}{2}d\mu$ as has been assumed by Maxwell throughout his work, but $\frac{1}{2}Hd\mu$ where H is a factor to be determined. In discussing the steady conduction of heat through a gas Clausius assumes that, in addition to the velocity attributed to the molecule according to Maxwell's theory, we must also suppose a velocity normal to the stratum and depending on the temperature of the stratum. On this assumption the factor H is investigated along with other modifications, and an expression for the assumed velocity is determined from the consideration that when the flow of heat is steady there is no movement of the mass. Clausius combining his own results with those of Maxwell points out that the expression contained in (28) of the paper involves as a result the motion of the gas. He also disputes the accuracy of expression (59) for the Conduction of Heat. In the introduction to the memoir published in the *Phil. Trans.*, 1866, it will be found that Maxwell expresses dissatisfaction with his former theory of the Diffusion of Gases, and admits the force of the objections made by Clausius to his expression for the Conduction of Heat. Ed.]

by the collisions of the opposite stream. When the densities are equal, the diffusions due to these two causes respectively are as 2 to 3.

PROP. XIV. *In a system of particles whose density, velocity, &c. are functions of* x, *to find the quantity of matter transferred across the plane of* yz, *due to the motion of agitation alone.*

If the number of particles, their velocity, or their length of path is greater on one side of this plane than on the other, then more particles will cross the plane in one direction than in the other; and there will be a transference of matter across the plane, the amount of which may be calculated.

Let there be taken a stratum whose thickness is dx, and area unity, at a distance x from the origin. The number of collisions taking place in this stratum in unit of time will be

$$N \frac{v}{l} dx.$$

The proportion of these which reach a distance between nl and $(n+dn)l$ before they strike another particle is

$$e^{-n} dn.$$

The proportion of these which pass through the plane yz is

$$\frac{nl+x}{2nl} \text{ when } x \text{ is between } -nl \text{ and } 0,$$

and $\qquad -\dfrac{nl-x}{2nl}$ when x is between 0 and $+nl$;

the sign being negative in the latter case, because the particles cross the plane in the negative direction. The mass of each particle is M; so that the quantity of matter which is projected from the stratum dx, crosses the plane yz in a positive direction, and strikes other particles at distances between nl and $(n+dn)l$ is

$$\frac{MNv\,(x \mp nl)}{2nl^2} dx\, e^{-n} dn \dots\dots\dots\dots\dots\dots\dots(26),$$

where x must be between $\pm nl$, and the upper or lower sign is to be taken according as x is positive or negative.

In integrating this expression, we must remember that N, v, and l are functions of x, not vanishing with x, and of which the variations are very small between the limits $x = -nl$ and $x = +nl$.

50

As we may have occasion to perform similar integrations, we may state here, to save trouble, that if U and r are functions of x not vanishing with x, whose variations are very small between the limits $x = +r$ and $x = -r$,

$$\int_{-r}^{+r} \pm Ux^m dx = \frac{2}{m+2} \frac{d}{dx}(Ur^{m+2}) \quad \dots \dots \dots \dots \dots (27).$$

When m is an odd number, the upper sign only is to be considered; when m is even or zero, the upper sign is to be taken with positive values of x, and the lower with negative values. Applying this to the case before us,

$$\int_{-nl}^{+nl} \frac{MNvx}{2nl^2} dx = \frac{1}{3} \frac{d}{dx}(MNvn^2l),$$

$$\int_{-nl}^{+nl} \mp \frac{MNv}{2l} dx = -\frac{1}{2} \frac{d}{dx}(MNvn^2l).$$

We have now to integrate

$$\int_{0}^{\infty} -\frac{1}{6} \frac{d}{dx}(MNvl) n^2 e^{-n} dn,$$

n being taken from 0 to ∞. We thus find for the quantity of matter transferred across unit of area by the motion of agitation in unit of time,

$$q = -\frac{1}{3} \frac{d}{dx}(\rho vl) \quad \dots \dots \dots \dots \dots \dots \dots (28),$$

where $\rho = MN$ is the density, v the mean velocity of agitation, and l the mean length of path.

PROP. XV. The quantity transferred, in consequence of a mean motion of translation V, would obviously be

$$Q = V\rho \quad \dots \dots \dots \dots \dots \dots \dots \dots \dots (29).$$

PROP. XVI. *To find the resultant dynamical effect of all the collisions which take place in a given stratum.*

Suppose the density and velocity of the particles to be functions of x, then more particles will be thrown into the given stratum from that side on which the density is greatest; and those particles which have greatest velocity will have the greatest effect, so that the stratum will not be generally in equilibrium, and the dynamical measure of the force exerted on the stratum will be the resultant momentum of all the particles which lodge in it during unit of time. We shall first take the case in which there is no mean motion of translation, and then consider the effect of such motion separately.

Let a stratum whose thickness is a (a small quantity compared with l), and area unity, be taken at the origin, perpendicular to the axis of x; and let another stratum, of thickness dx, and area unity, be taken at a distance x from the first.

If M_1 be the mass of a particle, N the number in unit of volume, v the velocity of agitation, l the mean length of path, then the number of collisions which take place in the stratum dx is

$$N \frac{v}{l} \, dx.$$

The proportion of these which reach a distance between nl and $(n+dn)\, l$ is

$$e^{-n} \, dn.$$

The proportion of these which have the extremities of their paths in the stratum a is

$$\frac{a}{2nl}.$$

The velocity of these particles, resolved in the direction of x, is

$$-\frac{vx}{nl},$$

and the mass is M; so that multiplying all these terms together, we get

$$\frac{NMv^2ax}{2n^2l^3} \, e^{-n} \, dx \, dn \dots \dots \dots \dots \dots \dots \dots \dots \dots \dots (30)$$

for the momentum of the particles fulfilling the above conditions.

To get the whole momentum, we must first integrate with respect to x from $x = -nl$ to $x = +nl$, remembering that l may be a function of x, and is a very small quantity. The result is

$$\frac{d}{dx} \left(\frac{NMv^2}{3} \right) ane^{-n} \, dn.$$

Integrating with respect to n from $n = 0$ to $n = \infty$, the result is

$$-a \frac{d}{dx} \left(\frac{NMv^2}{3} \right) = aX\rho \quad \dots \dots \dots \dots \dots \dots (31)$$

as the whole resultant force on the stratum a arising from these collisions. Now $\frac{NMv^2}{3} = p$ by Prop. XII., and therefore we may write the equation

$$-\frac{dp}{dx} = X\rho \quad \dots \dots \dots \dots \dots \dots \dots \dots (32),$$

the ordinary hydrodynamical equation.

PROP. XVII. *To find the resultant effect of the collisions upon each of several different systems of particles mixed together.*

Let M_1, M_2, &c. be the masses of the different kinds of particles, N_1, N_2, &c. the number of each kind in unit of volume, v_1, v_2, &c. their velocities of agitation, l_1, l_2 their mean paths, p_1, p_2, &c. the pressures due to each system of particles; then

$$\left. \begin{array}{l} \dfrac{1}{l_1} = A\rho_1 + B\rho_2 + \text{&c.} \\[2mm] \dfrac{1}{l_2} = C\rho_1 + D\rho_2 + \text{&c.} \end{array} \right\} \quad \dots \dots \dots \dots \dots \dots (33).$$

The number of collisions of the first kind of particles with each other in unit of time will be

$$N_1 v_1 A \rho_1.$$

The number of collisions between particles of the first and second kinds will be

$$N_1 v_1 B \rho_2, \quad \text{or} \quad N_2 v_2 C \rho_1, \quad \text{because} \quad v_1^2 B = v_2^2 C.$$

The number of collisions between particles of the second kind will be $N_2 v_2 D \rho_2$, and so on, if there are more kinds of particles.

Let us now consider a thin stratum of the mixture whose volume is unity.

The resultant momentum of the particles of the first kind which lodge in it during unit of time is

$$-\frac{dp_1}{dx}.$$

The proportion of these which strike particles of the first kind is

$$A\rho_1 l_1.$$

The whole momentum of these remains among the particles of the first kind. The proportion which strike particles of the second kind is

$$B\rho_2 l_1.$$

The momentum of these is divided between the striking particles in the ratio of their masses; so that $\dfrac{M_1}{M_1 + M_2}$ of the whole goes to particles of the first kind, and $\dfrac{M_2}{M_1 + M_2}$ to particles of the second kind.

The effect of these collisions is therefore to produce a force

$$-\frac{dp_1}{dx}\left(A\rho_1 l_1 + B\rho_2 l_1 \frac{M_1}{M_1 + M_2}\right)$$

on particles of the first system, and

$$-\frac{dp_1}{dx} B\rho_2 l_1 \frac{M_2}{M_1 + M_2}$$

on particles of the second system.

The effect of the collisions of those particles of the second system which strike into the stratum, is to produce a force

$$-\frac{dp_2}{dx} C\rho_1 l_2 \frac{M_1}{M_1 + M_2}$$

on the first system, and

$$-\frac{dp_2}{dx}\left(C\rho_1 l_2 \frac{M_2}{M_1 + M_2} + D\rho_2 l_2\right)$$

on the second.

The whole effect of these collisions is therefore to produce a resultant force

$$-\frac{dp_1}{dx}\left(A\rho_1 l_1 + B\rho_2 l_1 \frac{M_1}{M_1 + M_2}\right) - \frac{dp_2}{dx} C\rho_1 l_2 \frac{M_1}{M_1 + M_2} + \&c. \dots\dots\dots (34)$$

on the first system,

$$-\frac{dp_1}{dx} B\rho_2 l_1 \frac{M_2}{M_1 + M_2} - \frac{dp_2}{dx}\left(C\rho_1 l_2 \frac{M_2}{M_1 + M_2} + D\rho_2 l_2\right) + \&c. \dots\dots\dots (35)$$

on the second, and so on.

PROP. XVIII. *To find the mechanical effect of a difference in the mean velocity of translation of two systems of moving particles.*

Let V_1, V_2 be the mean velocities of translation of the two systems respectively, then $\dfrac{M_1 M_2}{M_1 + M_2}(V_1 - V_2)$ is the mean momentum lost by a particle of the first, and gained by a particle of the second at collision. The number of such collisions in unit of volume is

$$N_1 B \rho_2 v_1, \quad \text{or} \quad N_2 C \rho_1 v_2;$$

therefore the whole effect of the collisions is to produce a force

$$= - N_1 B \rho_2 v_1 \frac{M_1 M_2}{M_1 + M_2}(V_1 - V_2) \dots\dots\dots\dots\dots\dots(36)$$

on the first system, and an equal and opposite force

$$= + N_2 C \rho_1 v_2 \frac{M_1 M_2}{M_1 + M_2}(V_1 - V_2) \dots\dots\dots\dots\dots\dots(37)$$

on unit of volume of the second system.

PROP. XIX. *To find the law of diffusion in the case of two gases diffusing into each other through a plug made of a porous material, as in the case of the experiments of Graham.*

The pressure on each side of the plug being equal, it was found by Graham that the quantities of the gases which passed in opposite directions through the plug in the same time were directly as the square roots of their specific gravities.

We may suppose the action of the porous material to be similar to that of a number of particles fixed in space, and obstructing the motion of the particles of the moving systems. If L_1 is the mean distance a particle of the first kind would have to go before striking a fixed particle, and L_2 the distance for a particle of the second kind, then the mean paths of particles of each kind will be given by the equations

$$\frac{1}{l_1} = A\rho_1 + B\rho_2 + \frac{1}{L_1}, \quad \frac{1}{l_2} = C\rho_1 + D\rho_2 + \frac{1}{L_2} \dots\dots\dots\dots(38).$$

The mechanical effect upon the plug of the pressures of the gases on each side, and of the percolation of the gases through it, may be found by Props. XVII. and XVIII. to be

$$\frac{M_1 N_1 v_1 V_1}{L_1} + \frac{M_2 N_2 v_2 V_2}{L_2} - \frac{dp_1}{dx}\frac{l_1}{L_1} - \frac{dp_2}{dx}\frac{l_2}{L_2} = 0 \dots\dots\dots\dots(39);$$

and this must be zero, if the pressures are equal on each side of the plug. Now if Q_1, Q_2 be the quantities transferred through the plug by the mean motion of translation, $Q_1 = \rho_1 V_1 = M_1 N_1 V_1$; and since by Graham's law

$$\frac{Q_1}{Q_2} = -\sqrt{\frac{M_1}{M_2}} = -\frac{v_2}{v_1},$$

we shall have

$$M_1 N_1 v_1 V_1 = -M_2 N_2 v_2 V_2 = U \text{ suppose};$$

and since the pressures on the two sides are equal, $\dfrac{dp_2}{dx} = -\dfrac{dp_1}{dx}$, and the only way in which the equation of equilibrium of the plug can generally subsist is when $L_1 = L_4$ and $l_1 = l_2$. This implies that $A = C$ and $B = D$. Now we know that $v_1^3 B = v_2^3 C$. Let $K = 3\dfrac{A}{v_1^3}$, then we shall have

$$A = C = \tfrac{1}{3} K v_1^3, \quad B = D = \tfrac{1}{3} K v_2^3 \quad\dots\dots\dots\dots\dots\dots (40),$$

and

$$\frac{1}{l_1} = \frac{1}{l_2} = K (v_1 p_1 + v_2 p_2) + \frac{1}{L}\dots\dots\dots\dots\dots\dots\dots(41).$$

The diffusion is due partly to the motion of translation, and partly to that of agitation. Let us find the part due to the motion of translation.

The equation of motion of one of the gases through the plug is found by adding the forces due to pressures to those due to resistances, and equating these to the moving force, which in the case of slow motions may be neglected altogether. The result for the first is

$$\frac{dp_1}{dx}\left(A\rho_1 l_1 + B\rho_2 l_1 \frac{M_1}{M_1 + M_2}\right) + \frac{dp_2}{dx} C\rho_1 l_2 \frac{M_1}{M_1 + M_2}$$
$$+ N_1 B \rho_2 v_1 \frac{M_1 M_2}{M_1 + M_2}(V_1 - V_2) + \frac{\rho_1 v_1 V_1}{L} = 0 \dots\dots(42).$$

Making use of the simplifications we have just discovered, this becomes

$$\frac{dp}{dx}\frac{Kl}{v_1^2 + v_2^2}(v_1^3 p_1 + v_2^3 p_2) + K\frac{v_1 v_2}{v_1^2 + v_2^2}(p_1 v_2 + p_2 v_1) U + \frac{1}{L} U \dots\dots\dots(43),$$

whence

$$U = -\frac{dp}{dx}\frac{Kl(v_1^3 p_1 + v_2^3 p_2)}{Kv_1 v_2(p_1 v_2 + p_2 v_1) + \dfrac{v_1^2 + v_2^2}{L}} \dots\dots\dots\dots\dots (44);$$

whence the rate of diffusion due to the motion of translation may be found; for

$$Q_1 = \frac{U}{v_1}, \text{ and } Q_2 = -\frac{U}{v_2} \quad \dots\dots\dots\dots\dots\dots (45).$$

To find the diffusion due to the motion of agitation, we must find the value of q_1.

$$q_1 = -\tfrac{1}{3} \frac{d}{dx} (\rho_1 v_1 l_1),$$

$$= -\frac{L}{v_1} \frac{d}{dx} \frac{p_1}{1 + KL(v_1 p_1 + v_2 p_2)},$$

$$q_1 = -\frac{l^2}{v_1 L} \frac{dp}{dx} \{1 + KL v_2 (p_1 + p_2)\} \quad \dots\dots\dots\dots (46).$$

Similarly,
$$q_2 = +\frac{l^2}{v_2 L} \frac{dp}{dx} \{1 + KL v_1 (p_1 + p_2)\} \quad \dots\dots\dots\dots (47).$$

The whole diffusions are $Q_1 + q_1$ and $Q_2 + q_2$. The values of q_1 and q_2 have a term not following Graham's law of the square roots of the specific gravities, but following the law of equal volumes. The closer the material of the plug, the less will this term affect the result.

Our assumptions that the porous plug acts like a system of fixed particles, and that Graham's law is fulfilled more accurately the more compact the material of the plug, are scarcely sufficiently well verified for the foundation of a theory of gases; and even if we admit the original assumption that they are systems of moving elastic particles, we have not very good evidence as yet for the relation among the quantities A, B, C, and D.

PROP. XX. *To find the rate of diffusion between two vessels connected by a tube.*

When diffusion takes place through a large opening, such as a tube connecting two vessels, the question is simplified by the absence of the porous diffusion plug; and since the pressure is constant throughout the apparatus, the volumes of the two gases passing opposite ways through the tube at the same time must be equal. Now the quantity of gas which passes through the tube is due partly to the motion of agitation as in Prop. XIV., and partly to the mean motion of translation as in Prop. XV.

Let us suppose the volumes of the two vessels to be a and b, and the length of the tube between them c, and its transverse section s. Let a be filled with the first gas, and b with the second at the commencement of the experiment, and let the pressure throughout the apparatus be P.

Let a volume y of the first gas pass from a to b, and a volume y' of the second pass from b to a; then if p_1 and p_2 represent the pressures in a due to the first and second kinds of gas, and p'_1 and p'_2 the same in the vessel b,

$$p_1 = \frac{a-y}{a} P, \quad p_2 = \frac{y'}{a} P, \quad p'_1 = \frac{y}{b} P, \quad p'_2 = \frac{b-y'}{b} P \ldots\ldots\ldots\ldots(48).$$

Since there is still equilibrium,

$$p_1 + p_2 = p'_1 + p'_2,$$

which gives

$$y = y' \text{ and } p_1 + p_2 = P = p'_1 + p'_2 \ldots\ldots\ldots\ldots\ldots(49).$$

The rate of diffusion will be $+\dfrac{dy}{dt}$ for the one gas, and $-\dfrac{dy}{dt}$ for the other, measured in volume of gas at pressure P.

Now the rate of diffusion of the first gas will be

$$\frac{dy}{dt} = s\,\frac{k_1 q_1 + p_1 V_1}{P} = s\,\frac{-\frac{1}{3}v_1\dfrac{d}{dx}(p_1 l_1) + p_1 V_1}{P} \ldots\ldots\ldots\ldots(50);$$

and that of the second,

$$-\frac{dy}{dt} = s\,\frac{-\frac{1}{3}v_2\dfrac{d}{dx}(p_2 l_2) + p_2 V_2}{P} \ldots\ldots\ldots\ldots(51).$$

We have also the equation, derived from Props. XVI. and XVII.,

$$\frac{dp_1}{dx}\{A\rho_1 l_1(M_1 + M_2) + B\rho_2 l_1 M_1 - C\rho_1 l_2 M_1\} + B\rho_1 \rho_2 v_1 M_2(V_1 - V_2) = 0 \ldots..(52).$$

From these three equations we can eliminate V_1 and V_2, and find $\dfrac{dy}{dt}$ in terms of p and $\dfrac{dp}{dx}$, so that we may write

$$\frac{dy}{dt} = f\left(p_1,\ \frac{dp_1}{dx}\right) \ldots\ldots\ldots\ldots\ldots\ldots(53).$$

51

Since the capacity of the tube is small compared with that of the vessels, we may consider $\dfrac{dy}{dt}$ constant through the whole length of the tube. We may then solve the differential equation in p and x; and then making $p = p_1$ when $x = 0$, and $p = p'_1$ when $x = c$, and substituting for p_1 and p'_1 their values in terms of y, we shall have a differential equation in y and t, which being solved, will give the amount of gas diffused in a given time.

The solution of these equations would be difficult unless we assume relations among the quantities A, B, C, D, which are not yet sufficiently established in the case of gases of different density. Let us suppose that in a particular case the two gases have the same density, and that the four quantities A, B, C, D are all equal.

The volume diffused, owing to the motion of agitation of the particles, is then

$$-\tfrac{1}{3}\frac{s}{P}\frac{dp}{dx}\,vl,$$

and that due to the motion of translation, or the interpenetration of the two gases in opposite streams, is

$$-\frac{s}{P}\frac{dp}{dx}\frac{kl}{v}\,.$$

The values of v are distributed according to the law of Prop. IV., so that the mean value of v is $\dfrac{2a}{\sqrt{\pi}}$, and that of $\dfrac{1}{v}$ is $\dfrac{2}{\sqrt{\pi}a}$, that of k being $\tfrac{1}{2}a^2$. The diffusions due to these two causes are therefore in the ratio of 2 to 3, and their sum is

$$\frac{dy}{dt} = -\tfrac{4}{3}\sqrt{\frac{2k}{\pi}}\frac{sl}{P}\frac{dp}{dx} \quad\ldots\ldots\ldots\ldots\ldots\ldots (54).$$

If we suppose $\dfrac{dy}{dt}$ constant throughout the tube, or, in other words, if we regard the motion as *steady* for a short time, then $\dfrac{dp}{dx}$ will be constant and equal to $\dfrac{p'_1 - p_1}{c}$; or substituting from (48),

$$\frac{dy}{dt} = -\tfrac{4}{3}\sqrt{\frac{2k}{\pi}}\frac{sl}{abc}\{(a+b)\,y - ab\} \quad\ldots\ldots\ldots\ldots (55);$$

whence

$$y = \frac{ab}{a+b}\left(1 - e^{-\frac{4}{3}\sqrt{\frac{2k}{\pi}}\frac{sl}{abc}(a+b)t}\right)\ldots\ldots\ldots\ldots\ldots\ldots(56).$$

By choosing pairs of gases of equal density, and ascertaining the amount of diffusion in a given time, we might determine the value of l in this expression. The diffusion of nitrogen into carbonic oxide or of deutoxide of nitrogen into carbonic acid, would be suitable cases for experiment. The only existing experiment which approximately fulfils the conditions is one by Graham, quoted by Herapath from Brande's *Quarterly Journal of Science*, Vol. XVIII. p. 76.

A tube 9 inches long and 0·9 inch diameter, communicated with the atmosphere by a tube 2 inches long and 0·12 inch diameter; 152 parts of olefiant gas being placed in the tube, the quantity remaining after four hours was 99 parts.

In this case there is not much difference of specific gravity between the gases, and we have $a = 9 \times (0 \cdot 9)^2 \frac{\pi}{4}$ cubic inches, $b = \infty$, $c = 2$ inches, and $s = (0 \cdot 12)^2 \frac{\pi}{4}$ square inches;

$$l = \sqrt{\frac{\pi}{2k}} \frac{3}{4} \frac{ac}{s} \log_e 10 \cdot \frac{1}{t} \cdot \log_{10} \left(\frac{a}{a - y} \right) \quad \ldots\ldots\ldots\ldots\ldots (57);$$

$$\therefore \ l = 0 \cdot 00000256 \text{ inch } = \tfrac{1}{389000} \text{ inch} \ldots\ldots\ldots\ldots\ldots (58).$$

PROP. XXI. *To find the amount of energy which crosses unit of area in unit of time when the velocity of agitation is greater on one side of the area than on the other.*

The energy of a single particle is composed of two parts,—the *vis viva* of the centre of gravity, and the *vis viva* of the various motions of rotation round that centre, or, if the particle be capable of internal motions, the *vis viva* of these. We shall suppose that the whole *vis viva* bears a constant proportion to that due to the motion of the centre of gravity, or

$$E = \tfrac{1}{2} \beta M v^2,$$

where β is a coefficient, the experimental value of which is 1·634. Substituting E for M in Prop. XIV., we get for the transference of energy across unit of area in unit of time,

$$Jq = - \tfrac{1}{3} \frac{d}{dx} \left(\tfrac{1}{2} \beta M v^2 N v l \right),$$

where J is the mechanical equivalent of heat in foot-pounds, and q is the transfer of heat in thermal units.

Now $MN = \rho$, and $l = \dfrac{1}{A\rho}$, so that $MNl = \dfrac{1}{A}$;

$$\therefore \; Jq = -\tfrac{1}{2} \frac{\beta v^2}{A} \frac{dv}{dx} \; \dotfill \; (59).$$

Also, if T is the absolute temperature,

$$\frac{1}{T} \frac{dT}{dx} = \frac{2}{v} \frac{dv}{dx};$$

$$\therefore \; Jq = -\tfrac{3}{4}\beta plv \frac{1}{T} \frac{dT}{dx} \dotfill (60),$$

where p must be measured in dynamical units of force.

Let $J = 772$ foot-pounds, $p = 2116$ pounds to square foot, $l = \frac{1}{400000}$ inch, $v = 1505$ feet per second, $T = 522$ or $62°$ Fahrenheit; then

$$q = \frac{T' - T}{40000x} \dotfill (61),$$

where q is the flow of heat in thermal units per square foot of area; and T' and T are the temperatures at the two sides of a stratum of air x *inches* thick.

In Prof. Rankine's work on the Steam-engine, p. 259, values of the *thermal resistance*, or the reciprocal of the *conductivity*, are given for various substances as computed from a Table of conductivities deduced by M. Peclet from experiments by M. Despretz:—

Resistance.

Gold, Platinum, Silver	0·0036
Copper	0·0040
Iron	0·0096
Lead	0·0198
Brick	0·3306

Air by our calculation 40000

It appears, therefore, that the resistance of a stratum of air to the conduction of heat is about 10,000,000 times greater than that of a stratum of copper of equal thickness. It would be almost impossible to establish the value of the conductivity of a gas by direct experiment, as the heat radiated from the sides of the vessel would be far greater than the heat conducted through the air, even if currents could be entirely prevented*.

PART III.

ON THE COLLISION OF PERFECTLY ELASTIC BODIES OF ANY FORM.

When two perfectly smooth spheres strike each other, the force which acts between them always passes through their centres of gravity; and therefore their motions of rotation, if they have any, are not affected by the collision, and do not enter into our calculations. But, when the bodies are not spherical, the force of compact will not, in general, be in the line joining their centres of gravity; and therefore the force of impact will depend both on the motion of the centres and the motions of rotation before impact, and it will affect both these motions after impact.

In this way the velocities of the centres and the velocities of rotation will act and react on each other, so that finally there will be some relation established between them; and since the rotations of the particles about their three axes are quantities related to each other in the same way as the three velocities of their centres, the reasoning of Prop. IV. will apply to rotation as well as velocity, and both will be distributed according to the law

$$\frac{dN}{dx} = N \frac{1}{a\sqrt{\pi}} e^{-\frac{x}{a^2}}.$$

* [Clausius, in the memoir cited in the last foot-note, has pointed out two oversights in this calculation. In the first place the numbers have not been properly reduced to English measure, and have still to be multiplied by ·4356, the ratio of the English pound to the kilogramme. The numbers have, further, been calculated with one hour as the unit of time, whereas Maxwell has used them as if a second had been the unit. Taking account of these circumstances and using his own expression for the conduction which differs from (59) only in having $\frac{5}{12}$ in place of $\frac{1}{2}$ on the right-hand side, Clausius finds that the resistance of a stratum of air to the conduction of heat is 1400 times greater than that of a stratum of lead of the same thickness, or about 7000 times greater than that of copper. Ed.]

Also, by Prop. V., if x be the average velocity of one set of particles, and y that of another, then the average value of the sum or difference of the velocities is

$$\sqrt{x^2 + y^2};$$

from which it is easy to see that, if in each individual case

$$u = ax + by + cz,$$

where x, y, z are independent quantities distributed according to the law above stated, then the *average values* of these quantities will be connected by the equation

$$u^2 = a^2x^2 + b^2y^2 + c^2z^2.$$

PROP. XXII. *Two perfectly elastic bodies of any form strike each other: given their motions before impact, and the line of impact, to find their motions after impact.*

Let M_1 and M_2 be the centres of gravity of the two bodies. M_1X_1, M_1Y_1, and M_1Z_1 the principal axes of the first; and M_2X_2, M_2Y_2 and M_2Z_2 those of the second. Let I be the point of impact, and R_1IR_2 the line of impact.

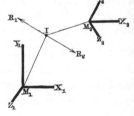

Let the co-ordinates of I with respect to M_1 be $x_1y_1z_1$, and with respect to M_2 let them be $x_2y_2z_2$.

Let the direction-cosines of the line of impact R_1IR_2 be $l_1m_1n_1$ with respect to M_1, and $l_2m_2n_2$ with respect to M_2.

Let M_1 and M_2 be the masses, and $A_1B_1C_1$ and $A_2B_2C_2$ the moments of inertia of the bodies about their principal axes.

Let the velocities of the centres of gravity, resolved in the direction of the principal axes of each body, be

$$U_1,\ V_1,\ W_1,\ \text{and}\ U_2,\ V_2,\ W_2,\ \text{before impact,}$$

and $\qquad\qquad U'_1,\ V'_1,\ W'_1,\ \text{and}\ U'_2,\ V'_2,\ W'_2,\ \text{after impact.}$

Let the angular velocities round the same axes be

$$p_1,\ q_1,\ r_1,\ \text{and}\ p_2,\ q_2,\ r_2,\ \text{before impact,}$$

and $\qquad\qquad p'_1,\ q'_1,\ r'_1,\ \text{and}\ p'_2,\ q'_2,\ r'_2,\ \text{after impact.}$

Let R be the impulsive force between the bodies, measured by the momentum it produces in each.

Then, for the velocities of the centres of gravity, we have the following equations :

$$U'_1 = U_1 + \frac{Rl_1}{M_1}, \quad U'_2 = U_2 - \frac{Rl_2}{M_2} \dots\dots\dots\dots\dots (62),$$

with two other pairs of equations in V and W.

The equations for the angular velocities are

$$p'_1 = p_1 + \frac{R}{A_1}(y_1 n_1 - z_1 m_1), \quad p'_2 = p_2 - \frac{R}{A_2}(y_2 n_2 - z_2 m_2) \dots\dots\dots (63),$$

with two other pairs of equations for q and r.

The condition of perfect elasticity is that the whole *vis viva* shall be the same after impact as before, which gives the equation

$$M_1(U'^2_1 - U^2_1) + M_2(U'^2_2 - U^2_2) + A_1(p'^2_1 - p^2_1) + A_2(p'^2_2 - p^2_2) + \&c. = 0 \dots (64).$$

The terms relating to the axis of x are here given; those relating to y and z may be easily written down.

Substituting the values of these terms, as given by equations (62) and (63), and dividing by R, we find

$$l_1(U'_1 + U_1) - l_2(U'_2 + U_2) + (y_1 n_1 - z_1 m_1)(p'_1 + p_1) - (y_2 n_2 - z_2 m_2)(p'_2 + p_2) + \&c. = 0 \dots (65).$$

Now if v_1 be the velocity of the striking-point of the first body before impact, resolved along the line of impact,

$$v_1 = l_1 U_1 + (y_1 n_1 - z_1 m_1) p_1 + \&c. ;$$

and if we put v_2 for the velocity of the other striking-point resolved along the same line, and v'_1 and v'_2 the same quantities after impact, we may write, equation (65),

$$v_1 + v'_1 - v_2 - v'_2 = 0 \dots\dots\dots\dots\dots\dots (66),$$

or

$$v_1 - v_2 = v'_2 - v'_1 \dots\dots\dots\dots\dots\dots\dots (67),$$

which shows that the velocity of separation of the striking-points resolved in the line of impact is equal to that of approach.

Substituting the values of the accented quantities in equation (65) by means of equations (63) and (64), and transposing terms in R, we find

$$2\left\{U_1 l_1 - U_2 l_2 + p_1\left(y_1 n_1 - z_1 m_1\right) - p_2\left(y_2 n_2 - z_2 m_2\right)\right\} + \&c.$$

$$= -R\left\{\frac{l_1^2}{M_1} + \frac{l_2^2}{M_2} + \frac{\left(y_1 n_1 - z_1 m_1\right)^2}{A_1} + \frac{\left(y_2 n_2 - z_2 m_2\right)^2}{A_2} + \&c.\right\} \dots\dots (68),$$

the other terms being related to y and z as these are to x. From this equation we may find the value of R; and by substituting this in equations (63), (64), we may obtain the values of all the velocities after impact.

We may, for example, find the value of U'_1 from the equation

$$\left.\begin{aligned}
U'_1 &\left\{\frac{l_1^2}{M_1} + \frac{l_2^2}{M_2} + \frac{\left(y_1 n_1 - z_1 m_1\right)^2}{A_1} + \frac{\left(y_2 n_2 - z_2 m_2\right)^2}{A_2} + \&c.\right\} \frac{M_1}{l_1} \\
= U_1 &\left\{-\frac{l_1^2}{M_1} + \frac{l_2^2}{M_2} + \frac{\left(y_1 n_1 - z_1 m_1\right)^2}{A_1} + \frac{\left(y_2 n_2 - z_2 m_2\right)^2}{A_2} + \&c.\right\} \frac{M_1}{l_1} \\
+ 2U_2 l_2 &- 2p_1\left(y_1 n_1 - z_1 m_1\right) + 2p_2\left(y_2 n_2 - z_2 m_2\right) - \&c.
\end{aligned}\right\} \dots\dots (69).$$

PROP. XXIII. *To find the relations between the average velocities of translation and rotation after many collisions among many bodies.*

Taking equation (69), which applies to an individual collision, we see that U'_1 is expressed as a linear function of U_1, U_2, p_1, p_2, &c., all of which are quantities of which the values are distributed among the different particles according to the law of Prop. IV. It follows from Prop. V., that if we square every term of the equation, we shall have a new equation between the *average values* of the different quantities. It is plain that, as soon as the required relations have been established, they will remain the same after collision, so that we may put $U_1'^2 = U_1^2$ in the equation of averages. The equation between the average values may then be written

$$\left(M_1 U_1^2 - M_2 U_2^2\right)\frac{l_2^2}{M_2} + \left(M_1 U_1^2 - A_1 p_1^2\right)\frac{\left(y_1 n_1 - z_1 m_1\right)^2}{A_1} + \left(M_1 U_1^2 - A_2 p_2^2\right)\frac{\left(y_2 n_2 - z_2 m_2\right)^2}{A_2} + \&c. = 0.$$

Now since there are collisions in every possible way, so that the values of l, m, n, &c. and x, y, z, &c. are infinitely varied, this equation cannot subsist unless

$$M_1 U_1^2 = M_2 U_2^2 = A_1 p_1^2 = A_2 p_2^2 = \&c.$$

The final state, therefore, of any number of systems of moving particles of any form is that in which the average *vis viva* of translation along each of the three axes is the same in all the systems, and equal to the average $\overline{vis\ viva}$ of rotation about each of the three principal axes of each particle.

Adding the *vires vivæ* with respect to the other axes, we find that the whole *vis viva* of translation is equal to that of rotation in each system of particles, and is also same for different systems, as was proved in Prop. VI.

This result (which is true, however nearly the bodies approach the spherical form, provided the motion of rotation is at all affected by the collisions) seems decisive against the unqualified acceptation of the hypothesis that gases are such systems of hard elastic particles. For the ascertained fact that γ, the ratio of the specific heat at constant pressure to that at constant volume, is equal to 1·408, requires that the ratio of the whole *vis viva* to the *vis viva* of translation should be

$$\beta = \frac{2}{3\,(\gamma - 1)} = 1\cdot634 \ ;$$

whereas, according to our hypothesis, $\beta = 2$.

We have now followed the mathematical theory of the collisions of hard elastic particles through various cases, in which there seems to be an analogy with the phenomena of gases. We have deduced, as others have done already, the relations of pressure, temperature, and density of a single gas. We have also proved that when two different gases act freely on each other (that is, when at the same temperature), the mass of the single particles of each is inversely proportional to the square of the molecular velocity ; and therefore, at equal temperature and pressure, *the number of particles in unit of volume is the same.*

We then offered an explanation of the internal friction of gases, and deduced from experiments a value of the mean length of path of a particle between successive collisions.

We have applied the theory to the law of diffusion of gases, and, from an experiment on olefiant gas, we have deduced a value of the length of path not very different from that deduced from experiments on friction.

Using this value of the length of path between collisions, we found that the resistance of air to the conduction of heat is 10,000,000 times that of copper, a result in accordance with experience.

Finally, by establishing a necessary relation between the motions of translation and rotation of all particles not spherical, we proved that a system of such particles could not possibly satisfy the known relation between the two specific heats of all gases.

[From the *Philosophical Transactions*, MDCCCLX.]

XXI. *On the Theory of Compound Colours, and the Relations of the Colours of the Spectrum.* Communicated by Professor STOKES, Sec. R.S.

(Received January 5,—Read March 22, 1860.)

§ I. *Introduction.*

ACCORDING to Newton's analysis of light*, every colour in nature is produced by the mixture, in various proportions, of the different kinds of light into which white light is divided by refraction. By means of a prism we may analyse any coloured light, and determine the proportions in which the different homogeneous rays enter into it; and by means of a lens we may recombine these rays, and reproduce the original coloured light.

Newton has also shewn† how to combine the different rays of the spectrum so as to form a single beam of light, and how to alter the proportions of the different colours so as to exhibit the result of combining them in any arbitrary manner.

The number of different kinds of homogeneous light being infinite, and the proportion in which each may be combined being also variable indefinitely, the results of such combinations could not be appreciated by the eye, unless the chromatic effect of every mixture, however complicated, could be expressed in some simpler form. Colours, as seen by the human eye of the normal type, can all be reduced to a few classes, and expressed by a few well-known names; and even those colours which have different names have obvious relations among themselves. Every colour, except purple, is similar to some colour of the spectrum‡,

---

* *Optics*, Book I. Part 2, Prop. 7.
† *Lectiones Opticæ*, Part 2, § 1, pp. 100 to 105; and *Optics*, Book I. Part 2, Prop. 11.
‡ *Optics*, Book I. Part 2, Prop. 4.

although less intense; and all purples may be compounded of blue and red, and diluted with white to any required tint. Brown colours, which at first sight seem different, are merely red, orange or yellow of feeble intensity, more or less diluted with white.

It appears therefore that the result of any mixture of colours, however complicated, may be defined by its relation to a certain small number of well-known colours. Having selected our standard colours, and determined the relations of a given colour to these, we have defined that colour completely as to its appearance. Any colour which has the same relation to the standard colours, will be identical in appearance, though its optical constitution, as revealed by the prism, may be very different.

We may express this by saying that two compound colours may be *chromatically* identical, but *optically* different. The *optical* properties of light are those which have reference to its origin and propagation through media, till it falls on the sensitive organ of vision; the *chromatical* properties of light are those which have reference to its power of exciting certain sensations of *colour*, perceived through the organ of vision.

The investigation of the chromatic relations of the rays of the spectrum must therefore be founded upon observations of the apparent identity of compound colours, as seen by an eye either of the normal or of some abnormal type; and the results to which the investigation leads must be regarded as partaking of a physiological, as well as of a physical character, and as indicating certain laws of sensation, depending on the constitution of the organ of vision, which may be different in different individuals. We have to determine the laws of the composition of colours in general, to reduce the number of standard colours to the smallest possible, to discover, if we can, what they are, and to ascertain the relation which the homogeneous light of different parts of the spectrum bears to the standard colours.

§ II. *History of the Theory of Compound Colours.*

The foundation of the theory of the composition of colours was laid by Newton*. He first shews that, by the mixture of homogeneal light, colours may be produced which are "like to the colours of homogeneal light as to the appearance of colour, but not as to the immutability of colour and consti-

---

* *Optics*, Book I. Part 2, Props. 4, 5, 6.

tution of light." Red and yellow give an orange colour, which is chromatically similar to the orange of the spectrum, but optically different, because it is resolved into its component colours by a prism, while the orange of the spectrum remains unchanged. When the colours to be mixed lie at a distance from one another in the spectrum, the resultant appears paler than that intermediate colour of the spectrum which it most resembles; and when several are mixed, the resultant may appear white. Newton* is always careful, however, not to call any mixture white, unless it agrees with common white light in its optical as well as its chromatical properties, and is a mixture of *all* the homogeneal colours. The theory of compound colours is first presented in a mathematical form in Prop. 6, "*In a mixture of primary colours, the quantity and quality of each being given, to know the colour of the compound.*" He divides the circumference of a circle into seven parts, proportional to the seven musical intervals, in accordance with his opinion about the proportions of the colours in the spectrum. At the centre of gravity of each of these arcs he places a little circle, whose area is proportional to the number of rays of the corresponding colour which enter into the given mixture. The position of the centre of gravity of all these circles indicates the nature of the resultant colour. A radius drawn through it points out that colour of the spectrum which it most resembles, and the distance from the centre determines the fulness of its colour.

With respect to this construction, Newton says, "This rule I conceive accurate enough for practice, though not mathematically accurate." He gives no reasons for the different parts of his rule, but we shall find that his method of finding the centre of gravity of the component colours is completely confirmed by my observations, and that it involves mathematically the theory of three elements of colour; but that the disposition of the colours on the circumference of a circle was only a provisional arrangement, and that the true relations of the colours of the spectrum can only be determined by direct observation.

Young† appears to have originated the theory, that the three elements of colour are determined as much by the constitution of the sense of sight as by anything external to us. He conceives that three different sensations may be excited by light, but that the proportion in which each of the three is excited depends on the nature of the light. He conjectures that these primary sensa-

---

* 7th and 8th Letters to Oldenburg.

† Young's *Lectures on Natural Philosophy*, Kelland's Edition, p. 345, or Quarto, 1807, Vol. I. p. 441 ; see also Young in *Philosophical Transactions*, 1801, or Works in Quarto, Vol. II. p. 617.

tions correspond to red, green, and violet. A blue ray, for example, though homogeneous in itself, he conceives capable of exciting both the green and the violet sensation, and therefore he would call blue a compound colour, though the colour of a simple kind of light. The *quality* of any colour depends, according to this theory, on the *ratios* of the intensities of the three sensations which it excites, and its *brightness* depends on the *sum* of these three intensities.

Sir David Brewster, in his paper entitled " On a New Analysis of Solar Light, indicating three Primary Colours, forming Coincident Spectra of equal length*," regards the actual colours of the spectrum as arising from the intermixture, in various proportions, of three primary kinds of light, red, yellow, and blue, each of which is variable in intensity, but uniform in colour, from one end of the spectrum to the other; so that every colour in the spectrum is really compound, and might be shewn to be so if we had the means of separating its elements.

Sir David Brewster, in his researches, employed coloured media, which, according to him, absorb the three elements of a single prismatic colour in different degrees, and change their proportions, so as to alter the colour of the light, without altering its refrangibility.

In this paper I shall not enter into the very important questions affecting the physical theory of light, which can only be settled by a careful inquiry into the phenomena of absorption. The physiological facts, that we have a threefold sensation of colour, and that the three elements of this sensation are affected in different proportions by light of different refrangibilities, are equally true, whether we adopt the physical theory that there are three kinds of light corresponding to these three colour-sensations, or whether we regard light of definite refrangibility as an undulation of known length, and therefore variable only in intensity, but capable of producing different chemical actions on different substances, of being absorbed in different degrees by different media, and of exciting in different degrees the three different colour-sensations of the human eye.

Sir David Brewster has given a diagram of three curves, in which the base-line represents the length of the spectrum, and the ordinates of the curves represent, by estimation, the intensities of the three kinds of light at each point of the spectrum. I have employed a diagram of the same kind to express the

* *Transactions of the Royal Society of Edinburgh*, Vol. XII. p. 123.

results arrived at in this paper, the ordinates being made to represent the intensities of each of the three elements of colour, as calculated from the experiments.

The most complete series of experiments on the mixture of the colours of the spectrum, is that of Professor Helmholtz*, of Königsberg. By using two slits at right angles to one another, he formed two pure spectra, the fixed lines of which were seen crossing one another when viewed in the ordinary way by means of a telescope. The colours of these spectra were thus combined in every possible way, and the effect of the combination of any two could be seen separately by drawing the eye back from the eye-piece of the telescope, when the compound colour was seen by itself at the eye-hole. The proportion of the components was altered by turning the combined slits round in their own plane.

One result of these experiments was, that a colour, chromatically identical with white, could be formed by combining yellow with indigo. M. Helmholtz was not then able to produce white with any other pair of simple colours, and considered that three simple colours were required in general to produce white, one from each of the three portions into which the spectrum is divided by the yellow and indigo.

Professor Grassmann† shewed that Newton's theory of compound colours implies that there are an infinite number of pairs of complementary colours in the spectrum, and pointed out the means of finding them. He also shewed how colours may be represented by lines, and combined by the method of the parallelogram.

In a second memoir‡, M. Helmholtz describes his method of ascertaining these pairs of complementary colours. He formed a pure spectrum by means of a slit, a prism, and a lens; and in this spectrum he placed an apparatus having two parallel slits which were capable of adjustment both in position and breadth, so as to let through any two portions of the spectrum, in any proportions. Behind this slit, these rays were united in an image of the prism, which was received on paper. By arranging the slits, the colour of this image may be reduced to white, and made identical with that of paper illuminated with white light. The wave-lengths of the component colours were then measured by observing the angle of diffraction through a grating. It was found that the

---

* Poggendorff's *Annalen*, Band LXXXVII. (*Philosophical Magazine*, 1852, December).
† *Ibid.* Band LXXXIX. (*Philosophical Magazine*, 1854, April).   ‡ *Ibid.* Band XCIV.

colours from red to green-yellow ($\lambda = 2082$) were complementary to colours ranging from green-blue ($\lambda = 1818$) to violet, and that the colours between green-yellow and green-blue have no homogeneous complementaries, but must be neutralized by mixtures of red and violet.

M. Helmholtz also gives a provisional diagram of the curve formed by the spectrum on Newton's diagram, for which his experiments did not furnish him with the complete data.

Accounts of experiments by myself on the mixture of artificial colours by rapid rotation, may be found in the *Transactions of the Royal Society of Edinburgh*, Vol. XXI. Pt. 2 (1855); in an appendix to Professor George Wilson's work on Colour-Blindness; in the *Report of the British Association* for 1856, p. 12; and in the *Philosophical Magazine*, July 1857, p. 40. These experiments shew that, for the normal eye, there are three, and only three, elements of colour, and that in the colour-blind one of these is absent. They also prove that chromatic observations may be made, both by normal and abnormal eyes, with such accuracy, as to warrant the employment of the results in the calculation of colour-equations, and in laying down colour-diagrams by Newton's rule.

The first instrument which I made (in 1852) to examine the mixtures of the colours of the spectrum was similar to that which I now use, but smaller, and it had no constant light for a term of comparison. The second was $6\frac{1}{2}$ feet long, made in 1855, and shewed *two* combinations of colour side by side. I have now succeeded in making the mixture much more perfect, and the comparisons more exact, by using white reflected light, instead of the second compound colour. An apparatus in which the light passes through the prisms, and is reflected back again in nearly the same path by a concave mirror, was shewn by me to the British Association in 1856. It has the advantage of being portable, and need not be more than half the length of the other, in order to produce a spectrum of equal length. I am so well satisfied with the working of this form of the instrument, that I intend to make use of it in obtaining equations from a greater variety of observers than I could meet with when I was obliged to use the more bulky instrument. It is difficult at first to get the observer to believe that the compound light can ever be so adjusted as to appear to his eyes identical with the white light in contact with it. He has to learn what adjustments are necessary to produce the requisite alteration under all circumstances, and he must never be satisfied till the two parts of the field are identical in colour and illumination. To do this thoroughly, implies not merely good eyes, but a power of judging as to the exact nature of the difference between two very pale and nearly identical tints, whether they differ in the amount of red, green, or blue, or in brightness of illumination.

In the following paper I shall first lay down the mathematical theory of Newton's diagram, with its relation to Young's theory of the colour-sensation. I shall then describe the experimental method of mixing the colours of the spectrum, and determining the wave-lengths of the colours mixed. The results of my experiments will then be given, and the chromatic relations of the spectrum exhibited in a system of colour-equations, in Newton's diagram, and in three curves of intensity, as in Brewster's diagram. The differences between the results of two observers will then be discussed, shewing on what they depend, and in what way such differences may affect the vision of persons otherwise free from defects of sight.

§ III. *Mathematical Theory of Newton's Diagram of Colours.*

Newton's diagram is a plane figure, designed to exhibit the relations of colours to each other.

Every point in the diagram represents a colour, simple or compound, and we may conceive the diagram itself so painted, that every colour is found at its corresponding point. Any colour, differing only in quantity of illumination from one of the colours of the diagram, is referred to it as a unit, and is measured by the ratio of the illumination of the given colour to that of the corresponding colour in the diagram. In this way the *quantity* of a colour is estimated. The resultant of mixing any two colours of the diagram is found by dividing the line joining them inversely as the quantity of each; then, if the sum of these quantities is unity, the resultant will have the illumination as well as the colour of the point so found; but if the sum of the components is different from unity, the *quantity* of the resultant will be measured by the sum of the components.

This method of determining the position of the resultant colour is mathematically identical with that of finding the centre of gravity of two weights, and placing a weight equal to their sum at the point so found. We shall therefore speak of the resultant tint as the sum of its components placed at their centre of gravity.

By compounding this resultant tint with some other colour, we may find the position of a mixture of three colours, at the centre of gravity of its components; and by taking these components in different proportions, we may obtain colours corresponding to every part of the triangle of which they are the angular points. In this way, by taking any three colours we should be able to construct a triangular portion of Newton's diagram by painting it with mixtures of the three colours. Of course these mixtures must be made to correspond with optical mixtures of light, not with mechanical mixtures of pigments.

Let us now take any colour belonging to a point of the diagram outside this triangle. To make the centre of gravity of the three weights coincide with this point, one or more of the weights must be made negative. This, though following from mathematical principles, is not capable of direct physical interpretation, as we cannot exhibit a negative colour.

The equation between the three selected colours, x, y, z, and the new colour u, may in the first case be written

$$u = x + y + z \dots\dots\dots\dots\dots\dots\dots\dots\dots (1),$$

x, y, z being the quantities of colour required to produce u. In the second case suppose that z must be made negative,

$$u = x + y - z \dots\dots\dots\dots\dots\dots\dots\dots\dots (2).$$

As we cannot realize the term $-z$ as a negative colour, we transpose it to the other side of the equation, which then becomes

$$u + z = x + y \dots\dots\dots\dots\dots\dots\dots\dots\dots (3),$$

which may be interpreted to mean, that the resultant tint, $u + z$, is identical with the resultant, $x + y$. We thus find a mixture of the new colour with one of the selected colours, which is chromatically equivalent to a mixture of the other two selected colours.

When the equation takes the form

$$u = x - y - z \dots\dots\dots\dots\dots\dots\dots\dots\dots (4),$$

two of the components being negative, we must transpose them thus,

$$u + y + z = x \dots\dots\dots\dots\dots\dots\dots\dots \dots (5),$$

which means that a mixture of certain proportions of the new colour and two of the three selected, is chromatically equivalent to the third. We may thus in all cases find the relation between any three colours and a fourth, and exhibit this relation in a form capable of experimental verification; and by proceeding in this way we may map out the positions of all colours upon Newton's diagram. Every colour in nature will then be defined by the position of the corresponding colour in the diagram, and by the ratio of its illumination to that of the colour in the diagram.

§ IV. *Method of representing Colours by Straight Lines drawn from a Point.*

To extend our ideas of the relations of colours, let us form a new geometrical conception by the aid of solid geometry.

Let us take as origin any point not in the plane of the diagram, and let us draw lines through this point to the different points of the diagram; then the direction of any of these lines will depend upon the position of the point of the diagram through which it passes, so that we may take this line as the representative of the corresponding colour on the diagram.

In order to indicate the *quantity* of this colour, let it be produced beyond the plane of the diagram in the same ratio as the given colour exceeds in illumination the colour on the diagram. In this way every colour in nature will be represented by a line drawn through the origin, whose *direction* indicates the *quality* of the colour, while its *length* indicates its *quantity*.

Let us find the resultant of two colours by this method. Let O be the origin and AB be a section of the plane of the diagram by that of the paper. Let OP, OQ be lines representing colours, A, B the

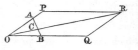

corresponding points in the diagram; then the quantity of P will be $\dfrac{OP}{OA} = p$, and that of Q will be $\dfrac{OQ}{OB} = q$. The resultant of these will be represented in the diagram by the point C, where $AC : CB :: q : p$, and the quantity of the resultant will be $p + q$, so that if we produce OC to R, so that $OR = (p+q)OC$, the line OR will represent the resultant of OP and OQ in direction and magnitude. It is easy to prove, from this construction, that OR is the diagonal of the parallelogram of which OP and OQ are two sides. It appears therefore that if colours are represented in quantity and quality by the magnitude and direction of straight lines, the rule for the composition of colours is identical with that for the composition of forces in mechanics. This analogy has been well brought out by Professor Grassmann in Poggendorff's *Annalen*, Bd. LXXXIX.

We may conceive an arrangement of actual colours in space founded upon this construction. Suppose each of these radiating lines representing a given colour to be itself illuminated with that colour, the brightness increasing from zero at the origin to unity, where it cuts the plane of the diagram, and becoming continually more intense in proportion to the distance from the origin. In this way every colour in nature may be matched, both in quality and quantity, by some point in this coloured space.

If we take any three lines through the origin as axes, we may, by co-ordinates parallel to these lines, express the position of any point in space. That point will correspond to a colour which is the resultant of the three colours represented by the three co-ordinates.

This system of co-ordinates is an illustration of the resolution of a colour into three components. According to the theory of Young, the human eye is capable of three distinct primitive sensations of colour, which by their composition in various proportions, produce the sensations of actual colour in all their varieties. Whether any kinds of light have the power of exciting these primitive sensations separately, has not yet been determined.

If colours corresponding to the three primitive sensations can be exhibited, then all colours, whether produced by light, disease, or imagination, are compounded of these, and have their places within the triangle formed by joining the three primaries. If the colours of the pure spectrum, as laid down on the diagram, form a triangle, the colours at the angles *may* correspond to the primitive sensations. If the curve of the spectrum does not reach the angles of the circumscribing triangle, then no colour in the spectrum, and therefore no colour in nature, corresponds to any of the three primary sensations.

The only data at present existing for determining the primary colours, are derived from the comparison of observations of colour-equations by colour-blind, and by normal eyes. The colour-blind equations differ from the others by the non-existence of one of the elements of colour, the relation of which to known colours can be ascertained. It appears, from observations made for me by two colour-blind persons*, that the elementary sensation which they do not possess is a red approaching to crimson, lying beyond both vermilion and carmine. These

---

* *Transactions of the Royal Society of Edinburgh*, Vol. XXI. Pt. 2, p. 286.

observations are confirmed by those of Mr Pole, and by others which I have obtained since. I have hopes of being able to procure a set of colour-blind equations between the colours of the spectrum, which will indicate the missing primary in a more exact manner.

The experiments which I am going to describe have for their object the determination of the position of the colours of the spectrum upon Newton's diagram, from actual observations of the mixtures of those colours. They were conducted in such a way, that in every observation the judgment of the observer was exercised upon two parts of an illuminated field, one of which was so adjusted as to be chromatically identical with the other, which, during the whole series of observations, remained of one constant intensity of white. In this way the effects of subjective colours were entirely got rid of, and all the observations were of the same kind, and therefore may claim to be equally accurate; which is not the case when comparisons are made between bright colours of different kinds.

The chart of the spectrum, deduced from these observations, exhibits the colours arranged very exactly along two sides of a triangle, the extreme red and violet forming doubtful portions of the third side. This result greatly simplifies the theory of colour, if it does not actually point out the three primary colours themselves.

§ V. *Description of an Instrument for making definite Mixtures of the Colours of the Spectrum.*

The experimental method which I have used consists in forming a combination of three colours belonging to different portions of the spectrum, the quantity of each being so adjusted that the mixture shall be white, and equal in intensity to a given white. Fig. 1, Plate VI. p. 444, represents the instrument for making the observations. It consists of two tubes, or long boxes, of deal, of rectangular section, joined together at an angle of about 100°.

The part AK is about five feet long, seven inches broad, and four deep; KN is about two feet long, five inches broad, and four deep; BD is a partition parallel to the side of the long box. The whole of the inside of the instrument is painted black, and the only openings are at the end AC, and at E. At the angle there is a lid, which is opened when the optical parts have to be adjusted or cleaned.

At E is a fine vertical slit; L is a lens; at P there are two equilateral prisms. The slit E, the lens L, and the prisms P are so adjusted, that when light is admitted at E a *pure spectrum* is formed at AB, the extremity of the long box. A mirror at M is also adjusted so as to reflect the light from E along the narrow compartment of the long box to BC. See Fig. 3.

At AB is placed the contrivance shewn in Fig. 2, Plate I. $A'B'$ is a rectangular frame of brass, having a rectangular aperture of 6×1 inches. On this frame are placed six brass sliders, X, Y, Z. Each of these carries a knife-edge of brass in the plane of the surface of the frame.

These six moveable knife-edges form three slits, X, Y, Z, which may be so adjusted as to coincide with any three portions of the pure spectrum formed by light from E. The intervals behind the sliders are closed by hinged shutters, which allow the sliders to move without letting light pass between them.

The inner edge of the brass frame is graduated to twentieths of an inch, so that the position of any slit can be read off. The breadth of the slit is ascertained by means of a wedge-shaped piece of metal, six inches long, and tapering to a point from a breadth of half an inch. This is gently inserted into each slit, and the breadth is determined by the distance to which it enters, the divisions on the wedge corresponding to the 200th of an inch difference in breadth, so that the unit of breadth is ·005 inch.

Now suppose light to enter at E, to pass through the lens, and to be refracted by the two prisms at P; a pure spectrum, shewing Fraunhofer's lines, is formed at AB, but only that part is allowed to pass which falls on the three slits X, Y, Z. The rest is stopped by the shutters. Suppose that the portion falling on X belongs to the red part of the spectrum; then, of the white light entering at E, only the red will come through the slit X. If we were to admit red light at X it would be refracted to E, by the principle in Optics, that the course of any ray may be reversed. If, instead of red light, we were to admit white light at X, still only red light would come to E; for all other light would be either more or less refracted, and would not reach the slit at E. Applying the eye at the slit E, we should see the prism P uniformly illuminated with red light, of the kind corresponding to the part of the spectrum which falls on the slit X when light is admitted at E.

Let the slit Y correspond to another portion of the spectrum, say the green; then, if white light is admitted at Y, the prism, as seen by an eye at E, will be uniformly illuminated with green light; and if white light be admitted at X

and Y simultaneously, the colour seen at E will be a compound of red and green, the proportions depending on the breadth of the slits and the intensity of the light which enters them. The third slit Z, enables us to combine any three kinds of light in any given proportions, so that an eye at E shall see the face of the prism at P uniformly illuminated with the colour resulting from the combination of the three. The position of these three rays in the spectrum is found by admitting the light at E, and comparing the position of the slits with the position of the principal fixed lines; and the breadth of the slits is determined by means of the wedge.

At the same time white light is admitted through BC to the mirror of black glass at M, whence it is reflected to E, past the edge of the prism at P, so that the eye at E sees through the lens a field consisting of two portions, separated by the edge of the prism; that on the left hand being compounded of three colours of the spectrum refracted by the prism, while that on the right hand is white light reflected from the mirror. By adjusting the slits properly, these two portions of the field may be made equal, both in colour and brightness, so that the edge of the prism becomes almost invisible.

In making experiments, the instrument was placed on a table in a room moderately lighted, with the end AB turned towards a large board covered with white paper, and placed in the open air, so as to be uniformly illuminated by the sun. In this way the three slits and the mirror M were all illuminated with white light of the same intensity, and all were affected in the same ratio by any change of illumination; so that if the two halves of the field were rendered equal when the sun was under a cloud, they were found nearly correct when the sun again appeared. No experiments, however, were considered good unless the sun remained uniformly bright during the whole series of experiments.

After each set of experiments light was admitted at E, and the position of the fixed lines D and F of the spectrum was read off on the scale at AB. It was found that after the instrument had been some time in use these positions were invariable, shewing that the eye-hole, the prisms, and the scale might be considered as rigidly connected.

§ VI. *Method of determining the Wave-length corresponding to any point of the Spectrum on the Scale* AB.

Two plane surfaces of glass were kept apart by two parallel strips of gold-beaters' leaf, so as to enclose a stratum of air of nearly uniform thickness. Light reflected from this stratum of air was admitted at E, and the spectrun formed by it was examined at AB by means of a lens. This spectrum consists of a large number of bright bands, separated by dark spaces at nearly uniform intervals, these intervals, however, being considerably larger as we approach the violet end of the spectrum.

The reason of these alternations of brightness is easily explained. By the theory of Newton's rings, the light reflected from a stratum of air consists of two parts, one of which has traversed a path longer than that of the other, by an interval depending on the thickness of the stratum and the angle of incidence. Whenever the interval of retardation is an exact multiple of a wave-length, these two portions of light destroy each other by interference; and when the interval is an odd number of half wave-lengths, the resultant light is a maximum.

In the ordinary case of Newton's rings, these alternations depend upon the varying thickness of the stratum; while in this case a pencil of rays of different wave-lengths, but all experiencing the same retardation, is analysed into a spectrum, in which the rays are arranged in order of their respective wave-lengths. Every ray whose wave-length is an exact submultiple of the retardation will be destroyed by interference, and its place will appear dark in the spectrum; and there will be as many dark bands seen as there are rays whose wave-lengths fulfil this condition.

If, then, we observe the positions of the dark bands on the scale AB, the wave-lengths corresponding to these positions will be a series of submultiples of the retardation.

Let us call the first dark band visible on the red side of the spectrum zero, and let us number them in order 1, 2, 3, &c. towards the violet end. Let N be the number of undulations corresponding to the band zero which are contained in the retardation R; then if n be the number of any other band, $N+n$ will be the number of the corresponding wave-lengths in the retardation, or in symbols,

$$R = (N+n)\,\lambda \quad\dots\dots\dots\dots\dots\dots\dots\dots\dots\dots\dots(6).$$

Now observe the position of two of Fraunhofer's fixed lines with respect to the dark bands, and let n_1, n_2 be their positions expressed in the number of bands, whole or fractional, reckoning from zero. Let λ_1, λ_2 be the wave-lengths of these fixed lines as determined by Fraunhofer, then

$$R = (N + n_1)\,\lambda_1 = (N + n_2)\,\lambda_2, \quad\dotfill (7);$$

whence

$$N = \frac{n_2\lambda_2 - n_1\lambda_1}{\lambda_1 - \lambda_2} = \frac{(n_2 - n_1)}{\lambda_1 - \lambda_2}\,\lambda_2 - n_1 \quad\dotfill (8),$$

and

$$R = \frac{n_2 - n_1}{\lambda_1 - \lambda_2}\,\lambda_1\lambda_2 \quad\dotfill (9).$$

Having thus found N and R, we may find the wave-length corresponding to the dark band n from the formula

$$\lambda = \frac{R}{N + n} \quad\dotfill (10).$$

In my experiments the line D corresponded with the seventh dark band, and F was between the 15th and 16th, so that $n_2 = 15 \cdot 7$. Here then for D,

and for F,

$$\left. \begin{array}{ll} n_1 = 7, & \lambda_1 = 2175 \\ n_2 = 15 \cdot 7, & \lambda_2 = 1794 \end{array} \right\} \text{ in Fraunhofer's measure} \dotfill (11),$$

whence we find

$$N = 34, \; R = 89175 \dotfill (12).$$

There were 22 bands visible, corresponding to 22 different positions on the scale AB, as determined 4th August, 1859.

TABLE I.

Band.	Scale.	Band.	Scale.	Band.	Scale.
$n = 1$	17	$n = 9$	36	$n = 16$	57
2	19	10	39	17	61
3	$21\frac{1}{4}$	11	42	18	65
4	$23\frac{1}{2}$	12	45	19	69
5	26	13	48	20	73
6	$28\frac{1}{2}$	14	51	21	77
7	31	15	54	22	82
8	$33\frac{1}{2}$				

Sixteen equidistant points on the scale were chosen for standard colours in the experiments to be described. The following Table gives the reading on the scale AB, the value of $N + n$, and the calculated wave-length for each of these :—

TABLE II.

Scale.	(N + n).	Wave-length.	Colour.
20	36·4	2450	Red.
24	38·3	2328	Scarlet.
28	39·8	2240	Orange.
32	41·4	2154	Yellow.
36	42·9	2078	Yellow-Green.
40	44·3	2013	Green.
44	45·7	1951	Green.
48	47·0	1879	Bluish green.
52	48·3	1846	Blue-green.
56	49·6	1797	Greenish blue.
60	50·8	1755	Blue.
64	51·8	1721	Blue.
68	52·8	1688	Blue.
72	53·7	1660	Indigo.
76	54·7	1630	Indigo.
80	55·6	1604	Indigo.

Having thus selected sixteen distinct points of the spectrum on which to operate, and determined their wave-lengths and apparent colours, I proceeded to ascertain the mathematical relations between these colours in order to lay them down on Newton's diagram. For this purpose I selected three of these as points of reference, namely, those at 24, 44, and 68 of the scale. I chose these points because they are well separated from each other on the scale, and because the colour of the spectrum at these points does not appear to the eye to vary very rapidly, either in hue or brightness, in passing from one point to another. Hence a small error of position will not make so serious an alteration of colour at these points, as if we had taken them at places of rapid variation; and we may regard the amount of the illumination produced by the light entering through the slits in these positions as sensibly proportional to the breadth of the slits.

(24) corresponds to a bright scarlet about one-third of the distance from C to D; (44) is a green very near the line E; and (68) is a blue about one-third of the distance from F to G.

§ VII. *Method of Observation.*

The instrument is turned with the end AB towards a board, covered with white paper, and illuminated by sunlight. The operator sits at the end AB, to move the sliders, and adjust the slits; and the observer sits at the end E, which is shaded from any bright light. The operator then places the slits so that their centres correspond to the three standard colours, and adjusts their breadths till the observer sees the prism illuminated with pure white light of the same intensity with that reflected by the mirror M. In order to do this, the observer must tell the operator what difference he observes in the two halves of the illuminated field, and the operator must alter the breadth of the slits accordingly, always keeping the centre of each slit at the proper point of the scale. The observer may call for more or less red, blue or green; and then the operator must increase or diminish the width of the slits X, Y, and Z respectively. If the variable field is darker or lighter than the constant field, the operator must widen or narrow all the slits in the same proportion. When the variable part of the field is nearly adjusted, it often happens that the constant white light from the mirror appears tinged with the complementary colour. This is an indication of what is required to make the resemblance of the two parts of the field of view perfect. When no difference can be detected between the two parts of the field, either in colour or in brightness, the observer must look away for some time, to relieve the strain on the eye, and then look again. If the eye thus refreshed still judges the two parts of the field to be equal, the observation may be considered complete, and the operator must measure the breadth of each slit by means of the wedge, as before described, and write down the result as a colour-equation, thus—

Oct. 18, J. $18{\cdot}5\,(24) + 27\,(44) + 37\,(68) = \mathrm{W}\,^{*}$..................(13).

This equation means that on the 18th of October the observer J. (myself) made an observation in which the breadth of the slit X was $18{\cdot}5$, as measured by the wedge, while its centre was at the division (24) of the scale; that the breadths of Y and Z were 27 and 37, and their positions (44) and (68); and that the illumination produced by these slits was exactly equal, in my estimation as an observer, to the constant white W.

The position of 'the slit X was then shifted from (24) to (28), and when the proper adjustments were made, I found a second colour-equation of this form—

Oct. 18, J. $\qquad$ $16 (28) + 21 (44) + 37 (68) = W$ .... (14).

Subtracting one equation from the other and remembering that the figures in brackets are merely symbols of position, not of magnitude, we find

$$16 (28) = 18{\cdot}5 (24) + 6 (44) \dots\dots\dots\dots\dots\dots\dots (15),$$

shewing that (28) can be made up of (24) and (44), in the proportion of 18·5 to 6.

In this way, by combining each colour with two standard colours, we may produce a white equal to the constant white. The red and yellow colours from (20) to (32) must be combined with green and blue, the greens from (36) to (52) with red and blue, and the blues from (56) to (80) with red and green.

The following is a specimen of an actual series of observations made in this way by another observer (K.) :—

TABLE III.

Oct. 13, 1859. $\qquad\qquad$ Observer (K.).

$(X)\qquad (Y)\qquad (Z)$
$18\frac{1}{2}(24) + 32\frac{1}{2}(44) + 32\ (68) = W^{*}.$
$17\frac{1}{2}(24) + 32\frac{1}{2}(44) + 63\ (80) = W.$
$18\ (24) + 32\frac{1}{2}(44) + 35\ (72) = W.$
$19\ (24) + 32\ (44) + 31\frac{1}{2}(68) = W^{*}.$
$19\ (24) + 30\frac{1}{2}(44) + 35\ (64) = W.$
$20\ (24) + 23\ (44) + 39\ (60) = W.$
$21\ (24) + 14\ (44) + 58\ (56) = W.$
$22\ (24) + 62\ (52) + 11\ (68) = W.$
$22\ (24) + 42\ (48) + 29\frac{1}{2}(68) = W.$
$19\ (24) + 31\frac{1}{2}(44) + 33\ (68) = W^{*}.$
$16\ (24) + 28\ (40) + 32\frac{1}{2}(68) = W.$
$6\ (24) + 27\ (36) + 32\frac{1}{2}(68) = W.$
$23\ (32) + 11\frac{1}{2}(44) + 32\frac{1}{2}(68) = W.$
$17\ (28) + 26\ (44) + 32\frac{1}{2}(68) = W.$
$20\ (24) + 33\frac{1}{2}(44) + 32\frac{1}{2}(68) = W^{*}.$
$46\ (20) + 33\ (44) + 30\ (68) = W.$

The equations marked with an asterisk (*) are those which involve the three standard colours, and since every other equation must be compared with them, they must be often repeated.

The following Table contains the *means* of four sets of observations by the same observer (K.):—

TABLE IV. (K.)

$$44 \cdot 3 \,(20) + 31 \cdot 0 \,(44) + 27 \cdot 7 \,(68) = W.$$
$$16 \cdot 1 \,(28) + 25 \cdot 6 \,(44) + 30 \cdot 6 \,(68) = W.$$
$$22 \cdot 0 \,(32) + 12 \cdot 1 \,(44) + 30 \cdot 6 \,(68) = W.$$
$$6 \cdot 4 \,(24) + 25 \cdot 2 \,(36) + 31 \cdot 3 \,(68) = W.$$
$$15 \cdot 3 \,(24) + 26 \cdot 0 \,(40) + 30 \cdot 7 \,(68) = W.$$
$$19 \cdot 8 \,(24) + 35 \cdot 0 \,(46) + 30 \cdot 2 \,(68) = W.$$
$$21 \cdot 2 \,(24) + 41 \cdot 4 \,(48) + 27 \cdot 0 \,(68) = W.$$
$$22 \cdot 0 \,(24) + 62 \cdot 0 \,(52) + 13 \cdot 0 \,(68) = W.$$
$$21 \cdot 7 \,(24) + 10 \cdot 4 \,(44) + 61 \cdot 7 \,(56) = W.$$
$$20 \cdot 5 \,(24) + 23 \cdot 7 \,(44) + 40 \cdot 5 \,(60) = W.$$
$$19 \cdot 7 \,(24) + 30 \cdot 3 \,(44) + 33 \cdot 7 \,(64) = W.$$
$$18 \cdot 0 \,(24) + 31 \cdot 2 \,(44) + 32 \cdot 3 \,(72) = W.$$
$$17 \cdot 5 \,(24) + 30 \cdot 7 \,(44) + 44 \cdot 0 \,(76) = W.$$
$$18 \cdot 3 \,(24) + 33 \cdot 2 \,(44) + 63 \cdot 7 \,(80) = W.$$

§ VIII. *Determination of the Average Error in Observations of different kinds.*

In order to estimate the degree of accuracy of these observations, I have taken the differences between the values of the three standard colours as originally observed, and their means as given by the above Table. The sum of all the errors of the red (24) from the means, was 31·1, and the number of observations was 42, which gives the average error ·74.

The sum of errors in green (44) was 48·0, and the number of observations 31, giving a mean error 1·55.

The sum of the errors in blue (68) was 46·9, and the number of observations 35, giving a mean error 1·16.

It appears therefore that in the observations generally, the average error does not exceed 1·5; and therefore the results, if confirmed by several observations, may safely be trusted to that degree of accuracy.

The equation between the three standard colours was repeatedly observed, in order to detect any alteration in the character of the light, or any other change of condition which would prevent the observations from being comparable with one another; and also because this equation is used in the reduction of all the others, and therefore requires to be carefully observed. There are twenty observations of this equation, the mean of which gives

$$18\cdot6\,(24) + 31\cdot4\,(44) + 30\cdot5\,(68) = W^* \quad\ldots\ldots\ldots\ldots\ldots(16)$$

as the standard equation.

We may use the twenty observations of this equation as a means of determining the relations between the errors in the different colours, and thus of estimating the accuracy of the observer in distinguishing colours.

The following Table gives the result of these operations, where R stands for (24), G for (44), and B for (68):—

TABLE V.—Mean Errors in the Standard Equation.

$(R) = \cdot54$	$(G - B) = \cdot99$	$(G + B) = 2\cdot31$	$\sqrt{G^2 + B^2} = 1\cdot67$
$(G) = 1\cdot22$	$(B - R) = \cdot85$	$(B + R) = 1\cdot59$	$\sqrt{B^2 + R^2} = 1\cdot26$
$(B) = 1\cdot15$	$(R - G) = \cdot86$	$(R + G) = 1\cdot57$	$\sqrt{R^2 + G^2} = 1\cdot33$

$$(R + G + B) = 2\cdot67 \qquad\qquad \sqrt{R^2 + G^2 + B^2} = 1\cdot76$$

The first column gives the mean difference between the observed value of each of the colours and the mean of all the observations. The second column shews the average error of the observed *differences* between the values of the standards, from the mean value of those differences. The third column shews the average error of the *sums* of two standards, from the mean of such sums. The fourth column gives the square root of the sum of the squares of the quantities in the first column. I have also given the average error of the sum of R, G and B, from its mean value, and the value of $\sqrt{R^2 + G^2 + B^2}$.

It appears from the first column that the red is more accurately observed than the green and blue.

§ IX. *Relative Accuracy in Observations of Colour and of Brightness.*

If the errors in the different colours occurred perfectly independent of each other, then the probable mean error in the sum or difference of any two colours would be the square root of the sum of their squares, as given in the fourth column. It will be seen, however, that the number in the second column is always less, and that in the third always greater, than that in the fourth; shewing that the errors are not independent of each other, but that positive errors in any colour coincide more often with positive than with negative errors in another colour. Now the *hue* of the resultant depends on the *ratios* of the components, while its *brightness* depends on their sum. Since, therefore, the difference of two colours is always more accurately observed than their sum, variations of *colour* are more easily detected than variations in *brightness*, and the eye appears to be a more accurate judge of the identity of colour of the two parts of the field than of their equal illumination. The same conclusion may be drawn from the value of the mean error of the sum of the three standards, which is 2·67, while the square root of the sum of the squares of the errors is 1·76.

§ X. *Reduction of the Observations.*

By eliminating W from the equations of page 428 by means of the standard equation, we obtain equations involving each of the fourteen selected colours of the spectrum, along with the three standard colours; and by transposing the selected colour to one side of the equation, we obtain its value in terms of the three standards. If any of the terms of these equations are negative, the equation has no physical interpretation as it stands, but by transposing the negative term to the other side it becomes positive, and then the equation may be verified.

The following Table contains the values of the fourteen selected tints in terms of the standards. To avoid repetition, the symbols of the standard colours are placed at the head of each column.

TABLE VI.

Observer (K.).	(24.)	(44.)	(68.)
44·3 (20) =	18·6	+ 0·4	+ 2·8
16·1 (28) =	18·6	+ 5·8	− 0·1
22·0 (32) =	18·6	+ 19·3	− 0·1
25·2 (36) =	12·2	+ 31·4	− 0·8
26·0 (40) =	3·3	+ 31·4	− 0·2
35·0 (46) = −	1·2	+ 31·4	+ 0·3
41·4 (48) = −	2·6	+ 31·4	+ 3·5
62·0 (52) = −	3·4	+ 31·4	+ 17·5
61·7 (56) = −	3·1	+ 21·0	+ 30·5
40·5 (60) = −	1·9	+ 7·7	+ 30·5
33·7 (64) = −	1·1	+ 1·1	+ 30·5
32·3 (72) = +	0·6	+ 0·2	+ 30·5
44·0 (76) = +	1·1	+ 0·7	+ 30·5
63·7 (80) = +	0·3	− 1·8	+ 30·5

From these equations we may lay down a chart of the spectrum on Newton's diagram by the following method :—Take any three points, A, B, C, and let A represent the standard colour (24), B (44), and C (68). Then, to find the position of any other colour, say (20), divide AC in P so that $(18\cdot6)\,AP = (2\cdot8)\,PC$, and then divide BP in Q so that $(18\cdot6 + 2\cdot8)\,PQ = (0\cdot4)\,QB$. At the point Q the colour corresponding to (20) must be placed. In this way the diagram of fig. 4, Plate VI., p. 444, has been constructed from the observations of all the colours.

§ XI.   *The Spectrum as laid down on Newton's Diagram.*

The curve on which these points lie has this striking feature, that two portions of it are nearly, if not quite, straight lines. One of these portions extends from (24) to (46), and the other from (48) to (64). The colour (20) and those beyond (64), are not far from the line joining (24) and (68). The spectrum, therefore, as exhibited in Newton's diagram, forms two sides of a triangle, with doubtful fragments of the third side. Now if three colours in Newton's diagram lie in a straight line, the middle one is a compound of the two others. Hence all the colours of the spectrum may be compounded of those which lie at the angles of this triangle. These correspond to the following colours :—

TABLE VII.

		Scale.	Wave-length.	Index in water.	Wave-length in water.
R	Scarlet . .	24	2328	1·332	1·747
G	Green. . .	46¾	1914	1·334	1·435
B	Blue . . .	64½	1717	1·339	1·282

All the other colours of the spectrum may be produced by combinations of these ; and since all natural colours are compounded of the colours of the spectrum, they may be compounded of these three primary colours. I have strong reason to believe that these are the three primary colours corresponding to three modes of sensation in the organ of vision, on which the whole system of colour, as seen by the normal eye, depends.

§ XII.   *Results found by a second Observer.*

We may now consider the results of three series of observations made by myself (J.) as observer, in order to determine the relation of one observer to another in the perception of colour. The standard colours are connected by the following equation, as determined by six observations:—

$$18 \cdot 1 \, (24) + 27 \cdot 5 \, (44) + 37 \, (68) = W^* \quad \dots \dots \dots \dots \dots \dots (17).$$

The average errors in these observations were—

TABLE VIII.

R, ·28	G + B, ·83	G − B, ·83	
G, ·83	B + R, ·42	B − R, ·28	R + G + B, ·95
B, ·16	R + G, ·95	R − G, ·72	

shewing that in this case, also, the power of distinguishing *colour* is more to be depended on than that of distinguishing degrees of *illumination*.

The average error in the other observations from the means was ·64 for red, 76 for green, and 1·02 for blue.

TABLE IX.

Observations by J., October 1859.

	(24.)	(44.)	(68.)
44·3 (20) =	18·1	− 2·5	+ 2·3
16·0 (28) =	18·1	+ 6·2	− 0·7
21·5 (32) =	18·1	+ 25·2	− 0·7
19·3 (36) =	8·1	+ 27·5	− 0·3
20·7 (40) =	2·1	+ 27·5	− 0·5
52·3 (48) = −	1·4	+ 27·5	+ 10·7
95·0 (52) = −	2·4	+ 27·5	+ 37·0
51·7 (56) = −	2·2	+ 4·8	+ 37·0
37·2 (60) = −	1·2	+ 0·8	+ 37·0
36·7 (64) = −	0·2	+ 0·8	+ 37·0
35·0 (72) = +	0·6	− 0·2	+ 37·0
40·0 (76) = +	0·9	+ 0·5	+ 37·0
51·0 (80) = +	1·1	+ 0·5	+ 37·0

§ XIII. Comparison of Results by Newton's Diagram.

The relations of the colours, as given by these observations, are laid down in fig. 5, Plate VI., p. 444. It appears from this diagram, that the positions of the colours lie nearly in a straight line from (24) to (44), and from (48) to (60). The colours beyond (60) are crowded together, as in the other diagram, and the observations are not yet sufficiently accurate to distinguish their relative positions accurately. The colour (20) at the red end of the spectrum is further from the line joining (24) and (68) than in the other diagram, but I have not obtained satisfactory observations of these extreme colours. It will be observed that (32), (36), and (40) are placed further to the right in fig. 5 than in fig. 4, shewing that the second observer (J.) sees more green in these colours than the first (K.), also that (48), (52), (56), and (60) are much further up in fig. 5, shewing that to the second observer they appear more blue and less green. These differences were well seen in making an observation. When the instrument was adjusted to suit the first observer (K.), then, if the selected colour were (32), (36), or (40), the second (J.), on looking into the instrument, saw it too green; but if (48), (52), (56), or (60) were the selected colour, then, if right to the first observer, it appeared too blue to the second. If the instrument were adjusted to suit the second observer, then, in the first case, the other saw red, and in the second green; shewing that there was a real difference in the eyes of these two individuals, producing constant and measurable differences in the apparent colour of objects.

§ XIV. *Comparison by Curves of Intensity of the Primaries.*

Figs. 6 and 7, Plate VI. p. 444, are intended to indicate the intensities of the three standard colours at different points of the spectrum. The curve marked (R) indicates the intensity of the red or (24), (G) that of green or (44), and (B) that of blue or (68). The curve marked (S) has its ordinates equal to the sum of the ordinates of the other three curves. The intensities are found by dividing every colour-equation by the coefficient of the colour on the left-hand side. Fig. 6 represents the results of observations by K., and fig. 7 represents those of J. It will be observed that the ordinates in fig. 7 are smaller between (48) and (56) than in fig. 6. This indicates the feeble intensity of certain kinds of light as seen by the eyes of J., which made it impossible to get observations of the colour (52) at all without making the slit so wide as to include all between (48) and (56).

This blindness of my eyes to the parts of the spectrum between the fixed lines E and F appears to be confined to the region surrounding the axis of vision, as the field of view, when adjusted for my eyes looking directly at the colour, is decidedly out of adjustment when I view it by indirect vision, turning the axis of my eye towards some other point. The prism then appears greener and brighter than the mirror, shewing that the parts of my eye at a distance from the axis are more sensitive to this blue-green light than the parts close to the axis.

It is to be noticed that this insensibility is not to all light of a green or blue colour, but to light of a definite refrangibility. If I had a species of colour-blindness rendering me totally or partially insensible to that element of colour which most nearly corresponds with the light in question, then the light from the mirror, as well as that from the prism, would appear to me deficient in that colour, and I should still consider them chromatically identical; or if there were any difference, it would be the same for all colours nearly the same in appearance, such as those just beyond the line F, which appear to me quite bright.

We must also observe that the peculiarity is confined to a certain portion of the retina, which is known to be of a yellow colour, and which is the seat of several ocular phenomena observed by Purkinje and Wheatstone, and of the sheaf or brushes seen by Haidinger in polarized light; and also that though, of the two observers whose results are given here, one is much more affected with this peculiarity than the other, both are less sensible to the light between E and F than to that on either side; and other observers, whose results are not here given, confirm this.

§ XV.   *Explanation of the Differences between the two Observers.*

I think, therefore, that the yellow spot at the foramen centrale of Soemmering will be found to be the cause of this phenomenon, and that it absorbs the rays between E and F, and would, if placed in the path of the incident light, produce a corresponding dark band in the spectrum formed by a prism.

The reason why white light does not appear yellow in consequence, is that this absorbing action is constant, and we reckon as white the *mean* of all the colours we are accustomed to see. This may be proved by wearing spectacles of any strong colour for some time, when we shall find that we judge white objects to be white, in spite of the rays which enter the eye being coloured.

Now ordinary white light is a mixture of all kinds of light, including that between E and F, which is partially absorbed. If, therefore, we compound an artificial white containing the absorbed ray as one of its three components, it will be much more altered by the absorption than the ordinary light, which contains many rays of nearly the same colour, which are not absorbed. On the other hand, if the artificial light do not contain the absorbed ray, it will be less altered than the ordinary light which contains it. Hence the greater the absorption the less green will those colours appear which are near the absorbed part, such as (48), (52), (56), and the more green will the colours appear which are not near it, such as (32), (36), (40). And these are the chief differences between fig. 4 and fig. 5.

I first observed this peculiarity of my eyes when observing the spectrum formed by a very long vertical slit. I saw an elongated dark spot running up and down in the blue, as if confined in a groove, and following the motion of the eye as it moved up or down the spectrum, but refusing to pass out of the blue into other colours. By increasing the breadth of the spectrum, the dark portion was found to correspond to the *foramen centrale*, and to be visible only when the eye is turned towards the blue-green between E and F. The spot may be well seen by first looking at a yellow paper, and then at a blue one, when the spot will be distinctly seen for a short time, but it soon disappears when the eye gets accustomed to the blue*.

I have been the more careful in stating this peculiarity of my eyes, as I have reason to believe that it affects most persons, especially those who can see Haidinger's brushes easily. Such persons, in comparing their vision with that of others, may be led to think themselves affected with partial colour-blindness, whereas their colour-vision may be of the ordinary kind, but the rays which reach their sense of sight may be more or less altered in their proportions by passing through the media of the eye. The existence of real, though partial colour-blindness will make itself apparent, in a series of observations, by the discrepancy between the observed values and the means being greater in certain colours than in others.

§ XVI. *General Conclusions.*

Neither of the observers whose results are given here shew any indications of colour-blindness, and when the differences arising from the absorption of the rays between E and F are put out of account, they agree in proving that there are three colours in the spectrum, red, green, and blue, by the mixtures of

* See the *Report of the British Association* for 1856, p. 12.

which colours chromatically identical with the other colours of the spectrum may be produced. The exact position of the red and blue is not yet ascertained; that of the green is $\frac{1}{4}$ from E towards F.

The orange and yellow of the spectrum are chromatically equivalent to mixtures of red and green. They are neither richer nor paler than the corresponding mixtures, and the only difference is that the mixture may be resolved by a prism, whereas the colour in the spectrum cannot be so resolved. This result seems to put an end to the pretension of yellow to be considered a primary element of colour.

In the same way the colours from the primary green to blue are chromatically identical with mixtures of these; and the extreme ends of the spectrum are probably equivalent to mixtures of red and blue, but they are so feeble in illumination that experiments on the same plan with the rest can give no result, but they must be examined by some special method. When observations have been obtained from a greater number of individuals, including those whose vision is dichromatic, the chart of the spectrum may be laid down independently of accidental differences, and a more complete discussion of the laws of the sensation of colour attempted.

POSTSCRIPT.

[Received May 8,—Read May 24, 1860.]

Since sending the above paper to the Royal Society, I have obtained some observations of the colour of the spectrum by persons whose vision is "dichromic," and who are therefore said to be "colour-blind."

The instrument used in making these observations was similar in principle to that formerly described, except that, in order to render it portable, the rays are reflected back through the prisms, nearly in their original direction; thus rendering one of the limbs of the instrument unnecessary, and allowing the other to be shortened considerably on account of the greater angular dispersion. The principle of reflecting light, so as to pass twice through the same prism, was employed by me in an instrument for combining colours made in 1856, and a reflecting instrument for observing the spectrum has been constructed independently by M. Porro.

Light from a sheet of paper illuminated by sunlight is admitted at the slits *X*, *Y*, *Z* (fig. 8, Plate VII. p. 444), falls on the prisms *P* and *P′* (angles = 45°), then on a concave silvered glass, *S*, radius 34 inches. The light, after reflexion, passes again through the prisms *P′* and *P*, and is reflected by a small mirror, *e*, to the slit *E*, where the eye is placed to receive the light compounded of the colours corresponding to the positions and breadths of the slits *X*, *Y*, and *Z*.

At the same time, another portion of the light from the illuminated paper enters the instrument at *BC*, is reflected at the mirror *M*, passes through the lens *L*, is reflected at the mirror *M′*, passes close to the edge of the prism *P*, and is reflected along with the coloured light at *e*, to the eye-slit at *E*.

In this way the compound colour is compared with a constant white light in optical juxtaposition with it. The mirror *M* is made of silvered glass, that at *M′* is made of glass roughened and blackened at the back, to reduce the intensity of the constant light to a convenient value for the experiments.

This instrument gives a spectrum in which the lines are very distinct, and the length of the spectrum from *A* to *H* is 3·6 inches. The outside measure of the box is 3 feet 6 inches, by 11 inches by 4 inches, and it can be carried about, and set up in any position, without readjustment. It was made by Messrs Smith and Ramage of Aberdeen.

In obtaining observations from colour-blind persons, two slits only are required to produce a mixture chromatically equivalent to white; and at one point of the spectrum the colour of the pure rays appears identical with white. This point is near the line *F*, a little on the less refrangible side. From this point to the more refrangible end of the spectrum appears to them "blue." The colours on the less refrangible side appear to them all of the same quality, but of different degrees of brightness; and when any of them are made sufficiently bright, they are called "yellow." It is convenient to use the term "yellow" in speaking of the colours from red to green inclusive, since it will be found that a dichromic person in speaking of red, green, orange, and brown, refers to different degrees of brightness or purity of a single colour, and not to different colours perceived by him. This colour we may agree to call "yellow," though it is not probable that the sensation of it is like that of yellow as perceived by us.

Of the three standard colours which I formerly assumed, the red appears to them "yellow," but so feeble that there is not enough in the whole red division of the spectrum to form an equivalent to make up the standard white.

The green at E appears a good "yellow," and the blue at $\frac{2}{3}$ from F towards G appears a good "blue." I have therefore taken these as standard colours for reducing dichromic observations. The three standard colours will be referred to as (104), (88), and (68), these being the positions of the red, green, and blue on the scale of the new instrument.

Mr James Simpson, formerly student of Natural Philosophy in my class, has furnished me with thirty-three observations taken in good sunlight. Ten of these were between the two standard colours, and give the following result:—

$$33 \cdot 7 \,(88) + 33 \cdot 1 \,(68) = W \dots \dots \dots \dots \dots (1).$$

The mean errors of these observations were as follows:—

Error of $(88) = 2 \cdot 5$; of $(68) = 2 \cdot 3$; of $(88) + (68) = 4 \cdot 8$; of $(88) - (68) = 1 \cdot 3$.

The fact that the mean error of the sum was so much greater than the mean error of the difference indicates that in this case, as in all others that I have examined, observations of equality of tint can be depended on much more than observations of equality of illumination or brightness.

From six observations of my own, made at the same time, I have deduced the "trichromic" equation

$$22 \cdot 6 \,(104) + 26 \,(88) + 37 \cdot 4 \,(68) = W \dots \dots \dots \dots (2).$$

If we suppose that the light which reached the organ of vision was the same in both cases, we may combine these equations by subtraction, and so find

$$22 \cdot 6 \,(104) - 7 \cdot 7 \,(88) + 4 \cdot 3 \,(68) = D \dots \dots \dots \dots (3),$$

where D is that colour, the absence of the sensation of which constitutes the defect of the dichromic eye. The sensation which I have in addition to those of the dichromic eye is therefore similar to the full red (104), but different from it, in that the red (104) has $7 \cdot 7$ of green (88) in it which must be removed, and $4 \cdot 3$ of blue (68) substituted. This agrees pretty well with the colour which Mr Pole* describes as neutral to him, though crimson to others. It must be remembered, however, that different persons of ordinary vision require different proportions of the standard colours, probably owing to differences in the absorptive powers of the media of the eye, and that the above equation (2), if observed by K., would have been

$$23 \,(104) + 32 \,(88) + 31 \,(68) = W \dots \dots \dots \dots (4).$$

* *Philosophical Transactions*, 1859, Part I. p. 329.

and the value of D, as deduced from these observers, would have been

$$23\,(104) - 1\cdot7\,(88) - 1\cdot1\,(68) = D \dotfill (5),$$

in which the defective sensation is much nearer to the red of the spectrum. It is probably a colour to which the extreme red of the spectrum tends, and which differs from the extreme red only in not containing that small proportion of "yellow" light which renders it visible to the colour-blind.

From other observations by Mr Simpson the following results have been deduced:—

TABLE a.

	(88.)	(68.)			(88.)	(68.)
$(99\cdot2+) =$	$33\cdot7$	$1\cdot9$				
$31\cdot3\,(96) =$	$33\cdot7$	$2\cdot1$		$100\,(96) =$	108	7
$28\quad(92) =$	$33\cdot7$	$1\cdot4$		$100\,(92) =$	120	5
$33\cdot7\,(88) =$	$33\cdot7$	0		$100\,(88) =$	100	0
$54\cdot7\,(84) =$	$33\cdot7$	$6\cdot1$		$100\,(84) =$	61	11
$71\quad(82) =$	$33\cdot7$	$15\cdot1$		$100\,(82) =$	47	21
$99\quad(80) =$	$33\cdot7$	$33\cdot1$		$100\,(80) =$	34	33
$70\quad(78) =$	$15\cdot7$	$33\cdot1$		$100\,(78) =$	22	47
$56\quad(76) =$	$5\cdot7$	$33\cdot1$		$100\,(76) =$	10	59
$36\quad(72) = -$	$0\cdot3$	$33\cdot1$		$100\,(72) = -$	1	92
$33\cdot1\,(68) =$	0	$33\cdot1$		$100\,(68) =$	0	100
$40\quad(64) =$	$0\cdot2$	$33\cdot1$		$100\,(64) =$	0	83
$55\cdot5\,(60) =$	$1\cdot7$	$33\cdot1$		$100\,(60) =$	3	60
$(57-) = -$	$0\cdot3$	$33\cdot1$				

In the Table on the left side $(99\cdot2+)$ means the whole of the spectrum beyond $(99\cdot2)$ on the scale, and $(57-)$ means the whole beyond (57) on the scale. The position of the fixed lines with reference to the scale was as follows:—

A, 116; a, 112; B, 110; C, 106; D, 98·3; E, 88; F, 79; G, 61; H, 44.

The values of the standard colours in different parts of the spectrum are given on the right side of the above Table, and are represented by the curves of fig. 9, Plate VII. p. 444, where the left-hand curve represents the intensity of the "yellow" element, and the right-hand curve that of the "blue" element of colour as it appears to the colour-blind.

The appearance of the spectrum to the colour-blind is as follows:—

From A to E the colour is pure "yellow" very faint up to D, and reaching a maximum between D and E. From E to one-third beyond F towards

G the colour is mixed, varying from "yellow" to "blue," and becoming neutral or "white" at a point near F. In this part of the spectrum, the total intensity, as given by the dotted line, is decidedly less than on either side of it, and near the line F, the retina close to the "yellow spot" is less sensible to light than the parts further from the axis of the eye. This peculiarity of the light near F is even more marked in the colour-blind than in the ordinary eye. Beyond F the "blue" element comes to a maximum between F and G, and then diminishes towards H; the spectrum from this maximum to the end being pure "blue."

In fig. 10, Plate VII. p. 444, these results are represented in a different manner. The point D, corresponding to the sensation wanting in the colour-blind, is taken as the origin of coordinates, the "yellow" element of colour is represented by distances measured horizontally to the right from D, and the "blue" element by distances measured vertically from the horizontal line through D. The numerals indicate the different colours of the spectrum according to the scale shewn in fig. 9, and the coordinates of each point indicate the composition of the corresponding colour. The triangle of colours is reduced, in the case of dichromic vision, to a straight line "B" "Y," and the proportions of "blue" and "yellow" in each colour are indicated by the ratios in which this line is cut by the line from D passing through the position of that colour.

The results given above were all obtained with the light of white paper, placed in clear sunshine. I have obtained similar results, when the sun was hidden, by using the light of uniformly illuminated clouds, but I do not consider these observations sufficiently free from disturbing circumstances to be employed in calculation. It is easy, however, by means of such observations, to verify the most remarkable phenomena of colour-blindness, as for instance, that the colours from red to green appear to differ only in brightness, and that the brightness may be made identical by changing the width of the slit; that the colour near F is a neutral tint, and that the eye in viewing it sees a dark spot in the direction of the axis of vision; that the colours beyond are all blue of different intensities, and that any "blue" may be combined with any "yellow" in such proportions as to form "white." These results I have verified by the observations of another colour-blind gentleman, who did not obtain sunlight for his observations; and as I have now the means of carrying the requisite apparatus easily, I hope to meet with other colour-blind observers, and to obtain their observations under more favourable circumstances.

On the Comparison of Colour-blind with ordinary Vision by means of Observations with Coloured Papers.

In March 1859 I obtained a set of observations by Mr Simpson, of the relations between six coloured papers as seen by him. The experiments were made with the colour-top in the manner described in my paper in the *Transactions of the Royal Society of Edinburgh*, Vol. XXI. pt. 2, p. 286; and the colour-equations were arranged so as to be equated to zero, as in those given in the *Philosophical Magazine*, July, 1857. The colours were—Vermilion (V), ultramarine (U), emerald-green (G), ivory-black (B), snow-white (W), and pale chrome-yellow (Y). These six colours afford fifteen colour-blind equations, since four colours enter into each equation. Fourteen of these were observed by Mr Simpson, and from these I deduced three equations, giving the relation of the three standards (V), (U), (G) to the other colours, according to his kind of vision. From these three equations I then deduced fifteen equations, admitting of comparison with the observed equations, and necessarily consistent in themselves.

The comparison of these equations furnishes a test of the truth of the theory that the colour-blind see by means of two colour-sensations, and that therefore every colour may be expressed in terms of *two* given colours, just as in ordinary vision it may be expressed in terms of three given colours. The one set of equations are each the result of a single observation; the other set are deduced from three equations in accordance with this theory, and the two sets agree to within an average error = 2·1.

TABLE *b.*

		V.	U.	G.	B.	W.	Y.	
1.	Observed ...	0	0	− 100	+ 45	+ 22	+ 33	= 0.
	Calculated ..	0	0	− 100	+ 37·5	+ 26·5	+ 36	= 0.
2.	Observed ...	0	+ 58	0	− 69	− 31	− 42	= 0.
	Calculated ..	0	+ 58·3	0	− 67·3	− 32·7	+ 41·7	= 0.
3.	Observed ...	0	+ 32	− 100	0	+ 12	+ 56	= 0.
	Calculated ..	0	+ 32·3	− 100	0	+ 8·3	+ 59·4	= 0.
4.	Observed ...	0	+ 38	− 89	− 11	0	+ 62	= 0.
	Calculated ..	0	+ 40	− 85	− 15	0	+ 60	= 0.
5.	Observed ...	0	+ 32	+ 68	− 60	− 40	0	= 0.
	Calculated ..	0	+ 34	+ 66	− 63·5	− 36·5	0	= 0.

TABLE b (*continued*).

		V.	U.	G.	B.	W.	Y.
6.	Observed . . . −	100	0	0	+82	+ 5	+ 13 = 0.
	Calculated . . −	100	0	0	+83·9	+ 4·5	+ 11·6 = 0.
7.	Observed . . . +	47	0	− 100	0	+ 22	+ 31 = 0.
	Calculated . . +	44·7	0	− 100	0	+ 24·5	+ 30·8 = 0.
8.	Observed . . . −	100	0	+ 20	+77	0	+ 3 = 0.
	Calculated . . −	100	0	+ 17	+77·5	0	+ 5·5 = 0.
9.	Not Observed.						
	Calculated . . +	96	0	− 31	−69	+ 4	0 = 0.
10.	Observed . . . −	70	+53	0	0	− 30	+ 47 = 0.
	Calculated . . −	73·5	+53	0	0	− 26·5	+ 47 = 0.
11.	Observed . . . −	100	+ 8	0	+71	0	+ 21 = 0.
	Calculated . . −	100	+ 8	0	+74·5	0	+ 17·5 = 0.
12.	Observed . . . +	85	+15	0	−88	− 12	0 = 0.
	Calculated . . +	86	+14	0	−88·5	− 11·5	0 = 0.
13.	Observed . . . −	20	+39	− 80	0	0	+ 61 = 0.
	Calculated . . −	19	+40	− 81	0	0	+ 60 = 0.
14.	Observed . . . −	66	+30	+ 70	0	− 34	0 = 0.
	Calculated . . −	70	+27	+ 73	0	− 30	0 = 0.
15.	Observed . . . +	100	− 2	− 27	−71	0	0 = 0.
	Calculated . . +	96	+ 4	− 24	−76	0	0 = 0.

But, according to our theory, colour-blind vision is not only dichromic, but the two elements of colour are identical with two of the three elements o colour as seen by the ordinary eye; so that it differs from ordinary visio only in not perceiving a particular colour, the relation of which to known colour may be numerically defined. This colour may be expressed under the form

$$a\mathrm{V} + b\mathrm{U} + c\mathrm{G} = \mathrm{D} \quad \dots\dots\dots\dots\dots\dots\dots\dots\dots (16),$$

where V, U, and G are the standard colours used in the experiments, and D i the colour which is visible to the ordinary eye, but invisible to the colour blind. If we know the value of D, we may always change an ordinary colour equation into a colour-blind equation by subtracting from it nD (n being chose so that one of the standard colours is eliminated), and adding n of black.

In September 1856 I deduced, from thirty-six observations of my own, th chromatic relations of the same set of six coloured papers. These observations with a comparison of them with the trichromic theory of vision, are to b found in the *Philosophical Magazine* for July 1857. The relations of th six colours may be deduced from two equations, of which the most convenient form is

V.	U.	G.	B.	W.	Y.
$+39\cdot7$	$+26\cdot6$	$+33\cdot7$	$-22\cdot7$	$-77\cdot3$	$0\quad=0$ ....(17).
$-62\cdot4$	$+18\cdot6$	$-37\cdot6$	0	$+45\cdot7$	$+35\cdot7=0$ ....(18).

The value of D, as deduced from a comparison of these equations with the colour-blind equations, is

$$1\cdot198\,V + 0\cdot078\,U - 0\cdot276\,G = D \quad\text{...................... (19).}$$

By making D the same thing as black (B), and eliminating W and Y respectively from the two ordinary colour-equations by means of D, we obtain three colour-blind equations, calculated from the ordinary equations and consistent with them, supposing that the colour (D) is black to the colour-blind.

The following Table is a comparison of the colour-blind equations deduced from Mr Simpson's observations alone, with those deduced from my observations and the value of D.

TABLE c.

	V.	U.	G.	B.	W.	Y.
(15) Calculated . .	$+96$	$+4$	-24	-76	0	0
By (19)	$+93\cdot9$	$+6\cdot1$	$-21\cdot7$	$-78\cdot3$	0	0
(14) Calculated . .	-70	$+27$	$+73$	0	-30	0
By (17) and (19) . .	-70	$+27\cdot2$	$-72\cdot8$	0	-30	0
(13) Calculated . .	-19	$+40$	-81	0	0	$+60$
By (18) and (19) . .	$-13\cdot6$	$+38\cdot5$	$-86\cdot4$	0	0	$+61\cdot5$

The average error here is 1·9, smaller than the average error of the individual colour-blind observations, shewing that the theory of colour-blindness being the want of a certain colour-sensation which is one of the three ordinary colour-sensations, agrees with observation to within the limits of error.

In fig. 11, Plate VII. p. 444, I have laid down the chromatic relations of these colours according to Newton's method. V (vermilion), U (ultramarine), and G (emerald-green) are assumed as standard colours, and placed at the angles of an equilateral triangle. The position of W (white) and Y (pale chrome-yellow) with respect to these are laid down from equations (17) and (18), deduced from my own observations. The positions of the defective colour, of white, and of yellow, as deduced from Mr Simpson's equations alone, are given at "d," "w," and "y." The positions of these points, as deduced from a combination of these equations with my own, are given at "D," "W," and "Y." The difference of these positions from those of "*d*," "*w*," and "*y*," shews the amount of discrepancy between observation and theory.

It will be observed that D is situated near V (vermilion), but that a line from D to W cuts UV at C near to V. D is therefore a red colour, not scarlet, but further from yellow. It may be called crimson, and may be *imitated* by a mixture of 86 vermilion and 14 ultramarine. This compound colour will be of the same *hue* as D; but since C lies between D and W, C must be regarded as D diluted with a certain amount of white; and therefore D must be imagined to be like C in hue, but without the intermixture of white which is unavoidable in actual pigments, and which reduces the purity of the tint.

Lines drawn from D through "W" and "Y," the colour-blind positions of white and yellow, pass through W and Y, their positions in ordinary vision. The reason why they do not coincide with W and Y, is that the white and yellow papers are much brighter than the colours corresponding to the points W and Y of the triangle V, U, G; and therefore lines from D, which represent them in intensity as well as in quality, must be longer than DW and DY in the proportion of their brightness.

Fig. 1.

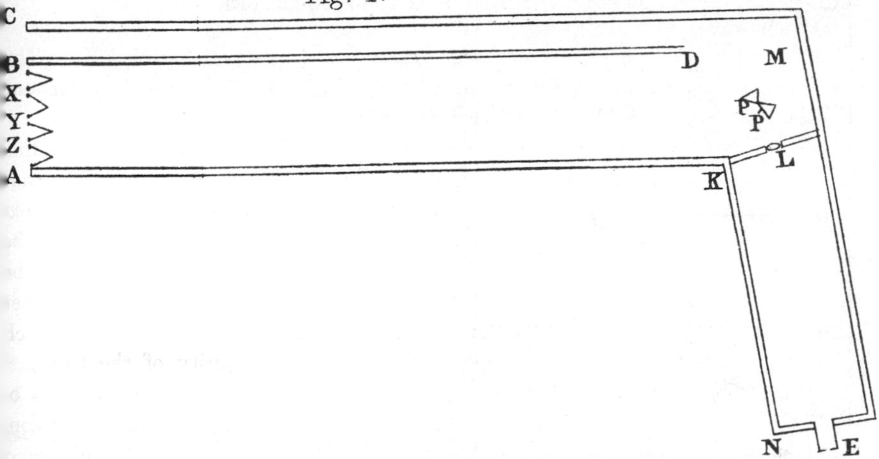
C
B
X
Y
Z
A
D
M
P
P
L
K
N
E

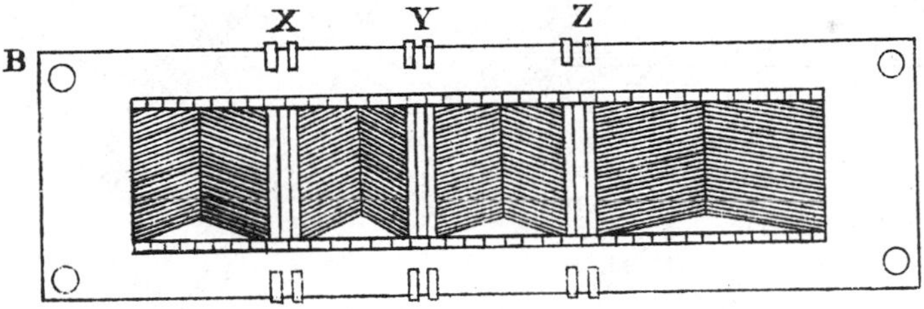
X
Y
Z
B

Fig. 2.

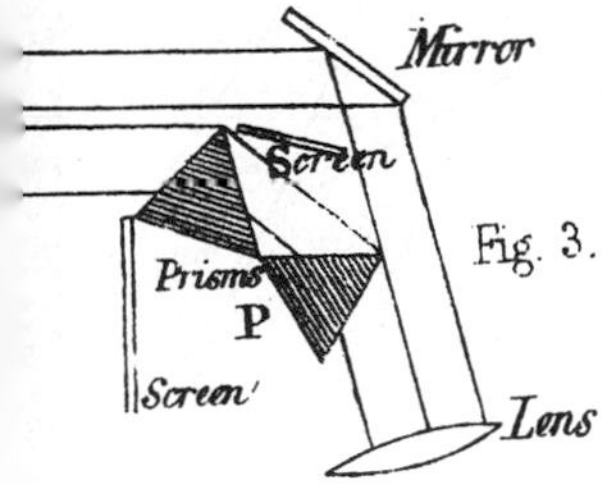
Mirror
Screen
Prisms
P
Screen
Lens

Fig. 3.

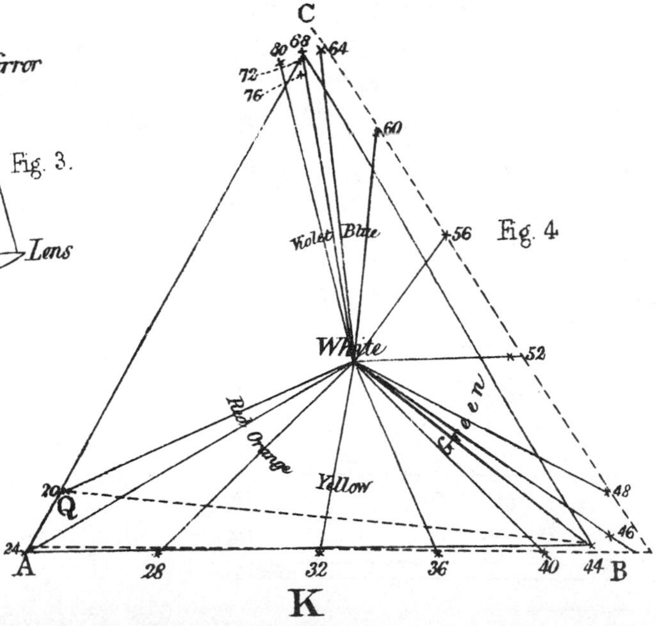
C
80
68
64
72
76
60
56
Violet Blue
White
52
Red
Orange
Green
Yellow
20
Q
48
46
24
A
28
32
36
40
44
B
K

Fig. 4

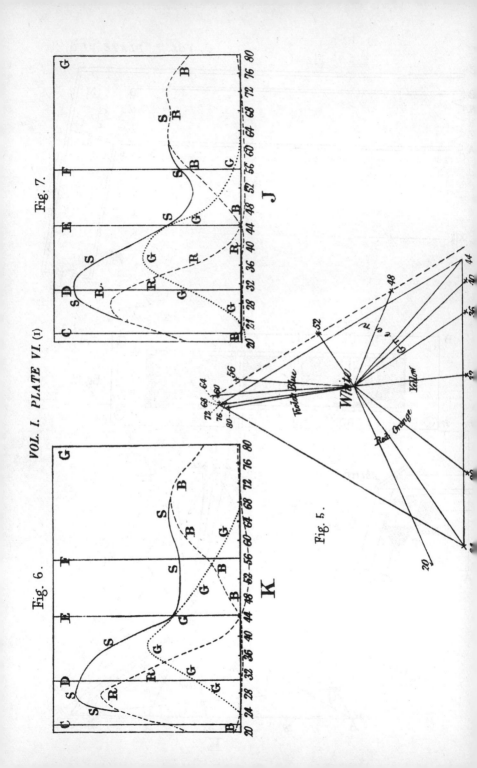

Fig. 7.

Fig. 6.

Fig. 5.

Fig. 8.

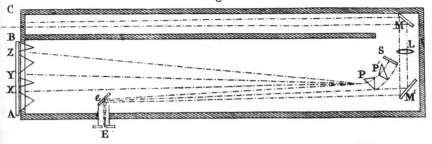

Fig. 9.

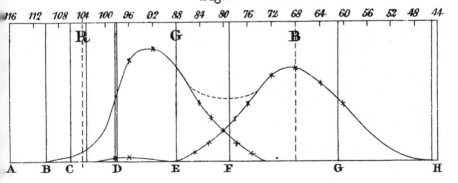

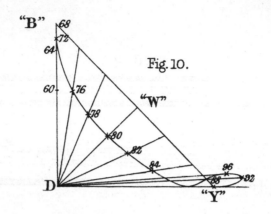

Fig. 10.

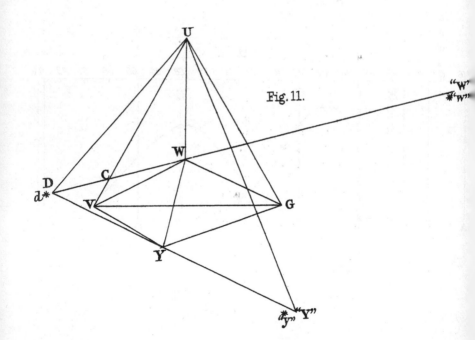

Fig. 11.

XXII. *On the Theory of Three Primary Colours.*

THE speaker commenced by shewing that our power of vision depends entirely on our being able to distinguish the intensity and quality of colours. The forms of visible objects are indicated to us only by differences in colour or brightness between them and surrounding objects. To classify and arrange these colours, to ascertain the physical conditions on which the differences of coloured rays depend, and to trace, as far as we are able, the physiological process by which these different rays excite in us various sensations of colour, we must avail ourselves of the united experience of painters, opticians, and physiologists. The speaker then proceeded to state the results obtained by these three classes of inquirers, to explain their apparent inconsistency by means of Young's Theory of Primary Colours, and to describe the tests to which he had subjected that theory.

Painters have studied the relations of colours, in order to imitate them by means of pigments. As there are only a limited number of coloured substances adapted for painting, while the number of tints in nature is infinite, painters are obliged to produce the tints they require by mixing their pigments in proper proportions. This leads them to regard these tints as actually compounded of other colours, corresponding to the pure pigments in the mixture. It is found, that by using three pigments only, we can produce all colours lying within certain limits of intensity and purity. For instance, if we take carmine (red), chrome yellow, and ultramarine (blue), we get by mixing the carmine and the chrome, all varieties of orange, passing through scarlet to crimson on the one side, and to yellow on the other; by mixing chrome and ultramarine we get all hues of green; and by mixing ultramarine with carmine, we get all hues of purple, from violet to mauve and crimson. Now these are all the strong colours that we ever see or can imagine : all others are like these, only less pure in tint. Our three colours can be mixed so as to form a neutral grey; and if this grey be mixed with any of the hues produced by mixing two colours only, all the tints of that hue will be exhibited, from the pure colour to neutral grey. If we could assume that the colour of a mixture of different kinds of paint is a true mixture of the colours of the pigments, and in the same proportion, then an analysis of colour might be made with the same ease as a chemical analysis of a mixture of substances.

The colour of a mixture of pigments, however, is often very different from a true mixture of the colours of the pure pigments. It is found to depend on the size of the particles, a finely ground pigment producing more effect than one coarsely ground. It has also been shewn by Professor Helmholtz, that when light falls on a mixture of pigments, part of it is acted on by one pigment only, and part of it by another; while a third portion is acted on by both pigments in succession before it is sent back to the eye. The two parts reflected directly from the pure pigments enter the eye together, and form a true mixture of colours; but the third portion, which has suffered absorption from both pigments, is often so considerable as to give its own character to the resulting tint. This is the explanation of the green tint produced by mixing most blue and yellow pigments.

In studying the mixture of colours, we must avoid these sources of error, either by mixing the rays of light themselves, or by combining the impressions of colours within the eye by the rotation of coloured papers on a disc.

The speaker then stated what the opticians had discovered about colour. White light, according to Newton, consists of a great number of different kinds of coloured light which can be separated by a prism. Newton divided these into seven classes, but we now recognize many thousand distinct kinds of light in the spectrum, none of which can be shewn to be a compound of more elementary rays. If we accept the theory that light is an undulation, then, as there are undulations of every different period from the one end of the spectrum to the other, there are an *infinite* number of possible kinds of light, no one of which can be regarded as compounded of any others.

Physical optics does not lead us to any theory of three primary colours, but leaves us in possession of an infinite number of pure rays with an infinitely more infinite number of compound beams of light, each containing any proportions of any number of the pure rays.

These beams of light, passing through the transparent parts of the eye, fall on a sensitive membrane, and we become aware of various colours. We know that the colour we see depends on the nature of the light; but the opticians say there are an infinite number of kinds of light; while the painters, and all who pay attention to what they see, tell us that they can account for all actual colours by supposing them mixtures of three primary colours.

The speaker then next drew attention to the physiological difficulties in accounting for the perception of colour. Some have supposed that the different kinds of light are distinguished by the time of their vibration. There are about 447 billions of vibrations of red light in a second; and 577 billions of vibrations of green light in the same time. It is certainly not by any mental process of which we are conscious that we distinguish between these infinitesimal portions of time, and it is difficult to conceive any mechanism by which the vibrations could be counted so that we should become conscious of the results, especially when many rays of different periods of vibration act on the same part of the eye at once.

Besides, all the evidence we have on the nature of nervous action goes to prove that whatever be the nature of the agent which excites a nerve, the sensation will differ only in being more or less acute. By acting on a nerve in various ways, we may produce the faintest sensation or the most violent pain; but if the intensity of the sensation is the same, its quality must be the same.

Now, we may perceive by our eyes a faint red light which may be made stronger and stronger till our eyes are dazzled. We may then perform the same experiment with a green light or a blue light. We shall thus see that our sensation of colour may differ in other ways, besides in being stronger or fainter. The sensation of colour, therefore, cannot be due to one nerve only.

The speaker then proceeded to state the theory of Dr Thomas Young, as the only theory which completely reconciles these difficulties in accounting for the perception of colour.

Young supposes that the eye is provided with three distinct sets of nervous fibres, each set extending over the whole sensitive surface of the eye. Each of these three systems of nerves, when excited, gives us a different sensation. One of them, which gives us the sensation we call red, is excited most by the red rays, but also by the orange and yellow, and slightly by the violet; another is acted on by the green rays, but also by the orange and yellow and part of the blue; while the third is acted on by the blue and violet rays.

If we could excite one of these sets of nerves without acting on the others, we should have the pure sensation corresponding to that set of nerves. This would be truly a primary colour, whether the nerve were excited by pure or by compound light, or even by the action of pressure or disease.

If such experiments could be made, we should be able to see the primary colours separately, and to describe their appearance by reference to the scale of colours in the spectrum.

But we have no direct consciousness of the contrivances of our own bodies, and we never feel any sensation which is not infinitely complex, so that we can never know directly how many sensations are combined when we see a colour. Still less can we isolate one or more sensations by artificial means, so that in general when a ray enters the eye, though it should be one of the pure rays of the spectrum, it may excite more than one of the three sets of nerves, and thus produce a compound sensation.

The terms simple and compound, therefore, as applied to colour-sensation, have by no means the same meaning as they have when applied to a ray of light.

The speaker then stated some of the consequences of Young's theory, and described the tests to which he had subjected it :—

1st. There are three primary colours.

2nd. Every colour is either a primary colour, or a mixture of primary colours.

3rd. Four colours may always be arranged in one of two ways. Either one of them is a mixture of the other three, or a mixture of two of them can be found, identical with a mixture of the other two.

4th. These results may be stated in the form of colour-equations, giving the numerical value of the amount of each colour entering into any mixture. By means of the Colour Top*, such equations can be obtained for coloured papers, and they may be obtained with a degree of accuracy shewing that the colour-judgment of the eye may be rendered very perfect.

The speaker had tested in this way more than 100 different pigments and mixtures, and had found the results agree with the theory of three primaries

---

* Described in the *Trans. of the Royal Society of Edinburgh*, Vol. XXI., and in the *Phil. Mag.*

in every case.   He had also examined all the colours of the spectrum with the same result.

The experiments with pigments do not indicate what colours are to be considered as primary; but experiments on the prismatic spectrum shew that all the colours of the spectrum, and therefore all the colours in nature, are equivalent to mixtures of three colours of the spectrum itself, namely, red, green (near the line E), and blue (near the line G).   Yellow was found to be a mixture of red and green.

The speaker, assuming red, green, and blue as primary colours, then exhibited them on a screen by means of three magic lanterns, before which were placed glass troughs containing respectively sulphocyanide of iron, chloride of copper, and ammoniated copper.

A triangle was thus illuminated, so that the pure colours appeared at its angles, while the rest of the triangle contained the various mixtures of the colours as in Young's triangle of colour.

The graduated intensity of the primary colours in different parts of the spectrum was exhibited by three coloured images, which, when superposed on the screen, gave an artificial representation of the spectrum.

Three photographs of a coloured ribbon taken through the three coloured solutions respectively, were introduced into the camera, giving images representing the red, the green, and the blue parts separately, as they would be seen by each of Young's three sets of nerves separately.   When these were superposed, a coloured image was seen, which, if the red and green images had been as fully photographed as the blue, would have been a truly-coloured image of the ribbon.   By finding photographic materials more sensitive to the less refrangible rays, the representation of the colours of objects might be greatly improved.

The speaker then proceeded to exhibit mixtures of the colours of the pure spectrum.   Light from the electric lamp was passed through a narrow slit, a lens and a prism, so as to throw a pure spectrum on a screen containing three moveable slits, through which three distinct portions of the spectrum were suffered to pass.   These portions were concentrated by a lens on a screen at a distance, forming a large, uniformly coloured image of the prism.

When the whole spectrum was allowed to pass, this image was white, as in Newton's experiment of combining the rays of the spectrum.   When portions of the spectrum were allowed to pass through the moveable slits, the image was uniformly illuminated with a mixture of the corresponding colours. In order to see these colours separately, another lens was placed between the moveable slits and the screen. A magnified image of the slits was thus thrown on the screen, each slit shewing, by its colour and its breadth, the quality and quantity of the colour which it suffered to pass. Several colours were thus exhibited, first separately, and then in combination. Red and blue, for instance, produced purple; red and green produced yellow; blue and yellow produced a pale pink; red, blue, and green produced white; and red and a bluish green near the line F produced a colour which appears very different to different eyes.

The speaker concluded by stating the peculiarities of colour-blind vision, and by shewing that the investigation into the theory of colour is truly a physiological inquiry, and that it requires the observations and testimony of persons of every kind in order to discover and explain the various peculiarities of vision.

[From the *Philosophical Magazine*, Vol. XXI.]

XXIII. *On Physical Lines of Force.*

PART I.

THE THEORY OF MOLECULAR VORTICES APPLIED TO MAGNETIC PHENOMENA.

IN all phenomena involving attractions or repulsions, or any forces depending on the relative position of bodies, we have to determine the *magnitude* and *direction* of the force which would act on a given body, if placed in a given position.

In the case of a body acted on by the gravitation of a sphere, this force is inversely as the square of the distance, and in a straight line to the centre of the sphere. In the case of two attracting spheres, or of a body not spherical, the magnitude and direction of the force vary according to more complicated laws. In electric and magnetic phenomena, the magnitude and direction of the resultant force at any point is the main subject of investigation. Suppose that the direction of the force at any point is known, then, if we draw a line so that in every part of its course it coincides in direction with the force at that point, this line may be called a *line of force*, since it indicates the direction of the force in every part of its course.

By drawing a sufficient number of lines of force, we may indicate the direction of the force in every part of the space in which it acts.

Thus if we strew iron filings on paper near a magnet, each filing will be magnetized by induction, and the consecutive filings will unite by their opposite poles, so as to form fibres, and these fibres will *indicate* the direction of the lines of force. The beautiful illustration of the presence of magnetic force afforded by this experiment, naturally tends to make us think of the lines of force as something real, and as indicating something more than the mere resultant of two forces, whose seat of action is at a distance, and which do not exist there at all until a magnet is placed in that part of the field. We are dissatisfied with the explanation founded on the hypothesis of attractive and repellent forces directed towards the magnetic poles, even though we may have satisfied ourselves that the phenomenon is in strict accordance with that hypothesis, and we cannot help thinking that in every place where we find these lines of force, some physical state or action must exist in sufficient energy to produce the actual phenomena.

My object in this paper is to clear the way for speculation in this direction, by investigating the mechanical results of certain states of tension and motion in a medium, and comparing these with the observed phenomena of magnetism and electricity. By pointing out the mechanical consequences of such hypotheses, I hope to be of some use to those who consider the phenomena as due to the action of a medium, but are in doubt as to the relation of this hypothesis to the experimental laws already established, which have generally been expressed in the language of other hypotheses.

I have in a former paper* endeavoured to lay before the mind of the geometer a clear conception of the relation of the lines of force to the space in which they are traced. By making use of the conception of currents in a fluid, I shewed how to draw lines of force, which should indicate by their number the amount of force, so that each line may be called a unit-line of force (see Faraday's *Researches*, 3122); and I have investigated the path of the lines where they pass from one medium to another.

In the same paper I have found the geometrical significance of the "Electrotonic State," and have shewn how to deduce the mathematical relations between the electrotonic state, magnetism, electric currents, and the electromotive force, using mechanical illustrations to assist the imagination, but not to account for the phenomena.

I propose now to examine magnetic phenomena from a mechanical point of view, and to determine what tensions in, or motions of, a medium are capable of producing the mechanical phenomena observed. If, by the same hypothesis, we can connect the phenomena of magnetic attraction with electromagnetic phenomena and with those of induced currents, we shall have found a theory which, if not true, can only be proved to be erroneous by experiments which will greatly enlarge our knowledge of this part of physics.

---

* See a paper "On Faraday's Lines of Force," *Cambridge Philosophical Transactions*, Vol. x. Part i. Page 155 of this volume.

The mechanical conditions of a medium under magnetic influence have been variously conceived of, as currents, undulations, or states of displacement or strain, or of pressure or stress.

Currents, issuing from the north pole and entering the south pole of a magnet, or circulating round an electric current, have the advantage of representing correctly the geometrical arrangement of the lines of force, if we could account on mechanical principles for the phenomena of attraction, or for the currents themselves, or explain their continued existence

Undulations issuing from a centre would, according to the calculations of Professor Challis, produce an effect similar to attraction in the direction of the centre; but admitting this to be true, we know that two series of undulations traversing the same space do not combine into one resultant as two attractions do, but produce an effect depending on relations of *phase* as well as intensity, and if allowed to proceed, they diverge from each other without any mutual action. In fact the mathematical laws of attractions are not analogous in any respect to those of undulations, while they have remarkable analogies with those of currents, of the conduction of heat and electricity, and of elastic bodies.

In the *Cambridge and Dublin Mathematical Journal* for January 1847, Professor William Thomson has given a "Mechanical Representation of Electric, Magnetic, and Galvanic Forces," by means of the displacements of the particles of an elastic solid in a state of strain. In this representation we must make the angular displacement at every point of the solid proportional to the magnetic force at the corresponding point of the magnetic field, the direction of the axis of rotation of the displacement corresponding to the direction of the magnetic force. The absolute displacement of any particle will then correspond in magnitude and direction to that which I have identified with the electrotonic state; and the relative displacement of any particle, considered with reference to the particle in its immediate neighbourhood, will correspond in magnitude and direction to the quantity of electric current passing through the corresponding point of the magneto-electric field. The author of this method of representation does not attempt to explain the origin of the observed forces by the effects due to these strains in the elastic solid, but makes use of the mathematical analogies of the two problems to assist the imagination in the study of both.

We come now to consider the magnetic influence as existing in the form of some kind of pressure or tension, or, more generally, of *stress* in the medium.

Stress is action and reaction between the consecutive parts of a body, and consists in general of pressures or tensions different in different directions at the same point of the medium.

The necessary relations among these forces have been investigated by mathematicians; and it has been shewn that the most general type of a stress consists of a combination of three principal pressures or tensions, in directions at right angles to each other.

When two of the principal pressures are equal, the third becomes an axis of symmetry, either of greatest or least pressure, the pressures at right angles to this axis being all equal.

When the three principal pressures are equal, the pressure is equal in every direction, and there results a stress having no determinate axis of direction, of which we have an example in simple hydrostatic pressure.

The general type of a stress is not suitable as a representation of a magnetic force, because a line of magnetic force has direction and intensity, but has no third quality indicating any difference between the *sides* of the line, which would be analogous to that observed in the case of polarized light*.

We must therefore represent the magnetic force at a point by a stress having a single axis of greatest or least pressure, and all the pressures at right angles to this axis equal. It may be objected that it is inconsistent to represent a line of force, which is essentially dipolar, by an axis of stress, which is necessarily isotropic; but we know that *every* phenomenon of action and reaction is isotropic in its *results*, because the effects of the force on the bodies between which it acts are equal and opposite, while the nature and origin of the force may be dipolar, as in the attraction between a north and a south pole.

Let us next consider the mechanical effect of a state of stress symmetrical about an axis. We may resolve it, in all cases, into a simple hydrostatic pressure, combined with a simple pressure or tension along the axis. When the axis is that of greatest pressure, the force along the axis will be a pressure. When the axis is that of least pressure, the force along the axis will be a tension.

If we observe the lines of force between two magnets, as indicated by iron filings, we shall see that whenever the lines of force pass from one pole to another, there is *attraction* between those poles; and where the lines of force from the poles avoid each other and are dispersed into space, the poles *repel*

---

* See Faraday's *Researches*, 3252.

each other, so that in both cases they are drawn in the direction of the resultant of the lines of force.

It appears therefore that the stress in the axis of a line of magnetic force is a *tension*, like that of a rope.

If we calculate the lines of force in the neighbourhood of two gravitating bodies, we shall find them the same in direction as those near two magnetic poles of the same name; but we know that the mechanical effect is that of attraction instead of repulsion. The lines of force in this case do not run between the bodies, but avoid each other, and are dispersed over space. In order to produce the effect of attraction, the stress along the lines of gravitating force must be a *pressure*.

Let us now suppose that the phenomena of magnetism depend on the existence of a tension in the direction of the lines of force, combined with a hydrostatic pressure; or in other words, a pressure greater in the equatorial than in the axial direction: the next question is, what mechanical explanation can we give of this inequality of pressures in a fluid or mobile medium? The explanation which most readily occurs to the mind is that the excess of pressure in the equatorial direction arises from the centrifugal force of vortices or eddies in the medium having their axes in directions parallel to the lines of force.

This explanation of the cause of the inequality of pressures at once suggests the means of representing the dipolar character of the line of force. Every vortex is essentially dipolar, the two extremities of its axis being distinguished by the direction of its revolution as observed from those points.

We also know that when electricity circulates in a conductor, it produces lines of magnetic force passing through the circuit, the direction of the lines depending on the direction of the circulation. Let us suppose that the direction of revolution of our vortices is that in which vitreous electricity must revolve in order to produce lines of force whose direction within the circuit is the same as that of the given lines of force.

We shall suppose at present that all the vortices in any one part of the field are revolving in the same direction about axes nearly parallel, but that in passing from one part of the field to another, the direction of the axes, the velocity of rotation, and the density of the substance of the vortices are subject to change. We shall investigate the resultant mechanical effect upon an element of the medium, and from the mathematical expression of this resultant we shall deduce the physical character of its different component parts.

Prop. I.—If in two fluid systems geometrically similar the velocities and densities at corresponding points are proportional, then the differences of pressure at corresponding points due to the motion will vary in the duplicate ratio of the velocities and the simple ratio of the densities.

Let l be the ratio of the linear dimensions, m that of the velocities, n that of the densities, and p that of the pressures due to the motion. Then the ratio of the *masses* of corresponding portions will be l^3n, and the ratio of the velocities acquired in traversing similar parts of the systems will be m; so that l^3mn is the ratio of the momenta acquired by similar portions in traversing similar parts of their paths.

The ratio of the surfaces is l^2, that of the forces acting on them is l^2p, and that of the times during which they act is $\dfrac{l}{m}$; so that the ratio of the impulse of the forces is $\dfrac{l^3p}{m}$, and we have now

$$l^3mn = \frac{l^3p}{m},$$

or
$$m^2n = p ;$$

that is, the ratio of the pressures due to the motion (p) is compounded of the ratio of the densities (n) and the duplicate ratio of the velocities (m^2), and does not depend on the linear dimensions of the moving systems.

In a circular vortex, revolving with uniform angular velocity, if the pressure at the axis is p_0, that at the circumference will be $p_1 = p_0 + \frac{1}{2}\rho v^2$, where ρ is the density and v the velocity at the circumference. The *mean pressure* parallel to the axis will be

$$p_0 + \tfrac{1}{4}\rho v^2 = p_2.$$

If a number of such vortices were placed together side by side with their axes parallel, they would form a medium in which there would be a pressure p_2 parallel to the axes, and a pressure p_1 in any perpendicular direction. If the vortices are circular, and have uniform angular velocity and density throughout, then

$$p_1 - p_2 = \tfrac{1}{4}\rho v^2.$$

If the vortices are not circular, and if the angular velocity and the density are not uniform, but vary according to the same law for all the vortices,

$$p_1 - p_2 = C\rho v^2,$$

where ρ is the mean density, and C is a numerical quantity depending on the distribution of angular velocity and density in the vortex. In future we shall write $\frac{\mu}{4\pi}$ instead of $C\rho$, so that

$$p_1 - p_2 = \frac{1}{4\pi}\mu v^2 \ldots\ldots\ldots\ldots\ldots\ldots\ldots (1),$$

where μ is a quantity bearing a constant ratio to the density, and v is the linear velocity at the circumference of each vortex.

A medium of this kind, filled with molecular vortices having their axes parallel, differs from an ordinary fluid in having different pressures in different directions. If not prevented by properly arranged pressures, it would tend to expand laterally. In so doing, it would allow the diameter of each vortex to expand and its velocity to diminish in the same proportion. In order that a medium having these inequalities of pressure in different directions should be in equilibrium, certain conditions must be fulfilled, which we must investigate.

PROP. II.—If the direction-cosines of the axes of the vortices with respect to the axes of x, y, and z be l, m, and n, to find the normal and tangential stresses on the co-ordinate planes.

The actual stress may be resolved into a simple hydrostatic pressure p_1 acting in all directions, and a simple tension $p_1 - p_2$, or $\frac{1}{4\pi}\mu v^2$, acting along the axis of stress.

Hence if p_{xx}, p_{yy}, and p_{zz} be the normal stresses parallel to the three axes, considered positive when they tend to increase those axes; and if p_{yz}, p_{zx}, and p_{xy} be the tangential stresses in the three co-ordinate planes, considered positive when they tend to increase simultaneously the symbols subscribed, then by the resolution of stresses*,

$$p_{xx} = \frac{1}{4\pi}\mu v^2 l^2 - p_1,$$

$$p_{yy} = \frac{1}{4\pi}\mu v^2 m^2 - p_1,$$

$$p_{zz} = \frac{1}{4\pi}\mu v^2 n^2 - p_1,$$

* Rankine's *Applied Mechanics*, Art. 106.

$$p_{yz} = \frac{1}{4\pi} \mu v^2 mn,$$

$$p_{zx} = \frac{1}{4\pi} \mu v^2 nl,$$

$$p_{xy} = \frac{1}{4\pi} \mu v^2 lm.$$

If we write $\qquad\qquad a = vl, \quad \beta = vm, \text{ and } \gamma = vn,$

then

$$\left. \begin{array}{ll} p_{xx} = \dfrac{1}{4\pi} \mu a^2 - p_1, & p_{yz} = \dfrac{1}{4\pi} \mu \beta\gamma \\[2ex] p_{yy} = \dfrac{1}{4\pi} \mu \beta^2 - p_1, & p_{zx} = \dfrac{1}{4\pi} \mu \gamma a \\[2ex] p_{zz} = \dfrac{1}{4\pi} \mu \gamma^2 - p_1, & p_{xy} = \dfrac{1}{4\pi} \mu a\beta \end{array} \right\} \dots\dots\dots\dots\dots (2).$$

PROP. III.—To find the resultant force on an element of the medium, arising from the variation of internal stress.

We have in general, for the force in the direction of x per unit of volume by the law of equilibrium of stresses [*],

$$X = \frac{d}{dx} p_{xx} + \frac{d}{dy} p_{xy} + \frac{d}{dz} p_{xz} \dots\dots\dots\dots\dots\dots(3).$$

In this case the expression may be written

$$X = \frac{1}{4\pi} \left\{ \frac{d(\mu a)}{dx} a + \mu a \frac{da}{dx} - 4\pi \frac{dp_1}{dx} + \frac{d(\mu\beta)}{dy} a + \mu\beta \frac{da}{dy} + \frac{d(\mu\gamma)}{dz} a + \mu\gamma \frac{da}{dz} \right\} \dots (4).$$

Remembering that $a \dfrac{da}{dx} + \beta \dfrac{d\beta}{dx} + \gamma \dfrac{d\gamma}{dx} = \dfrac{1}{2} \dfrac{d}{dx} (a^2 + \beta^2 + \gamma^2)$, this becomes

$$X = a \frac{1}{4\pi} \left\{ \frac{d}{dx} (\mu a) + \frac{d}{dy} (\mu\beta) + \frac{d}{dz} (\mu\gamma) \right\} + \frac{1}{8\pi} \mu \frac{d}{dx} (a^2 + \beta^2 + \gamma^2)$$

$$- \mu\beta \frac{1}{4\pi} \left(\frac{d\beta}{dx} - \frac{da}{dy} \right) + \mu\gamma \frac{1}{4\pi} \left(\frac{da}{dz} - \frac{d\gamma}{dx} \right) - \frac{dp_1}{dx} \dots\dots (5).$$

The expressions for the forces parallel to the axes of y and z may be written down from analogy.

* Rankine's *Applied Mechanics*, Art. 116.

We have now to interpret the meaning of each term of this expression.

We suppose a, β, γ to be the components of the force which would act upon that end of a unit magnetic bar which points to the north.

μ represents the magnetic inductive capacity of the medium at any point referred to air as a standard. μa, $\mu \beta$, $\mu \gamma$ represent the quantity of magnetic induction through unit of area perpendicular to the three axes of x, y z respectively.

The total amount of magnetic induction through a closed surface surrounding the pole of a magnet, depends entirely on the strength of that pole; so that if $dx\,dy\,dz$ be an element, then

$$\left(\frac{d}{dx}\mu a + \frac{d}{dy}\mu\beta + \frac{d}{dz}\mu\gamma\right) dx\,dy\,dz = 4\pi m\,dx\,dy\,dz \dots\dots\dots(6),$$

which represents the total amount of magnetic induction outwards through the surface of the element $dx\,dy\,dz$, represents the amount of "imaginary magnetic matter" within the element, of the kind which points north.

The *first term* of the value of X, therefore,

$$a\,\frac{1}{4\pi}\left(\frac{d}{dx}\mu a + \frac{d}{dy}\mu\beta + \frac{d}{dz}\mu\gamma\right) \dots\dots\dots\dots\dots(7),$$

may be written

$$am \dots\dots\dots\dots\dots\dots\dots\dots\dots(8),$$

where a is the intensity of the magnetic force, and m is the amount of magnetic matter pointing north in unit of volume.

The physical interpretation of this term is, that the force urging a north pole in the positive direction of x is the product of the intensity of the magnetic force resolved in that direction, and the strength of the north pole of the magnet.

Let the parallel lines from left to right in fig. 1 represent a field of magnetic force such as that of the earth, sn being the direction from south to north. The vortices, according to our hypothesis, will be in the direction shewn by the arrows in fig. 3, that is, in a plane perpendicular to the lines of force, and revolving in the direction of the hands of a watch when observed from s looking towards n. The parts of the vortices above the plane of the paper will be moving towards e, and the parts below that plane towards w.

We shall always mark by an arrow-head the direction in which we must look in order to see the vortices rotating in the direction of the hands of a watch. The arrow-head will then indicate the *northward* direction in the magnetic field, that is, the direction in which that end of a magnet which points to the north would set itself in the field.

Fig. 1.

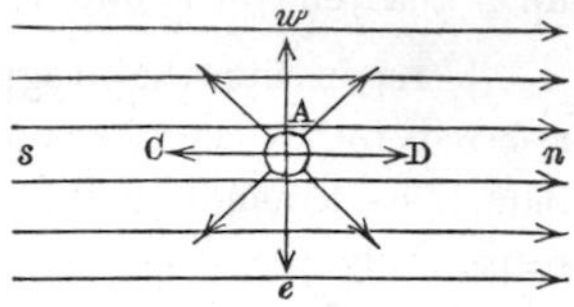

Now let A be the end of a magnet which points north. Since it repels the north ends of other magnets, the lines of force will be directed *from* A outwards in all directions. On the north side the line AD will be in the *same* direction with the lines of the magnetic field, and the velocity of the vortices will be *increased*. On the south side the line AC will be in the opposite direction, and the velocity of the vortices will be diminished, so that the lines of force are more powerful on the north side of A than on the south side.

Fig. 2.

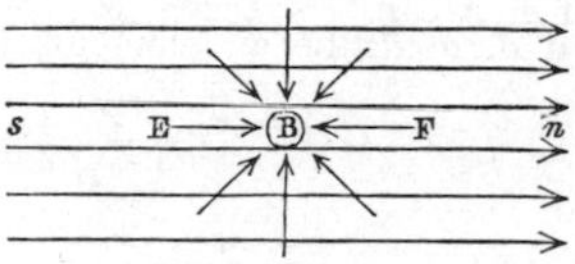

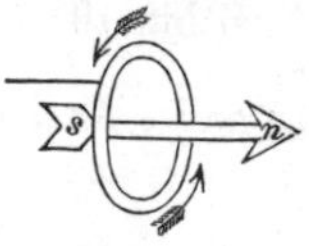

We have seen that the mechanical effect of the vortices is to produce a tension along their axes, so that the resultant effect on A will be to pull it more powerfully towards D than towards C; that is, A will tend to move to the north.

Fig. 3.

Let B in fig. 2 represent a south pole. The lines of force belonging to B will tend *towards* B, and we shall find that the lines of force are rendered stronger towards E than towards F, so that the effect in this case is to urge B towards the south.

It appears therefore that, on the hypothesis of molecular vortices, our first term gives a mechanical explanation of the force acting on a north or south pole in the magnetic field.

We now proceed to examine the second term,

$$\frac{1}{8\pi} \mu \frac{d}{dx} (\alpha^2 + \beta^2 + \gamma^2).$$

Here $\alpha^2 + \beta^2 + \gamma^2$ is the square of the intensity at any part of the field, and μ is the magnetic inductive capacity at the same place. Any body therefore placed in the field will be urged *towards places of stronger magnetic intensity* with a force depending partly on its own capacity for magnetic induction, and partly on the rate at which the square of the intensity increases.

If the body be placed in a fluid medium, then the medium, as well as the body, will be urged towards places of greater intensity, so that its hydrostatic pressure will be increased in that direction. The resultant effect on a body placed in the medium will be the *difference* of the actions on the body and on the portion of the medium which it displaces, so that the body will tend to or from places of greatest magnetic intensity, according as it has a greater or less capacity for magnetic induction than the surrounding medium.

In fig. 4 the lines of force are represented as converging and becoming more powerful towards the right, so that the magnetic tension at B is stronger than at A, and the body AB will be urged to the right. If the capacity for magnetic induction is greater in the body than in the surrounding medium, it will move to the right, but if less it will move to the left.

Fig. 4.   Fig. 5.

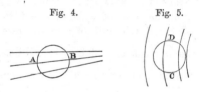

We may suppose in this case that the lines of force are converging to a magnetic pole, either north or south, on the right hand.

In fig. 5 the lines of force are represented as vertical, and becoming more numerous towards the right. It may be shewn that if the force increases towards the right, the lines of force will be curved towards the right. The effect of the magnetic tensions will then be to draw any body towards the right with a force depending on the excess of its inductive capacity over that of the surrounding medium.

We may suppose that in this figure the lines of force are those surrounding an electric current perpendicular to the plane of the paper and on the right hand of the figure.

These two illustrations will shew the mechanical effect on a paramagnetic or diamagnetic body placed in a field of varying magnetic force, whether the increase of force takes place along the lines or transverse to them. The form of the second term of our equation indicates the general law, which is quite independent of the direction of the lines of force, and depends solely on the manner in which the force *varies* from one part of the field to another.

We come now to the third term of the value of X,

$$-\mu\beta \, \frac{1}{4\pi} \left(\frac{d\beta}{dx} - \frac{d\alpha}{dy} \right).$$

Here $\mu\beta$ is, as before, the quantity of magnetic induction through unit of area perpendicular to the axis of y, and $\frac{d\beta}{dx} - \frac{d\alpha}{dy}$ is a quantity which would disappear if $\alpha dx + \beta dy + \gamma dz$ were a complete differential, that is, if the force acting on a unit north pole were subject to the condition that no work can be done upon the pole in passing round any closed curve. The quantity represents the work done on a north pole in travelling round unit of area in the direction from $+x$ to $+y$ parallel to the plane of xy. Now if an electric current whose strength is r is traversing the axis of z, which, we may suppose, points vertically upwards, then, if the axis of x is east and that of y north, a unit north pole will be urged round the axis of z in the direction from x to y, so that in one revolution the work done will be $= 4\pi r$. Hence $\frac{1}{4\pi} \left(\frac{d\beta}{dx} - \frac{d\alpha}{dy} \right)$ represents the *strength of an electric current parallel to* z through unit of area; and if we write

$$\frac{1}{4\pi}\left(\frac{d\gamma}{dy}-\frac{d\beta}{dz}\right)=p, \ \frac{1}{4\pi}\left(\frac{d\alpha}{dz}-\frac{d\gamma}{dx}\right)=q, \ \frac{1}{4\pi}\left(\frac{d\beta}{dx}-\frac{d\alpha}{dy}\right)=r \ \ldots\ldots\ldots (9),$$

then p, q, r will be the quantity of electric current per unit of area perpendicular to the axes of x, y, and z respectively.

The physical interpretation of the third term of X, $-\mu\beta r$, is that if $\mu\beta$ is the quantity of magnetic induction parallel to y, and r the quantity of electricity flowing in the direction of z, the element will be urged in the direction of $-x$, transversely to the direction of the current and of the lines of force; that is, an *ascending* current in a field of force magnetized towards the *north* would tend to move *west*.

To illustrate the action of the molecular vortices, let sn be the direction of magnetic force in the field, and let C be the section of an ascending magnetic current perpendicular to the paper. The lines of force due to this current will be circles drawn in the opposite direction from that of the hands of a watch; that is, in the direction *nwse*. At *e* the lines of force will be the sum of those of the field and of the current, and at *w* they will be the difference of the two sets of lines; so that the vortices on the east side of the current will be more powerful than those on the west side. Both sets of vortices have their equatorial parts turned towards *C*, so that they tend to expand towards *C*, but those on the east side have the greatest effect, so that the resultant effect on the current is to urge it towards the *west*.

Fig. 6.

The fourth term,

$$+\mu\gamma\,\frac{1}{4\pi}\left(\frac{da}{dz} - \frac{d\gamma}{dx}\right),\ \text{or}\ +\mu\gamma q \quad\text{.....................(10)},$$

may be interpreted in the same way, and indicates that a current *q* in the direction of *y*, that is, to the north, placed in a magnetic field in which the lines are vertically upwards in the direction of *z*, will be urged towards the *east*.

The fifth term,

$$-\frac{dp_1}{dx} \quad\text{.................................(11)},$$

merely implies that the element will be urged in the direction in which the hydrostatic pressure p_1 diminishes.

We may now write down the expressions for the components of the resultant force on an element of the medium per unit of volume, thus:

$$X = am + \frac{1}{8\pi}\,\mu\,\frac{d}{dx}\,(v^2) - \mu\beta r + \mu\gamma q - \frac{dp_1}{dx} \quad\text{...................(12)},$$

$$Y = \beta m + \frac{1}{8\pi}\,\mu\,\frac{d}{dy}\,(v^2) - \mu\gamma p + \mu ar - \frac{dp_1}{dy} \quad\text{...................(13)},$$

$$Z = \gamma m + \frac{1}{8\pi}\,\mu\,\frac{d}{dz}(v^2) - \mu aq + \mu\beta p - \frac{dp_1}{dz} \quad\text{...................(14)}.$$

The first term of each expression refers to the force acting on magnetic poles.

The second term to the action on bodies capable of magnetism by induction.

The third and fourth terms to the force acting on electric currents.

And the fifth to the effect of simple pressure.

Before going further in the general investigation, we shall consider equations (12, 13, 14), in particular cases, corresponding to those simplified cases of the actual phenomena which we seek to obtain in order to determine their laws by experiment.

We have found that the quantities p, q, and r represent the resolved parts of an electric current in the three co-ordinate directions. Let us suppose in the first instance that there is *no* electric current, or that p, q, and r vanish. We have then by (9),

$$\frac{d\gamma}{dy} - \frac{d\beta}{dz} = 0, \quad \frac{d\alpha}{dz} - \frac{d\gamma}{dx} = 0, \quad \frac{d\beta}{dx} - \frac{d\alpha}{dy} = 0 \dots\dots\dots\dots(15),$$

whence we learn that $\qquad \alpha dx + \beta dy + \gamma dz = d\phi \dots\dots\dots\dots\dots\dots(16),$

is an exact differential of ϕ, so that

$$\alpha = \frac{d\phi}{dx}, \quad \beta = \frac{d\phi}{dy}, \quad \gamma = \frac{d\phi}{dz} \dots\dots\dots\dots\dots\dots(17):$$

μ is proportional to the density of the vortices, and represents the " capacity for magnetic induction" in the medium. It is equal to 1 in air, or in whatever medium the experiments were made which determined the powers of the magnets, the strengths of the electric currents, &c.

Let us suppose μ constant, then

$$m = \frac{1}{4\pi} \left\{ \frac{d}{dx} (\mu\alpha) + \frac{d}{dy} (\mu\beta) + \frac{d}{dz} (\mu\gamma) \right\} = \frac{1}{4\pi} \mu \left(\frac{d^2\phi}{dx^2} + \frac{d^2\phi}{dy^2} + \frac{d^2\phi}{dz^2} \right) \dots\dots (18)$$

represents the amount of imaginary magnetic matter in unit of volume. That there may be no resultant force on that unit of volume arising from the action represented by the first term of equations (12, 13, 14), we must have $m = 0$, or

$$\frac{d^2\phi}{dx^2} + \frac{d^2\phi}{dy^2} + \frac{d^2\phi}{dz^2} = 0 \dots\dots\dots\dots\dots\dots (19).$$

Now it may be shewn that equation (19), if true within a given space, implies that the forces acting within that space are such as would result from a distribution of centres of force beyond that space, attracting or repelling inversely as the square of the distance.

Hence the lines of force in a part of space where μ is uniform, and where there are no electric currents, must be such as would result from the theory of "imaginary matter" acting at a distance. The assumptions of that theory are unlike those of ours, but the results are identical.

Let us first take the case of a single magnetic pole, that is, one end of a long magnet, so long that its other end is too far off to have a perceptible influence on the part of the field we are considering. The conditions then are, that equation (18) must be fulfilled at the magnetic pole, and (19) everywhere else. The only solution under these conditions is

$$\phi = -\frac{m}{\mu}\frac{1}{r} \dots\dots\dots\dots\dots\dots\dots\dots (20),$$

where r is the distance from the pole, and m the strength of the pole.

The repulsion at any point on a unit pole of the same kind is

$$\frac{d\phi}{dr} = \frac{m}{\mu}\frac{1}{r^2} \dots\dots\dots\dots\dots\dots\dots\dots (21).$$

In the standard medium $\mu = 1$; so that the repulsion is simply $\frac{m}{r^2}$ in that medium, as has been shewn by Coulomb.

In a medium having a greater value of μ (such as oxygen, solutions of salts of iron, &c.) the attraction, on our theory, ought to be *less* than in air, and in diamagnetic media (such as water, melted bismuth, &c.) the attraction between the same magnetic poles ought to be *greater* than in air.

The experiments necessary to demonstrate the difference of attraction of two magnets according to the magnetic or diamagnetic character of the medium in which they are placed, would require great precision, on account of the limited range of magnetic capacity in the fluid media known to us, and the small amount of the difference sought for as compared with the whole attraction.

Let us next take the case of an electric current whose quantity is C, flowing through a cylindrical conductor whose radius is R, and whose length is infinite as compared with the size of the field of force considered.

Let the axis of the cylinder be that of z, and the direction of the current positive, then within the conductor the quantity of current per unit of area is

$$r = \frac{C}{\pi R^2} = \frac{1}{4\pi}\left(\frac{d\beta}{dx} - \frac{d\alpha}{dy}\right)\dots\dots\dots\dots\dots\dots(22);$$

so that within the conductor

$$a = -2\frac{C}{R^2}y, \quad \beta = 2\frac{C}{R^2}x, \quad \gamma = 0\dots\dots\dots\dots\dots(23).$$

Beyond the conductor, in the space round it,

$$\phi = 2C \tan^{-1} \frac{y}{x} \quad \dots\dots\dots\dots\dots\dots\dots\dots\dots (24),$$

$$a = \frac{d\phi}{dx} = -2C \frac{y}{x^2 + y^2}, \quad \beta = \frac{d\phi}{dy} = 2C \frac{x}{x^2 + y^2}, \quad \gamma = \frac{d\phi}{dz} = 0 \dots\dots\dots (25).$$

If $\rho = \sqrt{x^2 + y^2}$ is the perpendicular distance of any point from the axis of the conductor, a unit north pole will experience a force $= \dfrac{2C}{\rho}$, tending to move it round the conductor in the direction of the hands of a watch, if the observer view it in the direction of the current.

Let us now consider a current running parallel to the axis of z in the plane of xz at a distance ρ. Let the quantity of the current be c', and let the length of the part considered be l, and its section s, so that $\dfrac{c'}{s}$ is its strength per unit of section. Putting this quantity for ρ in equations (12, 13, 14), we find

$$X = -\mu\beta \frac{c'}{s}$$

per unit of volume; and multiplying by ls, the volume of the conductor considered, we find

$$X = -\mu\beta c'l$$
$$= -2\mu \frac{Cc'l}{\rho} \quad \dots\dots\dots\dots\dots\dots\dots\dots (26),$$

shewing that the second conductor will be attracted towards the first with a force inversely as the distance.

We find in this case also that the amount of attraction depends on the value of μ, but that it varies directly instead of inversely as μ; so that the attraction between two conducting wires will be greater in oxygen than in air, and greater in air than in water.

We shall next consider the nature of electric currents and electromotive forces in connexion with the theory of molecular vortices.

PART II.

THE THEORY OF MOLECULAR VORTICES APPLIED TO ELECTRIC CURRENTS.

We have already shewn that all the forces acting between magnets, sub-stances capable of magnetic induction, and electric currents, may be mechanically accounted for on the supposition that the surrounding medium is put into such a state that at every point the pressures are different in different directions, the direction of least pressure being that of the observed lines of force, and the difference of greatest and least pressures being proportional to the square of the intensity of the force at that point.

Such a state of stress, if assumed to exist in the medium, and to be arranged according to the known laws regulating lines of force, will act upon the magnets, currents, &c. in the field with precisely the same resultant forces as those calculated on the ordinary hypothesis of direct action at a distance. This is true independently of any particular theory as to the *cause* of this state of stress, or the mode in which it can be sustained in the medium. We have therefore a satisfactory answer to the question, "Is there any mechanical hypothesis as to the condition of the medium indicated by lines of force, by which the observed resultant forces may be accounted for?" The answer is, the lines of force indicate the direction of *minimum pressure* at every point of the medium.

The second question must be, "What is the mechanical cause of this difference of pressure in different directions?" We have supposed, in the first part of this paper, that this difference of pressures is caused by molecular vortices, having their axes parallel to the lines of force.

We also assumed, perfectly arbitrarily, that the direction of these vortices is such that, on looking along a line of force from south to north, we should see the vortices revolving in the direction of the hands of a watch.

We found that the velocity of the circumference of each vortex must be proportional to the intensity of the magnetic force, and that the density of the substance of the vortex must be proportional to the capacity of the medium for magnetic induction.

We have as yet given no answers to the questions, "How are these vortices set in rotation?" and "Why are they arranged according to the known laws of lines of force about magnets and currents?" These questions are certainly of a higher order of difficulty than either of the former; and I wish to separate the suggestions I may offer by way of provisional answer to them, from the mechanical deductions which resolved the first question, and the hypothesis of vortices which gave a probable answer to the second.

We have, in fact, now come to inquire into the physical connexion of these vortices with electric currents, while we are still in doubt as to the nature of electricity, whether it is one substance, two substances, or not a substance at all, or in what way it differs from matter, and how it is connected with it.

We know that the lines of force are affected by electric currents, and we know the distribution of those lines about a current; so that from the force we can determine the amount of the current. Assuming that our explanation of the lines of force by molecular vortices is correct, why does a particular distribution of vortices indicate an electric current? A satisfactory answer to this question would lead us a long way towards that of a very important one, "What is an electric current?"

I have found great difficulty in conceiving of the existence of vortices in a medium, side by side, revolving in the same direction about parallel axes. The contiguous portions of consecutive vortices must be moving in opposite directions; and it is difficult to understand how the motion of one part of the medium can coexist with, and even produce, an opposite motion of a part in contact with it.

The only conception which has at all aided me in conceiving of this kind of motion is that of the vortices being separated by a layer of particles, revolving each on its own axis in the opposite direction to that of the vortices, so that the contiguous surfaces of the particles and of the vortices have the same motion.

In mechanism, when two wheels are intended to revolve in the same direction, a wheel is placed between them so as to be in gear with both, and this wheel is called an "idle wheel." The hypothesis about the vortices which I have to suggest is that a layer of particles, acting as idle wheels, is interposed between each vortex and the next, so that each vortex has a tendency to make the neighbouring vortices revolve in the same direction with itself.

In mechanism, the idle wheel is generally made to rotate about a *fixed* axle; but in epicyclic trains and other contrivances, as, for instance, in Siemens's governor for steam-engines *, we find idle wheels whose centres are capable of motion. In all these cases the motion of the centre is the half sum of the motions of the circumferences of the wheels between which it is placed. Let us examine the relations which must subsist between the motions of our vortices and those of the layer of particles interposed as idle wheels between them.

PROP. IV.—To determine the motion of a layer of particles separating two vortices.

Let the circumferential velocity of a vortex, multiplied by the three direction-cosines of its axis respectively, be a, β, γ, as in Prop. II. Let l, m, n be the direction-cosines of the normal to any part of the surface of this vortex, the outside of the surface being regarded positive. Then the components of the velocity of the particles of the vortex at this part of its surface will be

$$n\beta - m\gamma \text{ parallel to } x,$$
$$l\gamma - na \text{ parallel to } y,$$
$$ma - l\beta \text{ parallel to } z.$$

If this portion of the surface be in contact with another vortex whose velocities are a', β', γ', then a layer of very small particles placed between them will have a velocity which will be the mean of the superficial velocities of the vortices which they separate, so that if u is the velocity of the particles in the direction of x,

$$u = \tfrac{1}{2}m\left(\gamma' - \gamma\right) - \tfrac{1}{2}n\left(\beta' - \beta\right) \quad\ldots\ldots\ldots\ldots\ldots\ldots\ldots(27),$$

since the normal to the second vortex is in the opposite direction to that of the first.

PROP. V.—To determine the whole amount of particles transferred across unit of area in the direction of x in unit of time.

Let x_1, y_1, z_1 be the co-ordinates of the centre of the first vortex, x_2, y_2, z_2 those of the second, and so on. Let V_1, V_2, &c. be the volumes of the first, second, &c. vortices, and $\overline{V}$ the sum of their volumes. Let dS be an element of the surface separating the first and second vortices, and x, y, z its co-ordinates. Let ρ be the quantity of particles on every unit of surface. Then if p be the whole quantity of particles transferred across unit of area in unit of time in

* See Goodeve's *Elements of Mechanism*, p. 118.

the direction of x, the whole momentum parallel to x of the particles within the space whose volume is $\overline{V}$ will be $\overline{V}p$, and we shall have

$$\overline{V}p = \Sigma u \rho dS \quad \dots\dots\dots\dots\dots\dots\dots\dots\dots(28),$$

the summation being extended to every surface separating any two vortices within the volume $\overline{V}$.

Let us consider the surface separating the first and second vortices. Let an element of this surface be dS, and let its direction-cosines be l_1, m_1, n_1 with respect to the first vortex, and l_2, m_2, n_2 with respect to the second; then we know that

$$l_1 + l_2 = 0, \quad m_1 + m_2 = 0, \quad n_1 + n_2 = 0 \dots\dots\dots\dots\dots(29).$$

The values of α, β, γ vary with the position of the centre of the vortex; so that we may write

$$\alpha_2 = \alpha_1 + \frac{d\alpha}{dx}(x_2 - x_1) + \frac{d\alpha}{dy}(y_2 - y_1) + \frac{d\alpha}{dz}(z_2 - z_1) \dots\dots\dots(30),$$

with similar equations for β and γ.

The value of u may be written :—

$$u = \tfrac{1}{2}\frac{d\gamma}{dx}\{m_1(x - x_1) + m_2(x - x_2)\}$$

$$+ \tfrac{1}{2}\frac{d\gamma}{dy}\{m_1(y - y_1) + m_2(y - y_2)\} + \tfrac{1}{2}\frac{d\gamma}{dz}\{m_1(z - z_1) + m_2(z - z_2)\}$$

$$- \tfrac{1}{2}\frac{d\beta}{dx}\{n_1(x - x_1) + n_2(x - x_2)\} - \tfrac{1}{2}\frac{d\beta}{dy}\{n_1(y - y_1) + n_2(y - y_2)\}$$

$$- \tfrac{1}{2}\frac{d\beta}{dz}\{n_1(z - z_1) + n_1(z - z_2)\}\dots\dots\dots\dots\dots\dots\dots\dots\dots(31).$$

In effecting the summation of $\Sigma u \rho dS$, we must remember that round any closed surface $\Sigma l dS$ and all similar terms vanish; also that terms of the form $\Sigma l y dS$, where l and y are measured in different directions, also vanish; but that terms of the form $\Sigma l x dS$, where l and x refer to the same axis of co-ordinates, do not vanish, but are equal to the volume enclosed by the surface. The result is

$$\overline{V}p = \tfrac{1}{2}\rho\left(\frac{d\gamma}{dy} - \frac{d\beta}{dz}\right)(V_1 + V_2 + \&\text{c.})\dots\dots\dots\dots\dots(32);$$

or dividing by $\overline{V} = V_1 + V_2 + \&c.$,

$$p = \tfrac{1}{2}\rho \left(\frac{d\gamma}{dy} - \frac{d\beta}{dz} \right) \quad\dotsfill (33).$$

If we make

$$\rho = \frac{1}{2\pi} \quad\dotsfill (34),$$

then equation (33) will be identical with the first of equations (9), which give the relation between the quantity of an electric current and the intensity of the lines of force surrounding it.

It appears therefore that, according to our hypothesis, an electric current is represented by the transference of the moveable particles interposed between the neighbouring vortices. We may conceive that these particles are very small compared with the size of a vortex, and that the mass of all the particles together is inappreciable compared with that of the vortices, and that a great many vortices, with their surrounding particles, are contained in a single complete molecule of the medium. The particles must be conceived to roll without sliding between the vortices which they separate, and not to touch each other, so that, as long as they remain within the same complete molecule, there is no loss of energy by resistance. When, however, there is a general transference of particles in one direction, they must pass from one molecule to another, and in doing so, may experience resistance, so as to waste electrical energy and generate heat.

Now let us suppose the vortices arranged in a medium in any arbitrary manner. The quantities $\dfrac{d\gamma}{dy} - \dfrac{d\beta}{dz}$, &c. will then in general have values, so that there will at first be electrical currents in the medium. These will be opposed by the electrical resistance of the medium; so that, unless they are kept up by a continuous supply of force, they will quickly disappear, and we shall then have $\dfrac{d\gamma}{dy} - \dfrac{d\beta}{dz} = 0$, &c.; that is, $\alpha dx + \beta dy + \gamma dz$ will be a complete differential (see equations (15) and (16)); so that our hypothesis accounts for the distribution of the lines of force.

In Plate VIII. p. 488, fig. 1, let the vertical circle EE represent an electric current flowing from copper C to zinc Z through the conductor EE', as shewn by the arrows.

Let the horizontal circle MM' represent a line of magnetic force embracing the electric circuit, the north and south directions being indicated by the lines SN and NS.

Let the vertical circles V and V' represent the molecular vortices of which the line of magnetic force is the axis. V revolves as the hands of a watch, and V' the opposite way.

It will appear from this diagram, that if V and V' were contiguous vortices, particles placed between them would move downwards; and that if the particles were forced downwards by any cause, they would make the vortices revolve as in the figure. We have thus obtained a point of view from which we may regard the relation of an electric current to its lines of force as analogous to the relation of a toothed wheel or rack to wheels which it drives.

In the first part of the paper we investigated the relations of the statical forces of the system. We have now considered the connexion of the motions of the parts considered as a system of mechanism. It remains that we should investigate the dynamics of the system, and determine the forces necessary to produce given changes in the motions of the different parts.

Prop. VI.—To determine the actual energy of a portion of a medium due to the motion of the vortices within it.

Let a, β, γ be the components of the circumferential velocity, as in Prop. II., then the actual energy of the vortices in unit of volume will be proportional to the density and to the square of the velocity. As we do not know the distribution of density and velocity in each vortex, we cannot determine the numerical value of the energy directly; but since μ also bears a constant though unknown ratio to the mean density, let us assume that the energy in unit of volume is

$$E = C\mu\,(a^2 + \beta^2 + \gamma^2),$$

where C is a constant to be determined.

Let us take the case in which

$$a = \frac{d\phi}{dx}, \quad \beta = \frac{d\phi}{dy}, \quad \gamma = \frac{d\phi}{dz} \quad \dots\dots\dots\dots\dots (35).$$

Let
$$\phi = \phi_1 + \phi_2 \quad \dots\dots\dots\dots\dots\dots\dots (36),$$

and let
$$\frac{\mu}{4\pi}\left(\frac{d^2\phi_1}{dx^2} + \frac{d^2\phi_1}{dy^2} + \frac{d^2\phi_1}{dz^2}\right) = m_1, \text{ and } \frac{\mu}{4\pi}\left(\frac{d^2\phi_2}{dx^2} + \frac{d^2\phi_2}{dy^2} + \frac{d^2\phi_2}{dz^2}\right) = m_2 \dots\dots(37);$$

then ϕ_1 is the potential at any point due to the magnetic system m_1, and ϕ_2 that due to the distribution of magnetism represented by m_2. The actual energy of all the vortices is

$$E = \Sigma C\mu \left(a^2 + \beta^2 + \gamma^2\right) dV \ldots\ldots\ldots\ldots\ldots\ldots\ldots (38),$$

the integration being performed over all space.

This may be shewn by integration by parts (see Green's 'Essay on Electricity,' p. 10) to be equal to

$$E = -4\pi C\Sigma \left(\phi_1 m_1 + \phi_2 m_2 + \phi_1 m_2 + \phi_2 m_1\right) dV \ldots\ldots\ldots\ldots (39).$$

Or since it has been proved (Green's 'Essay,' p. 10) that

$$\Sigma \phi_1 m_2 dV = \Sigma \phi_2 m_1 dV,$$

$$E = -4\pi C \left(\phi_1 m_1 + \phi_2 m_2 + 2\phi_1 m_2\right) dV \ldots\ldots\ldots\ldots (40).$$

Now let the magnetic system m_1 remain at rest, and let m_2 be moved parallel to itself in the direction of x through a space δx; then, since ϕ_1 depends on m_1 only, it will remain as before, so that $\phi_1 m_1$ will be constant; and since ϕ_2 depends on m_2 only, the distribution of ϕ_2 about m_2 will remain the same, so that $\phi_2 m_2$ will be the same as before the change. The only part of E that will be altered is that depending on $2\phi_1 m_2$, because ϕ_1 becomes $\phi_1 + \dfrac{d\phi_1}{dx}\delta x$ on account of the displacement. The variation of actual energy due to the displacement is therefore

$$\delta E = -4\pi C\Sigma \left(2\frac{d\phi_1}{dx} m_2\right) dV \delta x \ldots\ldots\ldots\ldots (41).$$

But by equation (12) the work done by the mechanical forces on m_2 during the motion is

$$\delta W = \Sigma \left(\frac{d\phi_1}{dx} m_2 dV\right) \delta x \ldots\ldots\ldots\ldots (42);$$

and since our hypothesis is a purely mechanical one, we must have by the conservation of force,

$$\delta E + \delta W = 0 \ldots\ldots\ldots\ldots\ldots\ldots (43);$$

that is, the loss of energy of the vortices must be made up by work done in moving magnets, so that

$$-4\pi C\Sigma \left(2\frac{d\phi_1}{dx} m_2 dV\right) \delta x + \Sigma \left(\frac{d\phi_1}{dx} m_2 dV\right) \delta x = 0,$$

or

$$C = \frac{1}{8\pi} \ldots\ldots\ldots\ldots\ldots\ldots (44);$$

so that the energy of the vortices in unit of volume is

$$\frac{1}{8\pi}\mu\left(\alpha^2+\beta^2+\gamma^2\right)\dots\dots\dots\dots\dots(45);$$

and that of a vortex whose volume is V is

$$\frac{1}{8\pi}\mu\left(\alpha^2+\beta^2+\gamma^2\right)V\dots\dots\dots\dots(46).$$

In order to produce or destroy this energy, work must be expended on, or received from, the vortex, either by the tangential action of the layer of particles in contact with it, or by change of form in the vortex. We shall first investigate the tangential action between the vortices and the layer of particles in contact with them.

PROP. VII.—To find the energy spent upon a vortex in unit of time by the layer of particles which surrounds it.

Let P, Q, R be the forces acting on unity of the particles in the three co-ordinate directions, these quantities being functions of x, y, and z. Since each particle touches two vortices at the extremities of a diameter, the reaction of the particle on the vortices will be equally divided, and will be

$$-\tfrac{1}{2}P,\quad-\tfrac{1}{2}Q,\quad-\tfrac{1}{2}R$$

on each vortex for unity of the particles; but since the superficial density of the particles is $\dfrac{1}{2\pi}$ (see equation (34)), the forces on unit of surface of a vortex will be

$$-\frac{1}{4\pi}P,\quad-\frac{1}{4\pi}Q,\quad-\frac{1}{4\pi}R.$$

Now let dS be an element of the surface of a vortex. Let the direction-cosines of the normal be l, m, n. Let the co-ordinates of the element be x, y, z. Let the component velocities of the surface be u, v, w. Then the work expended on that element of surface will be

$$\frac{dE}{dt}=-\frac{1}{4\pi}\left(Pu+Qv+Rw\right)dS\dots\dots\dots\dots(47).$$

Let us begin with the first term, $PudS$. P may be written

$$P_0+\frac{dP}{dx}x+\frac{dP}{dy}y+\frac{dP}{dz}z\dots\dots\dots\dots\dots(48),$$

and

$$u=n\beta-m\gamma.$$

Remembering that the surface of the vortex is a closed one, so that

$$\Sigma nx dS = \Sigma mx dS = \Sigma my dS = \Sigma mz dS = 0,$$

and

$$\Sigma my dS = \Sigma nz dS = V,$$

we find

$$\Sigma P u dS = \left(\frac{dP}{dz}\beta - \frac{dP}{dy}\gamma\right) V \dots\dots\dots\dots\dots (49),$$

and the whole work done on the vortex in unit of time will be

$$\frac{dE}{dt} = -\frac{1}{4\pi} \Sigma (Pu + Qv + Rw) \, dS$$
$$= \frac{1}{4\pi} \left\{ a\left(\frac{dQ}{dz} - \frac{dR}{dy}\right) + \beta\left(\frac{dR}{dx} - \frac{dP}{dz}\right) + \gamma\left(\frac{dP}{dy} - \frac{dQ}{dx}\right) \right\} V \dots\dots (50).$$

PROP. VIII.—To find the relations between the alterations of motion of the vortices, and the forces P, Q, R which they exert on the layer of particles between them.

Let V be the volume of a vortex, then by (46) its energy is

$$E = \frac{1}{8\pi} \mu \left(a^2 + \beta^2 + \gamma^2\right) V \dots\dots\dots\dots\dots (51),$$

and

$$\frac{dE}{dt} = \frac{1}{4\pi} \mu V \left(a\frac{da}{dt} + \beta\frac{d\beta}{dt} + \gamma\frac{d\gamma}{dt}\right) \dots\dots\dots\dots (52).$$

Comparing this value with that given in equation (50), we find

$$a\left(\frac{dQ}{dz} - \frac{dR}{dy} - \mu\frac{da}{dt}\right) + \beta\left(\frac{dR}{dx} - \frac{dP}{dz} - \mu\frac{d\beta}{dt}\right) + \gamma\left(\frac{dP}{dy} - \frac{dQ}{dx} - \mu\frac{d\gamma}{dt}\right) = 0 \dots\dots (53).$$

This equation being true for all values of a, β, and γ, first let β and γ vanish, and divide by a. We find

Similarly,

and

$$\left.\begin{aligned} \frac{dQ}{dz} - \frac{dR}{dy} &= \mu\frac{da}{dt} \\ \frac{dR}{dx} - \frac{dP}{dz} &= \mu\frac{d\beta}{dt} \\ \frac{dP}{dy} - \frac{dQ}{dx} &= \mu\frac{d\gamma}{dt} \end{aligned}\right\} \dots\dots\dots\dots\dots\dots (54).$$

From these equations we may determine the relation between the alterations of motion $\frac{da}{dt}$, &c. and the forces exerted on the layers of particles between the vortices, or, in the language of our hypothesis, the relation between changes in the state of the magnetic field and the electromotive forces thereby brought into play.

In a memoir "On the Dynamical Theory of Diffraction" (*Cambridge Philosophical Transactions*, Vol. IX. Part 1, section 6), Professor Stokes has given a method by which we may solve equations (54), and find P, Q, and R in terms of the quantities on the right hand of those equations. I have pointed out[*] the application of this method to questions in electricity and magnetism.

Let us then find three quantities F, G, H from the equations

$$\left.\begin{aligned}
\frac{dG}{dz} - \frac{dH}{dy} &= \mu a \\
\frac{dH}{dx} - \frac{dF}{dz} &= \mu \beta \\
\frac{dF}{dy} - \frac{dG}{dx} &= \mu \gamma
\end{aligned}\right\} \quad \dots\dots\dots\dots\dots\dots (55),$$

with the conditions

$$\frac{1}{4\pi}\left(\frac{d}{dx}\mu a + \frac{d}{dy}\mu\beta + \frac{d}{dz}\mu\gamma\right) = m = 0 \dots\dots\dots\dots (56),$$

and

$$\frac{dF}{dx} + \frac{dG}{dy} + \frac{dH}{dz} = 0 \dots\dots\dots\dots\dots (57).$$

Differentiating (55) with respect to t, and comparing with (54), we find

$$P = \frac{dF}{dt}, \quad Q = \frac{dG}{dt}, \quad R = \frac{dH}{dt} \dots\dots\dots\dots\dots (58).$$

We have thus determined three quantities, F, G, H, from which we can find P, Q, and R by considering these latter quantities as the rates at which the former ones vary. In the paper already referred to, I have given reasons for considering the quantities F, G, H as the resolved parts of that which Faraday has conjectured to exist, and has called the *electrotonic state*. In that paper I have stated the mathematical relations between this electrotonic state and the lines of magnetic force as expressed in equations (55), and also between the electrotonic state and electromotive force as expressed in equations (58). We must now endeavour to interpret them from a mechanical point of view in connexion with our hypothesis.

---

[*] *Cambridge Philosophical Transactions*, Vol. X. Part I. Art. 3. "On Faraday's Lines of Force," pp. 205—209 of this vol.

We shall in the first place examine the process by which the lines of force are produced by an electric current.

Let *AB*, Plate VIII., p. 488, fig. 2, represent a current of electricity in the direction from *A* to *B*. Let the large spaces above and below *AB* represent the vortices, and let the small circles separating the vortices represent the layers of particles placed between them, which in our hypothesis represent electricity.

Now let an electric current from left to right commence in *AB*. The row of vortices *gh* above *AB* will be set in motion in the opposite direction to that of a watch. (We shall call this direction +, and that of a watch −.) We shall suppose the row of vortices *kl* still at rest, then the layer of particles between these rows will be acted on by the row *gh* on their lower sides, and will be at rest above. If they are free to move, they will rotate in the negative direction, and will at the same time move from right to left, or in the opposite direction from the current, and so form an *induced* electric current.

If this current is checked by the electrical resistance of the medium, the rotating particles will act upon the row of vortices *kl*, and make them revolve in the positive direction till they arrive at such a velocity that the motion of the particles is reduced to that of rotation, and the induced current disappears. If, now, the primary current *AB* be stopped, the vortices in the row *gh* will be checked, while those of the row *kl* still continue in rapid motion. The momentum of the vortices beyond the layer of particles *pq* will tend to move them from left to right, that is, in the direction of the primary current; but if this motion is resisted by the medium, the motion of the vortices beyond *pq* will be gradually destroyed.

It appears therefore that the phenomena of induced currents are part of the process of communicating the rotatory velocity of the vortices from one part of the field to another.

As an example of the action of the vortices in producing induced currents, let us take the following case:—Let *B*, Plate VIII., p. 488, fig. 3, be a circular ring, of uniform section, lapped uniformly with covered wire. It may be shewn that if an electric current is passed through this wire, a magnet placed within the coil of wire will be strongly affected, but no magnetic effect will be produced on any external point. The effect will be that of a magnet bent round till its two poles are in contact.

If the coil is properly made, no effect on a magnet placed outside it can be discovered, whether the current is kept constant or made to vary in strength; but if a conducting wire C be made to *embrace* the ring any number of times, an electromotive force will act on that wire whenever the current in the coil is made to vary; and if the circuit be *closed*, there will be an actual current in the wire C.

This experiment shews that, in order to produce the electromotive force, it is not necessary that the conducting wire should be placed in a field of magnetic force, or that lines of magnetic force should pass through the substance of the wire or near it. All that is required is that lines of force should pass through the circuit of the conductor, and that these lines of force should vary in quantity during the experiment.

In this case the vortices, of which we suppose the lines of magnetic force to consist, are all within the hollow of the ring, and outside the ring all is at rest. If there is no conducting circuit embracing the ring, then, when the primary current is made or broken, there is no action outside the ring, except an instantaneous pressure between the particles and the vortices which they separate. If there is a continuous conducting circuit embracing the ring, then, when the primary current is made, there will be a current in the opposite direction through C; and when it is broken, there will be a current through C in the same direction as the primary current.

We may now perceive that induced currents are produced when the electricity yields to the electromotive force,—this force, however, still existing when the formation of a sensible current is prevented by the resistance of the circuit.

The electromotive force, of which the components are P, Q, R, arises from the action between the vortices and the interposed particles, when the velocity of rotation is altered in any part of the field. It corresponds to the pressure on the axle of a wheel in a machine when the velocity of the driving wheel is increased or diminished.

The electrotonic state, whose components are F, G, H, is what the electromotive force would be if the currents, &c. to which the lines of force are due, instead of arriving at their actual state by degrees, had started instantaneously from rest with their actual values. It corresponds to the *impulse* which would act on the axle of a wheel in a machine if the actual velocity were suddenly given to the driving wheel, the machine being previously at rest.

If the machine were suddenly stopped by stopping the driving wheel, each wheel would receive an impulse equal and opposite to that which it received when the machine was set in motion.

This impulse may be calculated for any part of a system of mechanism, and may be called the *reduced momentum* of the machine for that point. In the varied motion of the machine, the actual force on any part arising from the variation of motion may be found by differentiating the reduced momentum with respect to the time, just as we have found that the electromotive force may be deduced from the electrotonic state by the same process.

Having found the relation between the velocities of the vortices and the electromotive forces when the centres of the vortices are at rest, we must extend our theory to the case of a fluid medium containing vortices, and subject to all the varieties of fluid motion. If we fix our attention on any one elementary portion of a fluid, we shall find that it not only travels from one place to another, but also changes its form and position, so as to be elongated in certain directions and compressed in others, and at the same time (in the most general case) turned round by a displacement of rotation.

These changes of form and position produce changes in the velocity of the molecular vortices, which we must now examine.

The alteration of form and position may always be reduced to three simple extensions or compressions in the direction of three rectangular axes, together with three angular rotations about any set of three axes. We shall first consider the effect of three simple extensions or compressions.

PROP. IX.—To find the variations of α, β, γ in the parallelopiped x, y, z when x becomes $x + \delta x$; y, $y + \delta y$; and z, $z + \delta z$; the volume of the figure remaining the same.

By Prop. II. we find for the work done by the vortices against pressure,

$$\delta W = p_1 \delta (xyz) - \frac{\mu}{4\pi} (\alpha^2 yz \delta x + \beta^2 zx \delta y + \gamma^2 xy \delta z) \dots\dots\dots\dots (59);$$

and by Prop. VI. we find for the variation of energy,

$$\delta E = \frac{\mu}{4\pi} (\alpha \delta\alpha + \beta \delta\beta + \gamma \delta\gamma) xyz \dots\dots\dots\dots (60).$$

The sum $\delta W + \delta E$ must be zero by the conservation of energy, and $\delta(xyz) = 0$, since xyz is constant; so that

$$a\left(\delta a - a\,\frac{\delta x}{x}\right) + \beta\left(\delta\beta - \beta\,\frac{\delta y}{y}\right) + \gamma\left(\delta\gamma - \gamma\,\frac{\delta z}{z}\right) = 0 \ldots\ldots\ldots (61).$$

In order that this should be true independently of any relations between a, β, and γ, we must have

$$\delta a = a\,\frac{\delta x}{x}, \quad \delta\beta = \beta\,\frac{\delta y}{y}, \quad \delta\gamma = \gamma\,\frac{\delta z}{z} \ldots\ldots\ldots\ldots\ldots (62).$$

Prop. X.—To find the variations of a, β, γ due to a rotation θ_1 about the axis of x from y to z, a rotation θ_2 about the axis of y from z to x, and a rotation θ_3 about the axis of z from x to y.

The axis of β will move away from the axis of x by an angle θ_3; so that β resolved in the direction of x changes from 0 to $-\beta\theta_3$.

The axis of γ approaches that of x by an angle θ_2; so that the resolved part of γ in direction x changes from 0 to $\gamma\theta_2$.

The resolved part of a in the direction of x changes by a quantity depending on the second power of the rotations, which may be neglected. The variations of a, β, γ from this cause are therefore

$$\delta a = \gamma\theta_2 - \beta\theta_3, \quad \delta\beta = a\theta_3 - \gamma\theta_1, \quad \delta\gamma = \beta\theta_1 - a\theta_2 \ldots\ldots\ldots\ldots (63).$$

The most general expressions for the distortion of an element produced by the displacement of its different parts depend on the nine quantities

$$\frac{d}{dx}\delta x, \quad \frac{d}{dy}\delta x, \quad \frac{d}{dz}\delta x; \quad \frac{d}{dx}\delta y, \quad \frac{d}{dy}\delta y, \quad \frac{d}{dz}\delta y; \quad \frac{d}{dx}\delta z, \quad \frac{d}{dy}\delta z, \quad \frac{d}{dz}\delta z;$$

and these may always be expressed in terms of nine other quantities, namely, three simple extensions or compressions,

$$\frac{\delta x'}{x'}, \quad \frac{\delta y'}{y'}, \quad \frac{\delta z'}{z'}$$

along three axes properly chosen, x', y', z', the nine direction-cosines of these axes with their six connecting equations, which are equivalent to three independent quantities, and the three rotations θ_1, θ_2, θ_3 about the axes of x, y, z.

Let the direction-cosines of x' with respect to x, y, z be l_1, m_1, n_1, those of y', l_2, m_2, n_2, and those of z', l_3, m_3, n_3; then we find

$$\frac{d}{dx}\,\delta x = l_1^2 \frac{\delta x'}{x'} + l_2^2 \frac{\delta y'}{y'} + l_3^2 \frac{\delta z'}{z'}$$

$$\frac{d}{dy}\,\delta x = l_1 m_1 \frac{\delta x'}{x'} + l_2 m_2 \frac{\delta y'}{y'} + l_3 m_3 \frac{\delta z'}{z'} - \theta_3 \qquad \Bigg\} \qquad \dots\dots\dots (64),$$

$$\frac{d}{dz}\,\delta x = l_1 n_1 \frac{\delta x'}{x'} + l_2 n_2 \frac{\delta y'}{y'} + l_3 n_3 \frac{dz'}{z'} + \theta_2$$

with similar equations for quantities involving δy and δz.

Let α', β', γ' be the values of α, β, γ referred to the axes x', y', z'; then

$$\alpha' = l_1 \alpha + m_1 \beta + n_1 \gamma$$

$$\beta' = l_2 \alpha + m_2 \beta + n_2 \gamma \qquad \Bigg\} \qquad \dots\dots\dots\dots (65).$$

$$\gamma' = l_3 \alpha + m_3 \beta + n_3 \gamma$$

We shall then have

$$\delta \alpha = l_1 \delta \alpha' + l_2 \delta \beta' + l_3 \delta \gamma' + \gamma \theta_2 - \beta \theta_3 \dots\dots\dots\dots(66),$$

$$= l_1 \alpha' \frac{\delta x'}{x'} + l_2 \beta' \frac{\delta y'}{y'} + l_3 \gamma' \frac{\delta z'}{z'} + \gamma \theta_2 - \beta \theta_3 \dots\dots\dots (67).$$

By substituting the values of α', β', γ', and comparing with equations (64), we find

$$\delta \alpha = \alpha \frac{d}{dx}\,\delta x + \beta \frac{d}{dy}\,\delta x + \gamma \frac{d}{dz}\,\delta x \dots\dots\dots\dots (68)$$

as the variation of α due to the change of form and position of the element. The variations of β and γ have similar expressions.

PROP. XI.—To find the electromotive forces in a moving body.

The variation of the velocity of the vortices in a moving element is due to two causes—the action of the electromotive forces, and the change of form and position of the element. The whole variation of α is therefore

$$\delta \alpha = \frac{1}{\mu}\left(\frac{dQ}{dz} - \frac{dR}{dy}\right)\delta t + \alpha \frac{d}{dx}\,\delta x + \beta \frac{d}{dy}\,\delta x + \gamma \frac{d}{dz}\delta x \dots\dots\dots\dots(69).$$

But since α is a function of x, y, z and t, the variation of α may be also written

$$\delta \alpha = \frac{d\alpha}{dx}\,\delta x + \frac{d\alpha}{dy}\,\delta y + \frac{d\alpha}{dz}\,\delta z + \frac{d\alpha}{dt}\,\delta t \dots\dots\dots\dots(70).$$

Equating the two values of $\delta \alpha$ and dividing by δt, and remembering that in the motion of an incompressible medium

$$\frac{d}{dx}\frac{dx}{dt} + \frac{d}{dy}\frac{dy}{dt} + \frac{d}{dz}\frac{dz}{dt} = 0 \dots\dots\dots\dots (71),$$

and that in the absence of free magnetism

$$\frac{da}{dx} + \frac{d\beta}{dy} + \frac{d\gamma}{dz} = 0 \dots\dots\dots\dots\dots(72),$$

we find

$$\frac{1}{\mu}\left(\frac{dQ}{dz} - \frac{dR}{dy}\right) + \gamma\frac{d}{dz}\frac{dx}{dt} - a\frac{d}{dz}\frac{dz}{dt} - a\frac{d}{dy}\frac{dy}{dt} + \beta\frac{d}{dy}\frac{dx}{dt}$$

$$+ \frac{d\gamma}{dz}\frac{dx}{dt} - \frac{da}{dz}\frac{dz}{dt} - \frac{da}{dy}\frac{dy}{dt} + \frac{d\beta}{dy}\frac{dx}{dt} - \frac{da}{dt} = 0 \dots\dots (73).$$

Putting

$$a = \frac{1}{\mu}\left(\frac{dG}{dz} - \frac{dH}{dy}\right) \dots\dots\dots\dots\dots (74),$$

and

$$\frac{da}{dt} = \frac{1}{\mu}\left(\frac{d^2G}{dz\,dt} - \frac{d^2H}{dy\,dt}\right) \dots\dots\dots\dots\dots(75),$$

where F, G, and H are the values of the electrotonic components for a fixed point of space, our equation becomes

$$\frac{d}{dz}\left(Q + \mu\gamma\frac{dx}{dt} - \mu a\frac{dz}{dt} - \frac{dG}{dt}\right) - \frac{d}{dy}\left(R + \mu a\frac{dy}{dt} - \mu\beta\frac{dx}{dt} - \frac{dH}{dt}\right) = 0 \dots\dots(76).$$

The expressions for the variations of β and γ give us two other equations which may be written down from symmetry. The complete solution of the three equations is

$$\left.\begin{array}{l} P = \mu\gamma\dfrac{dy}{dt} - \mu\beta\dfrac{dz}{dt} + \dfrac{dF}{dt} - \dfrac{d\Psi}{dx} \\[2ex] Q = \mu a\dfrac{dz}{dt} - \mu\gamma\dfrac{dx}{dt} + \dfrac{dG}{dt} - \dfrac{d\Psi}{dy} \\[2ex] R = \mu\beta\dfrac{dx}{dt} - \mu a\dfrac{dy}{dt} + \dfrac{dH}{dt} - \dfrac{d\Psi}{dz} \end{array}\right\} \dots\dots\dots\dots (77).$$

The first and second terms of each equation indicate the effect of the motion of any body in the magnetic field, the third term refers to changes in the electrotonic state produced by alterations of position or intensity of magnets or currents in the field, and Ψ is a function of x, y, z, and t, which is indeterminate as far as regards the solution of the original equations, but which may always be determined in any given case from the circumstances of the problem. The physical interpretation of Ψ is, that it is the *electric tension* at each point of space.

The physical meaning of the terms in the expression for the electromotive force depending on the motion of the body, may be made simpler by supposing the field of magnetic force uniformly magnetized with intensity a in the direction of the axis of x. Then if l, m, n be the direction-cosines of any portion of a linear conductor, and S its length, the electromotive force resolved in the direction of the conductor will be

$$e = S\left(Pl + Qm + Rn\right) \quad\text{..........................} (78),$$

or

$$e = S\mu a\left(m\,\frac{dz}{dt} - n\,\frac{dy}{dt}\right) \quad\text{.........................} (79),$$

that is, the product of μa, the quantity of magnetic induction over unit of area multiplied by $S\left(m\,\dfrac{dz}{dt} - n\,\dfrac{dy}{dt}\right)$, the area swept out by the conductor S in unit of time, resolved perpendicular to the direction of the magnetic force.

The electromotive force in any part of a conductor due to its motion is therefore measured by the *number* of lines of magnetic force which it crosses in unit of time; and the total electromotive force in a closed conductor is measured by the change of the number of lines of force which pass through it; and this is true whether the change be produced by the motion of the conductor or by any external cause.

In order to understand the mechanism by which the motion of a conductor across lines of magnetic force generates an electromotive force in that conductor, we must remember that in Prop. X. we have proved that the change of form of a portion of the medium containing vortices produces a change of the velocity of those vortices; and in particular that an extension of the medium in the direction of the axes of the vortices, combined with a contraction in all directions perpendicular to this, produces an increase of velocity of the vortices; while a shortening of the axis and bulging of the sides produces a diminution of the velocity of the vortices.

This change of the velocity of the vortices arises from the internal effects of change of form, and is independent of that produced by external electromotive forces. If, therefore, the change of velocity be prevented or checked, electromotive forces will arise, because each vortex will press on the surrounding particles in the direction in which it tends to alter its motion.

Let A, fig. 4, p. 488, represent the section of a vertical wire moving in the direction of the arrow from west to east, across a system of lines of magnetic force running north and south. The curved lines in fig. 4 represent the lines of fluid motion about the wire, the wire being regarded as stationary, and the fluid as having a motion relative to it. It is evident that, from this figure, we can trace the variations of form of an element of the fluid, as the form of the element depends, not on the absolute motion of the whole system, but on the relative motion of its parts.

In front of the wire, that is, on its east side, it will be seen that as the wire approaches each portion of the medium, that portion is more and more compressed in the direction from east to west, and extended in the direction from north to south; and since the axes of the vortices lie in the north and south direction, their velocity will continually tend to increase by Prop. X., unless prevented or checked by electromotive forces acting on the circumference of each vortex.

We shall consider an electromotive force as positive when the vortices tend to move the interjacent particles *upwards* perpendicularly to the plane of the paper.

The vortices appear to revolve as the hands of a watch when we look at them from south to north; so that each vortex moves upwards on its west side, and downwards on its east side. In front of the wire, therefore, where each vortex is striving to increase its velocity, the electromotive force upwards must be greater on its west than on its east side. There will therefore be a continual increase of upward electromotive force from the remote east, where it is zero, to the front of the moving wire, where the upward force will be strongest.

Behind the wire a different action takes place. As the wire moves away from each successive portion of the medium, that portion is extended from east to west, and compressed from north to south, so as to tend to diminish the velocity of the vortices, and therefore to make the upward electromotive force greater on the east than on the west side of each vortex. The upward electromotive force will therefore increase continually from the remote west, where it is zero, to the back of the moving wire, where it will be strongest.

It appears, therefore, that a vertical wire moving eastwards will experience an electromotive force tending to produce in it an upward current. If there is no conducting circuit in connexion with the ends of the wire, no current will be formed, and the magnetic forces will not be altered; but if such a circuit exists, there will be a current, and the lines of magnetic force and the velocity of the vortices will be altered from their state previous to the motion of the wire. The change in the lines of force is shewn in fig. 5. The vortices in front of the wire, instead of merely producing pressures, actually increase in velocity, while those behind have their velocity diminished, and those at the sides of the wire have the direction of their axes altered; so that the final effect is to produce a force acting on the wire as a resistance to its motion. We may now recapitulate the assumptions we have made, and the results we have obtained.

(1) Magneto-electric phenomena are due to the existence of matter under certain conditions of motion or of pressure in every part of the magnetic field, and not to direct action at a distance between the magnets or currents. The substance producing these effects may be a certain part of ordinary matter, or it may be an æther associated with matter. Its density is greatest in iron, and least in diamagnetic substances; but it must be in all cases, except that of iron, very rare, since no other substance has a large ratio of magnetic capacity to what we call a vacuum.

(2) The condition of any part of the field, through which lines of magnetic force pass, is one of unequal pressure in different directions, the direction of the lines of force being that of least pressure, so that the lines of force may be considered lines of tension.

(3) This inequality of pressure is produced by the existence in the medium of vortices or eddies, having their axes in the direction of the lines of force, and having their direction of rotation determined by that of the lines of force.

We have supposed that the direction was that of a watch to a spectator looking from south to north. We might with equal propriety have chosen the reverse direction, as far as known facts are concerned, by supposing resinous electricity instead of vitreous to be positive. The effect of these vortices depends on their density, and on their velocity at the circumference, and is independent of their diameter. The density must be proportional to the capacity of the substance for magnetic induction, that of the vortices in air being 1. The velocity must be very great, in order to produce so powerful effects in so rare a medium.

The size of the vortices is indeterminate, but is probably very small as compared with that of a complete molecule of ordinary matter*.

* The angular momentum of the system of vortices depends on their average diameter; so that if the diameter were sensible, we might expect that a magnet would behave as if it contained a revolving body

(4) The vortices are separated from each other by a single layer of round particles, so that a system of cells is formed, the partitions being these layers of particles, and the substance of each cell being capable of rotating as a vortex.

(5) The particles forming the layer are in *rolling contact* with both the vortices which they separate, but do not rub against each other. They are perfectly free to roll between the vortices and so to change their place, provided they keep within one *complete molecule* of the substance; but in passing from one molecule to another they experience resistance, and generate irregular motions, which constitute heat. These particles, in our theory, play the part of electricity. Their motion of translation constitutes an electric current, their rotation serves to transmit the motion of the vortices from one part of the field to another, and the tangential pressures thus called into play constitute electromotive force. The conception of a particle having its motion connected with that of a vortex by perfect rolling contact may appear somewhat awkward. I do not bring it forward as a mode of connexion existing in nature, or even as that which I would willingly assent to as an electrical hypothesis. It is, however, a mode of connexion which is mechanically conceivable, and easily investigated, and it serves to bring out the actual mechanical connexions between the known electro-magnetic phenomena; so that I venture to say that any one who understands the provisional and temporary character of this hypothesis, will find himself rather helped than hindered by it in his search after the true interpretation of the phenomena.

The action between the vortices and the layers of particles is in part tangential; so that if there were any slipping or differential motion between the parts in contact, there would be a loss of the energy belonging to the lines of force, and a gradual transformation of that energy into heat. Now we know that the lines of force about a magnet are maintained for an indefinite time without any expenditure of energy; so that we must conclude that wherever there is tangential action between different parts of the medium, there is no motion of slipping between those parts. We must therefore conceive that the vortices and particles roll together without slipping; and that the interior strata of each vortex receive their proper velocities from the exterior stratum without slipping, that is, the angular velocity must be the same throughout each vortex.

within it, and that the existence of this rotation might be detected by experiments on the free rotation of a magnet. I have made experiments to investigate this question, but have not yet fully tried the apparatus.

The only process in which electro-magnetic energy is lost and transformed into heat, is in the passage of electricity from one molecule to another. In all other cases the energy of the vortices can only be diminished when an equivalent quantity of mechanical work is done by magnetic action.

(6) The effect of an electric current upon the surrounding medium is to make the vortices in contact with the current revolve so that the parts next to the current move in the same direction as the current. The parts furthest from the current will move in the opposite direction; and if the medium is a conductor of electricity, so that the particles are free to move in any direction, the particles touching the outside of these vortices will be moved in a direction contrary to that of the current, so that there will be an induced current in the opposite direction to the primary one.

If there were no resistance to the motion of the particles, the induced current would be equal and opposite to the primary one, and would continue as long as the primary current lasted, so that it would prevent all action of the primary current at a distance. If there is a resistance to the induced current, its particles act upon the vortices beyond them, and transmit the motion of rotation to them, till at last all the vortices in the medium are set in motion with such velocities of rotation that the particles between them have no motion except that of rotation, and do not produce currents.

In the transmission of the motion from one vortex to another, there arises a force between the particles and the vortices, by which the particles are pressed in one direction and the vortices in the opposite direction. We call the force acting on the particles the electromotive force. The reaction on the vortices is equal and opposite, so that the electromotive force cannot move any part of the medium as a whole, it can only produce currents. When the primary current is stopped, the electromotive forces all act in the opposite direction.

(7) When an electric current or a magnet is moved in presence of a conductor, the velocity of rotation of the vortices in any part of the field is altered by that motion. The force by which the proper amount of rotation is transmitted to each vortex, constitutes in this case also an electromotive force, and, if permitted, will produce currents.

(8) When a conductor is moved in a field of magnetic force, the vortices in it and in its neighbourhood are moved out of their places, and are changed in form. The force arising from these changes constitutes the electromotive

force on a moving conductor, and is found by calculation to correspond with that determined by experiment.

We have now shewn in what way electro-magnetic phenomena may be imitated by an imaginary system of molecular vortices. Those who have been already inclined to adopt an hypothesis of this kind, will find here the conditions which must be fulfilled in order to give it mathematical coherence, and a comparison, so far satisfactory, between its necessary results and known facts. Those who look in a different direction for the explanation of the facts, may be able to compare this theory with that of the existence of currents flowing freely through bodies, and with that which supposes electricity to act at a distance with a force depending on its velocity, and therefore not subject to the law of conservation of energy.

The facts of electro-magnetism are so complicated and various, that the explanation of any number of them by several different hypotheses must be interesting, not only to physicists, but to all who desire to understand how much evidence the explanation of phenomena lends to the credibility of a theory, or how far we ought to regard a coincidence in the mathematical expression of two sets of phenomena as an indication that these phenomena are of the same kind. We know that partial coincidences of this kind have been discovered; and the fact that they are only partial is proved by the divergence of the laws of the two sets of phenomena in other respects. We may chance to find, in the higher parts of physics, instances of more complete coincidence, which may require much investigation to detect their ultimate divergence.

NOTE.

Since the first part of this paper was written, I have seen in Crelle's *Journal* for 1859, a paper by Prof. Helmholtz on Fluid Motion, in which he has pointed out that the lines of fluid motion are arranged according to the same laws as the lines of magnetic force, the path of an electric current corresponding to a line of axes of those particles of the fluid which are in a state of rotation. This is an additional instance of a *physical analogy*, the investigation of which may illustrate both electro-magnetism and hydrodynamics.

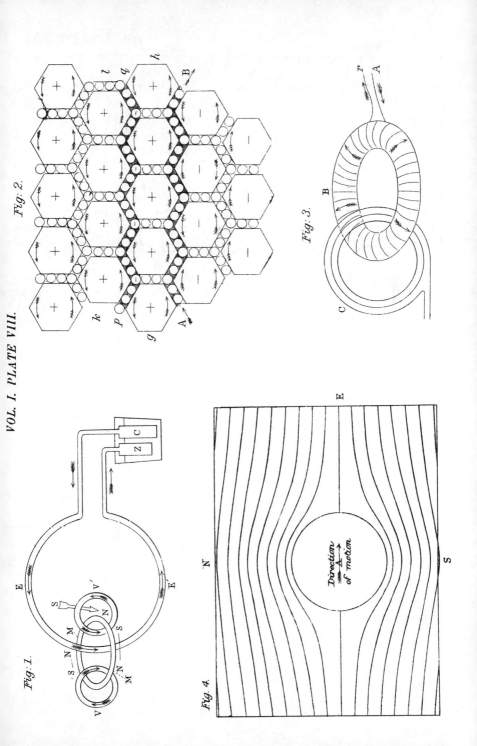

Fig: 1.

Fig: 2.

Fig: 3.

Fig. 4.

Direction
of motion

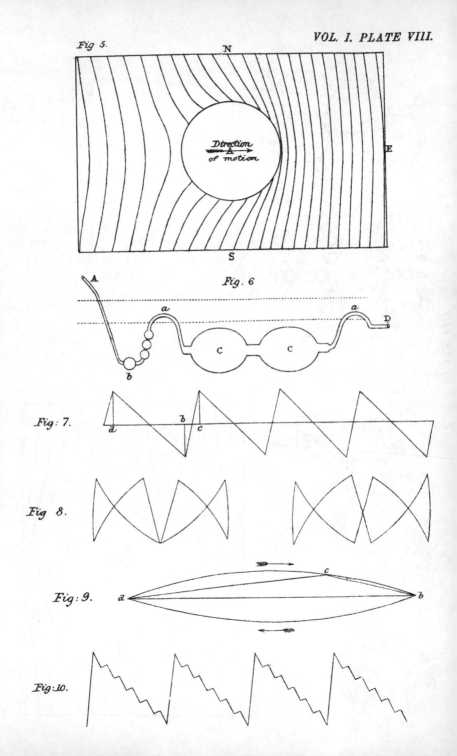

Fig 5.

Direction of motion

Fig. 6

Fig: 7.

Fig 8.

Fig: 9.

Fig: 10.

[From the *Philosophical Magazine* for January and February, 1862.]

PART III.

THE THEORY OF MOLECULAR VORTICES APPLIED TO STATICAL ELECTRICITY.

In the first part of this paper* I have shewn how the forces acting between magnets, electric currents, and matter capable of magnetic induction may be accounted for on the hypothesis of the magnetic field being occupied with innumerable vortices of revolving matter, their axes coinciding with the direction of the magnetic force at every point of the field.

The centrifugal force of these vortices produces pressures distributed in such a way that the final effect is a force identical in direction and magnitude with that which we observe.

In the second part† I described the mechanism by which these rotations may be made to coexist, and to be distributed according to the known laws of magnetic lines of force.

I conceived the rotating matter to be the substance of certain cells, divided from each other by cell-walls composed of particles which are very small compared with the cells, and that it is by the motions of these particles, and their tangential action on the substance in the cells, that the rotation is communicated from one cell to another.

I have not attempted to explain this tangential action, but it is necessary to suppose, in order to account for the transmission of rotation from the exterior to the interior parts of each cell, that the substance in the cells possesses elasticity of figure, similar in kind, though different in degree, to that observed in solid bodies. The undulatory theory of light requires us to admit this kind of elasticity in the luminiferous medium, in order to account for transverse vibrations. We need not then be surprised if the magneto-electric medium possesses the same property.

* *Phil. Mag.* March, 1861 [pp. 451—466 of this vol.].
† *Phil. Mag.* April and May, 1861 [pp. 467—488 of this vol.].

According to our theory, the particles which form the partitions between the cells constitute the matter of electricity. The motion of these particles constitutes an electric current; the tangential force with which the particles are pressed by the matter of the cells is electromotive force, and the pressure of the particles on each other corresponds to the tension or potential of the electricity.

If we can now explain the condition of a body with respect to the surrounding medium when it is said to be "charged" with electricity, and account for the forces acting between electrified bodies, we shall have established a connexion between all the principal phenomena of electrical science.

We know by experiment that electric tension is the same thing, whether observed in statical or in current electricity; so that an electromotive force produced by magnetism may be made to charge a Leyden jar, as is done by the coil machine.

When a difference of tension exists in different parts of any body, the electricity passes, or tends to pass, from places of greater to places of smaller tension. If the body is a conductor, an actual passage of electricity takes place; and if the difference of tensions is kept up, the current continues to flow with a velocity proportional inversely to the resistance, or directly to the conductivity of the body.

The electric resistance has a very wide range of values, that of the metals being the smallest, and that of glass being so great that a charge of electricity has been preserved* in a glass vessel for years without penetrating the thickness of the glass.

Bodies which do not permit a current of electricity to flow through them are called insulators. But though electricity does not flow through them, the electrical effects are propagated through them, and the amount of these effects differs according to the nature of the body; so that equally good insulators may act differently as dielectrics†.

Here then we have two independent qualities of bodies, one by which they allow of the passage of electricity through them, and the other by which they allow of electrical action being transmitted through them without any electricity being allowed to pass. A conducting body may be compared to a porous membrane which opposes more or less resistance to the passage of a fluid,

---

* By Professor W. Thomson.   † Faraday, *Experimental Researches*, Series XI.

while a dielectric is like an elastic membrane which may be impervious to the fluid, but transmits the pressure of the fluid on one side to that on the other.

As long as electromotive force acts on a conductor, it produces a current which, as it meets with resistance, occasions a continual transformation of electrical energy into heat, which is incapable of being restored again as electrical energy by any reversion of the process.

Electromotive force acting on a dielectric produces a state of polarization of its parts similar in distribution to the polarity of the particles of iron under the influence of a magnet*, and, like the magnetic polarization, capable of being described as a state in which every particle has its poles in opposite conditions.

In a dielectric under induction, we may conceive that the electricity in each molecule is so displaced that one side is rendered positively, and the other negatively electrical, but that the electricity remains entirely connected with the molecule, and does not pass from one molecule to another.

The effect of this action on the whole dielectric mass is to produce a general displacement of the electricity in a certain direction. This displacement does not amount to a current, because when it has attained a certain value it remains constant, but it is the commencement of a current, and its variations constitute currents in the positive or negative direction, according as the displacement is increasing or diminishing. The amount of the displacement depends on the nature of the body, and on the electromotive force; so that if h is the displacement, R the electromotive force, and E a coefficient depending on the nature of the dielectric,

$$R = -4\pi E^2 h ;$$

and if r is the value of the electric current due to displacement,

$$r = \frac{dh}{dt} .$$

These relations are independent of any theory about the internal mechanism of dielectrics; but when we find electromotive force producing electric displacement in a dielectric, and when we find the dielectric recovering from its state of electric displacement with an equal electromotive force, we cannot help

* See Prof. Mossotti, "Discussione Analitica," *Memorie della Soc. Italiana* (Modena), Vol. XXIV. Part 2, p. 49.

regarding the phenomena as those of an elastic body, yielding to a pressure, and recovering its form when the pressure is removed.

According to our hypothesis, the magnetic medium is divided into cells, separated by partitions formed of a stratum of particles which play the part of electricity. When the electric particles are urged in any direction, they will, by their tangential action on the elastic substance of the cells, distort each cell, and call into play an equal and opposite force arising from the elasticity of the cells. When the force is removed, the cells will recover their form, and the electricity will return to its former position.

In the following investigation I have considered the relation between the displacement and the force producing it, on the supposition that the cells are spherical. The actual form of the cells probably does not differ from that of a sphere sufficiently to make much difference in the numerical result.

I have deduced from this result the relation between the statical and dynamical measures of electricity, and have shewn, by a comparison of the electro-magnetic experiments of MM. Kohlrausch and Weber with the velocity of light as found by M. Fizeau, that the elasticity of the magnetic medium in air is the same as that of the luminiferous medium, if these two coexistent, coextensive, and equally elastic media are not rather one medium.

It appears also from Prop. XV. that the attraction between two electrified bodies depends on the value of E^2, and that therefore it would be less in turpentine than in air, if the quantity of electricity in each body remains the same. If, however, the *potentials* of the two bodies were given, the attraction between them would vary inversely as E^2, and would be greater in turpentine than in air.

PROP. XII. To find the conditions of equilibrium of an elastic sphere whose surface is exposed to normal and tangential forces, the tangential forces being proportional to the sine of the distance from a given point on the sphere.

Let the axis of z be the axis of spherical co-ordinates.

Let ξ, η, ζ be the displacements of any particle of the sphere in the directions of x, y, and z.

Let p_{xx}, p_{yy}, p_{zz} be the stresses normal to planes perpendicular to the three axes, and let p_{yz}, p_{zx}, p_{xy} be the stresses of distortion in the planes yz, zx, and xy.

Let μ be the coefficient of cubic elasticity, so that if

$$p_{xx} = p_{yy} = p_{zz} = p,$$

$$p = \mu \left(\frac{d\xi}{dx} + \frac{d\eta}{dy} + \frac{d\zeta}{dz} \right) \quad \ldots\ldots\ldots\ldots\ldots (80).$$

Let m be the coefficient of rigidity, so that

$$p_{xx} - p_{yy} = m \left(\frac{d\xi}{dx} - \frac{d\eta}{dy} \right), \quad \&c. \ldots\ldots\ldots\ldots(81).$$

Then we have the following equations of elasticity in an isotropic medium,

$$p_{xx} = (\mu - \tfrac{1}{3}m) \left(\frac{d\xi}{dx} + \frac{d\eta}{dy} + \frac{d\zeta}{dz} \right) + m \frac{d\xi}{dx} \quad \ldots\ldots\ldots\ldots\ldots(82);$$

with similar equations in y and z, and also

$$p_{yz} = \frac{m}{2} \left(\frac{d\eta}{dz} + \frac{d\zeta}{dy} \right), \quad \&c. \ldots\ldots\ldots\ldots\ldots (83).$$

In the case of the sphere, let us assume the radius $= a$, and

$$\xi = exz, \quad \eta = ezy, \quad \zeta = f(x^2 + y^2) + gz^2 + d \ldots\ldots\ldots\ldots(84).$$

Then

$$\left. \begin{aligned} p_{xx} &= 2\,(\mu - \tfrac{1}{3}m)\,(e+g)\,z + mez = p_{yy} \\[4pt] p_{zz} &= 2\,(\mu - \tfrac{1}{3}m)\,(e+g)\,z + 2mgz \\[4pt] p_{yz} &= \frac{m}{2}\,(e+2f)\,y \\[4pt] p_{zx} &= \frac{m}{2}\,(e+2f)\,z \\[4pt] p_{xy} &= 0 \end{aligned} \right\} \quad \ldots\ldots\ldots\ldots (85).$$

The equation of internal equilibrium with respect to z is

$$\frac{d}{dx}\,p_{zx} + \frac{d}{dy}\,p_{yz} + \frac{d}{dz}\,p_{zz} = 0 \ldots\ldots\ldots\ldots\ldots (86),$$

which is satisfied in this case if

$$m\,(e + 2f + 2g) + 2\,(\mu - \tfrac{1}{3}m)\,(e+g) = 0 \quad \ldots\ldots\ldots\ldots (87).$$

The tangential stress on the surface of the sphere, whose radius is a at an angular distance θ from the axis in plane xz,

$$T = (p_{xx} - p_{zz})\sin\theta\cos\theta + p_{zx}(\cos^2\theta - \sin^2\theta) \ldots\ldots\ldots\ldots(88)$$

$$= 2m\,(e + f - g)\,a\sin\theta\cos^2\theta - \frac{ma}{2}\,(e + 2f)\sin\theta \ldots\ldots\ldots\ldots(89).$$

In order that T may be proportional to $\sin \theta$, the first term must vanish, and therefore

$$g = e + f \dots\dots\dots\dots (90),$$

$$T = -\frac{ma}{2} (e + 2f) \sin \theta \dots\dots (91).$$

The normal stress on the surface at any point is

$$N = p_{xx} \sin^2 \theta + p_{yy} \cos^2 \theta + 2p_{xz} \sin \theta \cos \theta$$

$$= 2 (\mu - \tfrac{1}{3}m)(e + g) a \cos \theta + 2ma \cos \theta \{(e + f) \sin^2 \theta + g \cos^2 \theta\} \dots (92);$$

or by (87) and (90), $N = -ma (e + 2f) \cos \theta \dots\dots (93).$

The tangential displacement of any point is

$$t = \xi \cos \theta - \zeta \sin \theta = - (a^2 f + d) \sin \theta \dots\dots (94).$$

The normal displacement is

$$n = \xi \sin \theta + \zeta \cos \theta = \{a^2 (e + f) + d\} \cos \theta \dots\dots (95).$$

If we make $a^2 (e + f) + d = 0 \dots\dots (96),$

there will be no normal displacement, and the displacement will be entirely tangential, and we shall have

$$t = a^2 e \sin \theta \dots\dots (97).$$

The whole work done by the superficial forces is

$$U = \tfrac{1}{2} \Sigma (Tt) dS,$$

the summation being extended over the surface of the sphere.

The energy of elasticity in the substance of the sphere is

$$U = \tfrac{1}{2} \Sigma \left\{ \frac{d\xi}{dx} p_{xx} + \frac{d\eta}{dy} p_{yy} + \frac{d\zeta}{dz} p_{zz} + \left(\frac{d\eta}{dz} + \frac{d\zeta}{dy}\right) p_{yz} + \left(\frac{d\zeta}{dx} + \frac{d\xi}{dz}\right) p_{zx} + \left(\frac{d\xi}{dy} + \frac{d\eta}{dx}\right) p_{zy} \right\} dV,$$

the summation being extended to the whole contents of the sphere.

We find, as we ought, that these quantities have the same value, namely

$$U = -\tfrac{2}{3} \pi a^5 me (e + 2f) \dots\dots (98).$$

We may now suppose that the tangential action on the surface arises from a layer of particles in contact with it, the particles being acted on by their own mutual pressure, and acting on the surfaces of the two cells with which they are in contact.

We assume the axis of z to be in the direction of maximum variation of the pressure among the particles, and we have to determine the relation between an electromotive force R acting on the particles in that direction, and the electric displacement h which accompanies it.

PROP. XIII.—To find the relation between electromotive force and electric displacement when a uniform electromotive force R acts parallel to the axis of z.

Take any element δS of the surface, covered with a stratum whose density is ρ, and having its normal inclined θ to the axis of z; then the tangential force upon it will be

$$\rho R \delta S \sin \theta = 2\, T \delta S \quad\dots\dots\dots\dots\dots\dots\dots(99),$$

T being, as before, the tangential force on each side of the surface. Putting $\rho = \dfrac{1}{2\pi}$ as in equation (34)*, we find

$$R = -2\pi m a\, (e + 2f) \quad\dots\dots\dots\dots\dots\dots(100).$$

The displacement of electricity due to the distortion of the sphere is

$$\Sigma \delta S \tfrac{1}{2} \rho t \sin \theta \text{ taken over the whole surface} \dots\dots\dots (101);$$

and if h is the electric displacement per unit of volume, we shall have

$$\tfrac{4}{3}\pi a^3 h = \tfrac{2}{3} a^4 e \quad\dots\dots\dots\dots\dots\dots (102),$$

or

$$h = \frac{1}{2\pi}\, a e \quad\dots\dots\dots\dots\dots\dots\dots (103);$$

so that

$$R = 4\pi^2 m\, \frac{e + 2f}{e}\, h \quad\dots\dots\dots\dots (104),$$

or we may write

$$R = -4\pi E^2 h \quad\dots\dots\dots\dots\dots\dots\dots(105),$$

provided we assume

$$E^2 = -\pi m\, \frac{e + 2f}{e} \quad\dots\dots\dots\dots\dots (106).$$

Finding e and f from (87) and (90), we get

$$E^2 = \pi m\, \frac{3}{1 + \dfrac{5}{3}\dfrac{m}{\mu}} \quad\dots\dots\dots\dots\dots\dots(107).$$

The ratio of m to μ varies in different substances; but in a medium whose elasticity depends entirely upon forces acting between pairs of particles, this ratio is that of 6 to 5, and in this case

$$E^2 = \pi m \quad\dots\dots\dots\dots\dots\dots\dots\dots\dots(108).$$

* *Phil. Mag.* April, 1861 [p. 471 of this vol.].

When the resistance to compression is infinitely greater than the resistance to distortion, as in a liquid rendered slightly elastic by gum or jelly,

$$E^{2} = 3\pi m \dots (109).$$

The value of E^{2} must lie between these limits. It is probable that the substance of our cells is of the former kind, and that we must use the first value of E^{2}, which is that belonging to a hypothetically "perfect" solid*, in which

$$5m = 6\mu \dots (110),$$

so that we must use equation (108).

Prop. XIV.—To correct the equations (9)† of electric currents for the effect due to the elasticity of the medium.

We have seen that electromotive force and electric displacement are connected by equation (105). Differentiating this equation with respect to t, we find

$$\frac{dR}{dt} = -4\pi E^{2}\frac{dh}{dt} \dots (111),$$

shewing that when the electromotive force varies, the electric displacement also varies. But a variation of displacement is equivalent to a current, and this current must be taken into account in equations (9) and added to r. The three equations then become

$$\left.\begin{array}{l} p = \dfrac{1}{4\pi}\left(\dfrac{d\gamma}{dy} - \dfrac{d\beta}{dz} - \dfrac{1}{E^{2}}\dfrac{dP}{dt}\right) \\[2mm] q = \dfrac{1}{4\pi}\left(\dfrac{d\alpha}{dy} - \dfrac{d\gamma}{dx} - \dfrac{1}{E^{2}}\dfrac{dQ}{dt}\right) \\[2mm] r = \dfrac{1}{4\pi}\left(\dfrac{d\beta}{dx} - \dfrac{d\alpha}{dy} - \dfrac{1}{E^{2}}\dfrac{dR}{dt}\right) \end{array}\right\} \dots (112),$$

where p, q, r are the electric currents in the directions of x, y, and z; α, β, γ are the components of magnetic intensity; and P, Q, R are the electromotive forces. Now if e be the quantity of free electricity in unit of volume, then the equation of continuity will be

$$\frac{dp}{dx} + \frac{dq}{dy} + \frac{dr}{dz} + \frac{de}{dt} = 0 \dots (113).$$

* See Rankine "On Elasticity," *Camb. and Dub. Math. Journ.* 1851.
† *Phil. Mag.* March, 1861 [p. 462 of this vol.].

Differentiating (112) with respect to x, y, and z respectively, and substituting, we find

$$\frac{de}{dt} = \frac{1}{4\pi E^2} \frac{d}{dt} \left(\frac{dP}{dx} + \frac{dQ}{dy} + \frac{dR}{dz} \right) \dots\dots\dots\dots(114);$$

whence

$$e = \frac{1}{4\pi E^2} \left(\frac{dP}{dx} + \frac{dQ}{dy} + \frac{dR}{dz} \right) \dots\dots\dots\dots(115),$$

the constant being omitted, because $e = 0$ when there are no electromotive forces.

Prop. XV.—To find the force acting between two electrified bodies.

The energy in the medium arising from the electric displacements is

$$U = -\Sigma\tfrac{1}{2}\left(Pf + Qg + Rh\right)\delta V \dots\dots\dots\dots(116),$$

where P, Q, R are the forces, and f, g, h the displacements. Now when there is no motion of the bodies or alteration of forces, it appears from equations (77)[*] that

$$P = -\frac{d\Psi}{dx}, \quad Q = -\frac{d\Psi}{dy}, \quad R = -\frac{d\Psi}{dz} \dots\dots\dots\dots(118);$$

and we know by (105) that

$$P = -4\pi E^2 f, \quad Q = -4\pi E^2 g, \quad R = -4\pi E^2 h \dots\dots\dots(119);$$

whence

$$U = \frac{1}{8\pi E^2} \Sigma \left(\overline{\frac{d\Psi}{dx}}^2 + \overline{\frac{d\Psi}{dy}}^2 + \overline{\frac{d\Psi}{dz}}^2 \right) \delta V \dots\dots\dots(120).$$

Integrating by parts throughout all space, and remembering that Ψ vanishes at an infinite distance,

$$U = -\frac{1}{8\pi E^2} \Sigma \Psi \left(\frac{d^2\Psi}{dx^2} + \frac{d^2\Psi}{dy^2} + \frac{d^2\Psi}{dz^2} \right) \delta V \dots\dots\dots(121);$$

or by (115),

$$U = \tfrac{1}{2}\Sigma\,(\Psi e)\,\delta V \dots\dots\dots\dots(122).$$

Now let there be two electrified bodies, and let e_1 be the distribution of electricity in the first, and Ψ_1 the electric tension due to it, and let

$$e_1 = \frac{1}{4\pi E^2} \left(\frac{d^2\Psi_1}{dx^2} + \frac{d^2\Psi_1}{dy^2} + \frac{d^2\Psi_1}{dz^2} \right) \dots\dots\dots\dots(123).$$

Let e_2 be the distribution of electricity in the second body, and Ψ_2 the tension due to it; then the whole tension at any point will be $\Psi_1 + \Psi_2$, and the expansion for U will become

$$U = \tfrac{1}{2}\Sigma\,(\Psi_1 e_1 + \Psi_2 e_2 + \Psi_1 e_2 + \Psi_2 e_1)\,\delta V\dots\dots\dots\dots(124).$$

* *Phil. Mag.* May, 1861 [p. 482 of this vol.].

Let the body whose electricity is e_1 be moved in any way, the electricity moving along with the body, then since the distribution of tension Ψ_1 moves with the body, the value of $\Psi_1 e_1$ remains the same.

$\Psi_2 e_2$ also remains the same; and Green has shewn (Essay on Electricity, p. 10) that $\Psi_1 e_2 = \Psi_2 e_1$, so that the work done by moving the body against electric forces

$$W = \delta U = \delta \Sigma \, (\Psi_2 e_1) \, \delta V \dots\dots\dots\dots\dots\dots (125).$$

And if e_1 is confined to a small body,

$$W = e_1 \delta \Psi_2,$$

or

$$F dr = e_1 \frac{d\Psi_2}{dr} dr \dots\dots\dots\dots\dots\dots\dots (126),$$

where F is the resistance and dr the motion.

If the body e_2 be small, then if r is the distance from e_2, equation (123) gives

$$\Psi_2 = E^2 \frac{e_2}{r} ;$$

whence

$$F = - E^2 \frac{e_1 e_2}{r^2} \dots\dots\dots\dots\dots\dots\dots (127);$$

or the force is a repulsion varying inversely as the square of the distance.

Now let η_1 and η_2 be the same quantities of electricity measured statically, then we know by definition of electrical quantity

$$F = - \frac{\eta_1 \eta_2}{r^2} \dots\dots\dots\dots\dots\dots\dots (128);$$

and this will be satisfied provided

$$\eta_1 = E e_1 \text{ and } \eta_2 = E e_2 \dots\dots\dots\dots\dots\dots (129);$$

so that the quantity E previously determined in Prop. XIII. is the number by which the electrodynamic measure of any quantity of electricity must be multiplied to obtain its electrostatic measure.

That electric current which, circulating round a ring whose area is unity, produces the same effect on a distant magnet as a magnet would produce whose strength is unity and length unity placed perpendicularly to the plane of the ring, is a unit current; and E units of electricity, measured statically, traverse the section of this current in one second,—these units being such that any two of them, placed at unit of distance, repel each other with unit of force.

We may suppose either that E units of positive electricity move in the positive direction through the wire, or that E units of negative electricity move in the negative direction, or, thirdly, that $\frac{1}{2}E$ units of positive electricity move in the positive direction, while $\frac{1}{2}E$ units of negative electricity move in the negative direction at the same time.

The last is the supposition on which MM. Weber and Kohlrausch* proceed, who have found

$$\frac{1}{2}E = 155,370,000,000 \dots\dots\dots\dots (130),$$

the unit of length being the millimetre, and that of time being one second, whence

$$E = 310,740,000,000 \dots\dots\dots\dots (131).$$

PROP. XVI.—To find the rate of propagation of transverse vibrations through the elastic medium of which the cells are composed, on the supposition that its elasticity is due entirely to forces acting between pairs of particles.

By the ordinary method of investigation we know that

$$V = \sqrt{\frac{m}{\rho}} \dots\dots\dots\dots (132),$$

where m is the coefficient of transverse elasticity, and ρ is the density. By referring to the equations of Part I., it will be seen that if ρ is the density of the matter of the vortices, and μ is the "coefficient of magnetic induction,"

$$\mu = \pi\rho \dots\dots\dots\dots (133);$$

whence $$\pi m = V^2\mu \dots\dots\dots\dots (134);$$

and by (108), $$E = V\sqrt{\mu} \dots\dots\dots\dots (135).$$

In air or vacuum $\mu = 1$, and therefore

$$\left.\begin{array}{l} V = E \\ \quad = 310,740,000,000 \text{ millimetres per second} \\ \quad = 193,088 \text{ miles per second} \end{array}\right\} \dots\dots\dots (136).$$

* *Abhandlungen der König. Sächsischen Gesellschaft*, Vol. III. (1857), p. 260.

The velocity of light in air, as determined by M. Fizeau*, is 70,843 leagues per second (25 leagues to a degree) which gives

$$V = 314,858,000,000 \text{ millimetres}$$

$$= 195,647 \text{ miles per second } \dots\dots\dots\dots (137).$$

The velocity of transverse undulations in our hypothetical medium, calculated from the electro-magnetic experiments of MM. Kohlrausch and Weber, agrees so exactly with the velocity of light calculated from the optical experiments of M. Fizeau, that we can scarcely avoid the inference that *light consists in the transverse undulations of the same medium which is the cause of electric and magnetic phenomena.*

PROP. XVII.—To find the electric capacity of a Leyden jar composed of any given dielectric placed between two conducting surfaces.

Let the electric tensions or potentials of the two surfaces be Ψ_1 and Ψ_2. Let S be the area of each surface, and θ the distance between them, and let e and $-e$ be the quantities of electricity on each surface; then the capacity

$$C = \frac{e}{\Psi_1 - \Psi_2} \dots\dots\dots\dots\dots\dots\dots (138).$$

Within the dielectric we have the variation of Ψ perpendicular to the surface

$$= \frac{\Psi_1 - \Psi_2}{\theta}.$$

Beyond either surface this variation is zero.

Hence by (115) applied at the surface, the electricity on unit of area is

$$\frac{\Psi_1 - \Psi_2}{4\pi E^2 \theta} \dots\dots\dots\dots\dots\dots\dots (139);$$

and we deduce the whole capacity of the apparatus,

$$C = \frac{S}{4\pi E^2 \theta} \dots\dots\dots\dots\dots\dots\dots (140);$$

so that the quantity of electricity required to bring the one surface to a

---

* *Comptes Rendus*, Vol. XXIX. (1849), p. 90. In Galbraith and Haughton's *Manual of Astronomy*, M. Fizeau's result is stated at 169,944 geographical miles of 1000 fathoms, which gives 193,118 statute miles; the value deduced from aberration is 192,000 miles.

given tension varies directly as the surface, inversely as the thickness, and inversely as the square of E.

Now the coefficient of induction of dielectrics is deduced from the capacity of induction-apparatus formed of them; so that if D is that coefficient, D varies inversely as E^2, and is unity for air. Hence

$$D = \frac{V^2}{V_1^2 \mu} \dots\dots\dots\dots\dots\dots(141),$$

where V and V_1 are the velocities of light in air and in the medium. Now if i is the index of refraction, $\dfrac{V}{V_1} = i$, and

$$D = \frac{i^2}{\mu} \dots\dots\dots\dots\dots\dots(142);$$

so that the inductive power of a dielectric varies directly as the square of the index of refraction, and inversely as the magnetic inductive power.

In dense media, however, the optical, electric, and magnetic phenomena may be modified in different degrees by the particles of gross matter; and their mode of arrangement may influence these phenomena differently in different directions. The axes of optical, electric, and magnetic properties will probably coincide; but on account of the unknown and probably complicated nature of the reactions of the heavy particles on the ætherial medium, it may be impossible to discover any general numerical relations between the optical, electric, and magnetic ratios of these axes.

It seems probable, however, that the value of E, for any given axis, depends upon the velocity of light whose vibrations are parallel to that axis, or whose plane of polarization is perpendicular to that axis.

In a uniaxal crystal, the axial value of E will depend on the velocity of the extraordinary ray, and the equatorial value will depend on that of the ordinary ray.

In "positive" crystals, the axial value of E will be the least and in negative the greatest.

The value of D_1, which varies inversely as E^2, will, *cæteris paribus*, be greatest for the axial direction in positive crystals, and for the equatorial direction in negative crystals, such as Iceland spar. If a spherical portion of a crystal, radius $= a$, be suspended in a field of electric force which would act on unit of electricity with force = 1, and if D_1 and D_2 be the coefficients of dielectric induction along the two axes in the plane of rotation, then if θ be the inclination of the axis to the electric force, the moment tending to turn the sphere will be

$$\tfrac{3}{2} \frac{(D_1 - D_2)}{(2D_1 + 1)(2D_2 + 1)} \, I^2 a^3 \sin 2\theta \; \dots\dots\dots\dots (143),$$

and the axis of greatest dielectric induction (D_1) will tend to become parallel to the lines of electric force.

PART IV.

THE THEORY OF MOLECULAR VORTICES APPLIED TO THE ACTION OF MAGNETISM ON POLARIZED LIGHT.

The connexion between the distribution of lines of magnetic force and that of electric currents may be completely expressed by saying that the work done on a unit of imaginary magnetic matter, when carried round any closed curve, is proportional to the quantity of electricity which passes through the closed curve. The mathematical form of this law may be expressed as in equations (9)*, which I here repeat, where a, β, γ are the rectangular components of magnetic intensity, and p, q, r are the rectangular components of steady electric currents,

$$
\begin{aligned}
p &= \frac{1}{4\pi} \left(\frac{d\gamma}{dy} - \frac{d\beta}{dz} \right) \\
q &= \frac{1}{4\pi} \left(\frac{da}{dz} - \frac{d\gamma}{dx} \right) \\
r &= \frac{1}{4\pi} \left(\frac{d\beta}{dx} - \frac{da}{dy} \right)
\end{aligned}
\right\} \dots\dots\dots\dots\dots\dots (9).
$$

The same mathematical connexion is found between other sets of phenomena in physical science.

(1) If a, β, γ represent displacements, velocities, or forces, then p, q, r will be rotatory displacements, velocities of rotation, or moments of couples producing rotation, in the elementary portions of the mass.

---

* *Phil. Mag.* March, 1861 [p. 462 of this vol.].

(2) If a, β, γ represent rotatory displacements in a uniform and continuous substance, then p, q, r represent the *relative* linear displacement of a particle with respect to those in its immediate neighbourhood. See a paper by Prof. W. Thomson "On a Mechanical Representation of Electric, Magnetic, and Galvanic Forces," *Camb. and Dublin Math. Journal*, Jan. 1847.

(3) If a, β, γ represent the rotatory velocities of vortices whose centres are fixed, then p, q, r represent the velocities with which loose particles placed between them would be carried along. See the second part of this paper (*Phil. Mag.* April, 1861) [p. 469].

It appears from all these instances that the connexion between magnetism and electricity has the same mathematical form as that between certain pairs of phenomena, of which one has a *linear* and the other a *rotatory* character. Professor Challis* conceives magnetism to consist in currents of a fluid whose direction corresponds with that of the lines of magnetic force; and electric currents, on this theory, are accompanied by, if not dependent on, a rotatory motion of the fluid about the axis of the current. Professor Helmholtz† has investigated the motion of an incompressible fluid, and has conceived lines drawn so as to correspond at every point with the instantaneous axis of rotation of the fluid there. He has pointed out that the lines of fluid motion are arranged according to the same laws with respect to the lines of rotation, as those by which the lines of magnetic force are arranged with respect to electric currents. On the other hand, in this paper I have regarded magnetism as a phenomenon of rotation, and electric currents as consisting of the actual translation of particles, thus assuming the inverse of the relation between the two sets of phenomena.

Now it seems natural to suppose that all the direct effects of any cause which is itself of a longitudinal character, must be themselves longitudinal, and that the direct effects of a rotatory cause must be themselves rotatory. A motion of translation along an axis cannot produce a rotation about that axis unless it meets with some special mechanism, like that of a screw, which connects a motion in a given direction along the axis with a rotation in a given direction round it; and a motion of rotation, though it may produce tension along the axis, cannot of itself produce a current in one direction along the axis rather than the other.

* *Phil. Mag.* December, 1860, January and February, 1861.

† Crelle, *Journal*, Vol. LV. (1858), p. 25.

Electric currents are known to produce effects of transference in the direction of the current. They transfer the electrical state from one body to another, and they transfer the elements of electrolytes in opposite directions, but they do not* cause the plane of polarization of light to rotate when the light traverses the axis of the current.

On the other hand, the magnetic state is not characterized by any strictly longitudinal phenomenon. The north and south poles differ only in their names, and these names might be exchanged without altering the statement of any magnetic phenomenon; whereas the positive and negative poles of a battery are completely distinguished by the different elements of water which are evolved there. The magnetic state, however, is characterized by a well-marked rotatory phenomenon discovered by Faraday†—the rotation of the plane of polarized light when transmitted along the lines of magnetic force.

When a transparent diamagnetic substance has a ray of plane-polarized light passed through it, and if lines of magnetic force are then produced in the substance by the action of a magnet or of an electric current, the plane of polarization of the transmitted light is found to be changed, and to be turned through an angle depending on the intensity of the magnetizing force within the substance.

The direction of this rotation in diamagnetic substances is the same as that in which positive electricity must circulate round the substance in order to produce the actual magnetizing force within it; or if we suppose the horizontal part of terrestrial magnetism to be the magnetizing force acting on the substance, the plane of polarization would be turned in the direction of the earth's true rotation, that is, from west upwards to east.

In paramagnetic substances, M. Verdet‡ has found that the plane of polarization is turned in the opposite direction, that is, in the direction in which negative electricity would flow if the magnetization were effected by a helix surrounding the substance.

In both cases the absolute direction of the rotation is the same, whether the light passes from north to south or from south to north,—a fact which distinguishes this phenomenon from the rotation produced by quartz, turpentine, &c.,

---

* Faraday, *Experimental Researches*, 951—954, and 2216—2220.
† Ibid., Series XIX.
‡ *Comptes Rendus*, Vol. XLIII. p. 529; Vol. XLIV. p. 1209.

in which the absolute direction of rotation is reversed when that of the light is reversed. The rotation in the latter case, whether related to an axis, as in quartz, or not so related, as in fluids, indicates a relation between the direction of the ray and the direction of rotation, which is similar in its formal expression to that between the longitudinal and rotatory motions of a right-handed or a left-handed screw; and it indicates some property of the substance the mathematical form of which exhibits right-handed or left-handed relations, such as are known to appear in the external forms of crystals having these properties. In the magnetic rotation no such relation appears, but the direction of rotation is directly connected with that of the magnetic lines, in a way which seems to indicate that magnetism is really a phenomenon of rotation.

The transference of electrolytes in fixed directions by the electric current, and the rotation of polarized light in fixed directions by magnetic force, are the facts the consideration of which has induced me to regard magnetism as a phenomenon of rotation, and electric currents as phenomena of translation, instead of following out the analogy pointed out by Helmholtz, or adopting the theory propounded by Professor Challis.

The theory that electric currents are linear, and magnetic forces rotatory phenomena, agrees so far with that of Ampère and Weber; and the hypothesis that the magnetic rotations exist wherever magnetic force extends, that the centrifugal force of these rotations accounts for magnetic attractions, and that the inertia of the vortices accounts for induced currents, is supported by the opinion of Professor W. Thomson[*]. In fact the whole theory of molecular vortices developed in this paper has been suggested to me by observing the direction in which those investigators who study the action of media are looking for the explanation of electro-magnetic phenomena.

Professor Thomson has pointed out that the cause of the magnetic action on light must be a real rotation going on in the magnetic field. A *right-handed* circularly polarized ray of light is found to travel with a different velocity according as it passes from north to south, or from south to north, along a line of magnetic force. Now, whatever theory we adopt about the direction of vibrations in plane-polarized light, the geometrical arrangement of the parts of the medium during the passage of a right-handed circularly polarized ray is exactly the same whether the ray is moving north or south. The only difference

---

[*] See Nichol's *Cyclopædia*, art. "Magnetism, Dynamical Relations of," edition 1860; *Proceedings of Royal Society*, June 1856 and June 1861; and *Phil. Mag.* 1857.

is, that the particles describe their circles in opposite directions. Since, therefore, the *configuration* is the same in the two cases, the forces acting between particles must be the same in both, and the motions due to these forces must be equal in velocity if the medium was originally at rest; but if the medium be in a state of rotation, either as a whole or in molecular vortices, the circular vibrations of light may differ in velocity according as their direction is similar or contrary to that of the vortices.

We have now to investigate whether the hypothesis developed in this paper—that magnetic force is due to the centrifugal force of small vortices, and that these vortices consist of the same matter the vibrations of which constitute light—leads to any conclusions as to the effect of magnetism on polarized light. We suppose transverse vibrations to be transmitted through a magnetized medium. How will the propagation of these vibrations be affected by the circumstance that portions of that medium are in a state of rotation?

In the following investigation, I have found that the only effect which the rotation of the vortices will have on the light will be to make the plane of polarization rotate in the *same* direction as the vortices, through an angle proportional—

(A) to the thickness of the substance,

(B) to the resolved part of the magnetic force parallel to the ray,

(C) to the index of refraction of the ray,

(D) inversely to the square of the wave-length in air,

(E) to the *mean radius* of the vortices,

(F) to the capacity for magnetic induction.

A and B have been fully investigated by M. Verdet*, who has shewn that the rotation is strictly proportional to the thickness and to the magnetizing force, and that, when the ray is inclined to the magnetizing force, the rotation is as the cosine of that inclination. D has been supposed to give the true relation between the rotation of different rays; but it is probable that C must be taken into account in an accurate statement of the phenomena. The rotation varies, not exactly inversely as the square of the wave length, but a little faster; so that for the highly refrangible rays the rotation is greater than that given by this law, but more nearly as the index of refraction divided by the square of the wave-length.

* *Annales de Chimie et de Physique*, sér. 3, Vol. XLI. p. 370; Vol. XLIII. p. 37.

The relation (E) between the amount of rotation and the size of the vortices shews that different substances may differ in rotating power independently of any observable difference in other respects. We know nothing of the absolute size of the vortices; and on our hypothesis the optical phenomena are probably the only data for determining their relative size in different substances.

On our theory, the direction of the rotation of the plane of polarization depends on that of the mean moment of momenta, or *angular momentum,* of the molecular vortices; and since M. Verdet has discovered that magnetic substances have an effect on light opposite to that of diamagnetic substances, it follows that the molecular rotation must be opposite in the two classes of substances.

We can no longer, therefore, consider diamagnetic bodies as being those whose coefficient of magnetic induction is less than that of space empty of gross matter. We must admit the diamagnetic state to be the *opposite* of the paramagnetic; and that the vortices, or at least the influential majority of them, in diamagnetic substances, revolve in the direction in which positive electricity revolves in the magnetizing bobbin, while in paramagnetic substances they revolve in the opposite direction.

This result agrees so far with that part of the theory of M. Weber[*] which refers to the paramagnetic and diamagnetic conditions. M. Weber supposes the electricity in paramagnetic bodies to revolve the same way as the surrounding helix, while in diamagnetic bodies it revolves the opposite way. Now if we regard negative or resinous electricity as a substance the absence of which constitutes positive or vitreous electricity, the results will be those actually observed. This will be true independently of any other hypothesis than that of M. Weber about magnetism and diamagnetism, and does not require us to admit either M. Weber's theory of the mutual action of electric particles in motion, or our theory of cells and cell-walls.

I am inclined to believe that iron differs from other substances in the manner of its action as well as in the intensity of its magnetism; and I think its behaviour may be explained on our hypothesis of molecular vortices, by supposing that the particles of the *iron itself* are set in rotation by the tangential action of the vortices, in an opposite direction to their own. These large heavy particles would thus be revolving exactly as we have supposed the

---

[*] Taylor's *Scientific Memoirs,* Vol. v. p. 477.

infinitely small particles constituting electricity to revolve, but without being free like them to change their place and form currents.

The whole *energy* of rotation of the magnetized field would thus be greatly increased, as we know it to be; but the *angular momentum* of the iron particles would be opposite to that of the æthereal cells and immensely greater, so that the total angular momentum of the substance will be in the direction of rotation of the iron, or the reverse of that of the vortices. Since, however, the angular momentum depends on the absolute size of the revolving portions of the substance, it may depend on the state of aggregation or chemical arrangement of the elements, as well as on the ultimate nature of the components of the substance. Other phenomena in nature seem to lead to the conclusion that all substances are made up of a number of parts, finite in size, the particles composing these parts being themselves capable of internal motion.

PROP. XVIII.—To find the angular momentum of a vortex.

The angular momentum of any material system about an axis is the sum of the products of the mass, dm, of each particle multiplied by twice the area it describes about that axis in unit of time; or if A is the angular momentum about the axis of x,

$$A = \Sigma dm \left(y \frac{dz}{dt} - z \frac{dy}{dt} \right).$$

As we do not know the distribution of density within the vortex, we shall determine the relation between the angular momentum and the energy of the vortex which was found in Prop. VI.

Since the time of revolution is the same throughout the vortex, the mean angular velocity ω will be uniform and $= \dfrac{a}{r}$, where a is the velocity at the circumference, and r the radius. Then

$$A = \Sigma dm r^2 \omega,$$

and the energy

$$E = \tfrac{1}{2} \Sigma dm r^2 \omega^2 = \tfrac{1}{2} A \omega,$$

$$= \frac{1}{8\pi} \mu a^2 V \text{ by Prop. VI.*}$$

whence

$$A = \frac{1}{4\pi} \mu r a V \quad \dotfill \quad (144)$$

* *Phil. Mag.* April 1861 [p. 472 of this vol.].

for the axis of x, with similar expressions for the other axes, V being the volume, and r the radius of the vortex.

PROP. XIX.—To determine the conditions of undulatory motion in a medium containing vortices, the vibrations being perpendicular to the direction of propagation.

Let the waves be plane-waves propagated in the direction of z, and let the axis of x and y be taken in the directions of greatest and least elasticity in the plane xy. Let x and y represent the displacement parallel to these axes, which will be the same throughout the same wave-surface, and therefore we shall have x and y functions of z and t only.

Let X be the tangential stress on unit of area parallel to xy, tending to move the part next the origin in the direction of x.

Let Y be the corresponding tangential stress in the direction of y.

Let k_1 and k_2 be the coefficients of elasticity with respect to these two kinds of tangential stress; then, if the medium is at rest,

$$X = k_1 \frac{dx}{dz}, \quad Y = k_2 \frac{dy}{dz}.$$

Now let us suppose vortices in the medium whose velocities are represented as usual by the symbols a, β, γ, and let us suppose that the value of a is increasing at the rate $\frac{da}{dt}$, on account of the action of the tangential stresses alone, there being no electromotive force in the field. The angular momentum in the stratum whose area is unity, and thickness dz, is therefore increasing at the rate $\frac{1}{4\pi}\mu r \frac{da}{dt} dz$; and if the part of the force Y which produces this effect is Y', then the moment of Y' is $-Y'dz$, so that $Y' = -\frac{1}{4\pi}\mu r \frac{da}{dt}$.

The complete value of Y when the vortices are in a state of varied motion is

$$\left. \begin{aligned} Y &= k_2 \frac{dy}{dz} - \frac{1}{4\pi}\mu r \frac{da}{dt} \\ X &= k_1 \frac{dx}{dz} + \frac{1}{4\pi}\mu r \frac{d\beta}{dt} \end{aligned} \right\} \dots\dots\dots\dots\dots\dots (145).$$

Similarly,

The whole force acting upon a stratum whose thickness is dz and area unity, is $\dfrac{dX}{dz}\,dz$ in the direction of x, and $\dfrac{dY}{dz}\,dz$ in direction of y. The mass of the stratum is ρdz, so that we have as the equations of motion,

$$\left.\begin{aligned}
\rho\,\frac{d^2x}{dt^2}&=\frac{dX}{dz}=k_1\frac{d^2x}{dz^2}+\frac{d}{dz}\frac{1}{4\pi}\mu r\frac{d\beta}{dt}\\
\rho\,\frac{d^2y}{dt^2}&=\frac{dY}{dz}=k_2\frac{d^2y}{dz^2}-\frac{d}{dz}\frac{1}{4\pi}\mu r\frac{d\alpha}{dt}
\end{aligned}\right\}\ \ \dots\dots\dots\dots\dots(146).$$

Now the changes of velocity $\dfrac{d\alpha}{dt}$ and $\dfrac{d\beta}{dt}$ are produced by the motion of the medium containing the vortices, which distorts and twists every element of its mass; so that we must refer to Prop. X.* to determine these quantities in terms of the motion. We find there at equation (68),

$$da=a\,\frac{d}{dx}\,\delta x+\beta\,\frac{d}{dy}\,\delta x+\gamma\,\frac{d}{dz}\,\delta x\dots\dots\dots\dots\dots(68).$$

Since δx and δy are functions of z and t only, we may write this equation

$$\left.\begin{aligned}
\frac{d\alpha}{dt}&=\gamma\,\frac{d^2x}{dz\,dt}\\
\frac{d\beta}{dt}&=\gamma\,\frac{d^2y}{dz\,dt}
\end{aligned}\right\}\dots\dots\dots\dots\dots\dots(147),$$

and in like manner,

so that if we now put $k_1=a^2\rho$, $k_2=b^2\rho$, and $\dfrac{1}{4\pi}\dfrac{\mu r}{\rho}\gamma=c^2$, we may write the equations of motion

$$\left.\begin{aligned}
\frac{d^2x}{dt^2}&=a^2\frac{d^2x}{dz^2}+c^2\frac{d^2y}{dz^2dt}\\
\frac{d^2y}{dt^2}&=b^2\frac{d^2y}{dz^2}-c^2\frac{d^2x}{dz^2dt}
\end{aligned}\right\}\ \dots\dots\dots\dots\dots(148).$$

These equations may be satisfied by the values

$$\left.\begin{aligned}
x&=A\cos\,(nt-mz+\alpha)\\
y&=B\sin\,(nt-mz+\alpha)
\end{aligned}\right\}\dots\dots\dots\dots\dots(149),$$

provided

and

$$\left.\begin{aligned}
(n^2-m^2a^2)\,A&=m^2nc^2B\\
(n^2-m^2b^2)\,B&=m^2nc^2A
\end{aligned}\right\}\dots\dots\dots\dots\dots(150).$$

* *Phil. Mag.* May 1861 [p. 481 of this vol.].

Multiplying the last two equations together, we find

$$(n^2 - m^2a^2)(n^2 - m^2b^2) = m^4n^2c^4 \dots\dots\dots\dots\dots(151)$$

an equation quadratic with respect to m^2, the solution of which is

$$m^2 = \frac{2n^2}{a^2 + b^2 \mp \sqrt{(a^2 - b^2)^2 + 4n^2c^4}} \dots\dots\dots\dots(152).$$

These values of m^2 being put in the equations (150) will each give a ratio of A and B,

$$\frac{A}{B} = \frac{a^2 - b^2 \mp \sqrt{(a^2 - b^2)^2 + 4n^2c^4}}{2nc^2},$$

which being substituted in equations (149), will satisfy the original equations (148). The most general undulation of such a medium is therefore compounded of two elliptic undulations of different eccentricities travelling with different velocities and rotating in opposite directions. The results may be more easily explained in the case in which $a = b$; then

$$m^2 = \frac{n^2}{a^2 \mp nc^2} \text{ and } A = \mp B \dots\dots\dots\dots (153).$$

Let us suppose that the value of A is unity for both vibrations, then we shall have

$$\left.\begin{array}{l} x = \cos\left(nt - \dfrac{nz}{\sqrt{a^2 - nc^2}}\right) + \cos\left(nt - \dfrac{nz}{\sqrt{a^2 + nc^2}}\right) \\[2ex] y = -\sin\left(nt - \dfrac{nz}{\sqrt{a^2 - nc^2}}\right) + \sin\left(nt - \dfrac{nz}{\sqrt{a^2 + nc^2}}\right) \end{array}\right\} \dots\dots\dots(154).$$

The first terms of x and y represent a circular vibration in the negative direction, and the second term a circular vibration in the positive direction, the positive having the greatest velocity of propagation. Combining the terms, we may write

$$\left.\begin{array}{l} x = 2\cos(nt - pz)\cos qz \\ y = 2\cos(nt - pz)\sin qz \end{array}\right\} \dots\dots\dots\dots\dots (155),$$

where

$$\left.\begin{array}{l} p = \dfrac{n}{2\sqrt{a^2 - nc^2}} + \dfrac{n}{2\sqrt{a^2 + nc^2}} \\[2ex] q = \dfrac{n}{2\sqrt{a^2 - nc^2}} - \dfrac{n}{2\sqrt{a^2 + nc^2}} \end{array}\right\} \dots\dots\dots\dots(156).$$

and

These are the equations of an undulation consisting of a plane vibration whose periodic time is $\dfrac{2\pi}{n}$, and wave-length $\dfrac{2\pi}{p} = \lambda$, propagated in the direction of z with a velocity $\dfrac{n}{p} = v$, while the plane of the vibration revolves about the axis of z in the positive direction so as to complete a revolution when $z = \dfrac{2\pi}{q}$.

Now let us suppose c^2 small, then we may write

$$p = \frac{n}{a} \text{ and } q = \frac{n^2 c^2}{2a^3} \quad \dotfill (157);$$

and remembering that $c^2 = \dfrac{1}{4\pi} \dfrac{r}{\rho} \mu\gamma$, we find

$$q = \frac{\pi}{2} \frac{r}{\rho} \frac{\mu\gamma}{\lambda^2 v} \quad \dotfill (158).$$

Here r is the radius of the vortices, an unknown quantity. ρ is the density of the luminiferous medium in the body, which is also unknown; but if we adopt the theory of Fresnel, and make s the density in space devoid of gross matter, then

$$\rho = si^2 \quad \dotfill (159),$$

where i is the index of refraction.

On the theory of MacCullagh and Neumann,

$$\rho = s \quad \dotfill (160)$$

in all bodies.

μ is the coefficient of magnetic induction, which is unity in empty space or in air.

γ is the velocity of the vortices at their circumference estimated in the ordinary units. Its value is unknown, but it is proportional to the intensity of the magnetic force.

Let Z be the magnetic intensity of the field, measured as in the case of terrestrial magnetism, then the intrinsic energy in air per unit of volume is

$$\frac{1}{8\pi} Z^2 = \frac{1}{8\pi} \pi s \gamma^2,$$

where s is the density of the magnetic medium in air, which we have reason to believe the same as that of the luminiferous medium. We therefore put

$$\gamma = \frac{1}{\sqrt{\pi s}} Z \quad \dotfill (161),$$

λ is the wave-length of the undulation in the substance. Now if Λ be the wave-length for the same ray in air, and i the index of refraction of that ray in the body,

$$\lambda = \frac{\Lambda}{i} \dots\dots\dots\dots\dots\dots\dots\dots (162).$$

Also v, the velocity of light in the substance, is related to V, the velocity of light in air, by the equation

$$v = \frac{V}{i} \dots\dots\dots\dots\dots\dots\dots\dots (163).$$

Hence if z be the thickness of the substance through which the ray passes, the angle through which the plane of polarization will be turned will be in degrees,

$$\theta = \frac{180}{\pi} \, qz \dots\dots\dots\dots\dots\dots\dots (164);$$

or, by what we have now calculated,

$$\theta = 90^\circ \frac{1}{\sqrt{\pi}} \cdot \frac{r}{s^{\frac{3}{2}}} \frac{\mu i Z z}{\Lambda^2 V} \dots\dots\dots\dots\dots (165).$$

In this expression all the quantities are known by experiment except r, the radius of the vortices in the body, and s, the density of the luminiferous medium in air.

The experiments of M. Verdet* supply all that is wanted except the determination of Z in absolute measure; and this would also be known for all his experiments, if the value of the galvanometer deflection for a semi-rotation of the testing bobbin in a known magnetic field, such as that due to terrestrial magnetism at Paris, were once for all determined.

* *Annales de Chimie et de Physique*, sér. 3, Vol. XLI. p. 370.

[From the *London, Edinburgh, and Dublin Philosophical Magazine and Journal of Science.*
Vol. XXVII. Fourth Series.]

XXIV. *On Reciprocal Figures and Diagrams of Forces.*

RECIPROCAL figures are such that the properties of the first relative to the second are the same as those of the second relative to the first. Thus inverse figures and polar reciprocals are instances of two different kinds of reciprocity.

The kind of reciprocity which we have here to do with has reference to figures consisting of straight lines joining a system of points, and forming closed rectilinear figures; and it consists in the directions of all lines in the one figure having a constant relation to those of the lines in the other figure which correspond to them.

In plane figures, corresponding lines may be either parallel, perpendicular, or at any constant angle. Lines meeting in a point in one figure form a closed polygon in the other.

In figures in space, the lines in one figure are perpendicular to planes in the other, and the planes corresponding to lines which meet in a point form a closed polyhedron.

The conditions of reciprocity may be considered from a purely geometrical point of view; but their chief importance arises from the fact that either of the figures being considered as a system of points acted on by forces along the lines of connexion, the other figure is a diagram of forces, in which these forces are represented in plane figures by lines, and in solid figures by the areas of planes.

The properties of the "triangle" and "polygon" of forces have been long known, and the "diagram" of forces has been used in the case of the funicular polygon; but I am not aware of any more general statement of the method of drawing diagrams of forces before Professor Rankine applied it to frames, roofs, &c. in his *Applied Mechanics*, p. 137, &c. The "polyhedron of forces," or the equilibrium of forces perpendicular and proportional to the areas of the faces of a polyhedron, has, I believe, been enunciated independently at various times; but the application to a "frame" is given by Professor Rankine in the *Philosophical Magazine*, February, 1864.

I propose to treat the question geometrically, as reciprocal figures are subject to certain conditions besides those belonging to diagrams of forces.

On Reciprocal Plane Figures.

Definition.—Two plane figures are reciprocal when they consist of an equal number of lines, so that corresponding lines in the two figures are parallel, and corresponding lines which converge to a point in one figure form a closed polygon in the other.

Note.—If corresponding lines in the two figures, instead of being parallel are at right angles or any other angle, they may be made parallel by turning one of the figures round in its own plane.

Since every polygon in one figure has three or more sides, every point in the other figure must have three or more lines converging to it; and since every line in the one figure has two and only two extremities to which lines converge, every line in the other figure must belong to two, and only two closed polygons. The simplest plane figure fulfilling these conditions is that formed by the six lines which join four points in pairs. The reciprocal figure consists of six lines parallel respectively to these, the points in the one figure corresponding to triangles in the other.

General Relation between the Numbers of Points, Lines, and Polygons in Reciprocal Figures.

The effect of drawing a line, one of whose extremities is a point connected with the system of lines already drawn, is either to introduce one new point into the system, or to complete one new polygon, or to divide a polygon into two parts, according as it is drawn to an isolated point, or a point already connected with the system. Hence the sum of points and polygons in the system is increased by one for every new line. But the simplest figure consists of four points, four polygons, and six lines. Hence the sum of the points and polygons must always exceed the number of lines by two.

Note.—This is the same relation which connects the numbers of summits, faces, and edges of polyhedra.

Conditions of indeterminateness and impossibility in drawing reciprocal Diagrams.

Taking any line parallel to one of the lines of the figure for a base, every new point is to be determined by the intersection of two new lines. Calling s the number of points or summits, e the number of lines or edges, and f the number of polygons or faces, the assumption of the first line determines two points, and the remaining $s-2$ points are determined by $2(s-2)$ lines. Hence if

$$e = 2s - 3,$$

every point may be determined. If e be less, the form of the figure will be in some respects indeterminate; and if e be greater, the construction of the figure will be impossible, unless certain conditions among the directions of the lines are fulfilled.

These are the conditions of drawing any diagram in which the directions of the lines are arbitrarily given; but when one diagram is already drawn in which e is greater than $2s-3$, the directions of the lines will not be altogether arbitrary, but will be subject to $e-(2s-3)$ conditions.

Now if e', s', f' be the values of e, s, and f in the reciprocal diagram

$$e = e', \quad s = f', \quad f = s',$$
$$e = s + f - 2, \quad e' = s' + f' - 2.$$

Hence if $s = f$, $e = 2i - 2$; and there will be one condition connecting the directions of the lines of the original diagram, and this condition will ensure the possibility of constructing the reciprocal diagram. If

$$s > f, \quad e > 2s - 2, \quad \text{and} \quad e' < 2s' - 2;$$

so that the construction of the reciprocal diagram will be possible, but indeterminate to the extent of $s - f$ variables.

If $s < f$, the construction of the reciprocal diagram will be impossible unless $(s - f)$ conditions be fulfilled in the original diagram.

If any number of the points of the figure are so connected among themselves as to form an equal number of closed polygons, the conditions of constructing the reciprocal figure must be found by considering these points separately, and then examining their connexion with the rest.

Let us now consider a few cases of reciprocal figures in detail. The simplest case is that of the figure formed by the six lines connecting four points in a plane. If we now draw the six lines connecting the centres of the four circles which pass through three out of the four points, we shall have a reciprocal figure, the corresponding lines in the two figures being at right angles.

Fig. 1.

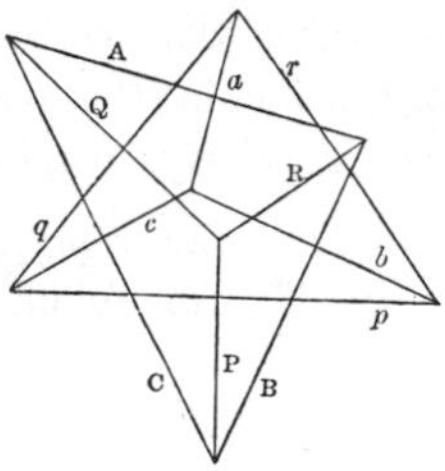

The reciprocal figure formed in this way is definite in size and position; but any figure similar to it and placed in any position is still reciprocal to the original figure. If the reciprocal figures are lettered as in fig. 1, we shall have the relation

$$\frac{AP}{ap} = \frac{BQ}{bq} = \frac{CR}{cr}.$$

In figures 2 and II. we have a pair of reciprocal figures in which the lines are more numerous, but the construction very easy. There are seven points in each figure corresponding to seven polygons in the other.

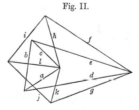

Fig. 2.   Fig. II.

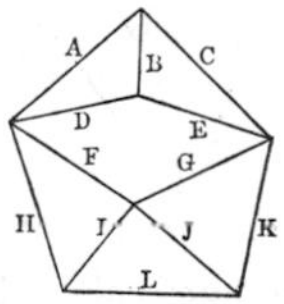

The four points of triple concourse of lines ABC, BDE, HIL, LJK correspond to four triangles, abc, bde, hil, ljk.

The three points of quadruple concourse $ADFH$, $CEGK$, $IFGJ$ correspond to three quadrilaterals, $adfh$, $cegk$, $ifgj$.

The five triangles ADB, EBC, GJK, IJL, HIF correspond to five points of triple concourse, adb, ebc, gjk, ijl, hif.

The quadrilateral *DEGF* corresponds to the point of quadruple concourse *degf*.

The pentagon *ACKLH* corresponds to the meeting of the five lines *acklh*.

In drawing the reciprocal of fig. 2, it is best to begin with a point of triple concourse. The reciprocal triangle of this point being drawn, determines three lines of the new figure. If the other extremities of any of the lines meeting in this point are points of triple concourse, we may in the same way determine more lines, two at a time. In drawing these lines, we have only to remember that those lines which in the first figure form a polygon, start from one point in the reciprocal figure. In this way we may proceed as long as we can always determine all the lines except two of each successive polygon.

The case represented in figs. 3 and III. is an instance of a pair of reciprocal figures fulfilling the conditions of possibility and determinateness, but

Fig. III.

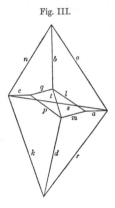

Fig. 3.

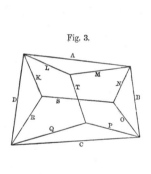

presenting a slight difficulty in drawing by the foregoing rule. Each figure has here eight points and eight polygons; but after we have drawn the lines *s*, *n*, *o*, *k*, *r*, we cannot proceed with the figure simply by drawing the last two lines of polygons, because the next polygons to be drawn are quadrilaterals, and we have only one side of each given. The easiest way to proceed is to produce *abcd* till they form a quadrilateral, then to draw a subsidiary figure similar to *tlmpq*, with *abcd* similarly situated, and then to reduce the latter figure to such a scale and position that *a*, *b*, *c*, *d* coincide in both figures.

In figures 4 and IV. the condition that the number of polygons is equal to the number of points is not fulfilled. In fig. 4 there are five points and

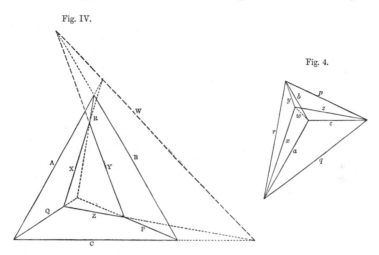

Fig. IV.

Fig. 4.

six triangles; in fig. IV. there are six points, two triangles, and three quadrilaterals. Hence if fig. 4 is given, fig. IV. is indeterminate to the extent of one variable, besides the elements of scale and position. In fact when we have drawn ABC and indicated the directions of P, Q, R, we may fix on any point of P as one of the angles of XYZ and complete the triangle XYZ. The size of XYZ is therefore indeterminate. Conversely, if fig. IV. is given, fig. 4 cannot be constructed unless one condition be fulfilled. That condition is that P, Q, and R meet in a point. When this is fulfilled, it follows by geometry that the points of concourse of A and X, B and Y, and C and Z lie in one straight line W, which is parallel to w in fig. 4. The condition may also be expressed by saying that fig. IV. must be a perspective projection of a polyhedron whose quadrilateral faces are planes. The planes of these faces intersect at the concourse of P, Q, R, and those of the triangular faces intersect in the line W.

Figs. 5 and V. represent another case of the same kind. In fig. 5 we have six points and eight triangles; fig. V. is therefore capable of two degrees of variability, and is subject to two conditions.

The conditions are that the four intersections of corresponding sides of opposite quadrilaterals in fig. V. shall lie in one straight line, parallel to the

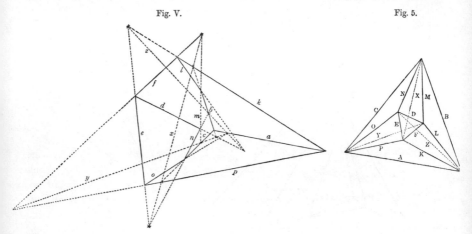

Fig. V.   Fig. 5.

line joining the opposite points of fig. 5 which correspond to these quadrilaterals. There are three such lines marked *x*, *y*, *z*, and four points of intersection lie on each line.

We may express this condition also by saying that fig. V. must be a perspective projection of a plane-sided polyhedron, the intersections of opposite planes being the lines *x*, *y*, *z*.

In fig. 6, let *ABCDE* be a portion of a polygon bounded by other polygons of which the edges are *PQRST*, one or more of these edges meeting each angle of the polygon.

In fig. VI., let *abcde* be lines parallel to *ABCDE* and meeting in a point, and let these be terminated by the lines *pqrst* parallel to *PQRST*, one or more of these lines completing each sector of fig. VI.

In fig. 6 draw *Y* through the intersections of *AC* and *PQ*, and in fig. VI. draw *y* through the intersections of *a*, *p* and *c*, *q*. Then the figures of six lines *ABCPQY* and *abcpqy* will be reciprocal, and *y* will be parallel to *Y*. Draw *X* parallel to *x*, and through the intersections of *TX* and *CE* draw *Z*, and in fig. VI. draw *z* through the intersections of *cx* and *et*; then *CDETXZ* and *cdetxz* will be reciprocal, and Z will be parallel to z. Then through the intersections of AE and YZ draw W, and through those of ay and ez draw w; and since $ACEYZW$ and *aceyzw* are reciprocal, W will be parallel to w.

Fig. 6.

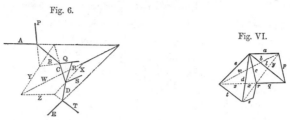

Fig. VI.

By going round the remaining sides of the polygon $ABCDE$ in the same way, we should find by the intersections of lines another point, the line joining which with the intersection of AE would be parallel to w, and therefore we should have three points in one line; namely, the intersection of Y and Z, the point determined by a similar process carried on on the other part of the circumference of the polygon, and the intersection of A and E; and we should find similar conditions for every pair of sides of every polygon.

Now the conditions of the figure 6 being a perspective projection of a plane-sided polyhedron are exactly the same. For A being the intersection of the faces AP and AB, and C that of BC and QC, the intersection AC will be a point in the intersection of the faces AP and CQ.

Similarly the intersection PQ will be another point in it, so that Y is the line of intersection of the faces AP and CQ.

In the same way Z is the intersection of ET and CQ, so that the intersection of Y and Z is a point in the intersection of AP and ET.

Another such point can be determined by going round the remaining sides of the polygon; and these two points, together with the intersections of the lines AE, must all be in one straight line, namely, the intersection of the faces AP and ET.

Hence the conditions of the possibility of reciprocity in plane figures are the same as those of each figure being the perspective projection of a plane-sided polyhedron. When the number of points is in every part of the figure equal to or less than the number of polygons, this condition is fulfilled of itself. When the number of points exceeds the number of polygons, there will be an impossible case, unless certain conditions are fulfilled so that certain sets of intersections lie in straight lines.

Application to Statics.

The doctrine of reciprocal figures may be treated in a purely geometrical manner, but it may be much more clearly understood by considering it as a method of calculating the forces among a system of points in equilibrium; for,

If forces represented in magnitude by the lines of a figure be made to act between the extremities of the corresponding lines of the reciprocal figure, then the points of the reciprocal figure will all be in equilibrium under the action of these forces.

For the forces which meet in any point are parallel and proportional to the sides of a polygon in the other figure.

If the points between which the forces are to act are known, the problem of determining the relations among the magnitudes of the forces so as to produce equilibrium will be indeterminate, determinate, or impossible, according as the construction of the reciprocal figure is so.

Reciprocal figures are mechanically reciprocal; that is, either may be taken as representing a system of points, and the other as representing the magnitudes of the forces acting between them.

In figures like 1, 2 and II., 3 and III., in which the equation

$$e = 2s - 2$$

is true, the forces are determinate in their ratios; so that one being given, the rest may be found.

When $e > 2s - 2$, as in figs. 4 and 5, the forces are indeterminate, so that more than one must be known to determine the rest, or else certain relations among them must be given, such as those arising from the elasticity of the parts of a frame.

When $e < 2s - 2$, the determination of the forces is impossible except under certain conditions. Unless these be fulfilled, as in figs. IV. and V., no forces along the lines of the figure can keep its points in equilibrium, and the figure, considered as a frame, may be said to be loose.

When the conditions are fulfilled, the pieces of the frame can support forces, but in such a way that a small disfigurement of the frame may produce infinitely great forces in some of the pieces, or may throw the frame into a loose condition at once.

The conditions, however, of the possibility of determining the ratios of the forces in a frame are not coextensive with those of finding a figure perfectly reciprocal to the frame. The condition of determinate forces is

$$e = 2s - 2 \; ;$$

the condition of reciprocal figures is that every line belongs to two polygons only, and

$$e = s + f - 2.$$

In fig. 7 we have six points connected by ten lines in such a way that the forces are all determinate; but since the line L is a side of three triangles, we cannot draw a reciprocal figure, for we should have to draw a straight line l with three ends.

If we attempt to draw the reciprocal figure as in fig. VII., we shall find that, in order to represent the reciprocals of all the lines of fig. 7 and fix their relations, we must repeat two of them, as h and e by h' and e, so as to form a parallelogram. Fig. VII. is then a complete representation of the relations of the force which would produce equilibrium in fig. 7; but it is redundant by the repetition of h and e, and the two figures are not reciprocal.

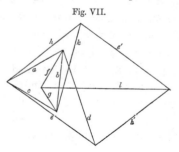

Fig. VII.

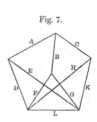

Fig. 7.

On Reciprocal Figures in three dimensions.

Definition.—Figures in three dimensions are reciprocal when they can be so placed that every line in the one figure is perpendicular to a plane face of the other, and every point of concourse of lines in the one figure is represented by a closed polyhedron with plane faces.

The simplest case is that of five points in space with their ten connecting lines, forming ten triangular faces enclosing five tetrahedrons. By joining the five points which are the centres of the spheres circumscribing these five tetrahedrons, we have a reciprocal figure of the kind described by Professor Rankine in the *Philosophical Magazine*, February 1864; and forces proportional to the areas of the triangles of one figure, if applied along the corresponding lines of connexion of the other figure, will keep its points in equilibrium.

In order to have perfect reciprocity between two figures, each figure must be made up of a number of closed polyhedra having plane faces of separation, and such that each face belongs to two and only two polyhedra, corresponding to the extremities of the reciprocal line in the other figure. Every line in the figure is the intersection of three or more plane faces, because the plane face in the reciprocal figure is bounded by three or more straight lines.

Let s be the number of points or summits, e the number of lines or edges, f the number of faces, and c the number of polyhedra or cells. Then if about one of the summits in which polyhedra meet, and σ edges and η faces, we describe a polyhedral cell, it will have ϕ faces and σ summits and η edges, and we shall have

$$\eta = \phi + \sigma - 2;$$

s, the number of summits, will be decreased by one and increased by σ;

c, the number of cells, will be increased by one;

f, the number of faces, will be increased by ϕ;

e, the number of edges, will be increased by η;

so that $e + c - (s + f)$ will be increased by $\eta + 1 - (\sigma + \phi - 1)$, which is zero, or this quantity is constant. Now in the figure of five points already discussed, $e = 10$, $c = 5$, $s = 5$, $f = 10$; so that generally

$$e + c = s + f,$$

in figures made up of cells in the way described.

The condition of a reciprocal figure being indeterminate, determinate, or impossible except in particular cases, is

$$e \gtreqless 3s - 5.$$

This condition is sufficient to determine the possibility of finding a system of forces along the edges which will keep the summits in equilibrium; but it is manifest that the mechanical problem may be solved, though the reciprocal figure cannot be constructed owing to the condition of all the sides of a face lying in a plane not being fulfilled, or owing to a face belonging to more than two cells. Hence the mechanical interest of reciprocal figures in space rapidly diminishes with their complexity.

Diagrams of forces in which the forces are represented by lines may be always constructed in space as well as in a plane, but in general some of the lines must be repeated.

Thus in the figure of five points, each point is the meeting place of four lines. The forces in these lines may be represented by five gauche quadrilaterals (that is, quadrilaterals not in one plane); and one of these being chosen, the other four may be applied to its sides and to each other so as to form five sides of a gauche hexahedron. The sixth side, that opposite the original quadrilateral, will be a parallelogram, the opposite sides of which are repetitions of the same line.

We have thus a complete but redundant diagram of forces consisting of eight points joined by twelve lines, two pairs of the lines being repetitions. This is a more convenient though less elegant construction of a diagram of forces, and it never becomes geometrically impossible as long as the problem is mechanically possible, however complicated the original figure may be.

[From the *Royal Society Transactions*, Vol. CLV.]

XXV. *A Dynamical Theory of the Electromagnetic Field.*

(Received October 27,—Read December 8, 1864.)

PART I.

INTRODUCTORY.

(1) THE most obvious mechanical phenomenon in electrical and magnetical experiments is the mutual action by which bodies in certain states set each other in motion while still at a sensible distance from each other. The first step, therefore, in reducing these phenomena into scientific form, is to ascertain the magnitude and direction of the force acting between the bodies, and when it is found that this force depends in a certain way upon the relative position of the bodies and on their electric or magnetic condition, it seems at first sight natural to explain the facts by assuming the existence of something either at rest or in motion in each body, constituting its electric or magnetic state, and capable of acting at a distance according to mathematical laws.

In this way mathematical theories of statical electricity, of magnetism, of the mechanical action between conductors carrying currents, and of the induction of currents have been formed. In these theories the force acting between the two bodies is treated with reference only to the condition of the bodies and their relative position, and without any express consideration of the surrounding medium.

These theories assume, more or less explicitly, the existence of substances the particles of which have the property of acting on one another at a distance by attraction or repulsion. The most complete development of a theory of this kind is that of M. W. Weber*, who has made the same theory include electrostatic and electromagnetic phenomena.

In doing so, however, he has found it necessary to assume that the force between two electric particles depends on their relative velocity, as well as on their distance.

This theory, as developed by MM. W. Weber and C. Neumann†, is exceedingly ingenious, and wonderfully comprehensive in its application to the phenomena of statical electricity, electromagnetic attractions, induction of currents and diamagnetic phenomena; and it comes to us with the more authority, as it has served to guide the speculations of one who has made so great an advance in the practical part of electric science, both by introducing a consistent system of units in electrical measurement, and by actually determining electrical quantities with an accuracy hitherto unknown.

(2) The mechanical difficulties, however, which are involved in the assumption of particles acting at a distance with forces which depend on their velocities are such as to prevent me from considering this theory as an ultimate one, though it may have been, and may yet be useful in leading to the coordination of phenomena.

I have therefore preferred to seek an explanation of the fact in another direction, by supposing them to be produced by actions which go on in the surrounding medium as well as in the excited bodies, and endeavouring to explain the action between distant bodies without assuming the existence of forces capable of acting directly at sensible distances.

(3) The theory I propose may therefore be called a theory of the *Electromagnetic Field*, because it has to do with the space in the neighbourhood of the electric or magnetic bodies, and it may be called a *Dynamical* Theory, because it assumes that in that space there is matter in motion, by which the observed electromagnetic phenomena are produced.

(4) The electromagnetic field is that part of space which contains and surrounds bodies in electric or magnetic conditions.

* " Electrodynamische Maassbestimmungen." *Leipzic Trans.* Vol. i. 1849, and Taylor's *Scientific Memoirs*, Vol. v. art. xiv.
† *Explicare tentatur quomodo fiat ut lucis planum polarizationis per vires electricas vel magneticas declinetur.*—Halis Saxonum, 1858.

It may be filled with any kind of matter, or we may endeavour to render it empty of all gross matter, as in the case of Geissler's tubes and other so-called vacua.

There is always, however, enough of matter left to receive and transmit the undulations of light and heat, and it is because the transmission of these radiations is not greatly altered when transparent bodies of measurable density are substituted for the so-called vacuum, that we are obliged to admit that the undulations are those of an æthereal substance, and not of the gross matter, the presence of which merely modifies in some way the motion of the æther.

We have therefore some reason to believe, from the phenomena of light and heat, that there is an æthereal medium filling space and permeating bodies, capable of being set in motion and of transmitting that motion from one part to another, and of communicating that motion to gross matter so as to heat it and affect it in various ways.

(5) Now the energy communicated to the body in heating it must have formerly existed in the moving medium, for the undulations had left the source of heat some time before they reached the body, and during that time the energy must have been half in the form of motion of the medium and half in the form of elastic resilience. From these considerations Professor W. Thomson has argued*, that the medium must have a density capable of comparison with that of gross matter, and has even assigned an inferior limit to that density.

(6) We may therefore receive, as a datum derived from a branch of science independent of that with which we have to deal, the existence of a pervading medium, of small but real density, capable of being set in motion, and of transmitting motion from one part to another with great, but not infinite, velocity.

Hence the parts of this medium must be so connected that the motion of one part depends in some way on the motion of the rest; and at the same time these connexions must be capable of a certain kind of elastic yielding, since the communication of motion is not instantaneous, but occupies time.

The medium is therefore capable of receiving and storing up two kinds of energy, namely, the "actual" energy depending on the motions of its parts, and "potential" energy, consisting of the work which the medium will do in recovering from displacement in virtue of its elasticity.

* "On the Possible Density of the Luminiferous Medium, and on the Mechanical Value of a Cubic Mile of Sunlight," *Transactions of the Royal Society of Edinburgh* (1854), p. 57.

The propagation of undulations consists in the continual transformation of one of these forms of energy into the other alternately, and at any instant the amount of energy in the whole medium is equally divided, so that half is energy of motion, and half is elastic resilience.

(7) A medium having such a constitution may be capable of other kinds of motion and displacement than those which produce the phenomena of light and heat, and some of these may be of such a kind that they may be evidenced to our senses by the phenomena they produce.

(8) Now we know that the luminiferous medium is in certain cases acted on by magnetism; for Faraday* discovered that when a plane polarized ray traverses a transparent diamagnetic medium in the direction of the lines of magnetic force produced by magnets or currents in the neighbourhood, the plane of polarization is caused to rotate.

This rotation is always in the direction in which positive electricity must be carried round the diamagnetic body in order to produce the actual magnetization of the field.

M. Verdet† has since discovered that if a paramagnetic body, such as solution of perchloride of iron in ether, be substituted for the diamagnetic body, the rotation is in the opposite direction.

Now Professor W. Thomson‡ has pointed out that no distribution of forces acting between the parts of a medium whose only motion is that of the luminous vibrations, is sufficient to account for the phenomena, but that we must admit the existence of a motion in the medium depending on the magnetization, in addition to the vibratory motion which constitutes light.

It is true that the rotation by magnetism of the plane of polarization has been observed only in media of considerable density; but the properties of the magnetic field are not so much altered by the substitution of one medium for another, or for a vacuum, as to allow us to suppose that the dense medium does anything more than merely modify the motion of the ether. We have therefore warrantable grounds for inquiring whether there may not be a motion of the ethereal medium going on wherever magnetic effects are observed, and

---

* *Experimental Researches*, Series XIX.

† *Comptes Rendus* (1856, second half year, p. 529, and 1857, first half year, p. 1209).

‡ *Proceedings of the Royal Society*, June 1856 and June 1861.

we have some reason to suppose that this motion is one of rotation, having the direction of the magnetic force as its axis.

(9) We may now consider another phenomenon observed in the electro-magnetic field. When a body is moved across the lines of magnetic force it experiences what is called an electromotive force; the two extremities of the body tend to become oppositely electrified, and an electric current tends to flow through the body. When the electromotive force is sufficiently powerful, and is made to act on certain compound bodies, it decomposes them, and causes one of their components to pass towards one extremity of the body, and the other in the opposite direction.

Here we have evidence of a force causing an electric current in spite of resistance; electrifying the extremities of a body in opposite ways, a condition which is sustained only by the action of the electromotive force, and which, as soon as that force is removed, tends, with an equal and opposite force, to produce a counter current through the body and to restore the original electrical state of the body; and finally, if strong enough, tearing to pieces chemical compounds and carrying their components in opposite directions, while their natural tendency is to combine, and to combine with a force which can generate an electromotive force in the reverse direction.

This, then, is a force acting on a body caused by its motion through the electromagnetic field, or by changes occurring in that field itself; and the effect of the force is either to produce a current and heat the body, or to decompose the body, or, when it can do neither, to put the body in a state of electric polarization,—a state of constraint in which opposite extremities are oppositely electrified, and from which the body tends to relieve itself as soon as the disturbing force is removed.

(10) According to the theory which I propose to explain, this "electro-motive force" is the force called into play during the communication of motion from one part of the medium to another, and it is by means of this force that the motion of one part causes motion in another part. When electromotive force acts on a conducting circuit, it produces a current, which, as it meets with resistance, occasions a continual transformation of electrical energy into heat, which is incapable of being restored again to the form of electrical energy by any reversal of the process.

(11) But when electromotive force acts on a dielectric it produces a state of polarization of its parts similar in distribution to the polarity of the parts of a mass of iron under the influence of a magnet, and like the magnetic polarization, capable of being described as a state in which every particle has its opposite poles in opposite conditions*.

In a dielectric under the action of electromotive force, we may conceive that the electricity in each molecule is so displaced that one side is rendered positively and the other negatively electrical, but that the electricity remains entirely connected with the molecule, and does not pass from one molecule to another. The effect of this action on the whole dielectric mass is to produce a general displacement of electricity in a certain direction. This displacement does not amount to a current, because when it has attained to a certain value it remains constant, but it is the commencement of a current, and its variations constitute currents in the positive or the negative direction according as the displacement is increasing or decreasing. In the interior of the dielectric there is no indication of electrification, because the electrification of the surface of any molecule is neutralized by the opposite electrification of the surface of the molecules in contact with it; but at the bounding surface of the dielectric, where the electrification is not neutralized, we find the phenomena which indicate positive or negative electrification.

The relation between the electromotive force and the amount of electric displacement it produces depends on the nature of the dielectric, the same electromotive force producing generally a greater electric displacement in solid dielectrics, such as glass or sulphur, than in air.

(12) Here, then, we perceive another effect of electromotive force, namely, electric displacement, which according to our theory is a kind of elastic yielding to the action of the force, similar to that which takes place in structures and machines owing to the want of perfect rigidity of the connexions.

(13) The practical investigation of the inductive capacity of dielectrics is rendered difficult on account of two disturbing phenomena. The first is the conductivity of the dielectric, which, though in many cases exceedingly small, is not altogether insensible. The second is the phenomenon called electric absorp-

---

* Faraday, *Experimental Researches*, Series XI.; Mossotti, *Mem. della Soc. Italiana* (Modena), Vol. XXIV. Part 2, p. 49.

tion*, in virtue of which, when the dielectric is exposed to electromotive force, the electric displacement gradually increases, and when the electromotive force is removed, the dielectric does not instantly return to its primitive state, but only discharges a portion of its electrification, and when left to itself gradually acquires electrification on its surface, as the interior gradually becomes depolarized. Almost all solid dielectrics exhibit this phenomenon, which gives rise to the residual charge in the Leyden jar, and to several phenomena of electric cables described by Mr F. Jenkin†.

(14) We have here two other kinds of yielding besides the yielding of the perfect dielectric, which we have compared to a perfectly elastic body. The yielding due to conductivity may be compared to that of a viscous fluid (that is to say, a fluid having great internal friction), or a soft solid on which the smallest force produces a permanent alteration of figure increasing with the time during which the force acts. The yielding due to electric absorption may be compared to that of a cellular elastic body containing a thick fluid in its cavities. Such a body, when subjected to pressure, is compressed by degrees on account of the gradual yielding of the thick fluid; and when the pressure is removed it does not at once recover its figure, because the elasticity of the substance of the body has gradually to overcome the tenacity of the fluid before it can regain complete equilibrium.

Several solid bodies in which no such structure as we have supposed can be found, seem to possess a mechanical property of this kind‡; and it seems probable that the same substances, if dielectrics, may possess the analogous electrical property, and if magnetic, may have corresponding properties relating to the acquisition, retention, and loss of magnetic polarity.

(15) It appears therefore that certain phenomena in electricity and magnetism lead to the same conclusion as those of optics, namely, that there is an æthereal medium pervading all bodies, and modified only in degree by their presence; that the parts of this medium are capable of being set in motion by electric currents and magnets; that this motion is communicated from one

---

* Faraday, *Experimental Researches*, 1233—1250.

† *Reports of British Association*, 1859, p. 248; and *Report of Committee of Board of Trade on Submarine Cables*, pp. 136 & 464.

‡ As, for instance, the composition of glue, treacle, &c., of which small plastic figures are made, which after being distorted gradually recover their shape.

part of the medium to another by forces arising from the connexions of those parts; that under the action of these forces there is a certain yielding depending on the elasticity of these connexions; and that therefore energy in two different forms may exist in the medium, the one form being the actual energy of motion of its parts, and the other being the potential energy stored up in the connexions, in virtue of their elasticity.

(16) Thus, then, we are led to the conception of a complicated mechanism capable of a vast variety of motion, but at the same time so connected that the motion of one part depends, according to definite relations, on the motion of other parts, these motions being communicated by forces arising from the relative displacement of the connected parts, in virtue of their elasticity. Such a mechanism must be subject to the general laws of Dynamics, and we ought to be able to work out all the consequences of its motion, provided we know the form of the relation between the motions of the parts.

(17) We know that when an electric current is established in a conducting circuit, the neighbouring part of the field is characterized by certain magnetic properties, and that if two circuits are in the field, the magnetic properties of the field due to the two currents are combined. Thus each part of the field is in connexion with both currents, and the two currents are put in connexion with each other in virtue of their connexion with the magnetization of the field. The first result of this connexion that I propose to examine, is the induction of one current by another, and by the motion of conductors in the field.

The second result, which is deduced from this, is the mechanical action between conductors carrying currents. The phenomenon of the induction of currents has been deduced from their mechanical action by Helmholtz * and Thomson †. I have followed the reverse order, and deduced the mechanical action from the laws of induction. I have then described experimental methods of determining the quantities L, M, N, on which these phenomena depend.

(18) I then apply the phenomena of induction and attraction of currents to the exploration of the electromagnetic field, and the laying down systems of lines of magnetic force which indicate its magnetic properties. By exploring

---

* "Conservation of Force," *Physical Society of Berlin*, 1847; and Taylor's *Scientific Memoirs*, 1853, p. 114.

† *Reports of the British Association*, 1848; *Philosophical Magazine*, Dec. 1851.

the same field with a magnet, I shew the distribution of its equipotential magnetic surfaces, cutting the lines of force at right angles.

In order to bring these results within the power of symbolical calculation, I then express them in the form of the General Equations of the Electromagnetic Field. These equations express—

(A) The relation between electric displacement, true conduction, and the total current, compounded of both.

(B) The relation between the lines of magnetic force and the inductive coefficients of a circuit, as already deduced from the laws of induction.

(C) The relation between the strength of a current and its magnetic effects, according to the electromagnetic system of measurement.

(D) The value of the electromotive force in a body, as arising from the motion of the body in the field, the alteration of the field itself, and the variation of electric potential from one part of the field to another.

(E) The relation between electric displacement, and the electromotive force which produces it.

(F) The relation between an electric current, and the electromotive force which produces it.

(G) The relation between the amount of free electricity at any point, and the electric displacements in the neighbourhood.

(H) The relation between the increase or diminution of free electricity and the electric currents in the neighbourhood.

There are twenty of these equations in all, involving twenty variable quantities.

(19) I then express in terms of these quantities the intrinsic energy of the Electromagnetic Field as depending partly on its magnetic and partly on its electric polarization at every point.

From this I determine the mechanical force acting, 1st, on a moveable conductor carrying an electric current; 2ndly, on a magnetic pole; 3rdly, on an electrified body.

The last result, namely, the mechanical force acting on an electrified body, gives rise to an independent method of electrical measurement founded on its electrostatic effects. The relation between the units employed in the two methods is shewn to depend on what I have called the "electric elasticity" of the medium, and to be a velocity, which has been experimentally determined by MM. Weber and Kohlrausch.

I then shew how to calculate the electrostatic capacity of a condenser, and the specific inductive capacity of a dielectric.

The case of a condenser composed of parallel layers of substances of different electric resistances and inductive capacities is next examined, and it is shewn that the phenomenon called electric absorption will generally occur, that is, the condenser, when suddenly discharged, will after a short time shew signs of a *residual* charge.

(20) The general equations are next applied to the case of a magnetic disturbance propagated through a non-conducting field, and it is shewn that the only disturbances which can be so propagated are those which are transverse to the direction of propagation, and that the velocity of propagation is the velocity v, found from experiments such as those of Weber, which expresses the number of electrostatic units of electricity which are contained in one electromagnetic unit.

This velocity is so nearly that of light, that it seems we have strong reason to conclude that light itself (including radiant heat, and other radiations if any) is an electromagnetic disturbance in the form of waves propagated through the electromagnetic field according to electromagnetic laws. If so, the agreement between the elasticity of the medium as calculated from the rapid alternations of luminous vibrations, and as found by the slow processes of electrical experiments, shews how perfect and regular the elastic properties of the medium must be when not encumbered with any matter denser than air. If the same character of the elasticity is retained in dense transparent bodies, it appears that the square of the index of refraction is equal to the product of the specific dielectric capacity and the specific magnetic capacity. Conducting media are shewn to absorb such radiations rapidly, and therefore to be generally opaque.

The conception of the propagation of transverse magnetic disturbances to the exclusion of normal ones is distinctly set forth by Professor Faraday* in his "Thoughts on Ray Vibrations." The electromagnetic theory of light, as

* *Philosophical Magazine*, May 1846, or *Experimental Researches*, III. p. 447.

proposed by him, is the same in substance as that which I have begun to develope in this paper, except that in 1846 there were no data to calculate the velocity of propagation.

(21) The general equations are then applied to the calculation of the coefficients of mutual induction of two circular currents and the coefficient of self-induction in a coil. The want of uniformity of the current in the different parts of the section of a wire at the commencement of the current is investigated, I believe for the first time, and the consequent correction of the coefficient of self-induction is found.

These results are applied to the calculation of the self-induction of the coil used in the experiments of the Committee of the British Association on Standards of Electric Resistance, and the value compared with that deduced from the experiments.

PART II.

ON ELECTROMAGNETIC INDUCTION.

Electromagnetic Momentum of a Current.

(22) We may begin by considering the state of the field in the neighbourhood of an electric current. We know that magnetic forces are excited in the field, their direction and magnitude depending according to known laws upon the form of the conductor carrying the current. When the strength of the current is increased, all the magnetic effects are increased in the same proportion. Now, if the magnetic state of the field depends on motions of the medium, a certain force must be exerted in order to increase or diminish these motions, and when the motions are excited they continue, so that the effect of the connexion between the current and the electromagnetic field surrounding it, is to endow the current with a kind of momentum, just as the connexion between the driving-point of a machine and a fly-wheel endows the driving-point with an additional momentum, which may be called the momentum of the fly-wheel reduced to the driving-point. The unbalanced force acting on the driving-point increases this momentum, and is measured by the rate of its increase.

In the case of electric currents, the resistance to sudden increase or diminution of strength produces effects exactly like those of momentum, but the amount of this momentum depends on the shape of the conductor and the relative position of its different parts.

Mutual Action of two Currents.

(23) If there are two electric currents in the field, the magnetic force at any point is that compounded of the forces due to each current separately, and since the two currents are in connexion with every point of the field, they will be in connexion with each other, so that any increase or diminution of the one will produce a force acting with or contrary to the other.

Dynamical Illustration of Reduced Momentum.

(24) As a dynamical illustration, let us suppose a body C so connected with two independent driving-points A and B that its velocity is p times that of A together with q times that of B. Let u be the velocity of A, v that of B, and w that of C, and let δx, δy, δz be their simultaneous displacements, then by the general equation of dynamics*,

$$C \frac{dw}{dt} \delta z = X \delta x + Y \delta y,$$

where X and Y are the forces acting at A and B.

But
$$\frac{dw}{dt} = p \frac{du}{dt} + q \frac{dv}{dt},$$

and
$$\delta z = p \delta x + q \delta y.$$

Substituting, and remembering that δx and δy are independent,

$$\left. \begin{aligned} X &= \frac{d}{dt} \left(C p^2 u + C p q v \right) \\ Y &= \frac{d}{dt} \left(C p q u + C q^2 v \right) \end{aligned} \right\} \quad \dots\dots\dots\dots\dots\dots\dots (1).$$

We may call $C p^2 u + C p q v$ the momentum of C referred to A, and $C p q u + C q^2 v$ its momentum referred to B; then we may say that the effect of the force X is to increase the momentum of C referred to A, and that of Y to increase its momentum referred to B.

* Lagrange, *Méc. Anal.* II. 2, § 5.

If there are many bodies connected with A and B in a similar way but with different values of p and q, we may treat the question in the same way by assuming

$$L = \Sigma\,(Cp^2), \quad M = \Sigma\,(Cpq), \quad \text{and} \quad N = \Sigma\,(Cq^2),$$

where the summation is extended to all the bodies with their proper values of C, p, and q. Then the momentum of the system referred to A is

$$Lu + Mv,$$

and referred to B,

$$Mu + Nv,$$

and we shall have

$$\left.\begin{aligned} X &= \frac{d}{dt}\,(Lu + Mv) \\[1mm] Y &= \frac{d}{dt}\,(Mu + Nv) \end{aligned}\right\} \quad \ldots\ldots\ldots\ldots\ldots\ldots\ldots (2),$$

where X and Y are the external forces acting on A and B.

(25) To make the illustration more complete we have only to suppose that the motion of A is resisted by a force proportional to its velocity, which we may call Ru, and that of B by a similar force, which we may call Sv, R and S being coefficients of resistance. Then if ξ and η are the forces on A and B,

$$\left.\begin{aligned} \xi &= X + Ru = Ru + \frac{d}{dt}\,(Lu + Mv) \\[1mm] \eta &= Y + Sv = Sv + \frac{d}{dt}(Mu + Nv) \end{aligned}\right\} \quad \ldots\ldots\ldots\ldots\ldots\ldots (3).$$

If the velocity of A be increased at the rate $\dfrac{du}{dt}$, then in order to prevent B from moving a force, $\eta = \dfrac{d}{dt}(Mu)$ must be applied to it.

This effect on B, due to an increase of the velocity of A, corresponds to the electromotive force on one circuit arising from an increase in the strength of a neighbouring circuit.

This dynamical illustration is to be considered merely as assisting the reader to understand what is meant in mechanics by Reduced Momentum. The facts of the induction of currents as depending on the variations of the quantity called Electromagnetic Momentum, or Electrotonic State, rest on the experiments of Faraday[*], Felici[†], &c.

---

[*] *Experimental Researches*, Series I., IX.   [†] *Annales de Chimie*, sér. 3, XXXIV. (1852), p. 64.

Coefficients of Induction for Two Circuits.

(26) In the electromagnetic field the values of L, M, N depend on the distribution of the magnetic effects due to the two circuits, and this distribution depends only on the form and relative position of the circuits. Hence L, M, N are quantities depending on the form and relative position of the circuits, and are subject to variation with the motion of the conductors. It will be presently seen that L, M, N are geometrical quantities of the nature of lines, that is, of one dimension in space; L depends on the form of the first conductor, which we shall call A, N on that of the second, which we shall call B, and M on the relative position of A and B.

(27) Let ξ be the electromotive force acting on A, x the strength of the current, and R the resistance, then Rx will be the resisting force. In steady currents the electromotive force just balances the resisting force, but in variable currents the resultant force $\xi - Rx$ is expended in increasing the "electromagnetic momentum," using the word momentum merely to express that which is generated by a force acting during a time, that is, a velocity existing in a body.

In the case of electric currents, the force in action is not ordinary mechanical force, at least we are not as yet able to measure it as common force, but we call it electromotive force, and the body moved is not merely the electricity in the conductor, but something outside the conductor, and capable of being affected by other conductors in the neighbourhood carrying currents. In this it resembles rather the reduced momentum of a driving-point of a machine as influenced by its mechanical connexions, than that of a simple moving body like a cannon ball, or water in a tube.

Electromagnetic Relations of two Conducting Circuits.

(28) In the case of two conducting circuits, A and B, we shall assume that the electromagnetic momentum belonging to A is

$$Lx + My,$$

and that belonging to B, $\qquad Mx + Ny,$

where L, M, N correspond to the same quantities in the dynamical illustration, except that they are supposed to be capable of variation when the conductors A or B are moved.

Then the equation of the current x in A will be

$$\xi = Rx + \frac{d}{dt}(Lx + My) \dotfill (4),$$

and that of y in B

$$\eta = Sy + \frac{d}{dt}(Mx + Ny) \dotfill (5),$$

where ξ and η are the electromotive forces, x and y the currents, and R and S the resistances in A and B respectively.

Induction of one Current by another.

(29) Case 1st. Let there be no electromotive force on B, except that which arises from the action of A, and let the current of A increase from 0 to the value x, then

$$Sy + \frac{d}{dt}(Mx + Ny) = 0,$$

whence

$$Y = \int_0^t y \, dt = -\frac{M}{S} x, \dotfill (6)$$

that is, a quantity of electricity Y, being the total induced current, will flow through B when x rises from 0 to x. This is induction by variation of the current in the primary conductor. When M is positive, the induced current due to increase of the primary current is negative.

Induction by Motion of Conductor.

(30) Case 2nd. Let x remain constant, and let M change from M to M', then

$$Y = -\frac{M' - M}{S} x ; \dotfill (7)$$

so that if M is increased, which it will be by the primary and secondary circuits approaching each other, there will be a negative induced current, the total quantity of electricity passed through B being Y.

This is induction by the relative motion of the primary and secondary conductors.

Equation of Work and Energy.

(31) To form the equation between work done and energy produced, multiply (1) by x and (2) by y, and add

$$\xi x + \eta y = Rx^2 + Sy^2 + x\,\frac{d}{dt}\,(Lx + My) + y\,\frac{d}{dt}\,(Mx + Ny)\ldots\ldots\ldots(8).$$

Here ξx is the work done in unit of time by the electromotive force ξ acting on the current x and maintaining it, and ηy is the work done by the electromotive force η. Hence the left-hand side of the equation represents the work done by the electromotive forces in unit of time.

Heat produced by the Current.

(32) On the other side of the equation we have, first,

$$Rx^2 + Sy^2 = H\ldots\ldots\ldots\ldots\ldots\ldots\ldots\ldots(9),$$

which represents the work done in overcoming the resistance of the circuits in unit of time. This is converted into heat. The remaining terms represent work not converted into heat. They may be written

$$\tfrac{1}{2}\,\frac{d}{dt}\,(Lx^2 + 2Mxy + Ny^2) + \tfrac{1}{2}\,\frac{dL}{dt}\,x^2 + \frac{dM}{dt}\,xy + \tfrac{1}{2}\,\frac{dN}{dt}\,y^2.$$

Intrinsic Energy of the Currents.

(33) If L, M, N are constant, the whole work of the electromotive forces which is not spent against resistance will be devoted to the development of the currents. The whole intrinsic energy of the currents is therefore

$$\tfrac{1}{2}Lx^2 + Mxy + \tfrac{1}{2}Ny^2 = E \ldots\ldots\ldots\ldots\ldots (10).$$

This energy exists in a form imperceptible to our senses, probably as actual motion, the seat of this motion being not merely the conducting circuits, but the space surrounding them.

Mechanical Action between Conductors.

(34) The remaining terms,

$$\tfrac{1}{2}\,\frac{dL}{dt}\,x^2 + \frac{dM}{dt}\,xy + \tfrac{1}{2}\,\frac{dN}{dt}\,y^2 = W \ldots\ldots\ldots\ldots (11)$$

represent the work done in unit of time arising from the variations of L, M, and N, or, what is the same thing, alterations in the form and position of the conducting circuits A and B.

Now if work is done when a body is moved, it must arise from ordinary mechanical force acting on the body while it is moved. Hence this part of the expression shews that there is a mechanical force urging every part of the conductors themselves in that direction in which L, M, and N will be most increased.

The existence of the electromagnetic force between conductors carrying currents is therefore a direct consequence of the joint and independent action of each current on the electromagnetic field. If A and B are allowed to approach a distance ds, so as to increase M from M to M' while the currents are x and y, then the work done will be

$$(M' - M)\,xy,$$

and the force in the direction of ds will be

$$\frac{dM}{ds}\,xy\dots\dots\dots\dots\dots\dots\dots\dots\dots\dots(12),$$

and this will be an attraction if x and y are of the same sign, and if M is increased as A and B approach.

It appears, therefore, that if we admit that the unresisted part of electro-motive force goes on as long as it acts, generating a self-persistent state of the current, which we may call (from mechanical analogy) its electromagnetic momentum, and that this momentum depends on circumstances external to the conductor, then both induction of currents and electromagnetic attractions may be proved by mechanical reasoning.

What I have called electromagnetic momentum is the same quantity which is called by Faraday * the electrotonic state of the circuit, every change of which involves the action of an electromotive force, just as change of momentum involves the action of mechanical force.

If, therefore, the phenomena described by Faraday in the Ninth Series of his *Experimental Researches* were the only known facts about electric currents, the laws of Ampère relating to the attraction of conductors carrying currents,

* *Experimental Researches*, Series I. 60, &c.

as well as those of Faraday about the mutual induction of currents, might be deduced by mechanical reasoning.

In order to bring these results within the range of experimental verification, I shall next investigate the case of a single current, of two currents, and of the six currents in the electric balance, so as to enable the experimenter to determine the values of L, M, N.

Case of a single Circuit.

(35) The equation of the current x in a circuit whose resistance is R, and whose coefficient of self-induction is L, acted on by an external electromotive force ξ, is

$$\xi - Rx = \frac{d}{dt} Lx \dots\dots\dots\dots\dots\dots\dots (13).$$

When ξ is constant, the solution is of the form

$$x = b + (a - b) e^{-\frac{R}{L}t},$$

where a is the value of the current at the commencement, and b is its final value.

The total quantity of electricity which passes in time t, where t is great, is

$$\int_0^t x \, dt = bt + (a - b) \frac{L}{R} \dots\dots\dots\dots\dots (14).$$

The value of the integral of x^2 with respect to the time is

$$\int_0^t x^2 dt = b^2 t + (a - b) \frac{L}{R} \left(\frac{3b + a}{2} \right) \dots\dots\dots\dots (15).$$

The actual current changes gradually from the initial value a to the final value b, but the values of the integrals of x and x^2 are the same as if a steady current of intensity $\frac{1}{2}(a + b)$ were to flow for a time $2\frac{L}{R}$, and were then succeeded by the steady current b. The time $2\frac{L}{R}$ is generally so minute a fraction of a second, that the effects on the galvanometer and dynamometer may be calculated as if the impulse were instantaneous.

If the circuit consists of a battery and a coil, then, when the circuit is first completed, the effects are the same as if the current had only half its final strength during the time $2\dfrac{L}{R}$. This diminution of the current, due to induction, is sometimes called the counter-current.

(36) If an additional resistance r is suddenly thrown into the circuit, as by breaking contact, so as to force the current to pass through a thin wire of resistance r, then the original current is $a = \dfrac{\xi}{R}$, and the final current is

$$b = \frac{\xi}{R+r}.$$

The current of induction is then $\frac{1}{2}\xi\dfrac{2R+r}{R(R+r)}$, and continues for a time $2\dfrac{L}{R+r}$. This current is greater than that which the battery can maintain in the two wires R and r, and may be sufficient to ignite the thin wire r.

When contact is broken by separating the wires in air, this additional resistance is given by the interposed air, and since the electromotive force across the new resistance is very great, a spark will be forced across.

If the electromotive force is of the form $E\sin pt$, as in the case of a coil revolving in the magnetic field, then

$$x = \frac{E}{\rho}\sin(pt - a),$$

where $\rho^2 = R^2 + L^2p^2$, and $\tan a = \dfrac{Lp}{R}$.

Case of two Circuits.

(37) Let R be the primary circuit and S the secondary circuit, then we have a case similar to that of the induction coil.

The equations of currents are those marked A and B, and we may here assume L, M, N as constant because there is no motion of the conductors. The equations then become

$$\left.\begin{aligned} Rx + L\frac{dx}{dt} + M\frac{dy}{dt} &= \xi \\ Sy + M\frac{dx}{dt} + N\frac{dy}{dt} &= 0 \end{aligned}\right\}\ \dots\dots\dots\dots\dots\dots\ (13^{*}).$$

To find the total quantity of electricity which passes, we have only to integrate these equations with respect to t; then if x_0, y_0 be the strengths of the currents at time 0, and x_1, y_1 at time t, and if X, Y be the quantities of electricity passed through each circuit during time t,

$$X = \frac{1}{R} \left\{ \xi t + L \left(x_0 - x_1 \right) + M \left(y_0 - y_1 \right) \right\}$$
$$Y = \frac{1}{S} \left\{ M \left(x_0 - x_1 \right) + N \left(y_0 - y_1 \right) \right\} \Biggr\} \quad \ldots\ldots\ldots\ldots (14^*).$$

When the circuit R is completed, then the total currents up to time t, when t is great, are found by making

$$x_0 = 0, \quad x_1 = \frac{\xi}{R}, \quad y_0 = 0, \quad y_1 = 0 \, ;$$

then
$$X = x_1 \left(t - \frac{L}{R} \right), \quad Y = -\frac{M}{S} x_1 \ldots\ldots\ldots\ldots (15^*).$$

The value of the total counter-current in R is therefore independent of the secondary circuit, and the induction current in the secondary circuit depends only on M, the coefficient of induction between the coils, S the resistance of the secondary coil, and x_1 the final strength of the current in R.

When the electromotive force ξ ceases to act, there is an extra current in the primary circuit, and a positive induced current in the secondary circuit, whose values are equal and opposite to those produced on making contact.

(38) All questions relating to the total quantity of transient currents, as measured by the impulse given to the magnet of the galvanometer, may be solved in this way without the necessity of a complete solution of the equations. The heating effect of the current, and the impulse it gives to the suspended coil of Weber's dynamometer, depend on the square of the current at every instant during the short time it lasts. Hence we must obtain the solution of the equations, and from the solution we may find the effects both on the galvanometer and dynamometer; and we may then make use of the method of Weber for estimating the intensity and duration of a current uniform while it lasts which would produce the same effects.

(39)   Let n_1, n_2 be the roots of the equation

$$(LN - M^2) n^2 + (RN + LS) n + RS = 0 \ldots\ldots\ldots\ldots\ldots(16),$$

and let the primary coil be acted on by a constant electromotive force Rc, so that c is the constant current it could maintain; then the complete solution of the equations for making contact is

$$x = \frac{c}{S} \frac{n_1 n_2}{n_1 - n_2} \left\{ \left(\frac{S}{n_1} + N\right) e^{n_1 t} - \left(\frac{S}{n_2} + N\right) e^{n_2 t} + S \frac{n_1 - n_2}{n_1 n_2} \right\} \ldots\ldots\ldots(17),$$

$$y = \frac{cM}{S} \frac{n_1 n_2}{n_1 - n_2} \{ e^{n_1 t} - e^{n_2 t} \} \ldots\ldots\ldots\ldots\ldots\ldots (18).$$

From these we obtain for calculating the impulse on the dynamometer,

$$\int x^2 dt = c^2 \left\{ t - \tfrac{3}{2} \frac{L}{R} - \tfrac{1}{2} \frac{M^2}{RN + LS} \right\} \ldots\ldots\ldots\ldots (19),$$

$$\int y^2 dt = c^2 \tfrac{1}{2} \frac{M^2 R}{S(RN + LS)} \ldots\ldots\ldots\ldots\ldots (20).$$

The effects of the current in the secondary coil on the galvanometer and dynamometer are the same as those of a uniform current

$$-\tfrac{1}{2} c \frac{MR}{RN + LS}$$

for a time

$$2 \left(\frac{L}{R} + \frac{N}{S}\right).$$

(40)   The equation between work and energy may be easily verified. The work done by the electromotive force is

$$\xi \int x dt = c^2 (Rt - L).$$

Work done in overcoming resistance and producing heat,

$$R \int x^2 dt + S \int y^2 dt = c^2 (Rt - \tfrac{3}{2} L).$$

Energy remaining in the system, $= \tfrac{1}{2} c^2 L.$

(41)   If the circuit R is suddenly and completely interrupted while carrying a current c, then the equation of the current in the secondary coil would be

$$y = c \frac{M}{N} e^{-\frac{S}{N} t}.$$

This current begins with a value $c \dfrac{M}{N}$, and gradually disappears.

The total quantity of electricity is $c\dfrac{M}{S}$, and the value of $\int y^2 dt$ is $c^2\dfrac{M^2}{2SN}$.

The effects on the galvanometer and dynamometer are equal to those of a uniform current $\frac{1}{2}c\dfrac{M}{N}$ for a time $2\dfrac{N}{S}$.

The heating effect is therefore greater than that of the current on making contact.

(42) If an electromotive force of the form $\xi = E\cos pt$ acts on the circuit R, then if the circuit S is removed, the value of x will be

$$x = \frac{E}{A}\sin(pt - \alpha),$$

where

$$A^2 = R^2 + L^2 p^2,$$

and

$$\tan\alpha = \frac{Lp}{R}.$$

The effect of the presence of the circuit S in the neighbourhood is to alter the value of A and α, to that which they would be if R became

$$R + p^2\frac{MS}{S^2 + p^2 N^2},$$

and L became

$$L - p^2\frac{MN}{S^2 + p^2 N^2}.$$

Hence the effect of the presence of the circuit S is to increase the apparent resistance and diminish the apparent self-induction of the circuit R.

On the Determination of Coefficients of Induction by the Electric Balance.

(43) The electric balance consists of six conductors joining four points, A, C, D, E, two and two. One pair, AC, of these points is connected through the battery B. The opposite pair, DE, is connected through the galvanometer G. Then if the resistances of the four remaining conductors are represented by P, Q, R, S, and the currents in them by x, $x - z$, y, and $y + z$,

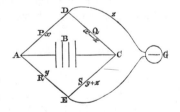

the current through G will be z. Let the potentials at the four points be A, C, D, E. Then the conditions of steady currents may be found from the equations

$$\left.\begin{array}{ll} Px = A - D, & Q\,(x - z) = D - C \\ Ry = A - E, & S\,(y + z) = E - C \\ Gz = D - E, & B\,(x + y) = -A + C + F \end{array}\right\} \ldots\ldots\ldots\ldots (21).$$

Solving these equations for z, we find

$$z\left\{\frac{1}{P} + \frac{1}{Q} + \frac{1}{R} + \frac{1}{S} + B\left(\frac{1}{P} + \frac{1}{R}\right)\left(\frac{1}{Q} + \frac{1}{S}\right) + G\left(\frac{1}{P} + \frac{1}{Q}\right)\left(\frac{1}{R} + \frac{1}{S}\right)\right.$$
$$\left. + \frac{BG}{PQRS}\,(P + Q + R + S)\right\} = F\left(\frac{1}{PS} - \frac{1}{QR}\right)\ldots\ldots(22).$$

In this expression F is the electromotive force of the battery, z the current through the galvanometer when it has become steady. P, Q, R, S the resistances in the four arms. B that of the battery and electrodes, and G that of the galvanometer.

(44) If $PS = QR$, then $z = 0$, and there will be no steady current, but a transient current through the galvanometer may be produced on making or breaking circuit on account of induction, and the indications of the galvanometer may be used to determine the coefficients of induction, provided we understand the actions which take place.

We shall suppose $PS = QR$, so that the current z vanishes when sufficient time is allowed, and

$$x\,(P + Q) = y\,(R + S) = \frac{F(P + Q)(R + S)}{(P + Q)(R + S) + B(P + Q)(R + S)} \ldots\ldots (23).$$

Let the induction coefficients between P, Q, R, S be given by the following Table, the coefficient of induction of P on itself being p, between P and Q, h, and so on.

Let g be the coefficient of induction of the galvanometer on itself, and let it be out of the reach of the inductive influence of P, Q, R, S (as it must be in order to avoid direct action of P, Q, R, S on the needle)   Let X, Y, Z be the integrals of x, y, z with respect to t. At

	P	Q	R	S
P	p	h	k	l
Q	h	q	m	n
R	k	m	r	o
S	l	n	o	s

making contact x, y, z are zero. After a time z disappears, and x and y reach constant values. The equations for each conductor will therefore be

$$
\left.
\begin{aligned}
PX & + (p+h)x + (k+l)y = \textstyle\int A dt - \int D dt \\
Q(X-Z) & + (h'+q)x + (m+n)y = \textstyle\int D dt - \int C dt \\
RY & + (k+m)x + (r+o)y = \textstyle\int A dt - \int E dt \\
S(Y+Z) & + (l+n)x + (o+s)y = \textstyle\int E dt - \int C dt \\
GZ & = \textstyle\int D dt - \int E dt.
\end{aligned}
\right\} \quad \dots\dots\dots(24).
$$

Solving these equations for Z, we find

$$
\left.
\begin{aligned}
Z \Big\{ \frac{1}{P} &+ \frac{1}{Q} + \frac{1}{R} + \frac{1}{S} + B\left(\frac{1}{P}+\frac{1}{R}\right)\left(\frac{1}{Q}+\frac{1}{S}\right) + G\left(\frac{1}{P}+\frac{1}{Q}\right)\left(\frac{1}{R}+\frac{1}{S}\right) \\
&+ \frac{BG}{PQRS}(P+Q+R+S) \Big\} \\
= -F\frac{1}{PS} \Big\{ \frac{p}{P} &- \frac{q}{Q} - \frac{r}{R} + \frac{s}{S} + h\left(\frac{1}{P}-\frac{1}{Q}\right) + k\left(\frac{1}{R}-\frac{1}{P}\right) + l\left(\frac{1}{R}+\frac{1}{Q}\right) \\
- m\left(\frac{1}{P}+\frac{1}{S}\right) &+ n\left(\frac{1}{Q}-\frac{1}{S}\right) + o\left(\frac{1}{S}-\frac{1}{R}\right) \Big\}
\end{aligned}
\right\} \quad \dots(25).
$$

(45) Now let the deflection of the galvanometer by the instantaneous current whose intensity is Z be α.

*Let the permanent deflection produced by making the ratio of PS to QR, ρ instead of unity, be θ.

Also let the time of vibration of the galvanometer needle from rest to rest be T.

Then calling the quantity

$$
\frac{p}{P} - \frac{q}{Q} - \frac{r}{R} + \frac{s}{S} + h\left(\frac{1}{P}-\frac{1}{Q}\right) + k\left(\frac{1}{R}-\frac{1}{P}\right) + l\left(\frac{1}{R}+\frac{1}{Q}\right) - m\left(\frac{1}{P}+\frac{1}{S}\right)
$$

$$
+ n\left(\frac{1}{Q}-\frac{1}{S}\right) + o\left(\frac{1}{S}-\frac{1}{R}\right) = \tau \quad \dots\dots(26),
$$

we find

$$
\frac{Z}{z} = \frac{2\sin\frac{1}{2}\alpha}{\tan\theta}\,\frac{T}{\pi} = \frac{\tau}{1-\rho} \quad \dots\dots\dots\dots\dots(27).
$$

* [In those circumstances the values of x and y found in Art. 44 require modification before being inserted in equation (24). This has been pointed out by Lord Rayleigh, who employed the method described in the text in his second determination of the British unit of resistance in absolute measure. See the *Philosophical Transactions*, 1882, Part II. pp. 677, 678.]

In determining τ by experiment, it is best to make the alteration of resistance in one of the arms by means of the arrangement described by Mr Jenkin in the Report of the British Association for 1863, by which any value of ρ from 1 to 1·01 can be accurately measured.

We observe (α) the greatest deflection due to the impulse of induction when the galvanometer is in circuit, when the connexions are made, and when the resistances are so adjusted as to give no permanent current.

We then observe (β) the greatest deflection produced by the permanent current when the resistance of one of the arms is increased in the ratio of 1 to ρ, the galvanometer not being in circuit till a little while after the connexion is made with the battery.

In order to eliminate the effects of resistance of the air, it is best to vary ρ till $\beta = 2\alpha$ nearly; then

$$\tau = T\,\frac{1}{\pi}(1-\rho)\,\frac{2\sin\frac{1}{2}\alpha}{\tan\frac{1}{2}\beta} \quad\text{.............................. (28)}.$$

If all the arms of the balance except P consist of resistance coils of very fine wire of no great length and doubled before being coiled, the induction coefficients belonging to these coils will be insensible, and τ will be reduced to $\frac{p}{P}$. The electric balance therefore affords the means of measuring the self-induction of any circuit whose resistance is known.

(46) It may also be used to determine the coefficient of induction between two circuits, as for instance, that between P and S which we have called m; but it would be more convenient to measure this by directly measuring the current, as in (37), without using the balance. We may also ascertain the equality of $\frac{p}{P}$ and $\frac{q}{Q}$ by there being no current of induction, and thus, when we know the value of p, we may determine that of q by a more perfect method than the comparison of deflections.

Exploration of the Electromagnetic Field.

(47) Let us now suppose the primary circuit A to be of invariable form, and let us explore the electromagnetic field by means of the secondary circuit B, which we shall suppose to be variable in form and position.

We may begin by supposing B to consist of a short straight conductor with its extremities sliding on two parallel conducting rails, which are put in connexion at some distance from the sliding-piece.

Then, if sliding the moveable conductor in a given direction increases the value of M, a negative electromotive force will act in the circuit B, tending to produce a negative current in B during the motion of the sliding-piece.

If a current be kept up in the circuit B, then the sliding-piece will itself tend to move in that direction, which causes M to increase. At every point of the field there will always be a certain direction such that a conductor moved in that direction does not experience any electromotive force in whatever direction its extremities are turned. A conductor carrying a current will experience no mechanical force urging it in that direction or the opposite.

This direction is called the direction of the line of magnetic force through that point.

Motion of a conductor across such a line produces electromotive force in a direction perpendicular to the line and to the direction of motion, and a conductor carrying a current is urged in a direction perpendicular to the line and to the direction of the current.

(48) We may next suppose B to consist of a very small plane circuit capable of being placed in any position and of having its plane turned in any direction. The value of M will be greatest when the plane of the circuit is perpendicular to the line of magnetic force. Hence if a current is maintained in B it will tend to set itself in this position, and will of itself indicate, like a magnet, the direction of the magnetic force.

On Lines of Magnetic Force.

(49) Let any surface be drawn, cutting the lines of magnetic force, and on this surface let any system of lines be drawn at small intervals, so as to lie side by side without cutting each other. Next, let any line be drawn on the surface cutting all these lines, and let a second line be drawn near it, its distance from the first being such that the value of M for each of the small spaces enclosed between these two lines and the lines of the first system is equal to unity.

In this way let more lines be drawn so as to form a second system, so that the value of M for every reticulation formed by the intersection of the two systems of lines is unity.

Finally, from every point of intersection of these reticulations let a line be drawn through the field, always coinciding in direction with the direction of magnetic force.

(50) In this way the whole field will be filled with lines of magnetic force at regular intervals, and the properties of the electromagnetic field will be completely expressed by them.

For, 1st, If any closed curve be drawn in the field, the value of M for that curve will be expressed by the *number* of lines of force which *pass through* that closed curve.

2ndly. If this curve be a conducting circuit and be moved through the field, an electromotive force will act in it, represented by the rate of decrease of the number of lines passing through the curve.

3rdly. If a current be maintained in the circuit, the conductor will be acted on by forces tending to move it so as to increase the number of lines passing through it, and the amount of work done by these forces is equal to the current in the circuit multiplied by the number of additional lines.

4thly. If a small plane circuit be placed in the field, and be free to turn, it will place its plane perpendicular to the lines of force. A small magnet will place itself with its axis in the direction of the lines of force.

5thly. If a long uniformly magnetized bar is placed in the field, each pole will be acted on by a force in the direction of the lines of force. The number of lines of force passing through unit of area is equal to the force acting on a unit pole multiplied by a coefficient depending on the magnetic nature of the medium, and called the coefficient of magnetic induction.

In fluids and isotropoic solids the value of this coefficient μ is the same in whatever direction the lines of force pass through the substance, but in crystallized, strained, and organized solids the value of μ may depend on the direction of the lines of force with respect to the axes of crystallization, strain, or growth.

In all bodies μ is affected by temperature, and in iron it appears to diminish as the intensity of the magnetization increases.

On Magnetic Equipotential Surfaces.

(51) If we explore the field with a uniformly magnetized bar, so long that one of its poles is in a very weak part of the magnetic field, then the magnetic forces will perform work on the other pole as it moves about the field. If we start from a given point, and move this pole from it to any other point, the work performed will be independent of the path of the pole between the two points; provided that no electric current passes between the different paths pursued by the pole.

Hence, when there are no electric currents but only magnets in the field, we may draw a series of surfaces such that the work done in passing from one to another shall be constant whatever be the path pursued between them. Such surfaces are called Equipotential Surfaces, and in ordinary cases are perpendicular to the Lines of magnetic force.

If these surfaces are so drawn that, when a unit pole passes from any one to the next in order, unity of work is done, then the work done in any motion of a magnetic pole will be measured by the strength of the pole multiplied by the number of surfaces which it has passed through in the positive direction.

(52) If there are circuits carrying electric currents in the field, then there will still be equipotential surfaces in the parts of the field external to the conductors carrying the currents, but the work done on a unit pole in passing from one to another will depend on the number of times which the path of the pole circulates round any of these currents. Hence the potential in each surface will have a series of values in arithmetical progression, differing by the work done in passing completely round one of the currents in the field.

The equipotential surfaces will not be continuous closed surfaces, but some of them will be limited sheets, terminating in the electric circuit as their common edge or boundary. The number of these will be equal to the amount of work done on a unit pole in going round the current, and this by the ordinary measurement $= 4\pi\gamma$, where γ is the value of the current.

These surfaces, therefore, are connected with the electric current as soap-bubbles are connected with a ring in M. Plateau's experiments. Every current γ has $4\pi\gamma$ surfaces attached to it. These surfaces have the current for their common edge, and meet it at equal angles. The form of the surfaces in other parts depends on the presence of other currents and magnets, as well as on the shape of the circuit to which they belong.

PART III.

GENERAL EQUATIONS OF THE ELECTROMAGNETIC FIELD.

(53) Let us assume three rectangular directions in space as the axes of x, y, and z, and let all quantities having direction be expressed by their components in these three directions.

Electrical Currents (p, q, r).

(54) An electrical current consists in the transmission of electricity from one part of a body to another. Let the quantity of electricity transmitted in unit of time across unit of area perpendicular to the axis of x be called p, then p is the component of the current at that place in the direction of x.

We shall use the letters p, q, r to denote the components of the current per unit of area in the directions of x, y, z.

Electrical Displacements (f, g, h).

(55) Electrical displacement consists in the opposite electrification of the sides of a molecule or particle of a body which may or may not be accompanied with transmission through the body. Let the quantity of electricity which would appear on the faces $dy \cdot dz$ of an element dx, dy, dz cut from the body be $f \cdot dy \cdot dz$, then f is the component of electric displacement parallel to x. We shall use f, g, h to denote the electric displacements parallel to x, y, z respectively.

The variations of the electrical displacement must be added to the currents p, q, r to get the total motion of electricity, which we may call p', q', r', so that

$$\left. \begin{array}{l} p' = p + \dfrac{df}{dt} \\[2mm] q' = q + \dfrac{dg}{dt} \\[2mm] r' = r + \dfrac{dh}{dt} \end{array} \right\} \quad \dotfill (A).$$

Electromotive Force (P, Q, R).

(56) Let P, Q, R represent the components of the electromotive force at any point. Then P represents the difference of potential per unit of length in a conductor placed in the direction of x at the given point. We may suppose an indefinitely short wire placed parallel to x at a given point and touched, during the action of the force P, by two small conductors, which are then insulated and removed from the influence of the electromotive force. The value of P might then be ascertained by measuring the charge of the conductors.

Thus if l be the length of the wire, the difference of potential at its ends will be Pl, and if C be the capacity of each of the small conductors the charge on each will be $\frac{1}{2}CPl$. Since the capacities of moderately large conductors, measured on the electromagnetic system, are exceedingly small, ordinary electromotive forces arising from electromagnetic actions could hardly be measured in this way. In practice such measurements are always made with long conductors, forming closed or nearly closed circuits.

Electromagnetic Momentum (F, G, H).

(57) Let F, G, H represent the components of electromagnetic momentum at any point of the field, due to any system of magnets or currents.

Then F is the total impulse of the electromotive force in the direction of x that would be generated by the removal of these magnets or currents from the field, that is, if P be the electromotive force at any instant during the removal of the system

$$F = \int P dt.$$

Hence the part of the electromotive force which depends on the motion of magnets or currents in the field, or their alteration of intensity, is

$$P = -\frac{dF}{dt}, \quad Q = -\frac{dG}{dt}, \quad R = -\frac{dH}{dt} \dots\dots\dots\dots (29).$$

Electromagnetic Momentum of a Circuit.

(58) Let s be the length of the circuit, then if we integrate

$$\int \left(F\frac{dx}{ds} + G\frac{dy}{ds} + H\frac{dz}{ds} \right) ds \dots\dots\dots\dots (30)$$

round the circuit, we shall get the total electromagnetic momentum of the circuit, or the number of lines of magnetic force which pass through it, the variations of which measure the total electromotive force in the circuit. This electromagnetic momentum is the same thing to which Professor Faraday has applied the name of the Electrotonic State.

If the circuit be the boundary of the elementary area $dy\,dz$, then its electromagnetic momentum is

$$\left(\frac{dH}{dy} - \frac{dG}{dz}\right) dy\,dz,$$

and this is the number of lines of magnetic force which pass through the area $dy\,dz$.

Magnetic Force (α, β, γ).

(59) Let α, β, γ represent the force acting on a unit magnetic pole placed at the given point resolved in the directions of x, y, and z.

Coefficient of Magnetic Induction (μ).

(60) Let μ be the ratio of the magnetic induction in a given medium to that in air under an equal magnetizing force, then the number of lines of force in unit of area perpendicular to x will be $\mu\alpha$ (μ is a quantity depending on the nature of the medium, its temperature, the amount of magnetization already produced, and in crystalline bodies varying with the direction).

(61) Expressing the electric momentum of small circuits perpendicular to the three axes in this notation, we obtain the following

Equations of Magnetic Force,

$$\left.\begin{aligned}
\mu\alpha &= \frac{dH}{dy} - \frac{dG}{dz} \\[4pt]
\mu\beta &= \frac{dF}{dz} - \frac{dH}{dx} \\[4pt]
\mu\gamma &= \frac{dG}{dx} - \frac{dF}{dy}
\end{aligned}\right\} \quad \dots\dots\dots\dots\dots\dots\dots (B).$$

Equations of Currents.

(62) It is known from experiment that the motion of a magnetic pole in the electromagnetic field in a closed circuit cannot generate work unless the circuit which the pole describes passes round an electric current. Hence, except in the space occupied by the electric currents,

$$a\,dx + \beta\,dy + \gamma\,dz = d\phi \quad \dots\dots\dots\dots\dots\dots\dots \text{(31)}$$

a complete differential of ϕ, the magnetic potential.

The quantity ϕ may be susceptible of an indefinite number of distinct values, according to the number of times that the exploring point passes round electric currents in its course, the difference between successive values of ϕ corresponding to a passage completely round a current of strength c being $4\pi c$.

Hence if there is no electric current,

$$\frac{d\gamma}{dy} - \frac{d\beta}{dz} = 0 \; ;$$

but if there is a current p',

Similarly,

$$\left.\begin{aligned}
\frac{d\gamma}{dy} - \frac{d\beta}{dz} &= 4\pi p' \\[4pt]
\frac{d\alpha}{dz} - \frac{d\gamma}{dx} &= 4\pi q' \\[4pt]
\frac{d\beta}{dx} - \frac{d\alpha}{dy} &= 4\pi r'
\end{aligned}\right\} \quad \dots\dots\dots\dots\dots\dots\dots \text{(C).}$$

We may call these the Equations of Currents.

Electromotive Force in a Circuit.

(63) Let ξ be the electromotive force acting round the circuit A, then

$$\xi = \int \left(P\frac{dx}{ds} + Q\frac{dy}{ds} + R\frac{dz}{ds} \right) ds \quad \dots\dots\dots\dots\dots \text{(32),}$$

where ds is the element of length, and the integration is performed round the circuit.

Let the forces in the field be those due to the circuits A and B, then the electromagnetic momentum of A is

$$\int \left(F\frac{dx}{ds} + G\frac{dy}{ds} + H\frac{dz}{ds} \right) ds = Lu + Mv \dots\dots\dots\dots (33),$$

where u and v are the currents in A and B, and

$$\xi = -\frac{d}{dt}(Lu + Mv) \dots\dots\dots\dots\dots\dots (34).$$

Hence, if there is no motion of the circuit A,

$$\left.\begin{aligned} P &= -\frac{dF}{dt} - \frac{d\psi}{dx} \\[1mm] Q &= -\frac{dG}{dt} - \frac{d\psi}{dy} \\[1mm] R &= -\frac{dH}{dt} - \frac{d\psi}{dz} \end{aligned}\right\} \dots\dots\dots\dots\dots (35),$$

where ψ is a function of x, y, z, and t, which is indeterminate as far as regards the solution of the above equations, because the terms depending on it will disappear on integrating round the circuit. The quantity ψ can always, however, be determined in any particular case when we know the actual conditions of the question. The physical interpretation of ψ is, that it represents the *electric potential* at each point of space.

Electromotive Force on a Moving Conductor.

(64) Let a short straight conductor of length a, parallel to the axis of x, move with a velocity whose components are $\dfrac{dx}{dt}$, $\dfrac{dy}{dt}$, $\dfrac{dz}{dt}$, and let its extremities slide along two parallel conductors with a velocity $\dfrac{ds}{dt}$. Let us find the alteration of the electromagnetic momentum of the circuit of which this arrangement forms a part.

In unit of time the moving conductor has travelled distances $\dfrac{dx}{dt}$, $\dfrac{dy}{dt}$, $\dfrac{dz}{dt}$ along the directions of the three axes, and at the same time the lengths of the parallel conductors included in the circuit have each been increased by $\dfrac{ds}{dt}$.

Hence the quantity

$$\int \left(F\frac{dx}{ds} + G\frac{dy}{ds} + H\frac{dz}{ds} \right) ds$$

will be increased by the following increments,

$$a\left(\frac{dF}{dx}\frac{dx}{dt} + \frac{dF}{dy}\frac{dy}{dt} + \frac{dF}{dz}\frac{dz}{dt}\right), \text{ due to motion of conductor,}$$

$$-a\frac{ds}{dt}\left(\frac{dF}{dx}\frac{dx}{ds} + \frac{dG}{dx}\frac{dy}{ds} + \frac{dH}{dx}\frac{dz}{ds}\right), \text{ due to lengthening of circuit.}$$

The total increment will therefore be

$$a\left(\frac{dF}{dy} - \frac{dG}{dx}\right)\frac{dy}{dt} - a\left(\frac{dH}{dx} - \frac{dF}{dz}\right)\frac{dz}{dt};$$

or, by the equations of Magnetic Force (8),

$$-a\left(\mu\gamma\frac{dy}{dt} - \mu\beta\frac{dz}{dt}\right).$$

If P is the electromotive force in the moving conductor parallel to x referred to unit of length, then the actual electromotive force is Pa; and since this is measured by the decrement of the electromagnetic momentum of the circuit, the electromotive force due to motion will be

$$P = \mu\gamma\frac{dy}{dt} - \mu\beta\frac{dz}{dt} \dots\dots\dots\dots\dots\dots\dots\dots\dots(36).$$

(65) The complete equations of electromotive force on a moving conductor may now be written as follows:—

Equations of Electromotive Force.

$$\left.\begin{array}{l} P = \mu\left(\gamma\dfrac{dy}{dt} - \beta\dfrac{dz}{dt}\right) - \dfrac{dF}{dt} - \dfrac{d\psi}{dx} \\[2mm] Q = \mu\left(a\dfrac{dz}{dt} - \gamma\dfrac{dx}{dt}\right) - \dfrac{dG}{dt} - \dfrac{d\psi}{dy} \\[2mm] R = \mu\left(\beta\dfrac{dx}{dt} - a\dfrac{dy}{dt}\right) - \dfrac{dH}{dt} - \dfrac{d\psi}{dz} \end{array}\right\} \dots\dots\dots\dots\dots\dots(D).$$

The first term on the right-hand side of each equation represents the electromotive force arising from the motion of the conductor itself. This electromotive force is perpendicular to the direction of motion and to the lines of magnetic force; and if a parallelogram be drawn whose sides represent in direction and magnitude the velocity of the conductor and the magnetic induction at that point of the field, then the area of the parallelogram will represent the electromotive force due to the motion of the conductor, and the direction of the force is perpendicular to the plane of the parallelogram.

The second term in each equation indicates the effect of changes in the position or strength of magnets or currents in the field.

The third term shews the effect of the electric potential ψ. It has no effect in causing a circulating current in a closed circuit. It indicates the existence of a force urging the electricity to or from certain definite points in the field.

Electric Elasticity.

(66) When an electromotive force acts on a dielectric, it puts every part of the dielectric into a polarized condition, in which its opposite sides are oppositely electrified. The amount of this electrification depends on the electromotive force and on the nature of the substance, and, in solids having a structure defined by axes, on the direction of the electromotive force with respect to these axes. In isotropic substances, if k is the ratio of the electromotive force to the electric displacement, we may write the

Equations of Electric Elasticity,

$$\left.\begin{array}{l} P = kf \\ Q = kg \\ R = kh \end{array}\right\} \dots\dots\dots\dots\dots\dots\dots\dots\dots (E).$$

Electric Resistance.

(67) When an electromotive force acts on a conductor it produces a current of electricity through it. This effect is additional to the electric displacement already considered. In solids of complex structure, the relation between the electromotive force and the current depends on their direction through the solid.

In isotropic substances, which alone we shall here consider, if ρ is the specific resistance referred to unit of volume, we may write the

Equations of Electric Resistance,

$$\left.\begin{array}{l} P = -\rho p \\ Q = -\rho q \\ R = -\rho r \end{array}\right\} \quad\dots\dots\dots\dots\dots\dots\dots\dots\dots\dots \text{(F)}.$$

Electric Quantity.

(68) Let e represent the quantity of free positive electricity contained in unit of volume at any part of the field, then, since this arises from the electrification of the different parts of the field not neutralizing each other, we may write the

Equation of Free Electricity,

$$e + \frac{df}{dx} + \frac{dg}{dy} + \frac{dh}{dz} = 0 \quad\dots\dots\dots\dots\dots\dots\dots\dots \text{(G)}.$$

(69) If the medium conducts electricity, then we shall have another condition, which may be called, as in hydrodynamics, the

Equation of Continuity,

$$\frac{de}{dt} + \frac{dp}{dx} + \frac{dq}{dy} + \frac{dr}{dz} = 0 \quad\dots\dots\dots\dots\dots\dots\dots \text{(H)}.$$

(70) In these equations of the electromagnetic field we have assumed twenty variable quantities, namely,

For Electromagnetic Momentum .... F   G   H
  „ Magnetic Intensity .... a β γ
  „ Electromotive Force .... P Q R
  „ Current due to true Conduction .... p q r
  „ Electric Displacement .... f g h
  „ Total Current (including variation of displacement) p' q' r'
  „ Quantity of Free Electricity .... e
  „ Electric Potential... Ψ

Between these twenty quantities we have found twenty equations, viz.

Three equations of Magnetic Force .... (B)

,,   Electric Currents .... (C)

,,   Electromotive Force .... (D)

,,   Electric Elasticity .... (E)

,,   Electric Resistance.............................. (F)

,,   Total Currents .... (A)

One equation of Free Electricity..................................... (G)

,,   Continuity.. (H)

These equations are therefore sufficient to determine all the quantities which occur in them, provided we know the conditions of the problem. In many questions, however, only a few of the equations are required.

Intrinsic Energy of the Electromagnetic Field.

(71) We have seen (33) that the intrinsic energy of any system of currents is found by multiplying half the current in each circuit into its electromagnetic momentum. This is equivalent to finding the integral

$$E = \tfrac{1}{2}\Sigma(Fp' + Gq' + Hr')\,dV \dots\dots\dots\dots\dots\dots(37)$$

over all the space occupied by currents, where p, q, r are the components of currents, and F, G, H the components of electromagnetic momentum.

Substituting the values of p', q', r' from the equations of Currents (C), this becomes

$$\frac{1}{8\pi}\Sigma\left\{F\left(\frac{d\gamma}{dy} - \frac{d\beta}{dz}\right) + G\left(\frac{d\alpha}{dz} - \frac{d\gamma}{dx}\right) + H\left(\frac{d\beta}{dx} - \frac{d\alpha}{dy}\right)\right\}dV.$$

Integrating by parts, and remembering that α, β, γ vanish at an infinite distance, the expression becomes

$$\frac{1}{8\pi}\Sigma\left\{\alpha\left(\frac{dH}{dy} - \frac{dG}{dz}\right) + \beta\left(\frac{dF}{dz} - \frac{dH}{dx}\right) + \gamma\left(\frac{dG}{dx} - \frac{dF}{dy}\right)\right\}dV,$$

where the integration is to be extended over all space. Referring to the equations of Magnetic Force (B), p. 556, this becomes

$$E = \frac{1}{8\pi}\Sigma\{\alpha\,.\,\mu\alpha + \beta\,.\,\mu\beta + \gamma\,.\,\mu\gamma\}\,dV \dots\dots\dots\dots (38),$$

where a, β, γ are the components of magnetic intensity or the force on a unit magnetic pole, and μa, $\mu\beta$, $\mu\gamma$ are the components of the quantity of magnetic induction, or the number of lines of force in unit of area.

In isotropic media the value of μ is the same in all directions, and we may express the result more simply by saying that the intrinsic energy of any part of the magnetic field arising from its magnetization is

$$\frac{\mu}{8\pi} I^2$$

per unit of volume, where I is the magnetic intensity.

(72) Energy may be stored up in the field in a different way, namely, by the action of electromotive force in producing electric displacement. The work done by a variable electromotive force, P, in producing a variable displacement, f, is got by integrating

$$\int P df$$

from $P = 0$ to the given value of P.

Since $P = kf$, equation (E), this quantity becomes

$$\int kf df = \tfrac{1}{2} kf^2 = \tfrac{1}{2} Pf.$$

Hence the intrinsic energy of any part of the field, as existing in the form of electric displacement, is

$$\tfrac{1}{2}\Sigma (Pf + Qg + Rh) dV.$$

The total energy existing in the field is therefore

$$E = \Sigma \left\{ \frac{1}{8\pi} (a\mu a + \beta\mu\beta + \gamma\mu\gamma) + \tfrac{1}{2}(Pf + Qg + Rh) \right\} dV \ldots\ldots\ldots (I).$$

The first term of this expression depends on the magnetization of the field, and is explained on our theory by actual motion of some kind. The second term depends on the electric polarization of the field, and is explained on our theory by strain of some kind in an elastic medium.

(73) I have on a former occasion [*] attempted to describe a particular kind of motion and a particular kind of strain, so arranged as to account for the phenomena. In the present paper I avoid any hypothesis of this kind; and in

[*] "On Physical Lines of Force," *Philosophical Magazine*, 1861—62. (In this vol. p. 451.)

using such words as electric momentum and electric elasticity in reference to the known phenomena of the induction of currents and the polarization of dielectrics, I wish merely to direct the mind of the reader to mechanical phenomena which will assist him in understanding the electrical ones. All such phrases in the present paper are to be considered as illustrative, not as explanatory.

(74) In speaking of the Energy of the field, however, I wish to be understood literally. All energy is the same as mechanical energy, whether it exists in the form of motion or in that of elasticity, or in any other form. The energy in electromagnetic phenomena is mechanical energy. The only question is, Where does it reside? On the old theories it resides in the electrified bodies, conducting circuits, and magnets, in the form of an unknown quality called potential energy, or the power of producing certain effects at a distance. On our theory it resides in the electromagnetic field, in the space surrounding the electrified and magnetic bodies, as well as in those bodies themselves, and is in two different forms, which may be described without hypothesis as magnetic polarization and electric polarization, or, according to a very probable hypothesis, as the motion and the strain of one and the same medium.

(75) The conclusions arrived at in the present paper are independent of this hypothesis, being deduced from experimental facts of three kinds:

1. The induction of electric currents by the increase or diminution of neighbouring currents according to the changes in the lines of force passing through the circuit.

2. The distribution of magnetic intensity according to the variations of a magnetic potential.

3. The induction (or influence) of statical electricity through dielectrics.

We may now proceed to demonstrate from these principles the existence and laws of the mechanical forces which act upon electric currents, magnets, and electrified bodies placed in the electromagnetic field.

PART IV.

MECHANICAL ACTIONS IN THE FIELD.

Mechanical Force on a Moveable Conductor.

(76) We have shewn (§§ 34 & 35) that the work done by the electro-magnetic forces in aiding the motion of a conductor is equal to the product of the current in the conductor multiplied by the increment of the electro-magnetic momentum due to the motion.

Let a short straight conductor of length a move parallel to itself in the direction of x, with its extremities on two parallel conductors. Then the increment of the electromagnetic momentum due to the motion of a will be

$$a\left(\frac{dF}{dx}\frac{dx}{ds} + \frac{dG}{dx}\frac{dy}{ds} + \frac{dH}{dx}\frac{dz}{ds}\right)\delta x.$$

That due to the lengthening of the circuit by increasing the length of the parallel conductors will be

$$-a\left(\frac{dF}{dx}\frac{dx}{ds} + \frac{dF}{dy}\frac{dy}{ds} + \frac{dF}{dz}\frac{dz}{ds}\right)\delta x.$$

The total increment is

$$a\delta x\left\{\frac{dy}{ds}\left(\frac{dG}{dx} - \frac{dF}{dy}\right) - \frac{dz}{ds}\left(\frac{dF}{dz} - \frac{dH}{dx}\right)\right\},$$

which is by the equations of Magnetic Force (B), p. 556,

$$a\delta x\left(\frac{dy}{ds}\mu\gamma - \frac{dz}{ds}\mu\beta\right).$$

Let X be the force acting along the direction of x per unit of length of the conductor, then the work done is $Xa\delta x$.

Let C be the current in the conductor, and let p', q', r' be its components, then

$$Xa\delta x = Ca\delta x\left(\frac{dy}{ds}\mu\gamma - \frac{dz}{ds}\mu\beta\right),$$

or

Similarly,

$$\left.\begin{array}{l} X = \mu\gamma q' - \mu\beta r' \\ Y = \mu a r' - \mu\gamma p' \\ Z = \mu\beta p' - \mu a q' \end{array}\right\} \quad \dots\dots\dots\dots\dots\dots\dots\dots\dots\dots\dots (\mathrm{J}).$$

These are the equations which determine the mechanical force acting on a conductor carrying a current. The force is perpendicular to the current and to the lines of force, and is measured by the area of the parallelogram formed by lines parallel to the current and lines of force, and proportional to their intensities.

Mechanical Force on a Magnet.

(77) In any part of the field not traversed by electric currents the distribution of magnetic intensity may be represented by the differential coefficients of a function which may be called the magnetic potential. When there are no currents in the field, this quantity has a single value for each point. When there are currents, the potential has a series of values at each point, but its differential coefficients have only one value, namely,

$$\frac{d\phi}{dx} = a, \quad \frac{d\phi}{dy} = \beta, \quad \frac{d\phi}{dz} = \gamma.$$

Substituting these values of a, β, γ in the expression (equation 38) for the intrinsic energy of the field, and integrating by parts, it becomes

$$-\Sigma \left\{ \phi \, \frac{1}{8\pi} \left(\frac{d\mu a}{dx} + \frac{d\mu\beta}{dy} + \frac{d\mu\gamma}{dz} \right) \right\} dV.$$

The expression

$$\Sigma \left(\frac{d\mu a}{dx} + \frac{d\mu\beta}{dy} + \frac{d\mu\gamma}{dz} \right) dV = \Sigma m \, dV \dots\dots\dots\dots (39)$$

indicates the number of lines of magnetic force which have their origin within the space V. Now a magnetic pole is known to us only as the origin or termination of lines of magnetic force, and a unit pole is one which has 4π lines belonging to it, since it produces unit of magnetic intensity at unit of distance over a sphere whose surface is 4π.

Hence if m is the amount of free positive magnetism in unit of volume, the above expression may be written $4\pi m$, and the expression for the energy of the field becomes

$$E = -\Sigma \left(\tfrac{1}{2} \phi m \right) dV \dots\dots\dots\dots\dots\dots (40).$$

If there are two magnetic poles m_1 and m_2 producing potentials ϕ_1 and ϕ_2 in the field, then if m_2 is moved a distance dx, and is urged in that direction by a force X, then the work done is Xdx, and the decrease of energy in the field is

$$d\{\tfrac{1}{2}(\phi_1 + \phi_2)(m_1 + m_2)\},$$

and these must be equal by the principle of Conservation of Energy.

Since the distribution ϕ_1 is determined by m_1, and ϕ_2 by m_2, the quantities $\phi_1 m_1$ and $\phi_2 m_2$ will remain constant.

It can be shewn also, as Green has proved (Essay, p. 10), that

$$m_1 \phi_2 = m_2 \phi_1,$$

so that we get $\qquad X dx = d\,(m_2 \phi_1),$

or $\qquad\qquad X = m_2 \dfrac{d\phi_1}{dx} = m_2 a_1,$

where a_1 represents the magnetic intensity due to m_1.

Similarly, $\qquad\qquad Y = m_2 \beta_1,$

$$Z = m_2 \gamma_1.$$

$$\left.\begin{array}{l}\\ \\ \\ \\ \\ \\ \end{array}\right\} \ \dots\dots\dots\dots\dots \text{(K)}.$$

So that a magnetic pole is urged in the direction of the lines of magnetic force with a force equal to the product of the strength of the pole and the magnetic intensity.

(78) If a single magnetic pole, that is, one pole of a very long magnet, be placed in the field, the only solution of ϕ is

$$\phi_1 = -\frac{m_1}{\mu}\frac{1}{r}\dots\dots\dots\dots\dots\dots\dots\dots(41),$$

where m_1 is the strength of the pole, and r the distance from it.

The repulsion between two poles of strength m_1 and m_2 is

$$m_2 \frac{d\phi_1}{dr} = \frac{m_1 m_2}{\mu r^2}\dots\dots\dots\dots\dots\dots\dots\dots(42).$$

In air or any medium in which $\mu = 1$ this is simply $\dfrac{m_1 m_2}{r^2}$, but in other media the force acting between two given magnetic poles is inversely proportional to the coefficient of magnetic induction for the medium. This may be explained by the magnetization of the medium induced by the action of the poles.

Mechanical Force on an Electrified Body.

(79) If there is no motion or change of strength of currents or magnets in the field, the electromotive force is entirely due to variation of electric potential, and we shall have (§ 65)

$$P = -\frac{d\Psi}{dx}, \quad Q = -\frac{d\Psi}{dy}, \quad R = -\frac{d\Psi}{dz}.$$

Integrating by parts the expression (I) for the energy due to electric displacement, and remembering that P, Q, R vanish at an infinite distance, it becomes

$$\tfrac{1}{2}\Sigma \left\{ \Psi \left(\frac{df}{dx} + \frac{dg}{dy} + \frac{dh}{dz} \right) dV, \right.$$

or by the equation of Free Electricity (G), p. 561,

$$-\tfrac{1}{2}\Sigma \left(\Psi e \right) dV.$$

By the same demonstration as was used in the case of the mechanical action on a magnet, it may be shewn that the mechanical force on a small body containing a quantity e_2 of free electricity placed in a field whose potential arising from other electrified bodies is Ψ_1, has for components

$$\left. \begin{aligned} X &= e_2 \frac{d\Psi_1}{dx} = -P_1 e_2 \\[1mm] Y &= e_2 \frac{d\Psi_1}{dy} = -Q_1 e_2 \\[1mm] Z &= e_3 \frac{d\Psi_1}{dz} = -R_1 e_2 \end{aligned} \right\} \quad \ldots\ldots\ldots\ldots\ldots\ldots\ldots\ldots \text{(D).}$$

So that an electrified body is urged in the direction of the electromotive force with a force equal to the product of the quantity of free electricity and the electromotive force.

If the electrification of the field arises from the presence of a small electrified body containing e_1 of free electricity, the only solution of Ψ_1 is

$$\Psi_1 = \frac{k}{4\pi} \frac{e_1}{r} \quad \ldots\ldots\ldots\ldots\ldots\ldots\ldots\ldots\ldots\ldots\ldots\ldots \text{(43),}$$

where r is the distance from the electrified body.

The repulsion between two electrified bodies e_1, e_2 is therefore

$$e_2 \frac{d\Psi_1}{dr} = \frac{k}{4\pi} \frac{e_1 e_2}{r^2} \quad \ldots\ldots\ldots\ldots\ldots\ldots\ldots\ldots \text{(44).}$$

Measurement of Electrostatic Effects.

(80) The quantities with which we have had to do have been hitherto expressed in terms of the Electromagnetic System of measurement, which is founded on the mechanical action between currents. The electrostatic system of measurement is founded on the mechanical action between electrified bodies, and is independent of, and incompatible with, the electromagnetic system; so that the units of the different kinds of quantity have different values according to the system we adopt, and to pass from the one system to the other, a reduction of all the quantities is required.

According to the electrostatic system, the repulsion between two small bodies charged with quantities η_1, η_2 of electricity is

$$\frac{\eta_1\eta_2}{r^2},$$

where r is the distance between them.

Let the relation of the two systems be such that one electromagnetic unit of electricity contains v electrostatic units; then $\eta_1 = ve_1$ and $\eta_2 = ve_2$, and this repulsion becomes

$$v^2\frac{e_1e_2}{r^2} = \frac{k}{4\pi}\frac{e_1e_2}{r^2} \text{ by equation (44)} \dots\dots\dots\dots (45),$$

whence k, the coefficient of "electric elasticity" in the medium in which the experiments are made, i. e. common air, is related to v, the number of electrostatic units in one electromagnetic unit, by the equation

$$k = 4\pi v^2 \dots\dots\dots\dots\dots\dots\dots\dots\dots\dots (46).$$

The quantity v may be determined by experiment in several ways. According to the experiments of MM. Weber and Kohlrausch,

$$v = 310,740,000 \text{ metres per second.}$$

(81) It appears from this investigation, that if we assume that the medium which constitutes the electromagnetic field is, when dielectric, capable of receiving in every part of it an electric polarization, in which the opposite sides of every element into which we may conceive the medium divided are oppositely electrified, and if we also assume that this polarization or electric displacement is proportional to the electromotive force which produces or maintains it, then we

can shew that electrified bodies in a dielectric medium will act on one another with forces obeying the same laws as are established by experiment.

The energy, by the expenditure of which electrical attractions and repulsions are produced, we suppose to be stored up in the dielectric medium which surrounds the electrified bodies, and not on the surface of those bodies themselves, which on our theory are merely the bounding surfaces of the air or other dielectric in which the true springs of action are to be sought.

Note on the Attraction of Gravitation.

(82) After tracing to the action of the surrounding medium both the magnetic and the electric attractions and repulsions, and finding them to depend on the inverse square of the distance, we are naturally led to inquire whether the attraction of gravitation, which follows the same law of the distance, is not also traceable to the action of a surrounding medium.

Gravitation differs from magnetism and electricity in this; that the bodies concerned are all of the same kind, instead of being of opposite signs, like magnetic poles and electrified bodies, and that the force between these bodies is an attraction and not a repulsion, as is the case between like electric and magnetic bodies.

The lines of gravitating force near two dense bodies are exactly of the same form as the lines of magnetic force near two poles of the same name; but whereas the poles are repelled, the bodies are attracted. Let E be the intrinsic energy of the field surrounding two gravitating bodies M_1, M_2, and let E' be the intrinsic energy of the field surrounding two magnetic poles, m_1, m_2 equal in numerical value to M_1, M_2, and let X be the gravitating force acting during the displacement δx, and X' the magnetic force,

$$X\delta x = \delta E, \qquad X'\delta x = \delta E';$$

now X and X' are equal in numerical value, but of opposite signs; so that

$$\delta E = -\delta E',$$

or

$$E = C - E'$$

$$= C - \Sigma \frac{1}{8\pi} (\alpha^2 + \beta^2 + \gamma^2)\, dV$$

where α, β, γ are the components of magnetic intensity. If R be the resultant gravitating force, and R' the resultant magnetic force at a corresponding part of the field,

$$R = -R', \text{ and } a^2 + \beta^2 + \gamma^2 = R^2 = R'^2.$$

Hence

$$E = C - \Sigma \frac{1}{8\pi} R^2 dV \dots\dots\dots\dots\dots\dots\dots\dots\dots\dots (47).$$

The intrinsic energy of the field of gravitation must therefore be less wherever there is a resultant gravitating force.

As energy is essentially positive, it is impossible for any part of space to have negative intrinsic energy. Hence those parts of space in which there is no resultant force, such as the points of equilibrium in the space between the different bodies of a system, and within the substance of each body, must have an intrinsic energy per unit of volume greater than

$$\frac{1}{8\pi} R^2,$$

where R is the greatest possible value of the intensity of gravitating force in any part of the universe.

The assumption, therefore, that gravitation arises from the action of the surrounding medium in the way pointed out, leads to the conclusion that every part of this medium possesses, when undisturbed, an enormous intrinsic energy, and that the presence of dense bodies influences the medium so as to diminish this energy wherever there is a resultant attraction.

As I am unable to understand in what way a medium can possess such properties, I cannot go any further in this direction in searching for the cause of gravitation.

PART V.

THEORY OF CONDENSERS.

Capacity of a Condenser.

(83) The simplest form of condenser consists of a uniform layer of insulating matter bounded by two conducting surfaces, and its capacity is measured by the quantity of electricity on either surface when the difference of potentials is unity.

Let S be the area of either surface, a the thickness of the dielectric, and k its coefficient of electric elasticity; then on one side of the condenser the potential is Ψ_1, and on the other side $\Psi_1 + 1$, and within its substance

$$\frac{d\Psi}{dx} = \frac{1}{a} = kf \dots\dots\dots\dots\dots\dots (48).$$

Since $\dfrac{d\Psi}{dx}$ and therefore f is zero outside the condenser, the quantity of electricity on its first surface $= -Sf$, and on the second $+Sf$. The capacity of the condenser is therefore $Sf = \dfrac{S}{ak}$ in electromagnetic measure.

Specific Capacity of Electric Induction (D).

(84) If the dielectric of the condenser be air, then its capacity in electrostatic measure is $\dfrac{S}{4\pi a}$ (neglecting corrections arising from the conditions to be fulfilled at the edges). If the dielectric have a capacity whose ratio to that of air is D, then the capacity of the condenser will be $\dfrac{DS}{4\pi a}$.

Hence
$$D = \frac{k_0}{k} \dots\dots\dots\dots\dots\dots\dots\dots (49),$$

where k_0 is the value of k in air, which is taken for unity.

Electric Absorption.

(85) When the dielectric of which the condenser is formed is not a perfect insulator, the phenomena of conduction are combined with those of electric displacement. The condenser, when left charged, gradually loses its charge, and in some cases, after being discharged completely, it gradually acquires a new charge of the same sign as the original charge, and this finally disappears. These phenomena have been described by Professor Faraday (*Experimental Researches*, Series XI.) and by Mr F. Jenkin (*Report of Committee of Board of Trade on Submarine Cables*), and may be classed under the name of "Electric Absorption."

(86) We shall take the case of a condenser composed of any number of parallel layers of different materials. If a constant difference of potentials between its extreme surfaces is kept up for a sufficient time till a condition of permanent steady flow of electricity is established, then each bounding surface will have a charge of electricity depending on the nature of the substances on each side of it. If the extreme surfaces be now discharged, these internal charges will gradually be dissipated, and a certain charge may reappear on the extreme surfaces if they are insulated, or, if they are connected by a conductor, a certain quantity of electricity may be urged through the conductor during the re-establishment of equilibrium.

Let the thickness of the several layers of the condenser be a_1, a_2, &c.

Let the values of k for these layers be respectively k_1, k_2, k_3, and let

$$a_1 k_2 + a_2 k_2 + \&c. = ak \dots\dots\dots\dots\dots (50),$$

where k is the "electric elasticity" of air, and a is the thickness of an equivalent condenser of air.

Let the resistances of the layers be respectively r_1, r_2, &c., and let $r_1 + r_2 + \&c. = r$ be the resistance of the whole condenser, to a steady current through it per unit of surface.

Let the electric displacement in each layer be f_1, f_2, &c.

Let the electric current in each layer be p_1, p_2, &c.

Let the potential on the first surface be Ψ_1, and the electricity per unit of surface e_1.

Let the corresponding quantities at the boundary of the first and second surface be Ψ_2 and e_2, and so on.   Then by equations (G) and (H),

$$e_1 = -f_1, \qquad \frac{de_1}{dt} = -p_1,$$

$$e_2 = f_1 - f_2, \qquad \frac{de_2}{dt} = p_1 - p_2, \qquad \left.\right\} \dots\dots\dots\dots\dots(51),$$

$$\text{\&c.} \qquad\qquad \text{\&c.}$$

But by equations (E) and (F),

$$\Psi_1 - \Psi_2 = a_1 k_1 f_1 = -r_1 p_1 \;\Big\}$$
$$\Psi_2 - \Psi_3 = a_2 k_2 f_2 = -r_2 p_2, \Big\} \dots\dots\dots\dots (52).$$
$$\text{\&c.} \qquad \text{\&c.} \qquad \text{\&c.}$$

After the electromotive force has been kept up for a sufficient time the current becomes the same in each layer, and

$$p_1 = p_2 = \text{\&c.} = p = \frac{\Psi}{r},$$

where Ψ is the total difference of potentials between the extreme layers.   We have then

and

$$f_1 = -\frac{\Psi}{r}\frac{r_1}{a_1 k_1}, \qquad f_2 = -\frac{\Psi}{r}\frac{r_2}{a_2 k_2}, \quad \text{\&c.} \;\Big\}$$
$$e_1 = \frac{\Psi}{r}\frac{r_1}{a_1 k_1}, \qquad e_2 = \frac{\Psi}{r}\left(\frac{r_2}{a_2 k_2} - \frac{r_1}{a k_1}\right), \quad \text{\&c.} \;\Big\} \dots\dots\dots (53).$$

These are the quantities of electricity on the different surfaces.

(87)   Now let the condenser be discharged by connecting the extreme surfaces through a perfect conductor so that their potentials are instantly rendered equal, then the electricity on the extreme surfaces will be altered, but that on the internal surfaces will not have time to escape.   The total difference of potentials is now

$$\Psi' = a_1 k_1 e'_1 + a_2 k_2(e'_1 + e_2) + a_3 k_3(e'_1 + e_2 + e_3), \quad \text{\&c.} = 0 \dots\dots\dots(54),$$

whence if e'_1 is what e_1 becomes at the instant of discharge,

$$e'_1 = \frac{\Psi}{r}\frac{r_1}{a_1 k_1} - \frac{\Psi}{ak} = e_1 - \frac{\Psi}{ak} \dots\dots\dots\dots\dots (55).$$

The instantaneous discharge is therefore $\dfrac{\Psi}{ak}$, or the quantity which would be discharged by a condenser of air of the equivalent thickness a, and it is unaffected by the want of perfect insulation.

(88) Now let us suppose the connexion between the extreme surfaces broken, and the condenser left to itself, and let us consider the gradual dissipation of the internal charges. Let Ψ' be the difference of potential of the extreme surfaces at any time t; then

$$\Psi' = a_1 k_1 f_1 + a_2 k_2 f_2 + \&\mathrm{c}\ldots\ldots\ldots\ldots\ldots\ldots\ldots\ldots (56);$$

but

$$a_1 k_1 f_1 = -r_1 \frac{df_1}{dt},$$

$$a_2 k_2 f_2 = -r_2 \frac{df_2}{dt}.$$

Hence $f_1 = A_1 e^{-\frac{a_1 k_1}{r_1}t}$, $f_2 = A_2 e^{-\frac{a_2 k_2}{r_2}t}$, &c.; and by referring to the values of e'_1, e_2, &c., we find

$$\left.\begin{array}{l} A_1 = \dfrac{\Psi}{r}\dfrac{r_1}{a_1 k_1} - \dfrac{\Psi}{ak} \\[2mm] A_2 = \dfrac{\Psi}{r}\dfrac{r_2}{a_2 k_2} - \dfrac{\Psi}{ak} \\[2mm] \&\mathrm{c}. \end{array}\right\} \ldots\ldots\ldots\ldots\ldots\ldots\ldots\ldots (57),$$

so that we find for the difference of extreme potentials at any time,

$$\Psi' = \Psi \left\{ \left(\frac{r_1}{r} - \frac{a_1 k_1}{ak}\right)e^{-\frac{a_1 k_1}{r_1}t} + \left(\frac{r_2}{r} - \frac{a_2 k_2}{ak}\right)e^{-\frac{a_2 k_2}{r_2}t} + \&\mathrm{c}. \right. \ldots\ldots\ldots (58).$$

(89) It appears from this result that if all the layers are made of the same substance, Ψ' will be zero always. If they are of different substances, the order in which they are placed is indifferent, and the effect will be the same whether each substance consists of one layer, or is divided into any number of thin layers and arranged in any order among thin layers of the other substances. Any substance, therefore, the parts of which are not mathematically homogeneous, though they may be apparently so, may exhibit phenomena of absorption. Also, since the order of magnitude of the coefficients is the same as that of the indices, the value of Ψ' can never change sign, but must start from zero, become positive, and finally disappear.

(90) Let us next consider the total amount of electricity which would pass from the first surface to the second, if the condenser, after being thoroughly saturated by the current and then discharged, has its extreme surfaces connected by a conductor of resistance R. Let p be the current in this conductor; then, during the discharge,

$$\Psi' = p_1 r_1 + p_2 r_2 + \&c. = pR \dots\dots\dots\dots\dots\dots\dots (59).$$

Integrating with respect to the time, and calling q_1, q_2, q the quantities of electricity which traverse the different conductors,

$$q_1 r_1 + q_2 r_2 + \&c. = qR \dots\dots\dots\dots\dots\dots\dots\dots (60).$$

The quantities of electricity on the several surfaces will be

$$e'_1 - q - q_1,$$
$$e_2 + q_1 - q_2,$$
$$\&c. \; ;$$

and since at last all these quantities vanish, we find

$$q_1 = e'_1 - q,$$
$$q_2 = e'_1 + e_2 - q \; ;$$

whence
$$qR = \frac{\Psi}{r}\left(\frac{r^2_1}{a_1 k_1} + \frac{r^2_2}{a_2 k_2} + \&c.\right) - \frac{\Psi r}{ak},$$

or
$$q = \frac{\Psi}{akrR}\left\{ a_1 k_1 a_2 k_2 \left(\frac{r_1}{a_1 k_1} - \frac{r_2}{a_2 k_2}\right)^2 + a_2 k_2 a_3 k_3 \left(\frac{r_2}{a_2 k_2} - \frac{r_3}{a_3 k_3}\right)^2 + \&c. \right\} \dots\dots (61),$$

a quantity essentially positive; so that, when the primary electrification is in one direction, the secondary discharge is always in the same direction as the primary discharge *.

---

* Since this paper was communicated to the Royal Society, I have seen a paper by M. Gaugain in the *Annales de Chimie* for 1864, in which he has deduced the phenomena of electric absorption and secondary discharge from the theory of compound condensers.

PART VI.

ELECTROMAGNETIC THEORY OF LIGHT.

(91) At the commencement of this paper we made use of the optical hypothesis of an elastic medium through which the vibrations of light are propagated, in order to shew that we have warrantable grounds for seeking, in the same medium, the cause of other phenomena as well as those of light. We then examined electromagnetic phenomena, seeking for their explanation in the properties of the field which surrounds the electrified or magnetic bodies. In this way we arrived at certain equations expressing certain properties of the electromagnetic field. We now proceed to investigate whether these properties of that which constitutes the electromagnetic field, deduced from electromagnetic phenomena alone, are sufficient to explain the propagation of light through the same substance.

(92) Let us suppose that a plane wave whose direction cosines are l, m, n is propagated through the field with a velocity V. Then all the electromagnetic functions will be functions of

$$w = lx + my + nz - Vt.$$

The equations of Magnetic Force (B), p. 556, will become

$$\mu a = m \frac{dH}{dw} - n \frac{dG}{dw},$$

$$\mu \beta = n \frac{dF}{dw} - l \frac{dH}{dw},$$

$$\mu \gamma = l \frac{dG}{dw} - m \frac{dF}{dw}.$$

If we multiply these equations respectively by l, m, n, and add, we find

$$l\mu a + m\mu\beta + n\mu\gamma = 0 \quad \dots\dots\dots\dots\dots\dots\dots (62),$$

which shews that the direction of the magnetization must be in the plane of the wave.

(93) If we combine the equations of Magnetic Force (B) with those of Electric Currents (C), and put for brevity

$$\frac{dF}{dx} + \frac{dG}{dy} + \frac{dH}{dz} = J, \text{ and } \frac{d^2}{dx^2} + \frac{d^2}{dy^2} + \frac{d^2}{dz^2} = \nabla^2 \quad \ldots\ldots\ldots\ldots (63),$$

$$\left. \begin{array}{l} 4\pi\mu p' = \dfrac{dJ}{dx} - \nabla^2 F \\[2mm] 4\pi\mu q' = \dfrac{dJ}{dy} - \nabla^2 G \\[2mm] 4\pi\mu r' = \dfrac{dJ}{dz} - \nabla^2 H \end{array} \right\} \quad \ldots\ldots\ldots\ldots\ldots (64).$$

If the medium in the field is a perfect dielectric there is no true conduction, and the currents p', q', r' are only variations in the electric displacement, or, by the equations of Total Currents (A),

$$p' = \frac{df}{dt}, \qquad q' = \frac{dg}{dt}, \qquad r' = \frac{dh}{dt} \quad \ldots\ldots\ldots\ldots (65).$$

But these electric displacements are caused by electromotive forces, and by the equations of Electric Elasticity (E),

$$P = kf, \qquad Q = kg, \qquad R = kh \quad \ldots\ldots\ldots\ldots (66).$$

These electromotive forces are due to the variations either of the electromagnetic or the electrostatic functions, as there is no motion of conductors in the field; so that the equations of electromotive force (D) are

$$\left. \begin{array}{l} P = -\dfrac{dF}{dt} - \dfrac{d\Psi}{dx} \\[2mm] Q = -\dfrac{dG}{dt} - \dfrac{d\Psi}{dy} \\[2mm] R = -\dfrac{dH}{dt} - \dfrac{d\Psi}{dz} \end{array} \right\} \quad \ldots\ldots\ldots\ldots\ldots (67).$$

(94) Combining these equations, we obtain the following :—

$$\left. \begin{array}{l} k\left(\dfrac{dJ}{dx} - \nabla^2 F\right) + 4\pi\mu\left(\dfrac{d^2 F}{dt^2} + \dfrac{d^2\Psi}{dxdt}\right) = 0 \\[2mm] k\left(\dfrac{dJ}{dy} - \nabla^2 G\right) + 4\pi\mu\left(\dfrac{d^2 G}{dt^2} + \dfrac{d^2\Psi}{dydt}\right) = 0 \\[2mm] k\left(\dfrac{dJ}{dz} - \nabla^2 H\right) + 4\pi\mu\left(\dfrac{d^2 H}{dt^2} + \dfrac{d^2\Psi}{dzdt}\right) = 0 \end{array} \right\} \quad \ldots\ldots\ldots\ldots (68).$$

If we differentiate the third of these equations with respect to y, and the second with respect to z, and subtract, J and Ψ disappear, and by remembering the equations (B) of magnetic force, the results may be written

$$\left.\begin{array}{c} k\nabla^2\mu a = 4\pi\mu \dfrac{d^2}{dt^2}\mu a \\[2mm] k\nabla^2\mu\beta = 4\pi\mu \dfrac{d^2}{dt^2}\mu\beta \\[2mm] k\nabla^2\mu\gamma = 4\pi\mu \dfrac{d^2}{dt^2}\mu\gamma \end{array}\right\} \quad\ldots\ldots\ldots\ldots\ldots\ldots (69).$$

(95) If we assume that a, β, γ are functions of $lx + my + nz - Vt = w$, the first equation becomes

$$k\mu\frac{d^2a}{dw^2} = 4\pi\mu^2 V^2\frac{d^2a}{dw^2} \ldots\ldots\ldots\ldots\ldots\ldots (70),$$

or
$$V = \pm\sqrt{\frac{k}{4\pi\mu}} \ldots\ldots\ldots\ldots\ldots\ldots\ldots (71).$$

The other equations give the same value for V, so that the wave is propagated in either direction with a velocity V.

This wave consists entirely of magnetic disturbances, the direction of magnetization being in the plane of the wave. No magnetic disturbance whose direction of magnetization is not in the plane of the wave can be propagated as a plane wave at all.

Hence magnetic disturbances propagated through the electromagnetic field agree with light in this, that the disturbance at any point is transverse to the direction of propagation, and such waves may have all the properties of polarized light.

(96) The only medium in which experiments have been made to determine the value of k is air, in which $\mu = 1$, and therefore, by equation (46),

$$V = v \ldots\ldots\ldots\ldots\ldots\ldots\ldots\ldots\ldots (72).$$

By the electromagnetic experiments of MM. Weber and Kohlrausch [*],

$$v = 310{,}740{,}000 \text{ metres per second}$$

* *Leipzig Transactions*, Vol. v. (1857), p. 260, or Poggendorff's *Annalen*, Aug. 1856, p. 10.

is the number of electrostatic units in one electromagnetic unit of electricity, and this, according to our result, should be equal to the velocity of light in air or vacuum.

The velocity of light in air, by M. Fizeau's * experiments, is

$$V = 314,858,000 ;$$

according to the more accurate experiments of M. Foucault †,

$$V = 298,000,000.$$

The velocity of light in the space surrounding the earth, deduced from the coefficient of aberration and the received value of the radius of the earth's orbit, is

$$V = 308,000,000.$$

(97)   Hence the velocity of light deduced from experiment agrees sufficiently well with the value of v deduced from the only set of experiments we as yet possess. The value of v was determined by measuring the electromotive force with which a condenser of known capacity was charged, and then discharging the condenser through a galvanometer, so as to measure the quantity of electricity in it in electromagnetic measure. The only use made of light in the experiment was to see the instruments. The value of V found by M. Foucault was obtained by determining the angle through which a revolving mirror turned, while the light reflected from it went and returned along a measured course. No use whatever was made of electricity or magnetism.

The agreement of the results seems to shew that light and magnetism are affections of the same substance, and that light is an electromagnetic disturbance propagated through the field according to electromagnetic laws.

(98)   Let us now go back upon the equations in (94), in which the quantities J and Ψ occur, to see whether any other kind of disturbance can be propagated through the medium depending on these quantities which disappeared from the final equations.

---

* *Comptes Rendus*, Vol. xxix. (1849), p. 90.

† Ibid. Vol. lv. (1862), pp. 501, 792.

If we determine χ from the equation

$$\nabla^2\chi = \frac{d^2\chi}{dx^2} + \frac{d^2\chi}{dy^2} + \frac{d^2\chi}{dz^2} = J \quad\dots\dots\dots\dots(73),$$

and F', G', H' from the equations

$$F' = F - \frac{d\chi}{dx}, \quad G' = G - \frac{d\chi}{dy}, \quad H' = H - \frac{d\chi}{dz}\dots\dots\dots(74),$$

then

$$\frac{dF'}{dx} + \frac{dG'}{dy} + \frac{dH'}{dz} = 0 \quad\dots\dots\dots\dots(75),$$

and the equations in (94) become of the form

$$k\nabla^2 F' = 4\pi\mu\left\{\frac{d^2F'}{dt^2} + \frac{d}{dxdt}\left(\Psi + \frac{d\chi}{dt}\right)\right\}\dots\dots\dots\dots(76).$$

Differentiating the three equations with respect to x, y, and z, and adding, we find that

$$\Psi = -\frac{d\chi}{dt} + \phi\,(x,\ y,\ z)\dots\dots\dots\dots(77),$$

and that

$$\left.\begin{array}{l} k\nabla^2 F' = 4\pi\mu\dfrac{d^2F'}{dt^2} \\[2mm] k\nabla^2 G' = 4\pi\mu\dfrac{d^2G'}{dt^2} \\[2mm] k\nabla^2 H' = 4\pi\mu\dfrac{d^2H'}{dt^2} \end{array}\right\} \quad\dots\dots\dots\dots (78).$$

Hence the disturbances indicated by F', G', H' are propagated with the velocity $V = \sqrt{\dfrac{k}{4\pi\mu}}$ through the field; and since

$$\frac{dF'}{dx} + \frac{dG'}{dy} + \frac{dH'}{dz} = 0,$$

the resultant of these disturbances is in the plane of the wave.

(99) The remaining part of the total disturbances F, G, H being the part depending on χ, is subject to no condition except that expressed in the equation

$$\frac{d\Psi}{dt} + \frac{d^2\chi}{dt^2} = 0.$$

If we perform the operation ∇^2 on this equation, it becomes

$$ke = \frac{dJ}{dt} - k\nabla^2\phi\,(x,\ y,\ z)\dots\dots\dots\dots\dots(79).$$

Since the medium is a perfect insulator, e, the free electricity, is immoveable, and therefore $\dfrac{dJ}{dt}$ is a function of x, y, z, and the value of J is either constant or zero, or uniformly increasing or diminishing with the time; so that no disturbance depending on J can be propagated as a wave.

(100) The equations of the electromagnetic field, deduced from purely experimental evidence, shew that transversal vibrations only can be propagated. If we were to go beyond our experimental knowledge and to assign a definite density to a substance which we should call the electric fluid, and select either vitreous or resinous electricity as the representative of that fluid, then we might have normal vibrations propagated with a velocity depending on this density. We have, however, no evidence as to the density of electricity, as we do not even know whether to consider vitreous electricity as a substance or as the absence of a substance.

Hence electromagnetic science leads to exactly the same conclusions as optical science with respect to the direction of the disturbances which can be propagated through the field; both affirm the propagation of transverse vibrations, and both give the same velocity of propagation. On the other hand, both sciences are at a loss when called on to affirm or deny the existence of normal vibrations.

Relation between the Index of Refraction and the Electromagnetic Character of the substance.

(101) The velocity of light in a medium, according to the Undulatory Theory, is

$$\frac{1}{i}V_0,$$

where i is the index of refraction and V_0 is the velocity in vacuum. The velocity, according to the Electromagnetic Theory, is

$$\sqrt{\frac{k}{4\pi\mu}},$$

where, by equations (49) and (71), $k = \dfrac{1}{D}k_0$, and $k_0 = 4\pi V_0^2$.

Hence $$D = \frac{i^2}{\mu} \dots\dots\dots\dots\dots\dots\dots(80),$$

or the Specific Inductive Capacity is equal to the square of the index of refraction divided by the coefficient of magnetic induction.

Propagation of Electromagnetic Disturbances in a Crystallized Medium.

(102) Let us now calculate the conditions of propagation of a plane wave in a medium for which the values of k and μ are different in different directions. As we do not propose to give a complete investigation of the question in the present imperfect state of the theory as extended to disturbances of short period, we shall assume that the axes of magnetic induction coincide in direction with those of electric elasticity.

(103) Let the values of the magnetic coefficient for the three axes be λ, μ, ν, then the equations of magnetic force (B) become

$$\left. \begin{aligned} \lambda a &= \frac{dH}{dy} - \frac{dG}{dz} \\[2mm] \mu\beta &= \frac{dF}{dz} - \frac{dH}{dx} \\[2mm] \nu\gamma &= \frac{dG}{dx} - \frac{dF}{dy} \end{aligned} \right\} \dots\dots\dots,\dots\dots\dots (81).$$

The equations of electric currents (C) remain as before.

The equations of electric elasticity (E) will be

$$\left. \begin{aligned} P &= 4\pi a^2 f \\ Q &= 4\pi b^2 g \\ R &= 4\pi c^2 h \end{aligned} \right\} \dots\dots\dots\dots\dots\dots (82),$$

where $4\pi a^2$, $4\pi b^2$, and $4\pi c^2$ are the values of k for the axes of x, y, z.

Combining these equations with (A) and (D), we get equations of the form

$$\frac{1}{\mu\nu}\left(\lambda\frac{d^2F}{dx^2} + \mu\frac{d^2F}{dy^2} + \nu\frac{d^2F}{dz^2}\right) - \frac{1}{\mu\nu}\frac{d}{dx}\left(\lambda\frac{dF}{dx} + \mu\frac{dG}{dy} + \nu\frac{dH}{dz}\right) = \frac{1}{a^2}\left(\frac{d^2F}{dt^2} + \frac{d^2\Psi}{dxdt}\right)\dots(83).$$

(104) If l, m, n are the direction-cosines of the wave, and V its velocity, and if

$$lx + my + nz - Vt = w \dots\dots\dots\dots\dots (84),$$

then F, G, H, and Ψ will be functions of w; and if we put F', G', H', Ψ' for the second differentials of these quantities with respect to w, the equations will be

$$
\left.
\begin{aligned}
\left\{ V^2 - a^2 \left(\frac{m^2}{\nu} + \frac{n^2}{\mu} \right) \right\} F' + \frac{a^2 lm}{\nu} G' + \frac{a^2 ln}{\mu} H' - l V \Psi' = 0 \\
\left\{ V^2 - b^2 \left(\frac{n^2}{\lambda} + \frac{l^2}{\nu} \right) \right\} G' + \frac{b^2 mn}{\lambda} H' + \frac{b^2 ml}{\nu} F' - m V \Psi' = 0 \\
\left\{ V^2 - c^2 \left(\frac{l^2}{\mu} + \frac{m^2}{\lambda} \right) \right\} H' + \frac{c^2 nl}{\mu} F' + \frac{c^2 nm}{\lambda} G' - n V \Psi' = 0
\end{aligned}
\right\} \quad \ldots\ldots\ldots (85).
$$

If we now put

$$
\left.
\begin{aligned}
V^4 - V^2 \frac{1}{\lambda\mu\nu} \left\{ l^2\lambda (b^2\mu + c^2\nu) + m^2\mu (c^2\nu + a^2\lambda) + n^2\nu (a^2\lambda + b^2\mu) \right\} \\
+ \frac{a^2 b^2 c^2}{\lambda\mu\nu} \left(\frac{l^2}{a^2} + \frac{m^2}{b^2} + \frac{n^2}{c^2} \right) (l^2\lambda + m^2\mu + n^2\nu) = U
\end{aligned}
\right\} \quad \ldots\ldots (86),
$$

we shall find

$$ F' V^2 U - l\Psi' VU = 0 \ldots\ldots\ldots\ldots\ldots\ldots (87), $$

with two similar equations for G' and H'. Hence either

$$ V = 0 \ldots\ldots\ldots\ldots\ldots\ldots\ldots\ldots\ldots\ldots\ldots\ldots (88), $$

$$ U = 0 \ldots\ldots\ldots\ldots\ldots\ldots\ldots\ldots\ldots\ldots\ldots\ldots (89), $$

or

$$ VF' = l\Psi', \quad VG' = m\Psi' \text{ and } VH' = n\Psi' \ldots\ldots\ldots (90). $$

The third supposition indicates that the resultant of F', G', H' is in the direction normal to the plane of the wave; but the equations do not indicate that such a disturbance, if possible, could be propagated, as we have no other relation between Ψ' and F', G', H'.

The solution $V = 0$ refers to a case in which there is no propagation.

* The solution $U = 0$ gives two values for V^2 corresponding to values of F', G', H', which are given by the equations

$$ \frac{l}{a^2} F' + \frac{m}{b^2} G' + \frac{n}{c^2} H' = 0 \ldots\ldots\ldots\ldots\ldots\ldots\ldots\ldots\ldots (91), $$

$$ \frac{a^2 l\lambda}{F'} (b^2\mu - c^2\nu) + \frac{b^2 m\mu}{G'} (c^2\nu - a^2\lambda) + \frac{c^2 n\nu}{H'} (a^2\lambda - b^2\mu) = 0 \ldots\ldots\ldots (92). $$

---

* [Although it is not expressly stated in the text it should be noticed that in finding equations (91) and (92) the quantity Ψ' is put equal to zero. See § 98 and also the corresponding treatment of this subject in the Electricity and Magnetism ii. § 796. It may be observed that the

(105) The velocities along the axes are as follows:—

Direction of propagation		x	y	z
Direction of the electric displacements	x		$\dfrac{a^2}{\nu}$	$\dfrac{a^2}{\mu}$
	y	$\dfrac{b^2}{\nu}$		$\dfrac{b^2}{\lambda}$
	z	$\dfrac{c^2}{\mu}$	$\dfrac{c^2}{\lambda}$	

Now we know that in each principal plane of a crystal the ray polarized in that plane obeys the ordinary law of refraction, and therefore its velocity is the same in whatever direction in that plane it is propagated.

If polarized light consists of electromagnetic disturbances in which the electric displacement is in the plane of polarization, then

$$a^2 = b^2 = c^2 \dots\dots\dots\dots\dots\dots\dots\dots\dots\dots (93).$$

If, on the contrary, the electric displacements are perpendicular to the plane of polarization,

$$\lambda = \mu = \nu \dots\dots\dots\dots\dots\dots\dots\dots\dots\dots (94).$$

We know, from the magnetic experiments of Faraday, Plücker, &c., that in many crystals λ, μ, ν are unequal.

equations referred to and the table given in § 105 may perhaps be more readily understood from a different mode of elimination. If we write

$$\lambda l^2 + \mu m^2 + \nu n^2 = P\lambda\mu\nu \quad \text{and} \quad \lambda l F' + \mu m G'' + \nu n H' = Q\lambda\mu\nu,$$

it is readily seen that

$$F' = l\,\frac{V\Psi' - a^2\lambda Q}{V^2 - a^2\lambda P},$$

with similar expressions for G'', H'. From these we readily obtain by reasoning similar to that in § 104, the equation corresponding to (86), viz.:

$$\frac{l^2\lambda}{V^2 - a^2\lambda P} + \frac{m^2\mu}{V^2 - b^2\mu P} + \frac{n^2\nu}{V^2 - c^2\nu P} = 0.$$

This form of the equation agrees with that given in the Electricity and Magnetism ii. § 797.

By means of this equation the equations (91) and (92) readily follow when $\Psi' = 0$. The ratios of F' : G' : H' for any direction of propagation may also be determined.]

The experiments of Knoblauch * on electric induction through crystals seem to shew that a, b and c may be different.

The inequality, however, of λ, μ, ν is so small that great magnetic forces are required to indicate their difference, and the differences do not seem of sufficient magnitude to account for the double refraction of the crystals.

On the other hand, experiments on electric induction are liable to error on account of minute flaws, or portions of conducting matter in the crystal.

Further experiments on the magnetic and dielectric properties of crystals are required before we can decide whether the relation of these bodies to magnetic and electric forces is the same, when these forces are permanent as when they are alternating with the rapidity of the vibrations of light.

Relation between Electric Resistance and Transparency.

(106) If the medium, instead of being a perfect insulator, is a conductor whose resistance per unit of volume is ρ, then there will be not only electric displacements, but true currents of conduction in which electrical energy is transformed into heat, and the undulation is thereby weakened. To determine the coefficient of absorption, let us investigate the propagation along the axis of x of the transverse disturbance G.

By the former equations

$$\frac{d^2G}{dx^2} = -4\pi\mu(q')$$

$$= -4\pi\mu\left(\frac{df}{dt} + q\right) \text{ by (A)},$$

$$\frac{d^2G}{dx^2} = +4\pi\mu\left(\frac{1}{k}\frac{d^2G}{dt^2} - \frac{1}{\rho}\frac{dG}{dt}\right) \text{ by (E) and (F)} \dots\dots\dots (95).$$

If G is of the form

$$G = e^{-px}\cos(qx + nt) \dots\dots\dots\dots\dots\dots (96),$$

we find that

$$p = \frac{2\pi\mu}{\rho}\frac{n}{q} = \frac{2\pi\mu}{\rho}\frac{V}{i} \dots\dots\dots\dots\dots (97),$$

where V is the velocity of light in air, and i is the index of refraction. The proportion of incident light transmitted through the thickness x is

$$e^{-2px} \dots\dots\dots\dots\dots\dots\dots (98).$$

* *Philosophical Magazine*, 1852.

Let R be the resistance in electromagnetic measure of a plate of the substance whose thickness is x, breadth b, and length l, then

$$R = \frac{l\rho}{bx},$$

$$2px = 4\pi\mu \frac{V}{i} \frac{l}{bR} \quad\quad\quad\quad\quad\quad\quad (99).$$

(107) Most transparent solid bodies are good insulators, whereas all good conductors are very opaque.

Electrolytes allow a current to pass easily and yet are often very transparent. We may suppose, however, that in the rapidly alternating vibrations of light, the electromotive forces act for so short a time that they are unable to effect a complete separation between the particles in combination, so that when the force is reversed the particles oscillate into their former position without loss of energy.

Gold, silver, and platinum are good conductors, and yet when reduced to sufficiently thin plates they allow light to pass through them. If the resistance of gold is the same for electromotive forces of short period as for those with which we make experiments, the amount of light which passes through a piece of gold-leaf, of which the resistance was determined by Mr C. Hockin, would be only 10^{-50} of the incident light, a totally imperceptible quantity. I find that between $\frac{1}{500}$ and $\frac{1}{1000}$ of green light gets through such gold-leaf. Much of this is transmitted through holes and cracks; there is enough, however, transmitted through the gold itself to give a strong green hue to the transmitted light. This result cannot be reconciled with the electromagnetic theory of light, unless we suppose that there is less loss of energy when the electromotive forces are reversed with the rapidity of the vibrations of light than when they act for sensible times, as in our experiments.

Absolute Values of the Electromotive and Magnetic Forces called into play in the Propagation of Light.

(108) If the equation of propagation of light is

$$F = A \cos \frac{2\pi}{\lambda} (z - Vt),$$

the electromotive force will be

$$P = -A \frac{2\pi}{\lambda} V \sin \frac{2\pi}{\lambda} (z - Vt);$$

and the energy per unit of volume will be

$$\frac{P^2}{8\pi\mu V^2},$$

where P represents the greatest value of the electromotive force. Half of this consists of magnetic and half of electric energy.

The energy passing through a unit of area is

$$W = \frac{P^2}{8\pi\mu V};$$

so that

$$P = \sqrt{8\pi\mu VW},$$

where V is the velocity of light, and W is the energy communicated to unit of area by the light in a second.

According to Pouillet's data, as calculated by Professor W. Thomson [*], the mechanical value of direct sunlight at the Earth is

83·4 foot-pounds per second per square foot.

This gives the maximum value of P in direct sunlight at the Earth's distance from the Sun,

$$P = 60,000,000,$$

or about 600 Daniell's cells per metre.

At the Sun's surface the value of P would be about

13,000 Daniell's cells per metre.

At the Earth the maximum magnetic force would be   193 [†].

At the Sun it would be 4·13.

These electromotive and magnetic forces must be conceived to be reversed twice in every vibration of light; that is, more than a thousand million million times in a second.

[*] *Transactions of the Royal Society of Edinburgh*, 1854 ("Mechanical Energies of the Solar System").

[†] The horizontal magnetic force at Kew is about 1·76 in metrical units.

PART VII.

CALCULATION OF THE COEFFICIENTS OF ELECTROMAGNETIC INDUCTION.

General Methods.

(109) The electromagnetic relations between two conducting circuits, A and B, depend upon a function M of their form and relative position, as has been already shewn.

M may be calculated in several different ways, which must of course all lead to the same result.

First Method. M is the electromagnetic momentum of the circuit B when A carries a unit current, or

$$M = \int \left(F \frac{dx}{ds'} + G \frac{dy}{ds'} + H \frac{dz}{ds'} \right) ds',$$

where F, G, H are the components of electromagnetic momentum due to a unit current in A, and ds' is an element of length of B, and the integration is performed round the circuit of B.

To find F, G, H, we observe that by (B) and (C)

$$\frac{d^2F}{dx^2} + \frac{d^2F}{dy^2} + \frac{d^2F}{dz^2} = -4\pi\mu p',$$

with corresponding equations for G and H, p', q', and r' being the components of the current in A.

Now if we consider only a single element ds of A, we shall have

$$p' = \frac{dx}{ds} ds, \qquad q' = \frac{dy}{ds} ds, \qquad r' = \frac{dz}{ds} ds,$$

and the solution of the equation gives

$$F = \frac{\mu}{\rho} \frac{dx}{ds} ds, \qquad G = \frac{\mu}{\rho} \frac{dy}{ds} ds, \qquad H = \frac{\mu}{\rho} \frac{dz}{ds} ds,$$

where ρ is the distance of any point from ds. Hence

$$M = \int\int \frac{\mu}{\rho}\left(\frac{dx}{ds}\frac{dx}{ds'} + \frac{dy}{ds}\frac{dy}{ds'} + \frac{dz}{ds}\frac{dz}{ds'}\right)dsds'$$

$$= \int\int \frac{\mu}{\rho}\cos\theta\,dsds',$$

where θ is the angle between the directions of the two elements ds, ds', and ρ is the distance between them, and the integration is performed round both circuits.

In this method we confine our attention during integration to the two linear circuits alone.

(110) *Second Method.* M is the number of lines of magnetic force which pass through the circuit B when A carries a unit current, or

$$M = \Sigma\,(\mu a l + \mu\beta m + \mu\gamma n)\,dS',$$

where μa, $\mu\beta$, $\mu\gamma$ are the components of magnetic induction due to unit current in A, S' is a surface bounded by the current B, and l, m, n are the direction-cosines of the normal to the surface, the integration being extended over the surface.

We may express this in the form

$$M = \mu\Sigma\frac{1}{\rho^2}\sin\theta\sin\theta'\sin\phi\,dS'ds,$$

where dS' is an element of the surface bounded by B, ds is an element of the circuit A, ρ is the distance between them, θ and θ' are the angles between ρ and ds and between ρ and the normal to dS' respectively, and ϕ is the angle between the planes in which θ and θ' are measured. The integration is performed round the circuit A and over the surface bounded by B.

This method is most convenient in the case of circuits lying in one plane, in which case $\sin\theta = 1$, and $\sin\phi = 1$.

(111) *Third Method.* M is that part of the intrinsic magnetic energy of the whole field which depends on the product of the currents in the two circuits, each current being unity.

Let α, β, γ be the components of magnetic intensity at any point due to the first circuit, α', β', γ' the same for the second circuit; then the intrinsic energy of the element of volume dV of the field is

$$\frac{\mu}{8\pi}\{(\alpha+\alpha')^2+(\beta+\beta')^2+(\gamma+\gamma')^2\}dV.$$

The ·part which depends on the product of the currents is

$$\frac{\mu}{4\pi}(\alpha\alpha'+\beta\beta'+\gamma\gamma')dV.$$

Hence if we know the magnetic intensities I and I' due to the unit current in each circuit, we may obtain M by integrating

$$\frac{\mu}{4\pi}\Sigma\mu I I' \cos\theta dV$$

over all space, where θ is the angle between the directions of I and I'.

Application to a Coil.

(112) To find the coefficient (M) of mutual induction between two circular linear conductors in parallel planes, the distance between the curves being everywhere the same, and small compared with the radius of either.

If r be the distance between the curves, and a the radius of either, then when r is very small compared with a, we find by the second method, as a first approximation,

$$M = 4\pi a\left(\log_e\frac{8a}{r} - 2\right).$$

To approximate more closely to the value of M, let a and a_1 be the radii of the circles, and b the distance between their planes; then

$$r^2 = (a - a_1)^2 + b^2.$$

We obtain M by considering the following conditions:—

1st. M must fulfil the differential equation

$$\frac{d^2M}{da^2} + \frac{d^2M}{db^2} + \frac{1}{a}\frac{dM}{da} = 0.$$

This equation being true for any magnetic field symmetrical with respect to the common axis of the circles, cannot of itself lead to the determination of M as a function of a, a_1, and b. We therefore make use of other conditions.

2ndly.   The value of M must remain the same when a and a_1 are exchanged.

3rdly.   The first two terms of M must be the same as those given above.

M may thus be expanded in the following series:—

$$M = 4\pi a \log \frac{8a}{r} \left\{ 1 + \frac{1}{2}\frac{a-a_1}{a} + \frac{1}{16}\frac{3b^2+(a_1-a)^2}{a^2} - \frac{1}{32}\frac{\{3b^2+(a-a_1)^2\}(a-a_1)}{a^3} + \&c. \right\}$$

$$- 4\pi a \left[2 + \frac{1}{2}\frac{a-a_1}{a} + \frac{1}{16}\frac{b^2-3(a-a_1)^2}{a^2} - \frac{1}{48}\frac{\{6b^2-(a-a_1)^2\}(a-a_1)}{a^3} + \&c. \right]$$

(113)   We may apply this result to find the coefficient of self-induction (L) of a circular coil of wire whose section is small compared with the radius of the circle.

Let the section of the coil be a rectangle, the breadth in the plane of the circle being c, and the depth perpendicular to the plane of the circle being b.

Let the mean radius of the coil be a, and the number of windings n; then we find, by integrating,

$$L = \frac{n^2}{b^2c^2}\iiiint M(xy\,x'y')\,dx\,dy\,dx'\,dy',$$

where $M(xy\,x'y')$ means the value of M for the two windings whose coordinates are xy and $x'y'$ respectively; and the integration is performed first with respect to x and y over the rectangular section, and then with respect to x' and y' over the same space.

$$L = 4\pi n^2 a \left\{ \log \frac{8a}{r} + \frac{1}{12} - \frac{4}{3}\left(\theta - \frac{\pi}{4}\right)\cot 2\theta - \frac{\pi}{3}\cos 2\theta - \frac{1}{6}\cot^2\theta\log\cos\theta - \frac{1}{6}\tan^2\theta\log\sin\theta \right\}$$

$$+ \frac{\pi n^2 r^2}{24a}\left\{ \log\frac{8a}{r}(2\sin^2\theta+1) + 3\cdot45 + 27\cdot475\cos^2\theta - 3\cdot2\left(\frac{\pi}{2}-\theta\right)\frac{\sin^3\theta}{\cos\theta} + \frac{1}{5}\frac{\cos^4\theta}{\sin^2\theta}\log\cos\theta \right.$$

$$+ \frac{13}{3}\frac{\sin^4\theta}{\cos^2\theta}\log\sin\theta \left. \right\} + \&c.$$

Here $a =$ mean radius of the coil.

  ,, $r =$ diagonal of the rectangular section $= \sqrt{b^2+c^2}$.

  ,, $\theta =$ angle between r and the plane of the circle.

  ,, $n =$ number of windings.

The logarithms are Napierian, and the angles are in circular measure.

In the experiments made by the Committee of the British Association for determining a standard of Electrical Resistance, a double coil was used, consisting of two nearly equal coils of rectangular section, placed parallel to each other, with a small interval between them.

The value of L for this coil was found in the following way.

The value of L was calculated by the preceding formula for six different cases, in which the rectangular section considered has always the same breadth, while the depth was

$$A, \quad B, \quad C, \quad A+B, \quad B+C, \quad A+B+C,$$

and $n = 1$ in each case.

Calling the results $\quad L(A), \quad L(B), \quad L(C), \quad$ &c.,

we calculate the coefficient of mutual induction $M(AC)$ of the two coils thus,

$$2ACM(AC) = (A+B+C)^2 L(A+B+C) - (A+B)^2 L(A+B)$$
$$- (B+C)^2 L(B+C) + B^2 L(B).$$

Then if n_1 is the number of windings in the coil A and n_2 in the coil C, the coefficient of self-induction of the two coils together is

$$L = n_1^2 L(A) + 2n_1 n_2 M(AC) + n_2^2 L(C).$$

(114) These values of L are calculated on the supposition that the windings of the wire are evenly distributed so as to fill up exactly the whole section. This, however, is not the case, as the wire is generally circular and covered with insulating material. Hence the current in the wire is more concentrated than it would have been if it had been distributed uniformly over the section, and the currents in the neighbouring wires do not act on it exactly as such a uniform current would do.

The corrections arising from these considerations may be expressed as numerical quantities, by which we must multiply the length of the wire, and they are the same whatever be the form of the coil.

Let the distance between each wire and the next, on the supposition that they are arranged in square order, be D, and let the diameter of the wire be d, then the correction for diameter of wire is

$$+ 2 \left(\log \frac{D}{d} + \tfrac{4}{3} \log 2 + \frac{\pi}{3} - \tfrac{11}{6} \right).$$

The correction for the eight nearest wires is

$$+0\cdot0236.$$

For the sixteen in the next row $+0\cdot00083.$

These corrections being multiplied by the length of wire and added to the former result, give the true value of L, considered as the measure of the potential of the coil on itself for unit current in the wire when that current has been established for some time, and is uniformly distributed through the section of the wire.

(115) But at the commencement of a current and during its variation the current is not uniform throughout the section of the wire, because the inductive action between different portions of the current tends to make the current stronger at one part of the section than at another. When a uniform electromotive force P arising from any cause acts on a cylindrical wire of specific resistance ρ, we have

$$p\rho = P - \frac{dF}{dt},$$

where F is got from the equation

$$\frac{d^2F}{dr^2} + \frac{1}{r}\frac{dF}{dr} = -4\pi\mu p,$$

r being the distance from the axis of the cylinder.

Let one term of the value of F be of the form Tr^n, where T is a function of the time, then the term of p which produced it is of the form

$$-\frac{1}{4\pi\mu} n^2 Tr^{n-2}.$$

Hence if we write

$$F = T + \frac{\mu\pi}{\rho}\left(-P + \frac{dT}{dt}\right)r^2 + \left|\frac{\mu\pi}{\rho}\right|^2 \frac{1}{1^2 \cdot 2^2}\frac{d^2T}{dt^2}r^4 + \&\text{c.}$$

$$p\rho = \left(P - \frac{dT}{dt}\right) - \frac{\mu\pi}{\rho}\frac{d^2T}{dt^2}r^2 - \left|\frac{\mu\pi}{\rho}\right|^2 \frac{1}{1^2 \cdot 2^2}\frac{d^3T}{dt^3}r^4 - \&\text{c.}$$

The total counter current of self-induction at any point is

$$\int\left(\frac{P}{\rho} - p\right)dt = \frac{1}{\rho}T + \frac{\mu\pi}{\rho^2}\frac{dT}{dt}r^2 + \frac{\mu^2\pi^2}{\rho^3}\frac{1}{1^2 2^2}\frac{d^2T}{dt^2}r^4 + \&\text{c.}$$

from $t = 0$ to $t = \infty$.

When $t=0$, $p=0$, $\therefore \left(\dfrac{dT}{dt}\right)_0 = P$, $\left(\dfrac{d^2T}{dt^2}\right)_0 = 0$, &c.

When $t=\infty$, $p=\dfrac{P}{\rho}$, $\therefore \left(\dfrac{dT}{dt}\right)_\infty = 0$, $\left(\dfrac{d^2T}{dt^2}\right)_\infty = 0$, &c.

$$\int_0^\infty \int_0^r 2\pi \left(\frac{P}{\rho} - p\right) rdrdt = \frac{1}{\rho} T\pi r^2 + \frac{1}{2}\frac{\mu\pi^2}{\rho^2}\frac{dT}{dt} r^4 + \frac{\mu^2\pi^3}{\rho^3}\frac{1}{1^2 . 2^2 . 3}\frac{d^2T}{dt^2} r^6 + \&c.$$

from $t=0$ to $=\infty$.

When $t=0$, $p=0$ throughout the section, $\therefore \left(\dfrac{dT}{dt}\right)_0 = P$, $\left(\dfrac{d^2T}{dt^2}\right)_0 = 0$, &c.

When $t=\infty$, $p=0$,,   ,,   ,, $\therefore \left(\dfrac{dT}{dt}\right)_\infty = 0$, $\left(\dfrac{d^2T}{dt^2}\right)_\infty = 0$, &c.

Also if l be the length of the wire, and R its resistance,

$$R = \frac{\rho l}{\pi r^2};$$

and if C be the current when established in the wire, $C = \dfrac{Pl}{R}$.

The total counter current may be written

$$\frac{l}{R}(T_\infty - T_0) - \tfrac{1}{2}\mu \frac{l}{R} C = - \frac{LC}{R} \text{ by § (35).}$$

Now if the current instead of being variable from the centre to the circumference of the section of the wire had been the same throughout, the value of F would have been

$$F = T + \mu\gamma \left(1 - \frac{r^2}{r_0^2}\right),$$

where γ is the current in the wire at any instant, and the total counter current would have been

$$\int_0^\infty \int_0^r \frac{1}{\rho}\frac{dF}{dt} 2\pi rdr = \frac{l}{R}(T_\infty - T_0) - \tfrac{3}{4}\mu \frac{l}{R} C = - \frac{L'C}{R}, \text{ say.}$$

Hence $L = L' - \tfrac{1}{4}\mu l$,

or the value of L which must be used in calculating the self-induction of a wire for variable currents is less than that which is deduced from the supposition of the current being constant throughout the section of the wire by $\tfrac{1}{4}\mu l$, where l is the length of the wire, and μ is the coefficient of magnetic induction for the substance of the wire.

(116)   The dimensions of the coil used by the Committee of the British Association in their experiments at King's College in 1864 were as follows :—

metre.

Mean radius.......................... $= a = \cdot158194$

Depth of each coil............... $= b = \cdot01608$

Breadth of each coil.............. $= c = \cdot01841$

Distance between the coils..... $= \cdot02010$

Number of windings.............. $n = 313$

Diameter of wire.................. $= \cdot00126$

The value of L derived from the first term of the expression is 437440 metres.

The correction depending on the radius not being infinitely great compared with the section of the coil as found from the second term is -7345 metres.

The correction depending on the diameter of the wire is per unit of length	$+ \cdot44997$
Correction of eight neighbouring wires	$+ \cdot0236$
For sixteen wires next to these	$+ \cdot0008$
Correction for variation of current in different parts of section	$- \cdot2500$
Total correction per unit of length	$\cdot22437$
Length	$311\cdot236$ metres.
Sum of corrections of this kind......................................	70 ,,
Final value of L by calculation....................................	430165 ,,

This value of L was employed in reducing the observations, according to the method explained in the Report of the Committee*. The correction depending on L varies as the square of the velocity. The results of sixteen experiments to which this correction had been applied, and in which the velocity varied from 100 revolutions in seventeen seconds to 100 in seventy-seven seconds,

---

* *British Association Reports*, 1863, p. 169.

were compared by the method of least squares to determine what further correction depending on the square of the velocity should be applied to make the outstanding errors a minimum.

The result of this examination shewed that the calculated value of L should be multiplied by 1·0618 to obtain the value of L, which would give the most consistent results.

We have therefore L by calculation...................................   430165 metres.

Probable value of L by method of least squares   456748   ,,

Result of rough experiment with the Electric Balance (see § 46)   410000   ,,

The value of L calculated from the dimensions of the coil is probably much more accurate than either of the other determinations.

[From the *Philosophical Magazine*, Vol. XXVII.]

* XXVI. *On the Calculation of the Equilibrium and Stiffness of Frames.*

THE theory of the equilibrium and deflections of frameworks subjected to the action of forces is sometimes considered as more complicated than it really is, especially in cases in which the framework is not simply stiff, but is strengthened (or weakened as it may be) by additional connecting pieces. I have therefore stated a general method of solving all such questions in the least complicated manner. The method is derived from the principle of Conservation of Energy, and is referred to in Lamé's *Leçons sur l'Elasticité*, Leçon 7me, as Clapeyron's Theorem; but I have not yet seen any detailed application of it.

If such questions were attempted, especially in cases of three dimensions, by the regular method of equations of forces, every point would have three equations to determine its equilibrium, so as to give $3s$ equations between e unknown quantities, if s be the number of points and e the number of connexions. There are, however, six equations of equilibrium of the system which must be fulfilled necessarily by the forces, on account of the equality of action and reaction in each piece. Hence if

$$e = 3s - 6,$$

the effect of any external force will be definite in producing tensions or pressures in the different pieces; but if $e > 3s - 6$, these forces will be indeterminate. This indeterminateness is got rid of by the introduction of a system of e equations of elasticity connecting the force in each piece with the change in its length. In order, however, to know the changes of length, we require to assume $3s$ displacements of the s points; 6 of these displacements, however, are equivalent to the motion of a rigid body so that we have $3s - 6$ displacements of points, e extensions and e forces to determine from $3s - 6$ equations of forces, e

---

* [Owing to an oversight this paper is out of its proper place; it should have been immediately before the memoir on "The Electro-magnetic Field." (No. XXV.)]

equations of extensions, and e equations of elasticity; so that the solution is always determinate.

The following method enables us to avoid unnecessary complexity by treating separately all pieces which are additional to those required for making the frame stiff, and by proving the identity in form between the equations of forces and those of extensions by means of the principle of work.

On the Stiffness of Frames.

Geometrical definition of a Frame. A frame is a system of lines connecting a number of points.

A stiff frame is one in which the distance between any two points cannot be altered without altering the length of one or more of the connecting lines of the frame.

A frame of s points in space requires *in general* $3s - 6$ connecting lines to render it stiff. In those cases in which stiffness can be produced with a smaller number of lines, certain conditions must be fulfilled, rendering the case one of a maximum or minimum value of one or more of its lines. The stiffness of such frames is of an inferior order, as a small disturbing force may produce a displacement infinite in comparison with itself.

A frame of s points in a plane requires in general $2s - 3$ connecting lines to render it stiff.

A frame of s points in a line requires $s - 1$ connecting lines.

A frame may be either simply stiff, or it may be self-strained by the introduction of additional connecting lines having tensions or pressures along them.

In a frame which is simply stiff, the forces in each connecting line arising from the application of a force of pressure or tension between any two points of the frame may be calculated either by equations of forces, or by drawing diagrams of forces according to known methods.

In general, the lines of connexion in one part of the frame may be affected by the action of this force, while those in other parts of the frame may not be so affected.

Elasticity and Extensibility of a connecting piece.

Let e be the extension produced in a piece by tension-unity acting in it, then e may be called its extensibility. Its elasticity, that is, the force required to produce extension-unity, will be $\dfrac{1}{e}$. We shall suppose that the effect of pressure in producing compression of the piece is equal to that of tension in producing extension, and we shall use e indifferently for extensibility and compressibility.

Work done against Elasticity.

Since the extension is proportional to the force, the whole work done will be the product of the extension and the mean value of the force; or if x is the extension and F the force,

$$x = eF,$$

$$\text{work} = \tfrac{1}{2}Fx = \tfrac{1}{2}eF^2 = \tfrac{1}{2}\frac{1}{e}x^2.$$

When the piece is inextensible, or $e = 0$, then all the work applied at one end is transmitted to the other, and the frame may be regarded as a machine whose efficiency is perfect. Hence the following

THEOREM. If p be the tension of the piece A due to a tension-unity between the points B and C, then an extension-unity taking place in A will bring B and C nearer by a distance p.

For let X be the tension and x the extension of A, Y the tension and y the extension of the line BC; then supposing all the other pieces inextensible, no work will be done except in stretching A, or

$$\tfrac{1}{2}Xx + \tfrac{1}{2}Yy = 0.$$

But $X = pY$, therefore $y = -px$, which was to be proved.

PROBLEM I. A tension F is applied between the points B and C of a frame which is simply stiff; to find the extension of the line joining D and E, all the pieces except A being inextensible, the extensibility of A being e.

Determine the tension in each piece due to unit tension between B and C, and let p be the tension in A due to this cause.

Determine also the tension in each piece due to unit tension between D and E, and let y be the tension in the piece A due to this cause.

Then the actual tension of A is Fp, and its extension is eFp, and the extension of the line DE due to this cause is $-Fepq$ by the last theorem.

COR. If the other pieces of the frame are extensible, the complete value of the extension in DE due to a tension F in BC is

$$- F\Sigma(epq),$$

where $\Sigma(epq)$ means the sum of the products of epq, which are to be found for each piece in the same way as they were found for A.

The extension of the line BC due to a tension F in BC itself will be

$$- F\Sigma(ep^2),$$

$\Sigma(ep^2)$ may therefore be called the resultant extensibility along BC.

PROBLEM II. A tension F is applied between B and C; to find the extension between D and E when the frame is not simply stiff, but has additional pieces R, S, T, &c. whose elasticities are known.

Let p and q, as before, be the tensions in the piece A due to unit tensions in BC and DE, and let r, s, t, &c. be the tensions in A due to unit tension in R, S, T, &c.; also let R, S, T be the tensions of R, S, T, and ρ, σ, τ their extensibilities. Then the tension A

$$= Fp + Rr + Ss + Tt + \&c.;$$

the extension of A

$$= e(Fp + Rr + Ss + Tt + \&c.);$$

the extension of R

$$= - F\Sigma(epr) - R\Sigma er^2 - S\Sigma ers - T\Sigma ert + \&c. = R\rho\;;$$

extension of S

$$= - F\Sigma(eps) - R\Sigma(ers) - S\Sigma es^2 - T\Sigma(est) = S\sigma\;;$$

extension of T

$$= - F\Sigma(ept) - R\Sigma(ert) - S\Sigma(est) - T\Sigma(et^2) = T\tau\;;$$

also extension of DE

$$= - F\Sigma(epq) - R\Sigma(eqr) - S\Sigma(eqs) - T\Sigma(eqt) = x,$$

the extension required. Here we have as many equations to determine R, S, T, &c. as there are of these unknown quantities, and by the last equation we determine x the extension of DE from F the tension in BC.

Thus, if there is only one additional connexion R, we find

$$R = - F\frac{\Sigma(epr)}{\Sigma(er^2) + \rho},$$

and

$$x = - F\left\{\Sigma(epq) + \frac{\Sigma(epr)\Sigma(eqr)}{\Sigma(er^2) + \rho}\right\}\;.$$

If there are two additional connexions R and S, with elasticities ρ and σ,

$$x = - F$$
$$\overline{\Sigma e(r^2+\rho)\Sigma e(s^2+\sigma)-(\Sigma(ers))^2}$$

$$\left\{ \begin{array}{l} \Sigma(epr)\Sigma(ers)\Sigma(eqs)+\Sigma(eps)\Sigma(eqr)\Sigma(ers)+\Sigma(epq)\Sigma e(r^2+\rho)\Sigma e(s^2+\sigma) \\ -\Sigma(epr)\Sigma(eqr)\Sigma e(s^2+\sigma)-\Sigma(eps)\Sigma(eqs)\Sigma e(r^2+\rho)-\Sigma(epq)(\Sigma(ers))^2 \end{array} \right\}.$$

The expressions for the extensibility, when there are many additional pieces, are of course very complicated.

It will be observed, however, that p and q always enter into the equations in the same way, so that we may establish the following general

THEOREM. The extension in BC, due to unity of tension along DE, is always equal to the tension in DE due to unity of tension in BC. Hence we have the following method of determining the displacement produced at any joint of a frame due to forces applied at other joints.

1st. Select as many pieces of the frame as are sufficient to render all its points stiff. Call the remaining pieces R, S, T, &c.

2nd. Find the tension on each piece due to unit of tension in the direction of the force proposed to be applied. Call this the value of p for each piece.

3rd. Find the tension on each piece due to unit of tension in the direction of the displacement to be determined. Call this the value of q for each piece.

4th. Find the tension on each piece due to unit of tension along R, S, T, &c., the additional pieces of the frame. Call these the values of r, s, t, &c. for each piece.

5th. Find the extensibility of each piece and call it e, those of the additional pieces being ρ, σ, τ, &c.

6th. R, S, T, &c. are to be determined from the equations

$$R\rho + R\Sigma(er^2) + S(ers) + T\Sigma(ert) + F\Sigma(epr) = 0,$$
$$S\sigma + R\Sigma(ers) + S(es^2) + T\Sigma(est) + F\Sigma(eps) = 0,$$
$$T\tau + R\Sigma(ert) + S(est) + T\Sigma(et^2) + F\Sigma(ept) = 0,$$

as many equations as there are quantities to be found.

7th. x, the extension required, is then found from the equation

$$x = - F\Sigma(epq) - R\Sigma(erq) - S\Sigma(eqs) - T\Sigma(eqt).$$

In structures acted on by weights in which we wish to determine the deflection at any point, we may regard the points of support as the extremities of pieces connecting the structure with the centre of the earth; and if the supports are capable of resisting a horizontal thrust, we must suppose them connected by a piece of equivalent elasticity. The deflection is then the shortening of a piece extending from the given point to the centre of the earth.

EXAMPLE. Thus in a triangular or Warren girder of length l, depth d, with a load W placed at a distance a from one end, 0; to find the deflection at a point distant b from the same end, due to the yielding of a piece of the boom whose extensibility is e, distant x from the same end.

The pressure of the support at $0 = W \dfrac{l-a}{l}$; and if x is less than a, the force at x will be $\dfrac{W}{dl} x(l-a)$, or

$$p = \frac{x(l-a)}{dl}.$$

If x is greater than a,

$$p = \frac{a(l-x)}{dl}.$$

Similarly, if x is less than b,

$$q = \frac{x(l-b)}{dl};$$

but if x is greater than b,

$$q = \frac{b(l-x)}{dl}.$$

The deflection due to x is therefore $Wepq$, where the proper values of p and q must be taken according to the relative position of a, b, and x.

If a, b, l, x represent the *number* of the respective pieces, reckoning from the beginning and calling the first joint 0, the second joint and the piece opposite 1, &c., and if L be the length of each piece, and the extensibility of each piece $= e$, then the deflection of b due to W at a will be, by summation of series,

$$= \frac{1}{6} WeL^2 . \frac{a(l-b)}{d^2 l} \{2b(l-a) - (b-a)^2 + 1\}.$$

This is the deflection due to the yielding of all the horizontal pieces. The greater the number of pieces, the less is the importance of the last term.

Let the inclination of the pieces of the web be a, then the force on a piece between 0 and a is $W \dfrac{l-a}{l \sin a}$, or

$$p' = \frac{l-a}{l \sin a} \text{ when } x < a,$$

and

$$p' = \frac{a}{l \sin a} \text{ when } x > a.$$

Also

$$q' = \frac{l-b}{l \sin a} \text{ when } x < b,$$

$$q' = \frac{b}{l \sin a} \text{ when } x > b.$$

If e' be the extensibility of a piece of the web, we have to sum $W \Sigma e' p' q'$ to get the deflection due to the yielding of the web,

$$= \frac{We'}{l^2 \sin^2 a} \, a(l-b)\{l + 2(b-a)\}.$$

INDEX TO VOL. I.

THE SCIENTIFIC PAPERS OF

JAMES CLERK MAXWELL

THE SCIENTIFIC PAPERS OF

JAMES CLERK MAXWELL

EDITED BY W. D. NIVEN, M.A., F.R.S.

VOLUME TWO

TABLE OF CONTENTS.

ERRATA. VOL. II.

Page   3, line   5, read   i. p. 25   instead of   xxxi. p. 30.

,,   73, ,, 14, ,,   60   ,,   76.

,, 188, ,, 27, ,,   p. (181)   ,.   p. (189).

,, 191, ,,   8, ,, $p_{yz} = -p\dfrac{d^2F}{dy\,dz}$,, $-p\dfrac{d^2F}{dx\,dy}$.

,, 201, ,, 10. insert H after the differential operator in equation (18).

In the Bakerian Lecture at page 18, line 21, the value of $\dfrac{\pi}{2}r^4$ is given as 1112·8, where r is the radius of each of the movable discs used in the experiments on Viscosity. But with the value of the diameter as given at page 4, line 14, this number should be 1220·8. The values of the quantity A in the fourth line of the Table given at page 19 should therefore all be increased by 108. The values of Q, the quantity in the fifth line, increase in the same proportion as the values of A. Hence according to equations (23) and (24) the values of μ, the coefficient of Viscosity, will be smaller than they appear in the text and will approximate to those obtained by more recent experiments. The above inaccuracy in the numerical reductions was pointed out by Mr Leahy, Pembroke College, Cambridge.

[From the *Philosophical Transactions*, Vol. CLVI.]

XXVII. THE BAKERIAN LECTURE.—*On the Viscosity or Internal Friction of Air and other Gases.*

Received November 23, 1865,—Read February 8, 1866.

THE gaseous form of matter is distinguished by the great simplification which occurs in the expression of the properties of matter when it passes into that state from the solid or liquid form. The simplicity of the relations between density, pressure, and temperature, and between the volume and the number of molecules, seems to indicate that the molecules of bodies, when in the gaseous state, are less impeded by any complicated mechanism than when they subside into the liquid or solid states. The investigation of other properties of matter is therefore likely to be more simple if we begin our research with matter in the form of a gas.

The viscosity of a body is the resistance which it offers to a continuous change of form, depending on the rate at which that change is effected.

All bodies are capable of having their form altered by the action of sufficient forces during a sufficient time. M. Kohlrausch* has shewn that torsion applied to glass fibres produces a permanent set which increases with the time of action of the force, and that when the force of torsion is removed the fibre slowly untwists, so as to do away with part of the set it had acquired. Softer solids exhibit the phenomena of plasticity in a greater degree; but the investigation of the relations between the forces and their effects is extremely difficult, as in most cases the state of the solid depends not only on the forces actually impressed on it, but on all the strains to which it has been subjected during its previous existence.

* "Ueber die elastische Nachwerkung bei der Torsion," Pogg. *Ann.* CXIX. 1863.

Professor W. Thomson* has shewn that something corresponding to internal friction takes place in the torsional vibrations of wires, but that it is much increased if the wire has been previously subjected to large vibrations. I have also found that, after heating a steel wire to a temperature below 120°, its elasticity was permanently diminished and its internal friction increased.

The viscosity of fluids has been investigated by passing them through capillary tubes†, by swinging pendulums in them‡, and by the torsional vibrations of an immersed disk§, and of a sphere filled with the fluid‖.

The method of transpiration through tubes is very convenient, especially for comparative measurements, and in the hands of Graham and Poiseuille it has given good results, but the measurement of the diameter of the tube is difficult, and on account of the smallness of the bore we cannot be certain that the action between the molecules of the gas and those of the substance of the tubes does not affect the result. The pendulum method is capable of great accuracy, and I believe that experiments are in progress by which its merits as a means of determining the properties of the resisting medium will be tested. The method of swinging a disk in the fluid is simple and direct. The chief difficulty is the determination of the motion of the fluid near the edge of the disk, which introduces very serious mathematical difficulties into the calculation of the result. The method with the sphere is free from the mathematical difficulty, but the weight of a properly constructed spherical shell makes it unsuitable for experiments on gases.

In the experiments on the viscosity of air and other gases which I propose to describe, I have employed the method of the torsional vibrations of disks, but instead of placing them in an open space, I have placed them each between two parallel fixed disks at a small but easily measurable distance, in which case, when the period of vibration is long, the mathematical difficulties of determining the motion of the fluid are greatly reduced. I have also used three

---

* *Proceedings of the Royal Society*, May 18, 1865.

† Liquids: Poiseuille, *Mém. de Savants Étrangers*, 1846. Gases: Graham, *Philosophical Transactions*, 1846 and 1849.'

‡ Baily, *Phil. Trans.* 1832; Bessel, *Berlin Acad.* 1826; Dubuat, *Principes d'Hydraulique*, 1786. All these are discussed in Professor Stokes's paper "On the Effect of the Internal Friction of Fluids on the Motion of Pendulums," *Cambridge Phil. Trans.* vol. IX. pt. 2 (1850).

§ Coulomb, *Mém. de l'Institut national*, III. p. 246; O. E. Meyer, Pogg. *Ann.* CXIII. (1861) p. 55, and *Crelle's Journal*, Bd. 59.

‖ Helmholtz and Pietrowski, *Sitzungsberichte der k. k. Akad.* April, 1860.

disks instead of one, so that there are six surfaces exposed to friction, which may be reduced to two by placing the three disks in contact, without altering the weight of the whole or the time of vibration. The apparatus was constructed by Mr Becker, of Messrs Elliott Brothers, Strand.

Description of the Apparatus.

Plate XXI. p. 30, fig. 1 represents the vacuum apparatus one-eighth of the actual size. *MQRS* is a strong three-legged stool supporting the whole. The top (*MM*) is in the form of a ring. *EE* is a brass plate supported by the ring *MM*. The under surface is ground truly plane, the upper surface is strengthened by ribs cast in the same piece with it. The suspension-tube *AC* is screwed into the plate *EE*, and is 4 feet in height. The glass receiver *N* rests on a wooden ring *PP* with three projecting pieces which rest on the three brackets *QQ*, of which two only are seen. The upper surfaces of the brackets and the under surfaces of the projections are so bevilled off, that by slightly turning the wooden ring in its own plane the receiver can be pressed up against the plate *EE*.

F, G, H, K are circular plates of glass of the form represented in fig. 2. Each has a hole in the centre 2 inches in diameter, and three holes near the circumference, by which it is supported on the screws *LL*.

Fig. 6 represents the mode of supporting and adjusting the glass plates. *LL* is one of the screws fixed under the plate *EE*. *S* is a nut, of which the upper part fits easily in the hole in the glass plate *F*, while the under part is of larger diameter, so as to support the glass plate and afford the means of turning the nut easily by hand. These nuts occupy little space, and enable the glass disks to be brought very accurately to their proper position.

ACB, fig. 1, is a siphon barometer, closed at *A* and communicating with the interior of the suspension-tube at *B*. The scale is divided on both sides, so that the difference of the readings gives the pressure within the apparatus. *T* is a thermometer, lying on the upper glass plate. *V* is a vessel containing pumice-stone soaked in sulphuric acid, to dry the air. Another vessel, containing caustic potash, is not shewn. *D* is a tube with a stopcock, leading to the air-pump or the gas generator. *C* is a glass window, giving a view of the suspended mirror *d*.

For high and low temperatures the tin vessel (fig. 10) was used. When the receiver was exhausted, the ring *P* was removed, and the tin vessel raised so as to envelope the receiver, which then rested on the wooden support YY. The tin vessel itself rested, by means of projections on the brackets QQ. The outside of the tin vessel was then well wrapped up in blankets, and the top of the brass plate EE covered with a feather cushion; and cold water, hot water, or steam was made to flow through the tin vessel till the thermometer T, seen through the window W, became stationary.

The moveable parts of the apparatus consist of—

The suspension-piece a, fitting air-tight into the top of the tube and holding the suspension-wire by a clip, represented in fig. 5.

The axis $cdek$, suspended to the wire by another clip at C.

The wire was a hard-drawn steel wire, one foot of which weighed 2·6 grains.

The axis carries the plane mirror d, by which its angular position is observed through the window C, and the three vibrating glass disks f, g, h, represented in fig. 3. Each disk is 10·56 inches diameter and about ·076 thick, and has a hole in the centre ·75 diameter. They are kept in position on the axis by means of short tubes of accurately known length, which support them on the axis and separate them from each other.

The whole suspended system weighs three pounds avoirdupoise.

In erecting the apparatus, the lower part of the axis ek is screwed off. The fixed disks are then screwed on, with a vibrating disk lying between each. Tubes of the proper lengths are then placed on the lower part of the axis and between the disks. The axis is then passed up from below through the disks and tubes, and is screwed to the upper part at e. The vibrating disks are now hanging by the wire and in their proper places, and the fixed disks are brought to their proper distances from them by means of the adjusting nuts.

ns is a small piece of magnetized steel wire attached to the axis.

When it is desired to set the disks in motion, a battery of magnets is placed under N, and so moved as to bring the initial arc of vibration to the proper value.

Fig. 4 is a brass ring whose moment of inertia is known. It is placed centrically on the vibrating disk by means of three radial wires, which keep it exactly in its place.

Fig. 7 is a tube containing two nearly equal weights, which slide inside it, and whose position can be read off by verniers.

The ring and the tube are used in finding the moment of inertia of the vibrating apparatus.

The extent and duration of the vibrations are observed in the ordinary way by means of a telescope, which shews the reflexion of a scale in the mirror d. The scale is on a circular arc of six feet radius, concentric with the axis of the instrument. The extremities of the scale correspond to an arc of vibration of 19° 36', and the divisions on the scale to 1·7. The readings are usually taken to tenths of a division.

Method of Observation.

When the instrument was properly adjusted, a battery of magnets was placed on a board below N, and reversed at proper intervals till the arc of vibration extended slightly beyond the limits of the scale. The magnets were then removed, and any accidental pendulous oscillations of the suspended disks were checked by applying the hand to the suspension-tube. The barometer and thermometer were then read off, and the observer took his seat at the telescope and wrote down the extreme limits of each vibration as shewn by the numbers on the scale. At intervals of five complete vibrations, the time of the transits of the middle point of the scale was observed (see Table I.). When the amplitude decreased rapidly, the observations were continued throughout the experiment ; but when the decrement was small, the observer generally left the room for an hour, or till the amplitude was so far reduced as to furnish the most accurate results.

In observing a quantity which decreases in a geometrical ratio in equal times, the most accurate value of the rate of decrement will be deduced from a comparison of the initial values with values which are to these in the ratio of e to 1, where $e = 2·71828$, the base of the Napierian system of logarithms. In practice, however, it is best to stop the experiment somewhat before the vibrations are so much reduced, as the time required would be better spent in beginning a new experiment.

In reducing the observations, the sum of every five maxima and of the consecutive five minima was taken, and the differences of these were written as the terms of the series the decrement of which was to be found.

In experiments where the law of decrement is uncertain, this rough method is inapplicable, and Gauss's method must be applied ; but the series of amplitudes in these experiments is so accurately geometrical, that no appreciable difference between the results of the two methods would occur.

The logarithm of each term of the series was then taken, and the mean logarithmic decrement ascertained by taking the difference of the first and last, of the second and last but one, and so on, multiplying each difference by the interval of the terms, and dividing the sum of the products by the sum of the squares of these intervals. Thus, if fifty observations were taken of the extreme limits of vibration, these were first combined by tens, so as to form five terms of a decreasing series. The logarithms of these terms were then taken. Twice the difference of the first and fifth of these logarithms was then added to the difference of the second and third, and the result divided by ten for the mean logarithmic decrement in five complete vibrations.

The times were then treated in the same way to get the mean time of five vibrations. The numbers representing the logarithmic decrement, and the time for five vibrations, were entered as the result of each experiment*.

The series found from ten different experiments were examined to discover any departure from uniformity in the logarithmic decrement depending on the amplitude of vibration. The logarithmic decrement was found to be constant in each experiment to within the limits of probable error; the deviations from uniformity were sometimes in one direction and sometimes in the opposite, and the ten experiments when combined gave no evidence of any law of increase or diminution of the logarithmic decrement as the amplitudes decrease. The forces which retard the disks are therefore as the first power of the velocity, and there is no evidence of any force varying with the square of the velocity, such as is produced when bodies move rapidly through the air. In these experiments the maximum velocity of the circumference of the moving disks was about $\frac{1}{12}$ inch per second. The changes of form in the air between the disks were therefore effected very slowly, and eddies were not produced†.

The retardation of the motion of the disks is, however, not due entirely to the action of the air, since the suspension wire has a viscosity of its own, which must be estimated separately. Professor W. Thomson has observed great changes in the viscosity of wires after being subjected to torsion and longitudinal strain. The wire used in these experiments had been hanging up for

---

* See Table II.

† The total moment of the resistances never exceeded that of the weight of $\frac{1}{30}$ grain acting at the edge of the disks.

some months before, and had been set into torsional vibrations with various weights attached to it, to determine its moment of torsion. Its moment of torsion and its viscosity seem to have remained afterwards nearly constant, till steam was employed to heat the lower part of the apparatus. Its viscosity then increased, and its moment of torsion diminished permanently, but when the apparatus was again heated, no further change seems to have taken place. During each course of experiments, care was taken not to set the disks vibrating beyond the limits of the scale, so that the viscosity of the wire may be supposed constant in each set of experiments.

In order to determine how much of the total retardation of the motion is due to the viscosity of the wire, the moving disks were placed in contact with each other, and fixed disks were placed at a measured distance above and below them. The weight and moment of inertia of the system remained as before, but the part of the retardation of the motion due to the viscosity of the air was less, as there were only two surfaces exposed to the action of the air instead of six. Supposing the effect of the viscosity of the wire to remain as before, the difference of retardation is that due to the action of the four additional strata of air, and is independent of the value of the viscosity of the wire.

In the experiments which were used in determining the viscosity of air, five different arrangements were adopted.

Arrangement 1. Three disks in contact, fixed disks at 1 inch above and below.

,, 2. ,, ,, ,, 0·5 inch.

,, 3. Three disks, each between two fixed disks at distance 0·683.

,, 4. ,, ,, ,, ,, ,, 0·425.

,, 5. ,, ,, ,, ,, ,, 0·18475.

By comparing the results of these different arrangements, the coefficient of viscosity was obtained, and the theory at the same time subjected to a rigorous test.

Definition of the Coefficient of Viscosity.

The final result of each set of experiments was to determine the value of the coefficient of viscosity of the gas in the apparatus. This coefficient may be best defined by considering a stratum of air between two parallel horizontal planes of indefinite extent, at a distance a from one another. Suppose the upper plane to be set in motion in a horizontal direction with a velocity of v feet per second, and to continue in motion till the air in the different parts of the stratum has taken up its final velocity, then the velocity of the air will increase uniformly as we pass from the lower plane to the upper. If the air in contact with the planes has the same velocity as the planes themselves, then the velocity will increase $\dfrac{v}{a}$ feet per second for every foot we ascend.

The friction between any two contiguous strata of air will then be equal to that between either surface and the air in contact with it. Suppose that this friction is equal to a tangential force f on every square foot, then

$$f = \mu \frac{v}{a},$$

where μ is the coefficient of viscosity, v the velocity of the upper plane, and a the distance between them.

If the experiment could be made with the two infinite planes as described, we should find μ at once, for

$$\mu = \frac{fa}{v}.$$

In the actual case the motion of the planes is rotatory instead of rectilinear, oscillatory instead of constant, and the planes are bounded instead of infinite.

It will be shewn that the rotatory motion may be calculated on the same principles as rectilinear motion; but that the oscillatory character of the motion introduces the consideration of the inertia of the air in motion, which causes the middle portions of the stratum to lag behind, as is shewn in fig. 8, where the curves represent the successive positions of a line of particles of air, which, if there were no motion, would be a straight line perpendicular to the planes.

The fact that the moving planes are bounded by a circular edge introduces another difficulty, depending on the motion of the air near the edge being different from that of the rest of the air.

The lines of equal motion of the air are shewn in fig. 9.

The consideration of these two circumstances introduces certain corrections into the calculations, as will be shewn hereafter.

In expressing the viscosity of the gas in absolute measure, the measures of all velocities, forces, &c. must be taken according to some consistent system of measurement.

If L, M, T represent the units of length, mass, and time, then the dimensions of f (a pressure per unit of surface) are $L^{-1}MT^{-2}$; a is a length, and v is a velocity whose dimensions are LT^{-1}, so that the dimensions of μ are $L^{-1}MT^{-1}$.

Thus if μ be the viscosity of a gas expressed in inch-grain-second measure, and μ' the same expressed in foot-pound-minute measure, then

$$\frac{\mu}{\mu'} \cdot \frac{1 \text{ inch}}{1 \text{ foot}} \cdot \frac{1 \text{ pound}}{1 \text{ grain}} \cdot \frac{1 \text{ second}}{1 \text{ minute}} = 1.$$

According to the experiments of MM. Helmholtz and Pietrowski*, the velocity of a fluid in contact with a surface is not always equal to that of the surface itself, but a certain amount of actual slipping takes place in certain cases between the surface and the fluid in immediate contact with it. In the case which we have been considering, if v_0 is the velocity of the fluid in contact with the fixed plane, and f the tangential force per unit of surface, then

$$f = \sigma v_0,$$

where σ is the coefficient of superficial friction between the fluid and the particular surface over which it flows, and depends on the nature of the surface as well as on that of the fluid. The coefficient σ is of the dimensions $L^{-2}MT^{-1}$. If v_1 be the velocity of the fluid in contact with the plane which is moving with velocity v, and if σ' be the coefficient of superficial friction for that plane,

$$f = \sigma'(v - v_1).$$

The internal friction of the fluid itself is

$$f = \frac{\mu}{a}(v_1 - v_0).$$

Hence

$$v = f\left(\frac{1}{\sigma} + \frac{1}{\sigma'} + \frac{a}{\mu}\right).$$

If we make $\frac{\mu}{\sigma} = \beta$, and $\frac{\mu}{\sigma'} = \beta'$, then

$$v = f\left(\frac{a + \beta + \beta'}{\mu}\right),$$

* *Sitzungsberichte der k. k. Akad.* April 1860.

or the friction is equal to what it would have been if there had been no slipping, and if the interval between the planes had been increased by $\beta + \beta'$. By changing the interval between the planes, a may be made to vary while $\beta + \beta'$ remains constant, and thus the value of $\beta + \beta'$ may be determined. In the case of air, the amount of slipping is so small that it produces no appreciable effect on the results of experiments. In the case of glass surfaces rubbing on air, the probable value of β, deduced from the experiments, was $\beta = \cdot0027$ inch. The distance between the moving surfaces cannot be measured so accurately as to give this value of β the character of an ascertained quantity. The probability is rather in favour of the theory that there is no slipping between air and glass, and that the value of β given above results from accidental discrepancy in the observations. I have therefore preferred to calculate the value of. μ on the supposition that there is no slipping between the air and the glass in contact with it.

The value of μ depends on the nature of the gas and on its physical condition. By making experiments in gas of different densities, it is shewn that μ remains constant, so that its value is the same for air at 0·5 inch and at 30 inches pressure, provided the temperature remains the same. This will be seen by examining Table IV., where the value of L, the logarithm of the decrement of arc in ten single vibrations, is the same for the same temperature, though the density is sixty times greater in some cases than in others. In fact the numbers in the column headed L' were calculated on the hypothesis that the viscosity is independent of the density, and they agree very well with the observed values.

It will be seen, however, that the value of L rises and falls with the temperature, as given in the second column of Table IV. These temperatures range from $51°$ to $74°$ Fahr., and were the natural temperatures of the room on different days in May 1865. The results agree with the hypothesis that the viscosity is proportional to $(461° + \theta)$, the temperature measured from absolute zero of the air-thermometer. In order to test this proportionality, the temperature was raised to $185°$ Fahr. by a current of steam sent round the space between the glass receiver and the tin vessel. The temperature was kept up for several hours, till the thermometer in the receiver became stationary, before the disks were set in motion. The ratio of the upper temperature ($185°$ F.) to the lower ($51°$), measured from $-461°$ F., was

$$1\cdot2605.$$

The ratio of the viscosity at the upper temperature to that at the lower was

$$1\cdot2624,$$

which shews that the viscosity is proportional to the absolute temperature very nearly. The simplicity of the other known laws relating to gases warrants us in concluding that the viscosity is really proportional to the temperature, measured from the absolute zero of the air-thermometer.

These relations between the viscosity of air and its pressure and temperature are the more to be depended on, since they agree with the results deduced by Mr. Graham from experiments on the transpiration of gases through tubes of small diameter. The constancy of the viscosity for all changes of density when the temperature is constant is a result of the Dynamical Theory of Gases*, whatever hypothesis we adopt as to the mode of action between the molecules when they come near one another. The relation between viscosity and temperature, however, requires us to make a particular assumption with respect to the force acting between the molecules. If the molecules act on one another only at a determinate distance by a kind of impact, the viscosity will be as the square root of the absolute temperature. This, however, is certainly not the actual law. If, as the experiments of Graham and those of this paper shew, the viscosity is as the first power of the absolute temperature, then in the dynamical theory, which is framed to explain the facts, we must assume that the force between two molecules is proportional inversely to the fifth power of the distance between them. The present paper, however, does not profess to give any explanation of the cause of the viscosity of air, but only to determine its value in different cases.

Experiments were made on a few other gases besides dry air.

Damp air, over water at 70° F. and 4 inches pressure, was found by the mean of three experiments to be about one-sixtieth part less viscous than dry air at the same temperature.

Dry hydrogen was found to be much less viscous than air, the ratio of its viscosity to that of air being ·5156.

A small proportion of air mixed with hydrogen was found to produce a large increase of viscosity, and a mixture of equal parts of air and hydrogen has a viscosity nearly equal to $1\frac{5}{8}$ of that of air.

The ratio of the viscosity of dry carbonic acid to that of air was found to be ·859.

* "Illustrations of the Dynamical Theory of Gases," *Philosophical Magazine*, Jan. 1860.

It appears from the experiments of Mr. Graham that the ratio of the transpiration time of hydrogen to that of air is ·4855, and that of carbonic acid to air ·807. These numbers are both smaller than those of this paper. I think that the discrepancy arises from the gases being less pure in my experiments than in those of Graham, owing to the difficulty of preventing air from leaking into the receiver during the preparation, desiccation, and admission of the gas, which always occupied at least an hour and a half before the experiment on the moving disks could be begun.

It appears to me that for comparative estimates of viscosity, the method of transpiration is the best, although the method here described is better adapted to determine the absolute value of the viscosity, and is less liable to the objection that in fine capillary tubes the influence of molecular action between the gas and the surface of the tube may possibly have some effect.

The actual value of the coefficient of viscosity in inch-grain-second measure, as determined by these experiments, is

$$·00001492(461° + \theta).$$

At 62° F. $\mu = ·007802.$

Professor Stokes has deduced from the experiments of Baily on pendulums

$$\sqrt{\frac{\mu}{\rho}} = ·116,$$

which at ordinary pressures and temperatures gives

$$\mu = ·00417,$$

or not much more than half the value as here determined. I have not found any means of explaining this difference.

In metrical units and Centigrade degrees

$$\mu = ·01878(1 + ·00365\theta).$$

M. O. E. Meyer gives as the value of μ in centimetres, grammes, and seconds, at 18° C.,

$$·000360.$$

This, when reduced to metre-gramme-second measure, is

$$\mu = ·0360.$$

I make μ, at 18° C., $= ·0200.$

Hence the value given by Meyer is 1·8 times greater than that adopted in this paper.

M. Meyer, however, has a different method of taking account of the disturbance of the air near the edge of the disk from that given in this paper. He supposes that when the disk is very thin the effect due to the edge is proportional to the thickness, and he has given in Crelle's *Journal* a vindication of this supposition. I have not been able to obtain a mathematical solution of the case of a disk oscillating in a large extent of fluid, but it can easily be shewn that there will be a finite increase of friction near the edge of the disk due to the want of continuity, even if the disk were infinitely thin. I think therefore that the difference between M. Meyer's result and mine is to be accounted for, at least in part, by his having under-estimated the effect of the edge of the disk. The effect of the edge will be much less in water than in air, so that any deficiency in the correction will have less influence on the results for liquids which are given in M. Meyer's very valuable paper.

Mathematical Theory of the Experiment.

A disk oscillates in its own plane about a vertical axis between two fixed horizontal disks, the amplitude of oscillation diminishing in geometrical progression, to find what part of the retardation is due to the viscosity of the air between it and the fixed disks.

That part of the surface of the disk which is not near the edge may be treated as part of an infinite disk, and we may assume that each horizontal stratum of the fluid oscillates as a whole. In fact, if the motion of every part of each stratum can be accounted for by the actions of the strata above and below it, there will be no mutual action between the parts of the stratum, and therefore no relative motion between its parts.

Let θ be the angle which defines the angular position of the stratum which is at the distance y from the fixed disk, and let r be the distance of a point of that stratum from the axis, then its velocity will be $r\dfrac{d\theta}{dt}$, and the tangential force on its lower surface arising from viscosity will be on unit of surface

$$-\mu r \frac{d^2\theta}{dy\,dt}=f \dots\dots\dots\dots\dots\dots\dots (1).$$

The tangential force on the upper surface will be

$$\mu r \left(\frac{d^2\theta}{dy\,dt} + \frac{d^3\theta}{dy^2\,dt} dy \right) ;$$

and the mass of the stratum per unit of surface is $\rho\,dy$, so that the equation of motion of each stratum is

$$\rho \frac{d^2\theta}{dt^2} = \mu \frac{d^3\theta}{dy^2\,dt} \quad\dots\dots\dots\dots\dots\dots\dots(2),$$

which is independent of r, shewing that the stratum moves as a whole.

The conditions to be satisfied are, that when $y = 0$, $\theta = 0$; and that when $y = b$,

$$\theta = Ce^{-lt} \cos (nt + a) \quad\dots\dots\dots\dots\dots\dots\dots(3).$$

The disk is suspended by a wire whose elasticity of torsion is such that the moment of torsion due to a torsion θ is $I\omega^2\theta$, where I is the moment of inertia of the disks. The viscosity of the wire is such that an angular velocity $\dfrac{d\theta}{dt}$ is resisted by a moment $2Ik\,\dfrac{d\theta}{dt}$. The equation of motion of the disks is then

$$I \left(\frac{d^2\theta}{dt^2} + 2k \frac{d\theta}{dt} + \omega^2\theta \right) + NA\mu \frac{d^2\theta}{dy\,dt} = 0 \quad\dots\dots\dots\dots\dots (4),$$

where $A = \int 2\pi r^3 dr = \frac{1}{2}\pi r^4$, the moment of inertia of each surface, and N is the number of surfaces exposed to friction of air.

The equation for the motion of the air may be satisfied by the solution

$$\theta = e^{-lt} \{ e^{py} \cos (nt + qy) - e^{-py} \cos (nt - qy) \} \quad\dots\dots\dots\dots\dots(5),$$

provided

$$2pq = \frac{\rho n}{\mu} \quad\dots\dots\dots\dots\dots\dots\dots\dots\dots (6),$$

and

$$q^2 - p^2 = \frac{\rho l}{\mu} \quad\dots\dots\dots\dots\dots\dots\dots\dots\dots (7);$$

and in order to fulfil the conditions (3) and (4),

$$2In(l - k)(e^{2pb} + e^{-2pb} - 2\cos 2qb) = NA\mu\{(pn - lq)(e^{2pb} - e^{-2pb}) + (qn + lp)\,2\sin 2qb\}\dots(8).$$

Expanding the exponential and circular functions, we find

$$2Ib(l - k) = NA\mu\{1 - \tfrac{1}{3}cl + \tfrac{1}{6}c^2(n^2 - 3l^2) + \tfrac{1}{23}c^3(n^2 l - l^3) + \tfrac{1}{120}c^4(\tfrac{7}{16}n^4 + \tfrac{215}{16}n^2 l^2 - \tfrac{145}{4}l^4)\} \; (9),$$

where $c = \dfrac{4b^2\rho}{\mu}$,

$l =$ observed Napierian logarithmic decrement of the amplitude in unit of time,

$k =$ the part of the decrement due to the viscosity of the wire.

When the oscillations are slow as in these experiments, when the disks are near one another, and when the density is small and the viscosity large, the series on the right-hand side of the equation is rapidly convergent.

When the time from rest to rest was thirty-six seconds, and the interval between the disks 1 inch, then for air of pressure 29·9 inches, the successive terms of the series were

$$1·0 - 0·00508 \quad +0·24866 \quad +0·00072 \quad +0·00386 = 1·24816;$$

but when the pressure was reduced to 1·44 inch, the series became

$$1·0 - 0·0002448 \quad +·0005768 + ·00000008 + ·00000002 = 1·0003321.$$

The series is also made convergent by diminishing the distance between the disks. When the distance was ·1847 inch, the first two terms only were sensible. When the pressure was 29·29, the series was

$$1 - ·000858 \quad +·000278 = 1 - ·00058.$$

At smaller pressures the series became sensibly = 1.

The motion of the air between the two disks is represented in fig. 8, where the upper disk is supposed fixed and the lower one oscillates. A row of particles of air which when at rest form a straight line perpendicular to the disks, will when in motion assume in succession the forms of the curves 1, 2, 3, 4, 5, 6. If the ratio of the density to the viscosity of the air is very small, or if the time of oscillation is very great, or if the interval between the disks is very small, these curves approach more and more nearly to the form of straight lines.

The chief mathematical difficulty in treating the case of the moving disks arises from the necessity of determining the motion of the air in the neighbourhood of the edge of the disk. If the disk were accompanied in its motion by an indefinite plane ring surrounding it and forming a continuation of its surface, the motion of the air would be the same as if the disk were of indefinite extent; but if the ring were removed, the motion of the air in the neighbourhood of the edge would be diminished, and therefore the effect of its viscosity on the parts of the disk near the edge would be increased. The actual effect of the air on the disk may be considered equal to that on a disk of greater radius forming part of an infinite plane.

Since the correction we have to consider is confined to the space immediately surrounding the edge of the disk, we may treat the edge as if it were the straight edge of an infinite plane parallel to xz, oscillating in the direction of z between two planes infinite in every direction at distance b. Let w be the velocity of the fluid in the direction of z, then the equation of motion is*

$$\rho \frac{dw}{dt} = \mu \left(\frac{d^2w}{dx^2} + \frac{d^2w}{dy^2} \right) \dots\dots\dots\dots\dots (10),$$

with the conditions

$$w = 0 \text{ when } y = \pm b \dots\dots\dots\dots\dots (11),$$

and

$$w = C \cos nt \text{ when } y = 0, \text{ and } x \text{ is positive} \dots (12).$$

I have not succeeded in finding the solution of the equation as it stands, but in the actual experiments the time of oscillation is so long, and the space between the disks is so small, that we may neglect $\dfrac{b^2 \rho n}{\mu}$, and the equation is reduced to

$$\frac{d^2w}{dx^2} + \frac{d^2w}{dy^2} = 0 \dots\dots\dots\dots\dots (13)$$

with the same conditions. For the method of treating these conditions I am indebted to Professor W. Thomson, who has shewn me how to transform these conditions into another set with which we are more familiar, namely, $w = 0$ when $x = 0$, and $w = 1$ when $y = 0$, and x is greater than $+1$, and $w = -1$ when x is less than -1. In this case we know that the lines of equal values of w are hyperbolas, having their foci at the points $y = 0$, $x = \pm 1$, and that the solution of the equation is

$$w = \frac{2}{\pi} \sin^{-1} \frac{r_1 - r_2}{2} \dots\dots\dots\dots\dots (14)$$

where r_1, r_2 are the distances from the foci.

If we put

$$\phi = \frac{2}{\pi} \log \left\{ \sqrt{(r_1 + r_2)^2 - 4} + r_1 + r_2 \right\} \dots\dots\dots\dots (15),$$

then the lines for which ϕ is constant will be ellipses orthogonal to the hyperbolas, and

$$\frac{d^2\phi}{dx^2} + \frac{d^2\phi}{dy^2} = 0; \dots\dots\dots\dots\dots (16);$$

and the resultant of the friction on any arc of a curve will be proportional

---

* Professor Stokes "On the Theories of the Internal Friction of Fluids in Motion, &c.," *Cambridge Phil. Trans.* Vol. VIII.

to $\phi_1 - \phi_0$, where ϕ_0 is the value of ϕ at the beginning, and ϕ_1 at the end of the given arc.

In the plane $y = 0$, when x is very great, $\phi = \dfrac{2}{\pi} \log 4x$, and when $x = 1$,

$\phi = \dfrac{2}{\pi} \log 2$, so that the whole friction between $x = 1$ and a very distant point

is $\dfrac{2}{\pi} \log 2x$.

Now let w and ϕ be expressed in terms of r and θ, the polar co-ordinates with respect to the origin as the pole; then the conditions may be stated thus:

When $\theta = \pm \dfrac{\pi}{2}$, $w = 0$. When $\theta = 0$ and r greater than 1, $w = 1$. When $\theta = \pi$ and r greater than 1, $w = -1$.

Now let x', y' be rectangular co-ordinates, and let

$$y' = \frac{2}{\pi} b\theta \text{ and } x' = \frac{2}{\pi} b \log r \quad\text{......................} (17),$$

and let w and ϕ be expressed in terms of x' and y'; the differential equations (13) and (16) will still be true; and when $y' = \pm b$, $w = 0$, and when $y' = 0$ and x' positive, $w = 1$.

When x' is great, $\phi = \dfrac{x'}{b} + \dfrac{2}{\pi} \log 4$, and when $x' = 0$, $\phi = \dfrac{2}{\pi} \log 2$, so that the whole friction on the surface is

$$\frac{x'}{b} + \frac{2}{\pi} \log 2 \quad\text{..................................} (18),$$

which is the same as if a portion whose breadth is $\dfrac{2b}{\pi} \log_e 2$ had been added to the surface at its edge.

The curves of equal velocity are represented in fig. 9 at u, v, w, x, y. They pass round the edge of the moving disk AB, and have a set of asymptotes U, V, W, X, Y, arranged at equal distances parallel to the disks.

The curves of equal friction are represented at o, p, q, r, s, t. The form of these curves approximates to that of straight lines as we pass to the left of the edge of the disk.

The dotted vertical straight lines O, P, Q, R, S, T represent the position of the corresponding lines of equal friction if the disk AB had been accompanied by an extension of its surface in the direction of B. The total friction on AB, or on any of the curves u, v, w, &c., is equal to that on a surface extending to the point C, on the supposition that the moving surface has an accompanying surface which completes the infinite plane.

In the actual case the moving disk is not a mere surface, but a plate of a certain thickness terminated by a slightly rounded edge. Its section may therefore be compared to the curve uu' rather than to the axis AB.

The total friction on the curve is still equal to that on a straight line extending to C, but the velocity corresponding to the curve u is less than that corresponding to the line AB.

If the thickness of the disk is 2β, and the distance between the fixed disks $= 2b$, so that the distance of the surfaces is $b - \beta$, the breadth of the strip which must be supposed to be added to the surface at the edge will be

$$a = \frac{2b}{\pi} \log_e 10 \left\{ \log_{10} 2 + \log_{10} \sin \frac{\pi (b - \beta)}{2b} \right\}^* \quad \ldots\ldots\ldots\ldots (19).$$

In calculating the moment of friction on this strip, we must suppose it to be at the same distance from the axis as the actual edge of the disk. Instead of $A = \frac{\pi}{2} r^4$ in equation (9), we must therefore put $A = \frac{\pi}{2} r^4 + 2\pi r^3 a$, and instead of b we must put $b - \beta$.

The actual value of $\frac{\pi}{2} r^4$ for each surface in inches $= 1112 \cdot 8$.

The value of I in inches and grains was 175337.

It was determined by comparing the times of oscillation of the axis and disks without the little magnet, with the times of the brass ring (fig. 4) and of the tube and weights (fig. 7). Four different suspension wires were used in these experiments.

The following Table gives the numbers required for the calculation of each of the five arrangements of the disks.

---

* This result is applicable to the calculation of the electrical capacity of a condenser in the form of a disk between two larger disks at equal distance from it.

Arrangement	Case 1	Case 2	Case 8	Case 4	Case 5
N = number of surfaces	2	2	6	6	6
$b - \beta$ = distance of surfaces	1·0	0·5	0·683	0·425	0·1847
$2\pi r^3 a$ = effect of edge	446·09	235·0	292·95	186·7	86·1
A = whole moment of each surface ...	1558·9	1347·8	1405·75	1299·5	1198·9
$\dfrac{N}{2}\dfrac{A}{Ib\log_e 10} = Q =$	·003815	·007398	·015110	·022448	·047640

If l is the Napierian logarithmic decrement per second, and L the observed decrement of the common logarithm (to base 10) of the arc in time T, then

$$L = lT \log_{10} e \quad\quad\quad\quad\quad\quad\quad (20).$$

If n is the coefficient of t in the periodic terms, and T the time of five complete vibrations,

$$nT = 10\pi \quad\quad\quad\quad\quad\quad\quad\quad\quad (21).$$

Let

$$K = kT \log_{10} e \quad\quad\quad\quad\quad\quad\quad (22),$$

then K is the part of the observed logarithmic decrement due to the viscosity of the wire, the yielding of the instrument, and the friction of the air on the axis, and is the same for all experiments as long as the wire is unaltered.

Let μ_0 be the value of μ at temperature zero, μ that at any other temperature θ, then if μ is proportional to the temperature from absolute zero,

$$\mu = (1 + a\theta)\,\mu_0 \quad\quad\quad\quad\quad\quad\quad (23),$$

where a is the coefficient of expansion of air per degree.

Equation (9) may now be written in the form

$$\mu_0 Q (1 + x)(1 + a\theta)\,T + K = L \quad\quad\quad\quad\quad (24),$$

where $1 + x$ is the series in equation (9), x being in most cases small, and may be calculated from an approximate value of μ_0.

The values of Q are to be taken from the Table according to the arrangement of disks in the experiment.

In this way I have combined the results of forty experiments on dry air in order to determine the values of μ_0 and K. Seven of these had the first arrangement, six had the second, six the third, nine the fourth, and twelve the fifth.

The values of Q for the five cases are roughly in the proportions of 1, 2, 4, 6, 12, so that it is easy to eliminate K and find μ_0. I had reason, however, to believe that the value of K was altered at a certain stage of the experiments when steam was first used to heat the air in the receiver. I therefore introduced two values of K, K_1 and K_2, into the experiments before and after this change respectively. The values of K_1 and K_2 deduced from these experiments were

In ten single vibrations.

$$K_1 = \cdot 01568$$
$$K_2 = \cdot 01901.$$

The value of μ in inch-grain-second measure at temperature θ^0 Fahrenheit is for air

$$\mu = \cdot 00001492 \, (461^0 + \theta^0).$$

The value of L was then calculated for each experiment and compared with the observed value. In this way the error of mean square of a single experiment was found. The probable error of μ, as determined from the equations, was calculated from this and found to be $0 \cdot 36$ per cent. of its value.

In order to estimate the value of the evidence in favour of there being a finite amount of slipping between the disks and the air in contact with them, the value of L for each of the forty experiments was found on the supposition that

$$\beta = \cdot 0027 \text{ inch and } \mu = (\cdot 000015419) \, (461^0 + \theta^0).$$

The error of mean square for each observation was found to be slightly greater than in the former case; the probable error of β was 40 per cent., and that of $\mu = 1 \cdot 6$ per cent.

I have no doubt that the true value of β is zero, that is, there is no slipping, and that the original value of μ is the best.

As the actual observations were very numerous, and the reduction of them would occupy a considerable space in this paper, I have given a specimen of the actual working of one experiment.

Table I. shews the readings of the scale as taken down at the time of observation, with the times of transit of the middle point of the scale after the fifth and sixth readings, with the sum of ten successive amplitudes deduced therefrom.

Table II. shews the results of this operation as extended to the rest of experiment 62, and gives the logarithmic decrement for each successive period of ten semivibrations, with the mean time and corresponding mean logarithmic decrement.

Table III. shews the method of combining forty experiments of different kinds. The observed decrement depends on two unknown quantities, the viscosity of air and that of the wire.

The experiments are grouped together according to the coefficients of μ and K that enter into them, and when the final results have been obtained, the decrements are calculated and compared with the results of observation. The calculated sums of the decrements are given in the last column.

Table IV. shews the results of the twelve experiments with the fifth arrangement. They are arranged in groups according to the pressure of the air, and it will be seen that the observed values of L are as independent of the pressure as the calculated values, in which the pressure is taken into account only in calculating the value of x in the fifth column. By arranging the values of $L - L'$ in order of temperature, it was found that within the range of atmospheric temperature during the course of the experiments the relation between the viscosity of air and its temperature does not perceptibly differ from that assumed in the calculation. Finally, the experiments were arranged in order of time, to determine whether the viscosity of the wire increased during the experiments, as it did when steam was first used to heat the apparatus. There did not appear any decided indication of any alteration in the wire.

Table V. gives the resultant value of μ in terms of the different units which are employed in scientific measurements.

Note, added February 6, 1866.—In the calculation of the results of the experiments, I made use of an erroneous value of the moment of inertia of the disks and axis $= 1 \cdot 012$ of the true value, as determined by six series of experiments with four suspension wires and two kinds of auxiliary weights. The numbers in the coefficients of m in Table IV. are therefore all too large, and the value of μ is also too large in the same proportion, and should be

$$\mu = \cdot 00001492 \, (461^\circ + \theta).$$

The same error ran through all the absolute values in other parts of the paper as sent in to the Royal Society, but to save trouble to the reader I have corrected them where they occur.

TABLE I.—Experiment 62.   Arrangement 5.   Dry air at pressure 0·55 inch.

Temperature 68° F.   May 9, 1865.

	Greater scale reading	Time 3ʰ +	Less scale reading	Time
		m s		m s
	8309		1740	
	8071	....	1968	
	7852	27 42·4	2180	28 18·8
	7650	....	2377	
	7460	....	2561	
Sum of greater readings	39342	....	10826	
Sum of less do.	10826			
	Difference 28516 = sum of 10 amplitudes.			

The observations were continued in the same way till five sets of readings of this kind were obtained. The following were the results.

TABLE II.

Times	Sum of ten amplitudes	Logarithm	Log. decrement
h m s			
3 28 0·6	28516	4·4550886	0·1587745
34 3·2	19784	4·2963141	0·1585171
40 5·8	13734	4·1377970	0·1587041
46 8·6	9530	3·9790929	0·1596806
52 11·2	6598	3·8194123	

Results of experiment 62.   Mean time of ten vibrations   = 362·66

Mean log. decrement . . .   =   0·1588574.

TABLE III.

Equations from which μ for air was determined; $m = \dfrac{\mu}{461^\circ + \theta}$.

Number of experiments	Arrangement	Result of observation	Result of calculation
3.	1	$6\cdot3647\,m + 3K_1 = \cdot00023167$	$\cdot00022779$
3.	2	$11\cdot2893\,m + 3K_1 = \cdot00028280$	$\cdot00030214$
6.	4	$71\cdot2412\,m + 6K_1 = \cdot00135467$	$\cdot00133897$
4.	1	$8\cdot7221\,m + 4K_2 = \cdot00034562$	$\cdot00034127$
3.	2	$11\cdot6680\,m + 3K_2 = \cdot00031505$	$\cdot00033335$
12.	5	$297\cdot7880\,m + 12K_2 = \cdot00511708$	$\cdot00512666$
3.	4	$36\cdot0551\,m + 3K_2 = \cdot00069607$	$\cdot00070159$
6.	3	$48\cdot8911\,m + 6K_2 = \cdot00108215$	$\cdot00105333$

Final result $\mu^* = \cdot00001510\ (461^\circ + \theta)$ with probable error $0\cdot36$ per cent.

$$K_1 = \cdot0000439, \qquad\qquad K_2 = \cdot0000524.$$

TABLE IV.—Experiments with Arrangement 5.

No. of experiment	Absolute temperature $461^\circ + \theta$	Pressure, in inches of mercury	Time of five double swings, in seconds	Correction for inertia of air $(1+x)$ in equation (24)	L = decrement of logarithm of arc in ten single vibrations		Diff. $L - L'$
					L' calculated	L observed	
62.	529	0·55	362·66		·15719	·15886	+ 167
77.	516	0·50	362·80	$1 - \cdot0000157$	·15378	·15260	− 118
80.	527	0·56	364·04		·15648	·15946	+ 279
63.	527·5	5·57	362·72		·15680	·15628	− 52
64.	535	5·97	362·94	$1 - \cdot000157$	·15875	·15838	− 37
81.	516	5·52	363·80		·15379	·15389	+ 10
65.	524	25·58	362·64		·15555	·15422	− 133
71.	513	19·87	362·50	$1 - \cdot000486$	·15299	·15144	− 155
72.	514·5	20·31	362·86		·15338	·15269	− 69
75.	517	29·90	363·8		·15398	·15377	− 21
76.	512·5	29·76	362·89	$1 - \cdot00058$	·15280	·15146	− 134
79.	521	28·22	363·9		·15502	·15510	+ 8

* This is the result derived from these equations, which is $1\cdot2$ per cent. too large.

TABLE V.—Results.

Coefficient of viscosity in dry air.   Units—the inch, grain, and second, and Fahrenheit temperature,

$$\mu = {\cdot}00001492\,(461 + \theta) = {\cdot}006876 + {\cdot}0000149\theta.$$

At 60° F. the mean temperature of the experiments, $\mu = {\cdot}007763$. Taking the foot as unit instead of the inch, $\mu = {\cdot}000179\,(461 + \theta)$. In metrical units (metre, gramme, second, and Centigrade temperature),

$$\mu = {\cdot}01878(1 + {\cdot}003650\theta).$$

The coefficient of viscosity of other gases is to be found from that of air by multiplying μ by the ratio of the transpiration time of the gas to that of air as determined by Graham*.

POSTSCRIPT.—Received December 7, 1865.

Since the above paper was communicated to the Royal Society, Professor Stokes has directed my attention to a more recent memoir of M. O. E. Meyer, "Ueber die innere Reibung der Gase," in Poggendorff's *Annalen*, cxxv. (1865). M. Meyer has compared the values of the coefficient of viscosity deduced from the experiments of Baily by Stokes, with those deduced from the experiments of Bessel and of Girault.   These values are ·000104, ·000275, and ·000384 respectively, the units being the centimetre, the gramme, and the second. M. Meyer's own experiments were made by swinging three disks on a vertical axis in an air-tight vessel.   The disks were sometimes placed in contact, and sometimes separate, so as to expose either two or six surfaces to the action of the air.   The difference of the logarithmic decrement of oscillation in these two arrangements was employed to determine the viscosity of the air.

The effects of the resistance of the air on the axis, mirror, &c., and of the viscosity of the suspending wires are thus eliminated.

The calculations are made on the supposition that the moving disks are so far from each other and from the surface of the receiver which contains them, that the effect of the air upon each is the same as if it were in an infinite space.

At the distance of 30 millims., and with a period of oscillation of fourteen seconds, the mutual effect of the disks would be very small in air at the

* *Philosophical Transactions*, 1849.

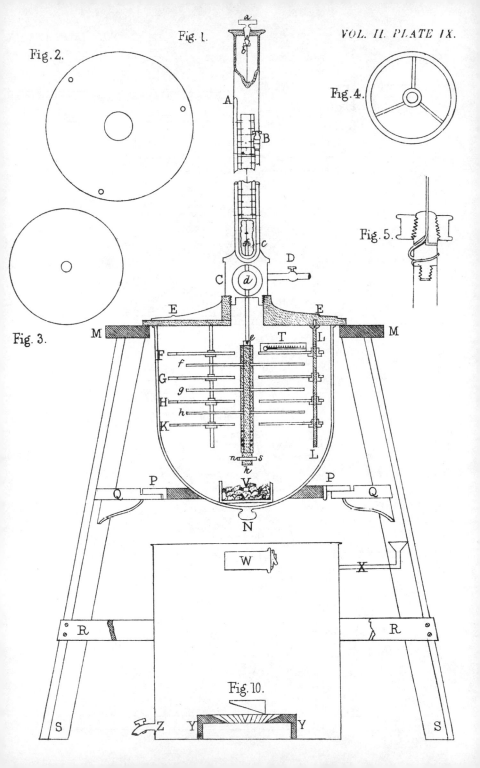

Fig. 2.

Fig. 1.

VOL. II. PLATE IX.

Fig. 4.

Fig. 3.

Fig. 5.

Fig. 10.

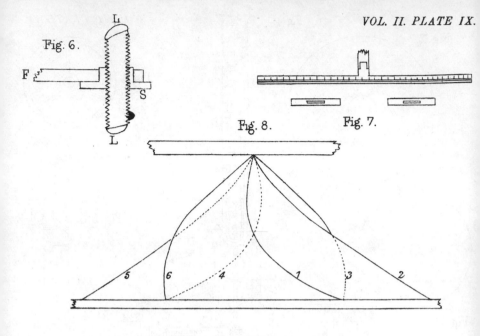

Fig. 6.

Fig. 7.

Fig. 8.

Fig. 9.

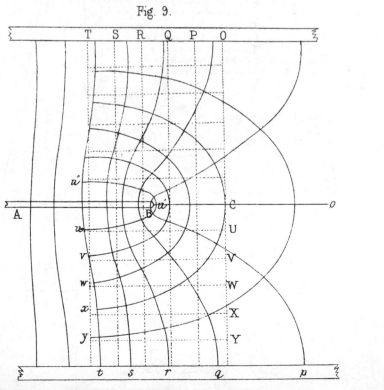

ordinary pressure. In November 1863 I made a series of experiments with an arrangement of three brass disks placed on a vertical axis exactly as in M. Meyer's experiments, except that I had then no air-tight apparatus, and the disks were protected from currents of air by a wooden box only.

I attempted to determine the viscosity of air by means of the observed mutual action between the disks at various distances. I obtained the values of this mutual action for distances under 2 inches, but I found that the results were so much involved with the unknown motion of the air near the edge of the disks, that I could place no dependence on the results unless I had a complete mathematical theory of the motion near the edge.

In M. Meyer's experiments the time of vibration is shorter than in most of mine. This will diminish the effect of the edge in comparison with the total effect, but in rarefied air both the mutual action and the effect of the edge are much increased. In his calculations, however, the effect of the three edges of the disks is supposed to be the same, whether they are in contact or separated. This, I think, will account for the large value which he has obtained for the viscosity, and for the fact that with the brass disks which vibrate in 14 seconds, he finds the apparent viscosity diminish as the pressure diminishes, while with the glass disks which vibrate in 8 seconds it first increases and then diminishes.

M. Meyer concludes that the viscosity varies much less than the pressure, and that it increases slightly with increase of temperature. He finds the value of μ in metrical units (centimetre-gramme-second) at various temperatures,

Temperature.	Viscosity.
8°·3 C.	·000333
21°·5 C.	·000323
34°·4 C.	·000366

In my experiments, in which fixed disks are interposed between the moving ones, the calculation is not involved in so great difficulties; and the value of μ is deduced directly from the observations, whereas the experiments of M. Meyer give only the value of $\sqrt{\mu\rho}$, from which μ must be determined. For these reasons I prefer the results deduced from experiments with fixed disks interposed between the moving ones.

M. Meyer has also given a mathematical theory of the internal friction of gases, founded on the dynamical theory of gases. I shall not say anything of this part of his paper, as I wish to confine myself to the results of experiment.

[From the *Philosophical Transactions*, Vol. CLVII.]

XXVIII. *On the Dynamical Theory of Gases.*

(Received May 16,—Read May 31, 1866.)

THEORIES of the constitution of bodies suppose them either to be continuous and homogeneous, or to be composed of a finite number of distinct particles or molecules.

In certain applications of mathematics to physical questions, it is convenient to suppose bodies homogeneous in order to make the quantity of matter in each differential element a function of the co-ordinates, but I am not aware that any theory of this kind has been proposed to account for the different properties of bodies. Indeed the properties of a body supposed to be a uniform *plenum* may be affirmed dogmatically, but cannot be explained mathematically.

Molecular theories suppose that all bodies, even when they appear to our senses homogeneous, consist of a multitude of particles, or small parts the mechanical relations of which constitute the properties of the bodies. Those theories which suppose that the molecules are at rest relative to the body may be called statical theories, and those which suppose the molecules to be in motion, even while the body is apparently at rest, may be called dynamical theories.

If we adopt a statical theory, and suppose the molecules of a body kept at rest in their positions of equilibrium by the action of forces in the directions of the lines joining their centres, we may determine the mechanical properties of a body so constructed, if distorted so that the displacement of each molecule is a function of its co-ordinates when in equilibrium. It appears from the mathematical theory of bodies of this kind, that the forces called into play by a small change of form must always bear a fixed proportion to those excited by a small change of volume.

Now we know that in fluids the elasticity of form is evanescent, while that of volume is considerable. Hence such theories will not apply to fluids. In solid bodies the elasticity of form appears in many cases to be smaller in proportion to that of volume than the theory gives*, so that we are forced to give up the theory of molecules whose displacements are functions of their co-ordinates when at rest, even in the case of solid bodies.

The theory of moving molecules, on the other hand, is not open to these objections. The mathematical difficulties in applying the theory are considerable, and till they are surmounted we cannot fully decide on the applicability of the theory. We are able, however, to explain a great variety of phenomena by the dynamical theory which have not been hitherto explained otherwise.

The dynamical theory supposes that the molecules of solid bodies oscillate about their positions of equilibrium, but do not travel from one position to another in the body. In fluids the molecules are supposed to be constantly moving into new relative positions, so that the same molecule may travel from one part of the fluid to any other part. In liquids the molecules are supposed to be always under the action of the forces due to neighbouring molecules throughout their course, but in gases the greater part of the path of each molecule is supposed to be sensibly rectilinear and beyond the sphere of sensible action of the neighbouring molecules.

I propose in this paper to apply this theory to the explanation of various properties of gases, and to shew that, besides accounting for the relations of pressure, density, and temperature in a single gas, it affords a mechanical explanation of the known chemical relation between the density of a gas and its equivalent weight, commonly called the Law of Equivalent Volumes. It also explains the diffusion of one gas through another, the internal friction of a gas, and the conduction of heat through gases.

The opinion that the observed properties of visible bodies apparently at rest are due to the action of invisible molecules in rapid motion is to be found in Lucretius. In the exposition which he gives of the theories of Democritus as modified by Epicurus, he describes the invisible atoms as all moving downwards with equal velocities, which, at quite uncertain times and places, suffer an imperceptible change, just enough to allow of occasional collisions taking place

---

* In glass, according to Dr Everett's second series of experiments (1866), the ratio of the elasticity of form to that of volume is greater than that given by the theory. In brass and steel it is less.— March 7, 1867.

between the atoms. These atoms he supposes to set small bodies in motion by an action of which we may form some conception by looking at the motes in a sunbeam. The language of Lucretius must of course be interpreted according to the physical ideas of his age, but we need not wonder that it suggested to Le Sage the fundamental conception of his theory of gases, as well as his doctrine of ultramundane corpuscles.

Professor Clausius, to whom we owe the most extensive developments of the dynamical theory of gases, has given* a list of authors who have adopted or given countenance to any theory of invisible particles in motion. Of these, Daniel Bernoulli, in the tenth section of his *Hydrodynamics*, distinctly explains the pressure of air by the impact of its particles on the sides of the vessel containing it.

Clausius also mentions a book entitled *Deux Traités de Physique Mécanique,* publiés par Pierre Prevost, comme simple Éditeur du premier et comme Auteur du second, Genève et Paris, 1818. The first memoir is by G. Le Sage, who explains gravity by the impact of "ultramundane corpuscles" on bodies. These corpuscles also set in motion the particles of light and various ethereal media, which in their turn act on the molecules of gases and keep up their motions. His theory of impact is faulty, but his explanation of the expansive force of gases is essentially the same as in the dynamical theory as it now stands. The second memoir, by Prevost, contains new applications of the principles of Le Sage to gases and to light. A more extensive application of the theory of moving molecules was made by Herapath†. His theory of the collisions of perfectly hard bodies, such as he supposes the molecules to be, is faulty, inasmuch as it makes the result of impact depend on the absolute motion of the bodies, so that by experiments on such hard bodies (if we could get them) we might determine the absolute direction and velocity of the motion of the earth ‡. This author, however, has applied his theory to the numerical results of experiment in many cases, and his speculations are always ingenious, and often throw much real light on the questions treated. In particular, the theory of temperature and pressure in gases and the theory of diffusion are clearly pointed out.

---

* Poggendorff's *Annalen*, Jan. 1862. Translated by G. C. Foster, B.A., *Phil. Mag.* June, 1862.

† *Mathematical Physics,* &c., by John Herapath, Esq. 2 vols. London: Whittaker and Co., and Herapath's *Railway Journal* Office, 1847.

‡ *Mathematical Physics,* &c., p. 134.

Dr Joule* has also explained the pressure of gases by the impact of their molecules, and has calculated the velocity which they must have in order to produce the pressure observed in particular gases.

It is to Professor Clausius, of Zurich, that we owe the most complete dynamical theory of gases. His other researches on the general dynamical theory of heat are well known, and his memoirs *On the kind of Motion which we call Heat*, are a complete exposition of the molecular theory adopted in this paper. After reading his investigation† of the distance described by each molecule between successive collisions, I published some propositions‡ on the motions and collisions of perfectly elastic spheres, and deduced several properties of gases, especially the law of equivalent volumes, and the nature of gaseous friction. I also gave a theory of diffusion of gases, which I now know to be erroneous, and there were several errors in my theory of the conduction of heat in gases which M. Clausius has pointed out in an elaborate memoir on that subject §.

M. O. E. Meyer‖ has also investigated the theory of internal friction on the hypothesis of hard elastic molecules.

In the present paper I propose to consider the molecules of a gas, not as elastic spheres of definite radius, but as small bodies or groups of smaller molecules repelling one another with a force whose direction always passes very nearly through the centres of gravity of the molecules, and whose magnitude is represented very nearly by some function of the distance of the centres of gravity. I have made this modification of the theory in consequence of the results of my experiments on the viscosity of air at different temperatures, and I have deduced from these experiments that the repulsion is inversely as the *fifth* power of the distance.

If we suppose an imaginary plane drawn through a vessel containing a great number of such molecules in motion, then a great many molecules will cross the plane in either direction. The excess of the mass of those which traverse the plane in the positive direction over that of those which traverse it in the negative direction, gives a measure of the flow of gas through the plane in the positive direction.

---

* *Some Remarks on Heat and the Constitution of Elastic Fluids*, Oct. 3, 1848.

† *Phil. Mag.* Feb. 1859.

‡ "Illustrations of the Dynamical Theory of Gases," *Phil. Mag.* 1860, January and July.

§ Poggendorff, Jan. 1862; *Phil. Mag.* June, 1862.

‖ "Ueber die innere Reibung der Gase" (Poggendorff, Vol. cxxv. 1865).

If the plane be made to move with such a velocity that there is no excess of flow of molecules in one direction through it, then the velocity of the plane is the mean velocity of the gas resolved normal to the plane.

There will still be molecules moving in both directions through the plane, and carrying with them a certain amount of momentum into the portion of gas which lies on the other side of the plane.

The quantity of momentum thus communicated to the gas on the other side of the plane during a unit of time is a measure of the force exerted on this gas by the rest. This force is called the pressure of the gas.

If the velocities of the molecules moving in different directions were independent of one another, then the pressure at any point of the gas need not be the same in all directions, and the pressure between two portions of gas separated by a plane need not be perpendicular to that plane. Hence, to account for the observed equality of pressure in all directions, we must suppose some cause equalizing the motion in all directions. This we find in the deflection of the path of one particle by another when they come near one another. Since, however, this equalization of motion is not instantaneous, the pressures in all directions are perfectly equalized only in the case of a gas at rest, but when the gas is in a state of motion, the want of perfect equality in the pressures gives rise to the phenomena of viscosity or internal friction. The phenomena of viscosity in all bodies may be described, independently of hypothesis, as follows :—

A distortion or strain of some kind, which we may call S, is produced in the body by displacement. A state of stress or elastic force which we may call F is thus excited. The relation between the stress and the strain may be written $F = ES$, where E is the coefficient of elasticity for that particular kind of strain. In a solid body free from viscosity, F will remain $= ES$, and

$$\frac{dF}{dt} = E \frac{dS}{dt}.$$

If, however, the body is viscous, F will not remain constant, but will tend to disappear at a rate depending on the value of F, and on the nature of the body. If we suppose this rate proportional to F, the equation may be written

$$\frac{dF}{dt} = E \frac{dS}{dt} - \frac{F}{T},$$

which will indicate the actual phenomena in an empirical manner. For if S be constant,

$$F = ESe^{-\frac{t}{T}},$$

shewing that F gradually disappears, so that if the body is left to itself it gradually loses any internal stress, and the pressures are finally distributed as in a fluid at rest.

If $\dfrac{dS}{dt}$ is constant, that is, if there is a steady motion of the body which continually increases the displacement,

$$F = ET \frac{dS}{dt} + Ce^{-\frac{t}{T}},$$

shewing that F tends to a constant value depending on the rate of displacement. The quantity ET, by which the rate of displacement must be multiplied to get the force, may be called the coefficient of viscosity. It is the product of a coefficient of elasticity, E, and a time T, which may be called the "time of relaxation" of the elastic force. In mobile fluids T is a very small fraction of a second, and E is not easily determined experimentally. In viscous solids T may be several hours or days, and then E is easily measured. It is possible that in some bodies T may be a function of F, and this would account for the gradual untwisting of wires after being twisted beyond the limit of perfect elasticity. For if T diminishes as F increases, the parts of the wire furthest from the axis will yield more rapidly than the parts near the axis during the twisting process, and when the twisting force is removed, the wire will at first untwist till there is equilibrium between the stresses in the inner and outer portions. These stresses will then undergo a gradual relaxation; but since the actual value of the stress is greater in the outer layers, it will have a more rapid rate of relaxation, so that the wire will go on gradually untwisting for some hours or days, owing to the stress on the interior portions maintaining itself longer than that of the outer parts. This phenomenon was observed by Weber in silk fibres, by Kohlrausch in glass fibres, and by myself in steel wires.

In the case of a collection of moving molecules such as we suppose a gas to be, there is also a resistance to change of form, constituting what may be called the linear elasticity, or "rigidity" of the gas, but this resistance gives way and diminishes at a rate depending on the amount of the force and on the nature of the gas.

Suppose the molecules to be confined in a rectangular vessel with perfectly elastic sides, and that they have no action on one another, so that they never strike one another, or cause each other to deviate from their rectilinear paths. Then it can easily be shewn that the pressures on the sides of the vessel due to the impacts of the molecules are perfectly independent of each other, so that the mass of moving molecules will behave, not like a fluid, but like an elastic solid. Now suppose the pressures at first equal in the three directions perpendicular to the sides, and let the dimensions a, b, c of the vessel be altered by small quantities, δa, δb, δc.

Then if the original pressure in the direction of a was p, it will become

$$p\left(1 - 3\frac{\delta a}{a} - \frac{\delta b}{b} - \frac{\delta c}{c}\right);$$

or if there is no change of volume,

$$\frac{\delta p}{p} = -2\frac{\delta a}{a},$$

shewing that in this case there is a "longitudinal" elasticity of form of which the coefficient is $2p$. The coefficient of "Rigidity" is therefore $= p$.

This rigidity, however, cannot be directly observed, because the molecules continually deflect each other from their rectilinear courses, and so equalize the pressure in all directions. The rate at which this equalization takes place is great, but not infinite; and therefore there remains a certain inequality of pressure which constitutes the phenomenon of viscosity.

I have found by experiment that the coefficient of viscosity in a given gas is independent of the density, and proportional to the absolute temperature, so that if ET be the viscosity, $ET \propto \dfrac{p}{\rho}$.

But $E = p$, therefore T, the time of relaxation, varies inversely as the density and is independent of the temperature. Hence the number of collisions producing a given deflection which take place in unit of time is independent of the temperature, that is, of the velocity of the molecules, and is proportional to the number of molecules in unit of volume. If we suppose the molecules hard elastic bodies, the number of collisions of a given kind will be proportional to the velocity, but if we suppose them centres of force, the angle of deflection will be smaller when the velocity is greater; and if the force is inversely as the fifth power of the distance, the number of deflections of a given kind will be independent of the velocity. Hence I have adopted this law in making my calculations.

The effect of the mutual action of the molecules is not only to equalize the pressure in all directions, but, when molecules of different kinds are present, to communicate motion from the one kind to the other. I formerly shewed that the final result in the case of hard elastic bodies is to cause the average *vis viva* of a molecule to be the same for all the different kinds of molecules. Now the pressure due to each molecule is proportional to its *vis viva*, hence the whole pressure due to a given number of molecules in a given volume will be the same whatever the mass of the molecules, provided the molecules of different kinds are permitted freely to communicate motion to each other.

When the flow of *vis viva* from the one kind of molecules to the other is zero, the temperature is said to be the same. Hence equal volumes of different gases at equal pressures and temperatures contain equal numbers of molecules.

This result of the dynamical theory affords the explanation of the "law of equivalent volumes" in gases.

We shall see that this result is true in the case of molecules acting as centres of force. A law of the same general character is probably to be found connecting the temperatures of liquid and solid bodies with the energy possessed by their molecules, although our ignorance of the nature of the connexions between the molecules renders it difficult to enunciate the precise form of the law.

The molecules of a gas in this theory are those portions of it which move about as a single body. These molecules may be mere points, or pure centres of force endowed with inertia, or the capacity of performing work while losing velocity. They may be systems of several such centres of force, bound together by their mutual actions, and in this case the different centres may either be separated, so as to form a group of points, or they may be actually coincident, so as to form one point.

Finally, if necessary, we may suppose them to be small solid bodies of a determinate form; but in this case we must assume a new set of forces binding the parts of these small bodies together, and so introduce a molecular theory of the second order. The doctrines that all matter is extended, and that no two portions of matter can coincide in the same place, being deductions from our experiments with bodies sensible to us, have no application to the theory of molecules.

The actual energy of a moving body consists of two parts, one due to the motion of its centre of gravity, and the other due to the motions of its parts relative to the centre of gravity. If the body is of invariable form, the motions of its parts relative to the centre of gravity consist entirely of rotation, but if the parts of the body are not rigidly connected, their motions may consist of oscillations of various kinds, as well as rotation of the whole body.

The mutual interference of the molecules in their courses will cause their energy of motion to be distributed in a certain ratio between that due to the motion of the centre of gravity and that due to the rotation, or other internal motion. If the molecules are pure centres of force, there can be no energy of rotation, and the whole energy is reduced to that of translation; but in all other cases the whole energy of the molecule may be represented by $\frac{1}{2}Mv^2\beta$, where β is the ratio of the total energy to the energy of translation. The ratio β will be different for every molecule, and will be different for the same molecule after every encounter with another molecule, but it will have an average value depending on the nature of the molecules, as has been shown by Clausius. The value of β can be determined if we know either of the specific heats of the gas, or the ratio between them.

The method of investigation which I shall adopt in the following paper, is to determine the mean values of the following functions of the velocity of all the molecules of a given kind within an element of volume:—

(a) the mean velocity resolved parallel to each of the coordinate axes;

(β) the mean values of functions of two dimensions of these component velocities;

(γ) the mean values of functions of three dimensions of these velocities.

The rate of translation of the gas, whether by itself, or by diffusion through another gas, is given by (a), the pressure of the gas on any plane, whether normal or tangential to the plane, is given by (β), and the rate of conduction of heat through the gas is given by (γ).

I propose to determine the variations of these quantities, due, 1st, to the encounters of the molecules with others of the same system or of a different system; 2nd, to the action of external forces such as gravity; and 3rd, to the passage of molecules through the boundary of the element of volume.

I shall then apply these calculations to the determination of the statical cases of the final distribution of two gases under the action of gravity, the equilibrium of temperature between two gases, and the distribution of temperature in a vertical column. These results are independent of the law of force between the molecules. I shall also consider the dynamical cases of diffusion, viscosity, and conduction of heat, which involve the law of force between the molecules.

On the Mutual Action of Two Molecules.

Let the masses of these molecules be M_1, M_2, and let their velocities resolved in three directions at right angles to each other be ξ_1, η_1, ζ_1 and ξ_2, η_2, ζ_2. The components of the velocity of the centre of gravity of the two molecules will be

$$\frac{\xi_1 M_1 + \xi_2 M_2}{M_1 + M_2}, \quad \frac{\eta_1 M_1 + \eta_2 M_2}{M_1 + M_2}, \quad \frac{\zeta_1 M_1 + \zeta_2 M_2}{M_1 + M_2}.$$

The motion of the centre of gravity will not be altered by the mutual action of the molecules, of whatever nature that action may be. We may therefore take the centre of gravity as the origin of a system of coordinates moving parallel to itself with uniform velocity, and consider the alteration of the motion of each particle with reference to this point as origin.

If we regard the molecules as simple centres of force, then each molecule will describe a plane curve about this centre of gravity, and the two curves will be similar to each other and symmetrical with respect to the line of apses. If the molecules move with sufficient velocity to carry them out of the sphere of their mutual action, their orbits will each have a pair of asymptotes inclined at an angle $\frac{\pi}{2} - \theta$ to the line of apses. The asymptotes of the orbit of M_1 will be at a distance b_1 from the centre of gravity, and those of M_2 at a distance b_2, where

$$M_1 b_1 = M_2 b_2.$$

The distance between two parallel asymptotes, one in each orbit, will be

$$b = b_1 + b_2.$$

If, while the two molecules are still beyond each other's action, we draw a straight line through M_1 in the direction of the relative velocity of M_1 to M_2, and draw from M_2 a perpendicular to this line, the length of this perpendicular will be b, and the plane including b and the direction of relative motion will be the plane of the orbits about the centre of gravity.

When, after their mutual action and deflection, the molecules have again reached a distance such that there is no sensible action between them, each will be moving with the same velocity relative to the centre of gravity that it had before the mutual action, but the direction of this relative velocity will be turned through an angle 2θ in the plane of the orbit.

The angle θ is a function of the relative velocity of the molecules and of b, the form of the function depending on the nature of the action between the molecules.

If we suppose the molecules to be bodies, or systems of bodies, capable of rotation, internal vibration, or any form of energy other than simple motion of translation, these results will be modified. The value of θ and the final velocities of the molecules will depend on the amount of internal energy in each molecule before the encounter, and on the particular form of that energy at every instant during the mutual action. We have no means of determining such intricate actions in the present state of our knowledge of molecules, so that we must content ourselves with the assumption that the value of θ is, on an average, the same as for pure centres of force, and that the final velocities differ from the initial velocities only by quantities which may in each collision be neglected, although in a great many encounters the energy of translation and the internal energy of the molecules arrive, by repeated small exchanges, at a final ratio, which we shall suppose to be that of 1 to $\beta - 1$.

We may now determine the final velocity of M_1 after it has passed beyond the sphere of mutual action between itself and M_2.

Let V be the velocity of M_1 relative to M_2, then the components of V are

$$\xi_1 - \xi_2, \quad \eta_1 - \eta_2, \quad \zeta_1 - \zeta_2.$$

The plane of the orbit is that containing V and b. Let this plane be inclined ϕ to a plane containing V and parallel to the axis of x; then, since the direction of V is turned round an angle 2θ in the plane of the orbit, while its magnitude remains the same, we may find the value of ξ_1 after the encounter. Calling it ξ'_1,

$$\xi'_1 = \xi_1 + \frac{M_2}{M_1 + M_2} \{(\xi_2 - \xi_1)\, 2 \sin^2\theta + \sqrt{(\eta_2 - \eta_1)^2 + (\zeta_2 - \zeta_1)^2}\, \sin 2\theta \cos \phi\} \quad \ldots \ldots (1).$$

There will be similar expressions for the components of the final velocity of M_1 in the other coordinate directions.

If we know the initial positions and velocities of M_1 and M_2 we can determine V, the velocity of M_1 relative to M_2; b the shortest distance between M_1 and M_2 if they had continued to move with uniform velocity in straight lines; and ϕ the angle which determines the plane in which V and b lie. From V and b we can determine θ, if we know the law of force, so that the problem is solved in the case of two molecules.

When we pass from this case to that of two systems of moving molecules, we shall suppose that the time during which a molecule is beyond the action of other molecules is so great compared with the time during which it is deflected by that action, that we may neglect both the time and the distance described by the molecules during the encounter, as compared with the time and the distance described while the molecules are free from disturbing force. We may also neglect those cases in which three or more molecules are within each other's spheres of action at the same instant.

On the Mutual Action of Two Systems of Moving Molecules.

Let the number of molecules of the first kind in unit of volume be N_1, the mass of each being M_1. The velocities of these molecules will in general be different both in magnitude and direction. Let us select those molecules the components of whose velocities lie between

$$\xi_1 \text{ and } \xi_1 + d\xi_1, \quad \eta_1 \text{ and } \eta_1 + d\eta_1, \quad \zeta_1 \text{ and } \zeta_1 + d\zeta_1,$$

and let the number of these molecules be dN_1. The velocities of these molecules will be very nearly equal and parallel.

On account of the mutual actions of the molecules, the number of molecules which at a given instant have velocities within given ·limits will be definite, so that

$$dN_1 = f_1\left(\xi_1 \eta_1 \zeta_1\right) d\xi_1 d\eta_1 d\zeta_1 \quad\dots\dots\dots\dots\dots\dots (2).$$

We shall consider the form of this function afterwards.

Let the number of molecules of the second kind in unit of volume be N_2, and let dN_2 of these have velocities between ξ_2 and $\xi_2 + d\xi_2$, η_2 and $\eta_2 + d\eta_2$, ζ_2 and $\zeta_2 + d\zeta_2$, where

$$dN_2 = f_2\left(\xi_2 \eta_2 \zeta_2\right) d\xi_2 d\eta_2 d\zeta_2.$$

The velocity of any of the dN_1 molecules of the first system relative to the dN_2 molecules of the second system is V, and each molecule M_1 will in the time δt describe a relative path $V\delta t$ among the molecules of the second system. Conceive a space bounded by the following surfaces. Let two cylindrical surfaces have the common axis $V\delta t$ and radii b and $b+db$. Let two planes be drawn through the extremities of the line $V\delta t$ perpendicular to it. Finally, let two planes be drawn through $V\delta t$ making angles ϕ and $\phi+d\phi$ with a plane through V parallel to the axis of x. Then the volume included between the four planes and the two cylindric surfaces will be $Vb\,db\,d\phi\,\delta t$.

If this volume includes one of the molecules M_2, then during the time δt there will be an encounter between M_1 and M_2, in which b is between b and $b+db$, and ϕ between ϕ and $\phi+d\phi$.

Since there are dN_1 molecules similar to M_1 and dN_2 similar to M_2 in unit of volume, the whole number of encounters of the given kind between the two systems will be

$$Vb\,db\,d\phi\,\delta t\,dN_1\,dN_2.$$

Now let Q be any property of the molecule M_1, such as its velocity in a given direction, the square or cube of that velocity or any other property of the molecule which is altered in a known manner by an encounter of the given kind, so that Q becomes Q' after the encounter, then during the time δt a certain number of the molecules of the first kind have Q changed to Q', while the remainder retain the original value of Q, so that

$$\delta Q\,dN_1 = (Q'-Q)\,Vb\,db\,d\phi\,\delta t\,dN_1\,dN_2,$$

or

$$\frac{\delta Q\,dN_1}{\delta t} = (Q'-Q)\,Vb\,db\,d\phi\,dN_1\,dN_2\quad\ldots\ldots\ldots\ldots\ldots\ldots(3).$$

Here $\dfrac{\delta Q\,dN_1}{\delta t}$ refers to the alteration in the sum of the values of Q for the dN_1 molecules, due to their encounters of the given kind with the dN_2 molecules of the second sort. In order to determine the value of $\dfrac{\delta Q N_1}{\delta t}$, the rate of alteration of Q among all the molecules of the first kind, we must perform the following integrations:—

1st, with respect to ϕ from $\phi=0$ to $\phi=2\pi$.

2nd, with respect to b from $b=0$ to $b=\infty$. These operations will give the results of the encounters of every kind between the dN_1 and dN_2 molecules.

3rd, with respect to dN_2, or $f_2(\xi_2\eta_2\zeta_2)\,d\xi_2d\eta_2d\zeta_2$.

4th, with respect to dN_1, or $f_1(\xi_1\eta_1\zeta_1)\,d\xi_1d\eta_1d\zeta_1$.

These operations require in general a knowledge of the forms of f_1 and f_2.

1st. *Integration with respect to ϕ.*

Since the action between the molecules is the same in whatever plane it takes place, we shall first determine the value of $\int_0^{2\pi}(Q'-Q)\,d\phi$ in several cases, making Q some function of ξ, η, and ζ.

(a) Let $Q=\xi_1$ and $Q'=\xi'_1$, then

$$\int_0^{2\pi}(\xi'_1-\xi_1)\,d\phi=\frac{M_2}{M_1+M_2}(\xi_2-\xi_1)\,4\pi\sin^2\theta \dots\dots\dots\dots (4).$$

(β) Let $Q=\xi_1^2$ and $Q'=\xi'_1^2$,

$$\int_0^{2\pi}(\xi'_1{}^2-\xi_1^2)\,d\phi=\frac{M_2}{(M_1+M_2)^2}[(\xi_2-\xi_1)(M_1\xi_1+M_2\xi_2)\,8\pi\sin^2\theta+M_2\{(\eta_2-\eta_1)^2$$
$$+(\zeta_2-\zeta_1)^2-2(\xi_2-\xi_1)^2\}\pi\sin^2 2\theta]\dots\dots(5).$$

By transformation of coordinates we may derive from this

$$\int_0^{2\pi}(\xi'_1\eta'_1-\xi_1\eta_1)\,d\phi=\frac{M_2}{(M_1+M_2)^2}[\{M_2\xi_2\eta_2-M_1\xi_1\eta_1+\tfrac12(M_1-M_2)(\xi_1\eta_2+\xi_2\eta_1)\}\,8\pi\sin^2\theta$$
$$-3M_2(\xi_2-\xi_1)(\eta_2-\eta_1)]\dots\dots(6),$$

with similar expressions for the other quadratic functions of ξ, η, ζ.

(γ) Let $Q=\xi_1(\xi_1^2+\eta_1^2+\zeta_1^2)$, and $Q'=\xi'_1(\xi'_1{}^2+\eta'_1{}^2+\zeta'_1{}^2)$; then putting
$$\xi_1^2+\eta_1^2+\zeta_1^2=V_1^2,\quad \xi_1\xi_2+\eta_1\eta_2+\zeta_1\zeta_2=U,\quad \xi_2^2+\eta_2^2+\zeta_2^2=V_2^2,$$
and $(\xi_2-\xi_1)^2+(\eta_2-\eta_1)^2+(\zeta_2-\zeta_1)^2=V^2$, we find

$$\left.\begin{aligned}
\int_0^{2\pi}(\xi'_1V'_1{}^2-\xi_1V_1^2)\,d\phi&=\frac{M_2}{M_1+M_2}4\pi\sin^2\theta\{(\xi_2-\xi_1)V_1^2+2\xi_1(U-V_1^2)\}\\
&+\left(\frac{M_2}{M_1+M_2}\right)^2(8\pi\sin^2\theta-3\pi\sin^2 2\theta)\,2(\xi_2-\xi_1)(U-V_1^2)\\
&+\left(\frac{M_2}{M_1+M_2}\right)^2(8\pi\sin^2\theta+2\pi\sin^2 2\theta)\,\xi_1V^2\\
&+\left(\frac{M_2}{M_1+M_2}\right)^3(8\pi\sin^2\theta-2\pi\sin^2 2\theta)\,2(\xi_2-\xi_1)V^2
\end{aligned}\right\}\ \dots(7).$$

These are the principal functions of ξ, η, ζ whose changes we shall have to consider; we shall indicate them by the symbols α, β, or γ, according as the function of the velocity is of one, two, or three dimensions.

2nd. *Integration with respect to* b.

We have next to multiply these expressions by bdb, and to integrate with respect to b from $b=0$ to $b=\infty$. We must bear in mind that θ is a function of b and V, and can only be determined when the law of force is known. In the expressions which we have to deal with, θ occurs under two forms only, namely, $\sin^2\theta$ and $\sin^2 2\theta$. If, therefore, we can find the two values of

$$B_1 = \int_0^\infty 4\pi bdb\,\sin^2\theta, \quad \text{and} \quad B_2 = \int_0^\infty \pi bdb\,\sin^2 2\theta \quad \ldots\ldots\ldots\ldots (8),$$

we can integrate all the expressions with respect to b.

B_1 and B_2 will be functions of V only, the form of which we can determine only in particular cases, after we have found θ as a function of b and V.

Determination of θ for certain laws of Force.

Let us assume that the force between the molecules M_1 and M_2 is repulsive and varies inversely as the nth power of the distance between them, the value of the moving force at distance unity being K, then we find by the equation of central orbits,

$$\frac{\pi}{2} - \theta = \int_0^{x'} \frac{dx}{\sqrt{1 - x^2 - \dfrac{2}{n-1}\left(\dfrac{x}{a}\right)^{n-1}}} \quad \ldots\ldots\ldots\ldots\ldots\ldots (9),$$

where $x = \dfrac{b}{r}$, or the ratio of b to the distance of the molecules at a given time: x is therefore a numerical quantity; a is also a numerical quantity and is given by the equation

$$a = b\left\{\frac{V^2 M_1 M_2}{K(M_1 + M_2)}\right\}^{\frac{1}{n-1}} \quad \ldots\ldots\ldots\ldots\ldots\ldots (10).$$

The limits of integration are $x = 0$ and $x = x'$, where x' is the least positive root of the equation

$$1 - x^2 - \frac{2}{n-1}\left(\frac{x}{a}\right)^{n-1} = 0 \quad \ldots\ldots\ldots\ldots (11).$$

It is evident that θ is a function of a and n, and when n is known θ may be expressed as a function of a only.

Also
$$b\,db = \left\{ \frac{K\,(M_1 + M_2)}{V^2 M_1 M_2} \right\}^{\frac{2}{n-1}} a\,da \dots\dots\dots\dots\dots (12);$$

so that if we put

$$A_1 = \int_0^\infty 4\pi a\,da \, \sin^2 \theta, \quad A_2 = \int_0^\infty \pi a\,da \, \sin^2 2\theta \dots\dots\dots (13),$$

A_1 and A_2 will be definite numerical quantities which may be ascertained when n is given, and B_1 and B_2 may be found by multiplying A_1 and A_2 by

$$\left\{ \frac{K\,(M_1 + M_2)}{M_1 M_2} \right\}^{\frac{2}{n-1}} V^{\frac{-4}{n-1}}.$$

Before integrating further we have to multiply by V, so that the form in which V will enter into the expressions which have to be integrated with respect to dN_1 and dN_2 will be

$$V^{\frac{n-5}{n-1}}.$$

It will be shewn that we have reason from experiments on the viscosity of gases to believe that $n = 5$. In this case V will disappear from the expressions of the form (3), and they will be capable of immediate integration with respect to dN_1 and dN_2.

If we assume $n = 5$ and put $a^4 = 2 \cot^2 2\phi$ and $x = \sqrt{1 - \tan^2 \phi} \cos \psi$,

$$\left. \begin{array}{l} \dfrac{\pi}{2} - \theta = \sqrt{\cos 2\phi} \displaystyle\int_0^{\frac{\pi}{2}} \dfrac{d\psi}{\sqrt{1 - \sin^2 \phi \sin^2 \psi}} \\[3mm] \qquad = \sqrt{\cos 2\phi}\, F_{\sin\phi}, \end{array} \right\} \dots\dots\dots\dots\dots (14),$$

where $F_{\sin\phi}$ is the complete elliptic function of the first kind and is given in Legendre's Tables. I have computed the following Table of the distance of the asymptotes, the distance of the apse, the value of θ, and of the quantities whose summation leads to A_1 and A_2.

ϕ	b	Distance of apse	θ	$\dfrac{\sin^2 \theta}{\sin^2 2\phi}$	$\dfrac{\sin^2 2\theta}{\sin^2 2\phi}$
0 0	infinite	infinite	0 0	0	0
5 0	2381	2391	0 31	·00270	·01079
10 0	1658	1684	1 53	·01464	·03689
15 0	1316	1366	4 47	·02781	·11048
20 0	1092	1172	8 45	·05601	·21885
25 0	916	1036	14 15	·10325	·38799
30 0	760	931	21 42	·18228	·62942
35 0	603	845	31 59	·31772	·71433
40 0	420	772	47 20	·55749	1·02427
41 0	374	758	51 32	·62515	·96763
42 0	324	745	56 26	·70197	·85838
43 0	264	732	62 22	·78872	·67868
44 0	187	719	70 18	·88745	·40338
44 30	132	713	76 1	·94190	·21999
45 0	0	707	90 0	1·00000	·00000

$$A_1 = \int 4\pi a da \, \sin^2 \theta = 2\cdot6595 \dots\dots\dots\dots\dots\dots(15),$$

$$A_2 = \int \pi a da \, \sin^2 2\theta = 1\cdot3682 \dots\dots\dots\dots\dots\dots(16).$$

The paths described by molecules about a centre of force S, repelling inversely as the fifth power of the distance, are given in the figure.

The molecules are supposed to be originally moving with equal velocities in parallel paths, and the way in which their deflections depend on the distance of the path from S is shewn by the different curves in the figure.

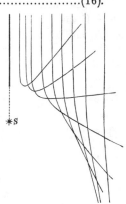

3rd. *Integration with respect to* dN_2.

We have now to integrate expressions involving various functions of ξ, η, ζ, and V with respect to all the molecules of the second sort. We may write the expression to be integrated

$$\iiint Q V^{\frac{n-5}{n-1}} f_2 \left(\xi_2 \eta_2 \zeta_2\right) d\xi_2 \, d\eta_2 \, d\zeta_2,$$

where Q is some function of ξ, η, ζ, &c., already determined, and f_2 is the function which indicates the distribution of velocity among the molecules of the second kind.

In the case in which $n = 5$, V disappears, and we may write the result of integration $\overline{Q}N_2$,

where $\overline{Q}$ is the mean value of Q for all the molecules of the second kind, and N_2 is the number of those molecules.

If, however, n is not equal to 5, so that V does not disappear, we should require to know the form of the function f_2 before we could proceed further with the integration.

The only case in which I have determined the form of this function is that of one or more kinds of molecules which have by their continual encounters brought about a distribution of velocity such that the number of molecules whose velocity lies within given limits remains constant. In the *Philosophical Magazine* for January 1860, I have given an investigation of this case, founded on the assumption that the probability of a molecule having a velocity resolved parallel to x lying between given limits is not in any way affected by the knowledge that the molecule has a given velocity resolved parallel to y. As this assumption may appear precarious, I shall now determine the form of the function in a different manner.

On the Final Distribution of Velocity among the Molecules of Two Systems acting on one another according to any Law of Force.

From a given point O let lines be drawn representing in direction and magnitude the velocities of every molecule of either kind in unit of volume. The extremities of these lines will be distributed over space in such a way that if an element of volume dV be taken anywhere, the number of such lines which will terminate within dV will be $f(r)\,dV$, where r is the distance of dV from O.

Let $OA = a$ be the velocity of a molecule of the first kind, and $OB = b$ that of a molecule of the second kind before they encounter one another, then

BA will be the velocity of A relative to B; and if we divide AB in G inversely as the masses of the molecules, and join OG, OG will be the velocity of the centre of gravity of the two molecules.

Now let $OA' = a'$ and $OB' = b'$ be the velocities of the two molecules after the encounter, $GA = GA'$ and $GB = GB'$, and $A'GB'$ is a straight line not necessarily in the plane of OAB. Also $AGA' = 2\theta$ is the angle through which the relative velocity is turned in the encounter in question. The relative motion of the molecules is completely defined if we know BA the relative velocity before the encounter, 2θ the angle through which BA is turned during the encounter, and ϕ the angle which defines the direction of the plane in which BA and $B'A'$ lie. All encounters in which the magnitude and direction of BA, and also θ and ϕ, lie within certain almost contiguous limits, we shall class as encounters of the given kind. The number of such encounters in unit of time will be

$$n_1 n_2 F de \dots\dots\dots\dots\dots\dots\dots\dots\dots(17),$$

where n_1 and n_2 are the numbers of molecules of each kind under consideration, and F is a function of the relative velocity and of the angle θ, and de depends on the limits of variation within which we class encounters as of the same kind.

Now let A describe the boundary of an element of volume dV while AB and $A'B'$ move parallel to themselves, then B, A', and B' will also describe equal and similar elements of volume.

The number of molecules of the first kind, the lines representing the velocities of which terminate in the element dV at A, will be

$$n_1 = f_1(a)\, dV \dots\dots\dots\dots\dots\dots\dots\dots(18).$$

The number of molecules of the second kind which have velocities corresponding to OB will be

$$n_2 = f_2(b)\, dV \dots\dots\dots\dots\dots\dots (19);$$

and the number of encounters of the given kind between these two sets of molecules will be

$$f_1(a) f_2(b)\, (dV)^2 F de \dots\dots\dots\dots\dots\dots(20).$$

The lines representing the velocities of these molecules after encounters of the given kind will terminate within elements of volume at A' and B', each equal to dV.

In like manner we should find for the number of encounters between molecules whose original velocities corresponded to elements equal to dV described about A' and B', and whose subsequent velocities correspond to elements equal to dV described about A and B,

$$f_1(a')f_2(b')(dV)^2F'de \dots\dots\dots\dots (21),$$

where F' is the same function of $B'A'$ and $A'GA$ that F is of BA and AGA'. F is therefore equal to F'.

When the number of pairs of molecules which change their velocities from OA, OB to OA', OB' is equal to the number which change from OA', OB' to OA, OB, then the final distribution of velocity will be obtained, which will not be altered by subsequent exchanges. This will be the case when

$$f_1(a)f_2(b)=f_1(a')f_2(b') \dots\dots\dots\dots(22).$$

Now the only relation between a, b and a', b' is

$$M_1a^2 + M_2b^2 = M_1a'^2 + M_2b'^2, \dots\dots\dots\dots(23),$$

whence we obtain
$$f_1(a) = C_1e^{-\frac{a^2}{a^2}}, \ f_2(b) = C_2e^{-\frac{b^2}{\beta^2}} \dots\dots\dots\dots(24),$$

where
$$M_1a^2 = M_2\beta^2 \dots\dots\dots\dots(25).$$

By integrating $\iiint C_1e^{-\frac{\xi^2+\eta^2+\zeta^2}{a^2}}d\xi\,d\eta\,d\zeta$, and equating the result to N_1, we obtain the value of C_1. If, therefore, the distribution of velocities among N_1 molecules is such that the number of molecules whose component velocities are between ξ and $\xi+d\zeta$, η and $\eta+d\eta$, and ζ and $\zeta+d\zeta$ is

$$dN_1 = \frac{N_1}{a^3\pi^{\frac{3}{2}}} e^{-\frac{\xi^2+\eta^2+\zeta^2}{a^2}}d\xi\,d\eta\,d\zeta \dots\dots\dots\dots(26),$$

then this distribution of velocities will not be altered by the exchange of velocities among the molecules by their mutual action.

This is therefore a possible form of the final distribution of velocities. It is also the only form; for if there were any other, the exchange between velocities represented by OA and OA' would not be equal. Suppose that the number of molecules having velocity OA' increases at the expense of OA. Then since the total number of molecules corresponding to OA' remains constant, OA' must communicate as many to OA'', and so on till they return to OA.

Hence if OA, OA', OA'', &c. be a series of velocities, there will be a tendency of each molecule to assume the velocities OA, OA', OA'', &c. in order, returning to OA. Now it is impossible to assign a reason why the successive velocities of a molecule should be arranged in this cycle, rather than in the reverse order. If, therefore, the direct exchange between OA and OA' is not equal, the equality cannot be preserved by exchange in a cycle. Hence the direct exchange between OA and OA' is equal, and the distribution we have determined is the only one possible.

This final distribution of velocity is attained only when the molecules have had a great number of encounters, but the great rapidity with which the encounters succeed each other is such that in all motions and changes of the gaseous system except the most violent, the form of the distribution of velocity is only slightly changed.

When the gas moves in mass, the velocities now determined are compounded with the motion of translation of the gas.

When the differential elements of the gas are changing their figure, being compressed or extended along certain axes, the values of the mean square of the velocity will be different in different directions. It is probable that the form of the function will then be

$$f_1(\xi\eta\zeta) = \frac{N_1}{\alpha\beta\gamma\pi^{\frac{3}{2}}} e^{-\left(\frac{\xi^2}{\alpha^2}+\frac{\eta^2}{\beta^2}+\frac{\zeta^2}{\gamma^2}\right)} \quad\ldots\ldots\ldots\ldots\ldots\ldots (27),$$

where α, β, γ are slightly different. I have not, however, attempted to investigate the exact distribution of velocities in this case, as the theory of motion of gases does not require it.

When one gas is diffusing through another, or when heat is being conducted through a gas, the distribution of velocities will be different in the positive and negative directions, instead of being symmetrical, as in the case we have considered. The want of symmetry, however, may be treated as very small in most actual cases.

The principal conclusions which we may draw from this investigation are as follows. Calling a the modulus of velocity,

1st. The mean velocity is $\qquad \bar{v} = \frac{2}{\sqrt{\pi}} a \ldots\ldots\ldots\ldots\ldots\ldots (28).$

2nd. The mean square of the velocity is $\overline{v^2} = \frac{3}{2} a^2 \ldots\ldots\ldots\ldots\ldots\ldots (29).$

3rd. The mean value of ξ^2 is $\qquad \overline{\xi^2} = \frac{1}{2} a^2 \ldots\ldots\ldots\ldots\ldots\ldots (30).$

4th. The mean value of ξ^4 is $\qquad$ $\overline{\xi^4} = \frac{3}{4}\alpha^4$ ....(31).

5th. The mean value of $\xi^2\eta^2$ is $\overline{\xi^2\eta^2} = \frac{1}{4}\alpha^4$ ....(32).

6th. When there are two systems of molecules

$$M_1\alpha^2 = M_2\beta^2 \qquad\dots\dots\dots\dots (33),$$

whence $\qquad\qquad M_1v_1^2 = M_2v_2^2 \qquad\dots\dots\dots\dots\dots (34),$

or the mean *vis viva* of a molecule will be the same in each system. This is a very important result in the theory of gases, and it is independent of the nature of the action between the molecules, as are all the other results relating to the final distribution of velocities. We shall find that it leads to the law of gases known as that of Equivalent Volumes.

Variation of Functions of the Velocity due to encounters between the Molecules.

We may now proceed to write down the values of $\dfrac{\delta\overline{Q}}{\delta t}$ in the different cases. We shall indicate the mean value of any quantity for all the molecules of one kind by placing a bar over the symbol which represents that quantity for any particular molecule, but in expressions where all such quantities are to be taken at their mean values, we shall, for convenience, omit the bar. We shall use the symbols δ_1 and δ_2 to indicate the effect produced by molecules of the first kind and second kind respectively, and δ_3 to indicate the effect of external forces. We shall also confine ourselves to the case in which $n = 5$, since it is not only free from mathematical difficulty, but is the only case which is consistent with the laws of viscosity of gases.

In this case V disappears, and we have for the effect of the second system on the first,

$$\frac{\delta Q}{\delta t} = N_2 \left\{ \frac{K(M_1 + M_2)}{M_1 M_2} \right\}^{\frac{1}{2}} A \int_0^\pi (Q' - Q)\,d\phi \dots\dots\dots\dots(35),$$

where the functions of ξ, η, ζ in $\int (Q' - Q)\,d\phi$ must be put equal to their mean values for all the molecules, and A_1 or A_2 must be put for A according as $\sin^2\theta$ or $\sin^2 2\theta$ occurs in the expressions in equations (4), (5), (6), (7). We thus obtain

(a) $\qquad \dfrac{\delta_2\xi_1}{\delta t} = \left\{ \dfrac{K}{M_1 M_2 (M_1 + M_2)} \right\}^{\frac{1}{2}} N_2 M_2 A_1 (\xi_2 - \xi_1) \dots\dots\dots\dots(36);$

$$(\beta) \quad \frac{\delta_2 \xi_1^2}{\delta t} = \left\{ \frac{K}{M_1 M_2 (M_1 + M_2)} \right\}^{\frac{1}{2}} \frac{N_2 M_2}{M_1 + M_2} \left\{ 2 A_1 (\xi_2 - \xi_1)(M_1 \xi_1 + M_2 \xi_2) \right. \\ \left. + A_2 M_2 (\overline{\eta_2 - \eta_1}^2 + \overline{\zeta_2 - \zeta_1}^2 - 2 \overline{\xi_2 - \xi_1}^2) \right\} \quad \cdots\cdots (37);$$

$$\frac{\delta_2 \xi_1 \eta_1}{\delta t} = \left\{ \frac{K}{M_1 M_2 (M_1 + M_2)} \right\}^{\frac{1}{2}} \frac{N_2 M_2}{M_1 + M_2} \left[A_1 \{ 2 M_2 \xi_2 \eta_2 - 2 M_1 \xi_1 \eta_1 \right. \\ \left. + (M_1 - M_2)(\xi_1 \eta_2 + \xi_2 \eta_1) \} - 3 A_2 M_2 (\xi_2 - \xi_1)(\eta_2 - \eta_1) \right] \quad \cdots(38);$$

$$(\gamma) \quad \frac{\delta_2 \xi_1 V_1^2}{\delta t} = \left\{ \frac{K}{M_1 M_2 (M_1 + M_2)} \right\}^{\frac{1}{2}} N_2 M_2 \left[A_1 \{ \overline{\xi_2 - \xi_1} V_1^2 + 2 \xi_1 (U - V_1^2) \} \right. \\ + \frac{M_2}{M_1 + M_2} (2 A_1 - 3 A_2) 2 (\xi_2 - \xi_1)(U - V_1^2) \\ + \frac{M_2}{M_1 + M_2} (2 A_1 + 2 A_2) \xi_1 V^2 \\ \left. + \left(\frac{M_2}{M_1 + M_2} \right)^2 (2 A_1 - 2 A_2) 2 (\xi_2 - \xi_1) V^2 \right] \quad \cdots\cdots (39),$$

using the symbol δ_2 to indicate variations arising from the action of molecules of the second system.

These are the values of the rate of variation of the mean values of ξ_1, ξ_1^2, $\xi_1 \eta_1$, and $\xi_1 V_1^2$, for the molecules of the first kind due to their encounters with molecules of the second kind. In all of them we must multiply up all functions of ξ, η, ζ, and take the mean values of the products so found. As this has to be done for all such functions, I have omitted the bar over each function in these expressions.

To find the rate of variation due to the encounters among the particles of the same system, we have only to alter the suffix $_{(2)}$ into $_{(1)}$ throughout, and to change K, the coefficient of the force between M_1 and M_2 into K_1, that of the force between two molecules of the first system. We thus find

$$(a) \quad \frac{\delta_1 \overline{\xi_1}}{\delta t} = 0 \quad \cdots\cdots\cdots\cdots\cdots\cdots\cdots\cdots\cdots\cdots\cdots\cdots\cdots\cdots\cdots\cdots\cdots\cdots\cdots (40);$$

$$(\beta) \quad \frac{\delta_1 \overline{\xi_1^2}}{dt} = \left(\frac{K_1}{2 M_1^3} \right)^{\frac{1}{2}} M_1 N_1 A_2 \{ \overline{\eta_1^2} + \overline{\zeta_1^2} - 2 \overline{\xi_1^2} - (\overline{\eta_1 . \eta_1} + \overline{\zeta_1 . \zeta_1} - 2 \overline{\xi_1 . \xi_1}) \} \quad \cdots\cdots (41);$$

$$\frac{\delta_1 \overline{\xi_1 \eta_1}}{\delta t} = \left(\frac{K_1}{2 M_1^3} \right)^{\frac{1}{2}} M_1 N_1 A_2 3 \{ \overline{\xi_1 . \eta_1} - \overline{\xi_1 \eta_1} \} \quad \cdots\cdots\cdots\cdots\cdots\cdots\cdots\cdots\cdots (42);$$

$$(\gamma) \quad \frac{\delta_1 \overline{\xi_1 V_1^2}}{\delta t} = \left(\frac{K_1}{2M_1^3}\right) M_1 N_1 A_2 3 \left(\overline{\xi_1 . V_1^2} - \overline{\xi_1 V_1^2}\right) \quad\dots\dots\dots\dots\dots\dots (43).$$

These quantities must be added to those in equations (36) to (39) in order to get the rate of variation in the molecules of the first kind due to their encounters with molecules of both systems. When there is only one kind of molecules, the latter equations give the rates of variation at once.

On the Action of External Forces on a System of Moving Molecules.

We shall suppose the external force to be like the force of gravity, producing equal acceleration on all the molecules. Let the components of the force in the three coordinate directions be X, Y, Z. Then we have by dynamics for the variations of ξ, ξ^2, and ξV^2 due to this cause,

$$(\alpha) \quad \frac{\delta_3 \xi}{\delta t} = X \dots\dots\dots\dots\dots\dots\dots\dots\dots\dots\dots\dots\dots\dots\dots (44);$$

$$(\beta) \quad \frac{\delta_3 . \xi^2}{\delta t} = 2\xi X \dots\dots\dots\dots\dots\dots\dots\dots\dots\dots\dots\dots (45);$$

$$\frac{\delta_3 . \xi \eta}{\delta t} = \eta X + \xi Y \dots\dots\dots\dots\dots\dots\dots\dots\dots\dots (46);$$

$$(\gamma) \quad \frac{\delta_3 . \xi V^2}{\delta t} = 2\xi (\xi X + \eta Y + \zeta Z) + X V^2 \dots\dots\dots\dots\dots (47);$$

where δ_3 refers to variations due to the action of external forces.

On the Total rate of change of the different functions of the velocity of the molecules of the first system arising from their encounters with molecules of both systems and from the action of external forces.

To find the total rate of change arising from these causes, we must add

$$\frac{\delta_1 Q}{\delta t}, \quad \frac{\delta_2 Q}{\delta t}, \quad \text{and} \quad \frac{\delta_3 Q}{\delta t},$$

the quantities already found. We shall find it, however, most convenient in the remainder of this investigation to introduce a change in the notation, and to substitute for

$$\xi, \ \eta, \ \text{and} \ \zeta, \quad u + \xi, \quad v + \eta, \ \text{and} \ w + \zeta \dots\dots\dots\dots (48),$$

where u, v, and w are so chosen that they are the mean values of the components of the velocity of all molecules of the same system in the immediate neighbourhood of a given point. We shall also write

$$M_1 N_1 = \rho_1, \quad M_2 N_2 = \rho_2 \dots \dots \dots \dots \dots (49),$$

where ρ_1 and ρ_2 are the densities of the two systems of molecules, that is, the mass in unit of volume. We shall also write

$$\left(\frac{K_1}{2M_1^2}\right)^{\frac{1}{2}} = k_1, \quad \left(\frac{K}{M_1 M_2 (M_1 + M_2)}\right)^{\frac{1}{2}} = k, \quad \text{and} \quad \left(\frac{K_2}{2M_2^3}\right)^{\frac{1}{2}} = k_2 \dots \dots (50);$$

ρ_1, ρ_2, k_1, k_2, and k are quantities the absolute values of which can be deduced from experiment. We have not as yet experimental data for determining M, N, or K.

We thus find for the rate of change of the various functions of the velocity,

(α) $\quad \dfrac{\delta u_1}{\delta t} = k A_1 \rho_2 (u_2 - u_1) + X \dots \dots \dots \dots \dots \dots \dots \dots \dots (51);$

(β) $\quad \dfrac{\delta . \xi_1^2}{\delta t} = k_1 A_2 \rho_1 \{\eta_1^2 + \zeta_1^2 - 2\xi_1^2\} + k\rho_2 \dfrac{M_2}{M_1 + M_2} \{2A_1 (u_2 - u_1)^2$

$$+ A_2 \overline{(v_2 - v_1}^2 + \overline{w_2 - w_1}^2 - 2\overline{u_2 - u_1}^2)\} + \frac{k\rho_2}{M_1 + M_2} \{2A_1 (M_2 \xi_2^2 - M_1 \xi_1^2)$$

$$+ A_2 M_2 (\eta_1^2 + \zeta_1^2 - 2\xi_1^2 + \eta_2^2 + \zeta_2^2 - 2\xi_2^2)\}$$

$$\left. \right\} .. (52);$$

also $\quad \dfrac{\delta . \xi \eta}{\delta t} = - 3k_1 A_2 \rho_1 \xi_1 \eta_1 + k\rho_2 \dfrac{M_2}{M_1 + M_2} (2A_1 - 3A_2)(u_2 - u_1)(v_2 - v_1)$

$$+ \frac{k\rho_2}{M_1 + M_2} \{2A_1 (M_2 \xi_2 \eta_2 - M_1 \xi_1 \eta_1) - 3A_2 M_2 (\xi_1 \eta_1 + \xi_2 \eta_2)\} \quad \left. \right\} \dots \dots \dots (53).$$

(γ) As the expressions for the variation of functions of three dimensions in mixed media are complicated, and as we shall not have occasion to use them, I shall give the case of a single medium,

$$\frac{\delta}{\delta t}(\xi_1^3 + \xi_1 \eta_1^2 + \xi_1 \zeta_1^2) = - 3k_1 \rho_1 A_2 (\xi_1^3 + \xi_1 \eta_1^2 + \xi_1 \zeta_1^2) + X (3\xi_1^2 + \eta_1^2 + \zeta_1^2)$$

$$+ 2Y\xi_1 \eta_1 + 2Z\xi_1 \zeta_1 \dots \dots \dots \dots (54).$$

Theory of a Medium composed of Moving Molecules.

We shall suppose the position of every moving molecule referred to three rectangular axes, and that the component velocities of any one of them, resolved in the directions of x, y, z, are

$$u+\xi, \quad v+\eta, \quad w+\zeta,$$

where u, v, w are the components of the mean velocity of all the molecules which are at a given instant in a given element of volume, and ξ, η, ζ are the components of the relative velocity of one of these molecules with respect to the mean velocity.

The quantities u, v, w may be treated as functions of x, y, z, and t, in which case differentiation will be expressed by the symbol d. The quantities ξ, η, ζ, being different for every molecule, must be regarded as functions of t for each molecule. Their variation with respect to t will be indicated by the symbol δ.

The mean values of ξ^2 and other functions of ξ, η, ζ for all the molecules in the element of volume may, however, be treated as functions of x, y, z, and t.

If we consider an element of volume which always moves with the velocities u, v, w, we shall find that it does not always consist of the same molecules, because molecules are continually passing through its boundary. We cannot therefore treat it as a mass moving with the velocity u, v, w, as is done in hydrodynamics, but we must consider separately the motion of each molecule. When we have occasion to consider the variation of the properties of this element during its motion as a function of the time we shall use the symbol ∂.

We shall call the velocities u, v, w the velocities of translation of the medium, and ξ, η, ζ the velocities of agitation of the molecules.

Let the number of molecules in the element $dx\,dy\,dz$ be $N\,dx\,dy\,dz$, then we may call N the number of molecules in unit of volume. If M is the mass of each molecule, and ρ the density of the element, then

$$MN = \rho \dotfill (55).$$

Transference of Quantities across a Plane Area.

We must next consider the molecules which pass through a given plane of unit area in unit of time, and determine the quantity of matter, of momentum, of heat, &c. which is transferred from the negative to the positive side of this plane in unit of time.

We shall first divide the N molecules in unit of volume into classes according to the value of ξ, η, and ζ for each, and we shall suppose that the number of molecules in unit of volume whose velocity in the direction of x lies between ξ and $\xi + d\xi$, η and $\eta + d\eta$, ζ and $\zeta + d\zeta$ is dN, dN will then be a function of the component velocities, the sum of which being taken for all the molecules will give N the total number of molecules. The most probable form of this function for a medium in its state of equilibrium is

$$dN = \frac{N}{a^3 \pi^{\frac{3}{2}}} e^{-\frac{\xi^2 + \eta^2 + \zeta^2}{a^2}} d\xi\, d\eta\, d\zeta \dots\dots\dots\dots\dots\dots(56).$$

In the present investigation we do not require to know the form of this function.

Now let us consider a plane of unit area perpendicular to x moving with a velocity of which the part resolved parallel to x is u'. The velocity of the plane relative to the molecules we have been considering is $u' - (u + \xi)$, and since there are dN of these molecules in unit of volume it will overtake

$$\{u' - (u + \xi)\}\, dN$$

such molecules in unit of time, and the number of such molecules passing from the negative to the positive side of the plane, will be

$$(u + \xi - u')\, dN.$$

Now let Q be any property belonging to the molecule, such as its mass, momentum, *vis viva*, &c., which it carries with it across the plane, Q being supposed a function of ξ or of ξ, η, and ζ, or to vary in any way from one molecule to another, provided it be the same for the selected molecules whose number is dN, then the quantity of Q transferred across the plane in the positive direction in unit of time is

$$\int (u - u' + \xi)\, Q dN,$$
or
$$(u - u') \int Q dN + \int \xi Q dN \dots\dots\dots\dots\dots\dots(57).$$

If we put $\overline{Q}N$ for $\int Q dN$, and $\overline{\xi Q}N$ for $\int \xi Q dN$, then we may call $\overline{Q}$ the mean value of Q, and $\overline{\xi Q}$ the mean value of ξQ, for all the particles in the element of volume, and we may write the expression for the quantity of Q which crosses the plane in unit of time

$$(u - u')\, \overline{Q}N + \overline{\xi Q}N \dots\dots\dots\dots\dots\dots(58).$$

(a) *Transference of Matter across a Plane—Velocity of the Fluid.*

To determine the quantity of matter which crosses the plane, make Q equal to M the mass of each molecule; then, since M is the same for all molecules of the same kind, $\overline{M} = M$; and since the mean value of ξ is zero, the expression is reduced to

$$(u - u') MN = (u - u') \rho \quad\quad\dots\dots\dots (59).$$

If $u = u'$, or if the plane moves with velocity u, the whole excess of matter transferred across the plane is zero; the velocity of the fluid may therefore be defined as the velocity whose components are u, v, w.

(β) *Transference of Momentum across a Plane—System of Pressures at any point of the Fluid.*

The momentum of any one molecule in the direction of x is $M(u + \xi)$. Substituting this for Q, we get for the quantity of momentum transferred across the plane in the positive direction

$$(u - u') u\rho + \overline{\xi^2}\rho \quad\quad\dots\dots\dots (60).$$

If the plane moves with the velocity u, this expression is reduced to $\overline{\xi^2}\rho$, where $\overline{\xi^2}$ represents the mean value of ξ^2.

This is the whole momentum in the direction of x of the molecules projected from the negative to the positive side of the plane in unit of time. The mechanical action between the parts of the medium on opposite sides of the plane consists partly of the momentum thus transferred, and partly of the direct attractions or repulsions between molecules on opposite sides of the plane. The latter part of the action must be very small in gases, so that wo may consider the pressure between the parts of the medium on opposite sides of the plane as entirely due to the constant bombardment kept up between them. There will also be a transference of momentum in the directions of y and z across the same plane,

$$(u - u') v\rho + \overline{\xi\eta}\rho \quad\quad\dots\dots\dots(61),$$

and

$$(u - u') w\rho + \overline{\xi\zeta}\rho \quad\quad\dots\dots\dots(62),$$

where $\overline{\xi\eta}$ and $\overline{\xi\zeta}$ represent the mean values of these products.

If the plane moves with the mean velocity u of the fluid, the total force exerted on the medium on the positive side by the projection of molecules into it from the negative side will be

a normal pressure $\overline{\xi^2}\rho$ in the direction of x,

a tangential pressure $\overline{\xi\eta}\rho$ in the direction of y,

and a tangential pressure $\overline{\xi\zeta}\rho$ in the direction of z.

If X, Y, Z are the components of the pressure on unit of area of a plane whose direction cosines are l, m, n,

$$\left.\begin{array}{l} X = l\overline{\xi^2}\rho + m\overline{\xi\eta}\rho + n\overline{\xi\zeta}\rho \\ Y = l\overline{\xi\eta}\rho + m\overline{\eta^2}\rho + n\overline{\eta\zeta}\rho \\ Z = l\overline{\xi\zeta}\rho + m\overline{\eta\zeta}\rho + n\overline{\zeta^2}\rho \end{array}\right\} \dots\dots\dots\dots\dots\dots (63),$$

When a gas is not in a state of violent motion the pressures in all directions are nearly equal, in which case, if we put

$$\overline{\xi^2}\rho + \overline{\eta^2}\rho + \overline{\zeta^2}\rho = 3p \dots\dots\dots\dots\dots\dots (64),$$

the quantity p will represent the mean pressure at a given point, and $\overline{\xi^2}\rho$, $\overline{\eta^2}\rho$, and $\overline{\zeta^2}\rho$ will differ from p only by small quantities; $\overline{\eta\zeta}\rho$, $\overline{\zeta\xi}\rho$, and $\overline{\xi\eta}\rho$ will then be also small quantities with respect to p.

Energy in the Medium—Actual Heat.

The actual energy of any molecule depends partly on the velocity of its centre of gravity, and partly on its rotation or other internal motion with respect to the centre of gravity. It may be written

$$\tfrac{1}{2}M\{(u + \xi)^2 + (v + \eta)^2 + (w + \zeta)^2\} + \tfrac{1}{2}EM \dots\dots\dots\dots(65),$$

where $\tfrac{1}{2}EM$ is the internal part of the energy of the molecule, the form of which is at present unknown. Summing for all the molecules in unit of volume, the energy is

$$\tfrac{1}{2}(u^2 + v^2 + w^2)\rho + \tfrac{1}{2}(\xi^2 + \eta^2 + \zeta^2)\rho + \tfrac{1}{2}\overline{E}\rho \dots\dots\dots\dots\dots(66).$$

The first term gives the energy due to the motion of translation of the medium in mass, the second that due to the agitation of the centres of gravity of the molecules, and the third that due to the internal motion of the parts of each molecule.

If we assume with Clausius that the ratio of the mean energy of internal motion to that of agitation tends continually towards a definite value $(\beta - 1)$, we may conclude that, except in very violent disturbances, this ratio is always preserved, so that

$$\overline{E} = (\beta - 1) (\xi^2 + \eta^2 + \zeta^2) \quad \dots\dots\dots\dots\dots\dots (67).$$

The total energy of the invisible agitation in unit of volume will then be

$$\tfrac{1}{2}\beta (\xi^2 + \eta^2 + \zeta^2) \dots\dots\dots\dots\dots\dots\dots\dots\dots (68),$$

or
$$\tfrac{3}{2}\beta p \dots\dots\dots\dots\dots\dots\dots\dots\dots\dots\dots (69).$$

This energy, being in the form of invisible agitation, may be called the total heat in the unit of volume of the medium.

(γ) *Transference of Energy across a Plane—Conduction of Heat.*

Putting
$$Q = \tfrac{1}{2}\beta (\xi^2 + \eta^2 + \zeta^2) M, \quad \text{and} \quad u = u' \quad \dots\dots\dots\dots\dots (70),$$

we find for the quantity of heat carried over the unit of area by conduction in unit of time

$$\tfrac{1}{2}\beta (\overline{\xi^3} + \overline{\xi\eta^2} + \overline{\xi\zeta^2}) \rho \quad \dots\dots\dots\dots\dots\dots (71),$$

where $\overline{\xi^3}$, &c. indicate the mean values of ξ^3, &c. They are always small quantities.

On the Rate of Variation of Q in an Element of Volume, Q being any property of the Molecules in that Element.

Let Q be the value of the quantity for any particular molecule, and $\overline{Q}$ the mean value of Q for all the molecules of the same kind within the element.

The quantity $\overline{Q}$ may vary from two causes. The molecules within the element may by their mutual action or by the action of external forces produce an alteration of $\overline{Q}$, or molecules may pass into the element and out of it, and so cause an increase or diminution of the value of $\overline{Q}$ within it. If we employ the symbol δ to denote the variation of Q due to actions of the first kind on the individual molecules, and the symbol ∂ to denote the actual variation of Q in an element moving with the mean velocity of the system of molecules under consideration, then by the ordinary investigation of the increase or diminution of matter in an element of volume as contained in treatises on Hydrodynamics,

$$\frac{\partial \overline{Q}N}{\partial t} = \frac{\delta \overline{Q}}{\delta t} N - \frac{d}{dx} \{(u-u')\,\overline{Q}N + \overline{\xi}QN\} \left. \right\} \dots\dots\dots(72),$$
$$- \frac{d}{dy} \{(v-v')\,\overline{Q}N + \eta\overline{QN}\} - \frac{d}{dz} \{(w-w')\,\overline{Q}N + \zeta\overline{QN}\}$$

where the last three terms are derived from equation (59) and two similar equations, and denote the quantity of Q which flows out of an element of volume, that element moving with the velocities u', v', w'. If we perform the differentiations and then make $u' = u$, $v' = v$, and $w' = w$, then the variation will be that in an element which moves with the actual mean velocity of the system of molecules, and the equation becomes

$$\frac{\partial \overline{Q}N}{\partial t} + \overline{Q}N \left(\frac{du}{dx} + \frac{dv}{dy} + \frac{dw}{dz} \right) + \frac{d}{dx}(\overline{\xi}QN) + \frac{d}{dy}(\overline{\eta}QN) + \frac{d}{dz}(\overline{\zeta}QN) = \frac{\delta Q}{\delta t} N \dots (73).$$

Equation of Continuity.

Put $Q = M$ the mass of a molecule; M is unalterable, and we have, putting $MN = \rho$,

$$\frac{\partial \rho}{\partial t} + \rho \left(\frac{du}{dx} + \frac{dv}{dy} + \frac{dw}{dz} \right) = 0 \dots\dots\dots\dots (74),$$

which is the ordinary equation of continuity in hydrodynamics, the element being supposed to move with the velocity of the fluid. Combining this equation with that from which it was obtained, we find

$$N \frac{\partial \overline{Q}}{\partial t} + \frac{d}{dx}(\overline{\xi}QN) + \frac{d}{dy}(\overline{\eta}QN) + \frac{d}{dz}(\overline{\zeta}QN) = N \frac{\delta Q}{\delta t} \dots\dots\dots(75),$$

a more convenient form of the general equation.

Equations of Motion (a).

To obtain the Equation of Motion in the direction of x, put $Q = M_1(u_1 + \xi_1)$, the momentum of a molecule in the direction of x.

We obtain the value of $\frac{\delta Q}{\delta t}$ from equation (51), and the equation may be written

$$\rho_1 \frac{\partial u_1}{\partial t} + \frac{d}{dz}(\rho_1 \overline{\xi_1^2}) + \frac{d}{dy}(\rho_1 \overline{\xi_1 \eta_1}) + \frac{d}{dz}(\rho_1 \overline{\xi_1 \zeta_1}) = kA_1\rho_1\rho_2(u_2 - u_1) + X\rho_1 \dots(76).$$

In this equation the first term denotes the efficient force per unit of volume, the second the variation of normal pressure, the third and fourth the variations of tangential pressure, the fifth the resistance due to the molecules of a different system, and the sixth the external force acting on the system.

The investigation of the values of the second, third, and fourth terms must be deferred till we consider the variations of the second degree.

Condition of Equilibrium of a Mixture of Gases.

In a state of equilibrium u_1 and u_2 vanish, $\rho_1 \xi_1^2$ becomes p_1, and the tangential pressures vanish, so that the equation becomes

$$\frac{dp_1}{dx} = X\rho_1 \dots\dots\dots\dots\dots\dots\dots\dots\dots\dots\dots(77),$$

which is the equation of equilibrium in ordinary hydrostatics.

This equation, being true of the system of molecules forming the first medium independently of the presence of the molecules of the second system, shews that if several kinds of molecules are mixed together, placed in a vessel and acted on by gravity, the final distribution of the molecules of each kind will be the same as if none of the other kinds had been present. This is the same mode of distribution as that which Dalton considered to exist in a mixed atmosphere in equilibrium, the law of diminution of density of each constituent gas being the same as if no other gases were present.

This result, however, can only take place after the gases have been left for a considerable time perfectly undisturbed. If currents arise so as to mix the strata, the composition of the gas will be made more uniform throughout.

The result at which we have arrived as to the final distribution of gases, when left to themselves, is independent of the law of force between the molecules.

Diffusion of Gases.

If the motion of the gases is slow, we may still neglect the tangential pressures. The equation then becomes for the first system of molecules

$$\rho_1 \frac{\partial u_1}{\partial t} + \frac{dp_1}{dx} = kA_1\rho_1\rho_2 (u_2 - u_1) + X\rho_1 \dots\dots\dots\dots\dots (78),$$

and for the second,

$$\rho_2 \frac{\partial u_2}{\partial t} + \frac{dp_2}{dx} = kA_1\rho_1\rho_2\left(u_1 - u_2\right) + X\rho_2 \quad\ldots\ldots\ldots\ldots (79).$$

In all cases of quiet diffusion we may neglect the first term of each equation. If we then put $p_1 + p_2 = p$, and $\rho_1 + \rho_2 = \rho$, we find by adding,

$$\frac{dp}{dx} = X\rho \quad\ldots\ldots\ldots\ldots\ldots\ldots\ldots\ldots\ldots\ldots (80).$$

If we also put $p_1u_1 + p_2u_2 = pu$, then the volumes transferred in opposite directions across a plane moving with velocity u will be equal, so that

$$p_1\left(u_1 - u\right) = p_2\left(u - u_2\right) = \frac{p_1p_2}{p\rho_1\rho_2 kA_1} \cdot \left(X\rho_1 \frac{dp_1}{dx}\right) \quad\ldots\ldots\ldots\ldots (81).$$

Here $p_1\left(u_1 - u\right)$ is the volume of the first gas transferred in unit of time across unit of area of the plane reduced to pressure unity, and at the actual temperature; and $p_2\left(u - u_2\right)$ is the equal volume of the second gas transferred across the same area in the opposite direction.

The external force X has very little effect on the quiet diffusion of gases in vessels of moderate size. We may therefore leave it out in our definition of the coefficient of diffusion of two gases.

When two gases not acted on by gravity are placed in different parts of a vessel at equal pressures and temperatures, there will be mechanical equilibrium from the first, and u will always be zero. This will also be approximately true of heavy gases, provided the denser gas is placed below the lighter. Mr Graham has described in his paper on the Mobility of Gases[*], experiments which were made under these conditions. A vertical tube had its lower tenth part filled with a heavy gas, and the remaining nine-tenths with a lighter gas. After the lapse of a known time the upper tenth part of the tube was shut off, and the gas in it analyzed, so as to determine the quantity of the heavier gas which had ascended into the upper tenth of the tube during the given time.

In this case we have $u = 0 \quad\ldots\ldots\ldots\ldots\ldots\ldots\ldots (82),$

$$p_1u_1 = -\frac{p_1p_2}{\rho_1\rho_2 kA_1}\frac{1}{p}\frac{dp_1}{dx} \quad\ldots\ldots\ldots\ldots\ldots\ldots (83),$$

[*] *Philosophical Transactions*, 1863.

and by the equation of continuity,

$$\frac{dp_1}{dt} + \frac{d}{dx}(p_1u_1) = 0 \quad\dots\dots\dots\dots\dots (84),$$

whence

$$\frac{dp_1}{dt} = \frac{p_1p_2}{\rho_1\rho_2kA_1}\frac{1}{p}\frac{d^2p_1}{dx^2} \quad\dots\dots\dots\dots\dots (85);$$

or if we put $D = \dfrac{p_1p_2}{\rho_1\rho_2kA_1}\dfrac{1}{p}$,

$$\frac{dp_1}{dt} = D\frac{d^2p_1}{dx^2} \quad\dots\dots\dots\dots\dots\dots (86).$$

The solution of this equation is

$$p_1 = C_1 + C_2e^{-n^2Dt}\cos(nx+a) + \&c. \quad\dots\dots\dots\dots (87).$$

If the length of the tube is a, and if it is closed at both ends,

$$p_1 = C_1 + C_2e^{-\frac{\pi^2D}{a^2}t}\cos\frac{\pi x}{a} + C_3e^{-4\frac{\pi^2D}{a^2}t}\cos 2\frac{\pi x}{a} + \&c. \quad\dots\dots\dots (88),$$

where C_1, C_2, C_3 are to be determined by the condition that when $t=0$, $p_1=p$, from $x=0$ to $x=\frac{1}{10}a$, and $p_1=0$ from $x=\frac{1}{10}a$ to $x=a$. The general expression for the case in which the first gas originally extends from $x=0$ to $x=b$, and in which after a time t the gas from $x=0$ to $x=c$ is collected, is

$$\frac{p_1}{p} = \frac{b}{a} + \frac{2a}{\pi^2c}\left\{e^{-\frac{\pi^2D}{a^2}t}\sin\frac{\pi b}{a}\sin\frac{\pi c}{a} + \frac{1}{2^2}e^{-4\frac{\pi^2D}{a^2}t}\sin\frac{2\pi b}{a}\sin\frac{2\pi c}{a} + \&c.\right\} \quad\dots(89),$$

where $\dfrac{p_1}{p}$ is the proportion of the first gas to the whole in the portion from $x=0$ to $x=c$.

In Mr Graham's experiments, in which one-tenth of the tube was filled with the first gas, and the proportion of the first gas in the tenth of the tube at the other end ascertained after a time t, this proportion will be

$$\frac{p_1}{p} = \frac{1}{10} - \frac{20}{\pi^2}\left\{e^{-\frac{\pi^2D}{a^2}t}\sin^2\frac{\pi}{10} - e^{-2^2\frac{\pi^2D}{a^2}t}\sin^2 2\frac{\pi}{10} + e^{-3^2\frac{\pi^2D}{a^2}t}\sin^2 3\frac{\pi}{10} - \&c.\right\} \quad\dots(90).$$

We find for a series of values of $\dfrac{p_1}{p}$ taken at equal intervals of time T,

where

$$T = \frac{\log_e 10}{10\pi^2}\frac{a^2}{D}.$$

Time.	$\frac{p_1}{p}$.
0	0
T	·01193
$2T$	·02305
$3T$	·03376
$4T$	·04366
$5T$	·05267
$6T$	·06072
$8T$	·07321
$10T$	·08227
$12T$	·08845
∞	·10000

Mr Graham's experiments on carbonic acid and air, when compared with this Table, give $T = 500$ seconds nearly for a tube 0·57 metre long. Now

$$D = \frac{\log_e 10}{10\pi^2}\, \frac{a^2}{T} \quad\dots\dots\dots\dots\dots\dots\dots\dots\dots(91),$$

whence $D = ·0235$

for carbonic acid and air, in inch-grain-second measure.

Definition of the Coefficient of Diffusion.

D is the volume of gas reduced to unit of pressure which passes in unit of time through unit of area when the total pressure is uniform and equal to p, and the pressure of either gas increases or diminishes by unity in unit of distance. D may be called the coefficient of diffusion. It varies directly as the square of the absolute temperature, and inversely as the total pressure p.

The dimensions of D are evidently L^2T^{-1}, where L and T are the standards of length and time.

In considering this experiment of the interdiffusion of carbonic acid and air, we have assumed that air is a simple gas. Now it is well known that the constituents of air can be separated by mechanical means, such as passing them through a porous diaphragm, as in Mr Graham's experiments on Atmolysis.

The discussion of the interdiffusion of three or more gases leads to a much more complicated equation than that which we have found for two gases, and it is not easy to deduce the coefficients of interdiffusion of the separate gases. It is therefore to be desired that experiments should be made on the interdiffusion of every pair of the more important pure gases which do not act chemically on each other, the temperature and pressure of the mixture being noted at the time of experiment.

Mr Graham has also published in Brande's *Journal* for 1829, pt. 2, p. 74, the results of experiments on the diffusion of various gases out of a vessel through a tube into air. The coefficients of diffusion deduced from these experiments are—

Air and Hydrogen	·026216
Air and Marsh-gas	·010240
Air and Ammonia	·00962
Air and Olefiant gas	·00771
Air and Carbonic acid	·00682
Air and Sulphurous acid	·00582
Air and Chlorine	·00486

The value for carbonic acid is only one third of that deduced from the experiment with the vertical column. The inequality of composition of the mixed gas in different parts of the vessel is, however, neglected; and the diameter of the tube at the middle part, where it was bent, was probably less than that given.

Those experiments on diffusion which lasted ten hours, all give smaller values of D than those which lasted four hours, and this would also result from the mixture of the gases in the vessel being imperfect.

Interdiffusion through a small hole.

When two vessels containing different gases are connected by a small hole, the mixture of gases in each vessel will be nearly uniform except near the hole; and the inequality of the pressure of each gas will extend to a distance from the hole depending on the diameter of the hole, and nearly proportional to that diameter.

Hence in the equation

$$\rho_1 \frac{\partial u_1}{dt} + \frac{dp_1}{dx} = kA\rho_1\rho_2 (u_2 - u_1) + X\rho \dots\dots\dots(92)$$

the term $\frac{dp_1}{dx}$ will vary inversely as the diameter of the hole, while u_1 and u_2 will not vary considerably with the diameter.

Hence when the hole is very small the right-hand side of the equation may be neglected, and the flow of either gas through the hole will be independent of the flow of the other gas, as the term $kA\rho_1\rho_2(u_2 - u_1)$ becomes comparatively insignificant.

One gas therefore will escape through a very fine hole into another nearly as fast as into a vacuum; and if the pressures are equal on both sides, the volumes diffused will be as the square roots of the specific gravities inversely, which is the law of diffusion of gases established by Graham*.

Variation of the invisible agitation (β).

By putting for Q in equation (75)

$$Q = \frac{M}{2}\{(u_1 + \xi_1)^2 + (v_1 + \eta_1)^2 + (w_1 + \zeta_1)^2 + (\beta - 1)(\xi_1^2 + \eta_1^2 + \zeta_1^2)\}\dots\dots(93),$$

and eliminating by means of equations (76) and (52), we find

$$\begin{aligned}
&\tfrac{1}{2}\rho_1 \frac{\partial}{\partial t} \beta_1 (\xi_1^2 + \eta_1^2 + \zeta_1^2) + \rho_1\xi_1^2 \frac{du_1}{dx} + \rho_1\eta_1^2 \frac{dv_1}{dy} + \rho_1\zeta_1^2 \frac{dw_1}{dz} + \rho_1\eta_1\zeta_1 \left(\frac{dv_1}{dz} + \frac{dw_1}{dy}\right)\\
&+ \rho_1\zeta_1\xi_1 \left(\frac{dw_1}{dx} + \frac{du_1}{dz}\right) + \rho_1\xi_1\eta_1 \left(\frac{du_1}{dy} + \frac{dv_1}{dx}\right) + \beta_1 \left\{\frac{d}{dx}(\rho_1\xi_1^3 + \rho_1\xi_1\eta_1^2 + \rho_1\xi_1\zeta_1^2)\right.\\
&\left. + \frac{d}{dy}(\rho_1\eta_1\xi_1^2 + \rho_1\eta_1^3 + \rho_1\eta_1\zeta_1^2) + \frac{d}{dz}(\rho_1\zeta_1\xi_1^2 + \rho_1\zeta_1\eta_1^2 + \rho_1\zeta_1^3)\right\}\\
&= \frac{k\rho_1\rho_2 A_1}{M_1 + M_2} [M_2\{(u_2 - u_1)^2 + (v_2 - v_1)^2 + (w_2 - w_1)^2\}\\
&\quad + M_2(\xi_2^2 + \eta_2^2 + \zeta_2^2) - M_1(\xi_1^2 + \eta_1^2 + \zeta_1^2)]
\end{aligned}\quad \dots(94).$$

In this equation the first term represents the variation of invisible agitation or heat; the second, third, and fourth represent the cooling by expansion; the

---

* *Trans. Royal Society of Edinburgh*, Vol. XII. p. 222.

fifth, sixth, and seventh the heating effect of fluid friction or viscosity; and the last the loss of heat by conduction. The quantities on the other side of the equation represent the thermal effects of diffusion, and the communication of heat from one gas to the other.

The equation may be simplified in various cases, which we shall take in order.

1st. *Equilibrium of Temperature between two Gases.—Law of Equivalent Volumes.*

We shall suppose that there is no motion of translation, and no transfer of heat by conduction through either gas. The equation (94) is then reduced to the following form,

$$\tfrac{1}{2}\rho_1 \frac{\partial}{\partial t} \beta_1 \left(\xi_1^2 + \eta_1^2 + \zeta_1^2\right) = \frac{k\rho_1\rho_2 A_1}{M_1 + M_2} \left\{ M_2\left(\xi_2^2 + \eta_2^2 + \zeta_2^2\right) - M_1\left(\xi_1^2 + \eta_1^2 + \zeta_1^2\right)\right\} \ \dots(95).$$

If we put

$$\frac{M_1}{M_1 + M_2}\left(\xi_1^2 + \eta_1^2 + \zeta_1^2\right) = Q_1, \text{ and } \frac{M_2}{M_1 + M_2}\left(\xi_2^2 + \eta_2^2 + \zeta_2^2\right) = Q_2 \dots (96),$$

we find

$$\frac{\partial}{\partial t}\left(Q_2 - Q_1\right) = -\frac{2kA_1}{M_1 + M_2}\left(M_2\rho_2\beta_1 + M_1\rho_1\beta_2\right)\left(Q_2 - Q_1\right) \dots (97),$$

or

$$Q_2 - Q_1 = Ce^{-nt}, \text{ where } n = \frac{2kA_1}{M_1 + M_2}\left(M_2\rho_2\beta_2 + M_1\rho_1\beta_1\right)\frac{1}{\beta_1\beta_2} \dots (98).$$

If, therefore, the gases are in contact and undisturbed, Q_1 and Q_2 will rapidly become equal. Now the state into which two bodies come by exchange of invisible agitation is called equilibrium of heat or equality of temperature. Hence when two gases are at the same temperature,

$$Q_1 = Q_2 \dots(99),$$

or

$$1 = \frac{Q_1}{Q_2} = \frac{M_1\left(\xi_1^2 + \eta_1^2 + \zeta_1^2\right)}{M_2\left(\xi_2^2 + \eta_2^2 + \zeta_2^2\right)}$$

$$= \frac{M_1 \dfrac{p_1}{\rho_1}}{M_2 \dfrac{p_2}{\rho_2}}.$$

Hence if the pressures as well as the temperatures be the same in two gases,

$$\frac{M_1}{\rho_1} = \frac{M_2}{\rho_2} \quad\text{......................................(100),}$$

or the masses of the individual molecules are proportional to the density of the gas.

This result, by which the relative masses of the molecules can be deduced from the relative densities of the gases, was first arrived at by Gay-Lussac from chemical considerations. It is here shewn to be a necessary result of the Dynamical Theory of Gases; and it is so, whatever theory we adopt as to the nature of the action between the individual molecules, as may be seen by equation (34), which is deduced from perfectly general assumptions as to the nature of the law of force.

We may therefore henceforth put $\frac{s_1}{s_2}$ for $\frac{M_1}{M_2}$, where s_1, s_2 are the specific gravities of the gases referred to a standard gas.

If we use θ to denote the temperature reckoned from absolute zero of a gas thermometer, M_0 the mass of a molecule of hydrogen, V_0^2 its mean square of velocity at temperature unity, s the specific gravity of any other gas referred to hydrogen, then the mass of a molecule of the other gas is

$$M = M_0 s \quad\text{...................................(101).}$$

Its mean square of velocity, $$V^2 = \frac{1}{s}\, V_0^2 \theta \quad\text{...............................(102).}$$

Pressure of the gas, $$p = \tfrac{1}{3}\, \frac{\rho}{s}\, \theta V_0^2 \quad\text{.............................. (103).}$$

We may next determine the amount of cooling by expansion.

Cooling by Expansion.

Let the expansion be equal in all directions, then

$$\frac{du}{dx} = \frac{dv}{dy} = \frac{dw}{dz} = -\frac{1}{3\rho}\, \frac{\partial \rho}{\partial t} \quad\text{......................... (104),}$$

and $\frac{du}{dy}$ and all terms of unsymmetrical form will be zero.

If the mass of gas is of the same temperature throughout there will be no conduction of heat, and the equation (94) will become

$$\tfrac{1}{2}\rho\beta\frac{\partial \overline{V^2}}{\partial t} - \tfrac{1}{3}\overline{V^2}\frac{\partial \rho}{\partial t} = 0 \quad \dots\dots\dots\dots\dots\dots (105),$$

or

$$2\frac{\partial \rho}{\rho} = 3\beta\frac{\partial \overline{V^2}}{\overline{V^2}} = 3\beta\frac{\partial \theta}{\theta} \quad \dots\dots\dots\dots\dots\dots (106),$$

or

$$\frac{\partial \theta}{\theta} = \frac{2}{3\beta}\frac{\partial \rho}{\rho} \quad \dots\dots\dots\dots\dots\dots (107),$$

which gives the relation between the density and the temperature in a gas expanding without exchange of heat with other bodies. We also find

$$\frac{\partial p}{p} = \frac{\partial \rho}{\rho} + \frac{\partial \theta}{\theta}$$

$$= \frac{2+3\beta}{3\beta}\frac{\partial \rho}{\rho}\dots\dots\dots\dots\dots\dots(108),$$

which gives the relation between the pressure and the density.

Specific Heat of Unit of Mass at Constant Volume.

The total energy of agitation of unit of mass is $\tfrac{1}{2}\beta V^2 = \tfrac{1}{2}E$, or

$$E = \frac{3\beta}{2}\frac{p}{\rho} \quad \dots\dots\dots\dots\dots\dots (109).$$

If, now, additional energy in the form of heat be communicated to it without changing its density,

$$\partial E = \frac{3\beta}{2}\frac{\partial p}{\rho} = \frac{3\beta}{2}\frac{p}{\rho}\frac{\partial \theta}{\theta}\dots\dots\dots\dots\dots\dots(110).$$

Hence the specific heat of unit of mass of constant volume is in dynamical measure

$$\frac{\partial E}{\partial \theta} = \frac{3\beta}{2}\frac{p}{\rho\theta} \quad \dots\dots\dots\dots\dots\dots (111).$$

Specific Heat of Unit of Mass at Constant Pressure.

By the addition of the heat ∂E the temperature was raised $\partial \theta$ and the pressure ∂p. Now, let the gas expand without communication of heat till the pressure sinks to its former value, and let the final temperature be $\theta + \partial'\theta$. The temperature will thus sink by a quantity $\partial \theta - \partial'\theta$, such that

$$\frac{\partial \theta - \partial'\theta}{\theta} = \frac{2}{2+3\beta} \frac{\partial p}{p} = \frac{2}{2+3\beta} \frac{\partial \theta}{\theta},$$

whence

$$\frac{\partial'\theta}{\theta} = \frac{3\beta}{2+3\beta} \frac{\partial \theta}{\theta} \quad\dots\dots\dots\dots\dots\dots(112);$$

and the specific heat of unit of mass at constant pressure is

$$\frac{\partial E}{\partial'\theta} = \frac{2+3\beta}{2} \frac{p}{\rho\theta} \quad\dots\dots\dots\dots\dots\dots(113).$$

The ratio of the specific heat at constant pressure to that of constant volume is known in several cases from experiment. We shall denote this ratio by

$$\gamma = \frac{2+3\beta}{3\beta} \quad\dots\dots\dots\dots\dots\dots(114),$$

whence

$$\beta = \tfrac{2}{3} \frac{1}{\gamma - 1} \quad\dots\dots\dots\dots\dots\dots(115).$$

The specific heat of unit of volume in ordinary measure is at constant volume

$$\frac{1}{\gamma - 1} \frac{p}{J\theta} \quad\dots\dots\dots\dots\dots\dots(116),$$

and at constant pressure

$$\frac{\gamma}{\gamma - 1} \frac{p}{J\theta} \quad\dots\dots\dots\dots\dots\dots(117),$$

where J is the mechanical equivalent of unit of heat.

From these expressions Dr Rankine* has calculated the specific heat of air, and has found the result to agree with the value afterwards determined experimentally by M. Regnault†.

---

* *Transactions of the Royal Society of Edinburgh*, Vol. xx. (1850).
† *Comptes Rendus*, 1853.

Thermal Effects of Diffusion.

If two gases are diffusing into one another, then, omitting the terms relating to heat generated by friction and to conduction of heat, the equation (94) gives

$$
\left.
\begin{aligned}
&\tfrac{1}{2}\rho_1 \frac{\partial}{\partial t}\, \beta_1\left(\xi_1^2+\eta_1^2+\zeta_1^2\right) + \tfrac{1}{2}\rho_2 \frac{\partial}{\partial t}\, \beta_2\left(\xi_2^2+\eta_2^2+\zeta_2^2\right) + p_1\left(\frac{du_1}{dx}+\frac{dv_1}{dy}+\frac{dw_1}{dz}\right) \\
&+ p_2\left(\frac{du_2}{dx}+\frac{dv_2}{dy}+\frac{dw_2}{dz}\right) = k\rho_1\rho_2 A_1\{(u_1-u_2)^2+(v_1-v_2)^2+(w_1-w_2)^2\}
\end{aligned}
\right\} \;\dots(118).
$$

By comparison with equations (78), and (79), the right-hand side of this equation becomes

$$
X\left(\rho_1 u_1+\rho_2 u_2\right) + Y\left(\rho_1 v_1+\rho_2 v_2\right) + Z\left(\rho_1 w_1+\rho_2 w_2\right)
$$

$$
-\left(\frac{dp_1}{dx}u_1+\frac{dp_1}{dy}v_1+\frac{dp_1}{dz}w_1\right)-\left(\frac{dp_2}{dx}u_2+\frac{dp_2}{dy}v_2+\frac{dp_2}{dz}w_2\right)
$$

$$
-\tfrac{1}{2}\rho_1\frac{\partial}{\partial t}\left(u_1^2+v_1^2+w_1^2\right)-\tfrac{1}{2}\rho_2\frac{\partial}{\partial t}\left(u_2^2+v_2^2+w_2^2\right).
$$

The equation (118) may now be written

$$
\left.
\begin{aligned}
&\tfrac{1}{2}\rho_1 \frac{\partial}{\partial t}\{u_1^2+v_1^2+w_1^2+\beta_1(\xi_1^2+\eta_1^2+\zeta_1^2)\} + \tfrac{1}{2}\rho_2 \frac{\partial}{\partial t}\{u_2^2+v_2^2+w_2^2+\beta_2(\xi_2^2+\eta_2^2+\zeta_2^2)\} \\
&= X(\rho_1 u_1+\rho_2 u_2) + Y(\rho_1 v_1+\rho_2 v_2) + Z(\rho_1 w_1+\rho_2 w_2) - \left(\frac{d.pu}{dx}+\frac{d.pv}{dy}+\frac{d.pw}{dz}\right)
\end{aligned}
\right\} \;\dots(119).
$$

The whole increase of energy is therefore that due to the action of the external forces *minus* the cooling due to the expansion of the mixed gases. If the diffusion takes place without alteration of the volume of the mixture, the heat due to the mutual action of the gases in diffusion will be exactly neutralized by the cooling of each gas as it expands in passing from places where it is dense to places where it is rare.

Determination of the Inequality of Pressure in different directions due to the Motion of the Medium.

Let us put $\qquad \rho_1\xi_1^2 = p_1 + q_1$ and $\rho_2\xi_2^2 = p_2 + q_2$ .... (120).

Then by equation (52),

$$\left.\begin{aligned}\frac{\delta q_1}{\delta t} &= -3k_1A_2\rho_1q_1 - \frac{k}{M_1+M_2}(2M_1A_1 + 3M_2A_2)\rho_2q_1 - k(3A_2 - 2A_1)\frac{M_1}{M_1+M_2}\,\rho_1q_2 \\ &\quad - k\rho_1\rho_2\frac{M_2}{M_1+M_2}(A_2 - \tfrac{2}{3}A_1)\left(\overline{2u_1 - u_2}^2 - \overline{v_1 - v_2}^2 - \overline{w_1 - w_2}^2\right)\end{aligned}\right\}...(121),$$

the last term depending on diffusion; and if we omit in equation (75) terms of three dimensions in ξ, η, ζ, which relate to conduction of heat, and neglect quantities of the form $\xi\eta\rho$ and $\rho\xi^2 - p$, when not multiplied by the large coefficients k, k_1, and k_2, we get

$$\frac{\partial q}{\partial t} + 2p\frac{du}{dx} - \tfrac{2}{3}p\left(\frac{du}{dx} + \frac{dv}{dy} + \frac{dw}{dz}\right) = \frac{\delta q}{\delta t} \qquad (122).$$

If the motion is not subject to any very rapid changes, as in all cases except that of the propagation of sound, we may neglect $\frac{\partial q}{\partial t}$. In a single system of molecules

$$\frac{\delta q}{\delta t} = -3kA_2\rho q \qquad (123),$$

whence $\qquad q = -\frac{2p}{3kA_2\rho}\left\{\frac{du}{dx} - \tfrac{1}{3}\left(\frac{du}{dx} + \frac{dv}{dy} + \frac{dw}{dz}\right)\right\}$ ....(124).

If we make $\qquad \tfrac{2}{3}\frac{1}{kA_2}\frac{p}{\rho} = \mu$ .... (125),

μ will be the coefficient of viscosity, and we shall have by equation (120),

$$\left.\begin{aligned}\rho\xi^2 &= p - 2\mu\left\{\frac{du}{dx} - \tfrac{1}{3}\left(\frac{du}{dx} + \frac{dv}{dy} + \frac{dw}{dz}\right)\right\} \\ \rho\eta^2 &= p - 2\mu\left\{\frac{dv}{dy} - \tfrac{1}{3}\left(\frac{du}{dx} + \frac{dv}{dy} + \frac{dw}{dz}\right)\right\} \\ \rho\zeta^2 &= p - 2\mu\left\{\frac{dw}{dz} - \tfrac{1}{3}\left(\frac{du}{dx} + \frac{dv}{dy} + \frac{dw}{dz}\right)\right\}\end{aligned}\right\} \qquad (126);$$

and by transformation of co-ordinates we obtain

$$\left. \begin{aligned} \rho \eta \zeta &= -\mu \left(\frac{dv}{dz} + \frac{dw}{dy} \right) \\ \rho \zeta \xi &= -\mu \left(\frac{dw}{dx} + \frac{du}{dz} \right) \\ \rho \xi \eta &= -\mu \left(\frac{du}{dy} + \frac{dv}{dx} \right) \end{aligned} \right\} \quad \dots\dots\dots\dots\dots\dots (127).$$

These are the values of the normal and tangential stresses in a simple gas when the variation of motion is not very rapid, and when μ, the coefficient of viscosity, is so small that its square may be neglected.

Equations of Motion corrected for Viscosity.

Substituting these values in the equation of motion (76), we find

$$\rho \frac{\partial u}{\partial t} + \frac{dp}{dx} - \mu \left\{ \frac{d^2u}{dx^2} + \frac{d^2u}{dy^2} + \frac{d^2u}{dz^2} \right\} - \tfrac{1}{3}\mu \frac{d}{dx} \left(\frac{du}{dx} + \frac{dv}{dy} + \frac{dw}{dz} \right) = X\rho \dots (128),$$

with two other equations which may be written down with symmetry. The form of these equations is identical with that of those deduced by Poisson[*] from the theory of elasticity, by supposing the strain to be continually relaxed at a rate proportional to its amount. The ratio of the third and fourth terms agrees with that given by Professor Stokes[†].

If we suppose the inequality of pressure which we have denoted by q to exist in the medium at any instant, and not to be maintained by the motion of the medium, we find, from equation (123),

$$q_1 = Ce^{-3kA_2\rho t} \quad \dots\dots\dots\dots\dots\dots\dots\dots\dots (129)$$

$$= Ce^{-\frac{t}{T}} \text{ if } T = \frac{1}{3kA_2\rho} = \frac{\mu}{p} \dots\dots\dots\dots (130);$$

the stress q is therefore relaxed at a rate proportional to itself, so that

$$\frac{\delta q}{q} = \frac{\delta t}{T} \dots\dots\dots\dots\dots\dots\dots\dots\dots (131).$$

We may call T the modulus of the time of relaxation.

[*] *Journal de l'École Polytechnique*, 1829, Tom. XIII. Cah. XX. p. 139.

[†] "On the Friction of Fluids in Motion and the Equilibrium and Motion of Elastic Solids," *Cambridge Phil. Trans.* Vol. VIII. (1845), p. 297, equation (2).

If we next make $k = 3$, so that the stress q does not become relaxed, the medium will be an elastic solid, and the equation

$$\frac{\partial (\rho \xi^2 - p)}{\partial t} + 2p \frac{du}{dx} - \tfrac{2}{3}p \left(\frac{du}{dx} + \frac{dv}{dy} + \frac{dw}{dz}\right) = 0 \ldots\ldots\ldots(132)$$

may be written $\dfrac{\partial}{\partial t} \left\{ (p_{xx} - p) + 2p \dfrac{da}{dx} - \tfrac{2}{3}p \left(\dfrac{da}{dx} + \dfrac{d\beta}{dy} + \dfrac{d\gamma}{dz}\right) \right\} = 0 \ldots\ldots\ldots(133),$

where a, β, γ are the displacements of an element of the medium, and p_{xx} is the normal pressure in the direction of x. If we suppose the initial value of this quantity zero, and p_{xx} originally equal to p, then, after a small displacement,

$$p_{xx} = p - p \left(\frac{da}{dx} + \frac{d\beta}{dy} + \frac{d\gamma}{dz}\right) - 2p \frac{da}{dx} \ldots\ldots\ldots\ldots\ldots(134);$$

and by transformation of co-ordinates the tangential pressure

$$p_{xy} = -p \left(\frac{da}{dy} + \frac{d\beta}{dx}\right) \ldots\ldots\ldots\ldots\ldots\ldots(135).$$

The medium has now the mechanical properties of an elastic solid, the rigidity of which is p, while the cubical elasticity is $\tfrac{5}{3}p$*.

The same result and the same ratio of the elasticities would be obtained if we supposed the molecules to be at rest, and to act on one another with forces depending on the distance, as in the statical molecular theory of elasticity. The coincidence of the properties of a medium in which the molecules are held in equilibrium by attractions and repulsions, and those of a medium in which the molecules move in straight lines without acting on each other at all, deserve notice from those who speculate on theories of physics.

The fluidity of our medium is therefore due to the mutual action of the molecules, causing them to be deflected from their paths.

$$\left.\begin{array}{l}\text{The coefficient of instantaneous rigidity of a gas is therefore } p \\ \text{The modulus of the time of relaxation is } T \\ \text{The coefficient of viscosity is } \mu = pT \end{array}\right\} \ldots (136).$$

Now p varies as the density and temperature conjointly, while T varies inversely as the density.

Hence μ varies as the absolute temperature, and is independent of the density.

* *Camb. Phil. Trans.* Vol. VIII. (1845), p. 311, equation (29).

This result is confirmed by the experiments of Mr Graham on the Transpiration of Gases*, and by my own experiments on the Viscosity or Internal Friction of Air and other Gases†.

The result that the viscosity is independent of the density, follows from the Dynamical Theory of Gases, whatever be the law of force between the molecules. It was deduced by myself‡ from the hypothesis of hard elastic molecules, and M. O. E. Meyer§ has given a more complete investigation on the same hypothesis.

The experimental result, that the viscosity is proportional to the absolute temperature, requires us to abandon this hypothesis, which would make it vary as the square root of the absolute temperature, and to adopt the hypothesis of a repulsive force inversely as the fifth power of the distance between the molecules, which is the only law of force which gives the observed result.

Using the foot, the grain, and the second as units, my experiments give for the temperature of 62° Fahrenheit, and in dry air,

$$\mu = 0{\cdot}0936.$$

If the pressure is 30 inches of mercury, we find, using the same units,

$$p = 477360000.$$

Since $pT = \mu$, we find that the modulus of the time of relaxation of rigidity in air of this pressure and temperature is

$$\frac{1}{5099100000}$$ of a second.

This time is exceedingly small, even when compared with the period of vibration of the most acute audible sounds; so that even in the theory of sound we may consider the motion as steady during this very short time, and use the equations we have already found, as has been done by Professor Stokes‖.

---

* *Philosophical Transactions*, 1846 and 1849.

† *Proceedings of the Royal Society*, February 8, 1866; *Philosophical Transactions*, 1866, p. 249.

‡ *Philosophical Magazine*, January 1860. [Vol. I. xx.]

§ Poggendorff's *Annalen*, 1865.

‖ "On the effect of the Internal Friction of Fluids on the motion of Pendulums," *Cambridge Transactions*, Vol. IX. (1850), art. 79.

Viscosity of a Mixture of Gases.

In a complete mixture of gases, in which there is no diffusion going on, the velocity at any point is the same for all the gases.

Putting

$$\tfrac{2}{3}\left(2\frac{du}{dx}-\frac{dv}{dy}-\frac{dw}{dz}\right)= U \quad\ldots\ldots\ldots\ldots\ldots(137),$$

equation (122) becomes

$$p_1 U = -3k_1 A_2 \rho_1 q_1 - \frac{k}{M_1+M_2}(2M_1 A_1 + 3M_2 A_2)\rho_2 q_1 - k(3A_2 - 2A_1)\frac{M_2}{M_1+M_2}\rho_2 q_x \ldots(138).$$

Similarly,

$$p_2 U = -3k_2 A_2 \rho_2 q_2 - \frac{k}{M_1+M_2}(2M_2 A_1 + 3M_1 A_2)\rho_1 q_2 - k(3A_2 - 2A_1)\frac{M_1}{M_1+M_2}\rho_1 q_{1r} \ldots(139).$$

Since $p = p_1 + p_2$ and $q = q_1 + q_2$, where p and q refer to the mixture, we shall have

$$\mu U = -q = -(q_1 + q_2),$$

where μ is the coefficient of viscosity of the mixture.

If we put s_1 and s_2 for the specific gravities of the two gases, referred to a standard gas, in which the values of p and ρ at temperature θ_0 and p_0 and ρ_0,

$$\mu = \frac{p_0\theta}{\rho_0\theta_0}\cdot\frac{Ep_1^2+Fp_1 p_2 + Gp_2^2}{3A_2 k_1 s_1 Ep_1^2 + Hp_1 p_2 + 3A_1 k_2 s_2 Gp_2^2}\quad\ldots\ldots\ldots\ldots(140),$$

where μ is the coefficient of viscosity of the mixture, and

$$\left.\begin{aligned}
E &= \frac{ks_1}{s_1+s_2}(2s_2 A_1 + 3s_1 A_2)\\[4pt]
F &= 3A_2(k_2 s_1 + k_1 s_2) - (3A_2 - 2A_1)k\frac{2s_1 s_2}{s_1+s_2}\\[4pt]
G &= \frac{ks_2}{s_1+s_2}(2s_1 A_1 + 3s_2 A_2)\\[4pt]
H &= 3A_2 s_1 s_2 (3k_1 k_2 A_2 + 2k^2 A_1)
\end{aligned}\right\}\quad\ldots\ldots\ldots\ldots(141).$$

This expression is reduced to μ_1 when $p_2 = 0$, and to μ_2 when $p_1 = 0$. For other values of p_1 and p_2 we require to know the value of k, the coefficient of mutual interference of the molecules of the two gases. This might be deduced from the observed values of μ for mixtures, but a better method is by making experiments on the interdiffusion of the two gases. The experiments of Graham on the transpiration of gases, combined with my experiments on the viscosity of air, give as values of k_1 for air, hydrogen, and carbonic acid,

$$\text{Air} \dots\dots\dots\dots k_1 = \quad 4\cdot81 \times 10^{10},$$
$$\text{Hydrogen} \dots\dots k_1 = 142\cdot8 \quad \times 10^{10},$$
$$\text{Carbonic acid} \dots k_1 = \quad 3\cdot9 \quad \times 10^{10}.$$

The experiments of Graham in 1863, referred to at page 58, on the interdiffusion of air and carbonic acid, give the coefficient of mutual interference of these gases,

$$\text{Air and carbonic acid} \dots\dots k = 5\cdot2 \times 10^{10};$$

and by taking this as the absolute value of k, and assuming that the ratios of the coefficients of interdiffusion given at page 76 are correct, we find

$$\text{Air and hydrogen} \dots\dots k = 29\cdot8 \times 10^{10}.$$

These numbers are to be regarded as doubtful, as we have supposed air to be a simple gas in our calculations, and we do not know the value of k between oxygen and nitrogen. It is also doubtful whether our method of calculation applies to experiments such as the earlier observations of Mr Graham.

I have also examined the transpiration-times determined by Graham for mixtures of hydrogen and carbonic acid, and hydrogen and air, assuming a value of k roughly, to satisfy the experimental results about the middle of the scale. It will be seen that the calculated numbers for hydrogen and carbonic acid exhibit the peculiarity observed in the experiments, that a small addition of hydrogen *increases* the transpiration-time of carbonic acid, and that in both series the times of mixtures depend more on the slower than on the quicker gas.

The assumed values of k in these calculations were—

$$\text{For hydrogen and carbonic acid } k = 12\cdot5 \times 10^{10},$$
$$\text{For hydrogen and air} \dots\dots\dots k = 18\cdot8 \times 10^{10};$$

and the results of observation and calculation are, for the times of transpiration of mixtures of—

Hydrogen and Carbonic acid		Observed	Calculated	Hydrogen and Air		Observed	Calculated
100	0	·4321	·4375	100	0	·4434	·4375
97·5	2·5	·4714	·4750	95	5	·5282	·5300
95	5	·5157	·5089	90	10	·5880	·6028
90	10	·5722	·5678	75	25	·7488	·7438
75	25	·6786	·6822	50	50	·8179	·8488
50	50	·7339	·7652	25	75	·8790	·8946
25	75	·7535	·7468	10	90	·8880	·8983
10	90	·7521	·7361	5	95	·8960	·8996
0	100	·7470	·7272	0	100	·9000	·9010

The numbers given are the ratios of the transpiration-times of mixtures to that of oxygen as determined by Mr Graham, compared with those given by the equation (140) deduced from our theory.

Conduction of Heat in a Single Medium (γ).

The rate of conduction depends on the value of the quantity

$$\tfrac{1}{2}\beta\rho\,(\overline{\xi^3}+\overline{\xi\eta^2}+\overline{\xi\zeta^2}),$$

where $\overline{\xi^3}$, $\overline{\xi\eta^2}$, and $\overline{\xi\zeta^2}$ denote the mean values of those functions of ξ, η, ζ for all the molecules in a given element of volume.

As the expressions for the variations of this quantity are somewhat complicated in a mixture of media, and as the experimental investigation of the conduction of heat in gases is attended with great difficulty, I shall confine myself here to the discussion of a single medium.

Putting

$$Q = M\,(u+\xi)\,\{u^2+v^2+w^2+2u\xi+2v\eta+2w\zeta+\beta\,(\xi^2+\eta^2+\zeta^2)\}\ldots\ldots\ldots(142),$$

and neglecting terms of the forms $\xi\eta$ and ξ^3 and $\xi\eta^2$ when not multiplied by the large coefficient k_1, we find by equations (75), (77), and (54),

$$\left.\begin{aligned}
\rho\,\frac{\partial}{\partial}\,\beta\,(\overline{\xi^3}+\overline{\xi\eta^2}+\overline{\xi\zeta^2})+\beta\,\frac{d}{dx}\cdot\rho\,(\overline{\xi^4}+\overline{\xi^2\eta^2}+\overline{\xi^2\zeta^2})-\beta\,(\overline{\xi^2}+\overline{\eta^2}+\overline{\zeta^2})\,\frac{dp}{dx}\\
-2\beta\overline{\xi^2}\,\frac{dp}{dx}=-3k_1\rho^2A_2\beta\,\{\overline{\xi^3}+\overline{\xi\eta^2}+\overline{\xi\zeta^2}\}
\end{aligned}\right\}\ \ldots\ldots\ldots\ (143).$$

The first term of this equation may be neglected, as the rate of conduction will rapidly establish itself. The second term contains quantities of four dimensions in ξ, η, ζ, whose values will depend on the distribution of velocity among the molecules. If the distribution of velocity is that which we have proved to exist when the system has no external force acting on it and has arrived at its final state, we shall have by equations (29), (31), (32),

$$\overline{\xi^4} = 3\overline{\xi^2} \cdot \overline{\xi^2} = 3\frac{p^2}{\rho^2} \quad\text{............(144)},$$

$$\overline{\xi^2\eta^2} = \overline{\xi^2} \cdot \overline{\eta^2} = \frac{p^2}{\rho^2} \quad\text{............(145)},$$

$$\overline{\xi^2\zeta^2} = \overline{\xi^2} \cdot \overline{\zeta^2} = \frac{p^2}{\rho^2} \quad\text{............(146)};$$

and the equation of conduction may be written

$$5\beta\,\frac{p^2}{\rho\theta}\frac{d\theta}{dx} = -3k_1\rho^2A_2\beta\,\{\xi^3 + \xi\eta^2 + \xi\zeta^2\} \quad\text{............(147)}.$$

[Addition made December 17, 1866.]

[*Final Equilibrium of Temperature.*]

[The left-hand side of equation (147), as sent to the Royal Society, contained a term $2(\beta-1)\frac{p}{\rho}\frac{dp}{dx}$, the result of which was to indicate that a column of air, when left to itself, would assume a temperature varying with the height, and greater above than below. The mistake arose from an error * in equation (143). Equation (147), as now corrected, shews that the flow of heat depends on the variation of temperature only, and not on the direction of the variation of pressure. A vertical column would therefore, when in thermal equilibrium, have the same temperature throughout.

When I first attempted this investigation I overlooked the fact that $\overline{\xi^4}$ is not the same as $\overline{\xi^2} \cdot \overline{\xi^2}$, and so obtained as a result that the temperature diminishes as the height increases at a greater rate than it does by expansion when air is carried up in mass. This leads at once to a condition of instability,

* The last term on the left-hand side was not multiplied by β.

which is inconsistent with the second law of thermodynamics. I wrote to Professor Sir W. Thomson about this result, and the difficulty I had met with, but presently discovered *one* of my mistakes, and arrived at the conclusion that the temperature would increase with the height. This does not lead to mechanical instability, or to any self-acting currents of air, and I was in some degree satisfied with it. But it is equally inconsistent with the second law of thermodynamics. In fact, if the temperature of any substance, when in thermic equilibrium, is a function of the height, that of any other substance must be the same function of the height. For if not, let equal columns of the two substances be enclosed in cylinders impermeable to heat, and put in thermal communication at the bottom. If, when in thermal equilibrium, the tops of the two columns are at different temperatures, an engine might be worked by taking heat from the hotter and giving it up to the cooler, and the refuse heat would circulate round the system till it was all converted into mechanical energy, which is in contradiction to the second law of thermodynamics.

The result as now given is, that temperature in gases, when in thermal equilibrium, is independent of height, and it follows from what has been said that temperature is independent of height in all other substances.

If we accept this law of temperature as the actual one, and examine our assumptions, we shall find that unless $\bar{\xi}^4 = 3\bar{\xi}^2 \cdot \bar{\xi}^2$, we should have obtained a different result. Now this equation is derived from the law of distribution of velocities to which we were led by independent considerations. We may therefore regard this law of temperature, if true, as in some measure a confirmation of the law of distribution of velocities.]

Coefficient of Conductivity.

If C is the coefficient of conductivity of the gas for heat, then the quantity of heat which passes through unit of area in unit of time measured as mechanical energy, is

$$C\frac{d\theta}{dx} = \frac{5}{6}\frac{\beta}{k_1 A_2}\frac{p^2}{\rho^2\theta}\frac{d\theta}{dx} \quad\dots\dots\dots\dots\dots\dots (148).$$

by equation (147).

Substituting for β its value in terms of γ by equation (115), and for k_1 its value in terms of μ by equation (125), and calling p_0, ρ_0, and θ_0 the simultaneous pressure, density, and temperature of the standard gas, and s the specific gravity of the gas in question, we find

$$C = \frac{5}{3\,(\gamma-1)}\;\frac{p_0}{\rho_0\theta_0}\;\frac{\mu}{s} \quad\ldots\ldots\ldots\ldots\ldots\ldots(149).$$

For air we have $\gamma = 1\cdot 409$, and at the temperature of melting ice, or $274^{\circ}\cdot 6$ C. above absolute zero, $\sqrt{\dfrac{p}{\rho}} = 918\cdot 6$ feet per second, and at $16^{\circ}\cdot 6$ C., $\mu = 0\cdot 0936$ in foot-grain-second measure. Hence for air at $16^{\circ}\cdot 6$ C. the conductivity for heat is

$$C = 1172 \quad\ldots\ldots\ldots\ldots\ldots\ldots\ldots\ldots\ldots (150).$$

That is to say, a horizontal stratum of air one foot thick, of which the upper surface is kept at 17° C., and the lower at 16° C., would in one second transmit through every square foot of horizontal surface a quantity of heat the mechanical energy of which is equal to that of 2344 grains moving at the rate of one foot per second.

Principal Forbes[*] has deduced from his experiments on the conduction of heat in bars, that a plate of wrought iron one foot thick, with its opposite surfaces kept 1° C. different in temperature, would, when the mean temperature is 25° C., transmit in one minute through every square foot of surface as much heat as would raise one cubic foot of water $0^{\circ}\cdot 0127$ C.

Now the dynamical equivalent in foot-grain-second measure of the heat required to raise a cubic foot of water 1° C. is $1\cdot 9157 \times 10^{10}$.

It appears from this that iron at 25° C. conducts heat 3525 times better than air at $16^{\circ}\cdot 6$ C.

M. Clausius, from a different form of the theory, and from a different value of μ, found that lead should conduct heat 1400 times better than air. Now iron is twice as good a conductor of heat as lead, so that this estimate is not far different from that of M. Clausius in actual value.

In reducing the value of the conductivity from one kind of measure to another, we must remember that its dimensions are MLT^{-3}, when expressed in absolute dynamical measure.

---

[*] "Experimental Inquiry into the Laws of the Conduction of Heat in Bars," *Edinburgh Transactions*, 1861—62.

Since all the quantities which enter into the expression for C are constant except μ, the conductivity is subject to the same laws as the viscosity, that is, it is independent of the pressure, and varies directly as the absolute temperature. The conductivity of iron diminishes as the temperature increases.

Also, since γ is nearly the same for air, oxygen, hydrogen, and carbonic oxide, the conductivity of these gases will vary as the ratio of the viscosity to the specific gravity. Oxygen, nitrogen, carbonic oxide, and air will have equal conductivity, while that of hydrogen will be about seven times as great.

The value of γ for carbonic acid is 1·27, its specific gravity is $\frac{11}{8}$ of oxygen, and its viscosity $\frac{8}{11}$ of that of oxygen. The conductivity of carbonic acid for heat is therefore about $\frac{7}{9}$ of that of oxygen or of air.

[From the *Proceedings of the Royal Society*, No. 91, 1867.]

XXIX. *On the Theory of the Maintenance of Electric Currents by Mechanical Work without the use of Permanent Magnets.*

THE machines lately brought before the Royal Society by Mr Siemens and Professor Wheatstone consist essentially of a fixed and a moveable electromagnet, the coils of which are put in connexion by means of a commutator.

The electromagnets in the actual machines have cores of soft iron, which greatly increase the magnetic effects due to the coils ; but, in order to simplify the expression of the theory as much as possible, I shall begin by supposing the coils to have no cores, and, to fix our ideas, we may suppose them in the form of rings, the smaller revolving within the larger on a common diameter.

The equations of the currents in two neighbouring circuits are given in my paper "On the Electromagnetic Field*," and are there numbered (4) and (5),

$$\xi = Rx + \frac{d}{dt}(Lx + My),$$

$$\eta = Sy + \frac{d}{dt}(Mx + Ny),$$

where x and y are the currents, ξ and η the electromotive forces, and R and S the resistances in the two circuits respectively. L and N are the coefficients of self-induction of the two circuits, that is, their potentials on themselves when the current is unity, and M is their coefficient of mutual induction, which depends on their relative position. In the electromagnetic system of measurement, L, M, and N are of the nature of lines, and R and S are velocities. L may be metaphorically called the "electric inertia" of the first circuit, N that of the second, and $L + 2M + N$ that of the combined circuit.

* *Philosophical Transactions*, 1865, p. 469.

Let us first take the case of the two circuits thrown into one, and the two coils relatively at rest, so that M is constant. Then

$$(R+S)\, x + \frac{d}{dt}\, (L+2M+N)\, x = 0 \quad\ldots\ldots\ldots\ldots\ldots\ldots (1),$$

whence

$$x = x_0 e^{-\frac{R+S}{L+2M+N} t} \quad\ldots\ldots\ldots\ldots\ldots\ldots\ldots\ldots (2),$$

where x_0 is the initial value of the current. This expression shews that the current, if left to itself in a closed circuit, will gradually decay.

If we put

$$\frac{L+2M+N}{R+S} = \tau \quad\ldots\ldots\ldots\ldots\ldots\ldots\ldots\ldots,..(3),$$

then

$$x = x_0 e^{-\frac{t}{\tau}} \quad\ldots\ldots\ldots\ldots\ldots\ldots\ldots\ldots\ldots (4).$$

The value of the time τ depends on the nature of the coils. In coils of similar outward form, τ varies as the square of the linear dimension, and inversely as the resistance of unit of length of a wire whose section is the sum of the sections of the wires passing through unit of section of the coil.

In the large experimental coil used in determining the B.A. unit of resistance in 1864, τ was about ·01 second. In the coils of electromagnets τ is much greater, and when an iron core is inserted there is a still greater increase.

Let us next ascertain the effect of a sudden change of position in the secondary coil, which alters the value of M from M_1 to M_2 in a time $t_2 - t_1$, during which the current changes from x_1 to x_2. Integrating equation (1) with respect to t, we get

$$(R+S) \int_{t_1}^{t_2} x\, dt + (L+2M_2+N)\, x_2 - (L+2M_1+N)\, x_1 = 0 \ldots\ldots\ldots\ldots (5).$$

If we suppose the time so short that we may neglect the first term in comparison with the others, we find, as the effect of a *sudden* change of position,

$$(L+2M_2+N)\, x_2 = (L+2M_1+N)\, x_1 \quad\ldots\ldots\ldots\ldots\ldots (6).$$

This equation may be interpreted in the language of the dynamical theory, by saying that the electromagnetic momentum of the circuit remains the same after a sudden change of position. To ascertain the effect of the commutator, let us suppose that, at a given instant, currents x and y exist in the two coils, that the two coils are then made into one circuit, and that x' is the current in the circuit the instant after completion; then the same equation (1) gives

$$(L+2M+N) x' = (L+M) x + (N+M) y \dots\dots\dots (7).$$

The equation shews that the electromagnetic momentum of the completed circuit is equal to the sum of the electromagnetic momenta of the separate coils just before completion.

The commutator may belong to one of four different varieties, according to the order in which the contacts are made and broken. If A, B be the ends of the first coil, and C, D those of the second, and if we enclose in brackets the parts in electric connexion, we may express the four varieties as in the following Table :—

(1)	(2)	(3)	(4)
$(AC)\,(BD)$	$(AC)\,(BD)$	$(AC)\,(BD)$	$(AC)\,(BD)$
$(ABCD)$	$(ABC)\,(D)$	$(A)\,(BCD)$	$(A)\,(B)\,(C)\,(D)$
$(AD)\,(BC)$	$(ABCD)$	$(ABCD)$	$(AD)\,(BC)$
	$(AD)\,(BC)$	$(AD)\,(BC)$	

In the first kind the circuit of both coils remains uninterrupted; and when the operation is complete, two equal currents in opposite directions are combined into one. In this case, therefore, $y = -x$, and

$$(L+2M+N) x' = (L-N) x \dots\dots\dots\dots (8).$$

When there are iron cores in the coils, or metallic circuits in which independent currents can be excited, the electrical equations are much more complicated, and contain as many independent variables as there can be independent electromagnetic quantities. I shall therefore, for the sake of preserving simplicity, avoid the consideration of the iron cores, except in so far as they simply increase the values of L, M, and N.

I shall also suppose that the secondary coil is at first in a position in which $M = 0$, and that it turns into a position in which $M = -M$, which will increase the current in the ratio of $L + N$ to $L - 2M + N$.

The commutator is then reversed. This will diminish the current in a ratio depending on the kind of commutator.

The secondary coil is then moved so that M changes from M to 0, which will increase the current in the ratio of $L + 2M + N$ to $L + N$.

During the whole motion the current has also been decaying at a rate which varies according to the value of $L+2M+N$; but since M varies from $+M$ to $-M$, we may, in a rough theory, suppose that in the expression for the decay of the current $M=0$.

If the secondary coil makes a semirevolution in time T, then the ratio of the current x_1, after a semirevolution, to the current x_0 before the semirevolution, will be

$$\frac{x_1}{x_0} = e^{-\frac{T}{\tau}} r,$$

where

$$\tau = \frac{L+N}{R+S} \dots\dots\dots\dots\dots\dots\dots\dots\dots\dots\dots\dots (9),$$

and r is a ratio depending on the kind of commutator.

For the first kind,

$$r = \frac{L-N}{L-2M+N} \dots\dots\dots\dots\dots\dots\dots\dots\dots (10).$$

By increasing the speed, T may be indefinitely diminished, so that the question of the maintenance of the current depends ultimately on whether r is greater or less than unity. When r is greater than 1 or less than -1, the current may be maintained by giving a sufficient speed to the machine; it will be always in one direction in the first case, and it will be a reciprocating current in the second.

When r lies between $+1$ and -1, no current can be maintained.

Let there be p windings of wire in the first coil and q windings in the second, then we may write

$$L = lp^2, \quad M = mpq, \quad N = nq^2 \dots\dots\dots\dots\dots\dots(11),$$

where l, m, n are quantities depending on the shape and relative position of the coils. Since $L-2M+N$ must always be a positive quantity, being the coefficient of self-induction of the whole circuit, $ln - m^2$, and therefore $LN - M^2$ must be positive. When the commutator is of the first kind, the ratio r is greater than unity, provided pm is greater than qn; and when

$$\frac{p}{q} = \frac{n}{m}\left(1 + \sqrt{1 - \frac{m^2}{ln}}\right),$$

$$r = \left(1 - \frac{m^2}{ln}\right)^{-\frac{1}{2}} \dots\dots\dots\dots\dots\dots\dots\dots (12),$$

which is the maximum value of r.

When the ratio of p to q lies between that of n to m and that of m to l, r lies between $+1$ and -1, and the current must decay; but when pl is less than qm, a reciprocating current may be kept up, and will increase most rapidly when

$$\frac{p}{q} = \frac{n}{m}\left(1 - \sqrt{1 - \frac{m^2}{ln}}\right),$$

and
$$r = -\left(1 - \frac{m^2}{ln}\right)^{-\frac{1}{2}} \dots\dots\dots\dots\dots\dots\dots\dots\dots\dots\dots (13).$$

When the commutator is of the second kind, the first step is to close both circuits, so as to render the currents in them independent. The second circuit is then broken, and the current in it is thus stopped. This produces an effect on the first circuit by induction determined by the equation

$$Lx + My = Lx' + My' \dots\dots\dots\dots\dots\dots\dots\dots\dots\dots(14).$$

In this case $M = -M_0$, $y = x$, and $y' = 0$, so that

$$(L - M)x = Lx' \dots\dots\dots\dots\dots\dots\dots\dots\dots\dots\dots(15);$$

where x is the original, and x' the new value of the current.

The next step is to throw the circuits into one, M being now positive. If x'' be the current after this operation,

$$(L + M)x' = (L + 2M + N)x'' \dots\dots\dots\dots\dots\dots\dots\dots (16).$$

The whole effect of this commutator is therefore to multiply the current by the ratio

$$\frac{L^2 - M^2}{L(L + 2M + N)}.$$

The whole effect of the semirotation is to multiply the current by the ratio

$$\frac{L + 2M + N}{L - 2M + N}.$$

The total effect of a semirevolution supposed instantaneous is to multiply the current by the ratio

$$r = \frac{L^2 - M^2}{L(L - 2M + N)}.$$

If p and q be the number of windings in the first and second coils respectively, the ratio r becomes

$$r = \frac{l^2 p^2 - m^2 q^2}{l(lp^2 - 2mpq + nq^2)};$$

which is greater than 1, provided $2lmp$ is greater than $(ln + m^2)q$. When

$$\frac{p}{q} = \tfrac{1}{2}\left(\frac{n}{m} + \frac{m}{l}\right) + \tfrac{1}{2}\sqrt{\frac{n^2}{m} + 2\frac{n}{l} - 3\frac{m^2}{l^2}},$$

we have for the maximum value of r,

$$r = 1 + \frac{2\dfrac{m}{l}}{\sqrt{\dfrac{n^2}{m^2} + 2\dfrac{n}{l} - 3\dfrac{m^2}{l^2}} + \dfrac{n}{m} - \dfrac{m}{l}}.$$

In the experiment of Professor Wheatstone, in which the ends of the primary coil were put in permanent connexion by a short wire, the equations are more complicated, as we have three currents instead of two to consider. The equations are

$$Rx + \frac{d}{dt}(Lx + My) = Sy + \frac{d}{dt}(Mx + Ny) = Qz + \frac{d}{dt}Kz \dots\dots\dots(17),$$

$$x + y + z = 0 \dots\dots\dots\dots\dots\dots\dots\dots(18),$$

where Q, K, and z are the resistance, self-induction, and current in the short wire. The resultant equations are of the second degree; but as they are only true when the magnetism of the cores is considered rigidly connected with the currents in the coils, an elaborate discussion of them would be out of place in what professes to be only a rough explanation of the theory of the experiments.

Such a rough explanation appears to me to be as follows:—

Without the shunt, the current in the secondary coil is always in rigid connexion with that in the primary coil, except when the commutator is changing. With the shunt, the two currents are in some degree independent; and the secondary coil, whose electric inertia is small compared with that of the primary, can have its current reversed and varied without being clogged by the sluggish primary coil.

On the other hand, the primary coil loses that part of the total current which passes through the shunt; but we know that an iron core, when highly magnetized, requires a great increase of current to increase its magnetism, whereas its magnetism can be maintained at a considerable value by a current much less powerful. In this way the diminution in resistance and self-induction due to the shunt may more than counterbalance the diminution of strength in the primary magnet.

Also, since the self-induction of the shunt is very small, all instantaneous currents will run through it rather than through the electromagnetic coils, and therefore it will receive more of the heating effect of variable currents than a comparison of the resistances alone would lead us to expect.

[Extracted from *The Quarterly Journal of Pure and Applied Mathematics*, No. 32, 1867.]

XXX. *On the Equilibrium of a Spherical Envelope.*

I propose to determine the distribution of stress in an indefinitely thin and inextensible spherical sheet, arising from the action of external forces applied to it at any number of points on its surface.

Notation. Let two systems of lines, cutting each other at right angles, be drawn upon any surface, and let their equations be

$$\phi_1(xyz) = G \text{ and } \phi_2(xyz) = H,$$

where each curve is found by putting G or H equal to a constant, and combining it with the equation of the surface itself, which we may denote by

$$\psi(xyz) = S.$$

Now let G be made constant, and let H vary, and let dS_1 be the element of length of the curve ($G = $ constant) intercepted between the two curves for which H varies by dH, then $\dfrac{dH}{dS_1}$ will be a function of H and G.

In the same way, making dS_2 an element of the curve ($H = $ constant) we may determine $\dfrac{dG}{dS_2}$ as a function of H and G.

Now let the element dS_1 experience a stress, consisting of a force X in the direction in which G increases, and Y in the direction in which H increases, acting on the positive side of the linear element dS_1, and equal and opposite forces acting on the negative side. These will constitute a longitudinal tension normal to dS_1, which we shall denote by and a shearing force on the element, which we shall call

$$p_{12} = \frac{Y}{dS_1}.$$

In like manner, if the element dS_2 is acted on by forces Y' and X', it will experience on its positive side a tension and a shearing force, the values of which will be

$$p_{22} = \frac{Y'}{dS_2} \quad \text{and} \quad p_{21} = \frac{X'}{dS_2}.$$

That the moments of these forces on the elements of area dS_1, dS_2 may vanish,

$$p_{12} = p_{21},$$

or the shearing force on dS_1 must be equal to that on dS_2.

When there is no shearing force, then p_{11} and p_{22} are called the *principal* stresses at the point, and if p_{12} vanishes everywhere, the curves, $(G = \text{constant})$ and $(H = \text{constant})$, are called lines of principal stress. In this case the conditions of equilibrium of the element $dS_1 dS_2$ are

$$\frac{dp_{11}}{dG}\frac{dS_1}{dH} + (p_{11} - p_{22})\frac{d^2S_1}{dGdH} = 0 \dots\dots\dots\dots\dots\dots (1),$$

$$\frac{dp_{22}}{dH}\frac{dS_2}{dG} + (p_{22} - p_{11})\frac{d^2S_2}{dGdH} = 0 \dots\dots\dots\dots\dots\dots (2),$$

$$\frac{p_{11}}{r_1} + \frac{p_{22}}{r_2} = N_1 - N_2 \dots\dots\dots\dots\dots\dots\dots\dots (3).$$

The first and second of these equations are the conditions of equilibrium in the directions of the first and second lines of principal tension respectively.

The third equation is the condition of equilibrium normal to the surface; r_1 and r_2 are the radii of curvature of normal sections touching the first and second lines of principal stress. They are not necessarily the principal radii of curvature. N_1 is the normal pressure of any fluid on the surface from the side on which r_1 and r_2 are reckoned positive, and N_2 is the normal pressure on the other side.

If the systems of curves G and H, instead of being lines of principal stress, had been lines of curvature, we should still have had the same equation (3), but r_1 and r_2 would have been the principal radii of curvature, and p_{11} and p_{22}

would have been the tensions in the principal planes of curvature, and not necessarily principal tensions.

In the case of a spherical surface not acted on by any fluid pressure, $r_1 = r_2$, and $N_1 = N_2 = 0$, so that the third equation becomes

$$p_{11} + p_{22} = 0 \dots\dots\dots\dots\dots\dots\dots\dots\dots\dots\dots(4),$$

whence we obtain from the first and second equations

$$p_{11} = C_1 \left(\frac{dH}{dS_1}\right)^2 = -C_2 \left(\frac{dG}{dS_2}\right)^2 = -p_{22}\dots\dots\dots\dots\dots(5),$$

where C_1 is a function of H, and C_2 of G. If then we draw two lines of the system $(H = \text{constant})$ at such a distance that $p_{11}(dS_1)^2 = (dh)^2$ at any point where $(dh)^2$ is constant, this equation will continue true through the whole length of these lines, that is, the principal stresses will be inversely as the square of the distance between the consecutive lines of stress. Since this is true of both sets of lines, we may assume the form of the functions G and H, so that they not only indicate lines of stress, but give the value of the stress at any point by the equations

$$p_{11} = \left(\frac{dH}{dS_1}\right)^2 = \left(\frac{dG}{dS_2}\right)^2 = -p_{22}\dots\dots\dots\dots\dots\dots(6),$$

where $(H = \text{constant})$ is a line of principal tension, and $(G = \text{constant})$ a line of principal pressure.

If we now draw on the spherical surface lines corresponding to values of G differing by unity, and also lines corresponding to values of H differing by unity, these two systems of lines will intersect everywhere at right angles, and the distance between two consecutive lines of one system will be equal to the distance between two consecutive lines of the other, and the principal stresses will be in the directions of the lines, and inversely as the square of the intervals between them.

Now if two systems of lines can be drawn on a surface so as to fulfil these conditions, we know from the theory of electrical conduction in a sheet of uniform conductivity, that if one set of the curves are taken as equipotential lines, the other set will be lines of flow, and that the two systems of lines will give a solution of some problem relating to the flow of electricity through a conducting sheet. But we know that unless electricity be brought to some point of the sheet, and carried off at another point, there can be no flow of electricity in the sheet. Hence, if such systems of lines exist, there must be some singular points, at which all the lines of flow meet, and at which $\frac{dH}{dS_1}$ is infinite.

If $\frac{dH}{dS_1}$ is nowhere infinite, there can be no systems of lines at all, and if $\frac{dH}{dS_1}$ is infinite at any point, there is an infinite stress at that point, which can only be maintained by the action of an external force applied at that point.

Hence a spherical surface, to which no external forces are applied, must be free from stress, and it can easily be shewn from this that, when the external forces are given, there can be only one system of stresses in the surface.

This is not true in the case of a plane surface. In a plane surface, equation (3) disappears, and we have only two differential equations connecting the stresses at any point, which are not sufficient to determine the distribution of stress, unless we have some other conditions, such as the equations of elasticity, by which the question may be rendered determinate.

The simplest case of a spherical surface acted on by external forces is that in which two equal and opposite forces P are applied at the extremities of a diameter. There will evidently be a tension along the meridian lines, combined with an equal and opposite pressure along the parallels of latitude, and the magnitude p of either of these stresses will be

$$p = \frac{P}{2\pi a \sin^2 \theta} \dots\dots\dots\dots\dots(7),$$

where a is the radius of the sphere, P the force at the poles, and θ the angular distance of a point of the surface from the pole. If ϕ is the longitude, and if r_1 and r_2 are the rectilineal distances of a point from the two poles respectively, and if we make

$$G = \log_e \frac{r_1}{r_2} \text{ and } H = \phi \dots\dots\dots\dots (8),$$

then G and H will give the lines of principal stress, and

$$p = \frac{P}{2\pi a} \left(\frac{dG}{dS_2}\right)^2 = \frac{P}{2\pi a} \left(\frac{dH}{dS_1}\right)^2 \dots\dots\dots\dots (9).$$

To pass from this case to that in which the two forces are applied at any points, I shall make use of the following property of inverse surfaces.

If a surface of any form is in equilibrium under any system of stresses, and if lines of principal stress be drawn on it, then if a second surface be the inverse of the first with respect to a given point, and if lines be drawn on it which are inverse to the lines of principal stress in the first surface, and if along these lines stresses are applied which are to those in the corresponding point of the first surface inversely as the squares of their respective distances from the point of inversion, then every part of the second surface will either be in equilibrium, or will be acted on by a resultant force in the direction of the point of inversion.

For, if we compare corresponding elements of lines of stress in the two surfaces, we shall find that the forces acting on them are in the same plane with the line through the point of inversion, and make equal angles with it. The moment of the force on either element about the point of inversion is therefore as the product of the length of the element, into its distance from the point of inversion into the intensity of the stress. But the length of the element is as its distance, and the stress is inversely as the square of the distance, therefore the 'moments of the stresses about the point of inversion are equal, and in the same plane. If now any portion of the first surface is in equilibrium, it will be in equilibrium as regards moments about the point of inversion. The corresponding portion of the second surface will also be in equilibrium as regards moments about the point of inversion. It is therefore either in equilibrium, or the resultant force acting on it passes through the point of inversion.

Now let the first surface be a sphere; we know that the second surface is also a sphere. In the first surface the condition of equilibrium normal to the surface is $p_{11} + p_{22} = 0$. In the second surface the stresses are to those in the first in the inverse ratio of the squares of the distances. Hence in the second surface also, $p_{11} + p_{22} = 0$, or there is equilibrium in the direction of the normal. But we have seen that the resultant, if any, is in the radius vector. Therefore, if we except the limiting case in which the radius vector is perpendicular to the normal, the equilibrium is complete in all directions.

We may now, by inverting the spherical surface, pass from the case of a sphere acted on by a pair of tensions applied at the extremities of a diameter to that in which the forces are applied at the extremities of any chord of the sphere, subtending at the centre an angle $= 2a$. The lines of tension will be circles passing through the extremities of the chord. Let the angle which one of these circles makes with the great circle through these points be ϕ. The angle ϕ is the same as the corresponding angle in the inverse surface.

The lines of pressure, being orthogonal to these, will be circles whose planes if produced pass through the polar of the chord. Let r_1, r_2 be the distances of any point on the sphere from the extremities of the chord, then $\dfrac{r_1}{r_2}$ is constant for each of these circles, and has the same value as it has in the inverse surface. Hence, if we make

$$G = \log_e \frac{r_1}{r_2} \text{ and } H = \phi \quad\text{......................} (10),$$

G and H will give the lines of principal stress, and the absolute value of the stress at any point will be

$$p = \frac{P \sin a}{2\pi a} \left(\frac{dG}{dS_2}\right)^2 = \frac{P \sin a}{2\pi a} \left(\frac{dH}{dS_1}\right)^2 \quad\text{.....................} (11).$$

If we draw tangent planes to the sphere at the extremities of the chord, and if q_1, q_2 are the perpendiculars from any point of the spherical surface on these planes, it is easy to shew that at that point

$$p = \frac{P a \sin^2 a}{2\pi q_1 q_2} \quad\text{...............................} (12).$$

If any number of forces, forming a system in equilibrium, be applied at different points of a spherical envelope, we may proceed as follows. First decompose the system of forces into a system of pairs of equal and opposite forces acting along chords of the sphere. To do this, if there are n forces applied at n points, draw a number of chords, which must be at least $3(n-2)$, so as to render all the points rigidly connected. Then determine the tension along each chord due to the external forces. If too many chords have been drawn, some of these tensions will involve unknown quantities. The n forces will now be transformed into as many pairs of equal and opposite forces as chords have been drawn.

Next find the distribution of stress in the spherical surface due to each of these pairs of forces, and combine them at every point by the rules for the composition of stress*. The result will be the actual distribution of stress, and if any unknown forces have been introduced in the process, they will disappear from the result.

The calculation of the resultant stress from the component stresses, when these are given in terms of unsymmetrical spherical co-ordinates of different systems, would be very difficult; I shall therefore shew how to effect the same object by a method derived from Mr Airy's valuable paper, "On the strains in the interior of beams†."

If we place the point of inversion on the surface of the sphere, the inverse surface is a plane, and if p_{xx}, p_{xy}, and p_{yy} represent the components of stress in the plane referred to rectangular axes, we have for equilibrium

$$\frac{dp_{xx}}{dx} + \frac{dp_{xy}}{dy} = 0 \dots\dots\dots\dots\dots\dots\dots (13),$$

$$\frac{dp_{xy}}{dx} + \frac{dp_{yy}}{dy} = 0\dots\dots\dots\dots\dots\dots\dots(14).$$

These equations are equivalent to the following:

$$p_{xx} = \frac{d^2F}{dy^2}, \quad p_{xy} = -\frac{d^2F}{dxdy}, \quad p_{yy} = \frac{d^2F}{dx^2}\dots\dots\dots\dots\dots (15),$$

where F is any function whatever of x and y.

The form of the function F cannot, in the case of a plane, be determined from the equations of equilibrium, as strains may exist independently of external forces. To solve the question we require to know not only the original strains, but the law of elasticity of the plane sheet, whether it is uniform, or variable from point to point, and in different directions at the same point. When, however, we have found two solutions of F corresponding to different cases, we can combine the results by simple addition, as the expressions (equation 15) are linear in form.

In the case of two forces acting on a sphere, let A, B (fig. 29) be the points corresponding to the points of application in the inverse plane; $AP = r_1$,

---

* Rankin's *Applied Mechanics*, p. 82.
† *Philosophical Transactions*, 1863, Part I. p. 49.

$BP = r_2$, angle $APB = XAT = \phi$. Bisect AB in C, and draw PD perpendicular to AB. Then the line of tension at P is a circle through A and B, for which ϕ is constant, and the line of pressure is an orthogonal circle for which the ratio of r_1 to r_2 is constant, and the angle ϕ and the logarithms of the ratio of r_1 to r_2 differ from the corresponding quantities in the sphere only by constants. We may therefore put

$$p_{11} = \frac{P \sin a}{2\pi a} \left(\frac{dG}{dS_2}\right)^2 = \frac{P \sin a}{2\pi a} \left(\frac{dH}{dS_1}\right)^2 = -p_{22},$$

where the values of G and H are the same as in equations (8) and (10).

Transforming these principal stresses into their components, we get

$$p_{xx} = \frac{P \sin a}{2\pi a} \left(\left|\frac{\overline{dG}}{dx}\right|^2 - \left|\frac{\overline{dG}}{dy}\right|^2\right) \dots\dots\dots\dots\dots\dots(16),$$

$$p_{xy} = \frac{P \sin a}{2\pi a} 2 \frac{dG}{dx}\frac{dG}{dy} \dots\dots\dots\dots\dots\dots\dots(17),$$

$$p_{yy} = \frac{P \sin a}{2\pi a} \left(\left|\frac{\overline{dG}}{dy}\right|^2 - \left|\frac{\overline{dG}}{dx}\right|^2\right) \dots\dots\dots\dots\dots\dots(18).$$

From the relations between G and H we have

$$\frac{dG}{dx} = -\frac{dH}{dy} \text{ and } \frac{dG}{dy} = \frac{dH}{dx} \dots\dots\dots\dots (19),$$

whence
$$\frac{d^2G}{dx^2} + \frac{d^2G}{dy^2} = 0 \text{ and } \frac{d^2H}{dx^2} + \frac{d^2H}{dy^2} = 0 \dots\dots\dots\dots (20).$$

The values of the component stresses, being expressed as functions of the second degree in G, cannot be compounded by adding together the corresponding values of G, we must, therefore, in order to express them as linear functions, find a value of F, such that

$$\frac{d^2F}{dy^2} = \frac{P \sin a}{2\pi a} \left\{\left(\frac{dG}{dx}\right)^2 - \left(\frac{dG}{dy}\right)^2\right\} = p_{xx} \dots\dots\dots\dots (21).$$

We shall then have, by differentiation with respect to x, and integration with respect to y,

$$-\frac{d^2F}{dxdy} = \frac{P \sin a}{2\pi a} 2 \frac{dG}{dx}\frac{dG}{dy} + f(x) \dots\dots\dots\dots (22),$$

and
$$\frac{d^2F}{dx^2} = \frac{P \sin a}{2\pi a} \left\{\left(\frac{dG}{dy}\right)^2 - \left(\frac{dG}{dx}\right)^2\right\} + yf(x) + f_1(x) \dots\dots\dots (23).$$

Since $\dfrac{d^2F}{dx^2} + \dfrac{d^2F}{dy^2} = 0$ in this case, the arbitrary functions must be zero, and we have to find the value of F from that of G by ordinary integration of (21). The result is

$$F = \frac{P \sin a}{2\pi a} \left\{ \frac{AD - AC}{AC} \log \frac{AP}{BP} + \frac{PD}{AC} \text{ (angle } APB) \right\} \dots\dots (24),$$

or if the co-ordinates of A and B are (a_1, b_1) and (a_2, b_2),

$$F = \frac{P \sin a}{2\pi a} \left\{ \tfrac{1}{2} \frac{(2x - a_1 - a_2)(a_2 - a_1) + (2y - b_1 - b_2)(b_2 - b_1)}{(a_2 - a_1)^2 + (b_2 - b_1)^2} \times \log \frac{(x - a_1)^2 + (y - b_1)^2}{(x - a_2)^2 + (y - b_2)^2} \right.$$

$$\left. + \frac{(2y - b_1 - b_2)(a_2 - a_1) - (2x - a_1 - a_2)(b_2 - b_1)}{(a_2 - a_1)^2 + (b_2 - b_1)^2} \left(\tan^{-1} \frac{y - b_2}{x - a_2} - \tan^{-1} \frac{y - b_1}{x - a_1} \right) \right\} \dots (25).$$

If we obtain the values of F for all the different pairs of forces acting on the sphere, and add them together, we shall find a new value of F, the second differential coefficients of which, with respect to x and y will give a system of components of stress in the plane, which, being transferred to the sphere by the process of inversion, will give the complete solution of the problem in the case of the sphere.

We have now solved the problem in the case of any number of forces applied to points of the spherical surface, and all other cases may be reduced to this, but it is worth while to notice certain special cases.

If two equal and opposite twists be applied at any two points of the sphere, we can determine the distribution of stress. For if we put

$$G = \log \frac{r_1}{r_2} + \phi \text{ and } H = \log \frac{r_1}{r_2} - \phi \dots\dots\dots\dots\dots (26),$$

the equations of equilibrium will still hold, and the principal stresses at any point will be inclined $45°$ to those in the case already considered.

If M be the moment of the couple in a plane perpendicular to the chord, the absolute value of the principal stresses at any point is

$$p = \frac{M \sin a}{4\pi a^2} \left(\frac{dG}{dS_2} \right)^2 \dots\dots\dots\dots\dots\dots (27).$$

In figure 30 are represented the stereographic projections of the principal lines of stress in the cases which we have considered. When a tension is applied along the chord AB, the lines of tension are the circles through AB,

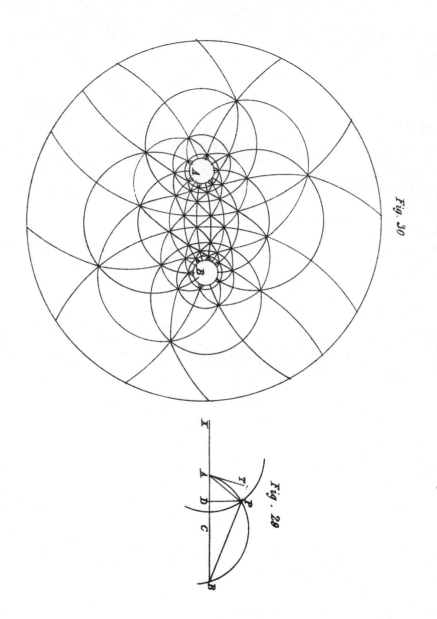

Fig. 30

Fig. 29

and the lines of pressure are the circles orthogonal to them. These circles are so drawn in the figure that the differences of the values of G and H are $\frac{1}{12}\pi$.

The spiral lines which pass through the intersections of these circles are the principal lines of stress in the case of twists applied to the spherical surface at the extremities of the chord AB.

In the case of a sphere acted on by fluid pressure, if the pressure is a function of the distance from a given point, we may take the line joining that point with the centre of the sphere as an axis, and then the lines of equal fluid pressure will be circles, and the fluid pressure N will be a function of θ, the angular distance from the pole. If we suppose the total effect of pressure balanced by a single force at the opposite pole, then we shall have for the equilibrium of the segment, whose radius is θ,

$$2 \sin^2 \theta p_{11} = a \int_0^\theta N \sin 2\theta d\theta \dots \dots \dots \dots (28),$$

and

$$p_{22} = Na - p_{11},$$

to determine p_{11} the tension in the meridian, and p_{22} that in the parallels of latitude.

[From the *Proceedings of the Royal Society of Edinburgh, Session* 1867–68.]

XXXI. *On the best Arrangement for producing a Pure Spectrum on a Screen.*

In experiments on the spectrum, it is usual to employ a slit through which the light is admitted, a prism to analyse the light, and one or more lenses to bring the rays of each distinct kind to a distinct focus on the screen. The most perfect arrangement is that adopted by M. Kirchhoff, in which two achromatic lenses are used, one before and the other after the passage of the light through the prism, so that every pencil consists of parallel rays while passing through the prism.

But when the observer has not achromatic lenses at his command, or when, as in the case of the highly refrangible rays, or the rays of heat, he is restricted in the use of materials, it may still be useful to be able to place the lenses and prism in such a way as to bring the rays of all colours to their foci at approximately the same distance from the prism.

We shall first examine the effect of the prism in changing the convergency or divergency of the pencils passing through it, and then that of the lens, so that by combining the prism and the lens we may cause their defects to disappear.

When a pencil of light is refracted through a plane surface, its convergency or divergency is less in that medium which has the greatest refractive index; and this change is greater as the angle of incidence is greater, and also as the index of refraction is greater.

When the pencil passes through a prism its convergency or divergency will be diminished as it enters, and will be increased when it emerges, and the emergent pencil will be more or less convergent or divergent than the incident one, according as the angle of emergence is greater or less than that of incidence. This effect will increase with the difference of these angles and with the refractive index.

When the angle of incidence is equal to that of emergence the convergence of the pencil is unaltered, but since the more refrangible rays have the greatest angle of emergence, their convergency or divergency will be greater than that of the less refrangible rays.

This effect will be increased by making the angle of incidence less, and that of emergence greater; and it will be diminished by increasing the angle of incidence, that is, by turning the prism round its edge towards the slit. If the angle of the prism is not too great, the convergency or divergency of all the pencils may be made the same (approximately) by turning the prism in this way.

This correction, however, diminishes the separation of the colours. It is inapplicable to a prism of large angle, and it takes no account of the chromatic aberration of the lens. By altering the arrangement, the lens may be made to correct the prism. The effect of a convex lens is to increase the convergency, and to diminish the divergency, of every pencil; but the change is greatest on the most refrangible rays. The prism, except when its base is very much turned towards the slit, makes the highly refrangible rays more convergent or more divergent than the less refrangible rays, according as they were convergent or divergent originally. If the rays pass through the prism before they reach the lens, the pencils will be divergent at incidence, and the more refrangible will be most divergent at emergence. If they then fall on the lens, they will be more converged than the rest; so that by a proper arrangement all may be brought to their foci at approximately the same distance. If the violet rays come to their focus first, we must turn the base of the prism more towards the light, and *vice versa*.

We proceed to the numerical calculation of the proper arrangement.

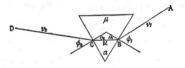

To find the variation of position of the focus of light passed through a prism as dependent on the nature of the light.

Let μ be the index of refraction of the prism, a its angle, ϕ_1 and ϕ_2 the angles of incidence and emergence, θ_1 and θ_2 the angles of the ray within the prism with the normals to the first and second surfaces, δ the difference of these angles—then by geometry

$$\theta_1 + \theta_2 = a, \qquad \theta_1 - \theta_2 = \delta,$$

and by the law of refraction,

$$\sin \phi_1 = \mu \sin \theta_1, \qquad \sin \phi_2 = \mu \sin \theta_2,$$

ϕ_1 is constant, being the angle of incidence for all kinds of light, but the other angles vary with μ, so that

$$\frac{d\theta_1}{d\mu} = -\frac{\sin \theta_1}{\mu \cos \theta_1}, \quad \frac{d\theta_2}{d\mu} = \frac{\sin \theta_1}{\mu \cos \theta_1}, \quad \frac{d\phi_2}{d\mu} = \frac{\sin a}{\cos \theta_1 \cos \phi_2}.$$

The last expression gives the dispersion, or breadth of the spectrum, and shews that it increases as the base of the prism is turned from the light.

As the slit is parallel to the edge of the prism, we have only to consider the primary foci of the pencils when we wish to render the image distinct.

Let v_1 be the distance of the focus of incident light from the prism, v_2 that of the emergent light, and u that within the prism, all measured to the right, then by the ordinary formula,

$$\frac{v_1}{\cos^2 \phi_1} = \frac{u}{\mu \cos^2 \theta_1}, \quad \frac{u}{\mu \cos^2 \theta_2} = \frac{v_2}{\cos^2 \phi_2},$$

$$v_1 \cos^2 \theta_1 \cos^2 \phi_2 = v_2 \cos^2 \theta_2 \cos^2 \phi_1.$$

Taking the differential coefficient of the logarithms of these quantities,

$$\frac{1}{v_1}\frac{dv_1}{d\mu} - \frac{2 \sin \theta_1}{\cos \theta_1}\frac{d\theta_1}{d\mu} - \frac{2 \sin \phi_2}{\cos \phi_2}\frac{d\phi_2}{d\mu} = \frac{1}{v_2}\frac{dv_2}{d\mu} - \frac{2 \sin \theta_2}{\cos \theta_2}\frac{d\theta_2}{d\mu},$$

$$\frac{1}{v_1}\frac{dv_1}{d\mu} - \frac{1}{v_2}\frac{dv_2}{d\mu} = \frac{2 \sin \phi_2 \sin a}{\cos \theta_1 \cos^2 \phi_2} - \frac{2 \sin^2 \theta_1}{\mu \cos^2 \theta_1} - \frac{2 \sin \theta_1 \sin \theta_2}{\mu \cos \theta_1 \cos \theta_2}.$$

Substituting for these angles their values in terms of a and δ we find

$$\frac{1}{v_1}\frac{dv_1}{d\mu} - \frac{1}{v_2}\frac{dv_2}{d\mu} = \frac{4 \sin a}{(\cos a + \cos \delta)^2} \cdot \frac{(\mu^2 - 1)\sin a - \sin \delta \{1 + \mu^2 \cos(a - \delta)\}}{1 - \frac{1}{2}\mu^2 \{1 - \cos(a - \delta)\}}.$$

The quantity on the right of this equation is always positive, unless the value of δ exceeds that given by the equation

$$(\mu^2 - 1)\sin a = \sin \delta \{1 + \mu^2 \cos(a - \delta)\}.$$

If $\mu = 1\cdot5$ and $a = 60°$, then $\delta = 22° 52'$, that is, the ray within the prism makes an angle of $11° 26'$ with the base, which corresponds to an angle of incidence $82° 50'$, or the incident ray is inclined $7° 10'$ to the face of the prism.

If two lenses* are used, of the same material with the prism, we may correct the defects of the prism without turning it so far from its position of least deviation.

Let a be the distance of the slit from the prism, and b that of the screen from the prism. Let f_1 be the focal length of the lens between the prism and slit, and f_2 that of the lens between the prism and the screen, then the condition of a flat image is

$$\frac{1}{v_1}\frac{dv_1}{d\mu} - \frac{1}{v_2}\frac{dv_2}{d\mu} = \frac{1}{\mu - 1}\left(\frac{v_1}{f_1} + \frac{v_2}{f_2}\right).$$

Let us first find the conditions of a flat spectrum $\delta = o$.

When $\delta = o$, $v_1 = v_2$, and we obtain the conditions

$$\frac{1}{a} - \frac{1}{f_1} = \frac{1}{f_2} - \frac{1}{b} = \left(\frac{1}{a} + \frac{1}{b}\right)\frac{(1+\cos a)^2\{1 - \frac{1}{2}\mu^2(1-\cos a)\}}{4(\mu-1)^2(\mu+1)\sin^2 a} = \left(\frac{1}{a} + \frac{1}{b}\right)c,$$

from which f_1 and f_2 may be found in terms of known quantities.

$$\frac{1}{f_1} = \frac{1}{a}(1-c) - \frac{1}{b}c,$$

$$\frac{1}{f_2} = \frac{1}{b}(1+c) + \frac{1}{a}c.$$

When a, the angle of the prism, is $60°$, then

$$c = \frac{3(4-\mu^2)}{16(\mu-1)^2(\mu+1)}.$$

If we now make $\mu = 1\cdot5$ we find $c = \cdot5025$, and

$$\frac{1}{f_1} = \frac{\cdot4975}{a} - \frac{\cdot5025}{b},$$

$$\frac{1}{f_2} = \frac{1\cdot5025}{b} + \frac{\cdot5025}{a}.$$

If $a = \frac{10}{21}b$, the first lens may be dispensed with, and the second lens will correct the defects of the prism.

* [These lenses are supposed to be close to the edge of the prism.]

If a is greater in proportion to b, a concave lens must be placed in front of the prism. The most convenient arrangement will be that in which the prism is placed in the position of least deviation, and the lens placed between the prism and the screen, while the distance from the slit to the prism is to that between the prism and the screen as $1-c$ is to c. For quartz, in which $\mu = 1\cdot584$ for the ordinary ray, $\dfrac{1}{c} = 2\cdot53$, so that the best arrangement is $a = 1\cdot53\,b$, or the lens should be placed on the side next the screen, and the distance from the slit which admits the light to the prism should be about one and a half times the distance from the prism to the screen.

[From the Proceedings of the *London Mathematical Society*, Vol. II.]

XXXII. *The Construction of Stereograms of Surfaces.*

To make a surface visible, lines must be drawn upon it; and to exhibit the nature of the surface, these lines ought to be traced on the surface according to some principle, as for instance the contour lines and lines of greatest slope on a surface may be drawn. Monge represents surfaces to the eye by their two systems of lines of curvature, which have the advantage of being independent of the direction assumed for the co-ordinate axes. For stereoscopic representation it is necessary to choose curves which are easily followed by the eye, and which are sufficiently different in form to prevent a curve of the one figure from being visually united with any other than the corresponding curve in the other figure. I have found the best way in practice to be as follows:—First determine how many curves are to be drawn on the surface, and at what intervals, and find the numerical values of the co-ordinates of points on these curves. A convenient method of drawing the figures according to Cartesian co-ordinates is to draw an equilateral triangle, find its centre of gravity, and take a point about $\frac{1}{30}$ of the side of the triangle distant horizontally from the centre of gravity as the origin, and the lines joining this point with the angles as unit axes. For the other figure, the point must be taken on the opposite side of the centre of gravity. I have found that this rule gives a convenient amount of relief to the figures. When the co-ordinates of a point are easily expressed in terms of tetrahedral co-ordinates x, y, z, w, I draw the two lines ($x = 0$, $y = 0$) and ($z = 0$, $w - 0$) in both figures. By means of a sector I divide the first line in P in the ratio of z to w, and the second in Q in the ratio of x to y; I then lay a rule along the line PQ (without drawing the line) and divide PQ in the ratio of $x + y$ to $z + w$, in order to find the point R in the figure. By drawing the two lines once for all in each figure, and performing the same process of finding ratios in each figure, we get each point without making any marks on the paper, which come to be very troublesome in complicated figures. In this way I have drawn the figures of cyclides, &c.

[Proceedings of the *London Mathematical Society*, Vol. II.]

XXXIII.   *On Reciprocal Diagrams in Space, and their relation to Airy's Function of Stress.*

LET F be any function of the co-ordinates x, y, z of a point in space, and let ξ, η, ζ be another system of co-ordinates which we may suppose referred to axes parallel to the axes of x, y, z, but at such a distance (in thought) that figures referred to x, y, z do not interfere with the figures referred to ξ, η, ζ.

We shall call the figure or figures referred to x, y, z the First Diagram, and those referred to ξ, η, ζ the Second Diagram.

Let the connection between the two diagrams be expressed thus—

$$\xi = \frac{dF}{dx}, \quad \eta = \frac{dF}{dy}, \quad \zeta = \frac{dF}{dz}.$$

When the form of F is known, ξ, η and ζ may be found for every value of x, y, z, and the form of the second diagram fixed.

To complete the second diagram, let a function ϕ of ξ, η, ζ be found from the equation

$$\phi = x\xi + y\eta + z\zeta - F;$$

then it is easily shewn that

$$x = \frac{d\phi}{d\xi}, \quad y = \frac{d\phi}{d\eta}, \quad z = \frac{d\phi}{d\zeta}.$$

Hence the first diagram is determined from the second by the same process that the second is determined from the first. They are therefore Reciprocal Diagrams both as regards their form and their functions.

But reciprocal diagrams have a mechanical significance which is capable of extensive applications, from the most elementary graphic methods for calculating the stresses of a roof to the most intricate questions about the internal molecular forces in solid bodies. I shall indicate two independent methods of representing internal stress by means of reciprocal diagrams.

First Method. Let a, b be any two contiguous points in the first diagram, and α, β the corresponding points in the second. Let an element of area be described about ab perpendicular to it. Then if the stress per unit of area on this surface is compounded of a *tension* parallel to $\alpha\beta$ and equal to $P\dfrac{\alpha\beta}{ab}$ and a *pressure* parallel to ab and equal to $P\left(\dfrac{d^2F}{dx^2} + \dfrac{d^2F}{dy^2} + \dfrac{d^2F}{dz^2}\right)$, P being a constant introduced for the sake of homogeneity, then a state of internal stress defined in this way will keep every point of the first figure in equilibrium.

The components of stress, as thus defined, will be

$$p_{xx} = P\left(\frac{d^2F}{dx^2} - \Delta^2 F\right), \quad p_{yy} = P\left(\frac{d^2F}{dy^2} - \Delta^2 F\right), \quad p_{zz} = P\left(\frac{d^2F}{dz^2} - \Delta^2 F\right),$$

$$p_{yz} = P\frac{d^2F}{dy\,dz}, \qquad p_{zx} = P\frac{d^2F}{dz\,dx}, \qquad p_{xy} = P\frac{d^2F}{dx\,dy},$$

and these are easily shewn to fulfil the conditions of equilibrium.

If any number of states of stress can be represented in this way, they can be combined by adding the values of their functions (F), since the quantities are linear. This method, however, is applicable only to certain states of stress; but if we write

$$p_{xx} = \frac{d^2B}{dz^2} + \frac{d^2C}{dy^2}, \quad p_{yy} = \frac{d^2C}{dx^2} + \frac{d^2A}{dz^2}, \quad p_{zz} = \frac{d^2A}{dy^2} + \frac{d^2B}{dx^2},$$

$$p_{yz} = -\frac{d^2A}{dy\,dz}, \qquad p_{zx} = -\frac{d^2B}{dz\,dx}, \qquad p_{xy} = -\frac{d^2C}{dx\,dy},$$

we get a general method at the expense of using three functions A, B, C, and of giving up the diagram of stress.

Second Method. Let a be any element of area in the first diagram, and α the corresponding area in the second. Let a uniform normal pressure equal to P per unit of area act on the area a, and let a force equal and parallel to the resultant of this pressure act on the area α, then a state of internal stress in the first figure defined in this way will keep every point of it in equilibrium.

The components of stress as thus defined will be

$$p_{xx} = P\left(\frac{d^2F}{dy^2}\frac{d^2F}{dz^2} - \overline{\frac{d^2F}{dy\,dz}}\Big|^2\right), \qquad p_{yy} = P\left(\frac{d^2F}{dz^2}\frac{d^2F}{dx^2} - \overline{\frac{d^2F}{dz\,dx}}\Big|^2\right),$$

$$p_{zz} = P\left(\frac{d^2F}{dx^2}\frac{d^2F}{dy^2} - \frac{d^2F}{dx\,dy}\right),$$

$$p_{yz} = P\left(\frac{d^2F}{dz\,dx}\frac{d^2F}{dx\,dy} - \frac{d^2F}{dx^2}\frac{d^2F}{dy\,dz}\right), \qquad p_{zx} = P\left(\frac{d^2F}{dx\,dy}\frac{d^2F}{dy\,dz} - \frac{d^2F}{dy^2}\frac{d^2F}{dz\,dx}\right),$$

$$p_{xy} = P\left(\frac{d^2F}{dy\,dz}\frac{d^2F}{dz\,dx} - \frac{d^2F}{dz^2}\frac{d^2F}{dx\,dy}\right).$$

This is a more complete, though not a perfectly general, representation of a state of stress ; but as the functions are not linear, it is difficult of application.

If however we confine ourselves to problems in two dimensions, either method leads to the expression of the three components of stress in terms of the function introduced by the Astronomer-Royal*.

$$p_{xx} = P\,\frac{d^2F}{dy^2}, \quad p_{xy} = -P\,\frac{d^2F}{dx\,dy}, \quad p_{yy} = P\,\frac{d^2F}{dx^2}.$$

Here $\qquad \xi = \dfrac{dF}{dx}, \quad y = \dfrac{dF}{dy}, \quad F + \phi = x\xi + y\eta,$

and if ab and $\alpha\beta$ be corresponding lines, the whole stress across the line ab is perpendicular to $\alpha\beta$ and equal to $P\alpha\beta$.

* "On Strains in the Interior of Beams." *Phil. Trans.* 1863.

[From the *Proceedings of the Royal Society*, No. 100, 1868.]

XXXIV.   *On Governors.*

A GOVERNOR is a part of a machine by means of which the velocity of the machine is kept nearly uniform, notwithstanding variations in the driving-power or the resistance.

Most governors depend on the centrifugal force of a piece connected with a shaft of the machine. When the velocity increases, this force increases, and either increases the pressure of the piece against a surface or moves the piece, and so acts on a break or a valve.

In one class of regulators of machinery, which we may call *moderators*[*], the resistance is increased by a quantity depending on the velocity. Thus in some pieces of clockwork the moderator consists of a conical pendulum revolving within a circular case. When the velocity increases, the ball of the pendulum presses against the inside of the case, and the friction checks the increase of velocity.

In Watt's governor for steam-engines the arms open outwards, and so contract the aperture of the steam-valve.

In a water-break invented by Professor J. Thomson, when the velocity is increased, water is centrifugally pumped up, and overflows with a great velocity, and the work is spent in lifting and communicating this velocity to the water.

In all these contrivances an increase of driving-power produces an increase of velocity, though a much smaller increase than would be produced without the moderator.

But if the part acted on by centrifugal force, instead of acting directly on the machine, sets in motion a contrivance which continually increases the

* See Mr C. W. Siemens "On Uniform Rotation," *Phil. Trans.* 1866, p. 657.

resistance as long as the velocity is above its normal value, and reverses its action when the velocity is below that value, the governor will bring the velocity to the same normal value whatever variation (within the working limits of the machine) be made in the driving-power or the resistance.

I propose at present, without entering into any details of mechanism, to direct the attention of engineers and mathematicians to the dynamical theory of such governors.

It will be seen that the motion of a machine with its governor consists in general of a uniform motion, combined with a disturbance which may be expressed as the sum of several component motions. These components may be of four different kinds :—

1. The disturbance may continually increase.
2. It may continually diminish.
3. It may be an oscillation of continually increasing amplitude.
4. It may be an oscillation of continually decreasing amplitude.

The first and third cases are evidently inconsistent with the stability of the motion ; and the second and fourth alone are admissible in a good governor. This condition is mathematically equivalent to the condition that all the possible roots, and all the possible parts of the impossible roots, of a certain equation shall be negative.

I have not been able completely to determine these conditions for equations of a higher degree than the third ; but I hope that the subject will obtain the attention of mathematicians.

The actual motions corresponding to these impossible roots are not generally taken notice of by the inventors of such machines, who naturally confine their attention to the way in which it is *designed* to act; and this is generally expressed by the real root of the equation. If, by altering the adjustments of the machine, its governing power is continually increased, there is generally a limit at which the disturbance, instead of subsiding more rapidly, becomes an oscillating and jerking motion, increasing in violence till it reaches the limit of action of the governor. This takes place when the possible part of one of the impossible roots becomes positive. The mathematical investigation of the motion may be rendered practically useful by pointing out the remedy for these disturbances.

This has been actually done in the case of a governor constructed by Mr Fleeming Jenkin, with adjustments, by which the regulating power of the governor could be altered. By altering these adjustments the regulation could be made more and more rapid, till at last a dancing motion of the governor, accompanied with a jerking motion of the main shaft, shewed that an alteration had taken place among the impossible roots of the equation.

I shall consider three kinds of governors, corresponding to the three kinds of moderators already referred to.

In the first kind, the centrifugal piece has a constant distance from the axis of motion, but its pressure on a surface on which it rubs varies when the velocity varies. In the *moderator* this friction is itself the retarding force. In the *governor* this surface is made moveable about the axis, and the friction tends to move it; and this motion is made to act on a break to retard the machine. A constant force acts on the moveable wheel in the opposite direction to that of the friction, which takes off the break when the friction is less than a given quantity.

Mr Jenkin's governor is on this principle. It has the advantage that the centrifugal piece does not change its position, and that its pressure is always the same function of the velocity. It has the disadvantage that the normal velocity depends in some degree on the coefficient of sliding friction between two surfaces which cannot be kept always in the same condition.

In the second kind of governor, the centrifugal piece is free to move further from the axis, but is restrained by a force the intensity of which varies with the position of the centrifugal piece in such a way that, if the velocity of rotation has the normal value, the centrifugal piece will be in equilibrium in every position. If the velocity is greater or less than the normal velocity, the centrifugal piece will fly out or fall in without any limit except the limits of motion of the piece. But a break is arranged so that it is made more or less powerful according to the distance of the centrifugal piece from the axis, and thus the oscillations of the centrifugal piece are restrained within narrow limits.

Governors have been constructed on this principle by Sir W. Thomson and by M. Foucault. In the first, the force restraining the centrifugal piece is that of a spring acting between a point of the centrifugal piece and a fixed point at a considerable distance, and the break is a friction-break worked by the reaction of the spring on the fixed point.

In M. Foucault's arrangement, the force acting on the centrifugal piece is the weight of the balls acting downward, and an upward force produced by weights acting on a combination of levers and tending to raise the balls. The resultant vertical force on the balls is proportional to their depth below the centre of motion, which ensures a constant normal velocity. The break is:— in the first place, the variable friction between the combination of levers and the ring on the shaft on which the force is made to act; and, in the second place, a centrifugal air-fan through which more or less air is allowed to pass, according to the position of the levers. Both these causes tend to regulate the velocity according to the same law.

The governors designed by the Astronomer-Royal on Mr Siemens's principle for the chronograph and equatorial of Greenwich Observatory depend on nearly similar conditions. The centrifugal piece is here a long conical pendulum, not far removed from the vertical, and it is prevented from deviating much from a fixed angle by the driving-force being rendered nearly constant by means of a differential system. The break of the pendulum consists of a fan which dips into a liquid more or less, according to the angle of the pendulum with the vertical. The break of the principal shaft is worked by the differential apparatus; and the smoothness of motion of the principal shaft is ensured by connecting it with a fly-wheel.

In the third kind of governor a liquid is pumped up and thrown out over the sides of a revolving cup. In the governor on this principle, described by Mr C. W. Siemens, the cup is connected with its axis by a screw and a spring, in such a way that if the axis gets ahead of the cup the cup is lowered and more liquid is pumped up. If this adjustment can be made perfect, the normal velocity of the cup will remain the same through a considerable range of driving-power.

It appears from the investigations that the oscillations in the motion must be checked by some force resisting the motion of oscillation. This may be done in some cases by connecting the oscillating body with a body hanging in a viscous liquid, so that the oscillations cause the body to rise and fall in the liquid.

To check the variations of motion in a revolving shaft, a vessel filled with viscous liquid may be attached to the shaft. It will have no effect on uniform rotation, but will check periodic alterations of speed.

Similar effects are produced by the viscosity of the lubricating matter in the sliding parts of the machine, and by other unavoidable resistances; so that it is not always necessary to introduce special contrivances to check oscillations.

I shall call all such resistances, if approximately proportional to the velocity, by the name of "viscosity," whatever be their true origin.

In several contrivances a differential system of wheel-work is introduced between the machine and the governor, so that the driving-power acting on the governor is nearly constant.

I have pointed out that, under certain conditions, the sudden disturbances of the machine do not act through the differential system on the governor, or *vice versâ*. When these conditions are fulfilled, the equations of motion are not only simple, but the motion itself is not liable to disturbances depending on the mutual action of the machine and the governor.

Distinction between Moderators and Governors.

In regulators of the first kind, let P be the driving-power and R the resistance, both estimated as if applied to a given axis of the machine. Let V be the normal velocity, estimated for the same axis, and $\frac{dx}{dt}$ the actual velocity, and let M be the moment of inertia of the whole machine reduced to the given axis.

Let the governor be so arranged as to increase the resistance or diminish the driving-power by a quantity $F\left(\frac{dx}{dt} - V\right)$, then the equation of motion will be

$$\frac{d}{dt}\left(M\frac{dx}{dt}\right) = P - R - F\left(\frac{dx}{dt} - V\right) \quad\dots\dots\dots\dots\dots\dots(1).$$

When the machine has obtained its final rate the first term vanishes, and

$$\frac{dx}{dt} = V + \frac{P - R}{F} \quad\dots\dots\dots\dots\dots\dots\dots\dots(2).$$

Hence, if P is increased or R diminished, the velocity will be permanently increased. Regulators of this kind, as Mr Siemens* has observed, should be called moderators rather than governors.

* " On Uniform Rotation," *Phil. Trans.* 1866, p. 657.

In the second kind of regulator, the force $F\left(\dfrac{dx}{dt} - V\right)$, instead of being applied directly to the machine, is applied to an independent moving piece, B, which continually increases the resistance, or diminishes the driving-power, by a quantity depending on the whole motion of B.

If y represents the whole motion of B, the equation of motion of B is

$$\frac{d}{dt}\left(B\frac{dy}{dt}\right) = F\left(\frac{dx}{dt} - V\right) \dots\dots\dots\dots\dots\dots\dots(3),$$

and that of M

$$\frac{d}{dt}\left(M\frac{dx}{dt}\right) = P - R - F\left(\frac{dx}{dt} - V\right) + Gy \dots\dots\dots\dots\dots(4),$$

where G is the resistance applied by B when B moves through one unit of space.

We can integrate the first of these equations at once, and we find

$$B\frac{dy}{dt} = F\left(x - Vt\right) \dots\dots\dots\dots\dots\dots\dots (5);$$

so that if the governor B has come to rest $x = Vt$, and not only is the velocity of the machine equal to the normal velocity, but the position of the machine is the same as if no disturbance of the driving-power or resistance had taken place.

Jenkin's Governor.—In a governor of this kind, invented by Mr Fleeming Jenkin, and used in electrical experiments, a centrifugal piece revolves on the principal axis, and is kept always at a constant angle by an appendage which slides on the edge of a loose wheel, B, which works on the same axis. The pressure on the edge of this wheel would be proportional to the square of the velocity; but a constant portion of this pressure is taken off by a spring which acts on the centrifugal piece. The force acting on B to turn it round is therefore

$$F'\left.\overline{\frac{dx}{dt}}\right|^2 - C';$$

and if we remember that the velocity varies within very narrow limits, we may write the expression

$$F\left(\frac{dx}{dt} - V_1\right),$$

where F is a new constant, and V_1 is the lowest limit of velocity within which the governor will act.

Since this force necessarily acts on B in the positive direction, and since it is necessary that the break should be taken off as well as put on, a weight W is applied to B, tending to turn it in the negative direction; and, for a reason to be afterwards explained, this weight is made to hang in a viscous liquid, so as to bring it to rest quickly.

The equation of motion of B may then be written

$$B\frac{d^2y}{dt^2} = F\left(\frac{dx}{dt} - V_1\right) - Y\frac{dy}{dt} - W \dots\dots\dots(6),$$

where Y is a coefficient depending on the viscosity of the liquid and on other resistances varying with the velocity, and W is the constant weight.

Integrating this equation with respect to t, we find

$$B\frac{dy}{dt} = F(x - V_1 t) - Yy - Wt \dots\dots\dots(7).$$

If B has come to rest, we have

$$x = \left(V_1 + \frac{W}{F}\right)t + \frac{Y}{F}y \dots\dots\dots(8),$$

or the position of the machine is affected by that of the governor, but the final velocity is constant, and

$$V_1 + \frac{W}{F} = V \dots\dots\dots(9),$$

where V is the normal velocity.

The equation of motion of the machine itself is

$$M\frac{d^2x}{dt^2} = P - R - F\left(\frac{dx}{dt} - V_1\right) - Gy \dots\dots\dots(10).$$

This must be combined with equation (7) to determine the motion of the whole apparatus. The solution is of the form

$$x = A_1 e^{n_1 t} + A_2 e^{n_2 t} + A_3 e^{n_3 t} + Vt \dots\dots\dots(11),$$

where n_1, n_2, n_3 are the roots of the cubic equation

$$MBn^3 + (MY + FB)n^2 + FYn + FG = 0 \dots\dots\dots(12).$$

If n be a pair of roots of this equation of the form $a \pm \sqrt{-1}\,b$, then the part of x corresponding to these roots will be of the form

$$e^{at}\cos(bt + \beta).$$

If a is a negative quantity, this will indicate an oscillation the amplitude of which continually decreases. If a is zero, the amplitude will remain constant, and if a is positive, the amplitude will continually increase.

One root of the equation (12) is evidently a real negative quantity. The condition that the real part of the other roots should be negative is

$$\left(\frac{F}{M}+\frac{Y}{B}\right)\frac{Y}{B} - \frac{G}{B} = \text{a positive quantity.}$$

This is the condition of stability of the motion. If it is not fulfilled there will be a dancing motion of the governor, which will increase till it is as great as the limits of motion of the governor. To ensure this stability, the value of Y must be made sufficiently great, as compared with G, by placing the weight W in a viscous liquid if the viscosity of the lubricating materials at the axle is not sufficient.

To determine the value of F, put the break out of gear, and fix the moveable wheel; then, if V and V' be the velocities when the driving-power is P and P',

$$F = \frac{P - P'}{V - V'}.$$

To determine G, let the governor act, and let y and y' be the positions of the break when the driving-power is P and P', then

$$G = \frac{P - P'}{y - y'}.$$

General Theory of Chronometric Centrifugal Pieces.

Sir W. Thomson's and M. Foucault's Governors.—Let A be the moment of inertia of a revolving apparatus, and θ the angle of revolution. The equation of motion is

$$\frac{d}{dt}\left(A\frac{d\theta}{dt}\right) = L \dots\dots\dots\dots\dots(1),$$

where L is the moment of the applied force round the axis.

Now, let A be a function of another variable ϕ (the divergence of the centrifugal piece), and let the kinetic energy of the whole be

$$\tfrac{1}{2}A\overline{\frac{d\theta}{dt}}\Big|^2 + \tfrac{1}{2}B\overline{\frac{d\phi}{dt}}\Big|^2,$$

where B may also be a function of ϕ, if the centrifugal piece is complex.

If we also assume that P, the potential energy of the apparatus, is a function of ϕ, then the force tending to *diminish* ϕ, arising from the action of gravity, springs, &c., will be $\dfrac{dP}{d\phi}$.

The whole energy, kinetic and potential, is

$$E = \tfrac{1}{2}A\overline{\frac{d\theta}{dt}}\Big|^2 + \tfrac{1}{2}B\overline{\frac{d\phi}{dt}}\Big|^2 + P = \int L d\theta \dots\dots\dots\dots\dots(2).$$

Differentiating with respect to t, we find

$$\left.\begin{aligned}
\frac{d\phi}{dt}\left(\tfrac{1}{2}\frac{dA}{d\phi}\overline{\frac{d\theta}{dt}}\Big|^2 + \tfrac{1}{2}\frac{dB}{d\phi}\overline{\frac{d\phi}{dt}}\Big|^2 + \frac{dP}{d\phi}\right) + A\frac{d\theta}{dt}\frac{d^2\theta}{dt^2} + B\frac{d\phi}{dt}\frac{d^2\phi}{dt^2} \\
= L\frac{d\theta}{dt} = \frac{d\theta}{dt}\left(\frac{dA}{d\phi}\frac{d\theta}{dt}\frac{d\phi}{dt} + A\frac{d^2\theta}{dt^2}\right)
\end{aligned}\right\} \dots\dots\dots(3),$$

whence we have, by eliminating L,

$$\frac{d}{dt}\left(B\frac{d\phi}{dt}\right) = \tfrac{1}{2}\frac{dA}{d\phi}\overline{\frac{d\theta}{dt}}\Big|^2 + \tfrac{1}{2}\frac{dB}{d\phi}\overline{\frac{d\phi}{dt}}\Big|^2 - \frac{dP}{d\phi} \dots\dots\dots\dots(4).$$

The first two terms on the right-hand side indicate a force tending to *increase* ϕ, depending on the squares of the velocities of the main shaft and of the centrifugal piece. The force indicated by these terms may be called the centrifugal force.

If the apparatus is so arranged that

$$P = \tfrac{1}{2}A\omega^2 + \text{const.} \dots\dots\dots\dots\dots\dots(5),$$

where ω is a constant velocity, the equation becomes

$$\frac{d}{dt}\left(B\frac{d\phi}{dt}\right) = \tfrac{1}{2}\frac{dA}{d\phi}\left(\overline{\frac{d\theta}{dt}}\Big|^2 - \omega^2\right) + \tfrac{1}{2}\frac{dB}{d\phi}\overline{\frac{d\phi}{dt}}\Big|^2 \dots\dots\dots\dots(6).$$

In this case the value of ϕ cannot remain constant unless the angular velocity is equal to ω.

A shaft with a centrifugal piece arranged on this principle has only one velocity of rotation without disturbance. If there be a small disturbance, the equations for the disturbance θ and ϕ may be written

$$A\frac{d^2\theta}{dt^2} + \frac{dA}{d\phi}\,\omega\,\frac{d\phi}{dt} = L \dotfill (7),$$

$$B\frac{d^2\phi}{dt^2} - \frac{dA}{d\phi}\,\omega\,\frac{d\theta}{dt} = 0 \dotfill (8).$$

The period of such small disturbances is $\frac{dA}{d\phi}(AB)^{-\frac{1}{2}}$ revolutions of the shaft. They will neither increase nor diminish if there are no other terms in the equations.

To convert this apparatus into a governor, let us assume viscosities X and Y in the motions of the main shaft and the centrifugal piece, and a resistance $G\phi$ applied to the main shaft. Putting $\frac{dA}{d\phi}\,\omega = K$, the equations become

$$A\frac{d^2\theta}{dt^2} + X\frac{d\theta}{dt} + K\frac{d\phi}{dt} + G\phi = L \dotfill (9),$$

$$B\frac{d^2\phi}{dt^2} + Y\frac{d\phi}{dt} - K\frac{d\theta}{dt} \quad\quad = 0 \dotfill (10).$$

The condition of stability of the motion indicated by these equations is that all the possible roots, or parts of roots, of the cubic equation

$$ABn^3 + (AY + BX)\,n^2 + (XY + K^2)\,n + GK = 0 \dotfill (11)$$

shall be negative; and this condition is

$$\left(\frac{X}{A} + \frac{Y}{B}\right)(XY + K^2) > GK \dotfill (12).$$

Combination of Governors.—If the break of Thomson's governor is applied to a moveable wheel, as in Jenkin's governor, and if this wheel works a steam-valve, or ʹ a more powerful break, we have to consider the motion of three pieces. Without entering into the calculation of the general equations of

motion of these pieces, we may confine ourselves to the case of small disturbances, and write the equations

$$A \frac{d^2\theta}{dt^2} + X \frac{d\theta}{dt} + K \frac{d\phi}{dt} + T\phi + J\psi = P - R,$$

$$\left. B \frac{d^2\phi}{dt^2} + Y \frac{d\phi}{dt} - K \frac{d\theta}{dt} \qquad\qquad = 0 \right\} \dots\dots\dots\dots(13),$$

$$C \frac{d^2\psi}{dt^2} + Z \frac{d\psi}{dt} - T\phi \qquad\qquad = 0$$

where θ, ϕ, ψ are the angles of disturbance of the main shaft, the centrifugal
arm, and the moveable wheel respectively, A, B, C their moments of inertia,
X, Y, Z the viscosity of their connexions, K is what was formerly denoted by
$\frac{dA}{d\phi} \omega$, and T and J are the powers of Thomson's and Jenkin's breaks respectively.

The resulting equation in n is of the form

$$\begin{vmatrix} An^2 + Xn & Kn + T & J \\ -K & Bn + Y & 0 \\ 0 & -T & Cn^2 + Zn \end{vmatrix} = 0 \dots\dots\dots\dots (14),$$

or

$$\left. \begin{aligned} n^5 + n^4 \left(\frac{X}{A} + \frac{Y}{B} + \frac{Z}{C} \right) + n^3 \left[\frac{XYZ}{ABC} \left(\frac{A}{X} + \frac{B}{Y} + \frac{C}{Z} \right) + \frac{K^2}{AB} \right] \\ + n^2 \left(\frac{XYZ + KTC + K^2Z}{ABC} \right) + n \frac{KTZ}{ABC} + \frac{KTJ}{ABC} = 0 \end{aligned} \right\} \dots\dots (15).$$

I have not succeeded in determining completely the conditions of stability
of the motion from this equation; but I have found two necessary conditions,
which are in fact the conditions of stability of the two governors taken
separately. If we write the equation

$$n^5 + pn^4 + qn^3 + rn^2 + sn + t = 0 \dots\dots\dots\dots\dots\dots (16),$$

then, in order that the possible parts of all the roots shall be negative, it is
necessary that

$$pq > r \text{ and } ps > t \dots\dots\dots\dots\dots\dots (17).$$

I am not able to shew that these conditions are sufficient. This compound
governor has been constructed and used.

On the Motion of a Liquid in a Tube revolving about a Vertical Axis.

Mr C. W. Siemens's Liquid Governor.—Let ρ be the density of the fluid, k the section of the tube at a point whose distance from the origin measured along the tube is s, r, θ, z the co-ordinates of this point referred to axes fixed with respect to the tube, Q the volume of liquid which passes through any section in unit of time. Also let the following integrals, taken over the whole tube, be

$$\int \rho k r^2 ds = A, \quad \int \rho r^2 d\theta = B, \quad \int \rho \frac{1}{a} ds = C \quad\quad\quad (1),$$

the lower end of the tube being in the axis of motion.

Let ϕ be the angle of position of the tube about the vertical axis, then the moment of momentum of the liquid in the tube is

$$H = A \frac{d\phi}{dt} + BQ \quad\quad\quad\quad (2).$$

The moment of momentum of the liquid thrown out of the tube in unit of time is

$$\frac{dH'}{dt} = \rho r^2 Q \frac{d\phi}{dt} + \rho \frac{r}{k} Q^2 \cos a \quad\quad\quad (3),$$

where r is the radius at the orifice, k its section, and a the angle between the direction of the tube there and the direction of motion.

The energy of motion of the fluid in the tube is

$$W = \tfrac{1}{2} A \overline{\frac{d\phi}{dt}}\Big|^2 + BQ \frac{d\phi}{dt} + \tfrac{1}{2} CQ^2 \quad\quad\quad (4).$$

The energy of the fluid which escapes in unit of time is

$$\frac{dW'}{dt} = \rho g Q (h + z) + \tfrac{1}{2} \rho r^2 Q \overline{\frac{d\phi}{dt}}\Big|^2 + \rho \frac{r}{k} \cos a \, Q^2 \frac{d\phi}{dt} + \tfrac{1}{2} \frac{\rho}{k^2} Q^3 \quad\quad\quad (5).$$

The work done by the prime mover in turning the shaft in unit of time is

$$L \frac{d\phi}{dt} = \frac{d\phi}{dt} \left(\frac{dH}{dt} + \frac{dH'}{dt} \right) \quad\quad\quad (6).$$

The work spent on the liquid in unit of time is

$$\frac{dW}{dt} + \frac{dW'}{dt}.$$

Equating this to the work done, we obtain the equations of motion

$$A \frac{d^2\phi}{dt^2} + B \frac{dQ}{dt} + \rho r^2 Q \frac{d\phi}{dt} + \rho \frac{r}{k} \cos \alpha Q^2 = L \dots\dots\dots (7),$$

$$B \frac{d^2\phi}{dt^2} + C \frac{dQ}{dt} + \tfrac{1}{2} \frac{\rho}{k^2} Q^2 + \rho g (h + z) - \tfrac{1}{2} \rho r^2 \overline{\frac{d\phi}{dt}}\Big|^2 = 0 \dots\dots\dots (8).$$

These equations apply to a tube of given section throughout. If the fluid is in open channels, the values of A and C will depend on the depth to which the channels are filled at each point, and that of k will depend on the depth at the overflow.

In the governor described by Mr C. W. Siemens in the paper already referred to, the discharge is practically limited by the depth of the fluid at the brim of the cup.

The resultant force at the brim is $f = \sqrt{g^2 + \omega^4 r^2}$.

If the brim is perfectly horizontal, the overflow will be proportional to $x^{\frac{3}{2}}$ (where x is the depth at the brim), and the mean square of the velocity relative to the brim will be proportional to x, or to $Q^{\frac{2}{3}}$.

If the breadth of overflow at the surface is proportional to x^n, where x is the height above the lowest point of overflow, then Q will vary as $x^{n+\frac{3}{2}}$, and the mean square of the velocity of overflow relative to the cup as x or as $\dfrac{1}{Q^{n+\frac{3}{2}}}$.

If $n = -\tfrac{1}{2}$, then the overflow and the mean square of the velocity are both proportional to x.

From the second equation we find for the mean square of velocity

$$\frac{Q^2}{k^2} = -\frac{2}{\rho} \left(B \frac{d^2\phi}{dt^2} + C \frac{dQ}{dt} \right) + r^2 \overline{\frac{d\phi}{dt}}\Big|^2 - 2g (h + z) \dots\dots\dots (9).$$

If the velocity of rotation and of overflow is constant, this becomes

$$\frac{Q^2}{k^2} = r^2 \overline{\frac{d\phi}{dt}}\Big|^2 - 2g (h + z) \dots\dots\dots (10).$$

From the first equation, supposing, as in Mr Siemens's construction, that $\cos \alpha = 0$ and $B = 0$, we find

$$L = \rho r^2 Q \frac{d\phi}{dt} \dots\dots\dots (11).$$

In Mr Siemens's governor there is an arrangement by which a fixed relation is established between L and z,

$$L = -Sz \dots\dots\dots\dots\dots\dots\dots\dots (12),$$

whence

$$\frac{Q^2}{k^2} = r^2 \overline{\frac{d\phi}{dt}}\bigg|^2 - 2gh + \frac{2g\rho}{S} r^2 Q \frac{d\phi}{dt} \dots\dots\dots\dots (13).$$

If the conditions of overflow can be so arranged that the mean square of the velocity, represented by $\dfrac{Q^2}{k^2}$, is proportional to Q, and if the strength of the spring which determines S is also arranged so that

$$\frac{Q^2}{k^2} = \frac{2g\rho}{S} r^2 \omega Q \dots\dots\dots\dots\dots\dots\dots (14),$$

the equation will become, if $2gh = \omega^2 r^2$,

$$0 = r^2 \left(\overline{\frac{d\phi}{dt}}\bigg|^2 - \omega^2\right) + \frac{2g\rho}{S} r^2 Q \left(\frac{d\phi}{dt} - \omega\right) \dots\dots\dots\dots (15),$$

which shews that the velocity of rotation and of overflow cannot be constant unless the velocity of rotation is ω.

The condition about the overflow is probably difficult to obtain accurately in practice; but very good results have been obtained within a considerable range of driving-power by a proper adjustment of the spring. If the rim is uniform, there will be a *maximum* velocity for a certain driving-power. This seems to be verified by the results given at p. 667 of Mr Siemens's paper.

If the flow of the fluid were limited by a hole, there would be a *minimum* velocity instead of a maximum.

The differential equation which determines the nature of small disturbances is in general of the fourth order, but may be reduced to the third by a proper choice of the value of the mean overflow.

Theory of Differential Gearing.

In some contrivances the main shaft is connected with the governor by a wheel or system of wheels which are capable of rotation round an axis, which is itself also capable of rotation about the axis of the main shaft. These two axes may be at right angles, as in the ordinary system of differential bevel wheels; or they may be parallel, as in several contrivances adapted to clockwork.

Let ξ and η represent the angular position about each of these axes respectively, θ that of the main shaft, and ϕ that of the governor; then θ and ϕ are linear functions of ξ and η, and the motion of any point of the system can be expressed in terms either of ξ and η or of θ and ϕ.

Let the velocity of a particle whose mass is m resolved in the direction of x be

$$\frac{dx}{dt} = p_1 \frac{d\xi}{dt} + q_1 \frac{d\eta}{dt} \dots\dots\dots\dots\dots\dots\dots\dots\dots (1),$$

with similar expressions for the other co-ordinate directions, putting suffixes 2 and 3 to denote the values of p and q for these directions. Then Lagrange's equation of motion becomes

$$\Xi \delta\xi + H\delta\eta - \Sigma m \left(\frac{d^2x}{dt^2} \delta x + \frac{d^2y}{dt^2} \delta y + \frac{d^2z}{dt^2} \delta z \right) = 0 \dots\dots\dots\dots (2),$$

where Ξ and H are the forces tending to increase ξ and η respectively, no force being supposed to be applied at any other point.

Now putting $\quad\quad \delta x = p_1\delta\xi + q_1\delta\eta, \dots\dots\dots\dots\dots\dots\dots (3),$

and $\quad\quad\quad\quad\quad \dfrac{d^2x}{dt^2} = p_1 \dfrac{d^2\xi}{dt^2} + q_1 \dfrac{d^2\eta}{dt^2} \dots\dots\dots\dots\dots\dots (4),$

the equation becomes

$$\left(\Xi - \Sigma m p^2 \frac{d^2\xi}{dt^2} - \Sigma m p q \frac{d^2\eta}{dt^2} \right) \delta\xi + \left(H - \Sigma m p q \frac{d^2\xi}{dt} - \Sigma m q^2 \frac{d^2\eta}{dt^2} \right) \delta\eta = 0 \dots (5);$$

and since $\delta\xi$ and $\delta\eta$ are independent, the coefficient of each must be zero.

If we now put

$$\Sigma (mp^2) = L, \quad \Sigma (mpq) = M, \quad \Sigma (mq^2) = N \dots\dots\dots\dots\dots (6),$$

where $\quad p^2 = p_1^2 + p_2^2 + p_3^2, \quad pq = p_1q_1 + p_2q_2 + p_3q_3, \quad$ and $\quad q^2 = q_1^2 + q_2^2 + q_3^2,$

the equations of motion will be

$$\Xi = L \frac{d^2\xi}{dt^2} + M \frac{d^2\eta}{dt^2} \dots\dots\dots\dots\dots\dots\dots\dots\dots\dots (7),$$

$$H = M \frac{d^2\xi}{dt^2} + N \frac{d^2\eta}{dt^2} \dots\dots\dots\dots\dots\dots\dots\dots\dots\dots (8).$$

If the apparatus is so arranged that $M = 0$, then the two motions will be independent of each other; and the motions indicated by ξ and η will be about conjugate axes—that is, about axes such that the rotation round one of them does not tend to produce a force about the other.

Now let Θ be the driving-power of the shaft on the differential system, and Φ that of the differential system on the governor; then the equation of motion becomes

$$\Theta\delta\theta + \Phi\delta\phi + \left(\Xi - L\frac{d^2\xi}{dt^2} - M\frac{d^2\eta}{dt^2}\right)\delta\xi + \left(\mathrm{H} - M\frac{d^2\xi}{dt^2} - N\frac{d^2\eta}{dt^2}\right)\delta\eta = 0 \ \ldots\ldots (9);$$

and if

$$\left.\begin{aligned}\delta\xi &= P\delta\theta + Q\delta\phi \\ \delta\eta &= R\delta\theta + S\delta\phi\end{aligned}\right\} \quad\ldots\ldots\ldots\ldots\ldots\ldots\ldots\ldots (10),$$

and if we put

$$\left.\begin{aligned}L' &= LP^2 + 2MPR & + NR^2 \\ M' &= LPQ + M(PS+QR) + NRS \\ N' &= LQ^2 + 2MQS & + NS^2\end{aligned}\right\} \quad\ldots\ldots\ldots\ldots (11),$$

the equations of motion in θ and ϕ will be

$$\left.\begin{aligned}\Theta + P\Xi + Q\mathrm{H} &= L'\frac{d^2\theta}{dt^2} + M'\frac{d^2\phi}{dt^2} \\ \Phi + R\Xi + S\mathrm{H} &= M'\frac{d^2\theta}{dt^2} + N'\frac{d^2\phi}{dt^2}\end{aligned}\right\} \quad\ldots\ldots\ldots\ldots\ldots (12).$$

If $M' = 0$, then the motions in θ and ϕ will be independent of each other. If M is also 0, then we have the relation

$$LPQ + MRS = 0\ldots\ldots\ldots\ldots\ldots\ldots\ldots\ldots\ldots (13);$$

and if this is fulfilled, the disturbances of the motion in θ will have no effect on the motion in ϕ. The teeth of the differential system in gear with the main shaft and the governor respectively will then correspond to the centres of percussion and rotation of a simple body, and this relation will be mutual.

In such differential systems a constant force, H, sufficient to keep the governor in a proper state of efficiency, is applied to the axis η, and the motion of this axis is made to work a valve or a break on the main shaft of the machine. Ξ in this case is merely the friction about the axis of ξ. If the moments of inertia of the different parts of the system are so arranged that $M' = 0$, then the disturbance produced by a blow or a jerk on the machine will act instantaneously on the valve, but will not communicate any impulse to the governor.

[From the *Philosophical Magazine*, for May, 1868.]

XXXV. *"Experiment in Magneto-Electric Induction."*

IN A LETTER TO W. R. GROVE, F.R.S.*

8, Palace Gardens Terrace, W.
March 27, 1868.

Dear Sir,

Since our conversation yesterday on your experiment on magneto-electric induction†, I have considered it mathematically, and now send you the result. I have left out of the question the secondary coil, as the peculiar effect you observed depends essentially on the strength of the current in the primary coil, and the secondary sparks merely indicate a strong alternating primary current. The phenomenon depends on the magneto-electric machine, the electro-magnet, and the condenser.

The machine produces in the primary wire an alternating electromagnetic force, which we may compare to a mechanical force alternately pushing and pulling at a body.

The resistance of the primary wire we may compare to the effect of a viscous fluid in which the body is made to move backwards and forwards.

The electromagnetic coil, on account of its self-induction, resists the starting and stopping of the current, just as the mass of a large boat resists the efforts of a man trying to move it backwards and forwards.

The condenser resists the accumulation of electricity on its surface, just as a railway-buffer resists the motion of a carriage towards a fixed obstacle.

* Communicated by Mr W. R. Grove, F.R.S.
† See *Phil. Mag.* S. 4. March 1868, p. 184.

Now let us suppose a boat floating in a viscous fluid, and kept in its place by buffers fore and aft abutting against fixed obstacles, or by elastic ropes attached to fixed moorings before and behind. If the buffers were away, the mass of the boat would not prevent a man from pulling the boat along with a long-continued pull; but if the man were to push and pull in alternate seconds of time, he would produce very little motion of the boat. The buffers will effectually prevent the man from moving the boat far from its position by a steady pull; but if he pushes and pulls alternately, the period of alternation being not very different from that in which the buffers would cause the boat to vibrate about its position of equilibrium, then the force which acts in each vibration is due, partly to the efforts of the man, but chiefly to the resilience of the buffers, and the man will be able to move the boat much further from its mean position than he would if he had pushed and pulled at the same rate at the same boat perfectly free.

Thus, when an alternating force acts on a massive body, the extent of the displacements may be much greater when the body is attracted towards a position of equilibrium by a force depending on the displacement than when the body is perfectly free.

The electricity in the primary coil when it is closed corresponds to a free body resisted only on account of its motion; and in this case the current produced by an alternating force is small. When the primary coil is interrupted by a condenser, the electricity is resisted with a force proportional to the accumulation, and corresponds to a body whose motion is restrained by a spring; and in this case the motion produced by a force which alternates with sufficient rapidity may be much greater than in the former case. I enclose the mathematical theory of the experiment, and remain,

Yours truly,

J. CLERK MAXWELL.

Mathematical Theory of the Experiment.

Let M be the revolving armature of the magneto-electric machine, N, S the poles of the magnets, x the current led through the coil of the electromagnet R, and interrupted by the condenser C. Let the plates of the condenser be connected by the additional conductor y.

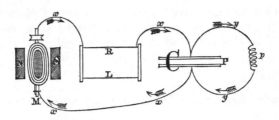

Let $M \sin \theta$ be the value of the potential of the magnets on the coil of the armature; then if the armature revolves with the angular velocity n, the electromotive force due to the machine is $Mn \cos nt$.

Let R be the resistance of the wire which forms the coil of the armature M and that of the fixed electromagnet.

Let L be the coefficient of self-induction, or the "electromagnetic mass" of these two coils taken together.

Let x be the value of the current in this wire at any instant, then Lx will be its "electromagnetic momentum."

Let C be the capacity of the condenser, and P the excess of potential of the upper plate at any instant, then the quantity of electricity on the upper plate is CP.

Let ρ be the resistance of the additional conductor, and y the current in it. We shall neglect the self induction of this current.

We have then for this conductor,
$$P = \rho y \dots\dots\dots (1).$$

For the charge of the condenser,
$$C \frac{dP}{dt} = x - y \dots\dots\dots (2).$$

For the current x,
$$Mn \cos nt + Rx + L \frac{dx}{dt} + P = 0 \dots\dots\dots (3).$$

If we assume
$$x = A \cos (nt + a),$$

we find
$$A^2 = \frac{M^2 n^2 \left(1 + C^2 \rho^2 n^2\right)}{\rho^2 \left\{(1 - LCn^2)^2 + R^2 C^2 n^2\right\} + 2R\rho + R^2 + Ln^2},$$
$$a = \cot^{-1} \frac{1}{C\rho n} - \cot^{-1} \frac{R + \rho - LC\rho n^2}{RC\rho n + Ln}.$$

The quantity of the alternating current is determined by A; and the value of a only affects the epoch of the maximum current. If we make $\rho = 0$, the effect is that of closing the circuit of x, and we find

$$A^2 = \frac{M^2 n^2}{R^2 + L^2 n^2}.$$

This expression shews that the condenser has no effect when the current is closed.

If we make $\rho = \infty$, the effect is that of removing the conductor y, and thus breaking the circuit. In this case

$$A^2 = \frac{M^2 n^2}{R^2 + \left(Ln - \dfrac{1}{Cn}\right)^2}.$$

This expression gives a greater value of A than when the circuit is closed, provided $2CLn^2$ is greater than unity, which may be ensured by increasing the capacity of the condenser, the self-induction of the electromagnetic coil, or the velocity of rotation.

If $CL^2 n = 1$, the expression is reduced to

$$A = \frac{Mn}{R}.$$

This is the greatest effect which can be produced with a given velocity, and is the same as if the current in the coil had no "electromagnetic momentum."

If the electromagnet has a secondary coil outside the primary coil so as to form an ordinary induction-coil, the intensity of the secondary current will depend essentially on that of the primary which has just been found. Although the reaction of the secondary current on the primary coil will introduce a greater complication in the mathematical expressions, the remarkable phenomenon described by Mr Grove does not require us to enter into this calculation, as the secondary sparks observed by him are a mere indication of what takes place in the primary coil.

[From the *Philosophical Transactions*, Vol. CLVIII.]

XXXVI. *On a Method of Making a Direct Comparison of Electrostatic with Electromagnetic Force; with a Note on the Electromagnetic Theory of Light.*

Received June 10,—Read June 18, 1868.

THERE are two distinct and independent methods of measuring electrical quantities with reference to received standards of length, time, and mass.

The electrostatic method is founded on the attractions and repulsions between electrified bodies separated by a fluid dielectric medium, such as air; and the electrical units are determined so that the repulsion between two small electrified bodies at a considerable distance may be represented numerically by the product of the quantities of electricity, divided by the square of the distance.

The electromagnetic method is founded on the attractions and repulsions observed between conductors carrying electric currents, and separated by air; and the electrical units are determined so that if two equal straight conductors are placed parallel to each other, and at a very small distance compared with their length, the attraction between them may be represented numerically by the product of the currents multiplied by the sum of the lengths of the conductors, and divided by the distance between them.

These two methods lead to two different units by which the quantity of electricity is to be measured. The ratio of the two units is an important physical quantity, which we propose to measure. Let us consider the relation of these units to those of space, time, and force (that of force being a function of space, time, and mass).

In the electrostatic system we have a force equal to the product of two quantities of electricity divided by the square of the distance. The unit of electricity will therefore vary directly as the unit of length, and as the square root of the unit of force.

In the electromagnetic system we have a force equal to the product of two currents multiplied by the ratio of two lines. The unit of current in this system therefore varies as the square root of the unit of force; and the unit of electrical quantity, which is that which is transmitted by the unit current in unit of time, varies as the unit of time and as the square root of the unit of force.

The ratio of the electromagnetic unit to the electrostatic unit is therefore that of a certain distance to a certain time, or, in other words, this ratio is a *velocity*; and this velocity will be of the same absolute magnitude, whatever standards of length, time, and mass we adopt.

The electromagnetic value of the resistance of a conductor is also a quantity of the nature of a velocity, and therefore we may express the ratio of the two electrical units in terms of the resistance of a known standard coil; and this expression will be independent of the magnitude of our standards of length, time and mass.

In the experiments here described no absolute measurements were made, either of length, time, or mass, the ratios only of these quantities being involved; and the velocity determined is expressed in terms of the British Association Unit of Resistance, so that whatever corrections may be discovered to be applicable to the absolute value of that unit must be also applied to the velocity here determined.

A resistance-coil whose resistance is equal to about 28·8 B. A. units would represent the velocity derived from the present experiments in a manner independent of all particular standards of measure.

The importance of the determination of this ratio in all cases in which electrostatic and electromagnetic actions are combined is obvious. Such cases occur in the ordinary working of all submarine telegraph-cables, in induction-coils, and in many other artificial arrangements. But a knowledge of this ratio is, I think, of still greater scientific importance when we consider that the velocity of propagation of electromagnetic disturbances through a dielectric medium depends on this ratio, and, according to my calculations*, is expressed by the very same number.

The first numerical determination of this quantity is that of Weber and Kohlrausch†, who measured the capacity of a condenser electrostatically by

* "A Dynamical Theory of the Electromagnetic Field," *Philosophical Transactions*, 1865.
† Pogg, *Ann.* Aug. 1856, Bd. xcix. p. 10.

comparison with the capacity of a sphere of known radius, and electromagnetically by passing the discharge from the condenser through a galvanometer.

The Electrical Committee of the British Association have turned their attention to the means of obtaining an accurate measurement of this velocity, and for this purpose have devised new forms of condensers and contact-breakers; and Sir William Thomson has obtained numerical values of continually increasing accuracy by the constant improvement of his own methods.

A velocity which is so great compared with our ordinary units of space and time is probably most easily measured by steps, and by the use of several different instruments; but as it seemed probable that the time occupied in the construction and improvement of these instruments would be considerable, I determined to employ a more direct method of comparing electrostatic with electromagnetic effects.

I should not, however, have been able to do this, had not Mr Gassiot, with his usual liberality, placed at my disposal his magnificent battery of 2600 cells charged with corrosive sublimate, with the use of his laboratory to work in.

To Mr Willoughby Smith I am indebted for the use of his resistance-coils, giving a resistance of more than a million B. A. units, and to Messrs Forde and Fleeming Jenkin for the use of a galvanometer and resistance-coils, a bridge and a key for double contacts.

Mr C. Hockin, who has greatly assisted me with suggestions since I first devised the experiment, undertook the whole work of the comparison of the currents by means of the galvanometer and shunts. He has also tested the resistances, and in fact done everything except the actual observation of equilibrium, which I undertook myself.

The electrical balance itself was made for me by Mr Becker.

The electrostatic force observed was that between two parallel disks, of which one, six inches diameter, was insulated and maintained at a high potential, while the other, four inches diameter, was at the same potential as the case of the instrument.

In order to insure a known quantity of electricity on the surface of this disk, it was surrounded by the "guard-ring" introduced by Sir W. Thomson, so that the surface of the disk when in position and that of the guard-ring were in one plane, at the same potential, and separated by a very narrow space. In this way the electrical action on the small disk was equal to that due to a uniform distribution over its front surface, while no electrical action could exist at its sides or back, as these were at the same potential with the surrounding surfaces.

The large disk was mounted on a slide worked by a micrometer-screw. The small disk was suspended on one arm of a torsion-balance so that in its position of equilibrium its surface and that of the guard-ring were in one plane.

If E is the difference of potential between the two disks in electromagnetic measure, the attraction between them is

$$\frac{E^2}{8v^2}\frac{a^2}{b^2} \quad\text{...} (1),$$

where a is the radius of the small disk, b its distance from the large one, and v is the velocity representing the ratio of the electromagnetic to the electrostatic unit of electricity.

The electromagnetic force observed was the repulsion between two circular coils, of which one was attached to the back of the suspended disk, and the other was placed behind the large disk, being separated from it by a plate of glass and a layer of Hooper's compound. A current was made to pass through these coils in opposite directions, so as to produce a repulsion

$$= 2\pi nn' \frac{2A}{B} y^2 \quad\text{...............................} (2),$$

where n and n' are the number of windings of each coil, y is the current, and

$$\frac{2A}{B} = \{E_c \tan^2\gamma - 2(F_c - E_c)\}\frac{b'\sin\gamma}{2\sqrt{a_1 a_2}} \quad\text{.....................} (3),$$

where

$$c = \sin\gamma = \frac{2\sqrt{a_1 a_2}}{\sqrt{(a_1 + a_2)^2 + b'^2}} \quad\text{.........................} (4);$$

a_1 and a_2 are the mean radii of the coils, and b' the mean distance of their planes, and E_c and F_c are the complete elliptic functions for modulus $c = \sin\gamma$.

When b' is small compared with a', $\frac{2A}{B}$ becomes very nearly $\frac{2a'}{b'}$.

If we take into account the fact that the section of each coil is of sensible area, this formula would require correction; but in these coils the depth was made equal to the breadth of the section, whence it follows, by the differential equation of the potential of two coils, given at p. 508 [*] of my paper on the Electromagnetic Field,

$$\frac{d^2M}{da^2} + \frac{d^2M}{db^2} - \frac{1}{a}\frac{dM}{da} = 0 \dots\dots\dots\dots\dots\dots(5),$$

that the correction is a factor of the form $\left(1 - \frac{1}{12}\frac{a'}{a'^2}\right)$, where a' is the depth of the coil—a correction which is in this case about $1 - \cdot000926$.

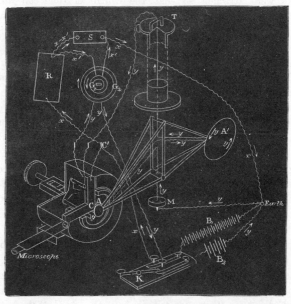

A. Suspended disk and coil.	K. Double key. g. Graduated glass scale.
A'. Counterpoise disk and coil.	C'. Electrode of fixed disk.
C. Fixed disk and coil.	x. Current through R.
B₁. Great battery. B₂. Small battery.	x'. Current through G₁. $x - x'$. Current through S.
G₁. Primary coil of galvanometer.	y. Current through the three coils and G₂.
G₂. Secondary coil. R. Great resistance.	S. Shunt. M. Mercury cup.
T. Torsion head and tangent screw.	

One quarter of the micrometer-box, disks, and coils is cut away to shew the interior. The case of the instrument is not shewn. The galvanometer and shunts were 10 feet from the Electric Balance.

* [Vol. I. p. 591.]

The suspended coil, besides the repulsion due to the fixed coil, experiences a couple due to the action of terrestrial magnetism. To balance this couple, a coil exactly similar was attached to the other arm of the torsion-balance, and the current in the second coil was made to flow in the opposite direction to that in the first. When the current was made to flow through both coils, no effect of terrestrial magnetism could be observed.

The torsion-balance consisted of a light brass frame, to which the suspended coils and disks were attached so that the centre of each coil was about eight inches from the vertical axis of suspension. This frame was suspended by a copper wire (No. 20), the upper end of which was attached to the centre of a torsion head, graduated, and provided with a tangent screw for small angular adjustments. The torsion head was supported by a hollow pillar, the base of which was clamped to the lid of the instrument so as to admit of small adjustments in every direction.

The fixed disk and coil were mounted on a slide worked by a micrometer-screw, and were protected by a cylindrical brass box, the front of which, forming the guard-ring, 7 inches in diameter, had a circular aperture 4·26 inches diameter, within which the suspended disk, 4·13 inches diameter, was free to move, leaving an interval of ·065 of an inch between the disk and the aperture. A glass scale with divisions of $\frac{1}{100}$ of an inch was attached to the suspended disk on the side which was not electrified, and this was viewed by a microscope attached to the side of the instrument and provided with cross wires at the focus.

The disk worked by the micrometer was carefully adjusted by the maker, so as to be parallel to the inner surface of the guard-ring, or front face of the micrometer-box. This front face of the micrometer-box, when in position in the instrument, was made vertical by means of three adjusting screws. The suspended disk was then pressed against the fixed disk by means of a slight spring, and the fixed disk was gradually moved forward by the micrometer-screw, while at the same time the graduated scale was observed through the microscope. In this way the graduations on the scale were compared with the readings of the micrometer. This was continued till the large disk came into contact with the guard-ring at one point, when the regularity of the motion was interrupted. A very small motion was then sufficient to bring the whole circumference of the disk into contact with the guard-ring, when the motion ceased altogether. This motion was not much more than one-thousandth of an inch.

This disk was then brought to the position of first contact, and the microscope was adjusted so that a known division of the glass scale was bisected by the cross wires. A small piece of silvered glass was fastened to the outside of the guard-ring, and another to the back of the suspended disk; and these were adjusted so as to be in one plane, and to give a continuous image of reflected objects when the disks were in contact and the surface of the suspended disk was therefore in the plane of the surface of the guard-ring. The fixed disk was then screwed back, and the torsion-balance was adjusted so that the suspended disk when in equilibrium was in precisely the same position as before. This was tested by observing the coincidence of the zero division of the glass scale with the cross wires of the microscope, and by examining the reflections from the two pieces of silvered glass. The torsion-balance could be moved bodily in any horizontal direction by adjusting the base of the pillar; it could be raised or lowered by a winch, and it could be turned about any horizontal axis by sliding weights, and round the vertical axis by a tangent screw of the torsion head. In this way the position of equilibrium of the suspended disk could be made to coincide with the plane of the guard-ring to the thousandth of an inch; and the adjustment when made continued very good from day to day, soft copper wire, stretched straight, not having the tendency to untwist gradually which I have observed in steel wire. The weight of the torsion piece was about 1 lb. 3 oz., and the time of a double oscillation about fourteen seconds. The oscillations of the suspended disk, when near its sighted position, were found to subside very rapidly, the energy of the motion being expended in pumping the air through the narrow aperture between the guard-plate and the suspended disk.

The electrical arrangements were as follows :—

One electrode of Mr Gassiot's great battery was connected with a key. When the key was pressed connexion was made to the fixed disk, and thence, through Mr Willoughby Smith's resistance-coils, to a point where the current was divided between the principal coil of the galvanometer and a shunt, S, consisting of Mr Jenkin's resistance-coils. These partial currents reunited at a point where they were put in connexion with the other electrode of the battery, with the case of the instrument, and with the earth.

Another battery was employed to send a current through the coils. One electrode of this battery was connected with a second contact piece of the key, so that, when the key was pressed, the current went first through the secondary coil of the galvanometer, consisting of thirty windings of thick wire, then through the fixed coil, then to the suspension wire, and so through the two suspended coils to the brass frame of the torsion-balance and the suspended disk. A stout copper wire, well amalgamated, hanging from the centre of the torsion-balance into a cup of mercury, made metallic communication to the case, to earth, and to the other electrode of the battery.

When these arrangements had been made, the observer at the microscope, when the suspended disk was stationary at zero, made simultaneous contact with both batteries by means of the key. If the disk was attracted, the great battery was the more powerful, and the micrometer was worked so as to increase the distance of the disk. If the disk was repelled, the fixed disk had to be moved nearer to the suspended disk, till a distance was found at which, when the scale was at rest and at zero, no effect was produced by the simultaneous action of the batteries. With the forces actually employed the equilibrium of the scale at zero was unstable; so that when the adjustment was nearly perfect the force was always directed from zero, and contacts had to be made as the scale was approaching zero, in such a way as to bring it to rest, if possible, at zero.

In the meantime the other observer at the galvanometer was taking advantage of these contacts to alter the shunt S, till the effects of the two currents on the galvanometer-needle balanced each other.

When a satisfactory case of equilibrium had been observed simultaneously at the galvanometer and at the torsion-balance, the micrometer-reading and the resistance of the shunt were set down as the results of the experiment.

The chief difficulties experienced arose from the want of constancy in the batteries, the ratio of the currents varying very rapidly after first making contact. I think that by increasing considerably the resistance of the great battery-circuit, the current could be made more uniform.

When a sufficient number of experiments on equilibrium had been made, a current was made to pass through the secondary coil of the galvanometer, and was then divided between a shunt of 31 units BA and the primary coil of the galvanometer with a resistance S' added. S' was then varied till the needle was in equilibrium. In this way the magnetic effects of the two coils were compared.

The resistance of the galvanometer and of all the coils were tested by

Mr Hockin, who also made all the observations with the galvanometer and its adjusting shunts.

To determine v from these experiments, we have first, since the attraction is equal to the repulsion,

$$\frac{E^2}{8v^2}\frac{a^2}{b^2} = 2\pi nn' \frac{2A}{B} y^2 \quad\dots\dots\dots\dots\dots\dots\dots(6).$$

If x is the current of the great battery passing through the great resistance R, and if x' of this passes through the galvanometer whose resistance is G, and $x - x'$ through the shunt S to earth, then

$$E = Rx + Gx' \quad\dots\dots\dots\dots\dots\dots\dots(7),$$

and

$$Gx' = S(x - x') \quad\dots\dots\dots\dots\dots\dots\dots(8).$$

Also if g_1 is the magnetic effect of the principal coil of the galvanometer, and g_2 that of the secondary coil, then when the needle is in equilibrium

$$g_1 x' = g_2 y \quad\dots\dots\dots\dots\dots\dots\dots(9).$$

In the comparison of the coils of the galvanometer, if x_1 and y_1 are the currents through each, we have

$$g_1 x_1 = g_2 y_1 \quad\dots\dots\dots\dots\dots\dots\dots(10).$$

But y_1 is divided into two parts, of which x_1 passes through the galvanometer G and the shunt S', and the other, $y_1 - x'$, passes through the shunt of 31 Ohms. Hence

$$x_1 (G + S') = (y_1 - x_1) 31 \quad\dots\dots\dots\dots\dots\dots(11).$$

From these equations we obtain as the value of v,

$$v = \frac{1}{4\sqrt{nn'}\pi}\frac{a}{b}\sqrt{\frac{B}{2A}}\left(\frac{RG}{S} + R + G\right)\frac{31}{G + S' + 31} \quad\dots\dots\dots(12),$$

an equation containing only known quantities on the right-hand side. Of these, n and n' are the numbers of windings on the two coils, a is the mean of the radii of the suspended disk and the aperture, b is the distance between the fixed disk and the suspended disk, $\frac{2A}{B}$ is found from a_1 and a_2, the mean radii of the coils, and b' their mean distance by equation (3).

R is the great resistance, G that of the galvanometer, S that of the shunt in the principal experiment, and S' that of the additional resistance in the comparison of galvanometer-coils.

In this expression the only quantities which must be determined in absolute measure are the resistances. The other quantities which must be measured are the ratios of the radius of the disk to its distance from the fixed disk, and the ratio of the radius of the coils to the distance between them. These ratios and the number of windings in the coils are of course abstract numbers.

In the experiments,

$$n = 144 \qquad\qquad n' = 121$$
$$a = 2 \cdot 0977 \text{ inches.} \qquad a' = 1 \cdot 934 \text{ inch.}$$

To determine a', the circumference of every layer of the coils was measured with watch-spring, the thickness of which was ·008 inch.

One turn of the micrometer-screw was found by Mr Hockin to be equal to ·0202 inch. If m is the micrometer-reading in terms of the screw,

$$b = m - 12 \cdot 70, \qquad\qquad b' = m + 26 \cdot 31.$$

In terms of the micrometer measure we have for a and a',

$$a = 103 \cdot 85 \text{ turns,} \qquad\qquad a' = 95 \cdot 75 \text{ turns.}$$

The resistances were determined by Mr Hockin as follows :

$$R = 1 \ 102 \ 000 \text{ Ohms.}$$
$$G = \qquad 46 \ 220 \quad ,,$$

The experiments were made for two days, using a small battery charged with bichromate of potash. The current due to this battery was found to diminish so rapidly that a set of Grove's cells was used on the third day, which was found to be more constant than the great battery. A proper combination of the two batteries would perhaps produce a current which would diminish according to the same law as that of the great battery. Another difficulty arose from the fact that when the connexions were made, but before the key was pressed, if the micrometer was touched by the hand the disk was attracted. This I have not been able satisfactorily to account for, except by leakage of electricity from the great battery through the floor. When the micrometer was not touched, the disk remained at its proper zero. In certain experiments I kept my hand always on the micrometer in order to be able to adjust it more accurately. These experiments gave a value of v much too small, on account of the additional attraction. When I discovered the attraction,

I took care to make the observations without touching the micrometer, and took advantage of the attraction to check the oscillations of the disk. The experiments in which these precautions were taken agree together as well as I could expect, and lead me to think that, with the experience I have acquired, still better results might be obtained by the same method. It must be borne in mind that none of the results were calculated till after the conclusion of all the experiments, and that the rejected experiments were condemned on account of errors observed while they were being made.

Any leakage arising from want of insulation of the fixed disk would introduce no error, as the difference of potentials between the two disks is measured by the current in the galvanometer, through a known resistance, independently of any leakage.

All that is essential to accuracy is that the position of equilibrium before making contact should be at true zero, the same as when there is no electrical action, and that this equilibrium should not be disturbed when simultaneous contact is made with both batteries.

Experiments on May 8. $S' = 1710$ Ohms.

Number of experiment	Great battery-cells	Small battery-cells	Distance of disks by micrometer	Resistance of shunt S	Value of v in Ohms
1	1000	6	12·41	6870	28·591
2	1000	6	12·36	6940	28·430
8*	1800	8	16·99	5074	28·886
9	1800	8	17·02	5110	28·686
10	1800	8	19·91	4430	28·910
11	1800	7	20·07	4410	28·850
12	2600	9	25·08	3700	28·762
13	2600	9	25·12	3690	28·795
14	2600	9	25·29	3680	28·735
15	2600	9	25·18	3690	28·752
16	2600	9	25·19	3695	28·709
17	1800	7	19·69	4435	29·474

Mean value of $v = 28·798$ Ohms, or B. A. units,

or 288,000,000 metres per second,

or 179,000 statute miles per second.

The "probable error" is about one-sixth per cent.

* In experiment 8 Mr Hockin and I changed places.

Experiments 3, 4, 5, 6, 7 were rejected on account of the micrometer being touched during the observation of equilibrium. These experiments gave an average value of $v = 27\cdot39$.

The value of v derived from these experiments is considerably smaller than that which was obtained by MM. Weber and Kohlrausch, which was $31\cdot074$ Ohms, or 310,740,000 metres per second.

Their method involved the determination of the electrostatic capacity of a condenser, the electrostatic determination of its potential when charged, and the electromagnetic determination of the quantity of electricity discharged through a galvanometer.

The capacity of the condenser was measured by dividing its charge repeatedly with a sphere of known radius. Now, since all condensers made with solid dielectrics exhibit the phenomena of "electric absorption," this method would give too large a value for the capacity, as the condenser would become recharged to a certain extent after each discharge, so that the repeated division of the charge would have too small an effect on the potential. The capacity being overestimated, the number of electrostatic units in the discharge would be overestimated, and the value of v would be too great.

In pointing out this as a probable source of error in the experiments of MM. Weber and Kohlrausch, I mean to indicate that I have such confidence in the ability and fidelity with which their investigation was conducted, that I am obliged to attribute the difference of their result from mine to a phenomenon the nature of which is now much better understood than when their experiments were made.

On the other hand, the result of present experiments depends on the accuracy of the experiments of the Committee of the British Association on Electric Resistance. The B. A. unit is about $8\cdot8$ per cent. larger than that determined by Weber in 1862, and about $1\cdot2$ per cent. less than that derived by Dr Joule from his experiments on the dynamical equivalent of heat by comparing the heating effects of direct mechanical agitation with those of electric currents.

I believe that Sir William Thomson's experiments, not yet published, give a value of v not very different from mine. His method, I believe, also depends on the value of the B. A. unit.

The lowest estimate of the velocity of light, that of the late M. Foucault, is

298,000,000 metres per second.

Note on the Electromagnetic Theory of Light.

In a paper on the Electromagnetic Field* some years ago, I laid before the Royal Society the reasons which led me to believe that light is an electromagnetic phenomenon, the laws of which can be deduced from those of electricity and magnetism, on the theory that all these phenomena are affections of one and the same medium. Two papers appeared in Poggendorff's *Annalen*, for 1867, bearing on the same subject. The first, by the late eminent mathematician Bernhardt Riemann, was presented in 1858 to the Royal Society of Göttingen, but was withdrawn before publication, and remained unknown till last year. Riemann shews that if for Laplace's equation we substitute

$$\frac{d^2 V}{dt^2} - a^2 \Delta^2 V + a^2 4\pi\rho = 0 \dots\dots\dots\dots\dots\dots (13),$$

V being the electrostatic potential, and a a velocity, the results will agree with known phenomena in all parts of electrical science. This equation is equivalent to a statement that the potential V is propagated through space with a certain velocity. The author, however, seems to avoid making explicit mention of any medium through which the propagation takes place, but he shews that this velocity is nearly, if not absolutely, equal to the known velocity of light.

The second paper, by M. Lorenz, shews that, on Weber's theory, periodic electric disturbances would be propagated with a velocity equal to that of light. The propagation of attraction through space forms part of this hypothesis also, though the medium is not explicitly recognised.

From the assumptions of both these papers we may draw the conclusions, first, that action and reaction are not always equal and opposite, and second, that apparatus may be constructed to generate any amount of work from its resources.

For let two oppositely electrified bodies A and B travel along the line joining them with equal velocities in the direction AB, then if either the potential or the attraction of the bodies at a given time is that due to their position at some former time (as these authors suppose), B, the foremost body, will attract A forwards more than A attracts B backwards.

---

* *Philosophical Transactions*, 1865, p. 459. [Vol. I. p. 527.]

Now let A and B be kept asunder by a rigid rod.

The combined system, if set in motion in the direction AB, will pull in that direction with a force which may either continually augment the velocity, or may be used as an inexhaustible source of energy.

I think that these remarkable deductions from the latest developments of Weber and Neumann's theory can only be avoided by recognizing the action of a medium in electrical phenomena.

The statement of the electromagnetic theory of light in my former paper was connected with several other electromagnetic investigations, and was therefore not easily understood when taken by itself. I propose, therefore, to state it in what I think the simplest form, deducing it from admitted facts, and shewing the connexion between the experiments already described and those which determine the velocity of light.

The connexion of electromagnetic phenomena may be stated in the following manner.

THEOREM A.—If a closed curve be drawn embracing an electric current, then the integral of the magnetic intensity taken round the closed curve is equal to the current multiplied by 4π.

The integral of the magnetic intensity may be otherwise defined as the work done on a unit magnetic pole carried completely round the closed curve.

This well-known theorem gives us the means of discovering the position and magnitude of electric currents, when we can ascertain the distribution of magnetic force in the field. It follows directly from the discovery of Œrsted.

THEOREM B.—If a conducting circuit embraces a number of lines of magnetic force, and if, from any cause whatever, the number of these lines is diminished, an electromotive force will act round the circuit, the total amount of which will be equal to the decrement of the number of lines of magnetic force in unit of time.

The number of lines of magnetic force may be otherwise defined as the integral of the magnetic intensity resolved perpendicular to a surface, multiplied by the element of surface, and by the coefficient of magnetic induction, the integration being extended over any surface bounded by the conducting circuit.

This theorem is due to Faraday, as the discoverer both of the facts and of this mode of expressing them, which I think the simplest and most comprehensive.

THEOREM C.—When a dielectric is acted on by electromotive force it experiences what we may call electric polarization. If the direction of the electromotive force is called positive, and if we suppose the dielectric bounded by two conductors, A on the negative, and B on the positive side, then the surface of the conductor A is positively electrified, and that of B negatively.

If we admit that the energy of the system so electrified resides in the polarized dielectric, we must also admit that within the dielectric there is a displacement of electricity in the direction of the electromotive force, the amount of this displacement being proportional to the electromotive force at each point, and depending also on the nature of the dielectric.

The energy stored up in any portion of the dielectric is half the product of the electromotive force and the electric displacement, multiplied by the volume of that portion.

It may also be shewn that at every point of the dielectric there is a mechanical tension along the lines of electric force, combined with an equal pressure in all directions at right angles to these lines, the amount of this tension on unit of area being equal to the amount of energy in unit of volume.

I think that these statements are an accurate rendering of the ideas of Faraday, as developed in various parts of his "Experimental Researches."

THEOREM D.—When the electric displacement increases or diminishes, the effect is equivalent to that of an electric current in the positive or negative direction.

Thus, if the two conductors in the last case are now joined by a wire, there will be a current in the wire from A to B.

At the same time, since the electric displacement in the dielectric is diminishing, there will be an action electromagnetically equivalent to that of an electric current from B to A through the dielectric.

According to this view, the current produced in discharging a condenser is a complete circuit, and might be traced within the dielectric itself by a galvanometer properly constructed. I am not aware that this has been done, so that this part of the theory, though apparently a natural consequence of the former, has not been verified by direct experiment. The experiment would certainly be a very delicate and difficult one.

Let us now apply these four principles to the electromagnetic theory of light, considered as a disturbance propagated in plane waves.

Let the direction of propagation be taken as the axis of z, and let all the quantities be functions of z and of t the time; that is, let every portion of any plane perpendicular to z be in the same condition at the same instant.

Let us also suppose that the magnetic force is in the direction of the axis of y, and let β be the magnetic intensity in that direction at any point.

Let the closed curve of Theorem A consist of a parallelogram in the plane yz, two of whose sides are b along the axis of y, and z along the axis of z. The integral of the magnetic intensity taken round this parallelogram is $b\,(\beta_0 - \beta)$, where β_0 is the value of β at the origin.

Now let p be the quantity of electric current in the direction of x per unit of area taken at any point, then the whole current through the parallelogram will be

$$\int_0^z bp\,dz,$$

and we have by (A),

$$b\,(\beta_0 - \beta) = 4\pi \int_0^z bp\,dz.$$

If we divide by b and differentiate with respect to z, we find

$$\frac{d\beta}{dz} = -4\pi p \dotfill (14).$$

Let us next consider a parallelogram in the plane of xz, two of whose sides are a along the axis of x, and z along the axis of z.

If P is the electromotive force per unit of length in the direction of x, then the total electromotive force round this parallelogram is $a\,(P - P_0)$.

If μ is the coefficient of magnetic induction, then the number of lines of force embraced by this parallelogram will be

$$\int_0^z a\mu\beta\,dz,$$

and since by (B) the total electromotive force is equal to the rate of diminution of the number of lines in unit of time,

$$a\,(P - P_0) = -\frac{d}{dt} \int_0^z a\mu\beta\,dz.$$

Dividing by a and differentiating with respect to z, we find

$$\frac{dP}{dz} = -\mu\,\frac{d\beta}{dt} \dotfill (15).$$

Let the nature of the dielectric be such that an electric displacement f is produced by an electromotive force P,

$$P = kf \dots\dots\dots\dots\dots\dots\dots\dots\dots\dots\dots (16),$$

where k is a quantity depending on the particular dielectric, which may be called its "electric elasticity."

Finally, let the current p, already considered, be supposed entirely due to the variation of f, the electric displacement, then

$$p = \frac{df}{dt} \dots\dots\dots\dots\dots\dots\dots\dots\dots (17).$$

We have now four equations, (14), (15), (16), (17), between the four quantities β, p, P, and f. If we eliminate p, P, and f, we find

$$\frac{d^2\beta}{dt^2} = \frac{k}{4\pi\mu} \frac{d^2\beta}{dz^2} \dots\dots\dots\dots\dots\dots\dots (18).$$

If we put
$$\frac{k}{4\pi\mu} = V^2 \dots\dots\dots\dots\dots\dots\dots (19),$$

the well-known solution of this equation is

$$\beta = \phi_1(z - Vt) + \phi_2(z + Vt) \dots\dots\dots\dots\dots (20),$$

shewing that the disturbance is propagated with the velocity V.

The other quantities p, P, and f can be deduced from β.

Thus, if
$$\left. \begin{aligned} \beta &= c \cos \frac{2\pi}{\lambda}(z - Vt) \\[2mm] p &= \frac{c}{2\lambda} \sin \frac{2\pi}{\lambda}(z - Vt) \\[2mm] P &= c\mu V \cos \frac{2\pi}{\lambda}(z - Vt) \\[2mm] f &= \frac{c}{4\pi V} \cos \frac{2\pi}{\lambda}(z - Vt) \end{aligned} \right\} \dots\dots\dots\dots (21).$$

I have in the next place to shew that the velocity V is the same quantity as that found from the experiments on electricity.

For this purpose let us consider a stratum of air of thickness b bounded by two parallel plane conducting surfaces of indefinite extent, the difference of whose potentials is E.

The electromotive force per unit of length between the surfaces is $P = \frac{1}{b} E$.

The electric displacement is $f = \frac{1}{k} P$.

The energy in unit of volume and the tension along the lines of force per unit of area is $\frac{1}{2} Pf$.

The attraction X on an area πa^2 of either surface is

$$\left. \begin{array}{l} X = \frac{1}{2} \pi a^2 Pf \\[1mm] \quad = \frac{1}{2} \frac{\pi}{k} \frac{a^2}{b^2} E^2 \end{array} \right\} \quad \dots\dots\dots\dots\dots\dots\dots\dots\dots(22).$$

If this area is separated by a small interval from the rest of the plane surface, as in the experiment, and if this interval is small compared with the radius of the disk, the lines of force belonging to the disk will be separated from those belonging to the rest of the surface by a surface of revolution, the section of which, at any sensible distance from the surface, will be a circle whose radius is a mean between those of the disk and the aperture. This radius must be taken for a in the equation (22)*.

Let us next consider the magnetic force near a long straight conductor carrying a current y. The magnetic force will be in the direction of a tangent to a circle whose axis is the current; and the intensity will be uniform round this circle. If the radius is b, and the magnetic intensity β, the integral round the circle will be $2\pi b\beta = 4\pi y$ by (A).

Hence $\qquad\qquad\qquad \beta = 2\frac{y}{b} \dots\dots\dots\dots\dots\dots\dots\dots\dots\dots\dots(23).$

Let a wire carrying a current y' be placed parallel to the first at a distance b, and let us consider a portion of this wire of length l. This portion will be urged across the lines of magnetic force, and the electromagnetic force Y will be equal to the product of the length of the portion, multiplied by

---

* [Note added Dec. 28, 1868.—I have since found that if a_1 is the radius of the disk, and a_2 that of the aperture of the guard-ring, and b the distance from the large fixed disk, then we must substitute for $\frac{a^2}{b^2}$ the more approximate expression $\frac{a^2_1}{b^2} + \frac{a^2_2 - a^2_1}{2b(b+a)}$, where a is a quantity which cannot exceed $\frac{\log_e 2}{\pi}(a_2 - a_1)$. —J. C. M.]

the current and by the number of lines which it crosses per unit of distance through which it moves, or, in symbols,

$$Y = ly'\mu\beta \\ = 2\mu \frac{l}{b} yy' \Bigg\} \quad \dots\dots\dots\dots\dots\dots(24).$$

If the two wires instead of being straight are circular, of radius a', and if b' the distance between them is very small compared with the radius, the attraction will be the same as if they were straight, and will be

$$Y = 2\mu \frac{2\pi a'}{b'} yy' \dots\dots\dots\dots\dots (25).$$

When b' is not very small compared with a', we must use the equation (3) to calculate the value of $\frac{2A}{B}$ by elliptic integrals.

Making $X = Y$ and comparing with equation (6), we find

$$v^2 = \frac{\mu k}{4\pi} \dots\dots\dots\dots\dots\dots(26);$$

but, by (19), $$V^2 = \frac{k}{4\pi\mu}.$$

Hence $$v = \mu V \dots\dots\dots\dots\dots (27),$$

where v is the electromagnetic ratio and V is the velocity of light.

But since all the experiments are made in air, for which μ is *assumed* equal to unity, as the standard medium with which all others are compared, we have finally

$$v = V \dots\dots\dots\dots\dots(28),$$

or the number of electrostatic units in one electromagnetic unit of electricity is numerically equal to the velocity of light.

[Extracted from *The Quarterly Journal of Pure and Applied Mathematics*, No. 34, 1867.]

XXXVII. *On the Cyclide.*

In optical treatises, the primary and secondary foci of a small pencil are sometimes represented by two straight lines cutting the axis of the pencil at right angles in planes at right angles to each other. Every ray of the pencil is supposed to pass through these two lines, thus forming what M. Plüker[*] has called a congruence of the first order.

The system of rays, as thus defined, does not fulfil the essential condition of all optical pencils, that the rays shall have a common wave-surface, for no surface can be drawn which shall cut all the rays of such a pencil at right angles.

Sir W. R. Hamilton has shewn, that the primary and secondary foci are in general the points of contact of the ray with the surface of centres of the wave-surface, which forms a double caustic surface. If we select a pencil of rays corresponding to a given small area on the wave-surface, their points of contact will lie on two small areas on the two sheets of the caustic surface. The sections of the pencil by planes perpendicular to its axis will appear, when the pencil is small enough, as two short straight lines in planes perpendicular to each other.

I propose to determine the form of the wave-surface, when one or both of the so-called focal lines is really a line, and not merely the projection of a small area of a curved surface.

Let us first determine the condition that all the normals of a surface may pass through *one* fixed curve.

Let R be a point on the surface, and RP a normal at P, meeting the fixed curve at P. Let PT be a tangent to the fixed curve at P, and RPT a plane through R and PT.

[*] *Philosophical Transactions*, 1864.

Of the two lines of curvature through R, the first touches the plane RPT, and the second is perpendicular to it. Hence, if the plane RPT turn about the tangent PT as an axis, it will always be normal to the second line of curvature. The second line of curvature is therefore a circle, and PT passes through its centre perpendicular to its plane.

All the normals belonging to the second line of curvature are of equal length, and equally inclined to PT, so that they may be considered either as the generating lines of a right cone whose axis is the tangent to the fixed curve, or as the radii of a sphere whose centre is at P, and which touches the surface all along the line of curvature.

The surface may therefore be defined as the envelope of a series of spheres, whose centres lie on the fixed curve, and whose radii vary according to any law.

If the normal passes through *two* fixed curves, the surface must also be the envelope of a second series of spheres whose centres lie on the second fixed curve, and each of which touches all the spheres of the first series.

If we take any three spheres of the first series, the surface may be defined as the envelope of all the spheres which touch the three given spheres in a continuous manner.

This is the definition given by Dupin, in his *Applications de Géométrie* (p. 200), of the surface of the fourth order called the Cyclide, because both series of its lines of curvature are circles.

If the three fixed spheres be given, they may either be all on the same side (inside or outside) of the touching sphere, or any one of the three may be on the opposite side from the other two. There are thus four different series of spheres which may be described touching the same three spheres, but we cannot pass continuously from one series to another, and the normals to the four corresponding cyclides pass through different fixed curves.

Let us next consider the nature of the two fixed curves. Since all the normals pass through both curves, and since all those which pass through a point P are equally inclined to the tangent at P, the second curve must lie on a right cone. If now the point P be taken so that its distance from a point Q in the second curve is a minimum, then PQ will be perpendicular to PT, and the right cone will become a plane, therefore the second curve is a plane conic. In the same way we may shew, that the first curve is a plane conic.

The two curves are therefore plane conics, such that the cone whose base is one of the conics, and its vertex any point of the other, is a right cone. The conics are therefore in planes at right angles to each other, and the foci of one are the vertices of the transverse axis of the other. We shall call these curves the focal conics of the cyclide.

Let the equations to a point on an ellipse be

$$x = c \cos a, \quad y = (c^2 - b^2)^{\frac{1}{2}} \sin a, \quad z = 0 \dots\dots\dots\dots\dots(1),$$

where a is the eccentric angle, and let the equations to a point on the hyperbola be

$$x = b \sec B, \quad y = 0, \quad z = (c^2 - b^2)^{\frac{1}{2}} \tan B \dots\dots\dots\dots(2),$$

where B is an angle, then these two conics fulfil the required conditions. For uniformity, we shall sometimes make use of the hyperbolic functions

$$\cos h\beta = \tfrac{1}{2} (e^{\beta} + e^{-\beta}), \text{ and } \sin h\beta = \tfrac{1}{2} (e^{\beta} - e^{-\beta}) \dots\dots\dots\dots(3),$$

and we shall suppose β and B so related, that

$$\begin{aligned} \cos h\beta &= \sec B, & \text{whence } \sin h\beta &= \tan B \\ \sec h\beta &= \cos B, & \tan h\beta &= \sin B \end{aligned} \Bigg\} \dots\dots\dots\dots(4).$$

The equations to a point in the hyperbola may then be written

$$x = b \cos h\beta, \quad y = 0, \quad z = (c^2 - b^2)^{\frac{1}{2}} \sin h\beta \dots\dots\dots\dots(5).$$

Construction of the Cyclide by Points. First Method.

Let P be a point on the ellipse, Q a point on the hyperbola, then

$$PQ = c \sec B - b \cos a \dots\dots\dots\dots\dots\dots(6).$$

Now take on PQ a point R, so that

$$PR = r - b \cos a \dots\dots\dots\dots\dots\dots(7),$$

or

$$QR = r - c \sec B \dots\dots\dots\dots\dots\dots(8),$$

where r is a constant, then if a and B vary, R will give a system of points on the cyclide (bcr).

For if P be fixed while Q varies, R will describe a circle, and if Q be fixed while P varies, R will describe another circle, and these circles cut at right angles, and are both at right angles to PQR at their intersection, and since P and Q are any points on the conics, the whole system of circles will form a cyclide.

The circle corresponding to P a fixed point on the ellipse, is in a plane which cuts that of xz along the line

$$x = \frac{br}{c}, \quad y = 0 \dots\dots\dots\dots\dots\dots\dots\dots\dots(9),$$

and makes with it an angle

$$\tan^{-1}\left\{\frac{c}{(c^2-b^2)^{\frac{1}{2}}}\tan a\right\}.$$

The circle corresponding to Q a fixed point in the hyperbola, is in a plane which cuts that of xy along the line

$$x = \frac{cr}{b}, \quad z = 0 \dots\dots\dots\dots\dots\dots\dots\dots\dots(10),$$

and makes with it an angle

$$\tan^{-1}\left\{\frac{b}{(c^2-b^2)^{\frac{1}{2}}}\sin B\right\}.$$

Hence the planes of all the circles of either series pass through one of two fixed lines, which are at right angles to each other, and at a minimum distance

$$= r\,\frac{c^2-b^2}{bc}\,.$$

The line of intersection of the planes of the two circles through the point R will therefore pass through both the fixed lines at points S and T, where the co-ordinates of S are

$$x = \frac{cr}{b}, \quad y = \frac{(c^2-b^2)^{\frac{1}{2}}}{b}\tan a, \quad z = 0 \dots\dots\dots\dots\dots(11),$$

and those of T,

$$x = \frac{br}{c}, \quad y = 0, \quad z = -\frac{(c^2-b^2)^{\frac{1}{2}}}{c}\sin B \dots\dots\dots\dots(12),$$

and it is easily shewn that

$$\frac{SR}{TR} = \frac{1 - \dfrac{r}{b}\sec a}{1 - \dfrac{r}{c}\cos B} = \rho \dots\dots\dots\dots\dots\dots(13).$$

Hence, we deduce the following :

Second Construction by Points.

Draw the two fixed lines, and find points S and T given by equations (11) and (12), then draw ST, and cut it in R, so that the ratio of the segments is that given by equation (13). R will be a point on the cyclide.

This construction is very convenient for drawing any projection of the cyclide, as the distances are measured along the projections of the fixed lines, and the line ST can be divided in the required ratio by means of a ruler and "sector," without making any marks on the paper, except the position of the required point R.

In this way I have drawn stereoscopic diagrams of four varieties of the cyclide, viewed from a position nearly in the line

$$x = y = z,$$

shewing the circles corresponding to various values of a and B^*.

On the Forms of the Cyclide.

We shall suppose b and c to be given, and trace the effect of giving different values to r. Since the cyclides corresponding to negative values of r differ from those corresponding to equal positive values merely by having the

---

* *Note on a Real-Image Stereoscope.* In ordinary stereoscopes the *virtual* images of two pictures are superposed, and the observer, looking through two lenses, or prisms, or at two mirrors, sees the figure apparently behind the optical apparatus. In a stereoscope, which I have had made by Elliott Brothers, the observer looks at a real image of the pictures, which appears in front of the instrument, and he is not conscious of using any optical apparatus.

This stereoscope consists of a frame to support the double picture, which may be a common stereoscopic slide inverted. One foot from this a frame is placed, containing side by side two convex lenses of half a foot focal length, and having their centres distant one and a quarter inches horizontally. One foot beyond these is placed a convex lens of two-thirds of a foot focal length and three inches diameter.

The observer stands about two feet from the large lens, so that with the right eye he sees an image of the left-hand picture, and with the left eye an image of the right-hand picture.

These images are formed by pencils which pass centrically through the two small lenses respectively, so that they are free from distortion, and they appear to be nearly at the same distance as the large lens, so that the observer fixing his eyes on the frame of the large lens sees the combined figures at once.

The figures of the cyclide, though constructed for this stereoscope, may be used with an ordinary stereoscope, or they may be united by squinting, which is a very effective method.

positive and negative ends of the axis of x reversed, we need study the positive values only.

(1) When r lies between zero and b, the section in the plane of the ellipse consists of two circles, whose centres are the foci, and which intersect at a point of the ellipse. The section in the plane of the hyperbola consists of two circles exterior to each other, whose centres are the vertices of the ellipse. The cyclide itself consists of two lobes exterior to each other, of which the negative one is the largest, and increases with r, while the positive lobe decreases. Each lobe terminates in two conical points, where it meets the other lobe. The cone of contact at these singular points is a right cone, whose axis is the tangent to the ellipse, and whose semi-vertical angle is

$$\cos^{-1}\left(\frac{b^2-r^2}{c^2-r^2}\right)^{\frac{1}{2}}.$$

The whole figure resembles two pairs of horns, each pair joined together by their bases, and the two pairs touching at the tips of the horns. Figure I.* represents a cyclide of this kind. The continuous curves represent the lines of curvature of both series. The dotted curves represent the ellipse and hyperbola through which the normals pass, and the dotted straight lines represent the axis of x, and the two straight lines through which the planes of the circles pass.

(2) When r lies between b and c, the cyclide consists of a single sheet in the form of a ring, the section of which is greatest on the negative side. Figure II. represents a cyclide of this kind.

(3) When r is greater than c, the cyclide again consists of two sheets, the one within the other, meeting each other in two conical points which are situated on the positive branch of the hyperbola. The semi-vertical angle at these points, is

$$\cos^{-1}\left(\frac{r^2-c^2}{r^2-b^2}\right)^{\frac{1}{2}}.$$

There is also in all forms of the cyclide, a singular tangent plane which touches the cyclide along a circle corresponding to $B=\pm\frac{\pi}{2}$. Figure III. repre-

* [Page 159].

sents such a cyclide. The outer sheet with its circles of contact and re-entering conical points, and the inner spindle with its conical points meeting those of the outer sheet, have a certain resemblance to the outer and inner sheets of Fresnel's Wave-Surface; and, if we bear in mind that the wave-surface has four such singular points while the cyclide has only two, we may find Figure III. useful in forming an idea of the singular points of the wave-surface.

If we give to r all values from $+\infty$ to $-\infty$, the cyclide assumes the forms (3), (2), (1), (-1), (-2), (-3) in succession, and every point of space is traversed four times by the surface. For when r is infinite, any given point R is within the spindle or inner sheet of (3). As r diminishes, the spindle contracts, and when $r = c$ it vanishes; so that for a certain value, r_1, greater than c, the surface of the spindle passes through the point R.

At this instant the outer sheet of the cyclide is still beyond R, but as r diminishes, the surface contracts, and finally vanishes when $r = -b$, before which it must have passed through a value r_2, for which the surface passes through R. At this instant the surface may have the form either of the outer sheet of (3), or of the ring cyclide of one sheet (2), or of the negative lobe of (1).

The positive lobe of (1) begins to appear when r becomes less than b, and increases as r diminishes, till when $r = -b$ it becomes a ring, and when $r = -c$ it becomes the outer sheet of the cyclide (-3).

This surface, therefore, for some value, r_3, of r, passes through the point R. This value r_3 is necessarily less than r_2.

When $r = -c$ ·the interior sheet of (-3) is developed, and increases indefinitely as r diminishes, so that for some value, r_4, of r, which is less than r_3, the point R is on the surface of this interior sheet. We thus see that the cyclide may be said to have four sheets, though not more than two can be real at once. These four sheets touch at three conical points.

The first sheet, corresponding to r_1, is the interior lobe of the cyclide (3), and always touches the second sheet at a conical point on the positive branch of the hyperbola.

The second sheet, corresponding to r_2, has three different forms, being either the outer sheet of (3), the ring cyclide of one sheet (2), or the negative lobe of (1). When the first sheet exists, it meets it at a conical point on the positive hyperbola, and when the third sheet exists, it meets it at a conical point on the ellipse.

The third sheet, corresponding to r_3, has also three different forms. It may be either the positive lobe of (1), the ring cyclide (-2), or the outer sheet of (-3). In the first case it has a conical point on the ellipse where it meets the second sheet. In the second case it has no conical point, and in the third it meets the fourth sheet in a conical point on the negative hyperbola.

The fourth sheet is the interior spindle of the cyclide (-3), and always meets the third sheet at a conical point on the negative hyperbola.

Parabolic Cyclides.

When the values of b, c, r, and x are each increased by the same quantity, and if this quantity is indefinitely increased, the two conics become in the limit two parabolas in perpendicular planes, the focus of one being the vertex of the other, and the cyclide becomes what we may call the parabolic cyclide.

When r lies between b and c, the cyclide consists of one infinite sheet, lying entirely between the planes $x = 2b - r$ and $x = 2c - r$. The portions of space on the positive and negative side of the sheet are linked together as the earth and the air are linked together by a bridge, the earth, of which the bridge forms part, embracing the air from below, and the air embracing the bridge from above. In fact the earth and bridge form a ring of which one side is much larger than the other.

A parabolic ring cyclide in which $2r = b + c$, is represented in Figure IV.

When r does not lie between b and c, the cyclide consists of a lobe with two conical points, and an infinite sheet with two conical points meeting those of the lobe.

Surfaces of Revolution.

When $b = 0$, the cyclide is the surface formed by the revolution of a circle of radius r about a line in its own plane distant c from the centre. If r is less than c, the form is that of an anchor ring. If r is greater than c, the surface consists of an outer and an inner sheet, meeting in two conical points. When $b = c$, the cyclide resolves itself into two spheres, which touch externally if r is less than b, and internally if r is greater than b. When $b = c = 0$, the two spheres become one.

If the origin be transferred to a conical point, and if the dimensions of the figure be then indefinitely increased, the cyclide becomes ultimately a right cone, having the same conical angle as the original cyclide. If $b = c$, the cone becomes a plane.

If b remains finite, while c, r, and x are each increased by the same indefinitely great quantity, the cyclide ultimately becomes a right cylinder, whose radius is $r - c$.

Inversion of the Cyclide.

Since every sphere, when inverted by means of the reciprocals of the radii drawn to a fixed point, becomes another sphere, every cyclide similarly inverted becomes another cyclide. There is, however, a certain relation between the parameters of the one cyclide and those of the other, namely

$$\frac{r^2 - b^2}{r^2 - c^2} = \frac{r'^2 - b'^2}{r'^2 - c'^2} \quad \dots\dots\dots\dots\dots\dots\dots \text{(14)},$$

or

$$\frac{r^2 - b^2}{r^2 - c^2} = \frac{r'^2 - c'^2}{r'^2 - b'^2} \quad \dots\dots\dots\dots\dots\dots\dots \text{(15)}.$$

If the point of inversion be taken on either of the circles

$$x^2 + y^2 - 2\frac{brx}{c} + b^2 + r^2 - c^2 = 0, \quad z = 0 \quad \dots\dots\dots\dots \text{(16)},$$

or

$$x^2 + z^2 - 2\frac{crx}{b} - b^2 - r^2 + c^2 = 0, \quad y = 0 \quad \dots\dots\dots\dots \text{(17)},$$

the cyclide will become a surface of revolution in which $b = 0$, and

$$\frac{r'^2}{c'^2} = \frac{c^2 - r^2}{c^2 - b^2} \quad \dots\dots\dots\dots\dots\dots\dots \text{(18)}$$

if the point of inversion be on the first circle, or

$$\frac{r'^2}{c'^2} = \frac{r^2 - b^2}{c^2 - b^2} \quad \dots\dots\dots\dots\dots\dots\dots \text{(19)}$$

if it be on the second.

When r is less than c, the first circle is real; and when r is greater than b, the second circle is real. In the ring-cyclide r is between b and c, and the cyclide can be transformed into an anchor ring in two different ways.

If the cyclide has conical points, and if one of them be made the point of inversion, the cyclide becomes a right cone, whose semi-vertical angle is $\cos^{-1}\left(\dfrac{b^2-r^2}{c^2-r^2}\right)^{\frac{1}{2}}$ if r is less than b, or $\cos^{-1}\left(\dfrac{r^2-c^2}{r^2-b^2}\right)^{\frac{1}{2}}$ if r is greater than b.

If the point of inversion be at any other point of the surface, the cyclide becomes a parabolic cyclide.

If the point of inversion be $x=\dfrac{bc}{r}$, $y=0$, $z=0$, the cyclide is inverse to itself.

On the Conjugate Isothermal Functions on the Cyclide.

DEFINITION. If on any surface two systems of curves be drawn, each individual curve being defined by the value of a parameter corresponding to it, and if the two systems of curves intersect everywhere at right angles, and if the intercept of a curve of the second system between two consecutive curves of the first system has the same ratio to the intercept of a curve of the first system between two consecutive curves of the second, as the difference of the parameters of the two curves of the first system has to the difference of the parameters of the two curves of the second system, then the two systems of curves are called conjugate isothermal lines, and the two parameters conjugate isothermal functions. If the surface be now supposed to be a uniform conducting lamina placed between non-conducting media, one set of these lines will be isothermal for heat or equipotential for electricity, and the other set will be lines of flow. (See Lamé on *Isothermal Functions*.)

This property of lines on a surface is not changed by inversion.

In the cyclide, we find the intercept ds of a line of curvature of the first system is

$$ds_1 = \frac{r-c\cos h\beta}{c\cos h\beta - b\cos a}\,(c^2-b^2)^{\frac{1}{2}}\,da \dots\dots\dots\dots\dots (20),$$

and the intercept ds_2 of a line of curvature of the second system is

$$ds_2 = \frac{r-b\cos a}{c\cos h\beta - b\cos a}\,(c^2-b^2)^{\frac{1}{2}}\,d\beta \dots\dots\dots\dots\dots (21).$$

If now θ be a function of a, and ϕ of β, such that

$$\frac{ds_1}{ds_2} = \frac{d\theta}{d\phi},$$

then θ and ϕ will be conjugate isothermal functions.

If $\qquad \theta = k \int \frac{da}{r - b \cos a}$ and $\phi = k \int \frac{d\beta}{r - c \cos h\beta}$ .... (22),

the condition will be satisfied. If r is greater than b, we find

$$\tan \frac{\theta}{(r^2 - b^2)^{\frac{1}{2}}} = \frac{(r^2 - b^2)^{\frac{1}{2}} \sin a}{b - r \cos a} \qquad .... (23).$$

It is more useful to have a expressed in terms of θ, thus :

$$\sin a = \frac{(r^2 - b^2)^{\frac{1}{2}} \sin \dfrac{\theta}{(r^2 - b^2)^{\frac{1}{2}}}}{r + b \cos \dfrac{\theta}{(r^2 - b^2)^{\frac{1}{2}}}}.$$

$$\cos a = \frac{b + r \cos \dfrac{\theta}{(r^2 - b^2)^{\frac{1}{2}}}}{r + b \cos \dfrac{\theta}{(r^2 - b^2)^{\frac{1}{2}}}} .... (24).$$

If r is less than b, we have only to write the hyperbolic functions of $\frac{\theta}{(r^2 - b^2)^{\frac{1}{2}}}$ instead of the circular functions of $\frac{\theta}{(r^2 - b^2)^{\frac{1}{2}}}$, and to write $(b^2 - r^2)^{\frac{1}{2}}$ for $(r^2 - b^2)^{\frac{1}{2}}$.

Similarly, we obtain for the relation between β and ϕ, when r is greater than c,

$$\tan B = \sin h\beta = \frac{(r^2 - c^2)^{\frac{1}{2}} \sin h \dfrac{\phi}{(r^2 - c^2)^{\frac{1}{2}}}}{r + c \cos h \dfrac{\phi}{(r^2 - c^2)^{\frac{1}{2}}}},$$

$$\sec B = \cos h\beta = \frac{c + r \cos h \dfrac{\phi}{(r^2 - c^2)^{\frac{1}{2}}}}{r + c \cos h \dfrac{\phi}{(r^2 - c^2)^{\frac{1}{2}}}} .... (25).$$

When r is less than c we must substitute $(c^2 - r^2)^{\frac{1}{2}}$ for $(r^2 - c^2)^{\frac{1}{2}}$ and turn the hyperbolic functions into circular functions.

Having found these conjugate isothermal functions we may deduce from them any number of other pairs, as θ_1 and ϕ_1, where

$$\frac{d\theta_1}{d\theta} = \frac{d\phi_1}{d\phi} \text{ and } \frac{d\theta_1}{d\phi} = -\frac{d\phi_1}{d\theta} \quad \dots\dots\dots\dots\dots\dots (26).$$

On Confocal Cyclides.

A system of cyclides in which the focal ellipse and hyperbola remain the same, while r has various values, may be called a confocal system. This system of cyclides and the two systems of right cones which have their vertices in one conic and pass through the other, form three systems of orthogonal surfaces, and therefore intersect along their lines of curvature. By inversion we may get three systems of cyclides intersecting orthogonally.

A system of confocal cyclides may also be considered as a system of wave surfaces in an isotropic medium, corresponding to a pencil of rays, each ray of which intersects the two focal conics. Each cyclide corresponds to a certain value of r, which we may call the length of the ray of that cyclide.

Now let us consider the system of confocal conicoids, whose equation is of the form

$$\frac{x^2}{\rho^2} + \frac{y^2}{\rho^2 - b^2} + \frac{z^2}{\rho^2 - c^2} = 1 \quad \dots\dots\dots\dots\dots\dots (27).$$

By putting $\rho = c$, we get the ellipse

$$\frac{x^2}{c^2} + \frac{y^2}{c^2 - b^2} = 1, \quad z = 0 \quad \dots\dots\dots\dots\dots\dots (28).$$

By putting $\rho = b$, we get the hyperbola

$$\frac{x^2}{b^2} - \frac{z^2}{c^2 - b^2} = 1, \quad y = 0 \quad \dots\dots\dots\dots\dots\dots (29).$$

These two conics therefore belong to the system and may be called its focal conics. If, with any point R for vertex, we draw cones through the ellipse and hyperbola, these will be confocal cones, whose three axes are normal to the three conicoids of the system which pass through R. The two cones will intersect at right angles along four generating lines r_1, r_2, r_3, r_4, which are normal to four cyclides passing through the point R.

The normal to the ellipsoid through R will be the real axis of the cone which passes through the ellipse, and will bisect the angle between r_1 and r_2, and also that between r_3 and r_4. If the ellipsoid were reflective, a ray incident in the direction r_1 would be reflected in the direction of r_2 reversed; hence, by the wave theory, $r_1 + r_2$ is constant for the ellipsoid. At the point of the ellipsoid ($\rho =$ constant) where it is cut by the axis of x,

$$x = \rho,$$
$$r_1 = x + c,$$
$$r_2 = x - c.$$

So that the equation of the ellipsoid ($r =$ constant) may be expressed in terms of r_1 and r_2 thus:

$$r_1 + r_2 = 2\rho \dots\dots\dots\dots\dots\dots\dots\dots\dots(30).$$

The normal to the ellipsoid also bisects the angle between r_3 and r_4, whence we deduce another form of the equation of the same ellipsoid

$$r_3 + r_4 = -2\rho \dots\dots\dots\dots\dots\dots\dots\dots(31).$$

Hence, the general relation among the values of r,

$$r_1 + r_2 + r_3 + r_4 = 0 \dots\dots\dots\dots\dots\dots\dots(32).$$

The normal to the hyperboloid of one sheet ($\mu =$ constant) bisects the angle between r_1 and r_3, and also that between r_2 and r_4, whence we obtain the equations

$$r_1 + r_3 = 2\mu = -(r_2 + r_4)\dots\dots\dots\dots\dots(33).$$

The normal to the hyperboloid of two sheets ($\nu =$ constant) bisects the angles between r_2 and r_3, and between r_1 and r_4, whence

$$r_2 + r_3 = 2\nu = -(r_1 + r_4)\dots\dots\dots\dots\dots(34).$$

These are the equations to the conicoids in terms of the four rays of the pencil. The equations to the four cyclides in terms of elliptic co-ordinates are easily deduced from them

$$\left.\begin{array}{l} r_1 = \rho + \mu - \nu \\ r_2 = \rho - \mu + \nu \\ r_3 = -\rho + \mu + \nu \\ r_4 = -\rho - \mu - \nu \end{array}\right\}\dots\dots\dots\dots\dots\dots(35).$$

Since the quantities $\qquad\qquad\rho,\ c,\ \mu,\ b,\ \nu,\ 0$

are in descending order of magnitude, it is evident that

$$r_1,\ \rho,\ r_2,\ r_3,\ -\rho,\ r_4$$

are also in descending order of magnitude.

The general equation to the cyclide in elliptic co-ordinates is

$$(r-\rho-\mu+\nu)\,(r-\rho+\mu-\nu)\,(r+\rho-\mu-\nu)\,(r+\rho+\mu+\nu)=0\ldots\ldots(36),$$

which may be expressed in Cartesian co-ordinates thus:

$$(x^2+y^2+z^2-r^2)^2-2\,(x^2+r^2)\,(b^2+c^2)-2\,(y^2-z^2)\,(c^2-b^2)+8bcrx+(c^2-b^2)^2=0\ldots(37).$$

When $b=c$ there are two focal points F and F'' and the values of the four rays are

$$\left.\begin{array}{l} r_1=\ \ \ RF+c\\ r_2=\ \ \ RF''-c\\ r_3=-RF+c\\ r_4=-RF''-c\end{array}\right\}\ldots\ldots\ldots\ldots\ldots\ldots\ldots\ldots\ldots\ldots(38).$$

The equation of the ellipsoid

$$2\rho=r_1+r_2=RF+RF''\ldots\ldots\ldots\ldots\ldots\ldots\ldots\ldots(39)$$

in this case expresses the property of the prolate spheroid, that the sum of the distances of any point from the two foci is constant.

In like manner, the equation

$$r_2+r_3=2\nu=RF''-RF\ldots\ldots\ldots\ldots\ldots\ldots\ldots\ldots(40)$$

expresses the property of the hyperboloid of revolution of two sheets, that the difference of the focal distances is constant.

In order to extend a property analogous to this to the other conicoids, let us conceive the following mechanical construction:

Suppose the focal ellipse and hyperbola represented by thin smooth wires, and let an indefinite thin straight rod always rest against the two curves, and let r be measured along the rod from a point fixed in the rod. Let a string whose length is $b+c$ be fastened at one end to the negative focus of the ellipse and at the other to the point $(+b)$ of the rod, and let the string slide on the ellipse at the same point as the rod rests on it. To keep the string always tight let another equal string pass from the positive focus of the ellipse round the curve to the point $(-b)$ of the rod. These strings will determine the point of the rod which rests on any given point of the ellipse.

Let the rod also rest on the hyperbola, so that either the positive portion of the rod rests on the positive branch of the hyperbola, or the negative portion of the rod rests on the negative branch.

Then the point r of the rod lies in the surface of the cyclide whose parameter is r, and as the rod is made to slide on the ellipse and hyperbola, the point r will explore the whole surface of the cyclide.

If we consider any point of space R, the rod will pass through it in four different positions corresponding to the four intersections of the cones whose vertex is R passing through the ellipse and hyperbola.

The first position, r_1, corresponds to the first sheet of the cyclide which passes through R. If we denote the intersection of the rod with the ellipse by E, and its intersection with the positive and negative branches of the hyperbola by $+H$ and $-H$, then the order of the intersections will be in this case

$$E, \ +H, \ R.$$

The second position, r_2, corresponds to the second sheet, and the order of intersections is either

$$E, \ R, \ +H \text{ or } -H, \ E, \ R.$$

The third position, r_3, corresponds to the third sheet, and the order of the intersections is either

$$R, \ E, \ +H, \text{ or } -H, \ R, \ E.$$

The fourth position, r_4, corresponds to the fourth sheet, and the order of the intersections is

$$R, \ -H, \ E,$$

the letters being always arranged in the order in which r increases.

The complete system of rays is an example of a linear congruence of the fourth order.

Now if two rods, each fulfilling the above conditions, intersect at R in any two of these four positions, and if a string of sufficient length be fastened to a sufficiently distant negative point of the first rod, be passed round the point R, and be fastened to a sufficiently distant negative point of the second rod, and if

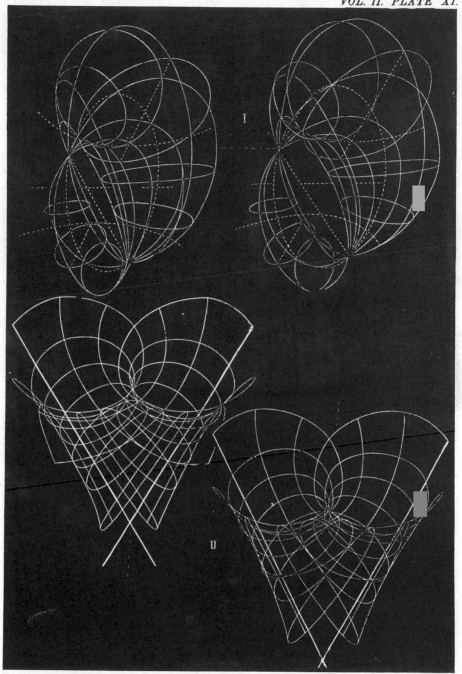

I HORNED CYCLIDE   II PARABOLIC CYCLIDE

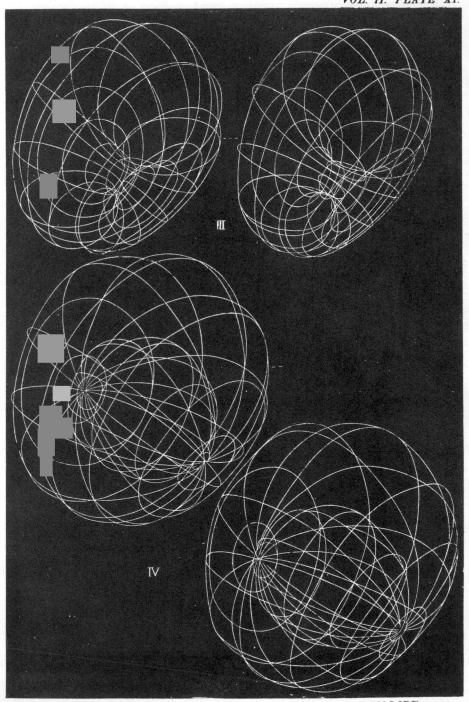

III RING CYCLIDE   IV SPINDLE CYCLIDE

the two rods be then moved always keeping the string tight at the point of intersection R, then R will trace out a conicoid.

If the rods are in the first and second positions, or in the third and fourth, the conicoid will be an ellipsoid.

If the rods are in the first and third positions, or in the second and fourth, the conicoid will be an hyperboloid of one sheet.

If the rods are in the first and fourth positions, or in the second and third, the conicoid will be an hyperboloid of two sheets.

In the parabolic confocal system, the fourth sheet of the cyclide is a plane, and r_4 is parallel to the axis of x. Hence if rays parallel to the axis of a paraboloid are reflected by the surface, they will all pass through the two focal parabolas of the system, and the wave surface after reflexion will be a cyclide, and if the rays are twice reflected, they will become again parallel to the axis.

[From the *Edinburgh Royal Society Proceedings*, Vol. VII.]

XXXVIII.   *On a Bow seen on the Surface of Ice.*

ON the 26th of January, about noon, I observed the appearance of a coloured bow on the frozen surface of the ditch which surrounds S. John's College, Cambridge. Its appearance and position seemed to correspond with those of an ordinary primary rainbow. I at once made a rough measurement of the angle on the board of a book which I had with me, and then borrowed from Dr Parkinson, President of S. John's College, a sextant with which I found that the angle between the bright red and the shadow of the large mirror was 41° 50′, and that for bright blue 40° 30′. The angle for the extreme red of the primary bow, as given in Parkinson's *Optics*, is 42° 20′, and that for violet 40° 32′. The bows formed by ice crystals are seen on the same side as the sun, and not on the opposite side. I suppose the bow which I saw to be formed by small drops of water lying on the ice. If the lower part of each drop were flattened, so as to bring the point at which the reflexion takes place nearer to the points of incidence and emergence, the effect would be of the same kind as that of a diminution of the index of refraction—that is, the angle of the bow would be increased. How a drop of water can lie upon ice without wetting it, and losing its shape altogether, I do not profess to explain.

Only a small part of the ice presented this appearance. It was best seen when the incident and emergent rays were nearly equally inclined to the horizontal. The ice was very thin, and I was not able to get near enough to the place where the bow appeared to see if the supposed water drops really existed.

[From the *Transactions of the Royal Society of Edinburgh,* Vol. XXVI.]

XXXIX. *On Reciprocal Figures, Frames, and Diagrams of Forces.*

(Received 17th Dec. 1869; read 7th Feb. 1870.)

Two figures are reciprocal when the properties of the first relative to the second are the same as those of the second relative to the first. Several kinds of reciprocity are known to mathematicians, and the theories of Inverse Figures and of Polar Reciprocals have been developed at great length, and have led to remarkable results. I propose to investigate a different kind of geometrical reciprocity, which is also capable of considerable development, and can be applied to the solution of mechanical problems.

A Frame may be defined geometrically as a system of straight lines connecting a number of points. In actual structures these lines are material pieces, beams, rods, or wires, and may be straight or curved; but the force by which each piece resists any alteration of the distance between the points which it joins acts in the straight line joining those points. Hence, in studying the equilibrium of a frame, we may consider its different points as mutually acting on each other with forces whose directions are those of the lines joining each pair of points. When the forces acting between the two points tend to draw them together, or to prevent them from separating, the action along the joining line is called a Tension. When the forces tend to separate the points, or to keep them apart, the action along the joining line is called a Pressure.

If we divide the piece joining the points by any imaginary section, the resultant of the whole internal force acting between the parts thus divided will be mechanically equivalent to the tension or pressure of the piece. Hence, in order to exhibit the mechanical action of the frame in the most elementary manner, we may draw it as a skeleton, in which the different points are joined by straight lines, and we may indicate by numbers attached to these lines the tensions or pressures in the corresponding pieces of the frame.

The diagram thus formed indicates the state of the frame in a way which is geometrical as regards the position and direction of the forces, but arithmetical as regards their magnitude.

But, by assuming that a line of a certain length shall represent a force of a certain magnitude, we may represent every force completely by a line. This is done in Elementary Statics, where we are told to draw a line from the point of application of the force in the direction in which the force acts, and to cut off as many units of length from the line as there are units of force in the force, and finally to mark the end of the line with an arrowhead, to shew that it is a force and not a piece of the frame, and that it acts in that direction and not the opposite.

By proceeding in this way, we should get a system of arrow-headed forces superposed on the skeleton of the frame, two equal and opposite arrows for every piece of the frame.

To test the equilibrium of these forces at any point of concourse, we should proceed by the construction of the parallelogram of forces, beginning with two of the forces acting at the point, completing the parallelogram, and drawing the diagonal, and combining this with the third force in the same way, till, when all the forces had been combined, the resultant disappeared. We should thus have to draw three new lines, one of which is an arrow, in taking in each force after the first, leaving at last not only a great number of useless lines, but a number of new arrows, not belonging to the system of forces, and only confusing to any one wishing to verify the process.

To simplify this process, we are told to construct the Polygon of Forces, by drawing in succession lines parallel and proportional to the different forces, each line beginning at the extremity of the last. If the forces acting at the point are in equilibrium, the polygon formed in this way will be a closed one.

Here we have for the first time a true Diagram of Forces, in which every force is not only represented in magnitude and direction by a straight line, but the equilibrium of the forces is manifest by inspection, for we have only to examine whether the polygon is closed or not. To secure this advantage, however, we have given up the attempt to indicate the position of the force, for the sides of the polygon do not pass through one point as the forces do. We must, therefore, give up the plan of representing the frame and its forces in one diagram, and draw one diagram of the frame and a separate diagram of the forces. By this method we shall not only avoid confusion, but we shall greatly simplify mechanical calculations, by reducing them to operations with the parallel ruler, in which no useless lines are drawn, but every line represents an actual force.

A Diagram of Forces is a figure, every line of which represents in magnitude and direction the force acting along a piece of the frame.

To express the relation between the diagram of the frame and the diagram of forces, the lines of the frame should each be indicated by a symbol, and the corresponding lines of the diagram of forces should be indicated by the same symbol, accented if necessary.

We have supposed the corresponding lines to be parallel, and it is necessary that they should be parallel when the frame is not in one plane; but if all the pieces of the frame are parallel to one plane, we may turn one of the diagrams round a right angle, and then every line will be perpendicular to the corresponding line.

If any number of lines meet at the same point in the frame, the corresponding lines in the diagram of forces form a closed polygon.

It is possible, in certain cases, to draw the diagram of forces so that if any number of lines meet in a point in the diagram of forces, the corresponding lines in the frame form a closed polygon.

In such cases, the two diagrams are said to be reciprocal in the sense in which we use it in this paper. If either diagram be taken as representing the frame, the lines of the other diagram will represent a system of forces which, if applied along the corresponding pieces of the frame, will keep it in equilibrium.

The properties of the "triangle" and "polygon" of forces have been long known, and a "diagram" of forces has been used in the case of the "funicular polygon," but I am not aware of any more general statement of the method of drawing diagrams of forces before Professor Rankine applied it to frames, roofs, &c., in his *Applied Mechanics*, p. 137, &c. The "polyhedron of forces," or the proposition that forces acting on a point perpendicular and proportional to the areas of the faces of a polyhedron are in equilibrium, has, I believe, been enunciated independently at various times, but the application of this principle to the construction of a diagram of forces in three dimensions was first made by Professor Rankine in the *Philosophical Magazine*, Feb. 1864.

In the *Philosophical Magazine* for April 1864, I stated some of the properties of reciprocal figures, and the conditions of their existence, and shewed that any plane rectilinear figure which is a perspective representation of a closed polyhedron with plane faces has a reciprocal figure. In Sept. 1867, I communicated to the British Association a method of drawing the reciprocal figure, founded on the theory of reciprocal polars*.

I have since found that the construction of diagrams of forces in which each force is represented by one line, had been independently discovered by Mr W. P. Taylor, and had been used by him as a practical method of determining the forces acting in frames for several years before I had taught it in King's College, or even studied it myself. I understand that he is preparing a statement of the application of the method to various kinds of structures in detail, so that it can be made use of by any one who is able to draw one line parallel to another.

Professor Fleeming Jenkin, in a paper recently published by the Society, has fully explained the application of the method to the most important cases occurring in practice.

In the present paper I propose, first, to consider plane diagrams of frames and of forces in an elementary way, as a practical method of solving questions about the stresses in actual frameworks, without the use of long calculations.

I shall then discuss the subject in a theoretical point of view, and give a method of defining reciprocal diagrams analytically, which is applicable to figures either of two or of three dimensions.

Lastly, I shall extend the method to the investigation of the state of stress in a continuous body, and shall point out the nature of the function of stress first discovered by the Astronomer Royal for stresses in two dimensions, extending the use of such functions to stresses in three dimensions.

On Reciprocal Plane Rectilinear Figures.

DEFINITION.—Two plane rectilinear figures are reciprocal when they consist of an equal number of straight lines, so that corresponding lines in the two figures are at right angles, and corresponding lines which meet in a point in the one figure form a closed polygon in the other.

* [See pp. 169 and 188].

Note.—It is often convenient to turn one of the figures round in its own plane 90°. Corresponding lines are then parallel to each other, and this is sometimes more convenient in comparing the diagrams by the eye.

Since every polygon in the one figure has three or more sides, every point in the other figure must have three or more lines meeting in it. Since every line in the one figure has two, and only two, extremities, every line in the other figure must be a side of two, and only two, polygons. If either of these figures be taken to represent the pieces of a frame, the other will represent a system of forces such that, these forces being applied as tensions or pressures along the corresponding pieces of the frame, every point of the frame will be in equilibrium.

The simplest example is that of a triangular frame without weight, ABC, jointed at the angles, and acted on by three forces, P, Q, R, applied at the angles. The directions of these three forces must meet in a point, if the frame is in equilibrium. We shall denote the lines of the figure by capital letters, and those of the reciprocal figure by the corresponding small letters; we shall denote points by the lines which meet in them, and polygons by the lines which bound them.

Here, then, are three lines, A, B, C, forming a triangle, and three other lines, P, Q, R, drawn from the angles and meeting in a point. Of these forces let that along P be given. Draw the first line p of the reciprocal diagram parallel to P, and of a length representing, on any convenient scale, the force along P. The forces along P, Q, R are in equilibrium, therefore, if from one extremity of p we draw q parallel to Q, and from the other extremity r parallel to R, so as to form a triangle pqr, then q and r will represent on the same scale the forces along Q and R.

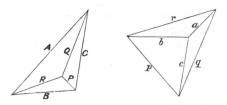

To determine whether these forces are tensions or pressures, make a point travel along p in the direction in which the force in P acts on the point of concourse of PQR, and let the point travel in the same direction round the polygon pqr. Then, the direction in which the point travels along any side of the polygon will be the direction in which the force acts along the corresponding piece of the frame on the point of concourse. If it acts from the point of concourse, the force is a tension; if towards it, it is a pressure.

The other extremity of P meets B and C, and the forces along these three pieces are in equilibrium. Hence, if we draw a triangle, having p for one side and lines parallel to B and C for the others, the sides of this triangle will represent the three forces.

Such a triangle may be described on either side of p, the two together would form a parallelogram of forces; but the theory of reciprocal figures indicates that only one of these triangles forms part of the diagram of forces.

The rule for such cases is as follows :—Of the two extremities of p, one corresponds to the closed figure PRB, and the other to the closed figure PQC, these being the polygons of which P is a side in the first figure.

We must, therefore, draw b parallel to B from the intersection of p and r, and not from the other extremity, and we must draw c parallel to C from the intersection of p and q.

We have now a second triangle, pbc, corresponding to the forces acting at the point of concourse of P, B, C. To determine whether these forces are tensions or pressures, we must make a point travel round pbc, so that its course along p is in the opposite direction to its course round pqr, because the piece P acts on the points PBC and PQR with equal and opposite forces.

If we now consider the equilibrium of the point of concourse of QC and A, we shall find that we have determined two of these forces by the lines q and c, and that the third force must be represented by the line a which completes the triangle qca.

We have now constructed a complete diagram of forces, in which each force is represented by a single line, and in which the equilibrium of the forces meeting at any point is expressed visibly by the corresponding lines in the other figure forming a closed polygon.

There are in this figure six lines, having four points of concourse, and forming four triangles. To determine the direction of the force along a given line at any point of concourse, we must make a point travel round the corresponding polygon in the other figure in a direction which is positive with respect to that polygon. For this purpose it is desirable to name the polygons in a determinate order of their sides, so arranged that, when we arrive at the same side in naming the two polygons which it divides, we travel along it in opposite directions. For instance, if *pqr* be one of the polygons, the others are *pbc*, *qca*, *rab*.

Note.—It may be observed, that after drawing the lines *p*, *q*, *r*, *b*, *c* with the parallel ruler, the line *a* was drawn by joining the points of concourse of *q*, *r* and *b*, *c*; but, since it represents the force in *A*, *a* is parallel to *A*. Hence the following geometrical theorem :—

If the lines *PQR*, drawn from the angles of the triangle *ABC*, meet in a point, then if *pqr* be a triangle with its corresponding sides parallel to *P*, *Q*, *R*, and if *a*, *b*, *c* be drawn from its corresponding angles parallel to *A*, *B*, *C*, the lines *a*, *b*, *c* will meet in a point.

A geometrical proof of this is easily obtained by finding the centres of the four circles circumscribing the triangles *ABC*, *AQR*, *BRP*, *CPQ*, and joining the four centres thus found by six lines.

These lines meet in the four centres, and are perpendicular to the six lines, *A*, *B*, *C*; *P*, *Q*, *R*; but by turning them round 90° they become parallel to the corresponding lines in the original figure.

The diagram formed in this way is definite in size and position, but any figure similar to it is a reciprocal diagram to the original figure. I have explained the construction of this, the simplest diagram of forces, more at length, as I wish to shew how, after the first line is drawn and its extremities fixed on, every other line is drawn in a perfectly definite position by means of the parallel ruler.

In any complete diagram of forces, those forces which act at a given point in the frame form a closed polygon. Hence, there will be as many closed polygons in the diagram as there are points in the frame. Also, since each piece of the frame acts with equal and opposite forces on the two points which form its extremities, the force in the diagram will be a side of two different polygons. These polygons might be drawn in any positions relatively to each other; but, in the diagrams here considered, they are placed so that each force is represented by one line, which forms the boundary between the two polygons to which it belongs.

If we regard the polygons as surfaces, rather than as mere outlines, every polygon will be bounded at every point of its outline by other polygons, so that the whole assemblage of polygons will form a continuous surface, which must either be an infinite surface or a closed surface.

The diagram cannot be infinite, because it is made up of a finite number of finite lines representing finite forces. It must, therefore, be a closed surface returning on itself, in such a way that every point in the plane of the diagram either does not belong to the diagram at all, or belongs to an even number of sheets of the diagram.

Any system of polygons, which are in contact with each other externally, may be regarded as a sheet of the diagram. When two polygons are on the same side of the line, which is common to them, that line forms part of the common boundary of two sheets of the diagram. If we reckon those areas positive, the boundary of which is traced in the direction of positive rotation round the area, then all the polygons in each sheet will be of the same sign as the sheet, but those sheets which have a common boundary will be of opposite sign. At every point in the diagram there will be the same number of positive as of negative sheets, and the whole area of the positive sheets will be equal to that of the negative sheets.

The diagram, therefore, may be considered as a plane projection of a closed polyhedron, the faces of the polyhedron being surfaces bounded by rectilinear polygons, which may or may not, as far as we yet know, lie each in one plane.

Let us next consider the plane projection of a given closed polyhedron. If any of the faces of this polyhedron are not plane, we may, by drawing additional lines, substitute for that face a system of triangles, each of which is necessarily in a plane. We may, therefore, consider the polyhedron as bounded by plane faces. Every angular point of this polyhedron will be defined by its projection on the plane and its height above it.

Let us now take a fixed point, which we shall call the origin, and draw from it a perpendicular to the plane. We shall call this line the axis. If we then draw from the origin a line perpendicular to one of the faces of the polyhedron, it will cut the plane at a point which may be said to correspond to the projection of that face. From this point draw a line perpendicular to the plane, and take on this line a point whose distance from the plane is equal to that of the intersection of the axis with the face of the polyhedron produced, but on the other side of the plane. This point in space will correspond to the face of the polyhedron. By repeating this process for every face of the polyhedron, we shall find for every face a corresponding point with its projection on the plane.

To every edge of the polyhedron will correspond the line which joins the points corresponding to the two faces which meet in that edge. Each of these lines is perpendicular to the projection of the other; for the perpendiculars from the origin to the two faces, lie in a plane perpendicular to the edge in which they meet, and the projection of the line corresponding to the edge is the intersection of this plane with the plane of projection. Hence, the edge is perpendicular to the projection of the corresponding line. The projection of the edge is therefore perpendicular to the projection of the corresponding line, and therefore to the corresponding line itself. In this way we may draw a diagram on the plane of projection, every line of which is perpendicular to the corresponding line in the original figure, and so that lines which meet in a point in the one figure form a closed polygon in the other.

If, in a system of rectangular co-ordinates, we make $z = 0$ the plane of projection, and $x = 0$, $y = 0$, $z = c$ the fixed point, then if the equation of a plane be

$$z = Ax + By + C,$$

the co-ordinates of the corresponding point will be

$$\xi = cA, \qquad \eta = cB, \qquad \zeta = -C,$$

and we may write the equation

$$c\,(z + \zeta) = x\xi + y\eta.$$

If we suppose ξ, η, ζ given as the co-ordinates of a point, then this equation, considering x, y, z as variable, is the equation of a plane corresponding to the point.

If we suppose x, y, z the co-ordinates of a point, and ξ, η, ζ as variable, the equation will be that of a plane corresponding to that point.

Hence, if a plane passes through the point xyz, the point corresponding to this plane lies in the plane corresponding to the point xyz.

These points and planes are reciprocally polar in the ordinary sense with respect to the paraboloid of revolution

$$2cz = x^2 + y^2.$$

We have thus arrived at a construction for reciprocal diagrams by considering each as a plane projection of a plane-sided polyhedron, these polyhedra being reciprocal to one another, in the geometrical sense, with respect to a certain paraboloid of revolution.

Each of the diagrams must fulfil the conditions of being a plane projection of a plane-sided polyhedron, for if any of the sides of the polyhedron of which it is the projection are not plane, there will be as many points corresponding to that side as there are different planes passing through three points of the side, and the other diagram will be indefinite.

Relation between the Number of Edges, Summits, and Faces of Polyhedra.

It is manifest that after a closed surface has been divided into separate faces by lines drawn upon it, every new line drawn from a point in the system, either introduces one new point into the system, or divides a face into two parts, according as it is drawn to an isolated point, or to a point already connected with the system. Hence the sum of points and faces is increased by one for every new line. If the closed surface is acyclic, or simply connected[*], like that of a solid body without any passage through it, then, if from any point we draw a closed curve on the surface, we divide the surface into two faces. We have here one line, one point, and two faces. Hence, if e be the number of lines, s the number of points, and f the number of faces, then in general

$$e - s - f = m$$

* See Riemann, *Crelle's Journal*, 1857, *Lehrsätze aus der analysis situs*, for space of two dimensions; also Cayley on the Partitions of a Close, *Phil. Mag.* 1861; Helmholtz, *Crelle's Journal*, 1858, *Wirbelbewegung*, for the application of the idea of multiple continuity to space of three dimensions; J. B. Listing, *Göttingen Trans.*, 1861, *Der Census Räumlicher Complexe*, a complete treatise on the subject of Cyclosis and Periphraxy.

On the importance of this subject see Gauss, *Werke*, v. 605, "Von der *Geometria Situs* die Leibnitz ahnte und in die nur einem Paar Geometern (Euler und Vandermonde) einen schwachen Blick zu thun vergönnt war, wissen und haben wir nach anderthalbhundert Jahren noch nicht viel mehr wie nichts."

Note added March 14, 1870.—Since this was written, I have seen Listing's *Census*. In his notation, the surface of an n-ly connected body (a body with $n - 1$ holes through it) is $(2n - 2)$ cyclic. If $2n - 2 = K_2$ expresses the degree of cyclosis, then Listing's general equation is—

$$s - (e - K_1) + (f - K_2 + \varpi_2) - (v - K_3 + \varpi_3 - w) = 0,$$

where s is the number of points, e the number of lines, K_1 the number of endless curves, f the number of faces, K_2 the number of degrees of cyclosis of the faces, ϖ_2 the number of periphractic or closed faces, v the number of regions of space, K_3 the number of degrees of cyclosis, ϖ_3 their number of degrees of periphraxy or the number of regions which they completely surround, and w is to be put $= 1$ or $= 0$, according as the system does or does not extend to infinity.

when m remains constant, however many lines be drawn. But in the case of a simple closed surface

$$m = -2.$$

If the closed surface is doubly connected, like that of a solid body with a hole through it, then if we draw one closed curve round the hole, and another closed curve through the hole, and round one side of the body, we shall have $e = 2$, $s = 1$, $f = 1$, so that $m = 0$. If the surface is n-ly connected, like that of a solid with $n-1$ holes through it, then we may draw n closed curves round the $n-1$ holes and the outside of the body, and $n-1$ other closed curves each through a hole and round the outside of the body.

We shall then have $4(n-1)$ segments of curves terminating in $2(n-1)$ points and dividing the surface into two faces, so that $e = 4(n-1)$, $s = 2(n-1)$, and $f = 2$, and

$$e - s - f = 2n - 4,$$

and this is the general relation between the edges, summits, and faces of a polyhedron whose surface is n-ly connected.

The plane reciprocal diagrams, considered as plane projections of such polyhedra, have the same relation between the numbers of their lines, points, and polygons. It is manifest that since

$$e_1 = e_2, \qquad s_1 = f_1, \qquad \text{and } f_1 = s_2,$$

where the suffixes refer to the first and second diagrams respectively

$$n_1 = n_2,$$

or the two diagrams are connected to the same degree.

On the Degrees of Freedom and Constraint of Frames.

To determine the positions of s points in space, with reference to a given origin and given axes, $3s$ data are required; but since the position of the origin and axes involve 6 data, the number of data required to determine the relative position of s points is $3s - 6$.

If, therefore, the lengths of $3s - 6$ lines joining selected pairs of a system of s points be given, and if these lengths are all independent of each other, then the distances between any other pair of points will be determinate, and the system will be rigidly connected.

If, however, the lines are so chosen that those which join pairs of points of a system of s' of the points are more than $3s' - 6$ in number, the lengths of these lines will not be independent of each other, and the lines of this partial system will only give $3s' - 6$ independent data to determine the complete system.

In a system of s points joined by e lines, there will in general be $3s - 6 - e$ $= p$ degrees of freedom, provided that in every partial system of s' points joined by e' lines, and having in itself p' degrees of freedom, p' is not negative. If in any such system p is negative, we may put $q = -p$, and call q the number of degrees of constraint, and there will be q equations connecting the lengths of the lines; and if the system is a material one, the stress along each piece will be a function of q independent variables. Such a system may be said to have q degrees of constraint. If p' is negative in any partial system, then the degrees of freedom of the complete system are $p - p'$, where p and p' are got from the number of points and lines in the complete and partial systems. If s points are connected by e lines, so as to form a polyhedron of f faces, enclosing a space n times connected, and if each of the faces has m sides, then

$$mf = 2e.$$

We have also

$$e - s - f = 2n - 4,$$

and

$$3s - e = p + 6,$$

whence

$$p = 6\,(1 - n) + \left(2 - \frac{6}{m}\right)e.$$

If all the faces of the polyhedron are triangles, $m = 3$, and we have

$$p = 6\,(1 - n).$$

If $n = 1$, or in the case of a simply connected polyhedron with triangular faces, $p = o$, that is to say, such a figure is a rigid system, which would be no longer rigid if any one of its lines were wanting. In such a figure, if made of material rods forming a closed web of triangles, the tensions and pressures in the rods would be completely determined by the external forces applied to the figure, and if there were no external force, there would be no stress in the rods.

In a closed surface of any kind, if we cover the surface* with a system of curves which do not intersect each other, and if we draw another system

---

* On the Bending of Surfaces, by J. Clerk Maxwell. *Cambridge Transactions*, 1856. [Vol. I. p. 80.]

intersecting these, and a third system passing diagonally through the intersections of the other two, the whole surface will be covered with small curvilinear triangles, and if we now substitute for the surface a system of rectilinear triangles having the same angular points, we shall have a polyhedron with triangular faces differing infinitely little from the surface, and such that the length of any line on the surface differs infinitely little from that of the corresponding line on the polyhedron. We may, therefore, in all questions about the transformation of surfaces by bending, substitute for them such polyhedra with triangular faces.

We thus find with respect to a simply connected closed inextensible surface—1st, That it is of invariable form*; 2nd, That the stresses in the surface depend entirely on the external applied forces†; 3rd, That if there is no external force, there is no stress in the surface.

In the limiting case of the curved surface, however, a kind of deformation is possible, which is not possible in the case of the polyhedron. Let us suppose that in some way a dimple has been formed on a convexo-convex part of the surface, so that the edge of the dimple is a plane closed curve, and the dimpled part is the reflexion in this plane of the original form of the surface. Then the length of any line drawn on the surface will remain unchanged.

Now let the dimple be gradually enlarged, so that its edge continually changes its position. Every line on the surface will still remain of the same length during the whole process, so that the process is possible in the case of an inextensible surface. In this way such a surface may be gradually turned outside in, and since the dimple may be formed from a mere point, a pressure applied at a single point on the outside of an inextensible surface will not be resisted, but will form a dimple which will increase till one part of the surface comes in contact with another.

In the case of closed surfaces doubly connected, $p = -6$, that is, such surfaces are not only rigid, but are capable of internal stress, independent of external forces, and the expression of this stress depends on six independent variables.

---

* This has been shewn by Professor Jellett, *Trans. R.I.A.*, Vol. XXII. p. 377.

† On the Equilibrium of a Spherical Envelope, by J. C. Maxwell. *Quarterly Journal of Mathematics*, 1867. [Vol. II. p. 86.]

In a polyhedron with triangular faces, if a number of the edges be taken away so as to form a hole with e_1 sides, the number of degrees of freedom is

$$p = e_1 - 6n + 3.$$

Hence, in order to make an n-ly connected polyhedron simply rigid without stress, we may cut out the edges till we have formed a hole having $6n - 3$ edges. The system will then be free from stress, but if any more edges be removed, the system will no longer be rigid.

Since in the limiting case of the inextensible surface, the smallest hole may be regarded as having an infinite number of sides, the smallest hole made in a closed inextensible surface connected to any degree will destroy its rigidity. Its flexibility, however, may be confined within very narrow limits.

In the case of a plane frame of s points, we have $2s$ data required to determine the points with reference to a given origin and axes; but since 3 arbitrary data are involved in the choice of origin and axis, the number of data required to determine the relative position of s points in a plane is $2s - 3$.

If we know the lengths of e lines joining certain pairs of these points, then in general the number of degrees of freedom of the frame will be

$$p = 2s - e - 3.$$

If, however, in any partial system of s' points connected by e' lines, the quantity $p' = 2s' - e' - 3$ be negative, or in other words, if a part of the frame be self-strained, this partial system will contribute only $2s' - 3$ equations independent of each other to the complete system, and the whole frame will have $p - p'$ degrees of freedom.

In a plane frame, consisting of a single sheet, every element of which is triangular, and in which the pieces form three systems of continuous lines, as at p. 173, if the frame contains e pieces connecting s points, s' of which are on the circumference of the frame and s_1 in the interior, then

$$3s - s' = e + 3.$$

Hence $$p = -(s - s') = -s_1,$$

a negative quantity, or such a frame is necessarily stiff; and if any of the points are in the interior of the frame, the frame has as many degrees of constraint as there are interior points—that is, the stresses in each piece will be functions of s_1 variables, and s_1 pieces may be removed from the frame without rendering it loose.

If there are n holes in the frame, so that s' points lie on the circumference of the frame or on those of the holes, and s_1 points lie in the interior, the degree of stiffness will be

$$-p = s_1 + 3n.$$

If a plane frame be a projection of a polyhedron of f faces, each of m sides, and enclosing a space n times connected, then

$$mf = 2e,$$

$$e - s - f = 2n - 4,$$

$$2s - e = p + 3,$$

whence

$$p = 5 - 4n + \left(1 - \frac{4}{m}\right)e.$$

If all the faces are quadrilaterals $m = 4$ and $p = 5 - 4n$, or a plane frame which is the projection of a closed polyhedron with quadrilateral faces, has one degree of freedom if the polyhedron is simply connected, as in the case of the projection of the solid bounded by six quadrilaterals, but if the polyhedron be doubly connected, the frame formed by its plane projection will have three degrees of stiffness. (See Diagram II.)

THEOREM.—If every one of a system of points in a plane is in equilibrium under the action of tensions and pressures acting along the lines joining the points, then if we substitute for each point a small smooth ring through which smooth thin rods of indefinite length corresponding to the lines are compelled to pass, then, if to each rod be applied a couple in the plane, whose moment is equal to the product of the length of the rod between the points multiplied by the tension or pressure in the former case, and tends to turn the rod in the positive or the negative direction, according as the force was a tension or a pressure, then every one of the system of rings will be in equilibrium. For each ring is acted on by a system of forces equal to the tensions and pressures in the former case, each to each, the whole system being turned round a right angle, and therefore the equilibrium of each point is undisturbed.

THEOREM.—In any system of points in equilibrium in a plane under the action of repulsions and attractions, the sum of the products of each attraction multiplied by the distance of the points between which it acts, is equal to the sum of the products of the repulsions multiplied each by the distance of the points between which it acts.

For since each point is in equilibrium under the action of a system of attractions and repulsions in one plane, it will remain in equilibrium if the system of forces is turned through a right angle in the positive direction. If this operation is performed on the systems of forces acting on all the points, then at the extremities of each line joining two points we have two equal forces at right angles to that line and acting in opposite directions, forming a couple whose magnitude is the product of the force between the points and their distance, and whose direction is positive if the force be repulsive, and negative if it be attractive. Now since every point is in equilibrium these two systems of couples are in equilibrium, or the sum of the positive couples is equal to that of the negative couples, which proves the theorem.

In a plane frame, loaded with weights in any manner, and supported by vertical thrusts, each weight must be regarded as attracted towards a horizontal base line, and each support of the frame as repelled from that line. Hence the following rule:

Multiply each load by the height of the point at which it acts, and each tension by the length of the piece on which it acts, and add all these products together.

Then multiply the vertical pressures on the supports of the frame each by the height at which it acts, and each pressure by the length of the piece on which it acts, and add the products together. This sum will be equal to the former sum.

If the thrusts which support the frame are not vertical, their horizontal components must be treated as tensions or pressures borne by the foundations of the structure, or by the earth itself.

The importance of this theorem to the engineer arises from the circumstance that the strength of a piece is in general proportional to its section, so that if the strength of each piece is proportional to the stress which it has to bear, its weight will be proportional to the product of the stress multiplied by the length of the piece. Hence these sums of products give an estimate of the total quantity of material which must be used in sustaining tension and pressure respectively.

The following method of demonstrating this theorem does not require the consideration of couples, and is applicable to frames in three dimensions.

Let the system of points be caused to contract, always remaining similar to its original form, and with its pieces similarly situated, and let the same forces continue to act upon it during this operation, so that every point is always in equilibrium under the same system of forces, and therefore no work is done by the system of forces as a whole.

Let the contraction proceed till the system is reduced to a point. Then the work done by each tension is equal to the product of that tension by the distance through which it has acted, namely, the original distance between the points. Also the work spent in overcoming each pressure is the product of that pressure by the original distance of the points between which it acts; and since no work is gained or lost on the whole, the sum of the first set of products must be equal to the sum of the second set. In this demonstration it is not necessary to suppose the points all in one plane. This demonstration is mathematically equivalent to the following algebraical proof:—

Let the co-ordinates of the n different points of the system be $x_1 y_1 z_1$, $x_2 y_2 z_2$, $x_p y_p z_p$, &c., and let the force between any two points p, q, be P_{pq}, and their distance r_{pq}, and let it be reckoned positive when it is a pressure, and negative when it is a tension, then the equation of equilibrium of any point p with respect to forces parallel to x is

$$(x_p - x_1)\frac{P_{p1}}{r_{p1}} + (x_p - x_2)\frac{P_{p2}}{r_{p2}} + \&c. + (x_p - x_q)\frac{P_{pq}}{r_{pq}} + \&c. = 0,$$

or generally, giving t all values from 1 to n,

$$\Sigma_1^n t \left\{ (x_p - x_t)\frac{P_{pt}}{r_{pt}} \right\} = 0.$$

Multiply this equation by x_p. There are n such equations, so that if each is multiplied by its proper co-ordinate and the sum taken, we get

$$\Sigma_1^n p \, \Sigma_1^n t \left\{ (x_p - x_t)^2 \frac{P_{pt}}{r_{pt}} \right\} = 0,$$

and adding the corresponding equations in y and z, we get

$$\Sigma_1^n p \, \Sigma_1^n t \, (P_{pt} \, r_{pt}) = 0,$$

which is the algebraic expression of the theorem.

GENERAL THEORY OF DIAGRAMS OF STRESS IN THREE DIMENSIONS.

First Method of Representing Stress in a Body.

DEFINITION. A diagram of stress is a figure having such a relation to a body under the action of internal forces, that if a surface A, limited by a closed curve, is drawn in the body, and if the corresponding limited surface a be drawn in the diagram of stress, then the resultant of the actual internal forces on the positive side of the surface A in the body is equal and parallel to the resultant of a uniform normal pressure p acting on the positive side of the surface a in the diagram of stress.

Let x, y, z be the co-ordinates of any point in the body, ξ, η, ζ those of the corresponding point in the diagram of stress, then ξ, η, ζ are functions of x, y, z, the nature of which we have to ascertain, so that the internal forces in the body may be in equilibrium. For the present we suppose no external forces, such as gravity, to act on the particles of the body. We shall consider such forces afterwards.

THEOREM 1.—If any closed surface is described in the body, and if the stress on any element of that surface is equal and parallel to the pressure on the corresponding element of surface in the diagram of stress, then the resultant stress on the whole closed surface will vanish; for the corresponding surface in the diagram of stress is a closed surface, and the resultant of a uniform normal pressure p on every element of a closed surface is zero by hydrostatics.

It does not, however, follow that the portion of the body within the closed surface is in equilibrium, for the stress on its surface may have a resultant moment.

THEOREM 2.—To ensure equilibrium of every part of the body, it is necessary and sufficient that

$$\xi = \frac{dF}{dx}, \qquad \eta = \frac{dF}{dy}, \qquad \zeta = \frac{dF}{dz},$$

where F is any function of x, y, and z.

Let us consider the elementary area in the body $dy\,dz$. The stress acting on this area will be a force equal and parallel to the resultant of a pressure p acting on the corresponding element of area in the diagram of stress. Resolving this pressure in the directions of the co-ordinate axes, we find the three components of stress on $dy\,dz$, which we may call $p_{xx}dy\,dz$, $p_{xy}dy\,dz$, and $p_{xz}dy\,dz$, each equal to p multiplied by the area of the projection of the corresponding element of the diagram of stress on the three co-ordinate planes. Now, the projection on the plane yz, is

$$\left(\frac{d\eta}{dy}\frac{d\zeta}{dz} - \frac{d\eta}{dz}\frac{d\zeta}{dy}\right) dy\,dz.$$

Hence we find for the component of stress in the direction of x

$$p_{xx} = p\left(\frac{d\eta}{dy}\frac{d\zeta}{dz} - \frac{d\eta}{dz}\frac{d\zeta}{dy}\right),$$

which we may write for brevity at present

$$p_{xx} = pJ(\eta,\ \zeta;\ y,\ z).$$

Similarly,

$$p_{xy} = pJ(\zeta,\ \xi;\ y,\ z), \qquad p_{xz} = pJ(\xi,\ \eta;\ y,\ z).$$

In the same way, we may find the components of stress on the areas $dz\,dx$ and $dx\,dy$—

$$p_{yx} = pJ(\eta,\ \zeta;\ z,\ x), \qquad p_{yy} = pJ(\zeta,\ \xi;\ z,\ x), \qquad p_{yz} = pJ(\xi,\ \eta;\ z,\ x),$$

$$p_{zx} = pJ(\eta,\ \zeta;\ x,\ y), \qquad p_{zy} = pJ(\zeta,\ \xi;\ x,\ y), \qquad p_{zz} = pJ(\xi,\ \eta;\ x,\ y).$$

Now, consider the equilibrium of the parallelopiped $dx\,dy\,dz$, with respect to the moment of the tangential stresses about its axes.

The moments of the forces tending to turn this elementary parallelopiped about the axis of x are

$$dz\,dx\,p_{yz}\,.\,dy - dx\,dy\,p_{zy}\,.\,dz.$$

To ensure equilibrium as respects rotation about the axis of x, we must have

$$p_{yz} = p_{zy}.$$

Similarly, for the moments about the axes of y and z, we obtain the equations

$$p_{zx} = p_{xz} \text{ and } p_{xy} = p_{yx}.$$

Now, let us assume for the present

$$\frac{d\xi}{dx} = A_1, \qquad \frac{d\xi}{dy} = B_3 + C_3, \qquad \frac{d\xi}{dz} = B_2 - C_2,$$

$$\frac{d\eta}{dx} = B_3 - C_3, \qquad \frac{d\eta}{dy} = A_2, \qquad \frac{d\eta}{dz} = B_1 + C_1,$$

$$\frac{d\zeta}{dx} = B_2 + C_2, \qquad \frac{d\zeta}{dy} = B_1 - C_1, \qquad \frac{d\zeta}{dz} = A_3.$$

Then the equation $p_{yz} = p_{zy}$ becomes

$$p\left(\frac{d\xi}{dz}\frac{d\eta}{dx} - \frac{d\xi}{dx}\frac{d\eta}{dz}\right) = p\left(\frac{d\zeta}{dx}\frac{d\xi}{dy} - \frac{d\zeta}{dy}\frac{d\xi}{dx}\right)$$

or $(B_2 - C_2)(B_3 - C_3) - A_1(B_1 + C_1) = (B_2 + C_2)(B_3 + C_3) - A_1(B_1 - C_1),$

$$0 = A_1 C_1 + B_3 C_2 + B_2 C_3.$$

Similarly, from the two other equations of equilibrium we should find

$$0 = A_2 C_2 + B_1 C_3 + B_3 C_1,$$
$$0 = A_3 C_3 + B_2 C_1 + B_1 C_2.$$

From these three equations it follows that

$$C_1 = 0, \quad C_2 = 0, \quad C_3 = 0.$$

Hence $$\frac{d\eta}{dz} = \frac{d\zeta}{dy}, \quad \frac{d\zeta}{dx} = \frac{d\xi}{dz}, \quad \frac{d\xi}{dy} = \frac{d\eta}{dx},$$

and $\xi dx + \eta dy + \zeta dz$ is a complete differential of some function, F, of x, y and z, whence it follows that

$$\xi = \frac{dF}{dx}, \quad \eta = \frac{dF}{dy}, \quad \zeta = \frac{dF}{dz}.$$

F may be called the function of stress, because when it is known, the diagram of stress may be formed, and the components of stress calculated. The form of the function F is limited only by the conditions to be fulfilled at the bounding surface of the body.

The six components of stress expressed in terms of F are

$$p_{xx} = p\left\{\frac{d^2F}{dy^2}\frac{d^2F}{dz^2} - \left(\frac{d^2F}{dydz}\right)^2\right\}, \; p_{yy} = p\left\{\frac{d^2F}{dz^2}\frac{d^2F}{dx^2} - \left(\frac{d^2F}{dzdx}\right)^2\right\}, \; p_{zz} = p\left\{\frac{d^2F}{dx^2}\frac{dF^2}{dy^2} - \left(\frac{d^2F}{dxdy}\right)\right\},$$

$$p_{yz} = p\left(\frac{d^2F}{dzdx}\frac{d^2F}{dxdy} - \frac{d^2F}{dx^2}\frac{d^2F}{dydz}\right), \; p_{zx} = p\left(\frac{d^2F}{dxdy}\frac{d^2F}{dydz} - \frac{d^2F}{dy^2}\frac{d^2F}{dzdx}\right),$$

$$p_{xy} = p\left(\frac{d^2F}{dydz}\frac{d^2F}{dzdx} - \frac{d^2F}{dz^2}\frac{d^2F}{dxdy}\right).$$

If $\frac{dF}{dz} = z$, F becomes Airy's function of stress in two dimensions, and we have

$$p_{xx} = p\frac{d^2F}{dy^2}, \quad p_{yy} = p\frac{d^2F}{dx^2}, \quad p_{xy} = -p\frac{d^2F}{dxdy}.$$

The system of stress in three dimensions deduced in this way from any function, F, satisfies the equations of equilibrium of internal stress. It is not, however, a general solution of these equations, as may be easily seen by taking the case in which p_{xx} and p_{yz} are both zero at all points. In this case, since there is no tangential action in planes parallel to xy, the stresses p_{xx}, p_{xy} and p_{yy} in each stratum must separately fulfil the conditions of equilibrium,

$$\frac{d}{dx}p_{xx} + \frac{d}{dy}p_{xy} = 0, \quad \frac{d}{dx}p_{xy} + \frac{d}{dy}p_{yy} = 0.$$

The complete solution of these equations is, as we have seen,

$$p_{xx} = \frac{d^2f}{dy^2}, \quad p_{xy} = -\frac{d^2f}{dxdy}, \quad p_{yy} = \frac{d^2f}{dx^2},$$

where f is any function of x and y, the form of which may be different for every different value of z, so that we may regard f as a perfectly general function of x, y, and z.

Again, if we consider a cylindrical portion of the body with its generating lines parallel to z, we shall see that there is no tangential action parallel to z between this cylinder and the rest of the body. Hence the longitudinal stress in this cylinder must be constant throughout its length, and is independent of the stress in any other part of the body.

Hence $\qquad\qquad p_{zz} = \phi(x, y)$,

where ϕ is a function of x and y only, but may be any such function. But expressing the stresses in terms of F under the conditions $p_{xz} = 0$, $p_{yz} = 0$, we find that if F is a perfectly general function of x and y

$$\frac{d^2F}{dxdz} = 0, \text{ and } \frac{d^2F}{dydz} = 0,$$

whence it follows that $\dfrac{dF}{dx}$ and $\dfrac{dF}{dy}$ are functions of x and y only, and that $\dfrac{dF}{dz}$ is a function of z only. Hence

$$F = G + Z,$$

when G is a function of x and y only, and Z a function of z only, and the components of stress are

$$p_{xx} = p\frac{d^2G}{dy^2}\frac{d^2Z}{dz^2}, \quad p_{yy} = p\frac{d^2G}{dx^2}\frac{d^2Z}{dz^2}, \quad p_{zz} = p\left\{\frac{d^2G}{dx^2}\frac{d^2G}{dy^2} - \left(\frac{d^2G}{dxdy}\right)^2\right\},$$

$$p_{yz} = 0, \qquad\qquad p_{zx} = 0, \qquad\qquad p_{xy} = -p\frac{d^2G}{dxdy}\frac{d^2Z}{dz^2}.$$

Here the function f which determines the stress in the strata parallel to xy is

$$f = pG\frac{d^2Z}{dz^2}$$

Now, this function is not sufficiently general, for instead of being any function of x, y, and z, it is the product of a function of x and y multiplied by a function of z.

Besides this, though the value of p_{zz} is, as it ought to be, a function of x and y only, it is not of the most general form, for it depends on G, the function which determines the stresses p_{xx}, p_{xy}, and p_{yy}, whereas the value of p_{zz} may be entirely independent of the values of these stresses. In fact, the equations give

$$p_{zz} = p\frac{p_{xx}p_{yy} - p_{xy}^2}{\left(\dfrac{d^2Z}{dz^2}\right)^2}.$$

This method, therefore, of representing stress in a body of three dimensions is a restricted solution of the equations of equilibrium.

On Reciprocal Diagrams in Three Dimensions.

Let us consider figures in two portions of space, which we shall call respectively the first and the second diagrams. Let the co-ordinates of any point in the first diagram be denoted by x, y, z, and those of the corresponding point in the second by ξ, η, ζ, measured in directions parallel to x, y, z respectively. Let F be a quantity varying from point to point of the first figure in any continuous manner; that is to say, if A, B are two points, and F_1, F_2 the values of F at those points; then, if B approaches A without limit, the value of F_2 approaches that of F_1 without limit. Let the co-ordinates (ξ, η, ζ) of a point in the second diagram be determined from x, y, z, those of the corresponding point in the first by the equations

$$\xi = \frac{dF}{dx}, \quad \eta = \frac{dF}{dy}, \quad \zeta = \frac{dF}{dz} \quad\dotfill (1).$$

This is equivalent to the statement, that the vector (ρ) of any point in the second diagram represents in direction and magnitude the rate of variation of F at the corresponding point of the first diagram.

Next, let us determine another function, ϕ, from the equation

$$x\xi + y\eta + z\zeta = F + \phi \quad\text{...........................} (2),$$

ϕ, as thus determined, will be a function of x, y, and z, since ξ, η, ζ are known in terms of these quantities. But, for the same reason, ϕ is a function of ξ, η, ζ. Differentiate ϕ with respect to ξ, considering x, y, and z functions of ξ, η, ζ,

$$\frac{d\phi}{d\xi} = x + \xi\frac{dx}{d\xi} + \eta\frac{dy}{d\xi} + \zeta\frac{dz}{d\xi} - \frac{dF}{d\xi}.$$

Substituting the values of ξ, η, ζ from (1)

$$\frac{d\phi}{d\xi} = x + \frac{dF}{dx}\frac{dx}{d\xi} + \frac{dF}{dy}\frac{dy}{d\xi} + \frac{dF}{dz}\frac{dz}{d\xi} - \frac{dF}{d\xi}$$

$$= x + \frac{dF}{d\xi} - \frac{dF}{d\xi}$$

$$= x.$$

Differentiating ϕ with respect to η and ζ, we get the three equations

$$x = \frac{d\phi}{d\xi}, \quad y = \frac{d\phi}{d\eta}, \quad z = \frac{d\phi}{d\zeta} \quad\text{.........................} (3),$$

or the vector (r) of any point in the first diagram represents in direction and magnitude the rate of increase of ϕ at the corresponding point of the second diagram.

Hence the first diagram may be determined from the second by the same process that the second was determined from the first, and the two diagrams, each with its own function, are reciprocal to each other.

The relation (2) between the functions expresses that the sum of the functions for two corresponding points is equal to the product of the distances of these points from the origin multiplied by the cosine of the angle between the directions of these distances.

Both these functions must be of two dimensions in space. Let F' be a linear function of xyz, which has the same value and rate of variation as F has at the point $x_0 y_0 z_0$

$$F' = F_0 + (x - x_0)\frac{dF_0}{dx} + (y - y_0)\frac{dF_0}{dy} + (z - z_0)\frac{dF_0}{dz} \quad\text{..............} (4).$$

The value of F' at the origin is found by putting x, y, and $z = 0$

$$F' = F_0 - x_0\xi - y_0\eta - z_0\zeta = -\phi \quad\text{........................} (5),$$

or the value of F' at the origin is equal and opposite to the value of ϕ at the point ξ, η, ζ.

If the rate of variation of F is nowhere infinite, the co-ordinates ξ, η, ζ, of the second diagram must be everywhere finite, and *vice versa*. Beyond the limits of the second diagram the values of x, y, z, in terms of ξ, η, ζ, must be impossible, and therefore the value of ϕ is also impossible. Within the limits of the second diagram, the function ϕ has an even number of values at every point, corresponding to an even number of points in the first diagram, which correspond to a single point in the second.

To find these points in the first diagram, let ρ be the vector of a given point in the second diagram, and let surfaces be drawn in the first diagram for which F is constant, and let points be found in each of these surfaces at which the tangent plane is perpendicular to ρ, these points will form one or more curves, which must be either closed or infinite, and the points on these curves correspond to the points in the second diagram which lie in the direction of the vector ρ. If p be the perpendicular from a point in the first diagram on a plane through the origin perpendicular to ρ, then all those points on these curves at which $\dfrac{dF}{dp} = \rho$ correspond to the given point in the second diagram. Now, since this point is within the second diagram, there are values of ρ both greater and less than the given one; and therefore $\dfrac{dF}{dp}$ is neither an absolute maximum nor an absolute minimum value. Hence there are in general an even number of points on the curve or curves which correspond to the given point. Some of these points may coincide, but at least two of them must be different, unless the given point is at the limit of the second diagram.

Let us now consider the two reciprocal diagrams with their functions, and ascertain in what the geometrical nature of their reciprocity consists.

(1) Let the first diagram be simply the point P_1, (x_1, y_1, z_1), at which $F = F_1$, then in the other diagram

$$\phi = x_1\xi + y_1\eta + z_1\zeta - F_1 \quad\text{.........................} (6),$$

or a point in one diagram is reciprocal to a space in the other, in which the function ϕ is a linear function of the co-ordinates.

(2) Let the first diagram contain a second point P_2, (x_2, y_2, z_2), at which $F = F_2$, then we must combine equation (6) with

$$\phi = x_2\xi + y_2\eta + z_2\zeta - F_2 \dots\dots\dots\dots\dots\dots\dots (7),$$

whence eliminating ϕ,

$$(x_1 - x_2)\,\xi + (y_1 - y_2)\,\eta + (z_1 - z_2)\,\zeta = F_1 - F_2.$$

If r_{12} is the length of the line drawn from the first point P_1 to the second P_2; and if $l_{12}m_{12}n_{12}$ are its direction cosines, this equation becomes

$$l_{12}\xi + m_{12}\eta + n_{12}\zeta = \frac{F_2 - F_1}{r_{12}},$$

or the reciprocal of the two points P_1 and P_2 is a plane, perpendicular to the line joining them, and such that the perpendicular from the origin on the plane multiplied by the length of the line P_1P_2 is equal to the excess of F_2 over F_1.

(3) Let there be a third point P_3 in the first diagram, whose co-ordinates are x_3, y_3, z_3 and for which $F = F_3$; then we must combine with equations (6) and (7)

$$\phi = x_3\xi + y_3\eta + z_3\zeta - F_3 \dots\dots\dots\dots\dots\dots\dots (8).$$

The reciprocal of the three points P_1, P_2, P_3 is a straight line perpendicular to the plane of the three points, and such that the perpendicular on this line from the origin represents, in direction and magnitude, the rate of most rapid increase of F in the plane $P_1P_2P_3$, F being a linear function of the co-ordinates whose values at the three points are those given.

(4) Let there be a fourth point P_4 for which $F = F_4$.

The reciprocal of the four points is a single point, and the line drawn from the origin to this point represents, in direction and magnitude, the rate of greatest increase of F, supposing F such a linear function of xyz that its values at the four points are those given. The value of ϕ at this point is that of F at the origin.

Let us next suppose that the value of F is continuous, that is, that F does not vary by a finite quantity when the co-ordinates vary by infinitesimal quantities, but that the form of the function ϕ is discontinuous, being a different linear function of xyz in different parts of space, bounded by definite surfaces.

The bounding surfaces of these parts of space must be composed of planes. For let the linear functions of xyz in contiguous portions of space be

$$F_1 = a_1 x + \beta_1 y + \gamma_1 z - \phi_1,$$
$$F_2 = a_2 x + \beta_2 y + \gamma_2 z - \phi_2,$$

then at the bounding surface, where $F_1 = F_2$

$$(a_1 - a_2)\, x + (\beta_1 - \beta_2)\, y + (\gamma_1 - \gamma_2)\, z = \phi_1 - \phi_2 \ldots\ldots\ldots\ldots (9),$$

and this is the equation of a plane.

Hence the portion of space in which any particular form of the value of F holds good must be a polyhedron or cell bounded by plane faces, and therefore having straight edges meeting in a number of points or summits.

Every face is the boundary of two cells, every edge belongs to three or more cells, and to two faces of each cell.

Every summit belongs to at least four cells, to at least three faces of each cell, and to two edges of each face.

The whole space occupied by the diagram is divided into cells in two different ways, so that every point in it belongs to two different cells, and has two values of F and its derivatives.

The reciprocal diagram is made up of cells in the same way, and the reciprocity of the two diagrams may be thus stated :—

1. Every summit in one diagram corresponds to a cell in the other.

The radius vector of the summit represents the rate of increase of the function within the cell, both in direction and magnitude.

The value of the function at the summit is equal and opposite to the value which the function in the cell would have if it were continued under the same algebraical form to the origin.

2. Every edge in the one diagram corresponds to a plane face in the other, which is the face of contact of the two cells corresponding to the two extremities of the edge.

The edge in the one diagram is perpendicular to the face in the other.

The distance of the plane from the origin represents the rate of increase of the function along the edge.

3. Every face in the one diagram corresponds to an edge in which as many cells meet as there are angles in the face, that is, at least three. Every face must belong to two, and only two cells, because the edge to which it corresponds has two, and only two extremities.

4. Every cell in the one diagram corresponds to a summit in the other. Every face of the cell corresponds and is perpendicular to an edge having an extremity in the summit. Since every cell must have four or more faces, every summit must have four or more edges meeting there.

Every edge of the cell corresponds to a face having an angle in the summit. Since every cell has at least six edges, every summit must be the point of concourse of at least six faces, which are the boundaries of cells.

Every summit of the cell corresponds to a cell having a solid angle at the summit. Since every cell has at least four summits, every summit must be the meeting place of at least four cells.

Mechanical Reciprocity of the Diagrams.

If along each of the edges meeting in a summit forces are applied proportional to the areas of the corresponding faces of the cell in the reciprocal diagram, and in a direction which is always inward with respect to the cell, then these forces will be in equilibrium at the summit.

This is the "Polyhedron of Forces," and may be proved by hydrostatics.

If the faces of the cell form a single closed surface which does not intersect itself, it is easy to understand what is meant by the inside and outside of the cell; but if the surface intersects itself, it is better to speak of the positive and negative sides of the surface. A cell, or portion of a cell, bounded by a closed surface, of which the positive side is inward, may be called a positive cell. If the surface intersects itself, and encloses another portion of space with its negative side inward, that portion of space forms a negative cell. If any portion of space is surrounded by n sheets of the surface of the same cell with their positive side inward, and by m sheets with their negative side inward, the space enclosed in this way must be reckoned $n - m$ times.

In passing to a contiguous cell, we must suppose that its face in contact with the first cell has its positive surface on the opposite side from that of the first cell. In this way, by making the positive side of the surface continuous throughout each cell, and by changing it when we pass to the next cell, we may settle the positive and negative side of every face of every cell, the sign of every face depending on which of the two cells it is considered for the moment to belong to.

If we now suppose forces of tension or pressure applied along every edge of the first diagram, so that the force on each extremity of the edge is in the direction of the positive normal to the corresponding face of the cell corresponding to that extremity, and proportional to the area of the face, then these pressures and tensions along the edges will keep every point of the diagram in equilibrium.

Another way of determining the nature of the force along any edge of the first diagram, is as follows :—

Round any edge of the first diagram draw a closed curve, embracing it and no other edge. However small the curve is, it will enter each of the cells which meet in the edge. Hence the reciprocal of this closed curve will be a plane polygon whose angles are the points reciprocal to these cells taken in order. The area of this polygon represents, both in direction and magnitude, the whole force acting through the closed curve, that is, in this case the stress along the edge. If, therefore, in going round the angles of the polygon, we travel in the same direction of rotation in space as in going round the closed curve, the stress along the edge will be a pressure ; but if the direction is opposite, the stress will be a tension.

This method of expressing stresses in three dimensions comprehends all cases in which Rankine's reciprocal figures are possible, and is applicable to certain cases of continuous stress. That it is not applicable to all such cases is easily seen by the example of p (189).

On Reciprocal Diagrams in two Dimensions.

If we make F a function of x and y only, all the properties already deduced for figures in three dimensions will be true in two; but we may form a more distinct geometrical conception of the theory by substituting cz for F

and $c\zeta$ for ϕ. We have then for the equations of relation between the two diagrams

$$\left.\begin{array}{cc} \xi = c\,\dfrac{dz}{dx}, & \eta = c\,\dfrac{dz}{dy} \\[2mm] x = c\,\dfrac{d\zeta}{d\xi}, & y = c\,\dfrac{d\zeta}{d\eta} \\[2mm] x\xi + y\eta = cz + c\zeta \end{array}\right\} \quad\dots\dots\dots\dots\dots\dots(10).$$

These equations are equivalent to the following definitions :—

Let z in the first diagram be given as a function of x and y, z will lie on a surface of some kind. Let x_0, y_0 be particular values of x and y, and let z_0 be the corresponding value of z. Draw a tangent plane to the surface at the point x_0, y_0, z_0, and from the point $\xi = 0$, $\eta = 0$, $\zeta = -c$; in the second diagram draw a normal to this tangent plane. It will cut the plane $\zeta = 0$ at the point ξ, η corresponding to xy, and the value of ζ is equal and opposite to the segment of the axis of z cut off by the tangent plane. The two surfaces may be defined as reciprocally polar (in the ordinary sense) with respect to the paraboloid of revolution

$$x^2 + y^2 = 2cz \dots\dots\dots\dots\dots\dots\dots\dots\dots\dots (11),$$

and the diagrams are the projections on the planes of xy and $\xi\eta$ of points and lines on these surfaces.

If one of the surfaces is a plane-faced polyhedron, the other will also be a plane-faced polyhedron, every face in the one corresponding to a point in the other, and every edge in the one corresponding to the line joining the points corresponding to the faces bounded by the edge. In the projected diagrams every line is perpendicular to the corresponding line, and lines which meet in a point in one figure form a closed polygon in the other.

These are the conditions of reciprocity mentioned at p. 169, and it now appears that if either of the diagrams is a projection of a plane-faced polyhedron, the other diagram can be drawn. If the first diagram cannot be a projection of a plane-faced polyhedron, let it be a projection of a polyhedron whose faces are polygons not in one plane. These faces must be conceived to be filled up by surfaces, which are either curved or made up of different plane portions. In the first case the polygon will correspond not to a point, but to a finite portion of a surface; in the second, it will correspond to several points, so that the lines, which correspond to the edges of such a polygon, will terminate in several points, and not in one, as is necessary for reciprocity.

Second Method of representing Stress in a Body.

Let a, b be any two consecutive points in the first diagram, distant s, and a, β the corresponding points in the second, distant σ, then if the direction cosines of the line ab are l, m, n and those of $a\beta$, λ, μ, ν

$$\left. \begin{aligned} \sigma\lambda &= sl\frac{d\xi}{dx} + sm\frac{d\xi}{dy} + sn\frac{d\xi}{dz} \\[1mm] \sigma\mu &= sl\frac{d\eta}{dx} + sm\frac{d\eta}{dy} + sn\frac{d\eta}{dz} \\[1mm] \sigma\nu &= sl\frac{d\zeta}{dx} + sm\frac{d\zeta}{dy} + sn\frac{d\zeta}{dz} \end{aligned} \right\} \dots\dots\dots\dots\dots\dots (12).$$

Hence

$$\frac{\sigma}{s}\left(l\lambda + m\mu + n\nu\right) = l^2\frac{d\xi}{dx} + m^2\frac{d\eta}{dy} + n^2\frac{d\zeta}{dz} + mn\left(\frac{d\eta}{dz} + \frac{d\zeta}{dy}\right) + nl\left(\frac{d\zeta}{dx} + \frac{d\xi}{dz}\right)$$
$$+ lm\left(\frac{d\xi}{dy} + \frac{d\eta}{dx}\right) \dots\dots (13).$$

If we put $l\lambda + m\mu + n\nu = \cos\epsilon$, where ϵ is the angle between s and σ, and if we take three sets of values of l, m, n, corresponding to three directions at right angles to each other, we find

$$\frac{\sigma_1}{s_1}\cos\epsilon_1 + \frac{\sigma_2}{s_2}\cos\epsilon_2 + \frac{\sigma_3}{s_3}\cos\epsilon_3 = \frac{d\xi}{dx} + \frac{d\eta}{dy} + \frac{d\zeta}{dz} = \frac{d^2F}{dx^2} + \frac{d^2F}{dy^2} + \frac{d^2F}{dz^2} \dots\dots (14).$$

Hence this quantity depends only on the position of the point, and not on the directions of s_1, s_2, s_3 or of x, y, z, let us call it $\Delta^2 F$.

Now, let us take an element of area perpendicular to s, and let us suppose that the stress on this element is compounded of a normal pressure $= p\Delta^2 F$, and a tension parallel to σ and equal to $p\dfrac{\sigma}{s}$.

By the rules for the composition of stress, we have for the components of the force on this element, in terms of the six components of stress,

$$X = lp_{xx} + mp_{xy} + np_{xz} = p\left(l\Delta^2 F - \lambda\,\frac{\sigma}{s}\right)$$
$$Y = lp_{xy} + mp_{yy} + np_{yz} = p\left(m\Delta^2 F - \mu\,\frac{\sigma}{s}\right) \Bigg\} \quad\ldots\ldots\ldots\ldots\ldots (15).$$
$$Z = lp_{xz} + mp_{yz} + np_{zz} = p\left(n\Delta^2 F - \nu\,\frac{\sigma}{s}\right)$$

Hence,

$$p_{xx} = p\left(\Delta^2 F - \frac{d\xi}{dx}\right) \quad = p\left(\Delta^2 F - \frac{d^2 F}{dx^2}\right) \quad = p\left(\frac{d^2 F}{dy^2} + \frac{d^2 F}{dz^2}\right)$$
$$p_{xx} = p\left(\frac{d^2 F}{dy^2} + \frac{d^2 F}{dz^2}\right),\ p_{yy} = p\left(\frac{d^2 F}{dz^2} + \frac{d^2 F}{dx^2}\right),\ p_{zz} = p\left(\frac{d^2 F}{dx^2} + \frac{d^2 F}{dy^2}\right) \Bigg\} \quad\ldots (16).$$
$$p_{yz} = -p\frac{d^2 F}{dx\,dy},\qquad p_{zx} = -p\frac{d^2 F}{dz\,dx},\qquad p_{xy} = -p\frac{d^2 F}{dx\,dy}$$

By substituting these values in the equations of equilibrium

$$\frac{dp_{xx}}{dx} + \frac{dp_{xy}}{dy} + \frac{dp_{xz}}{dz} = 0,\ \&c.\ \ldots\ldots\ldots\ldots\ldots\ldots (17),$$

it is manifest that they are fulfilled for any value of F.

The most general solution of these equations of equilibrium is contained in the values

$$p_{xx} = \frac{d^2 B}{dz^2} + \frac{d^2 C}{dy^2},\quad p_{yy} = \frac{d^2 C}{dx^2} + \frac{d^2 A}{dz^2},\quad p_{zz} = \frac{d^2 A}{dy^2} + \frac{d^2 B}{dx^2} \Bigg\} \quad\ldots\ldots (18).$$
$$p_{yz} = -\frac{d^2 A}{dy\,dz},\qquad p_{zx} = -\frac{d^2 B}{dz\,dx},\qquad p_{xy} = -\frac{d^2 C}{dx\,dy}$$

By making $A = B = C = pF$ we get a case which, though restricted in its generality, has remarkable properties with respect to diagrams of stress. We have seen that a distribution of stress according to the definition above (16), is consistent with itself, and will keep a body in equilibrium. Since the stresses are linear functions of F, any two systems of stress can be compounded by adding their respective functions, a process not applicable to the first method of representation by areas.

Let us ascertain what kind of stress is represented in this way in the case of the system of cells already considered.

Since F in each cell is a linear function of x, y, z, there can be no stress at any point within it. Let us take a and b two contiguous points in different cells, then α and β will be the points at a finite distance to which these cells are reciprocal, and $\Delta^2 F = \dfrac{\alpha\beta}{ab}$, which becomes infinite when ab vanishes.

If a and b are in the surface bounding the cells, α and β coincide. Hence there is a stress in this surface, uniform in all directions in the plane of the surface, and such that the stress across unit of length drawn on the surface is proportional to the distance between the points which are reciprocal to the two cells bounded by the surface, and this stress is a tension or a pressure according as the two points are similarly or oppositely situated to the two cells.

The kind of equilibrium corresponding to this case is therefore that of a system of liquid films, each having a tension like that of a soap bubble, depending on the nature of the fluid of which it is composed. If all the films are composed of the same fluid, their tensions must be equal, and all the edges of the reciprocal diagram must be equal.

On Airy's Function of Stress.

Mr Airy, in a paper "On the Strains in the Interior of Beams[*]," was, I believe, the first to point out that, in any body in equilibrium under the action of internal stress in two dimensions, the three components of the stress in any two rectangular directions are the three second derivatives, with respect to these directions, of a certain function of the position of a point in the body.

This important simplification of the theory of the equilibrium of stress in two dimensions does not depend on any theory of elasticity, or on the mode in which stress arises in the body, but solely on the two conditions of equilibrium of an element of a body acted on only by internal stress

$$\frac{d}{dx}\,p_{xx} + \frac{d}{dy}\,p_{xy} = 0, \text{ and } \frac{d}{dx}\,p_{xy} + \frac{d}{dy}\,p_{yy} = 0 \dots\dots\dots\dots(19),$$

whence it follows that

$$p_{xx} = \frac{d^2 F}{dy^2}, \quad p_{xy} = -\frac{d^2 F}{dx\,dy}, \quad \text{and} \quad p_{yy} = \frac{d^2 F}{dx^2} \dots\dots\dots\dots(20),$$

[*] *Phil. Trans.* 1863.

where F is a function of x and y, the form of which is (as far as these equations are concerned) perfectly arbitrary, and the value of which at any point is independent of the choice of axes of co-ordinates. Since the stresses depend on the second derivatives of F, any linear function of x and y may be added to F without affecting the value of the stresses deduced from F. Also, since the stresses are linear functions of F, any two systems of stress may be mechanically compounded by adding the corresponding values of F.

The importance of Airy's function in the theory of stress becomes even more manifest when we deduce from it the diagram of stress, the co-ordinates of whose points are

$$\xi = \frac{dF}{dy} \quad \text{and} \quad \eta = -\frac{dF}{dx} \quad \ldots\ldots\ldots\ldots\ldots\ldots (21).$$

For if s be the length of any curve in the original figure, and σ that of the corresponding curve in the diagram of stress, and if Xds, Yds are the components of the whole stress acting on the element ds towards the right hand of the curve s

$$Xds = p_{xx}\frac{dy}{ds}ds = \frac{d^2F}{dy^2}\frac{dy}{ds}ds = \frac{d\xi}{dy}\frac{dy}{ds}ds = \frac{d\xi}{d\sigma}d\sigma \left.\begin{matrix} \\ \\ \end{matrix}\right\}$$

and $\qquad Yds = -p_{yy}\frac{dx}{ds}ds = -\frac{d^2F}{dx^2}\frac{dx}{ds}ds = \frac{d\eta}{dx}\frac{dx}{ds}ds = \frac{d\eta}{d\sigma}d\sigma \quad \ldots\ldots\ldots(22).$

Hence the stress on the right hand side of the element ds of the original curve is represented, both in direction and magnitude, by the corresponding element $d\sigma$ of the curve in the diagram of stress, and, by composition, the resultant stress on any finite arc of the first curve s is represented in direction and magnitude by the straight line drawn from the beginning to the end of the corresponding curve σ.

If P_1, P_2 are the principal stresses at any point, and if P_1 is inclined a to the axis of x, then the component stresses are

$$\begin{aligned} p_{xx} &= P_1\cos^2 a + P_2\sin^2 a \\ p_{xy} &= (P_1 - P_2)\sin a \cos a \\ p_{yy} &= P_1\sin^2 a + P_2\cos^2 a \end{aligned} \right\} \quad \ldots\ldots\ldots\ldots\ldots\ldots (23).$$

Hence $\quad\quad$ $\tan 2a = \dfrac{p_{xy}}{p_{xx}-p_{yy}} = \dfrac{\dfrac{d^2F}{dx\,dy}}{\dfrac{d^2F}{dx^2}-\dfrac{d^2F}{dy^2}}$

$P_1+P_2 = \quad p_{xx}+p_{yy} = \dfrac{d^2F}{dx^2}+\dfrac{d^2F}{dy^2}$

$P_1P_2 = p_{xx}p_{yy}-p_{xy}{}^2 = \dfrac{d^2F}{dx^2}\dfrac{d^2F}{dy^2}-\left(\dfrac{d^2F}{dx\,dy}\right)^2$

$\left.\right\} \quad \ldots\ldots\ldots\ldots (24).$

Consider the area bounded by a closed curve s, and let us determine the surface integral of the sum of the principal stresses over the area within the curve. The integral is

$$\iint (P_1+P_2)\,dx\,dy = \iint \left(\dfrac{d^2F}{dx^2}+\dfrac{d^2F}{dy^2}\right)dx\,dy \ldots\ldots\ldots\ldots(25).$$

By a well-known theorem, corresponding in two dimensions to that of Green in three dimensions, the latter expression becomes, when once integrated,

$$\int \left(\dfrac{dF}{dy}\dfrac{dx}{ds} - \dfrac{dF}{dx}\dfrac{dy}{ds}\right) ds \ldots\ldots\ldots\ldots\ldots\ldots(26),$$

or

$$\int \left(\xi\dfrac{dx}{ds} + \eta\dfrac{dy}{ds}\right) ds \ldots\ldots\ldots\ldots\ldots\ldots (27).$$

These line integrals are to be taken round the closed curve s. If we take a point in the curve s as origin in the original body, and the corresponding point in σ as origin in the diagram of stress, then ξ and η are the components of the whole stress on the right hand of the curve from the origin to a given point. If ρ denote the line joining the origin with the point $\xi\eta$, then ρ will represent in direction and magnitude the whole stress on the arc σ.

The line integral may now be interpreted as the work done on a point which travels once round the closed curve s, and is everywhere acted on by a force represented in direction and magnitude by ρ. We may express this quantity in terms of the stress at every point of the curve, instead of the resultant stress on the whole arc, as follows:

For integrating (27) by parts it becomes,

$$-\int \left(x\dfrac{d\xi}{ds} + y\dfrac{dy}{ds}\right) ds = -\int (Xx + Yy)\,ds \ldots\ldots\ldots\ldots(28),$$

or if Rds is the actual stress on ds, and r is the radius vector of ds, and if R makes with r an angle ϵ, we obtain the result

$$\iint(P_1 + P_2)\, dx dy = -\int Rr \cos \epsilon \,.\, ds \dots\dots\dots\dots\dots (29).$$

This line integral, therefore, which depends only on the stress acting on the closed curve s, is equal to the surface integral of the sum of the principal stresses taken over the whole area within the curve.

If there is no stress on the curve s acting from without, then the surface integral vanishes. This is the extension to the case of continuous stress of the theorem, given at p. 176, that the algebraic sum of all the tensions multiplied each by the length of the piece in which it acts is zero for a system in equilibrium. In the case of a frame, the stress in each piece is longitudinal, and the whole pressure or tension of the piece is equal to the longitudinal stress multiplied by the section, so that the integral $\iint(P_1 + P_2)\, dx dy$ for each piece is its tension multiplied by its length.

If the closed curve s is a small circle, the corresponding curve σ will be an ellipse, and the stress on any diameter of the circle will be represented in direction and magnitude by the corresponding diameter of the ellipse. Hence, the principal axes of the ellipse represent in direction and magnitude the principal stresses at the centre of the circle.

Let us next consider the surface integral of the product of the principal stresses at every point taken over the area within the closed curve s.

$$\iint P_1 P_2 dx dy = \iint \left(\frac{d^2 F}{dx^2}\frac{d^2 F}{dy^2} - \overline{\frac{d^2 F}{dx dy}}\Big|^2\right) dx dy \dots\dots\dots\dots (30),$$

$$= \iint \left(\frac{d\xi}{dx}\frac{d\eta}{dy} - \frac{d\xi}{dy}\frac{d\eta}{dx}\right) dx dy,$$

or by transformation of variables

$$= \iint d\xi d\eta.$$

Hence the surface integral of the product of the principal stresses within the curve is equal to the area of the corresponding curve σ in the diagram of stress, and therefore depends entirely on the external stress on the curve s. This is seen from the construction of the curve σ in the diagram of stress, since each element $d\sigma$ represents the stress on the corresponding element ds of the original curve.

If ρ represents in direction and magnitude the resultant of the stress on the curve s from the origin to a point which moves round the curve, then the area traced out by ρ is equal to the surface-integral required. If Xds and Yds are the components of the stress on the element ds, and l the whole length of the closed curve s, then the surface integral is equal to either of the quantities

$$\int_0^l Y \int_0^s Xds \,.\, ds, \quad \text{or} -\int_0^l X \int_0^s Yds \,.\, ds.$$

In a frame the stress in each piece is entirely longitudinal, so that the product of the principal stresses is zero, and therefore nothing is contributed to the surface-integral except at the points where the pieces meet or cross each other. To find the value of the integral for any one of these points, draw a closed curve surrounding it and no other point, and therefore cutting all the pieces which meet in that point in order. The corresponding figure in the diagram of stress will be a polygon, whose sides represent in magnitude and direction the tensions in the several pieces *taken in order*. The area of this polygon, therefore, represents the value of $\iint P_1 P_2 dx dy$ for the point of concourse, and is to be considered positive or negative, according as the tracing point travels round it in the positive or the negative cyclical direction.

Hence the following theorem, which is applicable to all plane frames, whether a diagram of forces can be drawn or not.

For each point of concourse or of intersection construct a polygon, by drawing in succession lines parallel and proportional to the forces acting on the point in the several pieces which meet in that point, taking the pieces in cyclical order round the point. The area of this polygon is to be taken positive or negative, according as it lies on the left or the right of the tracing point.

If, then, a closed curve be drawn surrounding the entire frame, and a polygon be drawn by drawing in succession lines parallel and proportional to all the external forces which act on the frame in the order in which their lines of direction meet the closed curve, then the area of this polygon is equal to the algebraic sum of the areas of the polygons corresponding to the various points of the frame.

In this theorem a polygon is to be drawn for every point, whether the lines of the frame meet or intersect, whether they are really jointed together, or whether two pieces simply cross each other without mechanical connection. In the latter case the polygon is a parallelogram, whose sides are parallel and proportional to the stresses in the two pieces, and it is positive or negative according as these stresses are of the same or of opposite signs.

If three or more pieces intersect, it is manifestly the same whether they intersect at one point or not, so that we have the following theorem :—

The area of a polygon of an even number of sides, whose opposite sides are equal and parallel, is equal to the sum of the areas of all the different parallelograms which can be formed with their sides parallel and equal to those of the polygon.

This is easily shewn by dividing the polygon into the different parallelograms.

On the Equilibrium of Stress in a Solid Body.

Let PQR be the longitudinal, and STU the tangential components of stress, as indicated in the following table of stresses and strains, taken from Thomson and Tait's *Natural Philosophy*, p. 511, § 669 :—

Components of the		Planes, of which Relative Motion, or across which Force, is reckoned	Direction of Relative Motion or of Force
Strain	Stress		
e	P	yz	x
f	Q	zx	y
g	R	xy	z
a	S	$\begin{cases} yx \\ zx \end{cases}$	$\begin{matrix} y \\ z \end{matrix}$
b	T	$\begin{cases} zy \\ xy \end{cases}$	$\begin{matrix} z \\ x \end{matrix}$
c	U	$\begin{cases} xz \\ yz \end{cases}$	$\begin{matrix} x \\ y \end{matrix}$

Then the equations of equilibrium of an element of the body are, by § 697 of that work,

$$\left.\begin{array}{l} \dfrac{dP}{dx} + \dfrac{dU}{dy} + \dfrac{dT}{dz} + X = 0 \\[2mm] \dfrac{dU}{dx} + \dfrac{dQ}{dy} + \dfrac{dS}{dz} + Y = 0 \\[2mm] \dfrac{dT}{dx} + \dfrac{dS}{dy} + \dfrac{dR}{dz} + Z = 0 \end{array}\right\} \quad \ldots\ldots\ldots\ldots\ldots\ldots (1).$$

If we assume three functions A, B, C, such that

$$\left.\begin{array}{lll} S = -\dfrac{d^2 A}{dy\,dz}, & T = -\dfrac{d^2 B}{dz\,dx}, & U = -\dfrac{d^2 C}{dx\,dy} \\[2mm] \end{array}\right\} \ldots\ldots\ldots (2),$$

and put
$$\begin{array}{lll} X = \dfrac{dV}{dx}, & Y = \dfrac{dV}{dy}, & Z = \dfrac{dV}{dz} \end{array}$$

then a sufficiently general solution of the equations of equilibrium is given by putting

$$\left.\begin{array}{l} P = \dfrac{d^2 B}{dz^2} + \dfrac{d^2 C}{dy^2} - V \\[2mm] Q = \dfrac{d^2 C}{dx^2} + \dfrac{d^2 A}{dz^2} - V \\[2mm] R = \dfrac{d^2 A}{dy^2} + \dfrac{d^2 B}{dx^2} - V \end{array}\right\} \quad \ldots\ldots\ldots\ldots\ldots\ldots\ldots (3).$$

I am not aware of any method of finding other relations between the components of stress without making further assumptions. The most natural assumption to make is that the stress arises from elasticity in the body. I shall confine myself to the case of an isotropic body, such that it can be deprived of all stress and strain by a removal of the applied forces. In this case, if a, β, γ are the components of displacement, and n the coefficient of rigidity, the equations of tangential elasticity are, by equation (6), §§ 670 and 694 of Thomson and Tait,

$$a = \frac{d\beta}{dz} + \frac{d\gamma}{dy} = \frac{1}{n} S = -\frac{1}{n} \frac{d^2 A}{dy\,dz} \quad \ldots\ldots\ldots\ldots\ldots\ldots (4),$$

with similar equations for b and c. A sufficiently general solution of these equations is given by putting

$$
\left. \begin{aligned}
a &= \frac{1}{2n} \frac{d}{dx}(A - B - C) \\
\beta &= \frac{1}{2n} \frac{d}{dy}(B - C - A) \\
\gamma &= \frac{1}{2n} \frac{d}{dz}(C - A - B)
\end{aligned} \right\} \dots\dots\dots\dots\dots\dots(5).
$$

The equations of longitudinal elasticity are of the form given in § 693,

$$
P = (k + \tfrac{4}{3}n)\frac{da}{dx} + (k - \tfrac{2}{3}n)\left(\frac{d\beta}{dy} + \frac{d\gamma}{dz}\right)\dots\dots\dots\dots\dots(6),
$$

where k is the co-efficient of cubical elasticity, with similar equations for Q and R. Substituting for P, a, β and γ in equation (6) their values from (3) and (5),

$$
2n\left(\frac{d^2B}{dz^2} + \frac{d^2C}{dy^2} - V\right) = (k + \tfrac{4}{3}n)\left(\frac{d^2A}{dx^2} - \frac{d^2B}{dx^2} - \frac{d^2C}{dx^2}\right)
$$
$$
+ (k - \tfrac{2}{3}n)\left(\frac{d^2B}{dy^2} - \frac{d^2C}{dy^2} - \frac{d^2A}{dy^2} + \frac{d^2C}{dz^2} - \frac{d^2A}{dz^2} - \frac{d^2B}{dz^2}\right).
$$

If we put

$$
\frac{d^2A}{dx^2} + \frac{d^2B}{dy^2} + \frac{d^2C}{dz^2} = p, \text{ and } \frac{d^2}{dx^2} + \frac{d^2}{dy^2} + \frac{d^2}{dz^2} = \Delta^2,
$$

this equation becomes

$$
(k + \tfrac{4}{3}n)(\Delta^2 A + \Delta^2 B + \Delta^2 C) - (k + \tfrac{1}{3}n)2p - 2nV = 2n\Delta^2 A\dots\dots\dots(7).
$$

We have also two other equations differing from this only in having B and C instead of A on the right hand side. Hence equating the three expressions on the right hand side we find

$$
\Delta^2 A = \Delta^2 B = \Delta^2 C = D^2, \text{ say, } \dots\dots\dots\dots\dots(8),
$$

$$
(3k + n)2p = (3k + 2n)3D^2 - 6nV\dots\dots\dots\dots\dots(9),
$$

and

$$
P + Q + R = \frac{9k}{2}\frac{D^2 - 2V}{3k + n} = 6k\frac{p - 3V}{3k + 2n}\dots\dots\dots\dots(10).
$$

These equations are useful when we wish to determine the stress rather than the strain in a body. For instance, if the co-efficients of elasticity, k

and n, are increased in the same ratio to any extent, the displacements of the body are proportionally diminished, but the stresses remain the same, and, though their distribution depends essentially on the elasticity of the various parts of the body, the values of the internal forces do not contain the coefficients of elasticity as factors.

There are two cases in which the functions may be treated as functions of two variables.

The first is when there is no stress, or a constant pressure in the direction of z, as in the case of a stratum originally of uniform thickness, in the direction of z, the thickness being small compared with the other dimensions of the body, and with the rate of variation of strain.

The second is when there is no strain, or a uniform longitudinal strain in the direction of z, as in the case of a prismatic body whose length in the direction of z is very great, the forces on the sides being functions of x and y only.

In both of these cases $S=0$ and $T=0$, so that we may write

$$P=\frac{d^2C}{dy^2}-V, \qquad U=-\frac{d^2C}{dxdy}, \qquad Q=\frac{d^2C}{dx^2}-V\ldots\ldots(11).$$

This method of expressing the stresses in two dimensions was first given by the Astronomer Royal, in the *Philosophical Transactions* for 1863. We shall write F instead of C, and call it Airy's Function of Stress in Two Dimensions.

Let us assume two functions, G and H, such that

$$F=\frac{d^2G}{dxdy}, \quad \text{and} \quad V=\frac{d^2H}{dxdy}\ldots\ldots\ldots\ldots\ldots(12),$$

then by Thomson and Tait, § 694, if a is the displacement in the direction of x

$$2n(\sigma+1)\frac{da}{dx}=P-\sigma(Q+R)\ldots\ldots\ldots\ldots\ldots(13).$$

Case I.—If $R=0$ this becomes

$$2n(\sigma+1)\frac{da}{dx}=\frac{d^2}{dxdy}\left\{\frac{d^2G}{dy^2}-\sigma\frac{d^2G}{dx^2}+(\sigma-1)H\right\}.$$

Integrating with respect to x we find the following equation for a—

$$2n(\sigma+1)a=\frac{d}{dy}\left\{\frac{d^2G}{dy^2}-\sigma\frac{d^2G}{dx^2}+(\sigma-1)H\right\}+Y\ldots\ldots\ldots(14),$$

where Y is a function of y only. Similarly for the displacement β in the direction of y,

$$2n\,(\sigma+1)\,\beta = \frac{d}{dx}\left\{\frac{d^2G}{dx^2} - \sigma\frac{d^2G}{dy^2} + (\sigma-1)\,H\right\} + X \ldots\ldots\ldots(15),$$

where X is a function of x only. Now the shearing stress U depends on the shearing strain and the rigidity, or

$$U = n\left(\frac{d\alpha}{dy} + \frac{d\beta}{dx}\right) \ldots\ldots\ldots\ldots\ldots\ldots\ldots (16).$$

Multiplying both sides of this equation by $2\,(\sigma+1)$ and substituting from (11), (14), and (15),

$$-2\,(\sigma+1)\frac{d^4G}{dx^2dy^2} = \frac{d^4G}{dy^4} - 2\sigma\frac{d^4G}{dx^2dy^2} + \frac{d^4G}{dx^4} + (\sigma-1)\left(\frac{d^2H}{dx^2} + \frac{d^2H}{dy^2}\right) + \frac{dX}{dx} + \frac{dY}{dy}..(17).$$

Hence
$$\left(\frac{d^2}{dx^2} + \frac{d^2}{dy^2}\right)^2 G + \frac{dX}{dx} + \frac{dY}{dy} = (1-\sigma)\left(\frac{d^2}{dx^2} + \frac{d^2}{dy^2}\right) \ldots\ldots\ldots (18),$$

an equation which must be fulfilled by G when the body is originally without strain.

CASE II.—In the second case, in which there is no strain in the direction of z, we have

$$\frac{dY}{dz} = R - \sigma\,(P+Q) = 0 \ldots\ldots\ldots\ldots\ldots\ldots\ldots(19).$$

Substituting for R in (13), and dividing by $\sigma+1$,

$$2n\frac{d\alpha}{dx} = (1-\sigma)\,P - \sigma Q = \frac{d^2}{dxdy}\left\{(1-\sigma)\frac{d^2G}{dy^2} - \sigma\frac{d^2G}{dx^2} + \sigma H\right\}\ldots\ldots(20),$$

with a similar equation for β. Proceeding as in the former case, we find

$$\left(\frac{d^2}{dx^2} + \frac{d^2}{dy^2}\right)^2 G + \frac{dX}{dx} + \frac{dY}{dy} = \frac{\sigma}{1-\sigma}\left(\frac{d^2}{dx^2} + \frac{d^2}{dy^2}\right) H \ldots\ldots\ldots(21).$$

This equation is identical with that of the first case, with the exception of the coefficient of the part due to H, which depends on the density of the body, and the value of σ, the ratio of lateral expansion to longitudinal compression.

Hence, if the external forces are given in the two cases of no stress and no strain in the direction of z, and if the density of the body or the intensity of the force acting on its substance is in the ratio of σ to $(1-\sigma)^2$ in the two cases, the internal forces will be the same in every part, and will be independent of the actual values of the coefficients of elasticity, provided the strains are small. The solutions of the cases treated by Mr Airy, as given in his paper, do not exactly fulfil the conditions deduced from the theory of elasticity. In fact, the consideration of elastic strain is not explicitly introduced into the investigation. Nevertheless, his results are statically possible, and exceedingly near to the truth in the cases of ordinary beams.

As an illustration of the theory of Airy's Function, let us take the case of

$$F = \frac{1}{2p}\, r^{2p} \cos 2p\theta \quad\dots\dots\dots\dots\dots\dots (22).$$

In this case we have for the co-ordinates of the point in the diagram corresponding to (xy)

$$\xi = \frac{dF}{dx} = r^{2p-1}\cos(2p-1)\,\theta, \qquad \eta = -r^{2p-1}\sin(2p-1)\,\theta \dots\dots(23),$$

and for the components of stress

$$\left. \begin{aligned} p_{xx} &= \frac{d\eta}{dy} = -(2p-1)\,r^{2p-2}\cos(2p-2)\,\theta = -\frac{d\xi}{dx} = -p_{yy} \\ p_{xy} &= \frac{d^2F}{dx\,dy} = (2p-1)\,r^{2p-2}\sin(2p-2)\,\theta \end{aligned} \right\} \dots\dots (24).$$

If we make
$$G = \frac{1}{p}\, r^p \cos p\theta, \quad \text{and} \quad H = \frac{1}{p}\, r^p \sin p\theta \dots\dots\dots\dots\dots(25),$$

then
$$\left. \begin{aligned} (2p-1)\left(\overline{\frac{dG}{dx}}\Big|^2 - \overline{\frac{dG}{dy}}\Big|^2 \right) &= p_{yy} = -p_{xx} \\ (2p-1)\, 2\,\frac{dG}{dx}\frac{dG}{dy} &= p_{xy} \end{aligned} \right\} \dots\dots\dots\dots (26).$$

Hence the curves for which G and H respectively are constant will be lines' of principal stress, and the stress at any point will be inversely as the square of the distance between the consecutive curves G or H.

If we make
$$\xi = \rho \cos\phi \text{ and } \eta = \rho\sin\phi$$
then we must have
$$\rho = r^{2p-1} \quad \text{and} \quad \phi = (2p-1)\,\theta \quad\text{\Large\}} \dots\dots\dots\dots\dots (27).$$

If we put q for $\dfrac{p}{2p-1}$ then $\dfrac{1}{p} + \dfrac{1}{q} = 2$ and $(2p-1)(2q-1) = 1$, so that if f, g, h in the diagram of stress correspond to F, G, H in the original figure, we have

$$f = \frac{1}{2q} \rho^{2q} \cos 2q\phi, \quad g = \frac{1}{q} \rho^q \cos q\phi, \quad h = \frac{1}{q} \rho^q \sin q\phi \dots\dots\dots(28).$$

Case of a Uniform Horizontal Beam.

As an example of the application of the condition that the stresses must be such as are consistent with an initial condition of no strain, let us take the case of a uniform rectangular beam of indefinite length placed horizontally with a load $= h$ per unit of length placed on its upper surface, the weight of the beam being k per unit of length. Let us suppose the beam to be supported by vertical forces and couples in a vertical plane applied at the ends; but let us consider only the middle portion of the beam, where the conditions applicable to the ends have no sensible effect. Let the horizontal distance x be reckoned from the vertical plane where there is no shearing force, and let the planes where there is no moment of bending be at distances $\pm a_0$ from the origin. Let y be reckoned from the lower edge of the beam, and let b be the depth of the beam. Then, if $U = -\dfrac{d^2 F}{dx\,dy}$ is the shearing stress, the total vertical shearing force through a vertical section at distance x is

$$\int_0^b U\,dy = \left(\frac{dF}{dx}\right)_{y=0} - \left(\frac{dF}{dx}\right)_{y=b},$$

and this must be equal and opposite to the weight of the beam and load from 0 to x, which is evidently $(h+k)x$.

Hence, $\dfrac{dF}{dx} = -(h+k)\,x\phi(y), \quad \text{where} \quad \phi(b) - \phi(0) = 1 \dots\dots\dots\dots(29).$

From this we find the vertical stress

$$Q = \frac{d^2 F}{dx^2} + \frac{k}{b} y = -(h+k)\,\phi(y) + \frac{k}{b} y.$$

The vertical stress is therefore a function of y only. It must vanish at the lower side of the beam, where $y = 0$, and it must be $-h$ on the upper side of the beam, where $y = b$. The shearing stress U must vanish at both sides of the beam, or $\phi'(y) = 0$, when $y = 0$, and when $y = b$. •

The simplest form of $\phi(y)$ which will satisfy these conditions is

$$\phi(y) = \frac{1}{b^3}(3by^2 - 2y^3).$$

Hence we find the following expression for the function of stress by integrating (29) with respect to x,

$$F = \frac{h+k}{2b^3}(a^2 - x^2)(3by^2 - 2y^3) + Y \ldots\ldots\ldots\ldots\ldots (30),$$

where a is a constant introduced in integration, and depends on the manner in which the beam is supported. From this we obtain the values of the vertical, horizontal, and shearing stresses,

$$Q = \frac{d^2F}{dx^2} + \frac{k}{b}y = \frac{k}{b}y - \frac{h+k}{b^3}(3by^2 - 2y^3) \ldots\ldots\ldots\ldots (31),$$

$$P = \frac{d^2F}{dy^2} = 3\frac{h+k}{b^3}(a^2 - x^2)(b - 2y) + \frac{d^2Y}{dy^2} \ldots\ldots\ldots\ldots (32),$$

$$U = -\frac{d^2F}{dxdy} = 6\frac{h+k}{b^3}xy(b - y) \ldots\ldots\ldots\ldots\ldots\ldots (33).$$

The values of Q and of U, the vertical and the shearing stresses, as given by these equations, are perfectly definite in terms of h and k, the load and the weight of the beam per unit of length. The value of P, the horizontal stress, however, contains an arbitrary function Y, which we propose to find from the condition that the beam was originally unstrained. We therefore determine α and β, the horizontal and vertical displacement of any point (x, y), by the method indicated by equations (13), (14), (15)

$$2n(\sigma+1)\alpha = \frac{h+k}{b^3}\{(3a^2x - x^3)(b - 2y) - \sigma x(3by^2 - 2y^3)\} - \sigma\frac{k}{b}xy + x\frac{d^2Y}{dy^2} + Y' \ (34),$$

$$2n(\sigma+1)\beta = -\frac{h+k}{b^3}\{(by^2 - \tfrac{1}{2}y^4) + 3\sigma(a^2 - x^2)(by - y^2)\} + \tfrac{1}{2}\frac{k}{b}y^2 - \sigma\frac{dY}{dy} + X' \ (35),$$

where X' is a function of x only, and Y' of y only. Deducing from these displacements the shearing strain, and comparing it with the value of the shearing stress, U, we find the equation

$$\frac{h+k}{b^3}\{6a^2x - 2x^3 + 12x(by - y^2)\} + \sigma\frac{k}{b}x = x\frac{d^3Y}{dy^3} + \frac{dX'}{dx} + \frac{dY'}{dy} \ldots\ldots\ldots (36).$$

Hence

$$\frac{d^3Y}{dy^3} = 12\frac{h+k}{b^3}(by - y^2) \ldots\ldots\ldots\ldots\ldots\ldots\ldots (37),$$

$$\frac{dX'}{dx} = 2\frac{h+k}{b^3}(3a^2x - 2x^3) + \sigma\frac{k}{b}x, \quad \frac{dY'}{dy} = 0 \ldots\ldots\ldots (38).$$

If the total longitudinal stress across any vertical section of the beam is zero, the value of $\dfrac{dF}{dy}$ must be the same when $y = 0$ and when $y = b$. From this condition we find the value of P by equation (32)

$$P = \frac{h+k}{b^3} \{3\,(a^2 - x^2) + 2y^2 - 2by - b^2\}\,(b - 2y) \dots \dots \dots (39).$$

The moment of bending at any vertical section of the beam is

$$\int_0^b Py\,dy = (h+k)\{\tfrac{1}{2}\,(x^2 - a^2) + \tfrac{1}{5}b^2\} \dots \dots \dots \dots (40).$$

This becomes zero when $x = \pm a_0$ where

$$a_0^2 = a^2 - \tfrac{2}{5}b^2 \dots \dots \dots \dots \dots \dots (41).$$

If we wish to compare this case with that of a beam of finite length supported at both ends and loaded uniformly, we must make the moment of bending zero at the supports, and the length of the beam between the supports must therefore be $2a_0$. Substituting a_0 for a in the value of P, we find

$$P = \frac{h+k}{b^3}\,(3a_0^2 - 3x^2 + 2y^2 - 2by + \tfrac{1}{5}b^2)\,(b - 2y) \dots \dots \dots (42).$$

If we suppose the beam to be cut off just beyond the supports, and supported by an intense pressure over a small area, we introduce conditions into the problem which are not fulfilled by this solution, and the investigation of which requires the use of Fourier's series. In order that our result may be true, we must suppose the beam to extend to a considerable distance beyond the supports on either side, and the vertical forces to be applied by means of frames clamped to the ends of the beam, as in Diagram Va, so that the stresses arising from the discontinuity at the extremities are insensible in the part of the beam between the supports.

This expression differs from that given by Mr Airy only in the terms in the longitudinal stress P depending on the function Y, which was introduced in order to fulfil the condition that, when no force is applied, the beam is unstrained. The effect of these terms is a maximum when $y = \cdot 12788\,b$, and is then equal to $(h+k)\,\cdot 314$, or less than a third of the pressure of the beam and its load on a flat horizontal surface when laid upon it so as to produce a uniform vertical pressure $h+k$.

EXPLANATION OF THE DIAGRAMS (Plates I. II. III.).

Diagrams I a. and I b. illustrate the necessity of the condition of the possibility of reciprocal diagrams, that each line must be a side of two, and only two, polygons. Diagram I a. is a skeleton of a frame such, that if the force along any one piece be given, the force along any other piece may be determined. But the piece N forms a side of four triangles, NFH, NGI, NJL, and NKM, so that if there could be a reciprocal diagram, the line corresponding to N would have four extremities, which is impossible. In this case we can draw a diagram of forces in which the forces H, I, J, and K are each represented by two parallel lines.

Diagrams II a. and II b. illustrate the case of a frame consisting of thirty-two pieces, meeting four and four in sixteen points, and forming sixteen quadrilaterals. Diagram II a. may be considered as a plane projection of a polyhedron of double continuity, which we may describe as a quadrilateral frame consisting of four quadrilateral rods, of which the ends are bevelled so as to fit exactly. The projection of this frame, considered as a plane frame, has three degrees of stiffness, so that three of the forces may be arbitrarily assumed.

In the reciprocal diagram II b. the lines are drawn by the method given at p. 168, so that each line is perpendicular to the corresponding line in the other figure. To make the corresponding lines parallel we have only to turn one of the figures round a right angle.

Diagrams III a. and III b. illustrate the principle as applied to a bridge designed by Professor F. Jenkin. The loads Q_1 Q_2, &c., are placed on the upper series of joints, and R_1 R_2, &c., on the lower series. The diagram III b. gives the stresses due to both sets of loads, the vertical lines of loads being different for the two series.

Diagrams IV a. and IV b. illustrate the application of Airy's Function to the construction of diagrams of continuous stress.

IV a. represents a cylinder exposed to pressure in a vertical and horizontal direction, and to tension in directions inclined 45° to these. The lines marked a, b, c, &c., are lines of pressure, and those marked o, p, q, are lines of tension. In this case the lines of pressure and tension are rectangular hyperbolas, the pressure is always equal to the tension, and varies inversely as the square of the distance between consecutive curves, or, what is the same thing, directly as the square of the distance from the centre.

IV b. represents the reciprocal diagram corresponding to the upper quadrant of the former one. The stress on any line in the first diagram is represented in magnitude and direction by the corresponding line in the second diagram, the correspondence being ascertained by that of the corresponding systems of lines a, b, c, &c., and o, p, q, &c.

We may also consider IV b. as a sector of a cylinder of 270°, exposed to pressure along the lines a, b, c, and to tension along o, p, q, the magnitude of the stress being in this case $r^{-\frac{2}{3}}$. The upper quadrant of IV a. is in this case the reciprocal figure. This figure illustrates the tendency of any strained body to be ruptured at a re-entering angle, for it is plain that at the angle the stress becomes indefinitely great.

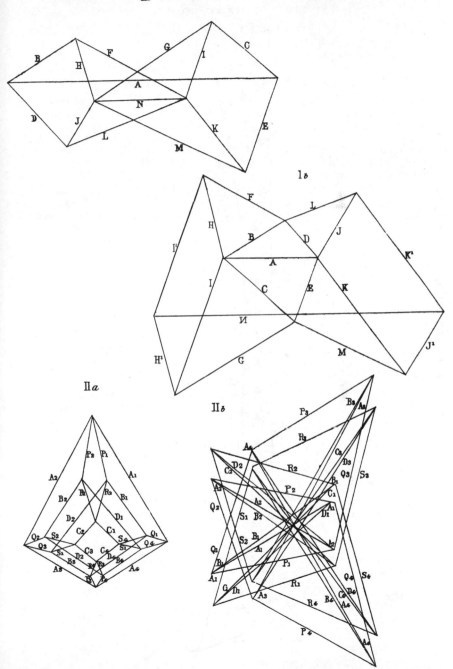

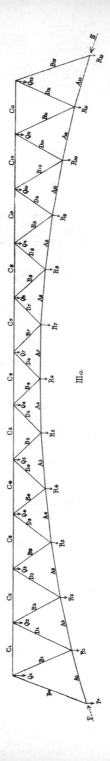

IIIa.

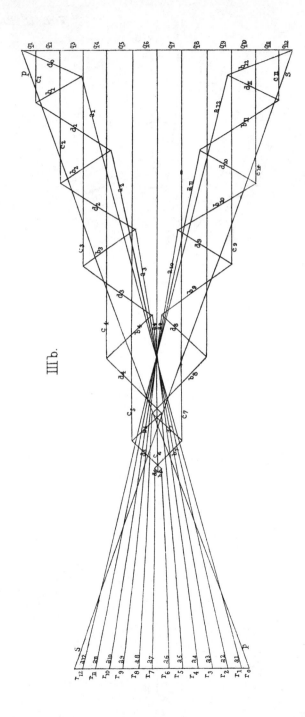

IIIb.

IVb.

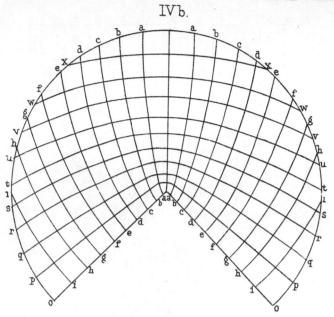

IVd.

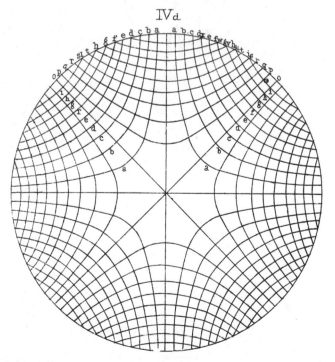

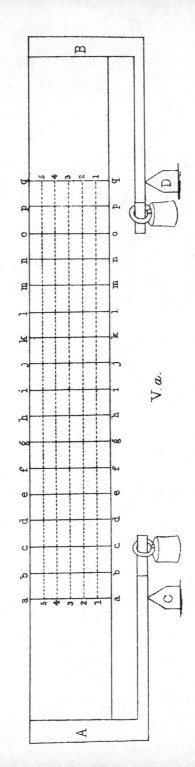

V. *a.*

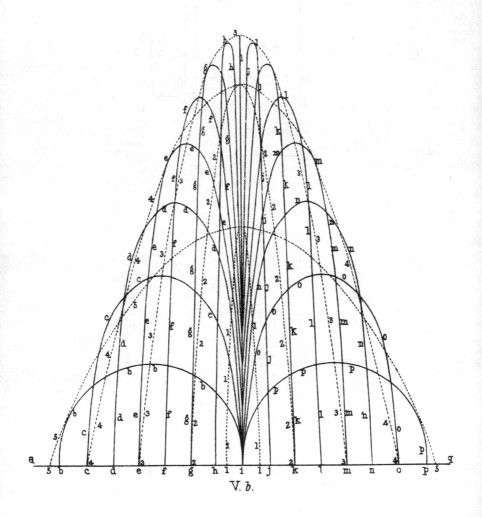

V. b.

In diagram IV a. :—

$$F = \tfrac{1}{4}r^4 \cos 4\theta, \qquad G = \tfrac{1}{2}r^2 \cos 2\theta, \qquad H = \tfrac{1}{2}r^2 \sin 2\theta.$$

In diagram IV b. :—

$$f = \tfrac{3}{4}\rho^{\frac{4}{3}} \cos \tfrac{4}{3}\,\phi, \qquad g = \tfrac{3}{2}\rho^{\frac{2}{3}} \cos \tfrac{2}{3}\,\phi, \qquad h = \tfrac{3}{2}\rho^{\frac{2}{3}} \sin \tfrac{2}{3}\,\phi.$$

Diagrams V a. and V b. illustrate Airy's theory of stress in beams.

V a. is the beam supported at C and D by means of bent pieces clamped to the ends of the beam at A and B, at such a distance from C and D, that the part of the beam between C and D is free from the local effects of the pressures of the clamps at A and B. The beam is divided into six strata by horizontal dotted lines, marked 1, 2, 3, 4, 5, 6, and into sixteen vertical slices by vertical lines marked a, b, c, &c.

The corresponding lines in the diagram V b. are marked with corresponding figures and letters. The stress across any line joining any two points in V a. is represented in magnitude by the line in V b., joining corresponding points, and is perpendicular to it in direction.

These illustrations of the application of the graphic method to cases of continuous stress, are intended rather to show the mathematical meaning of the method, than as practical aids to the engineer. In calculating the stresses in frames, the graphic method is really useful, and is less liable to accidental errors than the method of trigonometrical calculation. In cases of continuous stress, however, the symbolical method of calculation is still the best, although, as I have endeavoured to show in this paper, analytical methods may be explained, illustrated, and extended by considerations derived from the graphic method.

[From the *London Mathematical Society's Proceedings.* Vol. III.]

XL. *On the Displacement in a Case of Fluid Motion.*

IN most investigations of fluid motion, we consider the velocity at any point of the fluid as defined by its magnitude and direction, as a function of the coordinates of the point and of the time. We are supposed to be able to take a momentary glance at the system at any time, and to observe the velocities; but are not required to be able to keep our eye on a particular molecule during its motion. This method, therefore, properly belongs to the theory of a continuous fluid alike in all its parts, in which we measure the velocity by the volume which passes through unit of area rather than by the distance travelled by a molecule in unit of time. It is also the only method applicable to the case of a fluid, the motions of the individual molecules of which are not expressible as functions of their position, as in the motions due to heat and diffusion. When similar equations occur in the theory of the conduction of heat or electricity, we are constrained to use this method, for we cannot even define what is meant by the continued identity of a portion of heat or electricity.

The molecular theory, as it supposes each molecule to preserve its identity, requires for its perfection a determination of the position of each molecule at any assigned time. As it is only in certain cases that our present mathematical resources can effect this, I propose to point out a very simple case, with the results.

Let a cylinder of infinite length and of radius a move with its axis parallel to z, and always passing through the axis of x, with a velocity V, uniform or variable, in the direction of x, through an infinite, homogeneous, incompressible, perfect fluid. Let r be the distance of any point in the fluid from the axis of the cylinder; then it is easy to shew that. if x_0 is the value of x for the axis of the cylinder, and x that of the point, and

$$\phi = \frac{a^2}{r^2}(x - x_0), \text{ and } \psi = \left(1 - \frac{a^2}{r^2}\right)y,$$

$V\phi$ will satisfy the conditions of the velocity-potential, and $V\psi$ that of the stream function*; and, since the expression for ψ does not contain the time, its value will remain constant for a molecule during the whole of its motion.

If we consider the position of a particle as determined by the values of z, r, and ψ, then z and ψ will remain constant during the motion, and we have only to find r in terms of the time. For this purpose we observe that, if we put ψ in polar coordinates, it becomes

$$\psi = \left(1 - \frac{a^2}{r^2}\right) r \sin \theta,$$

and
$$\frac{dr}{dt} = \frac{V}{r}\frac{d\psi}{d\theta} = V\left(1 - \frac{a^2}{r^2}\right)\cos\theta.$$

Expressing $\cos\theta$ in terms of r and ψ, this becomes

$$\frac{dr}{dt} = \frac{V}{r^2}\sqrt{\{r^4 - (2a^2 + \psi^2)\,r^2 + a^4\}}.$$

If we make
$$\sqrt{(4a^2 + \psi^2)} + \psi = 2\beta, \text{ and } \frac{a^2}{\beta^2} = c,$$

then β will be the value of y when the axis of the cylinder is abreast of the particle, and

$$\frac{dr}{dt} = \frac{V}{r^2}\sqrt{(r^2 - \beta^2)}\sqrt{(r^2 - c^2\beta^2)};$$

and if we now use instead of r a new angular variable χ such that

$$\sin\chi = \frac{\beta}{r} = \frac{\sqrt{(4a^2 + \psi^2)} + \psi}{2r},$$

----

* The velocity-potential is a quantity such that its rate of variation along any line is equal to the velocity of the fluid resolved in the same direction. Whenever the motion of the fluid is irrotational, there is a velocity-potential.

The stream function exists in every case of the motion of an incompressible fluid in two dimensions, and is such that the total instantaneous flow across any curve, referred to unit of time, is equal to the difference of the values of the stream function at the extremities of the curve.

then we can express $\int V dt$ or x_0 in terms of elliptic functions of the first and second kinds,

$$\int V dt = x_0 = \beta \cot \chi \sqrt{(1 - c^2 \sin^2 \chi)} + \beta \{E_c(\chi) - F_c(\chi)\},$$

where the position of the axis of the cylinder is expressed in terms of the position of a molecule with respect to it.

Now let us take a molecule originally on the axis of y, at a distance η from the origin, and let the cylinder begin to move from an infinite distance on the negative side of the axis of x; then

$$\psi = \eta, \text{ and } 2\beta = \sqrt{(4a^2 + \eta^2)} + \eta, \text{ and } \frac{a^2}{\beta^2} = c;$$

and when the cylinder has passed from negative infinity to positive infinity in the direction of x, then the coordinates of the molecule will be

$$x = \frac{2a}{\sqrt{c}}(F_c - E_c), \text{ and } y = \frac{a(1-c)}{\sqrt{c}}.$$

It appears from this expression, that after the passage of the cylinder every particle is at the same distance as at first from the plane of xz, but that it is carried forward in the direction of the motion of the cylinder by a quantity which is infinite when $y = 0$, but finite for all other values of y.

The motion of a particle at any instant is always inclined to the axis of x at double the inclination of the line drawn to the axis of the cylinder. Hence it is in the forward direction till the inclination of this line is 45°, backward from 45° to 135°, and forward again afterwards. The forward motion is slower than the backward motion, but lasts for a longer time, and it appears that the final displacement of every particle is in the forward direction. It follows from this that the condition fulfilled by the fluid at an infinite distance is not that of being contained in a fixed vessel; for in that case there would have been, on the whole, a displacement backwards equal to that of the cylinder forwards. The problem actually solved differs from this only by the application of an infinitely small forward velocity to the infinite mass of fluid such as to generate a finite momentum.

In drawing the accompanying figures, I began by tracing the stream-lines in Fig. 1, p. 211, by means of the intersections of a system of straight lines equi-distant and parallel to the axis, with a system of circles touching the axis at

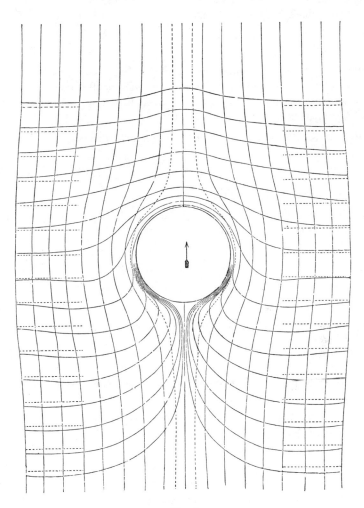

FIG. 1.

Fluid flowing past a fixed cylinder.

the origin and having their radii as the reciprocals of the natural numbers. (See Prof. Rankine's Papers on Stream-Lines in the *Phil. Trans.*)

The cylinder is $\frac{2}{3}$ inch radius, and the stream-lines are originally $\frac{4}{15}$ inch apart.

I then calculated the coordinates, x and y, of the final form of a transverse straight line from the values of the complete elliptic functions for values of c corresponding to every $5°$. The result is given in the continuous curve on the left of Fig. 2, p. 213.

I then traced the path of a particle in contact with the cylinder from the equation

$$\tan \tfrac{1}{2}\theta = e^{-\frac{2x_0}{a}},$$

where $x = x_0 + a \cos \theta$ and $y = a \sin \theta$.

The form of the path is the curve nearest the axis in Fig. 3. The dots indicate the positions at equal intervals of time.

The paths of particles not in contact with the cylinder might be calculated from Legendre's tables for incomplete functions, which I have not got.

I have therefore drawn them by eye so as to fulfil the following conditions :—

The radius of curvature is $\frac{1}{2} \dfrac{a^2 y}{a^2 \sin^2\theta + y^2}$, which, when y is large compared with a, becomes nearly $\dfrac{a^2}{2y}$.

The paths of particles at a great distance from the axis are therefore very nearly circles.

To draw the paths of intermediate particles, I observed that their two extremities must lie at the same distance from the axis of x as the asymptote of a certain stream-line, and the middle point of the path at a distance equal to that of the same stream-line when abreast of the cylinder; and, finally, that the distance between the extremities is the same as that given in Fig. 2.

In this way I drew the paths of different particles in Fig. 3. I then transferred these to Fig. 2, to shew the paths of a series of particles, originally in a straight line, and finally in the curve already described.

I then laid Fig. 1 on Fig. 2, and drew, through the intersections of the stream-lines and the paths of the corresponding particles in the fluid originally

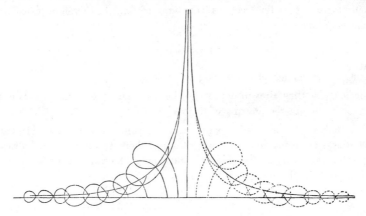

Fig. 2.

Paths of particles of the fluid when a cylinder moves through it.

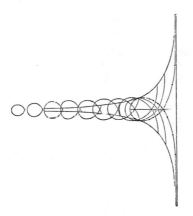

Fig. 3.

Paths of particles at different distances from the cylinder: radius of cylinder, $\frac{2}{3}$ inch. At great distances (β) the path is a circle of radius $\frac{a^2}{2\beta}$, and in this circle $\tan \frac{\theta}{2} = \frac{Vt}{\beta}$.

at rest, the lines which shew the form taken by a line of particles originally straight as it flows past the cylinder. This method, however, does not give the point where the line crosses the axis of x. I therefore calculated this from the equation

$$x = r + \tfrac{1}{2}a \log \frac{r-a}{r+a},$$

calculating r for values of x differing by $\tfrac{1}{3}$ inch.

The curves thus drawn appear to be as near the truth as I could get without a much greater amount of labour.

If a maker of "marbled" paper were to rule the surface of his bath with straight lines of paint at right angles, and then to draw a cylindrical ruler through the bath up to the middle, and apply the painted lines to his paper, he would produce the design of Fig. 1, p. 211.

[From the *British Association Report*, Vol. XL.]

XLI. *Address to the Mathematical and Physical Sections of the British Association.*

[Liverpool, *September* 15, 1870.]

AT several of the recent Meetings of the British Association the varied and important business of the Mathematical and Physical Section has been introduced by an Address, the subject of which has been left to the selection of the President for the time being. The perplexing duty of choosing a subject has not, however, fallen to me.

Professor Sylvester, the President of Section A at the Exeter Meeting, gave us a noble vindication of pure mathematics by laying bare, as it were, the very working of the mathematical mind, and setting before us, not the array of symbols and brackets which form the armoury of the mathematician, or the dry results which are only the monuments of his conquests, but the mathematician himself, with all his human faculties directed by his professional sagacity to the pursuit, apprehension, and exhibition of that ideal harmony which he feels to be the root of all knowledge, the fountain of all pleasure, and the condition of all action. The mathematician has, above all things, an eye for symmetry; and Professor Sylvester has not only recognized the symmetry formed by the combination of his own subject with those of the former Presidents, but has pointed out the duties of his successor in the following characteristic note :—

" Mr Spottiswoode favoured the Section, in his opening Address, with a combined history of the progress of Mathematics and Physics; Dr. Tyndall's address was virtually on the limits of Physical Philosophy; the one here in print," says Prof. Sylvester, " is an attempted faint adumbration of the nature of Mathematical Science in the abstract. What is wanting (like a fourth sphere resting on three others in contact) to build up the Ideal Pyramid is a discourse on the Relation of the two branches (Mathematics and Physics) to, their action and reaction upon, one another, a magnificent theme, with which it is to be hoped that some future President of Section A will crown the edifice and make the Tetralogy (symbolizable by $A + A'$, A, A', AA') complete."

The theme thus distinctly laid down for his successor by our late President is indeed a magnificent one, far too magnificent for any efforts of mine to realize. I have endeavoured to follow Mr Spottiswoode, as with far-reaching vision he distinguishes the systems of science into which phenomena, our knowledge of which is still in the nebulous stage, are growing. I have been carried by the penetrating insight and forcible expression of Dr Tyndall into that sanctuary of minuteness and of power where molecules obey the laws of their existence, clash together in fierce collision, or grapple in yet more fierce embrace, building up in secret the forms of visible things. I have been guided by Prof. Sylvester towards those serene heights

"Where never creeps a cloud, or moves a wind,
Nor ever falls the least white star of snow,
Nor ever lowest roll of thunder moans,
Nor sound of human sorrow mounts to mar
Their sacred everlasting calm."

But who will lead me into that still more hidden and dimmer region where Thought weds Fact, where the mental operation of the mathematician and the physical action of the molecules are seen in their true relation? Does not the way to it pass through the very den of the metaphysician, strewed with the remains of former explorers, and abhorred by every man of science? It would indeed be a foolhardy adventure for me to take up the valuable time of the Section by leading you into those speculations which require, as we know, thousands of years even to shape themselves intelligibly.

But we are met as cultivators of mathematics and physics. In our daily work we are led up to questions the same in kind with those of metaphysics; and we approach them, not trusting to the native penetrating power of our own minds, but trained by a long-continued adjustment of our modes of thought to the facts of external nature.

As mathematicians, we perform certain mental operations on the symbols of number or of quantity, and, by proceeding step by step from more simple to more complex operations, we are enabled to express the same thing in many different forms. The equivalence of these different forms, though a necessary consequence of self-evident axioms, is not always, to our minds, self-evident; but the mathematician, who by long practice has acquired a familiarity with many of these forms, and 'has become expert in the processes which lead from one to another, can often transform a perplexing expression into another which explains its meaning in more intelligible language.

As students of Physics we observe phenomena under varied circumstances, and endeavour to deduce the laws of their relations. Every natural phenomenon is, to our minds, the result of an infinitely complex system of conditions. What we set ourselves to do is to unravel these conditions, and by viewing the phenomenon in a way which is in itself partial and imperfect, to piece out its features one by one, beginning with that which strikes us first, and thus gradually learning how to look at the whole phenomenon so as to obtain a continually greater degree of clearness and distinctness. In this process, the feature which presents itself most forcibly to the untrained inquirer may not be that which is considered most fundamental by the experienced man of science; for the success of any physical investigation depends on the judicious selection of what is to be observed as of primary importance, combined with a voluntary abstraction of the mind from those features which, however attractive they appear, we are not yet sufficiently advanced in science to investigate with profit.

Intellectual processes of this kind have been going on since the first formation of language, and are going on still. No doubt the feature which strikes us first and most forcibly in any phenomenon, is the pleasure or the pain which accompanies it, and the agreeable or disagreeable results which follow after it. A theory of nature from this point of view is embodied in many of our words and phrases, and is by no means extinct even in our deliberate opinions.

It was a great step in science when men became convinced that, in order to understand the nature of things, they must begin by asking, not whether a thing is good or bad, noxious or beneficial, but of what kind is it? and how much is there of it? Quality and Quantity were then first recognized as the primary features to be observed in scientific inquiry.

As science has been developed, the domain of quantity has everywhere encroached on that of quality, till the process of scientific inquiry seems to have become simply the measurement and registration of quantities, combined with a mathematical discussion of the numbers thus obtained. It is this scientific method of directing our attention to those features of phenomena which may be regarded as quantities which brings physical research under the influence of mathematical reasoning. In the work of the Section we shall have abundant examples of the successful application of this method to the most recent conquests of science; but I wish at present to direct your attention to some of the reciprocal effects of the progress of science on those elementary conceptions which are sometimes thought to be beyond the reach of change.

If the skill of the mathematician has enabled the experimentalist to see that the quantities which he has measured are connected by necessary relations, the discoveries of physics have revealed to the mathematician new forms of quantities which he could never have imagined for himself.

Of the methods by which the mathematician may make his labours most useful to the student of nature, that which I think is at present most important is the systematic classification of quantities.

The quantities which we study in mathematics and physics may be classified in two different ways.

The student who wishes to master any particular science must make himself familiar with the various kinds of quantities which belong to that science. When he understands all the relations between these quantities, he regards them as forming a connected system, and he classes the whole system of quantities together as belonging to that particular science. This classification is the most natural from a physical point of view, and it is generally the first in order of time.

But when the student has become acquainted with several different sciences, he finds that the mathematical processes and trains of reasoning in one science resemble those in another so much that his knowledge of the one science may be made a most useful help in the study of the other.

When he examines into the reason of this, he finds that in the two sciences he has been dealing with systems of quantities, in which the mathematical forms of the relations of the quantities are the same in both systems, though the physical nature of the quantities may be utterly different.

He is thus led to recognize a classification of quantities on a new principle, according to which the physical nature of the quantity is subordinated to its mathematical form. This is the point of view which is characteristic of the mathematician; but it stands second to the physical aspect in order of time, because the human mind, in order to conceive of different kinds of quantities, must have them presented to it by nature.

I do not here refer to the fact that all quantities, as such, are subject to the rules of arithmetic and algebra, and are therefore capable of being submitted to those dry calculations which represent, to so many minds, their only idea of mathematics.

The human mind is seldom satisfied, and is certainly never exercising its highest functions, when it is doing the work of a calculating machine. What the man of science, whether he is a mathematician or a physical inquirer, aims at is, to acquire and develope clear ideas of the things he deals with. For this purpose he is willing to enter on long calculations, and to be for a season a calculating machine, if he can only at last make his ideas clearer.

But if he finds that clear ideas are not to be obtained by means of processes the steps of which he is sure to forget before he has reached the conclusion, it is much better that he should turn to another method, and try to understand the subject by means of well-chosen illustrations derived from subjects with which he is more familiar.

We all know how much more popular the illustrative method of exposition is found, than that in which bare processes of reasoning and calculation form the principal subject of discourse.

Now a truly scientific illustration is a method to enable the mind to grasp some conception or law in one branch of science, by placing before it a conception or a law in a different branch of science, and directing the mind to lay hold of that mathematical form which is common to the corresponding ideas in the two sciences, leaving out of account for the present the difference between the physical nature of the real phenomena.

The correctness of such an illustration depends on whether the two systems of ideas which are compared together are really analogous in form, or whether, in other words, the corresponding physical quantities really belong to the same mathematical class. When this condition is fulfilled, the illustration is not only convenient for teaching science in a pleasant and easy manner, but the recognition of the formal analogy between the two systems of ideas leads to a knowledge of both, more profound than could be obtained by studying each system separately.

There are men who, when any relation or law, however complex, is put before them in a symbolical form, can grasp its full meaning as a relation among abstract quantities. Such men sometimes treat with indifference the further statement that quantities actually exist in nature which fulfil this relation. The mental image of the concrete reality seems rather to disturb than to assist their contemplations.

But the great majority of mankind are utterly unable, without long training, to retain in their minds the unembodied symbols of the pure mathematician, so that, if science is ever to become popular, and yet remain scientific, it must be by a profound study and a copious application of those principles of the mathematical classification of quantities which, as we have seen, lie at the root of every truly scientific illustration.

There are, as I have said, some minds which can go on contemplating with satisfaction pure quantities presented to the eye by symbols, and to the mind in a form which none but mathematicians can conceive.

There are others who feel more enjoyment in following geometrical forms, which they draw on paper, or build up in the empty space before them.

Others, again, are not content unless they can project their whole physical energies into the scene which they conjure up. They learn at what a rate the planets rush through space, and they experience a delightful feeling of exhilaration. They calculate the forces with which the heavenly bodies pull at one another, and they feel their own muscles straining with the effort.

To such men momentum, energy, mass are not mere abstract expressions of the results of scientific inquiry. They are words of power, which stir their souls like the memories of childhood.

For the sake of persons of these different types, scientific truth should be presented in different forms, and should be regarded as equally scientific, whether it appears in the robust form and the vivid colouring of a physical illustration, or in the tenuity and paleness of a symbolical expression.

Time would fail me if I were to attempt to illustrate by examples the scientific value of the classification of quantities. I shall only mention the name of that important class of magnitudes having direction in space which Hamilton has called vectors, and which form the subject-matter of the Calculus of Quaternions, a branch of mathematics which, when it shall have been thoroughly understood by men of the illustrative type, and clothed by them with physical imagery, will become, perhaps under some new name, a most powerful method of communicating truly scientific knowledge to persons apparently devoid of the calculating spirit.

The mutual action and reaction between the different departments of human thought is so interesting to the student of scientific progress, that, at the risk of still further encroaching on the valuable time of the Section, I shall say a few words on a branch of physics which not very long ago would have been considered rather a branch of metaphysics. I mean the atomic theory, or, as it is now called, the molecular theory of the constitution of bodies.

Not many years ago if we had been asked in what regions of physical science the advance of discovery was least apparent, we should have pointed to the hopelessly distant fixed stars on the one hand, and to the inscrutable delicacy of the texture of material bodies on the other.

Indeed, if we are to regard Comte as in any degree representing the scientific opinion of his time, the research into what takes place beyond our own solar system seemed then to be exceedingly unpromising, if not altogether illusory.

The opinion that the bodies which we see and handle, which we can set in motion or leave at rest, which we can break in pieces and destroy, are composed of smaller bodies which we cannot see or handle, which are always in motion, and which can neither be stopped nor broken in pieces, nor in any way destroyed or deprived of the least of their properties, was known by the name of the Atomic theory. It was associated with the names of Democritus, Epicurus, and Lucretius, and was commonly supposed to admit the existence only of atoms and void, to the exclusion of any other basis of things from the universe.

In many physical reasonings and mathematical calculations we are accustomed to argue as if such substances as air, water, or metal, which appear to our senses uniform and continuous, were strictly and mathematically uniform and continuous.

We know that we can divide a pint of water into many millions of portions, each of which is as fully endowed with all the properties of water as the whole pint was; and it seems only natural to conclude that we might go on subdividing the water for ever, just as we can never come to a limit in subdividing the space in which it is contained. We have heard how Faraday divided a grain of gold into an inconceivable number of separate particles, and we may see Dr Tyndall produce from a mere suspicion of nitrite of butyle an immense cloud, the minute visible portion of which is still cloud, and therefore must contain many molecules of nitrite of butyle.

But evidence from different and independent sources is now crowding in upon us which compels us to admit that if we could push the process of subdivision still further we should come to a limit, because each portion would then contain only one molecule, an individual body, one and indivisible, unalterable by any power in nature.

Even in our ordinary experiments on very finely divided matter we find that the substance is beginning to lose the properties which it exhibits when in a large mass, and that effects depending on the individual action of molecules are beginning to become prominent.

The study of these phenomena is at present the path which leads to the development of molecular science.

That superficial tension of liquids which is called capillary attraction is one of these phenomena. Another important class of phenomena are those which are due to that motion of agitation by which the molecules of a liquid or gas are continually working their way from one place to another, and continually changing their course, like people hustled in a crowd.

On this depends the rate of diffusion of gases and liquids through each other, to the study of which, as one of the keys of molecular science, that unwearied inquirer into nature's secrets, the late Prof. Graham, devoted such arduous labour.

The rate of electrolytic conduction is, according to Wiedemann's theory, influenced by the same cause; and the conduction of heat in fluids depends probably on the same kind of action. In the case of gases, a molecular theory has been developed by Clausius and others, capable of mathematical treatment, and subjected to experimental investigation; and by this theory nearly every known mechanical property of gases has been explained on dynamical principles; so that the properties of individual gaseous molecules are in a fair way to become objects of scientific research.

Now Mr Stoney has pointed out[*] that the numerical results of experiments on gases render it probable that the mean distance of their particles at the ordinary temperature and pressure is a quantity of the same order of magnitude as a millionth of a millimetre, and Sir William Thomson has since[†] shewn, by several independent lines of argument, drawn from phenomena so different in themselves as the electrification of metals by contact, the tension of soap-bubbles, and the friction of air, that in ordinary solids and liquids the average distance between contiguous molecules is less than the hundred-millionth, and greater than the two-thousand-millionth of a centimetre.

[*] *Phil. Mag.* Aug. 1868.   [†] *Nature*, March 31, 1870.

These, of course, are exceedingly rough estimates, for they are derived from measurements some of which are still confessedly very rough; but if, at the present time, we can form even a rough plan for arriving at results of this kind, we may hope that, as our means of experimental inquiry become more accurate and more varied, our conception of a molecule will become more definite, so that we may be able at no distant period to estimate its weight with a greater degree of precision.

A theory, which Sir W. Thomson has founded on Helmholtz's splendid hydrodynamical theorems, seeks for the properties of molecules in the ring-vortices of a uniform, frictionless, incompressible fluid. Such whirling rings may be seen when an experienced smoker sends out a dexterous puff of smoke into the still air, but a more evanescent phenomenon it is difficult to conceive. This evanescence is owing to the viscosity of the air; but Helmholtz has shewn that in a perfect fluid such a whirling ring, if once generated, would go on whirling for ever, would always consist of the very same portion of the fluid which was first set whirling, and could never be cut in two by any natural cause. The generation of a ring-vortex is of course equally beyond the power of natural causes, but once generated, it has the properties of individuality, permanence in quantity, and indestructibility. It is also the recipient of impulse and of energy, which is all we can affirm of matter; and these ring-vortices are capable of such varied connexions and knotted self-involutions, that the properties of differently knotted vortices must be as different as those of different kinds of molecules can be.

If a theory of this kind should be found, after conquering the enormous mathematical difficulties of the subject, to represent in any degree the actual properties of molecules, it will stand in a very different scientific position from those theories of molecular action which are formed by investing the molecule with an arbitrary system of central forces invented expressly to account for the observed phenomena.

In the vortex theory we have nothing arbitrary, no central forces or occult properties of any other kind. We have nothing but matter and motion, and when the vortex is once started its properties are all determined from the original impetus, and no further assumptions are possible.

Even in the present undeveloped state of the theory, the contemplation of the individuality and indestructibility of a ring-vortex in a perfect fluid cannot fail to disturb the commonly received opinion that a molecule, in order to be permanent, must be a very hard body.

In fact one of the first conditions which a molecule must fulfil is, apparently, inconsistent with its being a single hard body. We know from those spectroscopic researches which have thrown so much light on different branches of science, that a molecule can be set into a state of internal vibration, in which it gives off to the surrounding medium light of definite refrangibility— light, that is, of definite wave-length and definite period of vibration. The fact that all the molecules (say, of hydrogen) which we can procure for our experiments, when agitated by heat or by the passage of an electric spark, vibrate precisely in the same periodic time, or, to speak more accurately, that their vibrations are composed of a system of simple vibrations having always the same periods, is a very remarkable fact.

I must leave it to others to describe the progress of that splendid series of spectroscopic discoveries by which the chemistry of the heavenly bodies has been brought within the range of human inquiry. I wish rather to direct your attention to the fact that, not only has every molecule of terrestrial hydrogen the same system of periods of free vibration, but that the spectroscopic examination of the light of the sun and stars shews that, in regions the distance of which we can only feebly imagine, there are molecules vibrating in as exact unison with the molecules of terrestrial hydrogen as two tuning-forks tuned to concert pitch, or two watches regulated to solar time.

Now this absolute equality in the magnitude of quantities, occurring in all parts of the universe, is worth our consideration.

The dimensions of individual natural bodies are either quite indeterminate, as in the case of planets, stones, trees, &c., or they vary within moderate limits, as in the case of seeds, eggs, &c.; but even in these cases small quantitative differences are met with which do not interfere with the essential properties of the body.

Even crystals, which are so definite in geometrical form, are variable with respect to their absolute dimensions.

Among the works of man we sometimes find a certain degree of uniformity.

There is a uniformity among the different bullets which are cast in the same mould, and the different copies of a book printed from the same type.

If we examine the coins, or the weights and measures, of a civilized country, we find a uniformity, which is produced by careful adjustment to standards made and provided by the state. The degree of uniformity of these national standards is a measure of that spirit of justice in the nation which has enacted laws to regulate them and appointed officers to test them.

This subject is one in which we, as a scientific body, take a warm interest; and you are all aware of the vast amount of scientific work which has been expended, and profitably expended, in providing weights and measures for commercial and scientific purposes.

The earth has been measured as a basis for a permanent standard of length, and every property of metals has been investigated to guard against any alteration of the material standards when made. To weigh or measure any thing with modern accuracy, requires a course of experiment and calculation in which almost every branch of physics and mathematics is brought into requisition.

Yet, after all, the dimensions of our earth and its time of rotation, though, relatively to our present means of comparison, very permanent, are not so by any physical necessity. The earth might contract by cooling, or it might be enlarged by a layer of meteorites falling on it, or its rate of revolution might slowly slacken, and yet it would continue to be as much a planet as before.

But a molecule, say of hydrogen, if either its mass or its time of vibration were to be altered in the least, would no longer be a molecule of hydrogen.

If, then, we wish to obtain standards of length, time, and mass which shall be absolutely permanent, we must seek them not in the dimensions, or the motion, or the mass of our planet, but in the wave-length, the period of vibration, and the absolute mass of these imperishable and unalterable and perfectly similar molecules.

When we find that here, and in the starry heavens, there are innumerable multitudes of little bodies of exactly the same mass, so many, and no more, to the grain, and vibrating in exactly the same time, so many times, and no more, in a second, and when we reflect that no power in nature can now alter in the least either the mass or the period of any one of them, we seem to have advanced along the path of natural knowledge to one of those points at which we must accept the guidance of that faith by which we understand that "that which is seen was not made of things which do appear."

One of the most remarkable results of the progress of molecular science is the light it has thrown on the nature of irreversible processes—processes, that is, which always tend towards and never away from a certain limiting state. Thus, if two gases be put into the same vessel, they become mixed, and the mixture tends continually to become more uniform. If two unequally heated portions of the same gas are put into the vessel, something of the kind takes place, and the whole tends to become of the same temperature. If two unequally heated solid bodies be placed in contact, a continual approximation of both to an intermediate temperature takes place.

In the case of the two gases, a separation may be effected by chemical means; but in the other two cases the former state of things cannot be restored by any natural process.

In the case of the conduction or diffusion of heat the process is not only irreversible, but it involves the irreversible diminution of that part of the whole stock of thermal energy which is capable of being converted into mechanical work.

This is Thomson's theory of the irreversible dissipation of energy, and it is equivalent to the doctrine of Clausius concerning the growth of what he calls Entropy.

The irreversible character of this process is strikingly embodied in Fourier's theory of the conduction of heat, where the formulæ themselves indicate, for all positive values of the time, a possible solution which continually tends to the form of a uniform diffusion of heat.

But if we attempt to ascend the stream of time by giving to its symbol continually diminishing values, we are led up to a state of things in which the formula has what is called a critical value; and if we inquire into the state of things the instant before, we find that the formula becomes absurd.

We thus arrive at the conception of a state of things which cannot be conceived as the physical result of a previous state of things, and we find that this critical condition actually existed at an epoch not in the utmost depths of a past eternity, but separated from the present time by a finite interval.

This idea of a beginning is one which the physical researches of recent times have brought home to us, more than any observer of the course of scientific thought in former times would have had reason to expect.

But the mind of man is not, like Fourier's heated body, continually settling down into an ultimate state of quiet uniformity, the character of which we can already predict; it is rather like a tree, shooting out branches which adapt themselves to the new aspects of the sky towards which they climb, and roots which contort themselves among the strange strata of the earth into which they delve. To us who breathe only the spirit of our own age, and know only the characteristics of contemporary thought, it is as impossible to predict the general tone of the science of the future as it is to anticipate the particular discoveries which it will make.

Physical research is continually revealing to us new features of natural processes, and we are thus compelled to search for new forms of thought appropriate to these features. Hence the importance of a careful study of those relations between Mathematics and Physics which determine the conditions under which the ideas derived from one department of physics may be safely used in forming ideas to be employed in a new department.

The figure of speech or of thought by which we transfer the language and ideas of a familiar science to one with which we are less acquainted may be called Scientific Metaphor.

Thus the words Velocity, Momentum, Force, &c. have acquired certain precise meanings in Elementary Dynamics. They are also employed in the Dynamics of a Connected System in a sense which, though perfectly analogous to the elementary sense, is wider and more general.

These generalized forms of elementary ideas may be called metaphorical terms in the sense in which every abstract term is metaphorical. The characteristic of a truly scientific system of metaphors is that each term in its metaphorical use retains all the formal relations to the other terms of the system which it had in its original use. The method is then truly scientific—that is, not only a legitimate product of science, but capable of generating science in its turn.

There are certain electrical phenomena, again, which are connected together by relations of the same form as those which connect dynamical phenomena. To apply to these the phrases of dynamics with proper distinctions and provisional reservations is an example of a metaphor of a bolder kind; but it is a legitimate metaphor if it conveys a true idea of the electrical relations to those who have been already trained in dynamics.

Suppose, then, that we have successfully introduced certain ideas belonging to an elementary science by applying them metaphorically to some new class of phenomena. It becomes an important philosophical question to determine in what degree the applicability of the old ideas to the new subject may be taken as evidence that the new phenomena are physically similar to the old.

The best instances for the determination of ·this question are those in which two different explanations have been given of the same thing.

The most celebrated case of this kind is that of the corpuscular and the undulatory theories of light. Up to a certain point the phenomena of light are equally well explained by both; beyond this point, one of them fails.

To understand the true relation of these theories in that part of the field where they seem equally applicable we must look at them in the light which Hamilton has thrown upon them by his discovery that to every brachistochrone problem there corresponds a problem of free motion, involving different velocities and times, but resulting in the same geometrical path. Professor Tait has written a very interesting paper on this subject.

According to a theory of electricity which is making great progress in Germany, two electrical particles act on one another directly at a distance, but with a force which, according to Weber, depends on their relative velocity, and according to a theory hinted at by Gauss, and developed by Riemann, Lorenz, and Neumann, acts not instantaneously, but after a time depending on the distance. The power with which this theory, in the hands of these eminent men, explains every kind of electrical phenomena must be studied in order to be appreciated.

Another theory of electricity, which I prefer, denies action at a distance and attributes electric action to tensions and pressures in an all-pervading medium, these stresses being the same in kind with those familiar to engineers, and the medium being identical with that in which light is supposed to be propagated.

Both these theories are found to explain not only the phenomena by the aid of which they were originally constructed, but other phenomena, which were not thought of or perhaps not known at the time; and both have independently arrived at the same numerical result, which gives the absolute velocity of light in terms of electrical quantities.

That theories apparently so fundamentally opposed should have so large a field of truth common to both is a fact the philosophical importance of which we cannot fully appreciate till we have reached a scientific altitude from which the true relation between hypotheses so different can be seen.

I shall only make one more remark on the relation between Mathematics and Physics. In themselves, one is an operation of the mind, the other is a dance of molecules. The molecules have laws of their own, some of which we select as most intelligible to us and most amenable to our calculation. We form a theory from these partial data, and we ascribe any deviation of the actual phenomena from this theory to disturbing causes. At the same time we confess that what we call disturbing causes are simply those parts of the true circumstances which we do not know or have neglected, and we endeavour in future to take account of them. We thus acknowledge that the so-called disturbance is a mere figment of the mind, not a fact of nature, and that in natural action there is no disturbance.

But this is not the only way in which the harmony of the material with the mental operation may be disturbed. The mind of the mathematician is subject to many disturbing causes, such as fatigue, loss of memory, and hasty conclusions; and it is found that, from these and other causes, mathematicians make mistakes.

I am not prepared to deny that, to some mind of a higher order than ours, each of these errors might be traced to the regular operation of the laws of actual thinking; in fact we ourselves often do detect, not only errors of calculation, but the causes of these errors. This, however, by no means alters our conviction that they are errors, and that one process of thought is right and another process wrong.

One of the most profound mathematicians and thinkers of our time, the late George Boole, when reflecting on the precise and almost mathematical character of the laws of right thinking as compared with the exceedingly perplexing though perhaps equally determinate laws of actual and fallible thinking, was led to another of those points of view from which Science seems to look out into a region beyond her own domain.

" We must admit," he says, " that there exist laws " (of thought) " which even the rigour of their mathematical forms does not preserve from violation. We must ascribe to them an authority, the essence of which does not consist in power, a supremacy which the analogy of the inviolable order of the natural world in no way assists us to comprehend."

[From the *Report of the British Association*, 1870.]

XLII. *On Colour-vision at different points of the Retina.*

It has long been known that near that point of the retina where it is intersected by the axis of the eye there is a yellowish spot, the existence of which can be shewn not only by the ophthalmoscope, but by its effect on vision. At the Cheltenham Meeting in 1856 the author pointed out a method of seeing this spot by looking at that part of a very narrow spectrum which lies near the line *F*. Since that time the spot has been described by Helmholtz and others; and the author has made a number of experiments, not yet published, in order to determine its effects on colour-vision.

One of the simplest methods of seeing the spot was suggested to the author by Prof. Stokes. It consists in looking at a white surface, such as that of a white cloud, through a solution of chloride of chromium made so weak that it appears of a bluish-green colour. If the observer directs his attention to what he sees before him before his eyes have got accustomed to the new tone of colour, he sees a pinkish spot like a wafer on a bluish-green ground; and this spot is always at the place he is looking at. The solution transmits the red end of the spectrum, and also a portion of bluish-green light near the line *F*. The latter portion is partially absorbed by the spot, so that the red light has the preponderance.

Experiments of a more accurate kind were made with an instrument the original conception of which is due to Sir Isaac Newton, and is described in his *Lectiones Opticæ*, though it does not appear to have been actually constructed till the author set it up in 1862, with a solid frame and careful adjustments. It consists of two parts, side by side. In the first part, white light is dispersed by a prism so as to form a spectrum. Certain portions of this spectrum are selected by being allowed to pass through slits in a screen. These selected portions are made to converge on a second prism, which unites them into a single beam of light, in which state they enter the eye. The second part of the instrument consists of an arrangement by which a beam of light from the very same source is weakened by two reflections from glass surfaces, and enters the eye alongside of the beam of compound colours.

The instrument is formed of three rectangular wooden tubes, the whole length being about nine feet. It contains two prisms, two mirrors, and six lenses, which are so adjusted that, in spite of the very different treatment to which the two portions of a beam of light are subjected, they shall enter the eye so as to form exactly equal and coincident images of the source of light. In fact, by looking through the instrument a man's face may be distinctly seen by means of the red, the green, or the blue light which it emits, or by any combination of these at pleasure.

The arrangement of the three slits is made by means of six brass slides, which can be worked with screws outside the instrument; and the breadth of the slits can be read off with a gauge very accurately.

In each observation three colours of the spectrum are mixed and so adjusted that their mixture is so exactly equivalent to the white light beside it, that the line which divides the two can no longer be seen.

It is found that in certain cases, when this adjustment is made so as to satisfy one person, a second will find the mixed colour of a green hue, while to a third it will appear of a reddish colour, compared with the white beam.

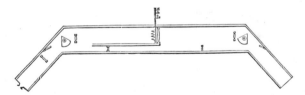

But, besides this, it is found that the mixed colour may be so adjusted that, if we look directly at it, it appears red, while if we direct the eye away from it, and cast a sidelong glance at it, we see it green. The cause of this is the yellow spot, which acts somewhat as a piece of yellow glass would do, absorbing certain kinds of light more than others; and the difference between different persons arises from different intensities of the absorbing spot. It is found in persons of every nation, but generally stronger in those of dark complexion. The degree of intensity does not seem to depend so much on the colour of the hair or the iris of the individual, as to run through families independent of outward complexion.

The same difference is found between different colour-blind persons; so that in the comparison of their vision with that of the normal eye, persons should be selected for comparison who have the yellow spot of nearly the same intensity.

In my own eye the part of the spectrum from A to E is seen decidedly better by the central part of the retina than by the surrounding parts. Near F this is reversed, and the central part gives a sensation of about half the intensity of the rest. Beyond G the central part is again the most sensitive, and it is decidedly so near H.

Before I conclude I wish to direct the attention of those who wish to study colour to the exceedingly simple and beautiful series of experiments described by Mr W. Benson in his works on colour. By looking through a prism at the black and white diagrams in his book, any one can see more of the true relations of colour than can be got from the most elaborately coloured theoretical arrangements of tints.

[From the *Philosophical Magazine* for December, 1870.]

XLIII. *On Hills and Dales.*

To the Editors of the Philosophical Magazine and Journal.

GENTLEMEN,

I FIND that in the greater part of the substance of the following paper I have been anticipated by Professor Cayley, in a memoir "On Contour and Slope Lines," published in the *Philosophical Magazine* in 1859 (S. 4. Vol. XVIII. p. 264). An exact knowledge of the first elements of physical geography, however, is so important, and loose notions on the subject are so prevalent, that I have no hesitation in sending you what you, I hope, will have no scruple in rejecting if you think it superfluous after what has been done by Professor Cayley.

I am, Gentlemen,

Your obedient Servant,

J. CLERK MAXWELL.

GLENLAIR, DALBEATTIE,
October 12, 1870.

1. ON CONTOUR-LINES AND MEASUREMENT OF HEIGHTS.

The results of the survey of the surface of a country are most conveniently exhibited by means of a map on which are traced contour-lines, each contour-line representing the intersection of a level surface with the surface of the earth, and being distinguished by a numeral which indicates the level surface to which it belongs.

When the extent of country surveyed is small, the contour-lines are defined with sufficient accuracy by the number of feet above the mean level of the sea; but when the survey is so extensive that the variation of the force of gravity must be taken into account, we must adopt a new definition of the height of a place in order to be mathematically accurate. If we could determine the exact form of the surface of equilibrium of the sea, so as to know its position in the interior of a continent, we might draw a normal to this surface from the top of a mountain, and call this the height of the mountain. This would be perfectly definite in the case when the surface of equilibrium is everywhere convex; but the lines of equal height would not be level surfaces.

Level surfaces are surfaces of equilibrium, and they are not equidistant. The only thing which is constant is the amount of work required to rise from one to another. Hence the only consistent definition of a level surface is obtained by assuming a standard station, say, at the mean level of the sea at a particular place, and defining every other level surface by the work required to raise unit of mass from the standard station to that level surface. This work must, of course, be expressed in absolute measure, not in local foot-pounds.

At every step, therefore, in ascertaining the difference of level of two places, the surveyor should ascertain the force of gravity, and multiply the linear difference of level observed by the numerical value of the force of gravity.

The height of a place, according to this system, will be defined by a number which represents, not a lineal quantity, but the half square of the velocity which an unresisted body would acquire in sliding along any path from that place to the standard station. This is the only definition of the height of a place consistent with the condition that places of equal height should be on the same level. If by any means we can ascertain the mean value of gravity along the line of force drawn from the place to the standard level surface, then, if we divide the number already found by this mean value, we shall obtain the length of this line of force, which may be called the linear height of the place.

On the Forms of Contour-lines.

Let us begin with a level surface entirely within the solid part of the earth, and let us suppose it to ascend till it reaches the bottom of the deepest sea. At that point it will touch the surface of the earth; and if it continues to ascend, a contour-line will be formed surrounding this bottom (or Immit, as it is called by Professor Cayley) and enclosing a region of depression. As the level surface continues to ascend, it will reach the next deepest bottom of the sea; and as it ascends it will form another contour-line, surrounding this point, and enclosing another region of depression below the level surface. As the level surface rises these regions of depression will continually expand, and new ones will be formed corresponding to the different lowest points of the earth's surface.

At first there is but one region of depression, the whole of the rest of the earth's surface forming a region of elevation surrounding it. The number of regions of elevation and depression can be altered in two ways.

1st. Two regions of depression may expand till they meet and so run into one. If a contour-line be drawn through the point where they meet, it forms a closed curve having a double point at this place. This contour-line encloses two regions of depression. We shall call the point where these two regions meet a Bar.

It may happen that more than two regions run into each other at once. Such cases are singular, and we shall reserve them for separate consideration.

2ndly. A region of depression may thrust out arms, which may meet each other and thus cut off a region of elevation in the midst of the region of depression, which thus becomes a cyclic region, while a new region of elevation is introduced. The contour-line through the point of meeting cuts off two regions of elevation from one region of depression, and the point itself is called a Pass. There may be in singular cases passes between more than two regions of elevation.

3rdly. As the level surface rises, the regions of elevation contract and at last are reduced to points. These points are called Summits or Tops.

Relation between the Number of Summits and Passes.

At first the whole earth is a region of elevation. For every new region of elevation there is a Pass, and for every region of elevation reduced to a point there is a Summit. And at last the whole surface of the earth is a

30—2

region of depression. Hence the number of Summits is one more than the number of Passes. If S is the number of Summits and P the number of passes,

$$S = P + 1.$$

Relation between the Number of Bottoms and Bars.

For every new region of depression there is a Bottom, and for every diminution of the number of these regions there is a Bar. Hence the number of Bottoms is one more than the number of Bars. If I is the number of Bottoms or Immits and B the number of Bars, then

$$I = B + 1.$$

From this it is plain that if, in the singular cases of passes and bars, we reckon a pass as single, double, or n-ple, according as two, three, or $n+1$ regions of elevation meet at that point, and a bar as single, double, or n-ple, as two, three, or $n+1$ regions of depression meet at that point, then the census may be taken as before, giving each singular point its proper number. If one region of depression meets another in several places at once, one of these must be taken as a bar and the rest as passes.

The whole of this theory applies to the case of the maxima and minima of a function of two variables which is everywhere finite, determinate, and continuous. The summits correspond to maxima and the bottoms to minima. If there are p maxima and q minima, there must be $p+q-2$ cases of stationary values which are neither maxima nor minima. If we regard those points in themselves, we cannot make any distinction among them; but if we consider the regions cut off by the curves of constant value of the function, we may call $p-1$ of them false maxima and $q-1$ of them false minima.

On Functions of Three Variables.

If we suppose the three variables to be the three co-ordinates of a point, and the regions where the function is greater or less than a given value to be called the positive and the negative regions, then, as the given value increases, for every negative region formed there will be a minimum, and the positive region will have an increase of its periphraxy. For every junction of two *different* negative regions there will be a false minimum, and the positive region will have a diminution of its periphraxy. Hence if there are q true minima there will be $q-1$ false minima.

There are different orders of these stationary points according to the number of regions which meet in them. The first order is when two negative regions meet surrounded by a positive region, the second order when three negative regions meet, and so on. Points of the second order count for two, those of the third for three, and so on, in this relation between the true minima and the false ones.

In like manner, when a negative region expands round a hollow part and at last surrounds it, thus cutting off a new positive region, the negative region acquires periphraxy, a new positive region is formed, and at the point of contact there is a false maximum.

When any positive region is reduced to a point and vanishes, the negative region loses periphraxy and there is a true maximum. Hence if there are p maxima there are $p-1$ false maxima.

But these are not the only forms of stationary points; for a negative region may thrust out arms which may meet in a stationary point. The negative and the positive region both become cyclic. Again, a cyclic region may close in so as to become acyclic, forming another kind of stationary point where the ring first fills up. If there are r points at which cyclosis is gained and r' points at which it is lost, then we know that

$$r = r';$$

but we cannot determine any relation between the number of these points and that of either the true or the false maxima and minima.

If the function of three variables is a potential function, the true maxima are points of stable equilibrium, the true minima points of equilibrium unstable in every direction, and at the other stationary points the equilibrium is stable in some directions and unstable in others.

On Lines of Slope.

Lines drawn so as to be everywhere at right angles to the contour-lines are called lines of slope. At every point of such a line there is an upward and a downward direction. If we follow the upward direction we shall *in general* reach a summit, and if we follow the downward direction we shall *in general* reach a bottom. In particular cases, however, we may reach a pass or a bar.

On Hills and Dales.

Hence each point of the earth's surface has a line of slope, which begins at a certain summit and ends in a certain bottom. Districts whose lines of slope run to the same bottom are called Basins or Dales. Those whose lines of slope come from the same summit may be called, for want of a better name, Hills.

Hence the whole earth may be naturally divided into Basins or Dales, and also, by an independent division, into hills, each point of the surface belonging to a certain dale and also to a certain hill.

On Watersheds and Watercourses.

Dales are divided from each other by Watersheds, and Hills by Watercourses.

To draw these lines, begin at a pass or a bar. Here the ground is level, so that we cannot begin to draw a line of slope; but if we draw a very small closed curve round this point, it will have highest and lowest points, the number of maxima being equal to the number of minima, and each one more than the index number of the pass or bar. From each maximum point draw a line of slope upwards till it reaches a summit. This will be a line of Watershed. From each minimum point draw a line of slope downwards till it reaches a bottom. This will be a line of Watercourse. Lines of Watershed are the only lines of slope which do not reach a bottom, and lines of Watercourse are the only lines of slope which do not reach a summit. All other lines of slope diverge from some summit and converge to some bottom, remaining throughout their course in the district belonging to that summit and that bottom, which is bounded by two watersheds and two watercourses.

In the pure theory of surfaces there is no method of determining a line of watershed or of watercourse, except by first finding a pass or a bar and drawing the line of slope from that point. In nature, water actually trickles down the lines of slope, which generally converge towards the mathematical watercourses, though they do not actually join them; but when the streams increase in quantity, they join and excavate courses for themselves; and these actually run into the main watercourse which bounds the district, and so cut out a river-bed, which, whether full or empty, forms a visible mark on the earth's surface. No such action takes place at a watershed, which therefore generally remains invisible..

There is another difficulty in the application of the mathematical theory, on account of the principal regions of depression being covered with water, so that very little is known about the positions of the singular points from which the lines of watershed must be drawn to the summits of hills near the coast. A complete division of the dry land into districts, therefore, requires some knowledge of the form of the bottom of the sea and of lakes.

On the Number of Natural Districts.

Let p_1 be the number of single passes, p_2 that of double passes, and so on. Let b_1, b_2, &c. be the numbers of single, double, &c. bars. Then the number of summits will be, by what we have proved,

$$S = 1 + p_1 + 2p_2 + \&c.,$$

and the number of bottoms will be

$$I = 1 + b_1 + 2b_2 + \&c.$$

The number of watersheds will be

$$W = 2\,(b_1 + p_1) + 3\,(b_2 + p_2) + \&c.$$

The number of watercourses will be the same.

Now, to find the number of faces, we have by Listing's rule

$$P - L + F - R = 0,$$

where P is the number of points, L that of lines, F that of faces, and R that of regions, there being in this case no instance of cyclosis or periphraxy. Here $R = 2$, viz. the earth and the surrounding space; hence

$$F = L - P + 2.$$

If we put L equal to the number of watersheds, and P equal to that of summits, passes, and bars, then F is the number of Dales, which is evidently equal to the number of bottoms.

If we put L for the number of watercourses, and P for the number of passes, bars, and bottoms, then F is the number of Hills, which is evidently equal to the number of summits.

If we put L equal to the whole number of lines, and P equal to the whole number of points, we find that F, the number of natural districts named from a hill and a dale together, is equal to W, the number of watersheds or watercourses, or to the whole number of summits, bottoms, passes, and bars diminished by 2.

Chart of an Inland Basin.

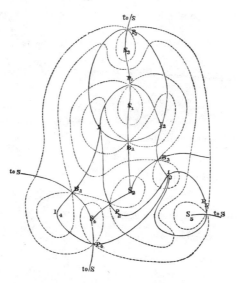

$I_1,\ I_2,\ I_3,\ I_4.$	Lowest points, Bottoms or Immits.
$S_1,\ S_2,\ S_4,\ S_5.$	Highest points, Tops or Summits.
$B_1,\ B_2,\ B_3.$	Bars between regions of depression.
$P_1,\ P_2,\ P_3,\ P_4,\ P_5.$	Passes between regions of elevation.
$I_1\ B_1\ I_2$ &c.	Lines of Watercourse.
$S_1\ P_1\ S_3$ &c.	Lines of Watershed.
Dotted line.	Contour-lines.

XLIV. *Introductory Lecture on Experimental Physics.*

The University of Cambridge, in accordance with that law of its evolution, by which, while maintaining the strictest continuity between the successive phases of its history, it adapts itself with more or less promptness to the requirements of the times, has lately instituted a course of Experimental Physics. This course of study, while it requires us to maintain in action all those powers of attention and analysis which have been so long cultivated in the University, calls on us to exercise our senses in observation, and our hands in manipulation. The familiar apparatus of pen, ink, and paper will no longer be sufficient for us, and we shall require more room than that afforded by a seat at a desk, and a wider area than that of the black board. We owe it to the munificence of our Chancellor, that, whatever be the character in other respects of the experiments which we hope hereafter to conduct, the material facilities for their full development will be upon a scale which has not hitherto been surpassed.

The main feature, therefore, of Experimental Physics at Cambridge is the Devonshire Physical Laboratory, and I think it desirable that on the present occasion, before we enter on the details of any special study, we should consider by what means we, the University of Cambridge, may, as a living body, appropriate and vitalise this new organ, the outward shell of which we expect soon to rise before us. The course of study at this University has always included Natural Philosophy, as well as Pure Mathematics. To diffuse a sound knowledge of Physics, and to imbue the minds of our students with correct dynamical principles, have been long regarded as among our highest functions, and very few of us can now place ourselves in the mental condition in which even such philosophers as the great Descartes were involved in the days before Newton had announced the true laws of the motion of bodies. Indeed the cultivation and diffusion of sound dynamical ideas has already effected a great change in the language and thoughts even of those who make no pretensions to science, and we are daily receiving fresh proofs that the popularisation of scientific doctrines is producing as great an alteration in the mental state of society as the material applications of science are effecting in its outward life. Such indeed is the respect paid to science, that the most absurd opinions may become current, provided they are expressed in language, the sound of which recals some well-known scientific phrase. If society is thus prepared to receive all kinds of scientific doctrines, it is our part to provide for the diffusion and cultivation, not only of true scientific principles, but of a spirit of sound criticism, founded on an examination of the evidences on which statements apparently scientific depend.

When we shall be able to employ in scientific education, not only the trained attention of the student, and his familiarity with symbols, but the keenness of his eye, the quickness of his ear, the delicacy of his touch, and the adroitness of his fingers, we shall not only extend our influence over a class of men who are not fond of cold abstractions, but, by opening at once all the gateways of knowledge, we shall ensure the association of the doctrines of science with those elementary sensations which form the obscure background of all our conscious thoughts, and which lend a vividness and relief to ideas, which, when presented as mere abstract terms, are apt to fade entirely from the memory.

In a course of Experimental Physics we may consider either the Physics or the Experiments as the leading feature. We may either employ the experiments to illustrate the phenomena of a particular branch of Physics, or we may make some physical research in order to exemplify a particular experimental method. In the order of time, we should begin, in the Lecture Room, with a course of lectures on some branch of Physics aided by experiments of illustration, and conclude, in the Laboratory, with a course of experiments of research.

Let me say a few words on these two classes of experiments,—Experiments of Illustration and Experiments of Research. The aim of an experiment of illustration is to throw light upon some scientific idea so that the student may be enabled to grasp it. The circumstances of the experiment are so arranged that the phenomenon which we wish to observe or to exhibit is brought into prominence, instead of being obscured and entangled among other phenomena, as it is when it occurs in the ordinary course of nature. To exhibit illustrative experiments, to encourage others to make them, and to cultivate in every way the ideas on which they throw light, forms an important part of our duty.

The simpler the materials of an illustrative experiment, and the more familiar they are to the student, the more thoroughly is he likely to acquire the idea which it is meant to illustrate. The educational value of such experiments is often inversely proportional to the complexity of the apparatus. The student who uses home-made apparatus, which is always going wrong, often learns more than one who has the use of carefully adjusted instruments, to which he is apt to trust, and which he dares not take to pieces.

It is very necessary that those who are trying to learn from books the facts of physical science should be enabled by the help of a few illustrative experiments to recognise these facts when they meet with them out of doors. Science appears to us with a very different aspect after we have found out that it is not in lecture rooms only, and by means of the electric light projected on a screen, that we may witness physical phenomena, but that we may find illustrations of the highest doctrines of science in games and gymnastics, in travelling by land and by water, in storms of the air and of the sea, and wherever there is matter in motion.

This habit of recognising principles amid the endless variety of their action can never degrade our sense of the sublimity of nature, or mar our enjoyment of its beauty. On the contrary, it tends to rescue our scientific ideas from that vague condition in which we too often leave them, buried among the other products of a lazy credulity, and to raise them into their proper position among the doctrines in which our faith is so assured, that we are ready at all times to act on them.

Experiments of illustration may be of very different kinds. Some may be adaptations of the commonest operations of ordinary life, others may be carefully arranged exhibitions of some phenomenon which occurs only under peculiar conditions. They all, however, agree in this, that their aim is to present some phenomenon to the senses of the student in such a way that he may associate with it the appropriate scientific idea. When he has grasped this idea, the experiment which illustrates it has served its purpose.

In an experiment of research, on the other hand, this is not the principal aim. It is true that an experiment, in which the principal aim is to see what happens under certain conditions, may be regarded as an experiment of research by those who are not yet familiar with the result, but in experimental researches, strictly so called, the ultimate object is to measure something which we have already seen—to obtain a numerical estimate of some magnitude.

Experiments of this class—those in which measurement of some kind is involved, are the proper work of a Physical Laboratory. In every experiment we have first to make our senses familiar with the phenomenon, but we must not stop here, we must find out which of its features are capable of measurement, and what measurements are required in order to make a complete specification of the phenomenon. We must then make these measurements, and deduce from them the result which we require to find.

This characteristic of modern experiments—that they consist principally of measurements,—is so prominent, that the opinion seems to have got abroad, that in a few years all the great physical constants will have been approximately estimated, and that the only occupation which will then be left to men of science will be to carry on these measurements to another place of decimals.

If this is really the state of things to which we are approaching, our Laboratory may perhaps become celebrated as a place of conscientious labour and consummate skill, but it will be out of place in the University, and ought rather to be classed with the other great workshops of our country, where equal ability is directed to more useful ends.

But we have no right to think thus of the unsearchable riches of creation, or of the untried fertility of those fresh minds into which these riches will continue to be poured. It may possibly be true that, in some of those fields of discovery which lie open to such rough observations as can be made without artificial methods, the great explorers of former times have appropriated most of what is valuable, and that the gleanings which remain are sought after, rather for their abstruseness, than for their intrinsic worth. But the history of science shews that even during that phase of her progress in which she devotes herself to improving the accuracy of the numerical measurement of quantities with which she has long been familiar, she is preparing the materials for the subjugation of new regions, which would have remained unknown if she had been contented with the rough methods of her early pioneers. I might bring forward instances gathered from every branch of science, shewing how the labour of careful measurement has been rewarded by the discovery of new fields of research, and by the development of new scientific ideas. But the history of the science of terrestrial magnetism affords us a sufficient example of what may be done by Experiments in Concert, such as we hope some day to perform in our Laboratory.

That celebrated traveller, Humboldt, was profoundly impressed with the scientific value of a combined effort to be made by the observers of all nations, to obtain accurate measurements of the magnetism of the earth; and we owe it mainly to his enthusiasm for science, his great reputation and his wide-spread influence, that not only private men of science, but the governments of most of the civilised nations, our own among the number, were induced to take part in the enterprise. But the actual working out of the scheme, and the arrangements by which the labours of the observers were so directed as to obtain the best results, we owe to the great mathematician Gauss, working along with Weber, the future founder of the science of electro-magnetic measurement, in the magnetic observatory of Göttingen, and aided by the skill of the instrument-maker Leyser. These men, however, did not work alone. Numbers of scientific men joined the Magnetic Union, learned the use of the new instruments and the new methods of reducing the observations; and in every city of Europe you might see them, at certain stated times, sitting, each in his cold wooden shed, with his eye fixed at the telescope, his ear attentive to the clock, and his pencil recording in his note-book the instantaneous position of the suspended magnet.

Bacon's conception of "Experiments in concert" was thus realised, the scattered forces of science were converted into a regular army, and emulation and jealousy became out of place, for the results obtained by any one observer were of no value till they were combined with those of the others.

The increase in the accuracy and completeness of magnetic observations which was obtained by the new method, opened up fields of research which were hardly suspected to exist by those whose observations of the magnetic needle had been conducted in a more primitive manner. We must reserve for its proper place in our course any detailed description of the disturbances to which the magnetism of our planet is found to be subject. Some of these disturbances are periodic, following the regular courses of the sun and moon. Others are sudden, and are called magnetic storms, but, like the storms of the atmosphere, they have their known seasons of frequency. The last and the most mysterious of these magnetic changes is that secular variation by which the whole character of the earth, as a great magnet, is being slowly modified, while the magnetic poles creep on, from century to century, along their winding track in the polar regions.

We have thus learned that the interior of the earth is subject to the influences of the heavenly bodies, but that besides this there is a constantly progressive change going on, the cause of which is entirely unknown. In each of the magnetic observatories throughout the world an arrangement is at work, by means of which a suspended magnet directs a ray of light on a prepared sheet of paper moved by clockwork. On that paper the never-resting heart of the earth is now tracing, in telegraphic symbols which will one day be interpreted, a record of its pulsations and its flutterings, as well as of that slow but ˌmighty working which warns us that we must not suppose that the inner history of our planet is ended.

But this great experimental research on Terrestrial Magnetism produced lasting effects on the progress of science in general. I need only mention one or two instances. The new methods of measuring forces were successfully applied by Weber to the numerical determination of all the phenomena of electricity, and very soon afterwards the electric telegraph, by conferring a commercial value on exact numerical measurements, contributed largely to the advancement, as well as to the diffusion of scientific knowledge.

But it is not in these more modern branches of science alone that this influence is felt. It is to Gauss, to the Magnetic Union, and to magnetic observers in general, that we owe our deliverance from that absurd method of estimating forces by a variable standard which prevailed so long even among men of science. It was Gauss who first based the practical measurement of magnetic force (and therefore of every other force) on those long established principles, which, though they are embodied in every dynamical equation, have been so generally set aside, that these very equations, though correctly given in our Cambridge textbooks, are usually explained there by assuming, in addition to the variable standard of force, a variable, and therefore illegal, standard of mass.

Such, then, were some of the scientific results which followed in this case from bringing together mathematical power, experimental sagacity, and manipu lative skill, to direct and assist the labours of a body of zealous observers. If therefore we desire, for our own advantage and for the honour of our University, that the Devonshire Laboratory should be successful, we must endeavour to maintain it in living union with the other organs and faculties of our learned body. We shall therefore first consider the relation in which we stand to those mathematical studies which have so long flourished among us, which deal with our own subjects, and which differ from our experimental studies only in the mode in which they are presented to the mind.

There is no more powerful method for introducing knowledge into the mind than that of presenting it in as many different ways as we can. When the ideas, after entering through different gateways, effect a junction in the citadel of the mind, the position they occupy becomes impregnable. Opticians tell us that the mental combination of the views of an object which we obtain from stations no further apart than our two eyes is sufficient to produce in our minds an impression of the solidity of the object seen; and we find that this impression is produced even when we are aware that we are really looking at two flat pictures placed in a stereoscope. It is therefore natural to expect that the knowledge of physical science obtained by the combined use of mathematical analysis and experimental research will be of a more solid, available, and enduring kind than that possessed by the mere mathematician or the mere experimenter.

But what will be the effect on the University, if men pursuing that course of reading which has produced so many distinguished Wranglers, turn aside to work experiments? Will not their attendance at the Laboratory count not merely as time withdrawn from their more legitimate studies, but as the introduction of a disturbing element, tainting their mathematical conceptions with material imagery, and sapping their faith in the formulæ of the textbooks? Besides this, we have already heard complaints of the undue extension of our studies, and of the strain put upon our questionists by the weight of learning which they try to carry with them into the Senate-House. If we now ask them to get up their subjects not only by books and writing, but at the same time by observation and manipulation, will they not break down altogether? The Physical Laboratory, we are told, may perhaps be useful to those who are going out in Natural Science, and who do not take in Mathematics, but to attempt to combine both kinds of study during the time of residence at the University is more than one mind can bear.

No doubt there is some reason for this feeling. Many of us have already overcome the initial difficulties of mathematical training. When we now go on with our study, we feel that it requires exertion and involves fatigue, but we are confident that if we only work hard our progress will be certain.

Some of us, on the other hand, may have had some experience of the routine of experimental work. As soon as we can read scales, observe times, focus telescopes, and so on, this kind of work ceases to require any great mental effort. We may perhaps tire our eyes and weary our backs, but we do not greatly fatigue our minds.

It is not till we attempt to bring the theoretical part of our training into contact with the practical that we begin to experience the full effect of what Faraday has called "mental inertia"—not only the difficulty of recognising, among the concrete objects before us, the abstract relation which we have learned from books, but the distracting pain of wrenching the mind away from the symbols to the objects, and from the objects back to the symbols. This however is the price we have to pay for new ideas.

But when we have overcome these difficulties, and successfully bridged over the gulph between the abstract and the concrete, it is not a mere piece of knowledge that we have obtained: we have acquired the rudiment of a permanent mental endowment. When, by a repetition of efforts of this kind, we have more fully developed the scientific faculty, the exercise of this faculty in detecting scientific principles in nature, and in directing practice by theory, is no longer irksome, but becomes an unfailing source of enjoyment, to which we return so often, that at last even our careless thoughts begin to run in a scientific channel.

I quite admit that our mental energy is limited in quantity, and I know that many zealous students try to do more than is good for them. But the question about the introduction of experimental study is not entirely one of quantity. It is to a great extent a question of distribution of energy. Some distributions of energy, we know, are more useful than others, because they are more available for those purposes which we desire to accomplish.

Now in the case of study, a great part of our fatigue often arises, not from those mental efforts by which we obtain the mastery of the subject, but from those which are spent in recalling our wandering thoughts; and these efforts of attention would be much less fatiguing if the disturbing force of mental distraction could be removed.

This is the reason why a man whose soul is in his work always makes more progress than one whose aim is something not immediately connected with his occupation. In the latter case the very motive of which he makes use to stimulate his flagging powers becomes the means of distracting his mind from the work before him.

There may be some mathematicians who pursue their studies entirely for their own sake. Most men, however, think that the chief use of mathematics is found in the interpretation of nature. Now a man who studies a piece of mathematics in order to understand some natural phenomenon which he has seen, or to calculate the best arrangement of some experiment which he means to make, is likely to meet with far less distraction of mind than if his sole aim had been to sharpen his mind for the successful practice of the Law, or to obtain a high place in the Mathematical Tripos.

I have known men, who when they were at school, never could see the good of mathematics, but who, when in after life they made this discovery, not only became eminent as scientific engineers, but made considerable progress in the study of abstract mathematics. If our experimental course should help any of you to see the good of mathematics, it will relieve us of much anxiety, for it will not only ensure the success of your future studies, but it will make it much less likely that they will prove injurious to your health.

But why should we labour to prove the advantage of practical science to the University? Let us rather speak of the help which the University may give to science, when men well trained in mathematics and enjoying the advantages of a well-appointed Laboratory, shall unite their efforts to carry out some experimental research which no solitary worker could attempt.

At first it is probable that our principal experimental work must be the illustration of particular branches of science, but as we go on we must add to this the study of scientific methods, the same method being sometimes illustrated by its application to researches belonging to different branches of science.

We might even imagine a course of experimental study the arrangement of which should be founded on a classification of methods, and not on that of the objects of investigation. A combination of the two plans seems to me better than either, and while we take every opportunity of studying methods, we shall take care not to dissociate the method from the scientific research to which it is applied, and to which it owes its value.

We shall therefore arrange our lectures according to the classification of the principal natural phenomena, such as heat, electricity, magnetism and so on.

In the laboratory, on the other hand, the place of the different instruments will be determined by a classification according to methods, such as weighing and measuring, observations of time, optical and electrical methods of observation, and so on.

The determination of the experiments to be performed at a particular time must often depend upon the means we have at command, and in the case of the more elaborate experiments, this may imply a long time of preparation, during which the instruments, the methods, and the observers themselves, are being gradually fitted for their work. When we have thus brought together the requisites, both material and intellectual, for a particular experiment, it may sometimes be desirable that before the instruments are dismounted and the observers dispersed, we should make some other experiment, requiring the same method, but dealing perhaps with an entirely different class of physical phenomena.

Our principal work, however, in the Laboratory must be to acquaint ourselves with all kinds of scientific methods, to compare them, and to estimate their value. It will, I think, be a result worthy of our University, and more likely to be accomplished here than in any private laboratory, if, by the free and full discussion of the relative value of different scientific procedures, we succeed in forming a school of scientific criticism, and in assisting the development of the doctrine of method.

But admitting that a practical acquaintance with the methods of Physical Science is an essential part of a mathematical and scientific education, we may be asked whether we are not attributing too much importance to science altogether as part of a liberal education.

Fortunately, there is no question here whether the University should continue to be a place of liberal education, or should devote itself to preparing young men for particular professions. Hence though some of us may, I hope, see reason to make the pursuit of science the main business of our lives, it must be one of our most constant aims to maintain a living connexion between our work and the other liberal studies of Cambridge, whether literary, philological, historical or philosophical.

There is a narrow professional spirit which may grow up among men of science, just as it does among men who practise any other special business. But surely a University is the very place where we should be able to overcome this tendency of men to become, as it were, granulated into small worlds, which are all the more worldly for their very smallness. We lose the advantage of having men of varied pursuits collected into one body, if we do not endeavour to imbibe some of the spirit even of those whose special branch of learning is different from our own.

It is not so long ago since any man who devoted himself to geometry, or to any science requiring continued application, was looked upon as necessarily a misanthrope, who must have abandoned all human interests, and betaken himself to abstractions so far removed from the world of life and action that he has become insensible alike to the attractions of pleasure and to the claims of duty.

In the present day, men of science are not looked upon with the same awe or with the same suspicion. They are supposed to be in league with the material spirit of the age, and to form a kind of advanced Radical party among men of learning.

We are not here to defend literary and historical studies. We admit that the proper study of mankind is man. But is the student of science to be withdrawn from the study of man, or cut off from every noble feeling, so long as he lives in intellectual fellowship with men who have devoted their lives to the discovery of truth, and the results of whose enquiries have impressed themselves on the ordinary speech and way of thinking of men who never heard their names? Or is the student of history and of man to omit from his consideration the history of the origin and diffusion of those ideas which have produced so great a difference between one age of the world and another?

It is true that the history of science is very different from the science of history. We are not studying or attempting to study the working of those blind forces which, we are told, are operating on crowds of obscure people, shaking principalities and powers, and compelling reasonable men to bring events to pass in an order laid down by philosophers.

The men whose names are found in the history of science are not mere hypothetical constituents of a crowd, to be reasoned upon only in masses. We recognise them as men like ourselves, and their actions and thoughts, being more free from the influence of passion, and recorded more accurately than those of other men, are all the better materials for the study of the calmer parts of human nature.

But the history of science is not restricted to the enumeration of successful investigations. It has to tell of unsuccessful inquiries, and to explain why some of the ablest men have failed to find the key of knowledge, and how the reputation of others has only given a firmer footing to the errors into which they fell.

The history of the development, whether normal or abnormal, of ideas is of all subjects that in which we, as thinking men, take the deepest interest. But when the action of the mind passes out of the intellectual stage, in which truth and error are the alternatives, into the more violently emotional states of anger and passion, malice and envy, fury and madness; the student of science, though he is obliged to recognise the powerful influence which these wild forces have exercised on mankind, is perhaps in some measure disqualified from pursuing the study of this part of human nature.

But then how few of us are capable of deriving profit from such studies. We cannot enter into full sympathy with these lower phases of our nature without losing some of that antipathy to them which is our surest safeguard against a reversion to a meaner type, and we gladly return to the company of those illustrious men who by aspiring to noble ends, whether intellectual or practical, have risen above the region of storms into a clearer atmosphere, where there is no misrepresentation of opinion, nor ambiguity of expression, but where one mind comes into closest contact with another at the point where both approach nearest to the truth.

I propose to lecture during this term on Heat, and, as our facilities for experimental work are not yet fully developed, I shall endeavour to place before you the relative position and scientific connexion of the different branches of the science, rather than to discuss the details of experimental methods.

We shall begin with Thermometry, or the registration of temperatures, and Calorimetry, or the measurement of quantities of heat. We shall then go on to Thermodynamics, which investigates the relations between the thermal properties of bodies and their other dynamical properties, in so far as these relations may be traced without any assumption as to the particular constitution of these bodies.

The principles of Thermodynamics throw great light on all the phenomena of nature, and it is probable that many valuable applications of these principles have yet to be made; but we shall have to point out the limits of this science, and to shew that many problems in nature, especially those in which the Dissipation of Energy comes into play, are not capable of solution by the principles of Thermodynamics alone, but that in order to understand them, we are obliged to form some more definite theory of the constitution of bodies.

Two theories of the constitution of bodies have struggled for victory with various fortunes since the earliest ages of speculation : one is the theory of a universal plenum, the other is that of atoms and void.

The theory of the plenum is associated with the doctrine of mathematical continuity, and its mathematical methods are those of the Differential

Calculus, which is the appropriate expression of the relations of continuous quantity.

The theory of atoms and void leads us to attach more importance to the doctrines of integral numbers and definite proportions; but, in applying dynamical principles to the motion of immense numbers of atoms, the limitation of our faculties forces us to abandon the attempt to express the exact history of each atom, and to be content with estimating the average condition of a group of atoms large enough to be visible. This method of dealing with groups of atoms, which I may call the statistical method, and which in the present state of our knowledge is the only available method of studying the properties of real bodies, involves an abandonment of strict dynamical principles, and an adoption of the mathematical methods belonging to the theory of probability. It is probable that important results will be obtained by the application of this method, which is as yet little known and is not familiar to our minds. If the actual history of Science had been different, and if the scientific doctrines most familiar to us had been those which must be expressed in this way, it is possible that we might have considered the existence of a certain kind of contingency a self-evident truth, and treated the doctrine of philosophical necessity as a mere sophism.

About the beginning of this century, the properties of bodies were investigated by several distinguished French mathematicians on the hypothesis that they are systems of molecules in equilibrium. The somewhat unsatisfactory nature of the results of these investigations produced, especially in this country, a reaction in favour of the opposite method of treating bodies as if they were, so far at least as our experiments are concerned, truly continuous. This method, in the hands of Green, Stokes, and others, has led to results, the value of which does not at all depend on what theory we adopt as to the ultimate constitution of bodies.

One very important result of the investigation of the properties of bodies on the hypothesis that they are truly continuous is that it furnishes us with a test by which we can ascertain, by experiments on a real body, to what degree of tenuity it must be reduced before it begins to give evidence that its properties are no longer the same as those of the body in mass. Investigations of this kind, combined with a study of various phenomena of diffusion and of dissipation of energy, have recently added greatly to the evidence in favour of the hypothesis that bodies are systems of molecules in motion.

I hope to be able to lay before you in the course of the term some of the evidence for the existence of molecules, considered as individual bodies having definite properties. The molecule, as it is presented to the scientific imagination, is a very different body from any of those with which experience has hitherto made us acquainted.

In the first place its mass, and the other constants which define its properties, are absolutely invariable; the individual molecule can neither grow nor decay, but remains unchanged amid all the changes of the bodies of which it may form a constituent.

In the second place it is not the only molecule of its kind, for there are innumerable other molecules, whose constants are not approximately, but absolutely identical with those of the first molecule, and this whether they are found on the earth, in the sun, or in the fixed stars.

By what process of evolution the philosophers of the future will attempt to account for this identity in the properties of such a multitude of bodies, each of them unchangeable in magnitude, and some of them separated from others by distances which Astronomy attempts in vain to measure, I cannot conjecture. My mind is limited in its power of speculation, and I am forced to believe that these molecules must have been made as they are from the beginning of their existence.

I also conclude that since none of the processes of nature, during their varied action on different individual molecules, have produced, in the course of ages, the slightest difference between the properties of one molecule and those of another, the history of whose combinations has been different, we cannot ascribe either their existence or the identity of their properties to the operation of any of those causes which we call natural.

Is it true then that our scientific speculations have really penetrated beneath the visible appearance of things, which seem to be subject to generation and corruption, and reached the entrance of that world of order and perfection, which continues this day as it was created, perfect in number and measure and weight?

We may be mistaken. No one has as yet seen or handled an individual molecule, and our molecular hypothesis may, in its turn, be supplanted by some new theory of the constitution of matter; but the idea of the existence of unnumbered individual things, all alike and all unchangeable, is one which cannot enter the human mind and remain without fruit.

But what if these molecules, indestructible as they are, turn out to be not substances themselves, but mere affections of some other substance?

According to Sir W. Thomson's theory of Vortex Atoms, the substance of which the molecule consists is a uniformly dense *plenum*, the properties of which are those of a perfect fluid, the molecule itself being nothing but a certain motion impressed on a portion of this fluid, and this motion is shewn, by a theorem due to Helmholtz, to be as indestructible as we believe a portion of matter to be.

If a theory of this kind is true, or even if it is conceivable, our idea of matter may have been introduced into our minds through our experience of those systems of vortices which we call bodies, but which are not substances, but motions of a substance; and yet the idea which we have thus acquired of matter, as a substance possessing inertia, may be truly applicable to that fluid of which the vortices are the motion, but of whose existence, apart from the vortical motion of some of its parts, our experience gives us no evidence whatever.

It has been asserted that metaphysical speculation is a thing of the past, and that physical science has extirpated it. The discussion of the categories of existence, however, does not appear to be in danger of coming to an end in our time, and the exercise of speculation continues as fascinating to every fresh mind as it was in the days of Thales.

[From the *Proceedings of the Cambridge Philosophical Society*, Vol. II.]

XLV. *On the Solution of Electrical Problems by the Transformation of Conjugate Functions**.

THE general problem in electricity is to determine a function which shall have given values at the various surfaces which bound a region of space, and which shall satisfy Laplace's partial differential equation at every point within this region. The solution of this problem, when the conditions are arbitrarily given, is beyond the power of any known method, but it is easy to find any number of functions which satisfy Laplace's equation, and from any one of these we may find the form of a system of conductors for which the function is a solution of the problem.

The only known method for transforming one electrical problem into another is that of Electric Inversion, invented by Sir William Thomson; but in problems involving only two dimensions, any problem of which we know the solution may be made to furnish an inexhaustible supply of problems which we can solve.

The condition that two functions a and β of x and y may be conjugate is

$$a + \sqrt{-1}\,\beta = F(x + \sqrt{-1}\,y).$$

This condition may be expressed in the form of the two equations

$$\frac{da}{dx} - \frac{d\beta}{dy} = 0, \quad \frac{da}{dy} + \frac{d\beta}{dx} = 0.$$

If a denotes the "potential function," β is the "function of induction." As examples of the method, the theory of Thomson's Guard Ring and that of a wire grating, used as an electric screen, were illustrated by drawings of the lines of force and equipotential surfaces.

---

* [The author's treatment of this subject and a full explanation of the examples mentioned in the text will be found in the chapter on Conjugate Functions in his treatise on Electricity and Magnetism.]

[From the *Proceedings of the London Mathematical Society*, Vol. III. No. 34.]

XLVI. *On the Mathematical Classification of Physical Quantities.*

THE first part of the growth of a physical science consists in the discovery of a system of quantities on which its phenomena may be conceived to depend. The next stage is the discovery of the mathematical form of the relations between these quantities. After this, the science may be treated as a mathematical science, and the verification of the laws is effected by a theoretical investigation of the conditions under which certain quantities can be most accurately measured, followed by an experimental realisation of these conditions, and actual measurement of the quantities.

It is only through the progress of science in recent times that we have become acquainted with so large a number of physical quantities that a classification of them is desirable.

One very obvious classification of quantities is founded on that of the sciences in which they occur. Thus temperature, pressure, density, specific heat, latent heat, &c., are quantities occurring in the theory of the action of heat on bodies.

But the classification which I now refer to is founded on the mathematical or formal analogy of the different quantities, and not on the matter to which they belong. Thus a finite straight line, a force, a velocity of rotation, &c., are quantities, differing in their physical nature, but agreeing in their mathematical form. We may distinguish the two methods of classification by calling the first a physical, and the second a mathematical classification of quantities.

A knowledge of the mathematical classification of quantities is of great use both to the original investigator and to the ordinary student of the science. The most obvious case is that in which we learn that a certain system of quantities in a new science stand to one another in the same mathematical relations as a certain other system in an old science, which has already been reduced to a mathematical form, and its problems solved by mathematicians.

Thus, when Mossotti observed that certain quantities relating to electrostatic induction in dielectrics had been shewn by Faraday to be analogous to certain quantities relating to magnetic induction in iron and other bodies, he was enabled to make use of the mathematical investigation of Poisson relative to magnetic induction, merely translating it from the magnetic language into the electric, and from French into Italian.

Another example, by no means so obvious, is that which was originally pointed out by Sir William Thomson, of the analogy between problems in attractions and problems in the steady conduction of heat, by the use of which we are able to make use of many of the results of Fourier for heat in explaining electrical distributions, and of all the results of Poisson in electricity in explaining problems in heat.

But it is evident that all analogies of this kind depend on principles of a more fundamental nature ; and that, if we had a true mathematical classification of quantities, we should be able at once to detect the analogy between any system of quantities presented to us and other systems of quantities in known sciences, so that we should lose no time in availing ourselves of the mathematical labours of those who had already solved problems essentially the same.

All quantities may be classed together in one respect, that they may be defined by means of two factors, the first of which is a numerical quantity, and the second is a standard quantity of the same kind with that to be defined.

Thus number may be said to rule the whole world of quantity, and the four rules of arithmetic may be regarded as the complete equipment of the mathematician.

Position and form, which were formerly supposed to be in the exclusive possession of geometers, were reduced by Descartes to submit to the rules of arithmetic by means of that ingenious scaffolding of co-ordinate axes which he made the basis of his operations.

Since this great step was taken in mathematics, all quantities have been treated in the same way, and presented to the mind by means of numbers, or symbols which denote numbers, so that as soon as any science has been thoroughly reduced to the mathematical form, the solution of problems in that science, as a mental process, is supposed (at least by the outer world) to be carried on without the aid of any of the physical ideas of the science.

I need not say that this is not true, and that mathematicians, in solving physical problems, are very much aided by a knowledge of the science in which the problems occur.

At the same time, I think that the progress of science, both in the way of discovery, and in the way of diffusion, would be greatly aided if more attention were paid in a direct way to the classification of quantities.

A most important distinction was drawn by Hamilton when he divided the quantities with which he had to do into Scalar quantities, which are completely represented by one numerical quantity, and Vectors, which require three numerical quantities to define them.

The invention of the calculus of Quaternions is a step towards the knowledge of quantities related to space which can only be compared for its importance, with the invention of triple co-ordinates by Descartes. The ideas of this calculus, as distinguished from its operations and symbols, are fitted to be of the greatest use in all parts of science.

We may imagine another step in the advancement of science to be the invention of a method, equally appropriate, of conceiving dynamical quantities. As our conceptions of physical science are rendered more vivid by substituting for the mere numerical ideas of Cartesian mathematics the geometrical ideas of Hamiltonian mathematics, so in the higher sciences the ideas might receive a still higher development if they could be expressed in language as appropriate to dynamics as Hamilton's is to geometry.

Another advantage of such a classification is, that it guides us in the use of the four rules of arithmetic. We know that we must not apply the rules of addition or subtraction unless the quantities are of the same kind. In certain cases we may multiply or divide one quantity by another, but in other cases the result of the process is of no intellectual value.

It has been pointed out by Professor Rankine that the physical quantity called Energy or Work can be conceived as the product of two factors in many different ways.

The dimensions of this quantity are $\dfrac{ML^2}{T^2}$, where L, M, and T represent the concrete units of length, time, and mass. If we divide the energy into two factors, one of which contains L^2, both factors will be scalars. If, on the other hand, both factors contain L, they will be both vectors. The energy itself is always a scalar quantity.

Thus, if we take the mass and the square of the velocity as the factors, as is done in the ordinary definitions of vis-viva or kinetic energy, both factors are scalar, though one of them, the square of the velocity, has no distinct physical meaning.

Another division into apparently scalar factors is that into volume and hydrostatic pressure, though here we must consider the volume, not in itself, but as a quantity subject to increase and diminution, and this change of volume can only occur at the surface, and is due to a variation of the surface in the direction of the normal, so that it is not a scalar but a vector quantity. The pressure also, though the abstract conception of a hydrostatic pressure is scalar, must be conceived as applied at a surface, and thus becomes a directed quantity or vector.

The division of the energy into vector factors affords results always capable of satisfactory interpretation. Of the two factors, one is conceived as a tendency towards a certain change, and the other as that change itself.

Thus the elementary definition of Work regards it as the product of a force into the distance through which its point of application moves, resolved in the direction of the force. In the language of Quaternions, it is the scalar part of the product of the force and the displacement.

These two vectors, the force and the displacement, may be regarded as types of many other pairs of vectors, the products of which have for their scalar part some form of energy.

Thus, instead of dividing kinetic energy into the factors "mass" and "square of velocity," the latter of which has no meaning, we may divide it into "momentum" and "velocity," two vectors which, in the dynamics of a particle, are in the same direction, but, in generalized dynamics, may be in different directions, so that in taking their product we must remember the rule for finding the scalar part of it.

But it is when we have to deal with continuous bodies, and quantities distributed in space, that the general principle of the division of energy into two factors is most clearly seen.

When we regard energy as residing intrinsically in a body, we may measure its intensity by the amount contained in unit of volume. This is, of course, a scalar quantity.

Of the factors which compose it, one is referred to unit of length, and the other to unit of area. This gives what I regard as a very important distinction among vector quantities.

Vectors which are referred to unit of length I shall call Forces, using the word in a somewhat generalized sense, as we shall see. The operation of taking the integral of the resolved part of a force in the direction of a line for every element of that line, has always a physical meaning. In certain cases the result of the integration is independent of the path of the line between its extremities. The result is then called a Potential.

Vectors which are referred to unit of area I shall call Fluxes. The operation of taking the integral of the resolved part of a flux perpendicular to a surface for every element of the surface has always a physical meaning. In certain cases the result of the integration over a closed surface is independent, within certain restrictions, of the position of the surface. The result then expresses the Quantity of some kind of matter, either existing within the surface, or flowing out of it, according to the physical nature of the flux.

In many physical cases, the force and the flux are always in the same direction, and proportional to each other. The one is therefore used as the measure of the other, their symbols degenerate into one, and their ideas become confounded together. One of the most important mathematical results of the discovery of substances having different physical properties in different directions, has been to enable us to distinguish between the force and the flux, by letting us see that their directions may be different.

Thus, in the ordinary theory of fluids, in which the only motion considered is that which we can directly perceive, we may define the velocity equally well in two different ways. We may define it with reference to unit of length, as the number of such units described by a particle in unit of time; or we may define it with reference to unit of area, as the volume of the fluid which passes through unit of area in unit of time. If defined in the first way, it belongs to the category of forces; if defined in the second way, to the category of fluxes.

But if we endeavour to develope a more complete theory of fluids, which shall take into account the facts of diffusion, where one fluid has a different velocity from another in the same place; or if we accept the doctrine, that the molecules of a fluid, in virtue of the heat of the substance, are in a state of agitation; then though we may give a definition of the velocity of a single molecule with reference to unit of length, we cannot do so for the fluid; and the only way we have of defining the motion of the fluid is by considering it as a flux, and measuring it by the mass of the fluid which flows through unit of area.

This distinction is still more necessary when we come to heat and electricity. The flux of heat or of electricity cannot be even thought of in any way except as the quantity which flows through a given area in a given time. To form a conception of the velocity, properly so called, of either agent, would require us to conceive heat or electricity as a continuous substance having a known density.

We must therefore consider these quantities as fluxes. The forces corresponding to them are, in the case of heat, the rate of variation of temperature, and, in the case of electricity, the rate of variation of potential.

I have said enough to point out the distinction between forces and fluxes. In statical electricity the resultant force at a point is the rate of variation of potential, and the flux is a quantity, hitherto confounded with the force, which I have called the electric displacement.

In magnetism the resultant force is also the rate of variation of the potential, and the flux is what Faraday calls the magnetic induction, and is measured, as Thomson has shewn, by the force on a unit pole placed in a narrow crevasse cut perpendicular to the direction of magnetization of the magnet. I shall not detain the Society with the explanation of these quantities, but I must briefly state the nature of a ratio of a force to a flux in its most general form.

When one vector is a function of another vector, the ratio of the first to the second is, in general, a quaternion which is a function of the second vector.

When, if the second vector varies in magnitude only, the first is always proportional to it, and remains constant in direction, we have the important case of the function being a *linear* one. The first vector is then said to be a linear and vector function of the second. If a, β, γ are the Cartesian components of the first vector, and a, b, c those of the second, then

$$a = r_1 a + q_3 b + p_2 c,$$
$$\beta = p_3 a + r_2 b + q_1 c,$$
$$\gamma = q_2 a + p_1 b + r_3 c,$$

where the coefficients p, q, r are constants. When the p's are equal to the corresponding q's, the function is said to be self-conjugate. It may then be represented geometrically as the relation between the radius vector from the centre of an ellipsoid, and the perpendicular on the tangent plane.

We may remark that even here, where we may seem to have reached a purer air, uncontaminated by physical applications, one vector is essentially a line, while the other is defined as the normal to a plane, as in all the other pairs of vectors already mentioned*.

Another distinction among physical vectors is founded on a different principle, and divides them into those which are defined with reference to translation and those which are defined with reference to rotation. The remarkable analogies between these two classes of vectors is well pointed out by Poinsôt in his treatise on the motion of a rigid body. But the most remarkable illustration of them is derived from the two different ways in which it is possible to contemplate the relation between electricity and magnetism.

Helmholtz, in his great paper on Vortex Motion, has shewn how to construct an analogy between electro-magnetic and hydro-kinetic phenomena, in which magnetic force is represented by the velocity of the fluid, a species of translation, while electric current is represented by the rotation of the elements of the fluid. He does not propose this as an explanation of electro-magnetism; for though the analogy is perfect in form, the dynamics of the two systems are different.

According to Ampère and all his followers, however, electric currents are regarded as a species of translation, and magnetic force as depending on rotation. I am constrained to agree with this view, because the electric current is associated with electrolysis, and other undoubted instances of translation, while magnetism is associated with the rotation of the plane of polarization of light, which, as Thomson has shewn, involves actual motion of rotation.

The Hamiltonian operator $V\nabla$, applied to any vector function, converts it from translation to rotation, or from rotation to translation, according to the kind of vector to which it is applied.

I shall conclude by proposing for the consideration of mathematicians certain phrases to express the results of the Hamiltonian operator Δ. I should be greatly obliged to anyone who can give me suggestions on this subject, as I feel that the onomastic power is very faint in me, and that it can be successfully exercised only in societies.

∇ is the operation
$$i\,\frac{d}{dx} + j\,\frac{d}{dy} + k\,\frac{d}{dz},$$

where i, j, k are unit vectors parallel to x, y, z respectively. The result of

---

* The subject of linear equations in quaternions has been developed by Professor Tait, in several communications to the Royal Society of Edinburgh.

performing this operation twice on any subject is the well known operation (of Laplace)

$$\nabla^2 = -\left(\frac{d^2}{dx^2} + \frac{d^2}{dy} + \frac{d^2}{dz^2}\right).$$

The discovery of the square root of this operation is due to Hamilton; but most of the applications here given, and the whole development of the theory of this operation, are due to Prof. Tait, and are given in several papers, of which the first is in the *Proceedings of the Royal Society of Edinburgh*, April 28, 1862, and the most complete is that on "Green's and other allied Theorems," *Transactions of the Royal Society of Edinburgh*, 1869—70.

And, first, I propose to call the result of ∇^2 (Laplace's operation with the negative sign) the *Concentration* of the quantity to which it is applied.

For if Q be a quantity, either scalar or vector, which is a function of the position of a point; and if we find the integral of Q taken throughout the volume of a sphere whose radius is r; then, if we divide this by the volume of the sphere, we shall obtain $\overline{Q}$, the *mean* value of Q within the sphere. If Q_0 is the value of Q at the centre of the sphere, then, when r is small,

$$Q_0 - \overline{Q} = \frac{r^2}{10}\nabla^2 Q,$$

or the value of Q at the centre of the sphere exceeds the mean value of Q within the sphere by a quantity depending on the radius, and on $\nabla^2 Q$. Since, therefore, $\nabla^2 Q$ indicates the excess of the value of Q at the centre above its mean value in the sphere, I shall call it the concentration of $\dot{Q}$.

If Q is a scalar quantity, its concentration is, of course, also scalar. Thus, if Q is an electric potential, $\nabla^2 Q$ is the density of the matter which produces the potential.

If Q is a vector quantity, then both Q_0 and $\overline{Q}$ are vectors, and $\nabla^2 Q$ is also a vector, indicating the excess of the uniform force Q_0 applied to the whole substance of the sphere above the resultant of the actual force Q acting on all the parts of the sphere.

Let us next consider the Hamiltonian operator ∇. First apply it to a scalar function P. The quantity ∇P is a vector, indicating the direction in which P decreases most rapidly, and measuring the rate of that decrease. I venture, with much diffidence, to call this the *slope* of P. Lamé calls the *magnitude* of ∇P the "first differential parameter" of P, but its *direction* does not enter into his conception. We require a vector word, which shall indicate both direction and magnitude, and one not already employed in another mathematical sense. I have taken the liberty of extending the ordinary sense of the word slope from topography, where only two independent variables are used, to space of three dimensions.

If σ represents a vector function, $\nabla\sigma$ may contain both a scalar and a vector part, which may be written $S\nabla\sigma$ and $V\nabla\sigma$.

I propose to call the scalar part the *Convergence* of σ, because, if a closed surface be described about any point, the surface integral of σ, which expresses the effect of the vector σ considered as an inward flux through the surface, is equal to the volume integral of $S\nabla\sigma$ throughout the enclosed space. I think, therefore, that the convergence of a vector function is a very good name for the effect of that vector function in carrying its subject inwards towards a point.

But $\nabla\sigma$ has, in general, also a vector portion, and I propose, but with great diffidence, to call this vector the *Curl* or *Version* of the original vector function.

It represents the direction and magnitude of the rotation of the subject matter carried by the vector σ. I have sought for a word which shall neither, like Rotation, Whirl, or Twirl, connote motion, nor, like Twist, indicate a helical or screw structure which is not of the nature of a vector at all.

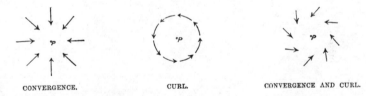

CONVERGENCE.　　　　CURL.　　　　CONVERGENCE AND CURL.

If we subtract from the general value of the vector function σ its value σ_0 at the point P, then the remaining vector $\sigma - \sigma_0$ will, when there is pure convergence, point towards P. When there is pure curl, it will point tangentially round P; and when there is both convergence and curl, it will point in a spiral manner.

The following statements are true :—

The slope of a scalar function has no curl.

The curl of a vector function has no convergence.

The convergence of the slope of a scalar function is its concentration.

The concentration of a vector function is the slope of its convergence, together with the curl of its curl.

The quaternion expressions, of which the above statements are a translation, were given by Prof. Tait, in his paper in the *Proceedings of the Royal Society of Edinburgh*, April 28th, 1862; but for the more complete mathematical treatment of the operator ∇, see a very able paper by Prof. Tait, "On Green's and other Allied Theorems" (*Transactions of the Royal Society of Edinburgh*, 1870), and another paper in the *Proceedings of the Royal Society of Edinburgh*, for 1870—71, p. 318.

[From the *Proceedings of the Royal Institution of Great Britain*, Vol. VI.]

XLVII. *On Colour Vision.*

ALL vision is colour vision, for it is only by observing differences of colour that we distinguish the forms of objects. I include differences of brightness or shade among differences of colour.

It was in the Royal Institution, about the beginning of this century, that Thomas Young made the first distinct announcement of that doctrine of the vision of colours which I propose to illustrate. We may state it thus:—We are capable of feeling three different colour-sensations. Light of different kinds excites these sensations in different proportions, and it is by the different combinations of these three primary sensations that all the varieties of visible colour are produced. In this statement there is one word on which we must fix our attention. That word is, Sensation. It seems almost a truism to say that colour is a sensation; and yet Young, by honestly recognising this elementary truth, established the first consistent theory of colour. So far as I know, Thomas Young was the first who, starting from the well-known fact that there are three primary colours, sought for the explanation of this fact, not in the nature of light, but in the constitution of man. Even of those who have written on colour since the time of Young, some have supposed that they ought to study the properties of pigments, and others that they ought to analyse the rays of light. They have sought for a knowledge of colour by examining something in external nature—something out of themselves.

Now, if the sensation which we call colour has any laws, it must be something in our own nature which determines the form of these laws; and I need not tell you that the only evidence we can obtain respecting ourselves is derived from consciousness.

The science of colour must therefore be regarded as essentially a mental science. It differs from the greater part of what is called mental science in the large use which it makes of the physical sciences, and in particular of optics and anatomy. But it gives evidence that it is a mental science by the numerous illustrations which it furnishes of various operations of the mind.

In this place we always feel on firmer ground when we are dealing with physical science. I shall therefore begin by shewing how we apply the discoveries of Newton to the manipulation of light, so as to give you an opportunity of feeling for yourselves the different sensations of colour.

Before the time of Newton, white light was supposed to be of all known things the purest. When light appears coloured, it was supposed to have become contaminated by coming into contact with gross bodies. We may still think white light the emblem of purity, though Newton has taught us that its purity does not consist in simplicity.

We now form the prismatic spectrum on the screen [*exhibited*]. These are the simple colours of which white light is always made up. We can distinguish a great many hues in passing from the one end to the other; but it is when we employ powerful spectroscopes, or avail ourselves of the labours of those who have mapped out the spectrum, that we become aware of the immense multitude of different kinds of light, every one of which has been the object of special study. Every increase of the power of our instruments increases in the same proportion the number of lines visible in the spectrum.

All light, as Newton proved, is composed of these rays taken in different proportions. Objects which we call coloured when illuminated by white light, make a selection of these rays, and our eyes receive from them only a part of the light which falls on them. But if they receive only the pure rays of a single colour of the spectrum they can appear only of that colour. If I place this disk, containing alternate quadrants of red and green paper, in the red rays, it appears all red, but the red quadrants brightest. If I place it in the green rays both papers appear green, but the red paper is now the darkest. This, then, is the optical explanation of the colours of bodies when illuminated with white light. They separate the white light into its component parts, absorbing some and scattering others.

Here are two transparent solutions [*exhibited*]. One appears yellow, it contains bichromate of potash; the other appears blue, it contains sulphate of copper. If I transmit the light of the electric lamp through the two solutions at once, the spot on the screen appears green. By means of the spectrum we shall be able to explain this. The yellow solution cuts off the blue end of the spectrum, leaving only the red, orange, yellow, and green. The blue solution cuts off the red end, leaving only the green, blue, and violet. The only light which can get through both is the green light, as you see. In the same way most blue and yellow paints, when mixed, appear green. The light which falls on the mixture is so beaten about between the yellow particles and the blue that the only light which survives is the green. But yellow and blue light when mixed do not make green, as you will see if we allow them to fall on the same part of the screen together.

It is a striking illustration of our mental processes that many persons have not only gone on believing, on the evidence of the mixture of pigments, that blue and yellow make green, but that they have even persuaded themselves that they could detect the separate sensations of blueness and of yellowness in the sensation of green.

We have availed ourselves hitherto of the analysis of light by coloured substances. We must now return, still under the guidance of Newton, to the prismatic spectrum. Newton not only

"Untwisted all the shining robe of day,"

but shewed how to put it together again. We have here a pure spectrum, but instead of catching it on a screen we allow it to pass through a lens large enough to receive all the coloured rays. These rays proceed, according to well-known principles in optics, to form an image of the prism on a screen placed at the proper distance. This image is formed by rays of all colours, and you see the result is white. But if I stop any of the coloured rays the image is no longer white, but coloured; and if I only let through rays of one colour, the image of the prism appears of that colour.

I have here an arrangement of slits by which I can select one, two, or three portions of the light of the spectrum, and allow them to form an image of the prism while all the rest are stopped. This gives me a perfect command of the colours of the spectrum, and I can produce on the screen every possible shade of colour by adjusting the breadth and the position of the slits through which the light passes. I can also, by interposing a lens in the passage of the light, shew you a magnified image of the slits, by which you will see the different kinds of light which compose the mixture.

The colours are at present red, green, and blue, and the mixture of the three colours is, as you see, nearly white. Let us try the effect of mixing two of these colours. Red and blue form a fine purple or crimson, green and blue form a sea-green or sky-blue, red and green form a yellow.

Here again we have a fact not universally known. No painter, wishing to produce a fine yellow, mixes his red with his green. The result would be a very dirty drab colour. He is furnished by nature with brilliant yellow pigments, and he takes advantage of these. When he mixes red and green paint, the red light scattered by the red paint is robbed of nearly all its brightness by getting among particles of green, and the green light fares no better, for it is sure to fall in with particles of red paint. But when the pencil with which we paint is composed of the rays of light, the effect of two coats of colour is very different. The red and the green form a yellow of great splendour, which may be shewn to be as intense as the purest yellow of the spectrum.

I have now arranged the slits to transmit the yellow of the spectrum. You see it is similar in colour to the yellow formed by mixing red and green. It differs from the mixture, however, in being strictly homogeneous in a physical point of view. The prism, as you see, does not divide it into two portions as it did the mixture. Let us now combine this yellow with the blue of the spectrum. The result is certainly not green; we may make it pink if our yellow is of a warm hue, but if we choose a greenish yellow we can produce a good white.

You have now seen the most remarkable of the combinations of colours— the others differ from them in degree, not in kind. I must now ask you to think no more of the physical arrangements by which you were enabled to see these colours, and to concentrate your attention upon the colours you saw, that is to say on certain sensations of which you were conscious. We are here surrounded by difficulties of a kind which we do not meet with in purely physical inquiries. We can all feel these sensations, but none of us can describe them. They are not only private property, but they are incommunicable. We have names for the external objects which excite our sensations, but not for the sensations themselves.

When we look at a broad field of uniform colour, whether it is really simple or compound, we find that the sensation of colour appears to our consciousness as one and indivisible. We cannot directly recognise the elementary sensations of which it is composed, as we can distinguish the component notes of a musical chord. A colour, therefore, must be regarded as a single thing, the quality of which is capable of variation.

To bring a quality within the grasp of exact science, we must conceive it as depending on the values of one or more variable quantities, and the first step in our scientific progress is to determine the number of these variables which are necessary and sufficient to determine the quality of a colour. We do not require any elaborate experiments to prove that the quality of colour can vary in three and only in three independent ways.

One way of expressing this is by saying, with the painters, that colour may vary in hue, tint, and shade.

The finest example of a series of colours, varying in hue, is the spectrum itself. A difference in hue may be illustrated by the difference between adjoining colours in the spectrum. The series of hues in the spectrum is not complete; for, in order to get purple hues, we must blend the red and the blue.

Tint may be defined as the degree of purity of a colour. Thus, bright yellow, buff, and cream-colour, form a series of colours of nearly the same hue, but varying in tint. The tints, corresponding to any given hue, form a series, beginning with the most pronounced colour, and ending with a perfectly neutral tint.

Shade may be defined as the greater or less defect of illumination. If we begin with any tint of any hue, we can form a gradation from that colour to black, and this gradation is a series of shades of that colour. Thus we may say that brown is a dark shade of orange.

The quality of a colour may vary in three different and independent ways. We cannot conceive of any others. In fact, if we adjust one colour to another, so as to agree in hue, in tint, and in shade, the two colours are absolutely indistinguishable. There are therefore three, and only three, ways in which a colour can vary.

I have purposely avoided introducing at this stage of our inquiry anything which may be called a scientific experiment, in order to shew that we may determine the number of quantities upon which the variation of colour depends by means of our ordinary experience alone.

Here is a point in this room: if I wish to specify its position, I may do so by giving the measurements of three distances—namely, the height above the floor, the distance from the wall behind me, and the distance from the wall at my left hand.

This is only one of many ways of stating the position of a point, but it is one of the most convenient. Now, colour also depends on three things. If we call these the intensities of the three primary colour sensations, and if we are able in any way to measure these three intensities, we may consider the colour as specified by these three measurements. Hence the specification of a colour agrees with the specification of a point in the room in depending on three measurements.

Let us go a step farther and suppose the colour sensations measured on some scale of intensity, and a point found for which the three distances, or co-ordinates, contain the same number of feet as the sensations contain degrees of intensity. Then we may say, by a useful geometrical convention, that the colour is represented, to our mathematical imagination, by the point so found in the room; and if there are several colours, represented by several points, the chromatic relations of the colours will be represented by the geometrical relations of the points. This method of expressing the relations of colours is a great help to the imagination. You will find these relations of colours stated in an exceedingly clear manner in Mr Benson's *Manual of Colour* one of the very few books on colour in which the statements are founded on legitimate experiments.

There is a still more convenient method of representing the relations of colours by means of Young's triangle of colours. It is impossible to represent on a plane piece of paper every conceivable colour, to do this requires space of three dimensions. If, however, we consider only colours of the same shade— that is, colours in which the sum of the intensities of the three sensations is the same, then the variations in tint and in hue of all such colours may be represented by points on a plane. For this purpose we must draw a plane cutting off equal lengths from the three lines representing the primary sensations. The part of this plane within the space in which we have been distributing our colours will be an equilateral triangle. The three primary colours will be at the three angles, white or gray will be in the middle, the tint or degree of purity of any colour will be expressed by its distance from the middle point, and its hue will depend on the angular position of the line which joins it with the middle point.

Thus the ideas of tint and hue can be expressed geometrically on Young's triangle. To understand what is meant by shade we have only to suppose the illumination of the whole triangle increased or diminished, so that by means of this adjustment of illumination Young's triangle may be made to exhibit every variety of colour. If we now take any two colours in the triangle and mix them in any proportions, we shall find the resultant colour in the line joining the component colours at the point corresponding to their centre of gravity.

I have said nothing about the nature of the three primary sensations, or what particular colours they most resemble. In order to lay down on paper the relations between actual colours, it is not necessary to know what the primary colours are. We may take any three colours, provisionally, as the angles of a triangle, and determine the position of any other observed colour with respect to these, so as to form a kind of chart of colours.

Of all colours which we see, those excited by the different rays of the prismatic spectrum have the greatest scientific importance. All light consists either of some one kind of these rays, or of some combination of them. The colours of all natural bodies are compounded of the colours of the spectrum. If therefore we can form a chromatic chart of the spectrum, expressing the relations between the colours of its different portions, then the colours of all natural bodies will be found within a certain boundary on the chart defined by the positions of the colours of the spectrum.

But the chart of the spectrum will also help us to the knowledge of the nature of the three primary sensations. Since every sensation is essentially a positive thing, every compound colour-sensation must be within the triangle of which the primary colours are the angles. In particular, the chart of the spectrum must be entirely within Young's triangle of colours, so that if any colour in the spectrum is identical with one of the colour-sensations, the chart of the spectrum must be in the form of a line having a sharp angle at the point corresponding to this colour.

I have already shewn you how we can make a mixture of any three of the colours of the spectrum, and vary the colour of the mixture by altering the intensity of any of the three components. If we place this compound colour side by side with any other colour, we can alter the compound colour till it appears exactly similar to the other. This can be done with the greatest exactness when the resultant colour is nearly white. I have therefore constructed an instrument which I may call a colour-box, for the purpose of making matches between two colours. It can only be used by one observer at a time, and it requires daylight, so I have not brought it with me to-night. It is nothing but the realisation of the construction of one of Newton's propositions in his *Lectiones Opticæ*, where he shews how to take a beam of light, to separate it into its components, to deal with these components as we please by means of slits, and afterwards to unite them into a beam again. The observer looks into the box through a small slit. He sees a round field of light consisting of two semicircles divided by a vertical diameter. The semicircle on the left consists of light which has been enfeebled by two reflexions at the surface of glass. That on the right is a mixture of colours of the spectrum, the positions and intensities of which are regulated by a system of slits.

The observer forms a judgment respecting the colours of the two semicircles. Suppose he finds the one on the right hand redder than the other, he says so, and the operator, by means of screws outside the box, alters the breadth of one of the slits, so as to make the mixture less red; and so on, till the right semicircle is made exactly of the same appearance as the left, and the line of separation becomes almost invisible.

When the operator and the observer have worked together for some time, they get to understand each other, and the colours are adjusted much more rapidly than at first.

When the match is pronounced perfect, the positions of the slits, as indicated by a scale, are registered, and the breadth of each slit is carefully measured by means of a gauge. The registered result of an observation is called a "colour equation." It asserts that a mixture of three colours is, in the opinion of the observer (whose name is given), identical with a neutral tint, which we shall call Standard White. Each colour is specified by the position of the slit on the scale, which indicates its position in the spectrum, and by the breadth of the slit, which is a measure of its intensity.

In order to make a survey of the spectrum we select three points for purposes of comparison, and we call these the three Standard Colours. The standard colours are selected on the same principles as those which guide the engineer in selecting stations for a survey. They must be conspicuous and invariable and not in the same straight line.

In the chart of the spectrum you may see the relations of the various colours of the spectrum to the three standard colours, and to each other. It is manifest that the standard green which I have chosen cannot be one of the true primary colours, for the other colours do not all lie within the triangle formed by joining them. But the chart of the spectrum may be described as consisting of two straight lines meeting in a point. This point corresponds to a green about a fifth of the distance from b towards F. This green has a wave length of about 510 millionths of a millimetre by Ditscheiner's measurement. This green is either the true primary green, or at least it is the nearest approach to it which we can ever see. Proceeding from this green towards the red end of the spectrum, we find the different colours lying almost. exactly in a straight line. This indicates that any colour is chromatically equivalent to a mixture of any two colours on opposite sides of it, and in the same straight line. The extreme red is considerably beyond the standard red, but it is in the same straight line, and therefore we might, if we had no other evidence, assume the extreme red as the true primary red. We shall see, however, that the true primary red is not exactly represented in colour by any part of the spectrum. It lies somewhat beyond the extreme red, but in the same straight line.

On the blue side of primary green the colour equations are seldom so accurate. The colours, however, lie in a line which is nearly straight. I have not been able to detect any measurable chromatic difference between the extreme indigo and the violet. The colours of this end of the spectrum are represented by a number of points very close to each other. We may suppose that the primary blue is a sensation differing little from that excited by the parts of the spectrum near G.

Now, the first thing which occurs to most people about this result is that the division of the spectrum is by no means a fair one. Between the red and the green we have a series of colours apparently very different from either, and having such marked characteristics that two of them, orange and yellow, have received separate names. The colours between the green and the blue, on the other hand, have an obvious resemblance to one or both of the extreme colours, and no distinct names for these colours have ever become popularly recognised.

I do not profess to reconcile this discrepancy between ordinary and scientific experience. It only shews that it is impossible by a mere act of introspection to make a true analysis of our sensations. Consciousness is our only authority; but consciousness must be methodically examined in order to obtain any trust-worthy results.

I have here, through the kindness of Professor Huxley, a picture of the structure upon which the light falls at the back of the eye. There is a minute structure of bodies like rods and cones or pegs, and it is conceivable that the mode in which we become aware of the shapes of things is by a consciousness which differs according to the particular rods on the ends of which the light falls, just as the pattern on the web formed by a Jacquard loom depends on the mode in which the perforated cards act on the system of moveable rods in that machine. In the eye we have on the one hand light falling on this wonderful structure, and on the other hand we have the sensation of sight. We cannot compare these two things; they belong to opposite categories. The whole of Metaphysics lies like a great gulf between them. It is possible that discoveries in physiology may be made by tracing the course of the nervous disturbance

"Up the fine fibres to the sentient brain;"

but this would make us no wiser than we are about those colour-sensations which we can only know by feeling them ourselves. Still, though it is impossible to become acquainted with a sensation by the anatomical study of the organ with which it is connected, we may make use of the sensation as a means of investigating the anatomical structure.

A remarkable instance of this is the deduction of Helmholtz's theory of the structure of the retina from that of Young with respect to the sensation of colour. Young asserts that there are three elementary sensations of colour; Helmholtz asserts that there are three systems of nerves in the retina, each of which has for its function, when acted on by light or any other disturbing agent, to excite in us one of these three sensations.

No anatomist has hitherto been able to distinguish these three systems of nerves by microscopic observation. But it is admitted in physiology that the only way in which the sensation excited by a particular nerve can vary is by degrees of intensity. The intensity of the sensation may vary from the faintest impression up to an insupportable pain; but whatever be the exciting cause, the sensation will be the same when it reaches the same intensity. If this doctrine of the function of a nerve be admitted, it is legitimate to reason from the fact that colour may vary in three different ways, to the inference that these three modes of variation arise from the independent action of three different nerves or sets of nerves.

Some very remarkable observations on the sensation of colour have been made by M. Sigmund Exner in Professor Helmholtz's physiological laboratory at Heidelberg. While looking at an intense light of a brilliant colour, he exposed his eye to rapid alternations of light and darkness by waving his fingers before his eyes. Under these circumstances a peculiar minute structure made its appearance in the field of view, which many of us may have casually observed.

M. Exner states that the character of this structure is different according to the colour of the light employed. When red light is used a veined structure is seen; when the light is green, the field appears covered with minute black dots, and when the light is blue, spots are seen, of a larger size than the dots in the green, and of a lighter colour.

Whether these appearances present themselves to all eyes, and whether they have for their physical cause any difference in the arrangement of the nerves of the three systems in Helmholtz's theory I cannot say, but I am sure that if these systems of nerves have a real existence, no method is more likely to demonstrate their existence than that which M. Exner has followed.

Colour Blindness.

The most valuable evidence which we possess with respect to colour vision is furnished to us by the colour-blind. A considerable number of persons in every large community are unable to distinguish between certain pairs of colours which to ordinary people appear in glaring contrast. Dr Dalton, the founder of the atomic theory of chemistry, has given us an account of his own case.

The true nature of this peculiarity of vision was first pointed out by Sir John Herschel in a letter written to Dalton in 1832, but not known to the world till the publication of Dalton's Life by Dr Henry. The defect consists in the absence of one of the three primary sensations of colour. Colour-blind vision depends on the variable intensities of two sensations instead of three. The best description of colour-blind vision is that given by Professor Pole in his account of his own case in the *Phil. Trans.*, 1859.

In all cases which have been examined with sufficient care, the absent sensation appears to resemble that which we call red. The point P on the chart of the spectrum represents the relation of the absent sensation to the colours of the spectrum, deduced from observations with the colour box furnished by Professor Pole.

If it were possible to exhibit the colour corresponding to this point on the chart, it would be invisible, absolutely black, to Professor Pole. As it does not lie within the range of the colours of the spectrum we cannot exhibit it; and, in fact, colour-blind people can perceive the extreme end of the spectrum which we call red, though it appears to them much darker than to us, and does not excite in them the sensation which we call red. In the diagram of the intensities of the three sensations excited by different parts of the spectrum, the upper figure, marked P, is deduced from the observations of Professor Pole; while the lower one, marked K, is founded on observations by a very accurate observer of the normal type.

The only difference between the two diagrams is that in the upper one the red curve is absent. The forms of the other two curves are nearly the same for both observers. We have great reason therefore to conclude that the colour sensations which Professor Pole sees are what we call green and blue. This is the result of my calculations; but Professor Pole agrees with every other colour-blind person whom I know in denying that green is one of his sensations. The colour-blind are always making mistakes about green things and confounding them with red. The colours they have no doubts about are certainly blue and yellow, and they persist in saying that yellow, and not green, is the colour which they are able to see.

To explain this discrepancy we must remember that colour-blind persons learn the names of colours by the same method as ourselves. They are told that the sky is blue, that grass is green, that gold is yellow, and that soldiers' coats are red. They observe difference in the colours of these objects, and they often suppose that they see the same colours as we do, only not so well. But if we look at the diagram we shall see that the brightest example of their second sensation in the spectrum is not in the green, but in the part which we call yellow, and which we teach them to call yellow. The figure of the spectrum below Professor Pole's curves is intended to represent to ordinary eyes what a colour-blind person would see in the spectrum. I hardly dare to draw your attention to it, for if you were to think that any painted picture would enable you to see with other people's vision I should certainly have lectured in vain.

On the Yellow Spot.

Experiments on colour indicate very considerable differences between the vision of different persons, all of whom are of the ordinary type. A colour, for instance, which one person on comparing it with white will pronounce pinkish, another person will pronounce greenish. This difference, however, does not arise from any diversity in the nature of the colour sensations in different persons. It is exactly of the same kind as would be observed if one of the persons wore yellow spectacles. In fact, most of us have near the middle of the retina a yellow spot through which the rays must pass before they reach the sensitive organ: this spot appears yellow because it absorbs the rays near the line F, which are of a greenish-blue colour. Some of us have this spot strongly developed. My own observations of the spectrum near the line F are of very little value on this account. I am indebted to Professor Stokes for the knowledge of a method by which anyone may see whether he has this yellow spot. It consists in looking at a white object through a solution of chloride of chromium, or at a screen on which light which has passed through this solution is thrown [*exhibited*]. This light is a mixture of red light with the light which is so strongly absorbed by the yellow spot. When it falls on the ordinary surface of the retina it is of a neutral tint, but when it falls on the yellow spot only the red light reaches the optic nerve, and we see a red spot floating like a rosy cloud over the illuminated field.

Very few persons are unable to detect the yellow spot in this way. The observer K, whose colour equations have been used in preparing the chart of the spectrum, is one of the very few who do not see everything as if through yellow spectacles. As for myself, the position of white light in the chart of the spectrum is on the yellow side of true white even when I use the outer parts of the retina; but as soon as I look direct at it, it becomes much yellower, as is shewn by the point WC. It is a curious fact that we do not see this yellow spot on every occasion, and that we do not think white objects yellow. But if we wear spectacles of any colour for some time, or if we live in a room lighted by windows all of one colour, we soon come to recognize white paper as white. This shews that it is only when some alteration takes place in our sensations, that we are conscious of their quality.

There are several interesting facts about the colour sensation which I can only mention briefly. One is that the extreme parts of the retina are nearly insensible to red. If you hold a red flower and a blue flower in your hand as far back as you can see your hand, you will lose sight of the red flower, while you still see the blue one. Another is, that when the light is diminished red objects become darkened more in proportion than blue ones. The third is, that a kind of colour blindness in which blue is the absent sensation can be produced artificially by taking doses of Santonine. This kind of colour blindness is described by Dr Edmund Rose, of Berlin. It is only temporary, and does not appear to be followed by any more serious consequences than headaches. I must ask your pardon for not having undergone a course of this medicine, even for the sake of becoming able to give you information at first hand about colour blindness.

[From the *Transactions of the Royal Society of Edinburgh,* Vol. XXVI.]

XLVIII. *On the Geometrical Mean Distance of Two Figures on a Plane.*

[Received January 5th; read January 15th, 1872.]

THERE are several problems of great practical importance in electro-magnetic measurements, in which the value of a quantity has to be calculated by taking the sum of the logarithms of the distances of a system of parallel wires from a given point. The calculation is in some respects analogous to that in which we find the potential at a point due to a given system of equal particles, by adding the reciprocals of the distances of the particles from the given point. There is this difference, however, that whereas the reciprocal of a line is completely defined when we know the unit of length, the logarithm of a line has no meaning till we know not only the unit of length, but the modulus of the system of logarithms.

In both cases, however, an additional clearness may be given to the statement of the result by dividing, by the number of wires in the first case, and by the number of particles in the second. The result in the first case is the logarithm of a distance, and in the second it is the reciprocal of a distance; and in both cases this distance is such that, if the whole system were concentrated at this distance from the given point, it would produce the same potential as it actually does.

In the first case, since the logarithm of the resultant distance is the arithmetical mean of the logarithms of the distances of the various components of the system, we may call the resultant distance the geometrical mean distance of the system from the given point.

In the second case, since the reciprocal of the resultant distance is the arithmetical mean of the reciprocals of the distances of the particles, we may call the resultant distance the harmonic mean distance of the system from the given point.

The practical use of these mean distances may be compared with that of several artificial lines and distances which are known in Dynamics as the radius of gyration, the length of the equivalent simple pendulum, and so on. The result of a process of integration is recorded, and presented to us in a form which we cannot misunderstand, and which we may substitute in those elementary formulæ which apply to the case of single particles. If we have any doubts about the value of the numerical co-efficients, we may test the expression for the mean distance by taking the point at a great distance from the system, in which case the mean distance must approximate to the distance of the centre of gravity.

Thus it is well known that the harmonic mean distance of two spheres, each of which is external to the other, is the distance between their centres, and that the harmonic mean distance of any figure from a thin shell which completely encloses it is equal to the radius of the shell.

I shall not discuss the harmonic mean distance, because the calculations which lead to it are well known, and because we can do very well without it. I shall, however, give a few examples of the geometric mean distance, in order to shew its use in electro-magnetic calculations, some of which seem to me to be rendered both easier to follow and more secure against error by a free use of this imaginary line.

If the co-ordinates of a point in the first of two plane figures be x and y, and those of a point in the second ξ and η, and if r denote the distance between these points, then R, the geometrical mean distance of the two figures, is defined by the equation

$$\log R \, . \, \iiiint dx\,dy\,d\xi\,d\eta = \iiiint \log r \, dx\,dy\,d\xi\,d\eta.$$

The following are some examples of the results of this calculation :—

(1) Let AB be a uniform line, and O a point not in the line, and let OP be the perpendicular from O on the line AB, produced if necessary, then if R is the geometric mean distance of O from the line AB,

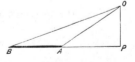

$$AB \, . \, (\log R + 1) = PB \, . \, \log OB - PA \log OA + OP \, . \, A\dot{O}B.$$

(2) The geometrical mean distance of P, a point in the line itself, from AB is found from the equation

$$AB\,(\log R + 1) = PB\log PB - PA\log PA.$$

When P lies between A and B, PA must be taken negative, but in taking the logarithm of PA we regard PA as a positive numerical quantity.

(3) If R is the geometric mean distance between two finite lines AB and CD, lying in the same straight line,

$$AB \, . \, CD\,(2\log R + 3) = AD^2\log AD + BC^2\log BC - AC^2\log AC - BD^2\log BD.$$

(4) If AB coincides with CD, we find for the geometric mean distance of all the points of AB from each other

$$R = ABe^{-\frac{3}{2}}.$$

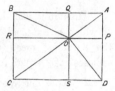

(5) If R is the geometric mean distance of the rectangle $ABCD$ from the point O in its plane, and POR and QOS are parallel to the sides of the rectangle through O,

$$ABCD\,(2\log R + 3) = 2OP\,.\,OQ\log OA + 2OQ\,.\,OR\log OB$$
$$+ 2OR\,.\,OS\log OC + 2OS\,.\,OP\log OD$$
$$+ OP^2\,.\,D\hat{O}A \qquad + OQ^2\,.\,A\hat{O}B$$
$$+ OR^2\,.\,B\hat{O}C \qquad + OS^2\,.\,COD$$

(6) If R is the geometric mean of the distances of all the points of the rectangle $ABCD$ from each other,

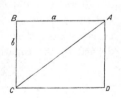

$$\log R = \log AC - \tfrac{1}{6}\frac{AB^2}{BC^2}\log\frac{AC}{AB} - \tfrac{1}{6}\frac{BC^2}{AB^2}\log\frac{AC}{BC}$$
$$+ \tfrac{2}{3}\frac{AB}{BC}B\hat{A}C + \tfrac{2}{3}\frac{BC}{AB}A\hat{C}B - \tfrac{25}{12}.$$

When the rectangle is a square, whose side $= a$,

$$\log R = \log a + \tfrac{1}{3}\log 2 + \frac{\pi}{3} - \tfrac{25}{12}$$
$$= \log a - 0{\cdot}8050866,$$
$$R = 0{\cdot}44705\,a.$$

(7) The geometric mean distance of a circular line of radius a, from a point in its plane at a distance r from the centre, is r if the point be without the circle, and a if the point be within the circle.

(8) The geometric mean distance of any figure from a circle which completely encloses it is equal to the radius of the circle. The geometric mean distance of any figure from the annular space between two concentric circles, both of which completely enclose it, is R, where

$$(a_1^2 - a_2^2)(\log R + \tfrac{1}{2}) = a_1^2 \log a_1 - a_2^2 \log a_2,$$

a_1 being the radius of the outer circle, and a_2 that of the inner. The geometric mean distance of any figure from a circle or an annular space between two concentric circles, the figure being completely external to the outer circle, is the geometric mean distance of the figure from the centre of the circle.

(9) The geometric mean distance of all the points of the annular space between two concentric circles from each other is R, where

$$(a_1^2 - a_2^2)^2 (\log R - \log a_1) = \tfrac{1}{4}(3a_2^2 - a_1^2)(a_1^2 - a_2^2) - a_2^4 \log \frac{a_1}{a_2}.$$

When a_2, the radius of the inner circle, vanishes, we find

$$R = ae^{-\frac{1}{4}}.$$

When a_2, the radius of the inner circle, becomes nearly equal to a_1, that of the outer circle,

$$R = a_1.$$

As an example of the application of this method, let us take the case of a coil of wire, in which the wires are arranged so that the transverse section of the coil exhibits the sections of the wires arranged in square order, the distance between two consecutive wires being D, and the diameter of each wire d.

Let the whole section of the coil be of dimensions which are small compared with the radius of curvature of the wires, and let the geometrical mean distance of the section from itself be R.

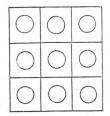

Let it be required to find the coefficient of induction of this coil on itself, the number of windings being n.

1st. If we begin by supposing that the wires fill up the whole section of the coil, without any interval of insulating matter, then if M is the coefficient of induction of a linear circuit of the same shape as the coil on a similar parallel circuit at a distance R, the coefficient of induction of the coil on itself will be

$$n^2 M.$$

2nd. The current, however, is not uniformly distributed over the section. It is confined to the wires. Now the coefficient of self-induction of a unit of length of a conductor is

$$C - 2 \log R,$$

where C is a constant depending on the form of the axis of the conductor, and R is the mean geometric distance of the section from itself.

Now for a square of side D,

$$\log R_1 = \log D + \tfrac{1}{3} \log 2 + \frac{\pi}{3} - \tfrac{25}{12},$$

and for a circle of diameter d

$$\log R_2 = \log d - \log 2 - \tfrac{1}{4}.$$

Hence
$$\log \frac{R_1}{R_2} = \log \frac{D}{d} + \tfrac{4}{3} \log 2 + \frac{\pi}{3} - \tfrac{11}{6},$$

and the coefficient of self-induction of the cylindric wire exceeds that of the square wire by

$$2 \left\{ \log \frac{D}{d} + 0 \cdot 1380606 \right\}$$

per unit of length.

3rd. We must also compare the mutual induction between the cylindric wire and the other cylindric wires next it with that between the square wire and the neighbouring square wires. The geometric mean distance of two squares side by side is to the distance of their centres of gravity as $0 \cdot 99401$ is to unity.

The geometric mean distance of two squares placed corner to corner is to the distance between their centres of gravity as $1 \cdot 0011$ is to unity.

Hence the correction for the eight wires nearest to the wire considered is

$$- 2 \times (0 \cdot 01971).$$

The correction for the wires at a greater distance is less than one-thousandth per unit of length.

The total self-induction of the coil is therefore

$$n^2 M + 2l \left\{ \log \frac{D}{d} + 0.11835 \right\},$$

where n is the number of windings, and l the length of wire.

For a circular coil of radius $= a$,

$$M = 4\pi a \left(\log 8a - \log R - 2 \right),$$

where R is the geometrical mean distance of the section of the coil from itself.

[From the *Proceedings of the Royal Society*, No. 132, 1872.]

XLIX. *On the Induction of Electric Currents in an Infinite Plane Sheet of Uniform Conductivity.*

1. WHEN, on account of the motion or the change of strength of any magnet or electro-magnet, a change takes place in the magnetic field, electro-motive forces are called into play, and, if the material in which they act is a conductor, electric currents are produced. This is the phenomenon of the induction of electric currents, discovered by Faraday.

I propose to investigate the case in which the conducting substance is in the form of a thin stratum or sheet, bounded by parallel planes, and of indefinite extent. A system of magnets or electro-magnets is supposed to exist on the positive side of this sheet, and to vary in any way by changing its position or its intensity. We have to determine the nature of the currents induced in the sheet, and their magnetic effect at any point, and, in particular, their reaction on the electro-magnetic system which gave rise to them. The induced currents are due, partly to the direct action of the external system, and partly to their mutual inductive action; so that the problem appears, at first sight, somewhat difficult.

2. The result of the investigation, however, may be presented in a remarkably simple form, by the aid of the principle of images which was first applied to problems in electricity and hydrokinetics by Sir W. Thomson. The essential part of this principle is, that we conceive the state of things on the positive side of a certain closed or infinite surface (which is really caused by actions having their seat on that surface) to be due to an imaginary system on the negative side of the surface, which, if it existed, and if the action of the

surface were abolished, would give rise to the actual state of things in the space on the positive side of the surface.

The state of things on the positive side of the surface is expressed by a mathematical function, which is different in form from that which expresses the state of things on the negative side, but which is identical with that which would be due to the existence, on the negative side, of a certain system which is called the Image.

The image, therefore, is what we should arrive at by *producing*, as it were, the mathematical function as far as it will go; just as, in optics, the virtual image is found by producing the rays, in straight lines, backwards from the place where their direction has been altered by reflexion or refraction.

3. The position of the image of a point in a plane surface is found by drawing a perpendicular from the point to the surface and producing it to an equal distance on the other side of the surface. If the image is of the same sign as the point, as it is in hydrokinetics when the surface is a rigid plane, it is called a positive image. If it is of the opposite sign, as in statical electricity, when the surface is a conductor, it is called a negative image. The image of a conducting circuit is reckoned positive when the electric current flows in the corresponding directions through corresponding parts of the object and the image. The image is reckoned negative when the direction of the current is reversed.

In the case of the plane conducting sheet, the imaginary system on the negative side of the sheet is not the simple image, positive or negative, of the real magnet or electro-magnet on the positive side, but consists of a moving train of images, the nature of which we now proceed to define.

4. Let the electric resistance of a rectangular portion of the sheet whose length is a, and whose breadth is $2\pi a$, be R.

R is to be measured on the electro-magnetic system, and is therefore a velocity, the value of which is independent of the magnitude of the line a. [If ρ denotes the specific resistance of the material of the sheet for a unit cube, and if c is the thickness of the sheet, then $R = \dfrac{\rho}{2\pi c}$; and if σ denotes the specific resistance of the sheet for a unit (or any other) square, $R = \dfrac{\sigma}{2\pi}$.]

5. Let us begin by dividing the time into a number of equal intervals, each equal to δt. The smaller we take these intervals the more accurate will be the definition of the train of images which we shall now describe.

6. At a given time t, let a positive image of the magnet or electro-magnet be formed on the negative side of the sheet.

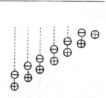

As soon as it is formed, let this image begin to move away from the sheet in the direction of the normal, with the velocity R, its form and intensity remaining constantly the same as that which the magnet had at the time t.

After an interval δt, that is to say, at the time $t + \delta t$, let a negative image, equal in magnitude and opposite in sign to this positive image, be formed in the original position of the positive image, and let it then begin to move along the normal, after the positive image, with the velocity R. The interval of time between the arrival of these images at any point will be δt, and the distance between corresponding points will be $R\delta t$.

7. Leaving this pair of images to pursue their endless journey, let us attend to the real magnet, or electro-magnet, as it is at the time $t + \delta t$. At this instant let a new positive image be formed of the magnet in its new position, and let this image also travel in the direction of the normal with the velocity R, and be followed after an interval of time δt by a corresponding negative image. Let these operations be repeated at equal intervals of time, each of these intervals being equal to δt.

8. Thus at any given instant there will be a train or trail of images, beginning with a single positive image, and followed by an endless succession of pairs of images. This trail, when once formed, continues unchangeable in form and intensity, and moves as a whole away from the conducting sheet with the constant velocity R.

9. If we now suppose the interval of time δt to be diminished without limit, and the train to be extended without limit in the negative direction, so as to include all the images which have been formed in all past time, the magnetic effect of this imaginary train at any point on the positive side of the

conducting sheet will be identical with that of the electric currents which actually exist in the sheet.

Before proceeding to prove this statement, let us take notice of the form which it assumes in certain cases.

10. Let us suppose the real system to be an electro-magnet, and that its intensity, originally zero, suddenly becomes I, and then remains constant. At this instant a positive image is formed, which begins to travel along the normal with velocity R. After an interval δt another positive image is formed; but at the same instant a second negative image is formed at the same place, which exactly neutralizes its effect. Hence the result is, that a single positive image travels by itself along the normal with velocity R. The magnetic effect of this image on the positive side of the sheet is equivalent to that of the currents of induction actually existing in the sheet, and the diminution of this effect, as the image moves away from the sheet, accurately represents the effect of the currents of induction, which gradually decay on account of the resistance of the sheet. After a sufficient time, the image is so distant that its effects are no longer sensible on the positive side of the sheet. If the current of the electro-magnet be now broken, there will be no more images; but the last negative image of the train will be left unneutralized, and will move away from the sheet with velocity R. The currents in the sheet will therefore be of the same magnitude as those which followed the excitement of the electro-magnet, but in the opposite direction.

11. It appears from this that, when the electro-magnet is increasing in intensity, it will be acted on by a repulsive force from the sheet, and when its intensity is diminishing, it will be attracted towards the sheet.

It also appears that if any system of currents is produced in the sheet and then left to itself, the effect of the decay of the currents, as observed at a point on the positive side of the sheet, will be the same as if the sheet, with its currents remaining constant, had been carried away in the negative direction with velocity R.

12. If a magnetic pole of strength m is brought from an infinite distance along a normal to the sheet with a uniform velocity v towards the sheet, it will be repelled with a force

$$\frac{m^2}{4z^2} \frac{v}{R+v},$$

where z is the distance from the sheet at the given instant.

This formula will not apply to the case of the pole moving away from the sheet, because in that case we must take account of the currents which are excited when the pole begins to move, which it does when near the sheet.

13. If the magnetic pole moves in a straight line parallel to the sheet, with uniform velocity v, it will be acted on by a force in the opposite direction to its motion, and equal to

$$\frac{m^2}{4z^2} v \frac{\sqrt{R^2 + v^2} + R - v}{(\sqrt{R^2 + v^2} + R)^2}.$$

Besides this retarding force, it is acted on by a force repelling it from the sheet, equal to

$$\frac{m^2}{4z^2} \frac{v^2}{R^2 + v^2 + R\sqrt{R^2 + v^2}}.$$

14. If the pole moves uniformly in a circle, the trail is in the form of a helix, and the calculation of its effect is more difficult; it is easy, however, to see that, besides the retarding force and the repelling force, there is also a force towards the centre of the circle.

15. It is shewn, in my treatise *On Electricity and Magnetism* (Vol. II. Art. 600), that the currents in any system are the same, whether the conducting system or the inducing system be in motion, provided the relative motion is the same. Hence the results already given are directly applicable to the case of Arago's rotating disk, provided the induced currents are not sensibly affected by the limitation arising from the edge of the disk. These will introduce other sets of images, which we shall not now investigate.

16. The greater the resistance of the sheet, whether from its thinness or from the low conducting-power of its material, the greater is the velocity R. Hence in most actual cases R is very great compared with v the velocity of the external system, and the trail of images is nearly normal to the sheet, and the induced currents differ little from those which arise from the direct action of the external system (see § 1).

17. If the conductivity of the sheet were infinite, or its resistance zero, R would be zero. The images, once formed, would remain stationary, and all except the last formed positive image would be neutralized. Hence the trail

would be reduced to a single positive image, and the sheet would exert a repulsive force $\frac{m^2}{4z^2}$ on the pole, whether the pole be in motion or at rest.

I need not say that this case does not occur in nature as we know it. Something of the kind is supposed to exist in the interior of molecules in Weber's Theory of Diamagnetism.

Mathematical Investigation.

18. Let the conducting sheet coincide with the plane of xy, and let its thickness be so small that we may neglect the variation of magnetic force at different points of the same normal within its substance, and that, for the same reason, the only currents which can produce sensible effects are those which are parallel to the surface of the sheet.

Current-function.

19. We shall define the currents in the sheet by means of the current-function ϕ. This function expresses the quantity of electricity which, in unit of time, crosses from right to left a curve drawn from a point at infinity to the point P.

This quantity will be the same for any two curves drawn from this point to P, provided no electricity enters or leaves the sheet at any point between these curves. Hence ϕ is a single-valued function of the position of the point P.

The quantity which crosses the element ds of any curve from right to left is

$$\frac{d\phi}{ds}\,ds.$$

By drawing ds first perpendicular to the axis of x, and then perpendicular to the axis of y, we obtain for the components of the electric current in the directions of x and of y respectively

$$u = \frac{d\phi}{dy}, \quad v = -\frac{d\phi}{dx} \dots\dots\dots\dots\dots\dots (1).$$

The curves for which ϕ is constant are called current lines.

20. The annular portion of the sheet included between the current lines ϕ and $\phi + \delta\phi$ is a conducting circuit round which an electric current of strength

$\delta\phi$ is flowing in the positive direction, that is, from x towards y. Such a circuit is equivalent in its magnetic effects to a magnetic shell of strength $\delta\phi$, having the circuit for its edge*.

The whole system of electric currents in the sheet will therefore be equivalent to a complex magnetic shell, consisting of all the simple shells, defined as above, into which it can be divided. The strength of the equivalent complex shell at any point will be ϕ.

We may suppose this shell to consist of two parallel plane sheets of imaginary magnetic matter at a very small distance c, the surface-density being $\dfrac{\phi}{c}$ on the positive sheet, and $-\dfrac{\phi}{c}$ on the negative sheet.

21. To find the magnetic potential due to this complex plane shell at any point not in its substance, let us begin by finding P, the potential at the point (ξ, η, ζ) due to a plane sheet of imaginary magnetic matter whose surface-density is ϕ, and which coincides with the plane of xy. The potential due to the positive sheet whose surface-density is $\dfrac{\phi}{c}$, and which is at a distance $\frac{1}{2}c$ on the positive side of the plane of xy, is

$$\frac{1}{c}\left(P - \tfrac{1}{2}c\,\frac{dP}{d\zeta} + \&\text{c.}\right).$$

That due to the negative sheet, at a distance $\frac{1}{2}c$ on the negative side of the plane of xy is

$$-\frac{1}{c}\left(P + \tfrac{1}{2}c\,\frac{dP}{d\zeta} + \&\text{c.}\right).$$

Hence the magnetic potential of the shell is

$$V = -\frac{dP}{d\zeta} \quad\dotfill (2).$$

This, therefore, is the value of the magnetic potential of the current-sheet at any given point on the positive side of it. Within the sheet there is no magnetic potential, and at any point (ξ, η, $-\zeta$) on the negative side of the sheet the potential is equal and of opposite sign to that at the point (ξ, η, ζ) on the positive side.

---

* W. Thomson, "Mathematical Theory of Magnetism," *Phil. Trans.* 1850.

22. At the positive surface the magnetic potential is

$$V = -\frac{dP}{d\zeta} = 2\pi\phi \dots\dots\dots\dots\dots\dots (3).$$

At the negative surface

$$\frac{dP}{d\zeta} = 2\pi\phi \dots\dots\dots\dots\dots\dots (4).$$

The normal component of magnetic force at the positive surface is

$$\gamma = -\frac{dV}{d\zeta} = \frac{d^2P}{d\zeta^2} \dots\dots\dots\dots\dots\dots(5).$$

In the case of the magnetic shell, the magnetic force is discontinuous at the surface; but in the case of the current-sheet this expression gives the value of γ within the sheet itself, as well as in the space outside.

23. Let F, G, H be the components of the electro-magnetic momentum at any point in the sheet, due to external electro-magnetic action as well as to that of the currents in the sheet, then the electromotive force in the direction of x is

$$-\frac{dF}{dt} - \frac{d\psi}{dx},$$

where ψ is the electric potential*; and by Ohm's law this is equal to σu, where σ is the specific resistance of the sheet.

Hence

$$\sigma u = -\frac{dF}{dt} - \frac{d\psi}{dx}$$

Similarly,

$$\left.\sigma u = -\frac{dG}{dt} - \frac{d\psi}{dy}\right\} \dots\dots\dots\dots\dots (6).$$

Let the external system be such that its magnetic potential is represented by $-\frac{dP_o}{dz}$, then the actual magnetic potential will be

$$V = -\frac{d}{dz}(P_o + P) \dots\dots\dots\dots\dots\dots(7),$$

and

$$F = \frac{d}{dy}(P_o + P), \quad G = -\frac{d}{dx}(P_o + P), \quad H = 0 \dots\dots\dots\dots(8).$$

* "Dynamical Theory of the Electromagnetic Field," *Phil. Trans.* 1865, p. 483.

Hence equations (6) become, by introducing the stream-function ϕ from (1),

$$\left.\begin{array}{l} \sigma \dfrac{d\phi}{dy} = -\dfrac{d^2}{dt\,dy}\,(P_0+P) - \dfrac{d\psi}{dx} \\[2mm] -\sigma \dfrac{d\phi}{dx} = \dfrac{d^2}{dt\,dx}\,(P_0+P) - \dfrac{d\psi}{dy} \end{array}\right\} \dots\dots\dots\dots\dots (9).$$

A solution of these equations is

$$\sigma\phi = -\frac{d}{dt}(P_0+P), \quad \psi = \text{constant} \dots\dots\dots\dots(10).$$

Substituting the value of ϕ in terms of P, as given in equation (4),

$$\frac{\sigma}{2\pi}\frac{dP}{dz} = -\frac{d}{dt}(P_0+P) \dots\dots\dots\dots\dots (11).$$

The quantity $\dfrac{\sigma}{2\pi}$ is evidently a velocity; let us therefore for conciseness call it R, then

$$R\frac{dP}{dz} + \frac{dP}{dt} + \frac{dP_0}{dt} = 0 \dots\dots\dots\dots\dots(12).$$

24. Let P_0' be the value of P_0 at the time $t-\tau$, and at a point on the negative side of the sheet, whose co-ordinates are x, y, $(z-R\tau)$, and let

$$Q = \int_0^\infty P_0'\,d\tau \dots\dots\dots\dots\dots (13).$$

At the upper limit when τ is infinite P_0' vanishes. Hence at the lower limit, when $\tau = 0$ and $P_0' = P_0$, we must have

$$P_0 = \frac{dQ}{dt} + R\frac{dQ}{dz} \dots\dots\dots\dots\dots(14);$$

but by equation (12)

$$\frac{dP_0}{dt} = -\frac{dP}{dt} - R\frac{dP}{dz} \dots\dots\dots\dots\dots (15).$$

Hence the equation will be satisfied if we make

$$P = -\frac{dQ}{dt} = -\frac{d}{dt}\int_0^\infty P_0'\,d\tau \dots\dots\dots\dots (16).$$

25. This, then, is a solution of the problem. Any other solution must differ from this by a system of closed currents, depending on the initial state of the sheet, not due to any external cause, and which therefore must decay

rapidly. Hence, since we assume an eternity of past time, this is the only solution of the problem.

This solution expresses P, a function due to the action of the induced current, in terms of P_0', and through this of P_0, a function of the same kind due to the external magnetic system. By differentiating P and P_0 with respect to z, we obtain the magnetic potential, and by differentiating them with respect to t, we obtain, by equation (10), the current-function. Hence the relation between P and P_0, as expressed by equation (16), is similar to the relation between the external system and its trail of images as expressed in the description of these images in the first part of this paper (§§ 6, 7, 8, 9), which is simply an explanation of the meaning of equation (16) combined with the definition of P_0' in § 24.

NOTE TO THE PRECEDING PAPER.

At the time when this paper was written, I was not able to refer to two papers by Prof. Felici, in Tortolini's *Annali di Scienze* for 1853 and 1854, in which he discusses the induction of currents in solid homogeneous conductors and in a plane conducting sheet, and to two papers by E. Jochmann in Crelle's *Journal* for 1864, and one in Poggendorff's *Annalen* for 1864, on the currents induced in a rotating conductor by a magnet.

Neither of these writers have attempted to take into account the inductive action of the currents on each other, though both have recognised the existence of such an action, and given equations expressing it. M. Felici considers the case of a magnetic pole placed almost in contact with a rotating disk. E. Jochmann solves the case in which the pole is at a finite distance from the plane of the disk. He has also drawn the forms of the current-lines and of the equipotential lines, in the case of a single pole, and in the case of two poles of opposite name at equal distances from the axis of the disk, but on opposite sides of it, and has pointed out why the current-lines are not, as Matteucci at first supposed, perpendicular to the equipotential lines, which he traced experimentally.

I am not aware that the principle of images, as described in the paper presented to the Royal Society, has been previously applied to the phenomena of induced currents, or that the problem of the induction of currents in an infinite plane sheet has been solved, taking into account the mutual induction of these currents, so as to make the solution applicable to a sheet of any degree of conductivity.

The statement in equation (10), that the motion of a magnetic system does not produce differences of potential in the infinite sheet, may appear somewhat strange, since we know that currents may be collected by electrodes touching the sheet at different points. These currents, however, depend entirely on the inductive action on the part of the circuit not included in the sheet; for if the whole circuit lies in the plane of the sheet, but is so arranged as not to interfere with the uniform conductivity of the sheet, there will be no difference of potential in any part of the circuit. This is pointed out by Felici, who shews that when the currents are induced by the instantaneous magnetization of a magnet, these currents are not accompanied with differences of potential in different parts of the sheet.

When the sheet is itself in motion, it appears, from Art. 600 of my treatise *On Electricity and Magnetism*, that the electric potential of any point, as measured by means of the electrodes of a fixed circuit, is

$$\psi = -\left(F \frac{\partial x}{\partial t} + G \frac{\partial y}{\partial t} + H \frac{\partial z}{\partial t} \right),$$

where $\frac{\partial x}{\partial t}$, $\frac{\partial y}{\partial t}$, $\frac{\partial z}{\partial t}$ are the components of the velocity of the part of the sheet to which the electrode is applied.

In the case of a sheet revolving with velocity ω about the axis of z, this becomes

$$\psi = \omega \left(x \frac{dP}{dx} + y \frac{dP}{dy} \right).$$

Note 2.—The velocity R for a copper plate of best quality 1 millimetre in thickness is about 25 metres per second. Hence it is only for *very* small velocities of the apparatus that we can obtain any approximation to the true result by neglecting the mutual induction of the currents.—Feb. 13.

[From the *Proceedings of the London Mathematical Society*, Vol. IV.]

L. *On the Condition that, in the Transformation of any Figure by Curvilinear Co-ordinates in Three Dimensions, every Angle in the new Figure shall be equal to the corresponding Angle in the original Figure.*

[Read May 9th, 1872.]

IN the corresponding problem in two dimensions, the only condition is

$$x + \sqrt{-1}\, y = f(\xi + \sqrt{-1}\, \eta) \quad \dots\dots\dots\dots\dots\dots\dots\dots (1),$$

where x, y are the co-ordinates in one system, and ξ, η in the other.

In three dimensions the solution is more restricted.

Let x, y, z be functions of ξ, η, ζ; then the point in the system x, y, z, for which ξ is constant, will be in a certain surface, and by giving ξ a series of values we obtain a series of such surfaces. There will be two other series of surfaces, corresponding to η and ζ respectively. If in the second system ξ, η, ζ are rectangular co-ordinates, the surfaces corresponding to ξ, η, ζ in the first system will intersect at right angles. The condition of this is

$$\frac{dx}{d\eta}\frac{dx}{d\zeta} + \frac{dy}{d\eta}\frac{dy}{d\zeta} + \frac{dz}{d\eta}\frac{dz}{d\zeta} = 0 \quad \dots\dots\dots\dots\dots\dots (2),$$

with two other equations in ζ and ξ, and ξ and η.

If we now write

$$\left.\begin{aligned}
a^2 &= \left(\frac{dx}{d\xi}\right)^2 + \left(\frac{dy}{d\xi}\right)^2 + \left(\frac{dz}{d\xi}\right)^2 \\
\beta^2 &= \left(\frac{dx}{d\eta}\right)^2 + \left(\frac{dy}{d\eta}\right)^2 + \left(\frac{dz}{d\eta}\right)^2 \\
\gamma^2 &= \left(\frac{dx}{d\zeta}\right)^2 + \left(\frac{dy}{d\zeta}\right)^2 + \left(\frac{dz}{d\zeta}\right)^2
\end{aligned}\right\} \quad \dots\dots\dots\dots\dots\dots (3);$$

38

and $d\xi$ is the intercept of the line ($\eta =$ const., $\zeta =$ const.) cut off between the surfaces ξ and $\xi + d\xi$.

The angle e, at which a line whose co-ordinates are functions of p cuts a line whose co-ordinates are functions of q, is found from the equation

$$\frac{dx}{dp}\frac{dx}{dq} + \frac{dy}{dp}\frac{dy}{dq} + \frac{dz}{dp}\frac{dz}{dq}$$

$$= \cos e \left\{ \left(\frac{dx}{dp}\right)^2 + \left(\frac{dy}{dp}\right)^2 + \left(\frac{dz}{dp}\right)^2 \right\}^{\frac{1}{2}} \left\{ \left(\frac{dx}{dq}\right)^2 + \left(\frac{dy}{dq}\right)^2 + \left(\frac{dz}{dq}\right)^2 \right\}^{\frac{1}{2}} \dots\dots (4).$$

Expressing this in terms of ξ, η, and ζ, it becomes

$$\alpha^2 \frac{d\xi}{dp}\frac{d\xi}{dq} + \beta^2 \frac{d\eta}{dp}\frac{d\eta}{dq} + \gamma^2 \frac{d\zeta}{dp}\frac{d\zeta}{dq}$$

$$= \cos e \left\{ \alpha^2 \left(\frac{d\xi}{dp}\right)^2 + \beta^2 \left(\frac{d\eta}{dp}\right)^2 + \gamma^2 \left(\frac{d\zeta}{dp}\right)^2 \right\}^{\frac{1}{2}} \times \left\{ \alpha^2 \left(\frac{d\xi}{dq}\right)^2 + \beta^2 \left(\frac{d\eta}{dq}\right)^2 + \gamma^2 \left(\frac{d\zeta}{dq}\right)^2 \right\}^{\frac{1}{2}} \dots (5).$$

In order that the angle e, at which these lines intersect in the system (x, y, z), should be always equal to the angle ϵ, at which the corresponding lines in the system (ξ, η, ζ) intersect, it is necessary and sufficient that

$$\alpha = \beta = \gamma \dots\dots\dots\dots\dots\dots\dots(6),$$

for these are the conditions that equations (4) and (5) should be of the same form.

Now consider the quadrilateral $ABCD$, cut off from the surface ($\zeta =$ const.) by the surfaces ξ, $\xi + d\xi$, η, and $\eta + d\eta$.

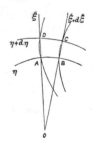

$$AB = \alpha d\xi,$$

$$AD = \beta d\eta,$$

$$CD = \left(\alpha + \frac{d\alpha}{d\eta} d\eta\right) d\xi,$$

$$BC = \left(\beta + \frac{d\beta}{d\xi} d\xi\right) d\eta.$$

Since the three sets of surfaces are orthogonal, their intersections are lines of curvature, by Dupin's Theorem. Hence AB is a line of curvature of the surface η, drawn parallel to α. Hence the normals at A and B will intersect at some point O. Let us call OA, *the radius of curvature of η in the plane of α, $R_{\eta a}$,* then

$$AB : DC :: R_{\eta a} : R_{\eta a} + AD.$$

Hence
$$R_{\eta a} = \frac{\alpha\beta}{\dfrac{d\alpha}{d\eta}}; \quad \text{similarly} \quad R_{\eta\gamma} = \frac{\beta\gamma}{\dfrac{d\gamma}{d\eta}}.$$

These values of the radii of curvature are true for any system of orthogonal surfaces, but since in this case $\alpha = \gamma$, we find

$$R_{\eta a} = R_{\eta\gamma};$$

or the principal radii of curvature of the surface η are equal to each other at every point of the surface. Hence the surfaces η must be spherical.

Since $\alpha = \beta = \gamma$, the other families of surfaces ξ and ζ must also be spherical.

Now take one of the points where three spherical surfaces meet at right angles for the origin, and invert the system. These spheres when inverted become three planes intersecting at right angles, and the other spheres become spheres, each intersecting at right angles two of these planes. Hence their centres lie in the lines of intersection of the planes. Let a, b, c be the distances, from the point of intersection of the three planes, of the centres of spheres belonging each to one of the three systems, and let their radii be p, q, r respectively. Then the conditions that these spheres intersect at right angles

are
$$q^2 + r^2 = b^2 + c^2, \quad r^2 + p^2 = c^2 + a^2, \quad p^2 + q^2 = a^2 + b^2,$$

whence
$$p^2 = a^2, \quad q^2 = b^2, \quad r^2 = c^2;$$

or all the spheres pass through the origin, and each system has a common tangent plane. Hence if we take these three planes as co-ordinate planes, and write

$$x^2 + y^2 + z^2 = r^2,$$
$$\xi^2 + \eta^2 + \zeta^2 = \rho^2;$$

we have $r\rho = R^2$, a constant quantity,

$$\frac{x}{\xi} = \frac{y}{\eta} = \frac{z}{\zeta};$$

whence
$$x = \xi \frac{R^2}{\rho^2}, \quad y = \eta \frac{R^2}{\rho^2}, \quad z = \zeta \frac{R^2}{\rho^2};$$

$$\xi = x \frac{R^2}{r^2}, \quad \eta = y \frac{R^2}{r^2}, \quad \zeta = z \frac{R^2}{r^2};$$

$$\alpha = \beta = \gamma = \frac{R^2}{\rho^2} = \frac{r^2}{R^2} = \frac{r}{\rho}.$$

It appears from this that the only method of transforming a figure of three dimensions, so that every angle in the system shall remain of the same magnitude, is the method of inversion or of reciprocal radii vectores.

[Reference may be made to "Méthodes de Transformation en Géométrie et en Physique mathématique," par J. N. Haton de Goupillière, especially § vii.; *Journal de l'École Polytechnique*, Tom. xxv., p. 188.]

[From *Nature*, Vol. VII.]

LI. *Reprint of Papers on Electrostatics and Magnetism.* By Sir W. Thomson,
D.C.L., LL.D., F.R.S., F.R.S.E., Fellow of St Peter's College, Cambridge,
and Professor of Natural Philosophy in the University of Glasgow. (London:
Macmillan and Co., 1872.)

To obtain any adequate idea of the present state of electro-magnetic science
we must study these papers of Sir W. Thomson's. It is true that a great deal
of admirable work has been done, chiefly by the Germans, both in analytical
calculation and in experimental researches, by methods which are independent
of, or at least different from, those developed in these papers, and it is the
glory of true science that all legitimate methods must lead to the same final
results. But if we are to count the gain to science by the number and value
of the ideas developed in the course of the inquiry, which preserve the results
of former thought in a form capable of being employed in future investigation,
we must place Sir W. Thomson's contributions to electro-magnetic science on
the very highest level.

One of the most valuable of these truly scientific, or *science-forming* ideas,
is that which forms the subject of the first paper in this collection. Two
scientific problems, each of the highest order of difficulty, had hitherto been
considered from quite different points of view. Cavendish and Poisson had
investigated the distribution of electricity on conductors on the hypothesis that
the particles of electricity exert on each other forces which vary inversely as
the square of the distance between them. On the other hand Fourier had
investigated the laws of the steady conduction of heat on the hypothesis that
the flow of heat from the hotter parts of a body to contiguous parts which
are colder is proportional to the rate at which the temperature varies from
point to point of the body. The physical ideas involved in these two problems

are quite different. In the one we have an attraction acting instantaneously at a distance, in the other heat creeping along from hotter to colder parts. The methods of investigation were also different. In the one the force on a given particle of electricity has to be determined as the resultant of the attraction of all the other particles. In the other we have to solve a certain partial differential equation which expresses a relation between the rates of variation of temperature in passing along lines drawn in three different directions through a point. Thomson, in this paper, points out that these two problems, so different, both in their elementary ideas and their analytical methods, are mathematically identical, and that, by a proper substitution of electrical for thermal terms in the original statement, any of Fourier's wonderful methods of solution may be applied to electrical problems. The electrician has only to substitute an electrified surface for the surface through which heat is supplied, and to translate temperature into electric potential, and he may at once take possession of all Fourier's solutions of the problem of the uniform flow of heat.

To render the results obtained in the prosecution of one branch of inquiry available to the students of another is an important service done to science, but it is still more important to introduce into a science a new set of ideas, belonging, as in this case, to what was, till then, considered an entirely unconnected science. This paper of Thomson's, published in February 1842, when he was a very young freshman at Cambridge, first introduced into mathematical science that idea of electrical action carried on by means of a continuous medium which, though it had been announced by Faraday, and used by him as the guiding idea of his researches, had never been appreciated by other men of science, and was supposed by mathematicians to be inconsistent with the laws of electrical action, as established by Coulomb, and built on by Poisson. It was Thomson who pointed out that the ideas employed by Faraday under the names of Induction, Lines of Force, &c., and implying an action transmitted from one part of a medium to another, were not only consistent with the results obtained by the mathematicians, but might be employed in a mathematical form so as to lead to new results. One of these new results, which was, we have reason to believe, obtained by this method, though demonstrated by Thomson by a very elegant adaptation of Newton's method in the theory of attraction, is the "Method of Electrical Images," leading to the "Method of Electrical Inversion."

Poisson had already, by means of Laplace's powerful method of spherical harmonics, determined, in the form of an infinite series, the distribution of electricity on a sphere acted on by an electrified system. No one, however, seems to have observed that when the external electrified system is reduced to a point, the resultant external action is equivalent to that of this point, together with an imaginary electrified point within the sphere, which Thomson calls the *electric image* of the external point.

Now if in an infinite conducting solid heat is flowing outwards uniformly from a very small spherical source, and part of this heat is absorbed at another small spherical surface, which we may call a *sink*, while the rest flows out in all directions through the infinite solid, it is easy, by Fourier's methods, to calculate the stationary temperature at any point in the solid, and to draw the isothermal surfaces. One of these surfaces is a sphere, and if, in the electrical problem, this sphere becomes a conducting surface in connection with the earth, and the external source of heat is transformed into an electrified point, the sink will become the *image* of that point, and the temperature and flow of heat at any point outside the sphere will become the electric potential and resultant force.

Thus Thomson obtained the rigorous solution of electrical problems relating to spheres by the introduction of an imaginary electrified system within the sphere. But this imaginary system itself next became the subject of examination, as the result of the transformation of the external electrified system by reciprocal *radii vectores*. By this method, called that of electrical inversion, the solution of many new problems was obtained by the transformation of problems already solved. A beautiful example of this method is suggested by Thomson in a letter to M. Liouville, dated October 8, 1845, and published in Liouville's *Journal*, for 1845, but which does not seem to have been taken up by any mathematician, till Thomson himself, in a hitherto unpublished paper (No. xv. of the book before us), wrote out the investigation complete. This, the most remarkable problem of electrostatics hitherto solved, relates to the distribution of electricity on a segment of spherical surface, or a *bowl*, as Thomson calls it, under the influence of any electrical forces. The solution includes a very important case of a flat circular dish, and of an infinite flat screen with a circular hole cut out of it.

If, however, the mathematicians were slow in making use of the physical method of electric inversion, they were more ready to appropriate the geometrical idea of inversion by reciprocal *radii vectores*, which is now well known to all geometers, having been, we suppose, discovered and re-discovered repeatedly, though, unless we are mistaken, most of these discoveries are later than 1845, the date of Thomson's paper.

But to return to physical science, we have in No. VII. a paper of even earlier date (1843), in which Thomson shews how the force acting on an electrified body can be exactly accounted for by the diminution of the atmospheric pressure on its electrified surface, this diminution being everywhere proportional to the square of the electrification per unit of area. Now this diminution of pressure is only another name for that *tension* along the lines of electric force, by means of which, in Faraday's opinion, the mutual action between electrified bodies takes place. This short paper, therefore, may be regarded as the germ of that course of speculation by which Maxwell has gradually developed the mathematical significance of Faraday's idea of the physical action of the lines of force.

We have dwelt, perhaps at too great length, on these youthful contributions to science, in order to shew how early in his career, Thomson laid a solid foundation for his future labours, both in the development of mathematical theories and in the prosecution of experimental research. Mathematicians however will do well to take note of the theorem in No. XIII., the applications of which to various branches of science will furnish them, if they be diligent, both occupation and renown for some time to come.

We must now turn to the next part of this volume, in which the mathematical electrician, now established as a Professor at Glasgow, turns his attention to the practical and experimental work of his science. In such work the mathematician, if he succeeds at all, proves himself no mere mathematician, but a thoroughly furnished man of science. And first we have an account of that research into atmospheric electricity which created a demand for electrometers; then a series of electrometers of gradually improving species; and lastly, an admirable report on electrometers and electrostatic measurements, in which the results of many years' experience are given in a most instructive and scientific form. In this report the different instruments are not merely described, but classified, so that the student is furnished with the means of devising a new instrument to suit his own wants. He may also study, in the recorded history of electrometers, the principles of natural selection, the conditions of the permanence of species, the retention of rudimentary organs in manufactured articles, and the tendency to reversion to older types in the absence of scientific control.

A good deal of Sir W. Thomson's practical electrical work is not referred to in this volume. It is to be hoped that he will yet find time to give some account of his many admirable telegraphic contrivances in galvanometers, suspended coils, and recording instruments, and to complete this collection by his papers on electrolysis, measurement of resistance, electric qualities of metals, thermo-electricity, and electro-magnetism in general*.

The second division of the book contains the theory of magnetism.

The first paper, communicated to the Royal Society in 1849 and 1850, is the best introduction to the theory of magnetism that we know of. The discussion of particular distributions of magnetisation is altogether original, and prepares the way for the theory of electro-magnets which follows. This paper on electro-magnets is interesting as having been in manuscript for twenty-three years, during which time a great deal has been done both at home and abroad on the same subject, but without in any degree trenching upon the ground occupied by Thomson in 1847. Though in these papers we find several formidable equations bristling with old English capitals, the reader will do well to observe that the most important results are often obtained without the use of this mathematical apparatus, and are always expressed in plain scientific English.

As regards the most interesting of all subjects, the history of the development of scientific ideas—we know of few statements so full of meaning as the note at p. 419 relating to Ampère's theory of magnetism, as depending on electric currents, flowing in circuits within the molecules of the magnet; he goes on to say: "From twenty to five-and-twenty years ago, when the materials of the present compilation were worked out, I had no belief in the reality of this theory; but I did not then know that motion is the very essence of what has been hitherto called matter. At the 1847 meeting of the British Association in Oxford, I learned from Joule the dynamical theory of heat, and was forced to abandon at once many, and gradually from year to year all other, statical preconceptions regarding the ultimate causes of apparently statical phenomena."

After a short, but sufficient, proof that the magnetic rotation of the plane of polarised light discovered by Faraday implies an actual rotatory motion of something, and that this motion is part of the phenomenon of magnetism, he

---

* [See *Mathematical and Physical Papers*, by Sir W. Thomson, Vol. I., Cambridge University Press, 1882.]

adds: "The explanation of all phenomena of electro-magnetic attraction or repulsion, and of electro-magnetic induction, is to be looked for simply in the inertia and pressure of the matter of which the motions constitute heat. Whether this matter is or is not electricity, whether it is a continuous fluid interpermeating the spaces between molecular nuclei, or is itself molecularly grouped; or whether all matter is continuous, and molecular heterogeneousness consists in finite vortical or other relative motions of contiguous parts of a body; it is impossible to decide, and perhaps in vain to speculate, in the present state of science."

The date of these remarks is 1856. In 1861 and 1862 appeared Maxwell's "theory of molecular vortices applied to magnetism, electricity, &c." which may be considered as a development of Thomson's idea in a form which, though rough and clumsy compared with the realities of nature, may have served its turn as a provisional hypothesis.

The concluding sections of the book before us are devoted to illustrations of magnetic force derived from the motion of a perfect fluid. They are not put forward as *explanations* of magnetic force, for in fact the forces are of the opposite kind to those of magnets. They belong more properly to that remarkable extension of the science of hydrokinetics which was begun by Helmholtz and so ably followed up by Thomson himself.

The conception of a perfectly homogeneous, incompressible frictionless fluid is as essential a part of pure dynamics as that of a circle is of pure geometry. It is true that the motions of ordinary fluids are very imperfect illustrations of those of the perfect fluid. But it is equally true that most of the objects which we are pleased to call circles are very imperfect representations of a true circle.

Neither a perfect fluid nor a perfect circle can be formed from the materials which we deal with, for they are assemblages of molecules, and therefore not homogeneous except when regarded roughly in large masses. The perfect circle is truly continuous and the perfect fluid is truly homogeneous.

It follows, however, from the investigations of Helmholtz and Thomson that if a motion of the kind called *rotational* is once set up in the fluid, the portion of the fluid to which this motion is communicated, retains for ever, during all its wanderings through the fluid mass, the character of the motion thus impressed on it.

This *vortex* then, as Helmholtz calls it, be it large or small, possesses that character of permanence and individuality which we attribute to a material molecule, while at the same time it is capable, while retaining its essential characteristics unchanged both in nature and value, of changing its form in an infinite variety of ways, and of executing the vibrations which excite those rays of the spectrum by which the species of the molecule may be discovered. It would puzzle one of the old-fashioned little round hard molecules to execute vibrations at all. There was no music in those spheres.

But besides this application of hydrokinetics to this new conception of the old atom, there is a vast field of high mathematical inquiry opened up by the papers of Helmholtz and Thomson. It is to be hoped that the latter will soon complete his papers on *Vortex Motion* and give them to the world. But why does no one else work in the same field? Has the multiplication of symbols put a stop to the development of ideas?

[From the *Proceedings of the Cambridge Philosophical Society*, Vol. II., 1876.]

LII. *On the Proof of the Equations of Motion of a Connected System.*

To deduce from the known motions of a system the forces which act on it is the primary aim of the science of Dynamics. The calculation of the motion when the forces are known, though a more difficult operation, is not so important, nor so capable of application to the analytical method of physical science.

The expressions for the forces which act on the system in terms of the motion of the system were first given by Lagrange in the fourth section of the second part of his *Mécanique Analytique.* Lagrange's investigation may be regarded from a mathematical point of view as a method of reducing the dynamical equations, of which there are originally three for every particle of the system, to a number equal to that of the degrees of freedom of the system. In other words it is a method of eliminating certain quantities called reactions from the equations.

The aim of Lagrange was, as he tells us himself, to bring dynamics under the power of the calculus, and therefore he had to express dynamical relations in terms of the corresponding relations of numerical quantities.

In the present day it is necessary for physical inquirers to obtain clear ideas in dynamics that they may be able to study dynamical theories of the physical sciences. We must therefore avail ourselves of the labours of the mathematician, and selecting from his symbols those which correspond to conceivable physical quantities, we must retranslate them into the language of dynamics.

In this way our words will call up the mental image, not of certain operations of the calculus, but of certain characteristics of the motion of bodies.

The nomenclature of dynamics has been greatly developed by those who in recent times have expounded the doctrine of the Conservation of Energy, and it will be seen that most of the following statement is suggested by the investigations in Thomson and Tait's *Natural Philosophy*, especially the method of beginning with the case of impulsive forces.

*I have applied this method in such a way as to get rid of the explicit consideration of the motion of any part of the system except the co-ordinates or variables on which the motion of the whole depends. It is important to the student to be able to trace the way in which the motion of each part is determined by that of the variables, but I think it desirable that the final equations should be obtained independently of this process. That this can be done is evident from the fact that the symbols by which the dependence of the motion of the parts on that of the variables was expressed, are not found in the final equations.

The whole theory of the equations of motion is no doubt familiar to mathematicians. It ought to be so, for it is the most important part of their science in its application to matter. But the importance of these equations does not depend on their being useful in solving problems in dynamics. A higher function which they must discharge is that of presenting to the mind in the clearest and most general form the fundamental principles of dynamical reasoning.

In forming dynamical theories of the physical sciences, it has been a too frequent practice to invent a particular dynamical hypothesis and then by means of the equations of motion to deduce certain results. The agreement of these results with real phenomena has been supposed to furnish a certain amount of evidence in favour of the hypothesis.

The true method of physical reasoning is to begin with the phenomena and to deduce the forces from them by a direct application of the equations of motion. The difficulty of doing so has hitherto been that we arrive, at least during the first stages of the investigation, at results which are so indefinite that we have no terms sufficiently general to express them without introducing some notion not strictly deducible from our premises.

It is therefore very desirable that men of science should invent some method of statement by which ideas, precise so far as they go, may be conveyed to the mind, and yet sufficiently general to avoid the introduction of unwarrantable details.

For instance, such a method of statement is greatly needed in order to express exactly what is known about the undulatory theory of light.

---

* [In the Author's treatise *On Electricity and Magnetism*, Vol. II. Part IV. Chap. V., the reader will find the subject treated at length from the point of view advocated in the text.]

[From the *Proceedings of the Cambridge Philosophical Society*, Vol. II., 1876.]

LIII. *On a Problem in the Calculus of Variations in which the solution is discontinuous.*

THE rider on the third question in the Senate-House paper of Wednesday, January 15, 1½ to 4, was set as an example of discontinuity introduced into a problem in a way somewhat different, I think, from any of those discussed in Mr Todhunter's essay*. In some of Mr Todhunter's cases the discontinuity was involved or its possibility implied in the statement of the problem, as when a curve is precluded from transgressing the boundary of a given region, or where its curvature must not be negative. In the case of figures of revolution considered as generated by a plane curve revolving about a line in its plane, this forms a boundary of the region within which the curve must lie, and therefore often forms part of the curve required for the solution.

In the problem now before us there is no discontinuity in the statement, and it is introduced into the problem by the continuous change of the co-efficients of a certain equation as we pass along the curve. At a certain point the two roots of this equation which satisfy the minimum condition coalesce with each other and with a maximum root. Beyond this point the root which formerly indicated a maximum indicates a minimum, and the other two roots become impossible.

---

* *Researches in the Calculus of Variations, &c.*

[The question referred to was set in 1873, and is as follows :—If the velocity of a carriage along a road is proportional to the cube of the cosine of the inclination of the road to the horizon, determine the path of quickest ascent from the bottom to the top of a hemispherical hill, and shew that it consists of the spherical curve described by a point of a great circle which rolls on a small circle described about the pole with a radius $\frac{\pi}{6}$, together with an arc of a great circle. How is the discontinuity introduced into this problem ?]

[From the *Proceedings of the Royal Institution of Great Britain*, Vol. VII.]

LIV.   *On Action at a Distance.*

I HAVE no new discovery to bring before you this evening. I must ask you to go over very old ground, and to turn your attention to a question which has been raised again and again ever since men began to think.

The question is that of the transmission of force. We see that two bodies at a distance from each other exert a mutual influence on each other's motion. Does this mutual action depend on the existence of some third thing, some medium of communication, occupying the space between the bodies, or do the bodies act on each other immediately, without the intervention of anything else?

The mode in which Faraday was accustomed to look at phenomena of this kind differs from that adopted by many other modern inquirers, and my special aim will be to enable you to place yourselves at Faraday's point of view, and to point out the scientific value of that conception of *lines of force* which, in his hands, became the key to the science of electricity.

When we observe one body acting on another at a distance, before we assume that this action is direct and immediate, we generally inquire whether there is any material connection between the two bodies; and if we find strings, or rods, or mechanism of any kind, capable of accounting for the observed action between the bodies, we prefer to explain the action by means of these intermediate connections, rather than to admit the notion of direct action at a distance.

Thus, when we ring a bell by means of a wire, the successive parts of the wire are first tightened and then moved, till at last the bell is rung at a distance by a process in which all the intermediate particles of the wire have taken part one after the other. We may ring a bell at a distance in other ways, as by forcing air into a long tube, at the other end of which is a cylinder with a piston which is made to fly out and strike the bell. We may also use a wire; but instead of pulling it, we may connect it at one end with a voltaic battery, and at the other with an electro-magnet, and thus ring the bell by electricity.

Here are three different ways of ringing a bell. They all agree, however, in the circumstance that between the ringer and the bell there is an unbroken line of communication, and that at every point of this line some physical process goes on by which the action is transmitted from one end to the other. The process of transmission is not instantaneous, but gradual; so that there is an interval of time after the impulse has been given to one extremity of the line of communication, during which the impulse is on its way, but has not reached the other end.

It is clear, therefore, that in many cases the action between bodies at a distance may be accounted for by a series of actions between each successive pair of a series of bodies which occupy the intermediate space; and it is asked, by the advocates of mediate action, whether, in those cases in which we cannot perceive the intermediate agency, it is not more philosophical to admit the existence of a medium which we cannot at present perceive, than to assert that a body can act at a place where it is not.

To a person ignorant of the properties of air, the transmission of force by means of that invisible medium would appear as unaccountable as any other example of action at a distance, and yet in this case we can explain the whole process, and determine the rate at which the action is passed on from one portion to another of the medium.

Why then should we not admit that the familiar mode of communicating motion by pushing and pulling with our hands is the type and exemplification of all action between bodies, even in cases in which we can observe nothing between the bodies which appears to take part in the action?

Here for instance is a kind of attraction with which Professor Guthrie has made us familiar. A disk is set in vibration, and is then brought near a light suspended body, which immediately begins to move towards the disk, as if drawn towards it by an invisible cord. What is this cord? Sir W. Thomson has pointed out that in a moving fluid the pressure is least where the velocity is greatest. The velocity of the vibratory motion of the air is greatest nearest the disk. Hence the pressure of the air on the suspended body is less on the side nearest the disk than on the opposite side, the body yields to the greater pressure, and moves toward the disk.

The disk, therefore, does not act where it is not. It sets the air next it in motion by pushing it, this motion is communicated to more and more distant portions of the air in turn, and thus the pressures on opposite sides of the suspended body are rendered unequal, and it moves towards the disk in consequence of the excess of pressure. The force is therefore a force of the old school—a case of *vis a tergo*—a shove from behind.

The advocates of the doctrine of action at a distance, however, have not been put to silence by such arguments. What right, say they, have we to assert that a body cannot act where it is not? Do we not see an instance of action at a distance in the case of a magnet, which acts on another magnet not only at a distance, but with the most complete indifference to the nature of the matter which occupies the intervening space? If the action depends on something occupying the space between the two magnets, it cannot surely be a matter of indifference whether this space is filled with air or not, or whether wood, glass, or copper, be placed between the magnets.

Besides this, Newton's law of gravitation, which every astronomical observation only tends to establish more firmly, asserts not only that the heavenly bodies act on one another across immense intervals of space, but that two portions of matter, the one buried a thousand miles deep in the interior of the earth, and the other a hundred thousand miles deep in the body of the sun, act on one another with precisely the same force as if the strata beneath which each is buried had been non-existent. If any medium takes part in transmitting this action, it must surely make some difference whether the space between the bodies contains nothing but this medium, or whether it is occupied by the dense matter of the earth or of the sun.

But the advocates of direct action at a distance are not content with instances of this kind, in which the phenomena, even at first sight, appear to favour their doctrine. They push their operations into the enemy's camp, and maintain that even when the action is apparently the pressure of contiguous portions of matter, the contiguity is only apparent—that a space *always* intervenes between the bodies which act on each other. They assert, in short, that so far from action at a distance being impossible, it is the only kind of action which ever occurs, and that the favourite old *vis a tergo* of the schools has no existence in nature, and exists only in the imagination of schoolmen.

The best way to prove that when one body pushes another it does not touch it, is to measure the distance between them. Here are two glass lenses, one of which is pressed against the other by means of a weight. By means of the electric light we may obtain on the screen an image of the place where the one lens presses against the other. A series of coloured rings is formed on the screen. These rings were first observed and first explained by Newton. The particular colour of any ring depends on the distance between the surfaces of the pieces of glass. Newton formed a table of the colours corresponding to different distances, so that by comparing the colour of any ring with Newton's table, we may ascertain the distance between the surfaces at that ring. The colours are arranged in rings because the surfaces are spherical, and therefore the interval between the surfaces depends on the distance from the line joining the centres of the spheres. The central spot of the rings indicates the place where the lenses are nearest together, and each successive ring corresponds to an increase of about the 4000th part of a millimètre in the distance of the surfaces.

The lenses are now pressed together with a force equal to the weight of an ounce; but there is still a measurable interval between them, even at the place where they are nearest together. They are not in optical contact. To prove this, I apply a greater weight. A new colour appears at the central spot, and the diameters of all the rings increase. This shews that the surfaces are now nearer than at first, but they are not yet in optical contact, for if they were, the central spot would be black. I therefore increase the weights, so as to press the lenses into optical contact.

But what we call optical contact is not real contact. Optical contact indicates only that the distance between the surfaces is much less than a wavelength of light. To shew that the surfaces are not in real contact, I remove the weights. The rings contract, and several of them vanish at the centre. Now it is possible to bring two pieces of glass so close together, that they will not tend to separate at all, but adhere together so firmly, that when torn asunder the glass will break, not at the surface of contact, but at some other place. The glasses must then be many degrees nearer than when in mere optical contact.

Thus we have shewn that bodies begin to press against each other whilst still at a measurable distance, and that even when pressed together with great force they are not in absolute contact, but may be brought nearer still, and that by many degrees.

Why, then, say the advocates of direct action, should we continue to maintain the doctrine, founded only on the rough experience of a pre-scientific age, that matter cannot act where it is not, instead of admitting that all the facts from which our ancestors concluded that contact is essential to action were in reality cases of action at a distance, the distance being too small to be measured by their imperfect means of observation?

If we are ever to discover the laws of nature, we must do so by obtaining the most accurate acquaintance with the facts of nature, and not by dressing up in philosophical language the loose opinions of men who had no knowledge of the facts which throw most light on these laws. And as for those who introduce ætherial, or other media, to account for these actions, without any direct evidence of the existence of such media, or any clear understanding of how the media do their work, and who fill all space three and four times over with æthers of different sorts, why the less these men talk about their philosophical scruples about admitting action at a distance the better.

If the progress of science were regulated by Newton's first law of motion, it would be easy to cultivate opinions in advance of the age. We should only have to compare the science of to-day with that of fifty years ago; and by producing, in the geometrical sense, the line of progress, we should obtain the science of fifty years hence.

The progress of science in Newton's time consisted in getting rid of the celestial machinery with which generations of astronomers had encumbered the heavens, and thus "sweeping cobwebs off the sky."

Though the planets had already got rid of their crystal spheres, they were still swimming in the vortices of Descartes. Magnets were surrounded by effluvia, and electrified bodies by atmospheres, the properties of which resembled in no respect those of ordinary effluvia and atmospheres.

When Newton demonstrated that the force which acts on each of the heavenly bodies depends on its relative position with respect to the other bodies, the new theory met with violent opposition from the advanced philosophers of the day, who described the doctrine of gravitation as a return to the exploded method of explaining everything by occult causes, attractive virtues, and the like.

Newton himself, with that wise moderation which is characteristic of all his speculations, answered that he made no pretence of explaining the mechanism by which the heavenly bodies act on each other. To determine the mode in which their mutual action depends on their relative position was a great step in science, and this step Newton asserted that he had made. To explain the process by which this action is effected was a quite distinct step, and this step Newton, in his *Principia*, does not attempt to make.

But so far was Newton from asserting that bodies really do act on one another at a distance, independently of anything between them, that in a letter to Bentley, which has been quoted by Faraday in this place, he says:—

"It is inconceivable that inanimate brute matter should, without the mediation of something else, which is not material, operate upon and affect other matter without mutual contact, as it must do if gravitation, in the sense of Epicurus, be essential and inherent in it.......That gravity should be innate, inherent, and essential to matter, so that one body can act upon another at a distance, through a vacuum, without the mediation of anything else, by and through which their action and force may be conveyed from one to another, is to me so great an absurdity, that I believe no man who has in philosophical matters a competent faculty of thinking can ever fall into it."

Accordingly, we find in his *Optical Queries,* and in his letters to Boyle, that Newton had very early made the attempt to account for gravitation by means of the pressure of a medium, and that the reason he did not publish these investigations "proceeded from hence only, that he found he was not able, from experiment and observation, to give a satisfactory account of this medium, and the manner of its operation in producing the chief phenomena of nature*."

The doctrine of direct action at a distance cannot claim for its author the discoverer of universal gravitation. It was first asserted by Roger Cotes, in his preface to the *Principia*, which he edited during Newton's life. According to Cotes, it is by experience that we learn that all bodies gravitate. We do not learn in any other way that they are extended, movable, or solid. Gravitation, therefore, has as much right to be considered an essential property of matter as extension, mobility, or impenetrability.

And when the Newtonian philosophy gained ground in Europe, it was the opinion of Cotes rather than that of Newton that became most prevalent, till at last Boscovich propounded his theory, that matter is a congeries of mathematical points, each endowed with the power of attracting or repelling the others according to fixed laws. In his world, matter is unextended, and contact

---

* Maclaurin's *Account of Newton's Discoveries.*

is impossible. He did not forget, however, to endow his mathematical points with inertia. In this some of the modern representatives of his school have thought that he "had not quite got so far as the strict modern view of 'matter' as being but an expression for modes or manifestations of 'force'*."

But if we leave out of account for the present the development of the ideas of science, and confine our attention to the extension of its boundaries, we shall see that it was most essential that Newton's method should be extended to every branch of science to which it was applicable—that we should investigate the forces with which bodies act on each other in the first place, before attempting to explain *how* that force is transmitted. No men could be better fitted to apply themselves exclusively to the first part of the problem, than those who considered the second part quite unnecessary.

Accordingly Cavendish, Coulomb, and Poisson, the founders of the exact sciences of electricity and magnetism, paid no regard to those old notions of "magnetic effluvia" and "electric atmospheres," which had been put forth in the previous century, but turned their undivided attention to the determination of the law of force, according to which electrified and magnetized bodies attract or repel each other. In this way the true laws of these actions were discovered, and this was done by men who never doubted that the action took place at a distance, without the intervention of any medium, and who would have regarded the discovery of such a medium as complicating rather than as explaining the undoubted phenomena of attraction.

We have now arrived at the great discovery by Örsted of the connection between electricity and magnetism. Örsted found that an electric current acts on a magnetic pole, but that it neither attracts it nor repels it, but causes it to move round the current. He expressed this by saying that "the electric conflict acts in a revolving manner."

The most obvious deduction from this new fact was that the action of the current on the magnet is not a push-and-pull force, but a rotatory force, and accordingly many minds were set a-speculating on vortices and streams of æther whirling round the current.

But Ampère, by a combination of mathematical skill with experimental ingenuity, first proved that two electric currents act on one another, and then analysed this action into the resultant of a system of push-and-pull forces between the elementary parts of these currents.

* Review of Mrs Somerville, *Saturday Review*, Feb. 13, 1869.

The formula of Ampère, however, is of extreme complexity, as compared with Newton's law of gravitation, and many attempts have been made to resolve it into something of greater apparent simplicity.

I have no wish to lead you into a discussion of any of these attempts to improve a mathematical formula. Let us turn to the independent method of investigation employed by Faraday in those researches in electricity and magnetism which have made this Institution one of the most venerable shrines of science.

No man ever more conscientiously and systematically laboured to improve all his powers of mind than did Faraday from the very beginning of his scientific career. But whereas the general course of scientific method then consisted in the application of the ideas of mathematics and astronomy to each new investigation in turn, Faraday seems to have had no opportunity of acquiring a technical knowledge of mathematics, and his knowledge of astronomy was mainly derived from books.

Hence, though he had a profound respect for the great discovery of Newton, he regarded the attraction of gravitation as a sort of sacred mystery, which, as he was not an astronomer, he had no right to gainsay or to doubt, his duty being to believe it in the exact form in which it was delivered to him. Such a dead faith was not likely to lead him to explain new phenomena by means of direct attractions.

Besides this, the treatises of Poisson and Ampère are of so technical a form, that to derive any assistance from them the student must have been thoroughly trained in mathematics, and it is very doubtful if such a training can be begun with advantage in mature years.

Thus Faraday, with his penetrating intellect, his devotion to science, and his opportunities for experiments, was debarred from following the course of thought which had led to the achievements of the French philosophers, and was obliged to explain the phenomena to himself by means of a symbolism which he could understand, instead of adopting what had hitherto been the only tongue of the learned.

This new symbolism consisted of those lines of force extending themselves in every direction from electrified and magnetic bodies, which Faraday in his mind's eye saw as distinctly as the solid bodies from which they emanated.

The idea of lines of force and their exhibition by means of iron filings was nothing new. They had been observed repeatedly, and investigated mathematically as an interesting curiosity of science. But let us hear Faraday himself, as he introduces to his reader the method which in his hands became so powerful*.

"It would be a voluntary and unnecessary abandonment of most valuable aid if an experimentalist, who chooses to consider magnetic power as represented by lines of magnetic force, were to deny himself the use of iron filings. By their employment he may make many conditions of the power, even in complicated cases, visible to the eye at once, may trace the varying direction of the lines of force and determine the relative polarity, may observe in which direction the power is increasing or diminishing, and in complex systems may determine the neutral points, or places where there is neither polarity nor power, even when they occur in the midst of powerful magnets. By their use probable results may be seen at once, and many a valuable suggestion gained for future leading experiments."

Experiment on Lines of Force.

In this experiment each filing becomes a little magnet. The poles of opposite names belonging to different filings attract each other and stick together, and more filings attach themselves to the exposed poles, that is, to the ends of the row of filings. In this way the filings, instead of forming a confused system of dots over the paper, draw together, filing to filing, till long fibres of filings are formed, which indicate by their direction the lines of force in every part of the field.

The mathematicians saw in this experiment nothing but a method of exhibiting at one view the direction in different places of the resultant of two forces, one directed to each pole of the magnet; a somewhat complicated result of the simple law of force.

But Faraday, by a series of steps as remarkable for their geometrical definiteness as for their speculative ingenuity, imparted to his conception of these lines of force a clearness and precision far in advance of that with which the mathematicians could then invest their own formulæ.

In the first place, Faraday's lines of force are not to be considered merely as individuals, but as forming a system, drawn in space in a definite manner

* *Exp. Res.* 3284.

so that the number of the lines which pass through an area, say of one square inch, indicates the intensity of the force acting through the area. Thus the lines of force become definite in number. The strength of a magnetic pole is measured by the number of lines which proceed from it; the electro-tonic state of a circuit is measured by the number of lines which pass through it.

In the second place, each individual line has a continuous existence in space and time. When a piece of steel becomes a magnet, or when an electric current begins to flow, the lines of force do not start into existence each in its own place, but as the strength increases new lines are developed within the magnet or current, and gradually grow outwards, so that the whole system expands from within, like Newton's rings in our former experiment. Thus every line of force preserves its identity during the whole course of its existence, though its shape and size may be altered to any extent.

I have no time to describe the methods by which every question relating to the forces acting on magnets or on currents, or to the induction of currents in conducting circuits, may be solved by the consideration of Faraday's lines of force. In this place they can never be forgotten. By means of this new symbolism, Faraday defined with mathematical precision the whole theory of electro-magnetism, in language free from mathematical technicalities, and applicable to the most complicated as well as the simplest cases. But Faraday did not stop here. He went on from the conception of geometrical lines of force to that of physical lines of force. He observed that the motion which the magnetic or electric force tends to produce is invariably such as to shorten the lines of force and to allow them to spread out laterally from each other. He thus perceived in the medium a state of stress, consisting of a tension, like that of a rope, in the direction of the lines of force, combined with a pressure in all directions at right angles to them.

This is quite a new conception of action at a distance, reducing it to a phenomenon of the same kind as that action at a distance which is exerted by means of the tension of ropes and the pressure of rods. When the muscles of our bodies are excited by that stimulus which we are able in some unknown way to apply to them, the fibres tend to shorten themselves and at the same time to expand laterally. A state of stress is produced in the muscle, and the limb moves. This explanation of muscular action is by no means complete. It gives no account of the cause of the excitement of the state of stress, nor does it even investigate those forces of cohesion which enable the muscles to support this stress. Nevertheless, the simple fact, that it substitutes a kind of action which extends continuously along a material substance for one of which we know only a cause and an effect at a distance from each other, induces us to accept it as a real addition to our knowledge of animal mechanics.

For similar reasons we may regard Faraday's conception of a state of stress in the electro-magnetic field as a method of explaining action at a distance by means of the continuous transmission of force, even though we do not know how the state of stress is produced.

But one of Faraday's most pregnant discoveries, that of the magnetic rotation of polarised light, enables us to proceed a step farther. The phenomenon, when analysed into its simplest elements, may be described thus :— Of two circularly polarised rays of light, precisely similar in configuration, but rotating in opposite directions, that ray is propagated with the greater velocity which rotates in the same direction as the electricity of the magnetizing current.

It follows from this, as Sir W. Thomson has shewn by strict dynamical reasoning, that the medium when under the action of magnetic force must be in a state of rotation—that is to say, that small portions of the medium, which we may call molecular vortices, are rotating, each on its own axis, the direction of this axis being that of the magnetic force.

Here, then, we have an explanation of the tendency of the lines of magnetic force to spread out laterally and to shorten themselves. It arises from the centrifugal force of the molecular vortices.

The mode in which electromotive force acts in starting and stopping the vortices is more abstruse, though it is of course consistent with dynamical principles.

We have thus found that there are several different kinds of work to be done by the electro-magnetic medium if it exists. We have also seen that magnetism has an intimate relation to light, and we know that there is a theory of light which supposes it to consist of the vibrations of a medium. How is this luminiferous medium related to our electro-magnetic medium ?

It fortunately happens that electro-magnetic measurements have been made from which we can calculate by dynamical principles the velocity of progagation of small magnetic disturbances in the supposed electro-magnetic medium.

This velocity is very great, from 288 to 314 millions of metres per second, according to different experiments. Now the velocity of light, according to

Foucault's experiments, is 298 millions of metres per second. In fact, the different determinations of either velocity differ from each other more than the estimated velocity of light does from the estimated velocity of propagation of small electro-magnetic disturbance. But if the luminiferous and the electro-magnetic media occupy the same place, and transmit disturbances with the same velocity, what reason have we to distinguish the one from the other? By considering them as the same, we avoid at least the reproach of filling space twice over with different kinds of æther.

Besides this, the only kind of electro-magnetic disturbances which can be propagated through a non-conducting medium is a disturbance transverse to the direction of propagation, agreeing in this respect with what we know of that disturbance which we call light. Hence, for all we know, light also may be an electro-magnetic disturbance in a non-conducting medium. If we admit this, the electro-magnetic theory of light will agree in every respect with the undulatory theory, and the work of Thomas Young and Fresnel will be established on a firmer basis than ever, when joined with that of Cavendish and Coulomb by the key-stone of the combined sciences of light and electricity—Faraday's great discovery of the electro-magnetic rotation of light.

The vast interplanetary and interstellar regions will no longer be regarded as waste places in the universe, which the Creator has not seen fit to fill with the symbols of the manifold order of His kingdom. We shall find them to be already full of this wonderful medium; so full, that no human power can remove it from the smallest portion of space, or produce the slightest flaw in its infinite continuity. It extends unbroken from star to star; and when a molecule of hydrogen vibrates in the dog-star, the medium receives the impulses of these vibrations; and after carrying them in its immense bosom for three years, delivers them in due course, regular order, and full tale into the spectroscope of Mr Huggins, at Tulse Hill.

But the medium has other functions and operations besides bearing light from man to man, and from world to world, and giving evidence of the absolute unity of the metric system of the universe. Its minute parts may have rotatory as well as vibratory motions, and the axes of rotation form those lines of magnetic force which extend in unbroken continuity into regions which no eye has seen, and which, by their action on our magnets, are telling us in language not yet interpreted, what is going on in the hidden underworld from minute to minute and from century to century.

And these lines must not be regarded as mere mathematical abstractions. They are the directions in which the medium is exerting a tension like that of a rope, or rather, like that of our own muscles. The tension of the medium in the direction of the earth's magnetic force is in this country one grain weight on eight square feet. In some of Dr Joule's experiments, the medium has exerted a tension of 200 lbs. weight per square inch.

But the medium, in virtue of the very same elasticity by which it is able to transmit the undulations of light, is also able to act as a spring. When properly wound up, it exerts a tension, different from the magnetic tension, by which it draws oppositely electrified bodies together, produces effects through the length of telegraph wires, and when of sufficient intensity, leads to the rupture and explosion called lightning.

These are some of the already discovered properties of that which has often been called vacuum, or nothing at all. They enable us to resolve several kinds of action at a distance into actions between contiguous parts of a continuous substance. Whether this resolution is of the nature of explication or complication, I must leave to the metaphysicians.

[From *Nature*, Vol. VII.]

LV. *Elements of Natural Philosophy.* By Professors Sir W. Thomson and P. G. Tait. Clarendon Press Series. (Macmillan and Co., 1873.)

NATURAL Philosophy, which is the good old English name for what is now called Physical Science, has been long taught in two very different ways. One method is to begin by giving the student a thorough training in pure mathematics, so that when dynamical relations are afterwards presented to him in the form of mathematical equations, he at once appreciates the language, if not the ideas, of the new subject. The progress of science, according to this method, consists in bringing the different branches of science in succession under the power of the calculus. When this has been done for any particular science, it becomes in the estimation of the mathematician like an Alpine peak which has been scaled, retaining little to reward original explorers, though perhaps still of some use, as furnishing occupation to professional guides.

The other method of diffusing physical science is to render the senses familiar with physical phenomena, and the ear with the language of science, till the student becomes at length able both to perform and to describe experiments of his own. The investigator of this type is in no danger of having no more worlds to conquer, for he can always go back to his former measurements, and carry them forward to another place of decimals.

Each of these types of men of science is of service in the great work of subduing the earth to our use, but neither of them can fully accomplish the still greater work of strengthening their reason and developing new powers of thought. The pure mathematician endeavours to transfer the actual effort of thought from the natural phenomena to the symbols of his equations, and the pure experimentalist is apt to spend so much of his mental energy on matters of detail and calculation, that he has hardly any left for the higher forms of thought. Both of them are allowing themselves to acquire an unfruitful familiarity with the facts of nature, without taking advantage of the opportunity of awakening those powers of thought which each fresh revelation of nature is fitted to call forth.

There is, however, a third method of cultivating physical science, in which each department in turn is regarded, not merely as a collection of facts to be co-ordinated by means of the formulæ laid up in store by the pure mathematicians, but as itself a new mathesis by which new ideas may be developed.

Every science must have its fundamental ideas—modes of thought by which the process of our minds is brought into the most complete harmony with the process of nature—and these ideas have not attained their most perfect form as long as they are clothed with the imagery, not of the phenomena of the science itself, but of the machinery with which mathematicians have been accustomed to work problems about pure quantities.

Poinsôt has pointed out several of his dynamical investigations as instances of the advantage of keeping before the mind the things themselves rather than arbitrary symbols of them ; and the mastery which Gauss displayed over every subject which he handled is, as he said himself, due to the fact that he never allowed himself to make a single step, without forming a distinct idea of the result of that step.

The book before us shews that the Professors of Natural Philosophy at Glasgow and Edinburgh have adopted this third method of diffusing physical science. It appears from their preface that it has been since 1863 a text-book in their classes, and that it is designed for use in schools and in the junior classes in Universities. The book is therefore primarily intended for students whose mathematical training has not been carried beyond the most elementary stage.

The matter of the book however bears but small resemblance to that of the treatises usually put into the hands of such students. We are very soon introduced to the combination of harmonic motions, to irrotational strains, to Hamilton's characteristic function, &c., and in every case the reasoning is conducted by means of dynamical ideas, and not by making use of the analysis of pure quantity.

The student, if he has the opportunity of continuing his mathematical studies, may do so with greater relish when he is able to see in the mathematical equations the symbols of ideas which have been already presented to his mind in the more vivid colouring of dynamical phenomena. The differential calculus, for example, is at once recognised as the method of reasoning applicable to quantities in a state of continuous change. This is Newton's conception of Fluxions, and all attempts to banish the ideas of time and motion from the mind must fail, since continuity cannot be conceived by us except by following in imagination the course of a point which continues to exist while it moves in space.

The arrangement of the book differs from that which has hitherto been adopted in text-books. It has been usual to begin with those parts of the subject in which the idea of change, though implicitly involved in the very conception of force, is not explicitly developed so as to bring into view the different configurations successively assumed by the system. For this reason, the first place has generally been assigned to the doctrine of the equilibrium of forces and the equivalence of systems of forces. The science of pure statics, as thus set forth, is conversant with the relations of forces and of systems of forces to each other, and takes no account of the nature of the material systems to which they may be applied, or whether these systems are at rest or in motion. The concrete illustrations usually given relate to systems of forces in equilibrium, acting on bodies at rest, but the equilibrium of the forces is established by reasoning which has nothing to do with the nature of the body, or with its being at rest.

The practical reason for beginning with statics seems to be that the student is not supposed capable of following the changes of configuration which take place in moving systems. He is expected, however, to be able to follow trains of reasoning about forces, the idea of which can never be acquired apart from that of motion, and which can only be thought of apart from motion by a process of abstraction.

Professors Thomson and Tait, on the contrary, begin with kinematics, the science of mere motion considered apart from the nature of the moving body and the causes which produce its motion. This science differs from geometry only by the explicit introduction of the idea of time as a measurable quantity. (The idea of time as a mere sequence of ideas is as necessary in geometry as in every other department of thought.) Hence kinematics, as involving the smallest number of fundamental ideas, has a metaphysical precedence over statics, which involves the idea of force, which in its turn implies the idea of matter as well as that of motion.

In kinematics, the conception of displacement comes before that of velocity, which is the rate of displacement. And here we cannot but regret that the authors, one of whom at least is an ardent disciple of Hamilton, have not at once pointed out that every displacement is a vector, and taken the opportunity of explaining the addition of vectors as a process, which, applied primarily to displacements, is equally applicable to velocities, or the rates of change of displacement, and to accelerations, or the rates of change of velocities. For it is only in this way that the method of Newton, to which we are glad to see that our authors have reverted, can be fully understood, and the "parallelogram of forces" deduced from the "parallelogram of velocities." Another conception of Hamilton's, however, that of the hodograph, is early introduced and employed with great effect. The fundamental idea of the hodograph is the same as that of vectors in general. The velocity of a body, being a vector, is defined by its magnitude and direction, so that velocities may be represented by straight lines, and these straight lines may be moved parallel to themselves into whatever position is most suitable for exhibiting their geometrical relations, as for instance in the hodograph they are all drawn from one point. The same idea is made use of in the theorems of the "triangle" and the "polygon" of forces, and in the more general method of "diagrams of stress," in which the lines which represent the stresses are drawn, not in the positions in which they actually exist, but in those positions which most fully exhibit their geometrical relations. We are sorry that a certain amount of slight is thrown on these methods in § 411, where a different proposition is called the *true* triangle of forces.

It is when a writer proceeds to set forth the first principle of dynamics that his true character as a sound thinker or otherwise becomes conspicuous. And here we are glad to see that the authors follow Newton, whose Leges Motûs, more perhaps than any other part of his great work, exhibit the unimproveable completeness of that mind without a flaw.

We would particularly recommend to writers on philosophy, first to deduce from the best philosophical data at their command a definition of equal intervals of time, and then to turn to § 212, where such a definition is given as a logical conversion of Newton's First Law.

But it is in the exposition of the Third Law, which affirms that the actions between bodies are mutual, that our authors have brought to light a doctrine, which, though clearly stated by Newton, remained unknown to generations of students and commentators, and even when acknowledged by the whole scientific world was not known to be contained in a paragraph of the *Principia* till it was pointed out by our authors in an article on "Energy" in *Good Words*, October 1862.

Our limits forbid us from following the authors as they carry the student through the theories of varying action, kinetic force, electric images, and elastic solids. We can only express our sympathy with the efforts of men, thoroughly conversant with all that mathematicians have achieved, to divest scientific truths of that symbolic language in which the mathematicians have left them, and to clothe them in words, developed by legitimate methods from our mother tongue, but rendered precise by clear definitions, and familiar by well-rounded statements.

Mathematicians may flatter themselves that they possess new ideas which mere human language is as yet unable to express. Let them make the effort to express these ideas in appropriate words without the aid of symbols, and if they succeed they will not only lay us laymen under a lasting obligation, but, we venture to say, they will find themselves very much enlightened during the process, and will even be doubtful whether the ideas as expressed in symbols had ever quite found their way out of the equations into their minds.

[From the *Proceedings of the London Mathematical Society*, Vol. IV.]

LVI. *On the Theory of a System of Electrified Conductors, and other Physical Theories involving Homogeneous Quadratic Functions.*

[Read April 10th, 1873.]

THE theory of homogeneous functions of the second degree is useful in several parts of natural philosophy.

The general form of such a function may be written

$$V = \tfrac{1}{2}(A_{11}x_1^2 + 2A_{12}x_1x_2 + \&\text{c.}) \dots\dots\dots\dots\dots\dots(1),$$

or more concisely

$$V_x = \tfrac{1}{2}\sum_{r=1}^{r=n}\sum_{s=1}^{s=n}(A_{rs}x_rx_s) \dots\dots\dots\dots\dots (1^*),$$

in which each term consists of a product of two out of n variables $x_1, \dots x_n$, which may or may not be different, and of a coefficient A_{rs} belonging to that pair of variables.

Differentiating V with respect to each of the n variables in succession, we get n new quantities $\xi_1, \dots \xi_n$ of the form

$$\frac{dV}{dx_r} = \xi_r = \sum_{s=1}^{s=n}(A_{rs}x_s) \dots\dots\dots\dots\dots\dots\dots(2).$$

Multiplying each ξ by its corresponding x, and taking half the sum of the products, we obtain a second expression for V,

$$V = \tfrac{1}{2}\sum_{r=1}^{r=n}(x_r\xi_r) \dots\dots\dots\dots\dots\dots\dots (3).$$

Since each of the n quantities ξ is a linear function of the n variables x, we may, by solving the n equations of the form (2), obtain expressions for each x in terms of the ξ's

$$x_s = \sum_{r=1}^{r=n}(a_{sr}\xi_r) \dots\dots\dots\dots\dots\dots\dots\dots(4);$$

and by substituting these values of the x's in (3), we obtain a third expression for V,

$$V_\xi = \tfrac{1}{2} \sum_{s=1}^{s=n} \sum_{r=1}^{r=n} (a_{sr} \xi_s \xi_r) \dots\dots\dots\dots\dots\dots\dots\dots(5).$$

The first and last of these expressions for V are distinguished by the suffixes x and ξ, in order to shew that the first is expressed in terms of the variables x and the last in terms of the variables ξ. The coefficients A and a may be functions of any number, m, of variables. Let y_t be one of these variables.

Since V_x, V, and V_ξ are three different expressions for the same quantity,

$$V_x + V_\xi = 2V = \sum_{r=1}^{r=n} (x_r \xi_r) \dots\dots\dots\dots\dots\dots\dots(6).$$

If we now suppose the three sets of variables x, ξ and y to vary in any consistent manner, and remember that V_x is a function of the x's and y's, V_ξ of the ξ's and y's, and V of the x's and ξ's, we find

$$\sum_{r=1}^{r=n} \left\{ \left(\frac{dV_x}{dx_r} - \xi_r \right) \delta x_r \right\} + \sum_{s=1}^{s=n} \left\{ \left(\frac{dV_\xi}{d\xi_s} - x_s \right) \delta \xi_s \right\} + \sum_{t=1}^{t=m} \left\{ \left(\frac{dV_x}{dy_t} + \frac{dV_\xi}{dy_t} \right) \delta y_t \right\} = 0 \dots (7).$$

The three sets of variations δx, $\delta \xi$, and δy are not independent of each other, for if the variations δy and either of the other sets be given, the other set may be determined. Hence we cannot immediately deduce any definite results from this equation. But we know, from equation (2), that the coefficients of the variations δx vanish of themselves, and the remaining variations $\delta \xi$ and δy are all independent of each other, so that we may equate the coefficient of each of them to zero. We thus obtain two sets of equations,

$$x_s = \frac{dV_\xi}{d\xi_s} \dots\dots\dots\dots\dots\dots\dots\dots (8),$$

and

$$\frac{dV_x}{dy_t} + \frac{dV_\xi}{dy_t} = 0 \dots\dots\dots\dots\dots\dots\dots (9).$$

In this purely algebraical theory of quadratic functions, of the two sets of variables x and ξ, either may be taken as the primary set. In the physical applications of the theory, however, the variables form two classes which are not interchangeable.

Thus, in kinetics, the variables are the components of velocity and those of momentum; in the theory of elasticity, they are stresses and strains; in electro-magnetism, they are electric currents and the "electrotonic state" of circuits; and in electrostatics, they are the potentials and the charges of conductors.

Now, if a change takes place in the configuration of the system, by which the energy (whether potential or kinetic) of the system is diminished, while the momenta, the strains, the electrotonic states, or the charges remain constant, the displacement will be aided by a force of such a magnitude that the work done by the force during the displacement is equal to the *diminution* of the energy of the system.

For the momenta, the strains, the electrotonic states, and the charges do not require for their maintenance the application of energy from without the system.

The same change of configuration, if effected under the condition that the velocities, stresses, potentials, or electric currents remain constant, would, by equation (9), *increase* the energy of the system by exactly the same amount as it was diminished in the former case. The work done by the system during the displacement will be the same as before, so that energy must in this case be supplied from without to an amount double of this work, in order to satisfy these new conditions.

For it is only by external compulsion that the velocities of the system can be maintained constant when the configuration changes. Work must be done on an elastic system to keep the stress constant while the strain varies. The currents in a conducting circuit tend to vary when the electrotonic state of the circuit varies, and can only be kept constant by battery power. The same agency must be employed to maintain the potential of a conductor constant during the displacement of the system of conductors.

Hence, when momenta, strains, electrotonic states, or charges are maintained constant, the internal forces of the system tend to produce displacements which would *diminish* the energy of the system.

If, on the other hand, the velocities, stresses, electric currents, or potentials are maintained constant, the internal forces tend to produce displacements which would *increase* the energy of the system.

This distinction between the two sets of physical quantities is of great importance in the theory of classification of such quantities. The characteristic of the first set is inherent persistence. Any persistence which we may observe in the second set is only apparent, and arises from the second set being functions of the first set when the configuration of the system either does not vary or is not such as to cause a variation of the coefficients A and a.

[From the *Proceedings of the London Mathematical Society*, Vol. IV.]

LVII. *On the Focal Lines of a Refracted Pencil.*

[Read April 10th, 1873.]

HAMILTON has shewn, by means of his Characteristic Function, that in whatever manner a pencil may be refracted, the rays always pass through two focal lines, the planes through which and the axis of the pencil are at right angles to each other. The same method leads to the following geometrical construction for finding the focal lines of any thin pencil after refraction through a curved surface, the focal lines of the incident pencil and the nature of the curvature of the surface being given.

1. The characteristic function of a thin pencil whose axis coincides with the axis of z, and whose rays pass through focal lines in the planes of xz and yz at distances a and b from the origin respectively, is for points near the origin

$$V = K + \mu \left(z - \frac{x^2}{2a} - \frac{y^2}{2b} \right) \quad \ldots\ldots\ldots\ldots\ldots\ldots\ldots (1).$$

If we turn this system of rays round the axis of z, through an angle ϕ reckoned from x towards y, the expression for V becomes

$$V = K + \mu \left(z - \frac{x^2}{2A} - \frac{y^2}{2B} - \frac{xy}{2C} \right) \quad \ldots\ldots\ldots\ldots\ldots (2),$$

where

$$\left. \begin{aligned}
\frac{1}{A} &= \frac{1}{a} \cos^2 \phi + \frac{1}{b} \sin^2 \phi \\
\frac{1}{B} &= \frac{1}{a} \sin^2 \phi + \frac{1}{b} \cos^2 \phi \\
\frac{1}{C} &= \left(\frac{1}{a} - \frac{1}{b} \right) \sin 2\phi
\end{aligned} \right\} \quad \ldots\ldots\ldots\ldots\ldots\ldots\ldots (3).$$

If we now turn the system round the axis of y, through an angle θ from z towards x, we find

$$V = K + \mu \left\{ z \cos \theta + x \sin \theta - \frac{x^2 \cos^2 \theta}{2A} - \frac{y^2}{2B} - \frac{xy \cos \theta}{2C} \right.$$
$$\left. - \frac{(2x \cos \theta + z \sin \theta) z \sin \theta}{2A} - \frac{yz \sin \theta}{2C} \right\} \dots \dots (4).$$

2. Now consider two portions of a pencil, close to the origin but in different media, whose indices of refraction are μ_1, μ_2 respectively, and let the coefficients belonging to these portions be distinguished by corresponding suffixes ($_1$ and $_2$).

Let the media be separated by the surface whose equation is

$$z = \frac{x^2}{2A} + \frac{y^2}{2B} + \frac{xy}{2C} \dots \dots \dots (5).$$

Then, since the characteristic function is continuous at this surface, we have the condition $V_1 - V_2 = 0$ when z has the value given in (5).

Substituting this value of z in the expressions for V_1 and V_2, and neglecting terms of the third degree in x and y, we obtain

$$\left(\frac{x^2}{2A} + \frac{y^2}{2B} + \frac{xy}{2C} \right) (\mu_1 \cos \theta_1 - \mu_2 \cos \theta_2) + x (\mu_1 \sin \theta_1 - \mu_2 \sin \theta_2)$$
$$- \mu_1 \left(\frac{x^2 \cos^2 \theta_1}{2A_1} + \frac{y^2}{2B_1} + \frac{xy \cos \theta_1}{2C_1} \right) + \mu_2 \left(\frac{x^2 \cos^2 \theta_2}{2A_2} + \frac{y^2}{2B_2} + \frac{xy \cos \theta_2}{2C_2} \right) = 0 \dots (6).$$

That the term in x may vanish, we must have

$$\mu_1 \sin \theta_1 = \mu_2 \sin \theta_2 \dots \dots \dots \dots (7),$$

the ordinary law of refraction.

Equating to zero the coefficients of x^2, y^2, and xy, we find

$$\frac{\cos^2 \theta_1}{A_1 \sin \theta_1} - \frac{\cos^2 \theta_2}{A_2 \sin \theta_2} = \frac{1}{A} (\cot \theta_1 - \cot \theta_2) \dots \dots \dots (8),$$

$$\frac{1}{B_1 \sin \theta_1} - \frac{1}{B_2 \sin \theta_2} = \frac{1}{B} (\cot \theta_1 - \cot \theta_2) \dots \dots \dots (9),$$

$$\frac{\cot \theta_1}{C_1} - \frac{\cot \theta_2}{C_2} = \frac{1}{C} (\cot \theta_1 - \cot \theta_2) \dots \dots \dots (10).$$

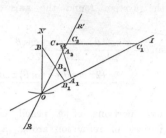

3. These relations of the quantities A, B, C may be found by the following construction :—

Let IO be the incident and OR the refracted ray, and let ON be the normal to the surface; $NOI = \theta_1$, $NOR' = \theta_2$.

Find the points A, B, C, whose co-ordinates are

for A, $x = A\,\dfrac{\cos^2\theta_1 - \cos^2\theta_2}{\cot\theta_1 - \cot\theta_2}$, $z = A\,\dfrac{\cos^2\theta_1\cot\theta_1 - \cos^2\theta_2\cot\theta_2}{\cot\theta_1 - \cot\theta_2}$ .... (11);

for B, $x = 0$, $z = B$ .... (12);

for C, $x = C\,\dfrac{\cos\theta_1 - \cos\theta_2}{\cot\theta_1 - \cot\theta_2}$, $z = C\,\dfrac{\cos\theta_1\cot\theta_1 - \cos\theta_2\cot\theta_2}{\cot\theta_1 - \cot\theta_2}$ ....(13).

The positions of these points depend only on the form of the surface and on the directions of the axes of the incident and refracted pencil. The point B is absolutely fixed, being the centre of curvature of a normal section of the surface perpendicular to the plane of refraction.

Let OA_1, OB_1, OC_1 be the values of A_1, B_1, C_1 for the incident ray. To find the corresponding quantities for the refracted ray, draw the straight lines AA_1, BB_1, CC_1 intersecting the refracted ray in A_2, B_2, C_2. OA_2, OB_2, and OC_2 are the required values of A_2, B_2, C_2.

When any of these quantities becomes infinite, the line must be drawn in a given direction. For A_1, B_1, or C_1 infinite, it must be parallel to the incident ray. For A_2, B_2, or C_2 infinite, it must be parallel to the refracted ray. For B infinite, it must be parallel to the normal; for A infinite, it must make with the normal an angle whose tangent is

$$\frac{\cos^2\theta_1 - \cos^2\theta_2}{\cos^2\theta_1\cot\theta_1 - \cos^2\theta_2\cot\theta_2}\ldots\ldots\ldots\ldots\ldots\ldots\ldots(14);$$

and for C infinite the tangent of the angle must be

$$\frac{\cos \theta_1 - \cos \theta_2}{\cos \theta_1 \cot \theta_1 - \cos \theta_2 \cot \theta_2} \quad \dots\dots\dots\dots\dots\dots(15).$$

If the plane of refraction cuts the surface along a line of curvature, $C = \infty$, and if one of the focal lines of the incident pencil is in the plane of refraction, $C_1 = \infty$. The points A_1, B_1 then coincide with the focal lines of the incident pencil, and A_2, B_2 with those of the refracted pencil.

That A_1 may coincide with B_1, and A_2 with B_2, the line joining both pairs of points must be on the line AB. There is therefore one, and only one, point on the axis of the incident pencil from which a pencil may diverge so that, after refraction, it still diverges from or converges to a single point.

4. When the quantity C has a finite value, the plane of refraction is not a plane of symmetry, and we have to deduce the quantities a, b, ϕ from A, B, C. The following construction enables us to pass from either of these systems to the other :—

Let OA, OB, OC be the values of A, B, C.

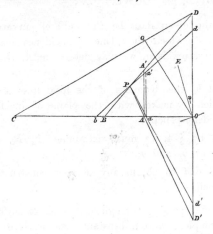

Draw AA' perpendicular and equal to AO. Join BA', and produce to D, a point on the perpendicular to OA through O. Cut off OD' equal to OD, but in the opposite direction. Join $D'A$, and produce to P, where $D'A$ meets BD.

Join CD, and draw OQ perpendicular to CD from O.

Make Od, Od' each equal to OQ. Draw dP, $d'P$ cutting OA in b and a. Bisect the angle DOQ by OE.

Then $Oa = a$, $Ob = b$, and $DOE = \phi$, the angle which the first focal line makes with the plane of xz.

5. If a, b, and ϕ are given, the construction is easily reversed, thus:

Let $Oa = a$, $Ob = b$, and $DOE = \phi$.

Draw aa' perpendicular and equal to aO. Draw ba' cutting OD, the perpendicular to aO from O in d. Cut off Od' equal and opposite to Od. Draw $d'a$ cutting bd in P.

Draw $OQ = Od$ so that the angle $DOE = OEQ$.

Draw CQD perpendicular to OQ, cutting Oa in C and Od in D.

Make OD' equal and opposite to OD. Draw DP, $D'P$ cutting Oa in B and A.

Then $OA = A$, $OB = B$, and $OC = C$.

6. If therefore the given data be the radii of curvature of the refracting surface and the angle, ϕ, which the plane of incidence makes with the principal section whose curvature is a, we may determine A, B, C for the refracting surface.

Then from a_1 and b_1, the distances of the focal lines of the incident pencil, and ϕ_1 the angle which a_1 makes with the plane of incidence, we must find A_1, B_1, C_1 for the incident pencil.

From these data, by § 4, we must determine A_2, B_2, C_2 for the refracted pencil, and from these a_2, b_2, and ϕ_2.

I have not been able to obtain any simpler construction for the general case of a refracted pencil.

7. For a pencil after passing through any series of surfaces the construction is necessarily more complex, as ten constants are involved in the general term of the second degree of the characteristic function, which is of the form

$$V = \tfrac{1}{2}a_1x_1^2 + \tfrac{1}{2}b_1y_1^2 + c_1x_1y_1 + \tfrac{1}{2}a_2x_2^2 + \tfrac{1}{2}b_2y_2^2 + c_2x_2y_2 + px_1x_2 + qx_1y_2 + ry_1x_2 + sy_1y_2;$$

and if
$$V_1 = \tfrac{1}{2} A_1 x_1^2 + \tfrac{1}{2} B_1 y_1^2 + C_1 x_1 y_1,$$

and
$$V_2 = \tfrac{1}{2} A_2 x_2^2 + \tfrac{1}{2} B_2 y_2^2 + C_2 x_2 y_2,$$

and we put
$$D = (A_1 + a_1)(B_1 + b_1) - (C_1 + c_1)^2,$$

$$(A_2 - a_2) D + p^2 (B_1 + b_1) + r^2 (A_1 + a_1) - 2pr (C_1 + c_1) = 0,$$

$$(B_2 - b_2) D + q^2 (B_1 + b_1) + s^2 (A_1 + a_1) - 2qs (C_1 + c_1) = 0,$$

$$(C_2 - c_2) D + pq (B_1 + b_1) + rs (A_1 + a_1) - (ps + qr)(C_1 + c_1) = 0.$$

These equations enable us to determine A_2, B_2, C_2 when A_1, B_1, C_1 are given.

Here we must observe that the quantities A, B, C, &c., do not represent lines, as in the first part of this paper, but the reciprocals of lines.

[From *Nature*, Vol. VIII.]

LVIII. *An Essay on the Mathematical Principles of Physics, &c.* By the Rev. James Challis, M.A., F.R.S., F.R.A.S., Plumian Professor of Astronomy and Experimental Philosophy in the University of Cambridge, and Fellow of Trinity College. (Cambridge : Deighton, Bell, and Co., 1873.)

THIS Essay is a sort of abstract or general account of the mathematical and physical researches on which the author has been so long engaged, portions of which have appeared from time to time in the *Philosophical Magazine,* and also in his larger work on the "Principles of Mathematics and Physics." It is always desirable that mathematical results should be expressed in intelligible language, as well as in the symbolic form in which they were at first obtained, and we have to thank Professor Challis for this Essay, which though, or rather because, it hardly contains a single equation, sets forth his system more clearly than has been done in some of his previous mathematical papers.

The aim of this Essay, and of the author's long-continued labours, is to advance the theoretical study of Physics. He regards the material universe as "a vast and wonderful *mechanism,* of which not the least wonderful quality is, its being so constructed that we can understand it." The Book of Nature, in fact, contains elementary chapters, and, to those who know where to look for them, the mastery of one chapter is a preparation for the study of the next. The discovery of the calculation necessary to determine the acceleration of a particle whose position is given in terms of the time led to the Newtonian epoch of Natural Philosophy. The study from the cultivation of which our author looks for the "inauguration of a new scientific epoch," is that of the motion of fluids, commonly called Hydrodynamics. The scientific method which he recommends is that described by Newton as the "foundation of all philosophy," namely, that the properties which we attribute to the least parts of matter must be consistent with those of which experiments on sensible bodies have made us cognizant.

The world, according to Professor Challis, is made up of atoms and æther. The atoms are spheres, unalterable in magnitude, and endowed with inertia, but with no other property whatever. The æther is a perfect fluid, endowed with inertia, and exerting a pressure proportional to its density. It is truly continuous (and therefore does not consist of atoms), and it fills up all the interstices of the atoms.

Here, then, we have set before us with perfect clearness the two constituents of the universe: the atoms, which we can picture in our minds as so many marbles; and the æther, which behaves exactly as air would do if Boyle's law were strictly accurate, if its temperature were invariable, if it were destitute of viscosity, and if gravity did not act on it.

We have no difficulty, therefore, in forming an adequate conception of the properties of the elements from which we have to construct a world. The hypothesis is at least an honest one. It attributes to the elements of things no properties except those which we can clearly define. It stands, therefore, on a different scientific level from those waxen hypotheses in which the atoms are endowed with a new system of attractive or repulsive forces whenever a new phenomenon has to be explained.

But the task still before us is a herculean one. It is no less than to explain all actions between bodies or parts of bodies, whether in apparent contact or at stellar distances, by the motions of this all-embracing æther, and the pressure thence resulting.

One kind of motion of the æther is evidently a wave-motion, like that of sound-waves in air. How will such waves affect an atom? Will they propel it forward like the driftwood which is flung upon the shore, or will they draw it back like the shingle which is carried out by the returning wave? Or will they make it oscillate about a fixed position without any advance or recession on the whole?.

We have no intention of going through the calculations necessary to solve this problem. They are not contained in this Essay, and Professor Challis admits that he has been unable to determine the absolute amount of the constant term which indicates the permanent effect of the waves on an atom. This is unfortunate, as it gives us no immediate prospect of making those numerical comparisons with observed facts which are necessary for the verification of the theory.   Let us, however, suppose this purely mathematical difficulty surmounted, and let us admit with Professor Challis that if the wave-length of the undulations is very small compared with the diameter of the atom, the atom will be urged in the direction of wave-propagation, or in other words *repelled* from the origin of the waves.   If on the other hand the wave-length is very great compared with the diameter of the atom, the atom will be urged in the direction opposite to that in which the waves travel, that is, it will be *attracted* towards the source of the waves.

The amount of this attraction or repulsion will depend on the mean of the square of the velocity of the periodic motion of the particles of the æther, and since the amplitude of a diverging wave is inversely as the distance from the centre of divergence, the force will be inversely as the square of this distance, according to Newton's law.

We must remember, however, that the problem is only imperfectly solved, as we do not know the absolute value of this force, and we have not yet arrived at an explanation of the fact that the attraction of gravitation is in exact proportion to the mass of the attracted body, whatever be its chemical nature.   (See p. 36.)

Admitting these results, and supposing the great ocean of æther to be traversed by waves, these waves impinge on the atoms, and are reflected in the form of diverging waves.   These, in their turn, beat other atoms, and cause attraction or repulsion, according as their wave-length is great or small.   Thus the waves of shortest period perform the office of repelling atom from atom, and rendering their collision for ever impossible.   Other waves, somewhat longer, bind the atoms together in molecular groups.   Others contribute to the elasticity of bodies of sensible size, while the long waves are the cause of universal gravitation, holding the planets in their courses, and preserving the most ancient heavens in all their freshness and strength.   Then besides the waves of æther, our author contemplates its streams, spiral and otherwise, by which he accounts for electric, magnetic, and galvanic phenomena.

Without pretending to have verified all or any of the calculations on which this theory is based, or to have compared the electric, magnetic, and galvanic phenomena, as described in the Essay, with those actually observed, we may venture to make a few remarks upon the theory of action at a distance here put forth.

The explanation of any action between distant bodies by means of a clearly conceivable process going on in the intervening medium is an achievement of the highest scientific value. Of all such actions, that of gravitation is the most universal and the most mysterious. Whatever theory of the constitution of bodies holds out a prospect of the ultimate explanation of the process by which gravitation is effected, men of science will be found ready to devote the whole remainder of their lives to the development of that theory.

The only theory hitherto put forth as a dynamical theory of gravitation is that of Lesage, who adopts the Lucretian theory of atoms and void.

Gravitation on this theory is accounted for by the impact of atoms of incalculable minuteness, which are flying through the heavens with inconceivable velocity and in every possible direction. These "ultramundane corpuscules" falling on a solitary heavenly body would strike it on every side with equal impetus, and would have no effect upon it in the way of resultant force. If, however, another heavenly body were in existence, each would screen the other from a portion of the corpuscular bombardment, and the two bodies would be attracted to each other. The merits and the defects of this theory have been recently pointed out by Sir W. Thomson. If the corpuscules are perfectly elastic one body cannot protect the other from the storm, for it will reflect exactly as many corpuscules as it intercepts. If they are inelastic, as Lesage supposes, what becomes of them after collision? Why are not bodies always growing by the perpetual accumulation of them? How do they get swept away? and what becomes of their energy? Why do they not volatilise the earth in a few minutes? I shall not enter on Sir W. Thomson's improvement of this theory, as it involves a different kind of hydrodynamics from that cultivated in the Essay, but in whatever way we regard Lesage's theory, the cause of gravitation in the universe can be represented only as depending on an ever fresh supply of something *from without*.

Though Professor Challis has not, as far as we can see, stated in what manner his æthereal waves are originally produced, it would seem that on his theory also the primary waves, by whose action the waves diverging from the atoms are generated, must themselves be propagated from somewhere *outside* the world of stars.

On either theory, therefore, the universe is not even temporarily automatic, but must be fed from moment to moment by an agency external to itself.

If the corpuscules of the one theory, or the æthereal waves of the other, were from any cause to be supplied at a different rate, the value of every force in the universe would suffer change.

On both theories, too, the preservation of the universe is effected only by the unceasing expenditure of enormous quantities of work, so that the conservation of energy in physical operations, which has been the subject of so many measurements, and the study of which has led to so many discoveries, is apparent only, and is merely a kind of "moveable equilibrium" between supply and destruction.

It may seem a sort of anticlimax to descend from these highest heavens of invention down to the "equations of condition" of fluid motion. But it would not be right to pass by the fact that the fluids treated of in this Essay are not in all respects similar to those met with elsewhere. In all their motions they obey a law, which our author was the first to lay down, in addition— or perhaps in some cases in opposition—to those prescribed for them by Lagrange, Poisson, &c.

It is true that a perfect fluid, originally at rest, and afterwards acted on only by such forces as occur in nature, will freely obey this law, and that not only in the form laid down by Professor Challis, in which its rigour is partially relaxed by the introduction of an arbitrary factor, but in its original severe simplicity, as the condition of the existence of a velocity-potential.

But, on the one hand, problems in which the motion is assumed to violate this condition have been solved by Helmholtz and Sir W. Thomson, who tell us what the fluid will then do; and, on the other hand, Professor Challis's fluid is able, in virtue of the new equation, to transmit plane waves consisting of transverse displacements. As this is what takes place in the luminiferous æther, other physicists refuse to regard that æther as a fluid, because, according to their definition, the action between any contiguous portions of a fluid is entirely normal to the surface which separates them.

It is not necessary, however, for us to say any more on this subject, as the Essay before us does not contain, in an explicit form, the equation referred to, but is devoted rather to the exposition of those wider theories of the constitution of matter and the phenomena of nature, some of which we have endeavoured to describe.

[From *Nature*, Vol. VIII.]

LIX. *On Loschmidt's Experiments on Diffusion in relation to the Kinetic Theory of Gases.*

THE kinetic theory asserts that a gas consists of separate molecules, each moving with a velocity amounting, in the case of hydrogen, to 1,800 metres per second. This velocity, however, by no means determines the rate at which a group of molecules set at liberty in one part of a vessel full of the gas will make their way into other parts. In spite of the great velocity of the molecules, the direction of their course is so often altered and reversed by collision with other molecules, that the process of diffusion is comparatively a slow one.

The first experiments from which a rough estimate of the rate of diffusion of one gas through another can be deduced are those of Graham*. Professor Loschmidt, of Vienna, has recently† made a series of most valuable and accurate experiments on the interdiffusion of gases in a vertical tube, from which he has deduced the coefficient of diffusion of ten pairs of gases. These results I consider to be the most valuable hitherto obtained as data for the construction of a molecular theory of gases.

There are two other kinds of diffusion capable of experimental investigation, and from which the same data may be derived, but in both cases the experimental methods are exposed to much greater risk of error than in the case of diffusion. The first of these is the diffusion of momentum, or the lateral communication of sensible motion from one stratum of a gas to another. This is the explanation, on the kinetic theory, of the viscosity or internal friction of gases. The investigation of the viscosity of gases requires experiments of great delicacy, and involving very considerable corrections before the true

* *Brande's Journal* for 1829, pt. ii. p. 74, "On the Mobility of Gases," *Phil. Trans.* 1863.
† *Sitzb. d. k. Akad. d. Wissench.* 10 März. 1870.

coefficient of viscosity is obtained. Thus the numbers obtained by myself in 1865 are nearly double of those calculated by Prof. Stokes from the experiments of Baily on pendulums, but not much more than half those deduced by O. E. Meyer from his own experiments. The other kind of diffusion is that of the energy of agitation of the molecules. This is called the conduction of heat. The experimental investigation of this subject is confessedly so difficult, that it is only recently that Prof. Stefan of Vienna*, by means of a very ingenious method, has obtained the first experimental determination of the conductivity of air. This result is, as he says, in striking agreement with the kinetic theory of gases.

The experiments on the interdiffusion of gases, as conducted by Prof. Loschmidt and his pupils, appear to be far more independent of disturbing causes than any experiments on viscosity or conductivity. The interdiffusing gases are left to themselves in a vertical cylindrical vessel, the heavier gas being underneath. No disturbing effect due to currents seems to exist, and the results of different experiments with the same pair of gases appear to be very consistent with each other.

They prove conclusively that the coefficient of diffusion varies inversely as the pressure, a result in accordance with the kinetic theory, whatever hypothesis we adopt as to the nature of the mutual action of the molecules during their encounters.

They also shew that the coefficient of diffusion increases as the temperature rises, but the range of temperature in the experiments appears to be too small to enable us to decide whether it varies as T^2, as it should be according to the theory of a force inversely as the fifth power of the distance adopted in my paper in the *Phil. Trans.* 1866, or as $T^{\frac{3}{2}}$ as it should do according to the theory of elastic spherical molecules, which was the hypothesis originally developed by Clausius, by myself in the *Phil. Mag.* 1860, and by O. E. Meyer.

In comparing the coefficients of diffusion of different pairs of gases, Prof. Loschmidt has made use of a formula according to which the coefficient of diffusion should vary inversely as the geometric mean of the atomic weights of the two gases. I am unable to see any ground for this hypothesis in the kinetic theory, which in fact leads to a different result, involving the diameters of the molecules, as well as their masses. The numerical results obtained by

* *Sitzb. d. k. Akad.* Feb. 22, 1872.

Prof. Loschmidt do not agree with his formula in a manner corresponding to the accuracy of his experiments. They agree in a very remarkable manner with the formula derived from the kinetic theory.

I have recently been revising the theory of gases founded on that of the collisions of elastic spheres, using, however, the methods of my paper on the dynamical theory of gases (*Phil. Trans.* 1866) rather than those of my first paper in the *Phil. Mag.*, 1860, which are more difficult of application, and which led me into great confusion, especially in treating of the diffusion of gases.

The coefficient of interdiffusion of two gases, according to this theory, is

$$D_{12} = \frac{1}{2\sqrt{6\pi}} \frac{V}{N} \sqrt{\frac{1}{w_1} + \frac{1}{w_2}} \frac{1}{s_{12}^2} \quad \ldots \ldots \ldots \ldots \ldots \ldots \ldots (1),$$

where w_1 and w_2 are the molecular weights of the two gases, that of hydrogen being unity.

s_{12} is the distance between the centres of the molecules at collision in centimetres.

V is the "velocity of mean square" of a molecule of hydrogen at $0°$ C.

$$V = \sqrt{\frac{3p}{\rho}} = 185,900 \text{ centimetres per second.}$$

N is the number of molecules in a cubic centimetre at $0°$ C. and 76 cm. B. (the same for all gases).

D_{12} is the coefficient of interdiffusion of the two gases in $\dfrac{(\text{centimetre})^2}{\text{second}}$ measure.

We may simplify this expression by writing

$$a^2 = \frac{1}{2\sqrt{6\pi}} \frac{V}{N}, \quad \sigma_{12}^2 = \frac{1}{D_{12}} \sqrt{\frac{1}{w_1} + \frac{1}{w_2}} \quad \ldots \ldots \ldots \ldots \ldots \ldots (2).$$

Here a is a quantity the same for all gases, but involving the unknown number N.

σ is a quantity which may be deduced from the corresponding experiment of M. Loschmidt. We have thus

$$s_{12} = a\sigma_{12} \quad \ldots \ldots \ldots \ldots \ldots \ldots \ldots \ldots \ldots \ldots \ldots \ldots (3),$$

or the distance between the centres of the molecules at collision is proportional to the quantity σ, which may be deduced from experiment.

If d_1 and d_2 are the diameters of the two molecules,

$$s_{12} = \tfrac{1}{2}(d_1 + d_2).$$

Hence if $\qquad\qquad d = a\delta \ldots\ldots \sigma_{12} = \tfrac{1}{2}(\delta_1 + \delta_2) \quad\ldots\ldots\ldots\ldots\ldots\ldots\ldots (4).$

Now M. Loschmidt has determined D for the six pairs of gases which can be formed from Hydrogen, Oxygen, Carbonic Oxide, and Carbonic Acid. The six values of σ deduced from these experiments ought not to be independent, since they may be deduced from the four values of δ belonging to the two gases. Accordingly we find, by assuming

TABLE I.

$$\delta\,(H) \ = 1\cdot739$$
$$\delta\,(O) \ = 2\cdot283$$
$$\delta\,(CO) = 2\cdot461$$
$$\delta\,(CO_2) = 2\cdot775$$

σ_{12}	Calculated $\tfrac{1}{2}(\delta_1 + \delta_2)$	Observed $\sqrt{\dfrac{1}{D}}\sqrt{\dfrac{1}{w_1} + \dfrac{1}{w_2}}$
For H and O	2·011	1·992
For H and CO	2·100	2·116
For H and CO_2	2·257	2·260
For O and CO	3·372	2·375
For O and CO_2	2·529	2·545
For CO and CO_2	2·618	2·599

Note.—These numbers must be multiplied by 0·6 to reduce them to (centimetre-second) measure from the (metre-hour) measure employed by Loschmidt.

The agreement of these numbers furnishes, I think, evidence of considerable strength in favour of this form of the kinetic theory, and if it should be confirmed by the comparison of results obtained from a greater number of pairs of gases it will be greatly strengthened.

Evidence, however, of a higher order may be furnished by a comparison between the results of experiments of entirely different kinds, as for instance, the coefficients of diffusion and those of viscosity. If μ denotes the coefficient of viscosity, and ρ the density of a gas at $0°$C. and 760 mm. B., the theory gives

$$\frac{\mu}{\rho} = a^2 \sqrt{\frac{2}{w}} \frac{1}{d^2} \quad \dots\dots\dots\dots\dots\dots\dots\dots(5),$$

so that the following relation exists between the viscosities of two gases and their coefficient of interdiffusion—

$$D_{12} = \tfrac{1}{2}\left(\frac{\mu_1}{\rho_1} + \frac{\mu_2}{\rho_2}\right) \quad \dots\dots\dots\dots\dots\dots\dots (6).$$

Calculating from the data of Table I., the viscosities of the gases, and comparing them with those found by O. E. Meyer and by myself, and reducing all to centimetre, gramme, second measure, and $0°$C.—

TABLE II.

Coefficient of Viscosity.

Gas.	Loschmidt.	O. E. Meyer.	Maxwell.
H	0·000116	0·000134	0·000097
O	0 000270	0·000306	
CO	0·000217	0·000266	
CO$_2$	0·000214	0·000231	0·000161

The numbers given by Meyer are greater than those derived from Loschmidt. Mine, on the other hand, are much smaller. I think, however, that of the three, Loschmidt's are to be preferred as an estimate of the absolute value of the quantities, while those of Meyer, derived from Graham's experiments, may possibly give the ratios of the viscosities of different gases more correctly. Loschmidt has also given the coefficients of interdiffusion of four other pairs of gases, but as each of these contains a gas not contained in any other pair, I have made no use of them.

In the form of the theory as developed by Clausius, an important part is played by a quantity called the *mean length of the uninterrupted path of a*

44—2

molecule, or, more concisely, the *mean path*. Its value, according to my calculations, is

$$l = \frac{1}{\sqrt{2}\pi s^2 N} = \frac{\sqrt{12}}{\sqrt{\pi} V} \frac{1}{\delta^2} \ast \quad \dots \dots \dots (7).$$

Its value in tenth-metres (1 metre × 10⁻¹⁰) is

TABLE III.

For Hydrogen . . .	965	Tenth-metres at 0° C. and 760 B.
For Oxygen . . .	560	
For Carbonic Oxide . .	482	
For Carbonic Acid . .	430	

(The wave-length of the hydrogen ray F is 4,861 tenth-metres, or about ten times the mean path of a molecule of carbonic oxide.)

We may now proceed for a few steps on more hazardous ground, and inquire into the actual size of the molecules. Prof. Loschmidt himself in his paper "Zur Grösse der Luftmolecüle" (*Acad. Vienna*, Oct. 12, 1865), was the first to make this attempt. Independently of him and of each other, Mr G. J. Stoney (*Phil. Mag.*, Aug. 1868), and Sir W. Thomson (*Nature*, March 31, 1870), have made similar calculations. We shall follow the track of Prof. Loschmidt.

The volume of a spherical molecule is $\frac{\pi}{6} s^3$, where s is its diameter. Hence if N is the number of molecules in unit of volume, the space actually filled by the molecules is $\frac{\pi}{6} N s^3$.

This, then, would be the volume to which a cubic centimetre of the gas would be reduced if it could be so compressed as to leave no room whatever between the molecules. This, of course, is impossible ; but we may, for the sake of clearness, call the quantity

$$\epsilon = \frac{\pi}{6} N s^3 \quad \dots \dots \dots \dots (8)$$

---

* The difference between this value and that given by M. Clausius in his paper of 1858, arises from his assuming that all the molecules have equal velocities, while I suppose the velocities to be distributed according to the "law of errors."

the ideal coefficient of condensation. The actual coefficient of condensation, when the gas is reduced to the liquid or even the solid form, and exposed to the greatest degree of cold and pressure, is of course greater than ϵ.

Multiplying equations (7) and (8), we find

$$s = 6 \sqrt{2}\epsilon l \quad\dots\dots\dots\dots\dots\dots\dots\dots\dots\dots (9),$$

where s is the diameter of a molecule, ϵ the coefficient of condensation, and l the mean path of a molecule.

Of these quantities, we know l approximately already, but with respect to ϵ we only know its superior limit. It is only by ascertaining whether calculations of this kind, made with respect to different substances, lead to consistent results, that we can obtain any confidence in our estimates of ϵ.

M. Lorenz Meyer* has compared the "molecular volumes" of different substances, as estimated by Kopp from measurements of the density of these substances and their compounds, with the values of s^3 as deduced from experiments on the viscosity of gases, and has shewn that there is a considerable degree of correspondence between the two sets of numbers.

The "molecular volume" of a substance here spoken of is the volume in cubic centimetres of as much of the substance in the liquid state as contains as many molecules as one gramme of hydrogen. Hence if ρ_0 denote the density of hydrogen, and $\mathfrak{v}$ the molecular volume of a substance, the actual coefficient of condensation is

$$\epsilon' = \rho_0\mathfrak{v}\dots\dots\dots\dots\dots\dots\dots\dots\dots\dots\dots\dots(10).$$

These "molecular volumes" of liquids are estimated at the boiling-points of the liquids, a very arbitrary condition, for this depends on the pressure, and there is no reason in the nature of things for fixing on 760 mm. B. as a standard pressure merely because it roughly represents the ordinary pressure of our atmosphere. What would be better, if it were not impossible to obtain it, would be the volume at -273° C. and ∞ B.

But the volume relations of potassium with its oxide and its hydrated oxide as described by Faraday seem to indicate that we have a good deal yet to learn about the volumes of atoms.

* _Annalen d. Chemie u. Pharmacie_ v. Supp. bd. 2, Heft (1867).

If, however, for our immediate purpose, we assume the smallest molecular volume of oxygen given by Kopp as derived from a comparison of the volume of tin with that of its oxide and put

$$\mathfrak{b}\,(O=16)=2\cdot7,$$

we find for the diameters of the molecules—

TABLE IV.

Hydrogen	5·8 tenth-metres.
Oxygen	7·6
Carbonic Oxide . .	8·3
Carbonic Acid . . .	9·3

The mass of a molecule of hydrogen on this assumption is

$$4\cdot6\times10^{-24}\ \text{gramme.}$$

The number of molecules in a cubic centimetre of any gas at 0° C. and 760 mm. B. is

$$N=19\times10^{18}.$$

Hence the side of a cube which, on an average, would contain one molecule would be

$$N^{-\frac{1}{3}}=37\ \text{tenth-metres.}$$

[From *Nature*, Vol. VIII.]

LX. *On the Final State of a System of Molecules in motion subject to forces of any kind.*

LET perfectly elastic molecules of different kinds be in motion within a vessel with perfectly elastic sides, and let each kind of molecules be acted on by forces which have a potential, the form of which may be different for different kinds of molecules.

Let x, y, z be the co-ordinates of a molecule, M, and ξ, η, ζ the components of its velocity, and let it be required to determine the number of molecules of a given kind which, on an average, have their co-ordinates between x and $x + dx$, y and $y + dy$, z and $z + dz$, and also their component velocities between ξ and $\xi + d\xi$, η and $\eta + d\eta$, and ζ and $\zeta + d\zeta$. This number must depend on the co-ordinates and the components of velocities and on the limits of these quantities. We may therefore write it

$$dN = f(x, y, z, \xi, \eta, \zeta)\, dx\,dy\,dz\,d\xi\,d\eta\,d\zeta \dots\dots\dots\dots(1).$$

We shall begin by investigating the manner in which this quantity depends on the components of velocity, before we proceed to determine in what way it depends on the co-ordinates.

If we distinguish by suffixes the quantities corresponding to different kinds of molecules, the whole number of molecules of the first and second kind within a given space which have velocities within given limits may be written

$$f_1(\xi_1, \eta_1, \zeta_1)\, d\xi_1.\ d\eta_1.\ d\zeta_1 = n_1 \dots\dots\dots\dots\dots(2),$$

and
$$f_2(\xi_2, \eta_2, \zeta_2)\, d\xi_2.\ d\eta_2.\ d\zeta_2 = n_2 \dots\dots\dots\dots\dots(3).$$

The number of pairs which can be formed by taking one molecule of each kind is $n_1.\ n_2$.

Let a pair of molecules encounter each other, and after the encounter let their component velocities be ξ_1', η_1', ζ_1' and ξ_2', η_2', ζ_2'. The nature of the encounter is completely defined when we know $\xi_2-\xi_1$, $\eta_2-\eta_1$, $\zeta_2-\zeta_1$ the velocity of the second molecule relative to the first before the encounter, and x_2-x_1, y_2-y_1, z_2-z_1 the position of the centre of the second molecule relative to the first at the instant of the encounter. When these quantities are given, $\xi_2'-\xi_1'$, $\eta_2'-\eta_1'$ and $\zeta_2'-\zeta_1'$, the components of the relative velocity after the encounter, are determinable.

Hence putting a, β, γ for these relative velocities, and a, b, c for the relative positions, we find for the number of molecules of the first kind having velocities between the limits ξ_1 and $\xi_1+d\xi$, &c., which encounter molecules of the second kind having velocities between the limits ξ_2 and $\xi_2+d\xi$, &c., in such a way that the relative velocities lie between a and $a+da$, &c., and the relative positions between a and $a+da$, &c.

$$f_1(\xi_1, \eta_1, \zeta_1)\,d\xi d\eta d\zeta . f_2(\xi_2, \eta_2, \zeta_2)\,d\xi d\eta d\zeta . \phi(abca\beta\gamma)\,da\,db\,dc\,da\,d\beta\,d\gamma \ldots (4),$$

and after the encounter the velocity of M_1 will be between the limits ξ_1' and $\xi_1'+d\xi$, &c. and that of M_2 between the limits ξ_2' and $\xi_2'+d\xi$, &c.

The differences of the limits of velocity are equal for both kinds of molecules, and both before and after the encounter.

When the state of motion of the system is in its permanent condition, as many pairs of molecules change their velocities from V_1, V_2 to V_1', V_2' as from V_1', V_2' to V_1, V_2, and the circumstances of the encounter in the one case are precisely similar to those in the second. Hence, omitting for the sake of brevity the quantities $d\xi$, &c., and ϕ, which are of the same value in the two cases, we find

$$f_1(\xi_1, \eta_1, \zeta_1)f_2(\xi_2, \eta_2, \zeta_2)=f_1(\xi_1', \eta_1', \zeta_1')f_2(\xi_2', \eta_2', \zeta_2') \ldots\ldots\ldots\ldots (5),$$

writing

$$\log f(\xi, \eta, \zeta)=F(MV^2, l, m, n) \ldots\ldots\ldots\ldots\ldots (6),$$

where l, m, n are the direction-cosines of the velocity, V, of the molecule M.

Taking the logarithm of both sides of equation (5),

$$F_1(M_1V_1^2l_1m_1n_1) + F_2(M_2V_2^2l_2m_2n_2) = F_1(M_1V_1'^2l_1'm_1'n_1') + F_2(M_2V_2'^2l_2'm_2'n_2') \ldots (7).$$

The only necessary relation between the variables before and after the encounter is

$$M_1V_1^2 + M_2V_2^2 = M_1V_1'^2 + M_2V_2'^2 \ldots\ldots\ldots\ldots\ldots\ldots (8).$$

If the right-hand side of the equations (7) and (8) are constant, the left-hand sides will also be constant; and since l_1, m_1, n_1 are independent of l_2, m_2, n_2 we must have

$$F_1 = AM_1V_1^2 \text{ and } F_2 = AM_2V_2^2 \quad\dots\dots\dots\dots (9),$$

where A is a quantity independent of the components of velocity, or

$$f_1(\xi_1, \eta_1, \zeta_1) = C_1 e^{AM_1V_1^2} \quad\dots\dots\dots\dots\dots (10),$$

$$f_2(\xi_2, \eta_2, \zeta_2) = C_2 e^{AM_2V_2^2} \quad\dots\dots\dots\dots\dots (11).$$

This result as to the distribution of the velocities of the molecules at a given place is independent of the action of finite forces on the molecules during their encounter, for such forces do not affect the velocities during the infinitely short time of the encounter.

We may therefore write equation (1)

$$dN = Ce^{AM(\xi^2+\eta^2+\zeta^2)} \, d\xi \, d\eta \, d\zeta \, dx \, dy \, dz \quad\dots\dots\dots\dots (12),$$

where C is a function of x, y, z which may be different for different kinds of molecules, while A is the same for every kind of molecule, though it may, for aught we know as yet, vary from one place to another.

Let us now suppose that the kind of molecules under consideration are acted on by a force whose potential is ψ. The variations of x, y, z arising from the motion of the molecules during a time δt are

$$\delta x = \xi \delta t, \ \delta y = \eta \delta t, \ \delta z = \zeta \delta t \quad\dots\dots\dots\dots\dots (13),$$

and those of ξ, η, ζ in the same time due to the action of the force, are

$$\delta \xi = -\frac{d\psi}{dx} \delta t, \ \delta \eta = -\frac{d\psi}{dy} \delta t, \ \delta \zeta = -\frac{d\psi}{dz} \delta t \quad\dots\dots\dots (14).$$

If we make

$$c = \log C \quad\dots\dots\dots\dots\dots\dots (15),$$

$$\log \frac{dN}{d\xi d\eta d\zeta dx dy dz} = c + AM(\xi^2 + \eta^2 + \zeta^2) \quad\dots\dots\dots\dots(16).$$

The variation of this quantity due to the variations δx_1, δy_1, δz_1, $\delta \xi_1$, $\delta \eta_1$, $\delta \zeta_1$, is

$$\left.\begin{array}{c} \left(\xi \dfrac{dc}{dx} + \eta \dfrac{dc}{dy} + \zeta \dfrac{dc}{dz}\right) \delta t - 2AM \left(\xi \dfrac{d\psi}{dx} + \eta \dfrac{d\psi}{dy} + \zeta \dfrac{d\psi}{dz}\right) \delta t \\[2mm] + M(\xi^2 + \eta^2 + \zeta^2) \left(\xi \dfrac{dA}{dx} + \eta \dfrac{dA}{dy} + \zeta \dfrac{dA}{dz}\right) \delta t \end{array}\right\} \dots\dots(17).$$

Since the number of the molecules does not vary during their motion, this quantity is zero, whatever the values of ξ, η, ζ. Hence we have in virtue of the last term

$$\frac{dA}{dx} = 0, \quad \frac{dA}{dy} = 0, \quad \frac{dA}{dz} = 0 \dots\dots\dots\dots\dots\dots(18),$$

or A is constant throughout the whole region traversed by the molecules.

Next, comparing the first and second terms, we find

$$c = AM(2\psi + B)\dots\dots\dots\dots\dots\dots(19).$$

We thus obtain as the complete form of dN

$$dN_1 = e^{AM_1(\xi_1^2 + \eta_1^2 + \zeta_1^2 + 2\psi_1 + B_1)} \, dx \, dy \, dz \, d\xi \, d\eta \, d\zeta \dots\dots\dots\dots(20),$$

when A is an absolute constant, the same for every kind of molecule in the vessel, but B_1 belongs to the first kind only. To determine these constants, we must integrate this quantity with respect to the six variables, and equate the result to the number of molecules of the first kind. We must then, by integrating $dN_1 \frac{1}{2} M_1 (\xi_1^2 + \eta_1^2 + \zeta_1^2 + 2\psi_1)$ determine the whole energy of the system, and equate it to the original energy. We shall thus obtain a sufficient number of equations to determine the constant A, common to all the molecules, and B_1, B_2, &c. those belonging to each kind.

The quantity A is essentially negative. Its value determines that of the mean kinetic energy of all the molecules in a given place, which is $-\frac{3}{2}\frac{1}{A}$, and therefore, according to the kinetic theory, it also determines the temperature of the medium at that place. Hence, since A_1, in the permanent state of the system, is the same for every part of the system, it follows that the temperature is everywhere the same, whatever forces act upon the molecules.

The number of molecules of the first kind in the element $dx\,dy\,dz$,

$$\left(-\frac{\pi}{A}\right)^{\frac{3}{2}} e^{AM_1(2\psi_1 + B_1)} \, dx \, dy \, dz \dots\dots\dots\dots\dots (21).$$

The effect of the force whose potential is ψ_1 is therefore to cause the molecules of the first kind to accumulate in greater numbers in those parts of the vessel towards which the force acts, and the distribution of each different kind of molecules in the vessel is determined by the forces which act on them in the same way as if no other molecules were present. This agrees with Dalton's doctrine of the distribution of mixed gases.

Michael Faraday.

From a Photograph by John Watkins, 34 Parliament Street.

[From *Nature*, Vol. VIII.]

LXI. *Faraday.*

[Michael Faraday, born September 22, 1791, died August 25, 1867.]

WITH this number of *Nature* we present to our subscribers the first of what we hope will be a long series of Portraits of Eminent Men of Science.

This first portrait is one of Faraday, engraved on steel, by Jeens, from a photograph by Watkins.   Those who had the happiness of knowing Faraday best will best appreciate the artist's skill—he has indeed surpassed himself, for the engraving is more life-like than the photograph.   We could ill spare such a memorial of such a man, one in which all the beautiful simplicity of his life beams upon us.   There is no posturing here!

There is no need that we should accompany the portrait with a memoir of Faraday.   Bence Jones, Tyndall, and Gladstone have already lovingly told the story of the grand and simple life which has shed and will long continue to shed such lustre on English Science, and their books have carried the story home to millions; nor is there any need that we should state why we have chosen to commence our series with Faraday; everybody will acknowledge the justice of our choice.

But there is great need just now that some of the lessons to be learnt from Faraday's life should be insisted upon, and we regard it as a fortunate circumstance that we have thus the opportunity of insisting upon them while our Scientific Congress is in session, and before the echoes of the Address of the President of the British Association for the Advancement of Science have died away.

In the first place, then, we regard Faraday at once as the most useful and the most noble type of a scientific man.   The nation is bigger and stronger in that Faraday has lived, and the nation would be bigger and stronger still were there more Faradays among us now.   Professor Williamson, in his admirable

45—2

address, acknowledges that the present time is "momentous." In truth the question of the present condition of Science and the ways of improving it, is occupying men's minds more than it has ever done before; and it is now conceded on all sides that this is a national question, and not only so, but one of fundamental importance. Now what is the present condition of English Science? It is simply this, that while the numbers of our professors and their emoluments are increasing, while the number of students is increasing, while practical instruction is being introduced and text-books multiplied, while the number and calibre of popular lecturers and popular writers in Science is increasing, original research, the fountain-head of a nation's wealth, is decreasing.

Now a scientific man is useful as such to a nation according to the amount of new knowledge with which he endows that nation. This is the test which the nation, as a whole, applies, and Faraday's national reputation rests on it. Let the nation know then that the real difficulty at present is this; we want more Faradays; in other words more men working at new knowledge.

It is refreshing to see this want so clearly stated in the Presidential Address:

"The first thing wanted for the work of advancing science is a supply of well-qualified workers. The second thing is to place and keep them under the conditions most favourable to their efficient activity. The most suitable men must be found while still young, and trained to the work. Now I know only one really effectual way of finding the youths who are best endowed by nature for the purpose; and that is to systematise and develop the natural conditions which accidentally concur in particular cases, and enable youths to rise from the crowd.

"Investigators, once found, ought to be placed in the circumstances most favourable to their efficient activity.

"The first and most fundamental condition for this is, that their desire for the acquisition of knowledge be kept alive and fostered. They must not merely retain the hold which they have acquired on the general body of their science; they ought to strengthen and extend that hold, by acquiring a more complete and accurate knowledge of its doctrines and methods; in a word, they ought to be more thorough students than during their state of preliminary training.

"They must be able to live by their work, without diverting any of their energies to other pursuits; and they must feel security against want, in the event of illness or in their old age.

"They must be supplied with intelligent and trained assistants to aid in the conduct of their researches, and whatever buildings, apparatus, and materials may be required for conducting those researches effectively.

"The desired system must therefore provide arrangements favourable to the maintenance and development of the true student-spirit in investigators, while providing them with permanent means of subsistence, sufficient to enable them to feel secure and tranquil in working at science alone, yet not sufficient to neutralise their motives for exertion; and at the same time it must give them all external aids, in proportion to their wants and powers of making good use of them."

Whether the scheme proposed by Dr Williamson to bring such a state of things about will have the full success he anticipates is a matter of second-rate importance; what is of importance is, that the need of some scheme is now fully recognised.

So far the remarks we have made have been suggested by Faraday's usefulness. It is to be hoped that the nobleness of his simple, undramatic life, will live as long in men's memories as the discoveries which have immortalised his name. Here was no hunger after popular applause, no jealousy of other men's work, no swerving from the well-loved, self-imposed task of "working, finishing, publishing."

"The simplicity of his heart, his candour, his ardent love of the truth, his fellow-interest in all the successes, and ingenuous admiration of all the discoveries of others, his natural modesty in regard to what he himself discovered, his noble soul—independent and bold—all these combined, gave an incomparable charm to the features of the illustrious physicist."

Such was his portrait as sketched by Dumas, a man cast in the same mould. All will recognise its truth. Can men of science find a nobler exemplar on which to fashion their own life? Nay, if it were more widely followed than it is, should we not hear less of men falling away from the "brilliant promise" of their youth, tempted by "fees," or the "applications of Science," or the advantages attendant upon a popular exposition of other men's work? Should we not hear a little less frequently than we do that research is a sham, and that all attempts to aid it savour of jobbery?

Lastly we may consider Faraday's place in the general history of Science; this is far from easy. Our minds are still too much occupied with the memory of the outward form and expression of his scientific work to be able to compare him aright with the other great men among whom we shall have to place him.

Every great man of the first rank is unique. Each has his own office and his own place in the historic procession of the sages. That office did not exist even in the imagination, till he came to fill it, and none can succeed to his place when he has passed away. Others may gain distinction by adapting the exposition of science to the varying language of each generation of students, but their true function is not so much didactic as pædagogic—not to teach the use of phrases which enable us to persuade ourselves that we understand a science, but to bring the student into living contact with the two main sources of mental growth, the fathers of the sciences, for whose personal influence over the opening mind there is no substitute, and the material things to which their labours first gave a meaning.

Faraday is, and must always remain, the father of that enlarged science of electro-magnetism which takes in at one view, all the phenomena which former inquirers had studied separately, besides those which Faraday himself discovered by following the guidance of those convictions, which he had already obtained, of the unity of the whole science.

Before him came the discovery of most of the fundamental phenomena, the electric and magnetic attractions and repulsions, the electric current and its effects. Then came Cavendish, Coulomb, and Poisson, who by following the path pointed out by Newton, and making the forces which act between bodies the principal object of their study, founded the mathematical theories of electric and magnetic forces. Then Örsted discovered the cardinal fact of electro-magnetic force, and Ampère investigated the mathematical laws of the mechanical action between electric currents.

Thus the field of electro-magnetic Science was already very large when Faraday first entered upon his public career. It was so large that to take in at one view all its departments required a stretch of thought for which a special preparation was necessary. Accordingly, we find Faraday endeavouring in the first place to obtain, from each of the known sources of electric action, all the phenomena which any one of them was able to exhibit. Having thus established the unity of nature of all electric manifestations, his next aim was to form a conception of electrification, or electric action, which would embrace them all. For this purpose it was necessary that he should begin by getting rid of those parasitical ideas, which are so apt to cling to every scientific term, and to invest it with a luxuriant crop of connotative meanings flourishing at the expense of the meaning which the word was intended to denote. He therefore endeavoured to strip all such terms as "electric fluid," "current," and "attraction" of every meaning except that which is warranted by the phenomena themselves, and to invent new terms, such as "electrolysis," "electrode," "dielectric," which suggest no other meaning than that assigned to them by their definitions.

He thus undertook no less a task than the investigation of the facts, the ideas, and the scientific terms of electro-magnetism, and the result was the remodelling of the whole according to an entirely new method.

That old and popular phrase, "electric fluid," which is now, we trust, banished for ever into the region of newspaper paragraphs, had done what it could to keep men's minds fixed upon those particular parts of bodies where the "fluid" was supposed to exist.

Faraday, on the other hand, by inventing the word "dielectric," has encouraged us to examine all that is going on in the air or other medium between the electrified bodies.

It is needless to multiply instances of this kind. The terms, field of force, lines of force, induction, &c., are sufficient to recall them. They all illustrate the general principles of the growth of science, in the particular form of which Faraday is the exponent.

We have, first, the careful observation of selected phenomena, then the examination of the received ideas, and the formation, when necessary, of new ideas; and, lastly, the invention of scientific terms adapted for the discussion of the phenomena in the light of the new ideas.

The high place which we assign to Faraday in electro-magnetic science may appear to some inconsistent with the fact that electro-magnetic science is an exact science, and that in some of its branches it had already assumed a mathematical form before the time of Faraday, whereas Faraday was not a professed mathematician, and in his writings we find none of those integrations of differential equations which are supposed to be of the very essence of an exact science. Open Poisson and Ampère, who went before him, or Weber and Neumann, who came after him, and you will find their pages full of symbols, not one of which Faraday would have understood. It is admitted that Faraday made some great discoveries, but if we put these aside, how can we rank his scientific method so high without disparaging the mathematics of these eminent men?

It is true that no one can essentially cultivate any exact science without understanding the mathematics of that science. But we are not to suppose that the calculations and equations which mathematicians find so useful constitute the whole of mathematics. The calculus is but a part of mathematics.

The geometry of position is an example of a mathematical science established without the aid of a single calculation. Now Faraday's lines of force occupy the same position in electro-magnetic science that pencils of lines do in the geometry of position. They furnish a method of building up an exact mental image of the thing we are reasoning about. The way in which Faraday made use of his idea of lines of force in co-ordinating the phenomena of magneto-electric induction * shews him to have been in reality a mathematician of a very high order—one from whom the mathematicians of the future may derive valuable and fertile methods.

For the advance of the exact sciences depends upon the discovery and development of appropriate and exact ideas, by means of which we may form a mental representation of the facts, sufficiently general, on the one hand, to stand for any particular case, and sufficiently exact, on the other, to warrant the deductions we may draw from them by the application of mathematical reasoning.

From the straight line of Euclid to the lines of force of Faraday this has been the character of the ideas by which science has been advanced, and by the free use of dynamical as well as geometrical ideas we may hope for a further advance. The use of mathematical calculations is to compare the results of the application of these ideas with our measurements of the quantities concerned in our experiments. Electrical science is now in the stage in which such measurements and calculations are of the greatest importance.

We are probably ignorant even of the name of the science which will be developed out of the materials we are now collecting, when the great philosopher next after Faraday makes his appearance.

---

* To estimate the *intensity* of Faraday's scientific power, we cannot do better than read the first and second series of his *Researches* and compare them, first, with the statements in Bence Jones's *Life of Faraday*, which tells us the tales of the first discovery of the facts, and of the final publication of the results, and second, with the whole course of electro-magnetic science since, which has added no new idea to those set forth, but has only verified the truth and scientific value of every one of them.

[From *Nature*, Vol. VIII.]

LXII. *Molecules**.

AN atom is a body which cannot be cut in two. A molecule is the smallest possible portion of a particular substance. No one has ever seen or handled a single molecule. Molecular science, therefore, is one of those branches of study which deal with things invisible and imperceptible by our senses, and which cannot be subjected to direct experiment.

The mind of man has perplexed itself with many hard questions. Is space infinite, and if so in what sense? Is the material world infinite in extent, and are all places within that extent equally full of matter? Do atoms exist, or is matter infinitely divisible?

The discussion of questions of this kind has been going on ever since men began to reason, and to each of us, as soon as we obtain the use of our faculties, the same old questions arise as fresh as ever. They form as essential a part of the science of the nineteenth century of our era, as of that of the fifth century before it.

We do not know much about the science organisation of Thrace twenty-two centuries ago, or of the machinery then employed for diffusing an interest in physical research. There were men, however, in those days, who devoted their lives to the pursuit of knowledge with an ardour worthy of the most distinguished members of the British Association; and the lectures in which Democritus explained the atomic theory to his fellow-citizens of Abdera realised, not in golden opinions only, but in golden talents, a sum hardly equalled even in America.

To another very eminent philosopher, Anaxagoras, best known to the world as the teacher of Socrates, we are indebted for the most important service to

---

* A Lecture delivered before the British Association at Bradford.

the atomic theory, which, after its statement by Democritus, remained to be done. Anaxagoras, in fact, stated a theory which so exactly contradicts the atomic theory of Democritus that the truth or falsehood of the one theory implies the falsehood or truth of the other. The question of the existence or non-existence of atoms cannot be presented to us this evening with greater clearness than in the alternative theories of these two philosophers.

Take any portion of matter, say a drop of water, and observe its properties. Like every other portion of matter we have ever seen, it is divisible. Divide it in two, each portion appears to retain all the properties of the original drop, and among others that of being divisible. The parts are similar to the whole in every respect except in absolute size.

Now go on repeating the process of division till the separate portions of water are so small that we can no longer perceive or handle them. Still we have no doubt that the sub-division might be carried further, if our senses were more acute and our instruments more delicate. Thus far all are agreed, but now the question arises, Can this sub-division be repeated for ever ?

According to Democritus and the atomic school, we must answer in the negative. After a certain number of sub-divisions, the drop would be divided into a number of parts each of which is incapable of further sub-division. We should thus, in imagination, arrive at the atom, which, as its name literally signifies, cannot be cut in two. This is the atomic doctrine of Democritus, Epicurus, and Lucretius, and, I may add, of your lecturer.

According to Anaxagoras, on the other hand, the parts into which the drop is divided are in all respects similar to the whole drop, the mere size of a body counting for nothing as regards the nature of its substance. Hence if the whole drop is divisible, so are its parts down to the minutest sub-divisions, and that without end.

The essence of the doctrine of Anaxagoras is that parts of a body are in all respects similar to the whole. It was, therefore, called the doctrine of Homoiomereia. Anaxagoras did not of course assert this of the parts of organised bodies such as men and animals, but he maintained that those inorganic substances which appear to us homogeneous are really so, and that the universal experience of mankind testifies that every material body, without exception, is divisible.

The doctrine of atoms and that of homogeneity are thus in direct contradiction.

But we must now go on to molecules. Molecule is a modern word. It does not occur in *Johnson's Dictionary*. The ideas it embodies are those belonging to modern chemistry.

A drop of water, to return to our former example, may be divided into a certain number, and no more, of portions similar to each other. Each of these the modern chemist calls a molecule of water. But it is by no means an atom, for it contains two different substances, oxygen and hydrogen, and by a certain process the molecule may be actually divided into two parts, one consisting of oxygen and the other of hydrogen. According to the received doctrine, in each molecule of water there are two molecules of hydrogen and one of oxygen. Whether these are or are not ultimate atoms I shall not attempt to decide.

We now see what a molecule is, as distinguished from an atom.

A molecule of a substance is a small body such that if, on the one hand, a number of similar molecules were assembled together they would form a mass of that substance, while on the other hand, if any portion of this molecule were removed, it would no longer be able, along with an assemblage of other molecules similarly treated, to make up a mass of the original substance.

Every substance, simple or compound, has its own molecule. If this molecule be divided, its parts are molecules of a different substance or substances from that of which the whole is a molecule. An atom, if there is such a thing, must be a molecule of an elementary substance. Since, therefore, every molecule is not an atom, but every atom is a molecule, I shall use the word molecule as the more general term.

I have no intention of taking up your time by expounding the doctrines of modern chemistry with respect to the molecules of different substances. It is not the special but the universal interest of molecular science which encourages me to address you. It is not because we happen to be chemists or physicists or specialists of any kind that we are attracted towards this centre of all material existence, but because we all belong to a race endowed with faculties which urge us on to search deep and ever deeper into the nature of things.

We find that now, as in the days of the earliest physical speculations, all physical researches appear to converge towards the same point, and every inquirer, as he looks forward into the dim region towards which the path of discovery is leading him, sees, each according to his sight, the vision of the same Quest.

One may see the atom as a material point, invested and surrounded by potential forces. Another sees no garment of force, but only the bare and utter hardness of mere impenetrability.

But though many a speculator, as he has seen the vision recede before him into the innermost sanctuary of the inconceivably little, has had to confess that the quest was not for him, and though philosophers in every age have been exhorting each other to direct their minds to some more useful and attainable aim, each generation, from the earliest dawn of science to the present time, has contributed a due proportion of its ablest intellects to the quest of the ultimate atom.

Our business this evening is to describe some researches in molecular science, and in particular to place before you any definite information which has been obtained respecting the molecules themselves. The old atomic theory, as described by Lucretius and revived in modern times, asserts that the molecules of all bodies are in motion, even when the body itself appears to be at rest. These motions of molecules are in the case of solid bodies confined within so narrow a range that even with our best microscopes we cannot detect that they alter their places at all. In liquids and gases, however, the molecules are not confined within any definite limits, but work their way through the whole mass, even when that mass is not disturbed by any visible motion.

This process of diffusion, as it is called, which goes on in gases and liquids and even in some solids, can be subjected to experiment, and forms one of the most convincing proofs of the motion of molecules.

Now the recent progress of molecular science began with the study of the mechanical effect of the impact of these moving molecules when they strike against any solid body. Of course these flying molecules must beat against whatever is placed among them, and the constant succession of these strokes is, according to our theory, the sole cause of what is called the pressure of air and other gases.

This appears to have been first suspected by Daniel Bernoulli, but he had not the means which we now have of verifying the theory. The same theory was afterwards brought forward independently by Lesage, of Geneva, who, however, devoted most of his labour to the explanation of gravitation by the impact of atoms. Then Herapath, in his *Mathematical Physics*, published in 1847, made a much more extensive application of the theory to gases, and Dr Joule, whose absence from our meeting we must all regret, calculated the actual velocity of the molecules of hydrogen.

The further development of the theory is generally supposed to have begun with a paper by Krönig, which does not, however, so far as I can see, contain any improvement on what had gone before. It seems, however, to have drawn the attention of Professor Clausius to the subject, and to him we owe a very large part of what has been since accomplished.

We all know that air or any other gas placed in a vessel presses against the sides of the vessel, and against the surface of any body placed within it. On the kinetic theory this pressure is entirely due to the molecules striking against these surfaces, and thereby communicating to them a series of impulses which follow each other in such rapid succession that they produce an effect which cannot be distinguished from that of a continuous pressure.

If the velocity of the molecules is given, and the number varied, then since each molecule, on an average, strikes the sides of the vessel the same number of times, and with an impulse of the same magnitude, each will contribute an equal share to the whole pressure. The pressure in a vessel of given size is therefore proportional to the number of molecules in it, that is to the quantity of gas in it.

This is the complete dynamical explanation of the fact discovered by Robert Boyle, that the pressure of air is proportional to its density. It shews also that of different portions of gas forced into a vessel, each produces its own part of the pressure independently of the rest, and this whether these portions be of the same gas or not.

Let us next suppose that the velocity of the molecules is increased. Each molecule will now strike the sides of the vessel a greater number of times in a second, but, besides this, the impulse of each blow will be increased in the same proportion, so that the part of the pressure due to each molecule will vary as the *square* of the velocity. Now the increase of velocity corresponds, on our theory, to a rise of temperature, and in this way we can explain the effect of warming the gas, and also the law discovered by Charles that the proportional expansion of all gases between given temperatures is the same.

The dynamical theory also tells us what will happen if molecules of different masses are allowed to knock about together. The greater masses will go slower than the smaller ones, so that, on an average, every molecule, great or small, will have the same energy of motion.

The proof of this dynamical theorem, in which I claim the priority, has recently been greatly developed and improved by Dr Ludwig Boltzmann. The most important consequence which flows from it is that a cubic centimetre of every gas at standard temperature and pressure contains the same number of molecules. This is the dynamical explanation of Gay Lussac's law of the equivalent volumes of gases. But we must now descend to particulars, and calculate the actual velocity of a molecule of hydrogen.

A cubic centimetre of hydrogen, at the temperature of melting ice, and at a pressure of one atmosphere, weighs 0·00008954 grammes. We have to find at what rate this small mass must move (whether ·altogether or in separate molecules makes no difference) so as to produce the observed pressure on the sides of the cubic centimetre. This is the calculation which was first made by Dr Joule, and the result is 1,859 metres per second. This is what we are accustomed to call a great velocity. It is greater than any velocity obtained in artillery practice. The velocity of other gases is less, as you will see by the table, but in all cases it is very great as compared with that of bullets.

We have now to conceive the molecules of the air in this hall flying about in all directions, at a rate of about seventeen miles in a minute.

If all these molecules were flying in the same direction, they would constitute a wind blowing at the rate of seventeen miles a minute, and the only wind which approaches this velocity is that which proceeds from the mouth of a cannon. How, then, are you and I able to stand here? Only because the molecules happen to be flying in different directions, so that those which strike against our backs enable us to support the storm which is beating against our faces. Indeed, if this molecular bombardment were to cease, even for an instant, our veins would swell, our breath would leave us, and we should, literally, expire. But it is not only against us or against the walls of the hall that the molecules are striking. Consider the immense number of them, and the fact that they are flying in every possible direction, and you will see that they cannot avoid striking each other. Every time that two molecules come into collision, the paths of both are changed, and they go off in new directions. Thus each molecule is continually getting its course altered, so that in spite of its great velocity it may be a long time before it reaches any great distance from the point at which it set out.

I have here a bottle containing ammonia. Ammonia is a gas which you can recognise by its smell. Its molecules have a velocity of six hundred metres per second, so that if their course had not been interrupted by striking against the molecules of air in the hall, everyone in the most distant gallery would have smelt ammonia before I was able to pronounce the name of the gas. But instead of this, each molecule of ammonia is so jostled about by the molecules of air, that it is sometimes going one way and sometimes another, and like a hare which is always doubling, though it goes a great pace, it makes very little progress. Nevertheless, the smell of ammonia is now beginning to be perceptible at some distance from the bottle. The gas does diffuse itself through the air, though the process is a slow one, and if we could close up every opening of this hall so as to make it air-tight, and leave everything to itself for some weeks, the ammonia would become uniformly mixed through every part of the air in the hall.

This property of gases, that they diffuse through each other, was first remarked by Priestley. Dalton shewed that it takes place quite independently of any chemical action between the inter-diffusing gases. Graham, whose researches were especially directed towards those phenomena which seem to throw light on molecular motions, made a careful study of diffusion, and obtained the first results from which the rate of diffusion can be calculated.

Still more recently the rates of diffusion of gases into each other have been measured with great precision by Professor Loschmidt of Vienna.

He placed the two gases in two similar vertical tubes, the lighter gas being placed above the heavier, so as to avoid the formation of currents. He then opened a sliding valve, so as to make the two tubes into one, and after leaving the gases to themselves for an hour or so, he shut the valve, and determined how much of each gas had diffused into the other.

As most gases are invisible, I shall exhibit gaseous diffusion to you by means of two gases, ammonia and hydrochloric acid, which, when they meet, form a solid product. The ammonia, being the lighter gas, is placed above the hydrochloric acid, with a stratum of air between, but you will soon see that the gases can diffuse through this stratum of air, and produce a cloud of white smoke when they meet. During the whole of this process no currents or any other visible motion can be detected. Every part of the vessel appears as calm as a jar of undisturbed air.

But, according to our theory, the same kind of motion is going on in calm air as in the inter-diffusing gases, the only difference being that we can trace the molecules from one place to another more easily when they are of a different nature from those through which they are diffusing.

If we wish to form a mental representation of what is going on among the molecules in calm air, we cannot do better than observe a swarm of bees, when every individual bee is flying furiously, first in one direction and then in another, while the swarm, as a whole, either remains at rest, or sails slowly through the air.

In certain seasons, swarms of bees are apt to fly off to a great distance, and the owners, in order to identify their property when they find them on other people's ground, sometimes throw handfulls of flour at the swarm. Now let us suppose that the flour thrown at the flying swarm has whitened those bees only which happened to be in the lower half of the swarm, leaving those in the upper half free from flour.

If the bees still go on flying hither and thither in an irregular manner, the floury bees will be found in continually increasing proportions in the upper part of the swarm, till they have become equally diffused through every part of it. But the reason of this diffusion is not because the bees were marked with flour, but because they are flying about. The only effect of the marking is to enable us to identify certain bees.

We have no means of marking a select number of molecules of air, so as to trace them after they have become diffused among others, but we may communicate to them some property by which we may obtain evidence of their diffusion.

For instance, if a horizontal stratum of air is moving horizontally, molecules diffusing out of this stratum into those above and below will carry their horizontal motion with them, and so tend to communicate motion to the neighbouring strata, while molecules diffusing out of the neighbouring strata into the moving one will tend to bring it to rest. The action between the strata is somewhat like that of two rough surfaces, one of which slides over the other, rubbing on it. Friction is the name given to this action between solid bodies; in the case of fluids it is called internal friction, or viscosity.

It is, in fact, only another kind of diffusion—a lateral diffusion of momentum, and its amount can be calculated from data derived from observations of the first kind of diffusion, that of matter. The comparative values of the viscosity of different gases were determined by Graham in his researches on the transpiration of gases through long narrow tubes, and their absolute values have been deduced from experiments on the oscillation of discs by Oscar Meyer and myself.

Another way of tracing the diffusion of molecules through calm air is to heat the upper stratum of the air in a vessel, and to observe the rate at which this heat is communicated to the lower strata. This, in fact, is a third kind of diffusion—that of energy, and the rate at which it must take place was calculated from data derived from experiments on viscosity before any direct experiments on the conduction of heat had been made. Professor Stefan, of Vienna, has recently, by a very delicate method, succeeded in determining the conductivity of air, and he finds it, as he tells us, in striking agreement with the value predicted by the theory.

All these three kinds of diffusion—the diffusion of matter, of momentum, and of energy—are carried on by the motion of the molecules. The greater the velocity of the molecules and the further they travel before their paths are altered by collision with other molecules, the more rapid will be the diffusion. Now we know already the velocity of the molecules, and therefore, by experiments on diffusion, we can determine how far, on an average, a molecule travels without striking another. Professor Clausius, of Bonn, who first gave us precise ideas about the motion of agitation of molecules, calls this distance the mean path of a molecule. I have calculated, from Professor Loschmidt's diffusion experiments, the mean path of the molecules of four well-known gases. The average distance travelled by a molecule between one collision and another is given in the table. It is a very small distance, quite imperceptible to us even with our best microscopes. Roughly speaking, it is about the tenth part of the length of a wave of light, which you know is a very small quantity. Of course the time spent on so short a path by such swift molecules must be very small. I have calculated the number of collisions which each must undergo in a second. They are given in the table and are reckoned by thousands of millions. No wonder that the travelling power of the swiftest molecule is but small, when its course is completely changed thousands of millions of times in a second.

The three kinds of diffusion also take place in liquids, but the relation between the rates at which they take place is not so simple as in the case of gases. The dynamical theory of liquids is not so well understood as that of gases, but the principal difference between a gas and a liquid seems to be that in a gas each molecule spends the greater part of its time in describing its free path, and is for a very small portion of its time engaged in encounters with other molecules, whereas, in a liquid, the molecule has hardly any free path, and is always in a state of close encounter with other molecules.

Hence in a liquid the diffusion of motion from one molecule to another takes place much more rapidly than the diffusion of the molecules themselves, for the same reason that it is more expeditious in a dense crowd to pass on a letter from hand to hand than to give it to a special messenger to work his way through the crowd. I have here a jar, the lower part of which contains a solution of copper sulphate, while the upper part contains pure water. It has been standing here since Friday, and you see how little progress the blue liquid has made in diffusing itself through the water above. The rate of diffusion of a solution of sugar has been carefully observed by Voit. Comparing his results with those of Loschmidt on gases, we find that about as much diffusion takes place in a second in gases as requires a day in liquids.

The rate of diffusion of momentum is also slower in liquids than in gases, but by no means in the same proportion. The same amount of motion takes about ten times as long to subside in water as in air, as you will see by what takes place when I stir these two jars, one containing water and the other air. There is still less difference between the rates at which a rise of temperature is propagated through a liquid and through a gas.

In solids the molecules are still in motion, but their motions are confined within very narrow limits. Hence the diffusion of matter does not take place in solid bodies, though that of motion and heat takes place very freely. Nevertheless, certain liquids can diffuse through colloid solids, such as jelly and gum, and hydrogen can make its way through iron and palladium.

We have no time to do more than mention that most wonderful molecular motion which is called electrolysis. Here is an electric current passing through acidulated water, and causing oxygen to appear at one electrode and hydrogen at the other. In the space between, the water is perfectly calm; and yet two opposite currents of oxygen and of hydrogen must be passing through it. The physical theory of this process has been studied by Clausius, who has given reasons for asserting that in ordinary water the molecules are not only moving, but every now and then striking each other with such violence that the oxygen and hydrogen of the molecules part company, and dance about through the crowd, seeking partners which have become dissociated in the same way. In ordinary water these exchanges produce, on the whole, no observable effect; but no sooner does the electromotive force begin to act than it exerts its guiding influence on the unattached molecules, and bends the course of each toward its proper electrode, till the moment when, meeting with an unappropriated molecule of the opposite kind, it enters again into a more or less permanent union with it till it is again dissociated by another shock. Electrolysis, therefore, is a kind of diffusion assisted by electromotive force.

Another branch of molecular science is that which relates to the exchange of molecules between a liquid and a gas. It includes the theory of evaporation and condensation, in which the gas in question is the vapour of the liquid, and also the theory of the absorption of a gas by a liquid of a different substance. The researches of Dr Andrews on the relations between the liquid and the gaseous state have shewn us that though the statements in our elementary text-books may be so neatly expressed as to appear almost self-evident, their true interpretation may involve some principle so profound that, till the right man has laid hold of it, no one ever suspects that any thing is left to be discovered.

These, then, are some of the fields from which the data of molecular science are gathered. We may divide the ultimate results into three ranks, according to the completeness of our knowledge of them.

To the first rank belong the relative masses of the molecules of different gases, and their velocities in metres per second. These data are obtained from experiments on the pressure and density of gases, and are known to a high degree of precision.

In the second rank we must place the relative size of the molecules of different gases, the length of their mean paths, and the number of collisions in a second. These quantities are deduced from experiments on the three kinds of diffusion. Their received values must be regarded as rough approximations till the methods of experimenting are greatly improved.

There is another set of quantities which we must place in the third rank, because our knowledge of them is neither precise, as in the first rank, nor approximate, as in the second, but is only as yet of the nature of a probable conjecture. These are :—The absolute mass of a molecule, its absolute diameter, and the number of molecules in a cubic centimetre. We know the relative masses of different molecules with great accuracy, and we know their relative diameters approximately. From these we can deduce the relative densities of the molecules themselves. So far we are on firm ground.

The great resistance of liquids to compression makes it probable that their molecules must be at about the same distance from each other as that at which two molecules of the same substance in the gaseous form act on each other

47—2

during an encounter. This conjecture has been put to the test by Lorenz Meyer, who has compared the densities of different liquids with the calculated relative densities of the molecules of their vapours, and has found a remarkable correspondence between them.

Now Loschmidt has deduced from the dynamical theory the following remarkable proportion:—As the volume of a gas is to the combined volume of all the molecules contained in it, so is the mean path of a molecule to one-eighth of the diameter of a molecule.

Assuming that the volume of the substance, when reduced to the liquid form, is not much greater than the combined volume of the molecules, we obtain from this proportion the diameter of a molecule. In this way Loschmidt, in 1865, made the first estimate of the diameter of a molecule. Independently of him and of each other, Mr Stoney in 1868, and Sir W. Thomson in 1870, published results of a similar kind, those of Thomson being deduced not only in this way, but from considerations derived from the thickness of soap-bubbles, and from the electric properties of metals.

According to the Table, which I have calculated from Loschmidt's data, the size of the molecules of hydrogen is such that about two millions of them in a row would occupy a millimetre, and a million million million million of them would weigh between four and five grammes.

In a cubic centimetre of any gas at standard pressure and temperature there are about nineteen million million million molecules. All these numbers of the third rank are, I need not tell you, to be regarded as at present conjectural. In order to warrant us in putting any confidence in numbers obtained in this way, we should have to compare together a greater number of independent data than we have as yet obtained, and to shew that they lead to consistent results.

Thus far we have been considering molecular science as an inquiry into natural phenomena. But though the professed aim of all scientific work is to unravel the secrets of nature, it has another effect, not less valuable, on the mind of the worker. It leaves him in possession of methods which nothing but scientific work could have led him to invent; and it places him in a position from which many regions of nature, besides that which he has been studying, appear under a new aspect.

The study of molecules has developed a method of its own, and it has also opened up new views of nature.

When Lucretius wishes us to form a mental representation of the motion of atoms, he tells us to look at a sunbeam shining through a darkened room (the same instrument of research by which Dr Tyndall makes visible to us the dust we breathe), and to observe the motes which chase each other in all directions through it. This motion of the visible motes, he tells us, is but a result of the far more complicated motion of the invisible atoms which knock the motes about. In his dream of nature, as Tennyson tells us, he

> " Saw the flaring atom-streams
> And torrents of her myriad universe,
> Ruining along the illimitable inane,
> Fly on to clash together again, and make
> Another and another frame of things
> For ever."

And it is no wonder that he should have attempted to burst the bonds of Fate by making his atoms deviate from their courses at quite uncertain times and places, thus attributing to them a kind of irrational free will, which on his materialistic theory is the only explanation of that power of voluntary action of which we ourselves are conscious.

As long as we have to deal with only two molecules, and have all the data given us, we can calculate the result of their encounter; but when we have to deal with millions of molecules, each of which has millions of encounters in a second, the complexity of the problem seems to shut out all hope of a legitimate solution.

The modern atomists have therefore adopted a method which is, I believe, new in the department of mathematical physics, though it has long been in use in the section of Statistics. When the working members of Section F get hold of a report of the Census, or any other document containing the numerical data of Economic and Social Science, they begin by distributing the whole population into groups, according to age, income-tax, education, religious belief, or criminal convictions. The number of individuals is far too great to allow of their tracing the history of each separately, so that, in order to reduce their labour within human limits, they concentrate their attention on a small number of artificial groups. The varying number of individuals in each group, and not the varying state of each individual, is the primary datum from which they work.

This, of course, is not the only method of studying human nature. We may observe the conduct of individual men and compare it with that conduct which their previous character and their present circumstances, according to the best existing theory, would lead us to expect. Those who practise this method endeavour to improve their knowledge of the elements of human nature in much the same way as an astronomer corrects the elements of a planet by comparing its actual position with that deduced from the received elements. The study of human nature by parents and schoolmasters, by historians and statesmen, is therefore to be distinguished from that carried on by registrars and tabulators, and by those statesmen who put their faith in figures. The one may be called the historical, and the other the statistical method.

The equations of dynamics completely express the laws of the historical method as applied to matter, but the application of these equations implies a perfect knowledge of all the data. But the smallest portion of matter which we can subject to experiment consists of millions of molecules, not one of which ever becomes individually sensible to us. We cannot, therefore, ascertain the actual motion of any one of these molecules; so that we are obliged to abandon the strict historical method, and to adopt the statistical method of dealing with large groups of molecules.

The data of the statistical method as applied to molecular science are the sums of large numbers of molecular quantities. In studying the relations between quantities of this kind, we meet with a new kind of regularity, the regularity of averages, which we can depend upon quite sufficiently' for all practical purposes, but which can make no claim to that character of absolute precision which belongs to the laws of abstract dynamics.

Thus molecular science teaches us that our experiments can never give us anything more than statistical information, and that no law deduced from them can pretend to absolute precision. But when we pass from the contemplation of our experiments to that of the molecules themselves, we leave the world of chance and change, and enter a region where everything is certain and immutable.

The molecules are conformed to a constant type with a precision which is not to be found in the sensible properties of the bodies which they constitute. In the first place, the mass of each individual molecule, and all its other properties, are absolutely unalterable. In the second place, the properties of all molecules of the same kind are absolutely identical.

Let us consider the properties of two kinds of molecules, those of oxygen and those of hydrogen.

We can procure specimens of oxygen from very different sources—from the air, from water, from rocks of every geological epoch. The history of these specimens has been very different, and if, during thousands of years, difference of circumstances could produce difference of properties, these specimens of oxygen would shew it.

In like manner we may procure hydrogen from water, from coal, or, as Graham did, from meteoric iron. Take two litres of any specimen of hydrogen, it will combine with exactly one litre of any specimen of oxygen, and will form exactly two litres of the vapour of water.

Now if, during the whole previous history of either specimen, whether imprisoned in the rocks, flowing in the sea, or careering through unknown regions with the meteorites, any modification of the molecules had taken place, these relations would no longer be preserved.

But we have another and an entirely different method of comparing the properties of molecules. The molecule, though indestructible, is not a hard rigid body, but is capable of internal movements, and when these are excited, it emits rays, the wave-length of which is a measure of the time of vibration of the molecule.

By means of the spectroscope the wave-lengths of different kinds of light may be compared to within one ten-thousandth part. In this way it has been ascertained, not only that molecules taken from every specimen of hydrogen in our laboratories have the same set of periods of vibration, but that light, having the same set of periods of vibration, is emitted from the sun and from the fixed stars.

We are thus assured that molecules of the same nature as those of our hydrogen exist in those distant regions, or at least did exist when the light by which we see them was emitted.

From a comparison of the dimensions of the buildings of the Egyptians with those of the Greeks, it appears that they have a common measure. Hence, even if no ancient author had recorded the fact that the two nations employed the same cubit as a standard of length, we might prove it from the buildings themselves. We should also be justified in asserting that at some time or other a material standard of length must have been carried from one country to the other, or that both countries had obtained their standards from a common source.

But in the heavens we discover by their light, and by their light alone, stars so distant from each other that no material thing can ever have passed from one to another; and yet this light, which is to us the sole evidence of the existence of these distant worlds, tells us also that each of them is built up of molecules of the same kinds as those which we find on earth. A molecule of hydrogen, for example, whether in Sirius or in Arcturus, executes its vibrations in precisely the same time.

Each molecule, therefore, throughout the universe, bears impressed on it the stamp of a metric system as distinctly as does the metre of the Archives at Paris, or the double royal cubit of the Temple of Karnac.

No theory of evolution can be formed to account for the similarity of molecules, for evolution necessarily implies continuous change, and the molecule is incapable of growth or decay, of generation or destruction.

None of the processes of Nature, since the time when Nature began, have produced the slightest difference in the properties of any molecule. We are therefore unable to ascribe either the existence of the molecules or the identity of their properties to the operation of any of the causes which we call natural.

On the other hand, the exact equality of each molecule to all others of the same kind gives it, as Sir John Herschel has well said, the essential character of a manufactured article, and precludes the idea of its being eternal and self-existent.

Thus we have been led, along a strictly scientific path, very near to the point at which Science must stop. Not that Science is debarred from studying the internal mechanism of a molecule which she cannot take to pieces, any more than from investigating an organism which she cannot put together. But in tracing back the history of matter Science is arrested when she assures herself, on the one hand, that the molecule has been made, and on the other, that it has not been made by any of the processes we call natural.

Science is incompetent to reason upon the creation of matter itself out of nothing. We have reached the utmost limit of our thinking faculties when we have admitted that because matter cannot be eternal and self-existent it must have been created.

It is only when we contemplate, not matter in itself, but the form in which it actually exists, that our mind finds something on which it can lay hold.

That matter, as such, should have certain fundamental properties—that it should exist in space and be capable of motion, that its motion should be persistent, and so on, are truths which may, for anything we know, be of the kind which metaphysicians call necessary. We may use our knowledge of such truths for purposes of deduction, but we have no data for speculating as to their origin.

But that there should be exactly so much matter and no more in every molecule of hydrogen is a fact of a very different order. We have here a particular distribution of matter—a *collocation*—to use the expression of Dr Chalmers, of things which we have no difficulty in imagining to have been arranged otherwise.

The form and dimensions of the orbits of the planets, for instance, are not determined by any law of nature, but depend upon a particular collocation of matter. The same is the case with respect to the size of the earth, from which the standard of what is called the metrical system has been derived. But these astronomical and terrestrial magnitudes are far inferior in scientific importance to that most fundamental of all standards which forms the base of the molecular system. Natural causes, as we know, are at work, which tend to modify, if they do not at length destroy, all the arrangements and dimensions of the earth and the whole solar system. But though in the course of ages catastrophes have occurred and may yet occur in the heavens, though ancient systems may be dissolved and new systems evolved out of their ruins, the molecules out of which these systems are built—the foundation stones of the material universe—remain unbroken and unworn.

They continue this day as they were created—perfect in number and measure and weight, and from the ineffaceable characters impressed on them we may learn that those aspirations after accuracy in measurement, truth in statement, and justice in action, which we reckon among our noblest attributes as men, are ours because they are essential constituents of the image of Him who in the beginning created, not only the heaven and the earth, but the materials of which heaven and earth consist.

Table of Molecular Data.

		Hydrogen.	Oxygen.	Carbonic oxide.	Carbonic acid.
Rank I.	Mass of molecule (hydrogen = 1)	1	16	14	22
	Velocity (of mean square) metres per second at 0° C.	1859	465	497	396
	Mean path, tenth-metres	965	560	482	379
Rank II.	Collisions in a second (millions)	17750	7646	9489	9720
	Diameter, tenth-metres	5·8	7·6	8·3	9·3
Rank III.	Mass, twenty-fifth grammes	46	736	644	1012

Table of Diffusion. $\dfrac{(Centimetre)^2}{Second}$ measure.

	Calculated.	Observed.	
H & O	0·7086	0·7214	
H & CO	0·6519	0·6422	
H & CO₂	0·5575	0·5558	Diffusion of matter observed by Loschmidt.
O & CO	0·1807	0·1802	
O & CO₂	0·1427	0·1409	
CO & CO₂	0·1386	0·1406	
H	1·2990	1·49	
O	0·1884	0·213	
CO	0·1748	0·212	Diffusion of momentum (Graham and Meyer).
CO₂	0·1087	0·117	
Air		0·256	
Copper		1·077	Diffusion of temperature observed by Stefan.
Iron		0·183	
Cane Sugar in water		0·00000365	Voit.
(Or in a day		0·3144)	
Salt in water		0·00000116 Fick.	

$\dfrac{(Centimetre)^2}{Second}$

[From the *Proceedings of the Royal Society*, No. 148, 1873.]

LXIII. *On Double Refraction in a Viscous Fluid in Motion.*

ACCORDING to Poisson's* theory of the internal friction of fluids, a viscous fluid behaves as an elastic solid would do if it were periodically liquefied for an instant and solidified again, so that at each fresh start it becomes for the moment like an elastic solid free from strain. The state of strain of certain transparent bodies may be investigated by means of their action on polarized light. This action was observed by Brewster, and was shewn by Fresnel to be an instance of double refraction.

In 1866 I made some attempts to ascertain whether the state of strain in a viscous fluid in motion could be detected by its action on polarized light. I had a cylindrical box with a glass bottom. Within this box a solid cylinder could be made to rotate. The fluid to be examined was placed in the annular space between this cylinder and the sides of the box. Polarized light was thrown up through the fluid parallel to the axis, and the inner cylinder was then made to rotate. I was unable to obtain any result with solution of gum or sirup of sugar, though I observed an effect on polarized light when I compressed some Canada balsam which had become very thick and almost solid in a bottle.

It is easy, however, to observe the effect in Canada balsam, which is so fluid that it very rapidly assumes a level surface after being disturbed. Put some Canada balsam in a wide-mouthed square bottle; let light, polarized in a vertical plane, be transmitted through the fluid; observe the light through a Nicol's prism, and turn the prism so as to cut off the light; insert a spatula in the Canada balsam, in a vertical plane passing through the eye. Whenever the spatula is moved up or down in the fluid, the light reappears on both sides of the spatula; this continues only so long as the spatula is in motion. As soon as the motion stops, the light disappears, and that so quickly that I have hitherto been unable to determine the rate of relaxation of that state of strain which the light indicates.

If the motion of the spatula in its own plane, instead of being in the plane

---

* *Journal de l'École Polytechnique*, tome xiii. cah. xx. (1829).

of polarization, is inclined 45° to it, no effect is observed, shewing that the axes of strain are inclined 45° to the plane of shearing, as indicated by the theory.

I am not aware that this method of rendering visible the state of strain of a viscous fluid has been hitherto employed; but it appears capable of furnishing important information as to the nature of viscosity in different substances.

Among transparent solids there is considerable diversity in their action on polarized light. If a small portion is cut from a piece of unannealed glass at a place where the strain is uniform, the effect on polarized light vanishes as soon as the glass is relieved from the stress caused by the unequal contraction of the parts surrounding it.

But if a plate of gelatine is allowed to dry under longitudinal tension, a small piece cut out of it exhibits the same effect on light as it did before, shewing that a state of strain can exist without the action of stress. A film of gutta percha which has been stretched in one direction has a similar action on light. If a circular piece is cut out of such a stretched film and warmed, it contracts in the direction in which the stretching took place.

The body of a sea-nettle has all the appearance of a transparent jelly; and at one time I thought that the spontaneous contractions of the living animal might be rendered visible by means of polarized light transmitted through its body. But I found that even a very considerable pressure applied to the sides of the sea-nettle produced no effect on polarized light, and I thus found, what I might have learned by dissection, that the sea-nettle is not a true jelly, but consists of cells filled with fluid.

On the other hand, the crystalline lens of the eye, as Brewster observed, has a strong action on polarized light when strained either by external pressure or by the unequal contraction of its parts as it becomes dry.

I have enumerated these instances of the application of polarized light to the study of the structure of solid bodies as suggestions with respect to the application of the same method to liquids so as to determine whether a given liquid differs from a solid in having a very small "rigidity," or in having a small "time of relaxation"*, or in both ways. Those which, like Canada balsam, act strongly on polarized light, have probably a small "rigidity," but a sensible "time of relaxation." Those which do not shew this action are probably much more "rigid," and owe their fluidity to the smallness of their "time of relaxation."

---

* The "time of relaxation" of a substance strained in a given manner is the time required for the complete relaxation of the strain, supposing the rate of relaxation to remain the same as at the beginning of this time.

[From the *Proceedings of the London Mathematical Society*, Vol. VI.]

LXIV. *On Hamilton's Characteristic Function for a Narrow Beam of Light.*

[Read *January* 8th, 1874.]

HAMILTON'S characteristic function V is an expression for the time of propagation of light from the point whose co-ordinates are x_1, y_1, z_1 to the point whose co-ordinates are x_2, y_2, z_2. It is a function of these six co-ordinates of the two points. The axes to which the co-ordinates are referred may be different for the two points.

In isotropic media the differential equation of V may be written

$$\left(\frac{dV}{dx}\right)^2 + \left(\frac{dV}{dy}\right)^2 + \left(\frac{dV}{dz}\right)^2 = \mu^2 \dots\dots\dots\dots\dots (1),$$

where μ is the slowness of propagation at a point in the medium whose co-ordinates are x, y, z, and is a function of these co-ordinates. If the time of propagation through the unit of length in vacuum be taken as the unit of time, then μ is the index of refraction of the medium.

The form of the equation in doubly refracting media, as given by Hamilton, is not required for our present purpose.

Let $OPQR$ be the path of a ray of light. Let the part OP be in a homogeneous medium whose index of refraction is μ_1, and let QR be in a homogeneous medium whose index of refraction is μ_2. Between P and Q the ray may pass through any combination of media, singly or doubly refracting.

Fig. 1.

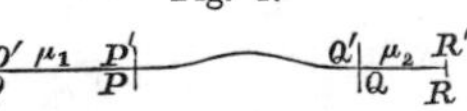

Let us consider the characteristic function from a point near to OP in the first medium to a point near to QR in the second.

Let the position of the first point be referred to rectangular axes, the origin of which is at P, and the axis of z_1 drawn in the direction PO. The axes of x_1 and y_1 may be turned at pleasure round that of z_1 into the position most suitable for our calculations.

Let the position of the second point be referred to Q as origin, to QR as axis of z_2, and to axes of x_2 and y_2 the position of which is of course independent of that chosen for x_1, y_1.

Let the ray from the first point $O'(x_1, y_1, z_1)$ to the second point $R'(x_2, y_2, z_2)$ pass through $P'(\xi_1, \eta_1, 0)$, and $Q'(\xi_2, \eta_2, 0)$.

We have then $\quad V_{O'R'} = V_{O'P'} + V_{P'Q'} + V_{Q'R'}$ .... (2).

Here
$$V_{O'P'} = \mu_1 O'P' = \mu_1 \sqrt{(x_1 - \xi_1)^2 + (y_1 - \eta_1)^2 + z_1^2}$$ ....(3),

and
$$V_{Q'R'} = \mu_2 Q'R' = \mu_2 \sqrt{(x_2 - \xi_2)^2 + (y_2 - \eta_2)^2 + z_2^2}$$ ....(4).

Also

$$\left.\begin{aligned}
V_{P'Q'} = V_{PQ} &+ \xi_1 \frac{dV}{d\xi_1} + \eta_1 \frac{dV}{d\eta_1} + \xi_2 \frac{dV}{d\xi_2} + \eta_2 \frac{dV}{\delta\eta_2} + \tfrac{1}{2}\xi_1^2 \frac{d^2V}{d\xi_1^2} \\
&+ \xi_1\eta_1 \frac{d^2V}{d\xi_1 d\eta_1} + \tfrac{1}{2}\eta_1^2 \frac{d^2V}{d\eta_1^2} + \tfrac{1}{2}\xi_2^2 \frac{d^2V}{d\xi_2^2} + \xi_2\eta_2 \frac{d^2V}{d\xi_2 d\eta_2} + \tfrac{1}{2}\eta_2^2 \frac{d^2V}{d\eta_2^2} \\
&+ \xi_1\xi_2 \frac{d^2V}{d\xi_1 d\xi_2} + \xi_1\eta_2 \frac{d^2V}{d\xi_1 d\eta_2} + \eta_1\xi_2 \frac{d^2V}{d\eta_1 d\xi_2} + \eta_1\eta_2 \frac{d^2V}{d\eta_1 d\eta_2}
\end{aligned}\right\} .....(5).$$

+ terms involving higher powers and products of ξ_1, η_1, ξ_2, η_2

Writing, for the sake of brevity, single symbols for the differential coefficients, we obtain for the value of $V_{O'R'}$ up to the terms of the second degree inclusive

$$\left.\begin{aligned}
V_{O'R'} = \mu_1 z_1 &+ \frac{\mu_1}{2z_1} \{(x_1 - \xi_1)^2 + (y_1 - \eta_1)^2\} + \mu_2 z_2 + \frac{\mu_2}{2z_2} \{(x_2 - \xi_2)^2 + (y_2 - \eta_2)^2\} \\
&+ V_{PQ} + f_1\xi_1 + g_1\eta_1 + f_2\xi_2 + g_2\eta_2 + \tfrac{1}{2}a_1\xi_1^2 + c_1\xi_1\eta_1 + \tfrac{1}{2}b_1\eta_1^2 \\
&+ p\xi_1\xi_2 + q\xi_1\eta_2 + r\eta_1\xi_2 + s\eta_1\eta_2 + \tfrac{1}{2}a_2\xi_2^2 + c_2\xi_2\eta_2 + \tfrac{1}{2}b_2\eta_2^2
\end{aligned}\right\} ..... (6).$$

This is the value of $V_{O'P'} + V_{P'Q'} + V_{Q'R'}$, supposing the course of the ray to be broken at P' and Q' in an arbitrary manner.

For the actual course of the ray the value of $V_{O'R'}$ must be stationary as regards variations of ξ_1, η_1, ξ_2, η_2. Hence, differentiating with respect to these variables, we obtain the four equations

$$\left.\begin{aligned}
\left(a_1+\frac{\mu_1}{z_1}\right)\xi_1 + \quad c_1\eta_1 \quad + \quad p\xi_2 \quad + \quad q\eta_2 \quad &= \mu_1\frac{x_1}{z_1}-f_1 \\
c_1\xi_1 \quad +\left(b_1+\frac{\mu_1}{z_1}\right)\eta_1+ \quad r\xi_2 \quad + \quad s\eta_2 \quad &= \mu_1\frac{y_1}{z_1}-g_1 \\
p\xi_1 \quad + \quad r\eta_1 \quad +\left(a_2+\frac{\mu_2}{z_2}\right)\xi_2+ \quad c_2\eta_2 \quad &= \mu_2\frac{x_2}{z_2}-f_2 \\
q\xi_1 \quad + \quad s\eta_1 \quad + \quad c_2\xi_2 \quad +\left(b_2+\frac{\mu_2}{z_2}\right)\eta_2 &= \mu_2\frac{y_2}{z_2}-g_2
\end{aligned}\right\}\dots\dots(7).$$

Since $OPQR$ is a ray of the system, the co-ordinates x_1, y_1; ξ_1, η_1; ξ_2, η_2; x_2, y_2, vanish together. Hence $f_1=g_1=f_2=g_2=0$, and if we write Δ for the determinant

$$\begin{vmatrix}
a_1+\dfrac{\mu_1}{z_1} & c_1 & p & q \\[2mm]
c_1 & b_1+\dfrac{\mu_1}{z_1} & r & s \\[2mm]
p & r & a_2+\dfrac{\mu_2}{z_2} & c_2 \\[2mm]
q & s & c_3 & b_2+\dfrac{\mu_2}{z_2}
\end{vmatrix} \dots\dots\dots\dots(8).$$

Then

$$\left.\begin{aligned}
\Delta\xi_1 &= \frac{\mu_1}{z_1}\left(x_1\frac{d\Delta}{da_1}+\tfrac{1}{2}y_1\frac{d\Delta}{dc_1}\right)+\tfrac{1}{2}\frac{\mu_2}{z_2}\left(x_2\frac{d\Delta}{dp}+y_2\frac{d\Delta}{dq}\right) \\
\Delta\eta_1 &= \frac{\mu_1}{z_1}\left(\tfrac{1}{2}x_1\frac{d\Delta}{dc_1}+y_1\frac{d\Delta}{db_1}\right)+\tfrac{1}{2}\frac{\mu_2}{z_2}\left(x_2\frac{d\Delta}{dr}+y_2\frac{d\Delta}{ds}\right) \\
\Delta\xi_2 &= \tfrac{1}{2}\frac{\mu_1}{z_1}\left(x_1\frac{d\Delta}{dp}+y_1\frac{d\Delta}{dr}\right)+\frac{\mu_2}{z_2}\left(x_2\frac{d\Delta}{da_2}+\tfrac{1}{2}y_2\frac{d\Delta}{dc_2}\right) \\
\Delta\eta_2 &= \tfrac{1}{2}\frac{\mu_1}{z_1}\left(x_1\frac{d\Delta}{dq}+y_1\frac{d\Delta}{ds}\right)+\frac{\mu_2}{z_2}\left(\tfrac{1}{2}x_2\frac{d\Delta}{dc_2}+y_2\frac{d\Delta}{db_2}\right)
\end{aligned}\right\}\dots\dots(9).$$

Substituting in (6), we obtain

$$\left.\begin{aligned}
V_{O'R'} = V_{OR}+\mu_1z_1+\mu_2z_2+\tfrac{1}{2}\mathfrak{A}_1x_1^2+\mathfrak{C}_1x_1y_1+\tfrac{1}{2}\mathfrak{B}_1y_1^2 \\
+\mathfrak{P}x_1x_2+\mathfrak{Q}x_1y_2+\mathfrak{R}_1x_2y_1+\mathfrak{S}y_1y_2+\tfrac{1}{2}\mathfrak{A}_2x_2^2+\mathfrak{C}_2x_2y_2+\tfrac{1}{2}\mathfrak{B}_2y_2^2
\end{aligned}\right\}\dots\dots(10);$$

where
$$\mathfrak{A}_1=\frac{\mu_1}{z_1}-\frac{\mu_1^2}{z_1^2\Delta}\frac{d\Delta}{da_1}, \qquad \mathfrak{C}_1=-\frac{\mu_1^2}{2z_1^2\Delta}\frac{d\Delta}{dc_1}, \qquad \mathfrak{B}_1=\frac{\mu_1}{z_1}-\frac{\mu_1^2}{z_1^2\Delta}\frac{d\Delta}{db_1},$$

$$\mathfrak{P}=-\frac{\mu_1\mu_2}{2z_1z_2\Delta}\frac{d\Delta}{dp}, \qquad \mathfrak{Q}=-\frac{\mu_1\mu_2}{2z_1z_2\Delta}\frac{d\Delta}{dq},$$

$$\mathfrak{R}=-\frac{\mu_1\mu_2}{2z_1z_2\Delta}\frac{d\Delta}{dr}, \qquad \mathfrak{S}=-\frac{\mu_1\mu_2}{2z_1z_2\Delta}\frac{d\Delta}{ds},$$

$$\mathfrak{A}_2=\frac{\mu_2}{z_2}-\frac{\mu_2^2}{z_2^2\Delta}\frac{d\Delta}{da_2}, \qquad \mathfrak{C}_2=-\frac{\mu_2^2}{2z_2^2\Delta}\frac{d\Delta}{dc_2}, \qquad \mathfrak{B}_2=\frac{\mu_2}{z_2}-\frac{\mu_2^2}{z_2^2\Delta}\frac{d\Delta}{db_2}$$

$$\left.\right\}\dots\dots(11).$$

This is the most general form of Hamilton's characteristic function for a pair of points, each of which is near the principal ray. It is a homogeneous function of the second degree in x_1, y_1, x_2, y_2, the coefficients of which are functions of z_1 and z_2.

By turning the axes of x_1 and y_1 about z_1, and those of x_2 and y_2 about z_2, we may get rid of two of the ten terms, and so reduce the expression to eight.

We may, for example, get rid of c_1 and c_2, and so of $\mathfrak{C}_1$ and $\mathfrak{C}_2$; but since, in the theory of pencils having two focal lines, terms may enter which must be added to $\mathfrak{C}_1$ and $\mathfrak{C}_2$, this transformation is not of much use.

It is better to begin by getting rid of q and r, by turning x_1 and y_1 round z_1, through an angle θ_1, such that

$$\tfrac{1}{2}\tan 2\theta_1=\frac{pr+qs}{p^2+q^2-r^2-s^2}\dots\dots\dots\dots\dots (12),$$

and also turning x_2 and y_2 round z_2, through an angle θ_2, such that

$$\tfrac{1}{2}\tan 2\theta_2=\frac{pq+rs}{p^2+r^2-q^2-s^2}\dots\dots\dots\dots\dots(13).$$

For these new axes the values of q and r are reduced to zero.

As an instance of the use of the characteristic function, let us find the form of the emergent pencil when that of the incident pencil is given.

The general form of the characteristic function of a pencil, whose axis is the axis of z, is

$$V_1=K+\mu\left(z-\frac{x^2}{2A}-\frac{xy}{2C}-\frac{y^2}{2B}\right)\dots\dots\dots\dots (14),$$

as in the *Proceedings of the London Mathematical Society*, Vol. IV., p. 337 (1873); where A, B, C are lines from which, by the construction there given, a and b, the co-ordinates of the focal lines, and ϕ, the angle which the line a makes with the plane xz, may be deduced.

The quantities a_1, &c., which occur as the coefficients of the characteristic function, are the reciprocals of lines.

Let
$$
\left.
\begin{aligned}
a_1 &= a_1 + \frac{1}{A_1}, & \beta_1 &= b_1 + \frac{1}{B_1}, & \gamma_1 &= c_1 + \frac{1}{C_1} \\
a_2 &= a_2 + \frac{1}{A_2}, & \beta_2 &= b_2 + \frac{1}{B_2}, & \gamma_2 &= c_2 + \frac{1}{C_2}
\end{aligned}
\right\} \dots\dots\dots\dots (15).
$$
also let
$$
a_1\beta_1 - \gamma_1^2 = \delta_1, \text{ and } a_2\beta_2 - \gamma_2^2 = \delta_2
$$

The condition that the incident pencil defined by A_1, B_1, C_1 should be conjugate to the emergent pencil defined by A_2, B_2, C_2, is that the value of the characteristic function must be the same for all rays of the pencil. Now a particular ray of the pencil may be defined either by the co-ordinates x_1, y_1, z_1 of a point through which it passes in the first medium, or by x_2, y_2, z_2 those of a point through which it passes in the second medium. In the first case, the coefficients of x_1^2, $x_1 y_1$, and y_1^2 will vanish, and in the second those of x_2^2, $x_2 y_2$, and y_2^2. If the one set of conditions is fulfilled, the other set will be fulfilled also. Hence we may write the conditions either in the form

$$
\frac{d\Delta}{da_1} = 0, \quad \frac{d\Delta}{d\beta_1} = 0, \quad \frac{d\Delta}{d\gamma_1} = 0 \dots\dots\dots\dots\dots (16),
$$

or in the form
$$
\frac{d\Delta}{da_2} = 0, \quad \frac{d\Delta}{d\beta_2} = 0, \quad \frac{d\Delta}{d\gamma_2} = 0 \dots\dots\dots\dots\dots (17),
$$

where
$$
\Delta =
\begin{vmatrix}
a_1 & \gamma_1 & p & q \\
\gamma_1 & \beta_1 & r & s \\
p & r & a_2 & \gamma_2 \\
q & s & \gamma_2 & \beta_2
\end{vmatrix}
\dots\dots\dots\dots\dots\dots (18),
$$

$$
\left.
\begin{aligned}
&= \delta_1\delta_2 - a_1 a_2 s^2 + 2a_1\gamma_2 rs - a_1\beta_2 r^2 + 2\gamma_1 a_2 qs - 2\gamma_1\gamma_2(ps+qr) + 2\gamma_1\beta_2 pr \\
&\quad - \beta_1 a_2 q^2 - 2\beta_1\gamma_2 pq - \beta_1\beta_2 p^2 + (ps-qr)^2
\end{aligned}
\right\} \dots (19).
$$

The conditions of conjugate pencils may therefore be written, either

$$
\left.
\begin{aligned}
a_2\delta_1 &= \beta_1 p^2 - 2\gamma_1 pr + a_1 r^2 \\
\gamma_2\delta_1 &= \beta_1 pq - \gamma_1 (ps + qr) + a_1 rs \\
\beta_2\delta_1 &= \beta_1 q^2 - 2\gamma_1 qs + a_1 s^2
\end{aligned}
\right\} \quad \dots\dots\dots\dots\dots (20),
$$

or in a form derived from this by exchanging the suffixes $_1$ and $_2$.

If the axes of co-ordinates are turned so that q and r vanish,

$$
\Delta = \delta_1\delta_2 - a_1 a_2 s^2 - 2\gamma_1\gamma_2 ps - \beta_1\beta_2 p^2 + p^2 s^2 \dots\dots\dots\dots (21),
$$

and

$$
\left.
\begin{aligned}
a_2\delta_1 &= \beta_1 p^2 \\
\gamma_2\delta_1 &= -\gamma_1 ps \\
\beta_2\delta_1 &= a_1 s^2
\end{aligned}
\right\} \dots\dots\dots\dots\dots\dots (22).
$$

If we write

$$
\left.
\begin{aligned}
a_1 &= X_1 p, \quad \beta_1 = Y_1 s, \quad \gamma_1 = Z_1\sqrt{ps} \\
a_2 &= X_2 p, \quad \beta_2 = Y_2 s, \quad \gamma_2 = Z_2\sqrt{ps}
\end{aligned}
\right\} \dots\dots\dots\dots (23),
$$

then X_1, Y_1, Z_1 will be inverse to X_2, Y_2, Z_2, and will satisfy the equations

$$
\left.
\begin{aligned}
X_1 X_2 + Z_1 Z_2 &= 1, \quad Z_1 X_2 + Y_1 Z_2 = 0 \\
Z_1 Z_2 + Y_1 Y_2 &= 1, \quad X_1 Z_2 + Z_1 Y_2 = 0
\end{aligned}
\right\} \dots\dots\dots\dots (24).
$$

Fig. 2.

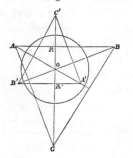

Fig. 3.

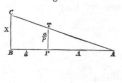

The relations between the quantities X_1, Y_1, Z_1 and X_2, Y_2, Z_2, are shewn in the annexed figure (Fig. 2).

Let $AR = X_1$ and $RB = Y_1$ in the same straight line, and $RO = Z_1$ perpendicular to AB. With O as centre and unity as radius describe a circle.

Draw $C'B'$ the polar of A, and $C'A'$ the polar of B, with respect to this circle. These lines meet BO and AO in B' and A' respectively. Join $A'B'$ cutting RO in R'. Then $B'R' = X_2$, $R'A' = Y_2$, and $OR' = Z_2$.

Since OR' is measured downwards, Z_2 is negative in the case represented by the figure. It is manifest that X_1, Y_1, and Z_1 may be found from X_2, Y_2, Z_2, by the same process.

The relation between the quantities A, B, C and X, Y, Z is shewn in Fig. 3.

Let a be one of the first three or the last three of the ten coefficients of the characteristic function $V_{P'Q'}$.

Since a is the reciprocal of a line, let BP represent the line $\dfrac{1}{a}$.

Draw PT perpendicular to BP so that PT is to the unit line as a to p.

Then, if $PA = A$, the line ATC will cut off from the line BC perpendicular to BA a part BC equal to X. For

$$BC = \frac{a}{p} + \frac{1}{A \cdot p} = \frac{a}{p} = X.$$

In this way X may be found when A is known, or A when X is known. The same method gives the relations between B and Y and between C and Z.

The geometrical process for finding the focal lines of the emergent pencil, when those of the incident pencil are given, is therefore as follows:—

From the distances a_1 and b_1 of the focal lines, and the angle ϕ_1 between the first of them and the plane of x_1z_1, deduce, by the method given in a former communication (Vol. IV., p. 337), A_1, B_1, and C_1*.

From A_1, B_1, C_1, find, by the construction of Fig. 3, X_1, Y_1, and Z_1.

From X_1, Y_1, Z_1, find, by the construction of Fig. 2, X_2, Y_2, and Z_2.

From X_2, Y_2, Z_2, find A_2, B_2, C_2.

From A_2, B_2, C_2, find a_2, b_2, ϕ_2.

Thus far we have been considering the most general case of a pencil passing through any number of media between P and Q, through surfaces of any form, the media before incidence at P and after emergence at Q being isotropic. When some of these media are doubly refracting, there may be two or more emergent pencils corresponding to one incident pencil. Our investigation is applicable only to one of these emergent pencils at a time. Each emergent pencil must be treated separately.

* [Page 337, Vol. II. of this Edition.]

In certain cases of practical importance the characteristic function may be greatly simplified. For instance, when the axis ray is refracted in one plane through the prisms of a spectroscope, the same positions of the axes of x and y which make q and r vanish, also make c_1 and c_2 vanish. The determinant Δ may now be written as the product of two factors

$$\Delta = \left\{ \left(a_1 + \frac{\mu_1}{z_1} \right) \left(a_2 + \frac{\mu_2}{z_2} \right) - p^2 \right\} \left\{ \left(b_1 + \frac{\mu_1}{z_1} \right) \left(b_2 + \frac{\mu_2}{z_2} \right) - s^2 \right\} \dots\dots(25),$$

$$V = V_{PQ} + \mu_1 z_1 + \mu_2 z_2$$

$$\left. \begin{array}{l} + \dfrac{\dfrac{\mu_1}{z_1} \left\{ a_1 \left(a_2 + \dfrac{\mu_2}{z_2} \right) - p^2 \right\} x_1^2 + \dfrac{\mu_1 \mu_2}{z_1 z_2} p x_1 x_2 + \dfrac{\mu_2}{z_2} \left\{ a_2 \left(a_1 + \dfrac{\mu_1}{z_1} \right) - p^2 \right\} x_2^2}{\left(a_1 + \dfrac{\mu_1}{z_1} \right) \left(a_2 + \dfrac{\mu_2}{z_2} \right) - p^2} \\[4ex] + \dfrac{\dfrac{\mu_1}{z_1} \left\{ b_1 \left(b_2 + \dfrac{\mu_2}{z_2} \right) - s^2 \right\} y_1^2 + \dfrac{\mu_1 \mu_2}{z_1 z_2} s y_1 y_2 + \dfrac{\mu_2}{z_2} \left\{ b_2 \left(b_1 + \dfrac{\mu_1}{z_1} \right) - s^2 \right\} y_2^2}{\left(b_1 + \dfrac{\mu_1}{z_1} \right) \left(b_2 + \dfrac{\mu_2}{z_2} \right) - s^2} \end{array} \right\} \dots(26).$$

If we write

$$\left. \begin{array}{ll} u_1 = \dfrac{\mu_1 a_2}{p^2 - a_1 a_2}, & u_2 = \dfrac{\mu_2 a_1}{p^2 - a_1 a_2} \\[2ex] v_1 = \dfrac{\mu_1 b_2}{s^2 - b_1 b_2}, & v_2 = \dfrac{\mu_2 b_1}{s^2 - b_1 b_2} \\[2ex] f_1 = - \dfrac{\mu_1 p}{p^2 - a_1 a_2}, & f_2 = - \dfrac{\mu_2 p}{p^2 - a_1 a_2} \\[2ex] g_1 = - \dfrac{\mu_1 s}{s^2 - b_1 b_2}, & g_2 = - \dfrac{\mu_2 s}{s^2 - b_1 b_2} \end{array} \right\} \dots\dots\dots\dots (27),$$

the characteristic function becomes

$$\left. \begin{array}{l} V = V_{PQ} + \mu_1 z_1 + \mu_2 z_2 + \frac{1}{2} \dfrac{\mu_1 (z_2 - u_2) x_1^2 + \mu_2 (z_1 - u_1) x_2^2 - (f_1 \mu_2 + f_2 \mu_1) x_1 x_2}{(z_1 - u_1)(z_2 - u_2) - f_1 f_2} \\[3ex] \qquad\qquad + \frac{1}{2} \dfrac{\mu_1 (z_2 - v_2) y_1^2 + \mu_2 (z_1 - v_1) y_2^2 - (g_1 \mu_2 + g_2 \mu_1) y_1 y_2}{(z_1 - v_1)(z_2 - v_2) - g_1 g_2} \end{array} \right\} \dots\dots (28).$$

Since in this case the terms of the characteristic function which involve x_1 and x_2 are separated from those which involve y_1 and y_2, we may consider either apart from the other. In the case of an optical instrument symmetrical about its axis,

$$u_1 = v_1, \quad u_2 = v_2, \quad f_1 = g_1, \text{ and } f_2 = g_2 \dots\dots\dots\dots\dots(29).$$

Let l_1, l_2 be the tangents of the angles which the incident and emergent rays, projected on the plane of xz, make with the axis of z,

$$l_1 = \frac{\dfrac{dV}{dx_1}}{\dfrac{dV}{dz_1}} = \frac{(z_2 - u_2)\, x_1 - f_2 x_2}{(z_1 - u_1)\,(z_2 - u_2) - f_1 f_2} \dots\dots\dots\dots\dots(30),$$

$$l_2 = \frac{(z_1 - u_1)\, x_2 - f_1 x_1}{(z_1 - u_1)\,(z_2 - u_2) - f_1 f_2} \dots\dots\dots\dots\dots(31).$$

If the incident ray is parallel to the axis, $l_1 = 0$, and the equation of the emergent ray is

$$(z_2 - u_2)\, x_1 - f_2 x_2 = 0 \dots\dots\dots\dots\dots(32).$$

The emergent ray cuts the plane of yz where

$$z_2 = u_2 \dots\dots\dots\dots\dots(33).$$

This therefore is the position of the *second principal focus*.

When

$$z_2 = u_2 + f_2, \quad x_1 = x_2 \dots\dots\dots\dots\dots(34),$$

or the ray is at the same distance from the plane of yz as before incidence. This gives the position of the *second principal plane*.

Its distance from the second principal focus is f_2, which is called the *second principal focal length*.

When

$$z_2 = u_2 + f_1 \text{ and } x_2 = 0, \quad l_1 = l_2 \dots\dots\dots\dots\dots(35),$$

or every ray which passes through this point is equally inclined to the plane of yz before and after passing through the instrument. This point is called the *second focal centre*.

The distance of the emergent ray from the axis of z, when $z = z_2$, is given by the equation

$$f_2 x_2 = (z_2 - u_2)\, x_1 - l_1 \{(z_1 - u_1)\,(z_2 - u_2) - f_1 f_2\} \dots\dots\dots\dots\dots(36).$$

When

$$(z_1 - u_1)\,(z_2 - u_2) - f_1 f_2 = 0 \dots\dots\dots\dots\dots(37),$$

the term multiplied by l_1 vanishes. Hence all the rays which pass through the point (x_1, z_1) pass through (x_2, z_2), whatever their inclination to the axis. The points x_1, z_1 and x_2, z_2 are therefore conjugate foci, and x_2 is the image of x_1.

In this case

$$\frac{x_2}{x_1} = \frac{z_2 - u_2}{f_2} = \frac{f_1}{z_1 - u_1} \quad\quad\quad\quad\quad\quad (38);$$

or, in words,—*The distance of the object from the axis is to the distance of the image from the axis as the distance of the object from the first principal focus is to the first principal focal length, or as the second principal focal length is to the distance of the image from the second principal focus.*

Let h_1 be the distance at which an object of diameter x_2 must be placed from the eye that it may subtend an angle equal to that which it subtends when placed at z_2, and seen through the instrument by an eye at z_1,

$$h_1 = \frac{x_2}{l_1} \text{ when } x_1 = 0, \text{ or } h_1 = \frac{\mu_1}{\dfrac{d^2 V}{dx_1 dx_2}} \quad\quad\quad\quad (39),$$

or

$$h_1 = \frac{1}{f_2} \{(z_1 - u_1)(z_2 - u_2) - f_1 f_2\} \quad\quad\quad\quad (40).$$

The quantity h_1 is that which occurs in Cotes' Theorem, and to which Smith gives the name of the "apparent distance."

Differentiating h_1 with respect to z_1 and z_2, we find

$$\frac{dh_1}{dz_1} = \frac{z_2 - u_2}{f_2}, \quad \frac{dh_1}{dz_2} = \frac{z_1 - u_1}{f_2}, \quad \frac{d^2 h_1}{dz_1 dz_2} = \frac{1}{f_2} \quad\quad\quad (41).$$

When the focal length is infinite, the instrument becomes a *télescope*, and the characteristic function is

$$V = V_1 + \mu_1 z_1 + \mu_2 z_2 + \tfrac{1}{2} \frac{\mu_1^2 x_1^2 + m^2 \mu_2^2 x_2^2 + 2m \mu_1 \mu_2 x_1 x_2}{\mu_1 (z_1 - u_1) - m^2 \mu_2 (z_2 - u_2)} + \text{a similar term in } y.$$

Here m is the angular magnification, and u_1, u_2 are the co-ordinates of any two conjugate foci. The linear magnification is $\dfrac{\mu_1}{\mu_2 m}$ and the elongation is $\dfrac{\mu_1}{\mu_2 m^2}$.

[From the *Cambridge Philosophical Proceedings*, Vol. II.]

LXV. On the Relation of Geometrical Optics to other parts of Mathematics and Physics.

THE study of geometrical optics may be made more interesting to the mathematician by treating the relation between the object and the image by the methods used in the geometry of homographic figures. The whole theory of images formed by simple or compound instruments when aberration is not considered is thus reduced to simple proportion, and this is found very convenient in the practical work of arranging lenses for an experiment, in order to produce a given effect.

As a preparation for physical optics the same elementary problems may be treated by Hamilton's method of the Characteristic Function. This function expresses, in terms of the co-ordinates of two points, the time taken by light in travelling from the one to the other, or more accurately the distance through which light would travel in a vacuum during this time, which we may call the *reduced path* of the light between the two points. The relation between this reduced path and the quantity which occurs in Cotes' celebrated but little known theorem, is called by Dr Smith the "apparent distance." The relations between the "apparent distance" and the positions of the foci conjugate to the two points, the principal foci and the principal focal lengths, were explained [*] ; and the general form of the characteristic function for a narrow pencil in the plane of xr was shewn to be

$$V = V_0 + \mu_1 r_1 + \mu_2 r_2 + \tfrac{1}{2} \frac{\mu_1 (r_2 - a_2) x_1^2 + \mu_2 (r_1 - a_1) x_2^2 - (f_1 \mu_2 + f_2 \mu_1) x_1 x_2}{(r_1 - a_1)(r_2 - a_2) - f_1 f_2} + \&c.,$$

* [i.e. to the Cambridge Philosophical Society at a meeting when the results of the foregoing paper LXIV. were communicated.]

where r_1, r_2 are measured from the instrument in opposite directions along the axis of the pencil in the media μ_1, μ_2, respectively, and x_1, x_2 are perpendicular to the axis.

a_1, a_2 are the values of r_1, r_2, for the principal foci, and f_1, f_2, the principal focal lengths, and $f_1\mu_2 = f_2\mu_1$.

If
$$\frac{r_1 - a_1}{f_1} = \frac{f_2}{r_2 - a_2} = \frac{x_1}{x_2},$$

the last term of V assumes the form $\frac{0}{0}$, and an infinite number of possible paths exist between the points (x_1, r_1), and (x_2, r_2), which are therefore conjugate foci.

Differentiating V with respect to x_1 and x_2 we obtain

$$\frac{d^2 V}{dx_1 dx_2} = \frac{1}{D} = -\tfrac{1}{2} \frac{f_1\mu_2 + f_2\mu_1}{(r_1 - a_1)(r_2 - a_2) - f_1 f_2} + \&c.,$$

D is the quantity in Cotes' Theorems which Dr Smith calls the Apparent Distance, or the distance at which the object must be placed that it may subtend the same angle as when viewed through the instrument.

We have also

$$f_1\mu_2 \frac{dD}{dr_1} = a_2 - r_2, \quad f_2\mu_1 \frac{dD}{dr_2} = a_1 - r_1.$$

[From *Nature*, Vol. x.]

LXVI.   *Plateau on Soap-Bubbles*.

On an Etruscan vase in the Louvre figures of children are seen blowing bubbles. Those children probably enjoyed their occupation just as modern children do. Our admiration of the beautiful and delicate forms, growing and developing themselves, the feeling that it is *our* breath which is turning dirty soap-suds into spheres of splendour, the fear lest by an irreverent touch we may cause the gorgeous vision to vanish with a sputter of soapy water in our eyes, our wistful gaze as we watch the perfected bubble when it sails away from the pipe's mouth to join, somewhere in the sky, all the other beautiful things that have vanished before it, assure us that, whatever our nominal age may be we are of the same family as those Etruscan children.

Here, for instance, we have a book, in two volumes, octavo, written by a distinguished man of science, and occupied for the most part with the theory and practice of bubble-blowing. Can the poetry of bubbles survive this? Will not the lovely visions which have floated before the eyes of untold generations collapse at the rude touch of Science, and "yield their place to cold material laws"? No, we need go no further than this book and its author to learn that the beauty and mystery of natural phenomena may make such an impression on a fresh and open mind that no physical obstacle can ever check the course of thought and study which it has once called forth.

M. Plateau in all his researches seems to have selected for his study those phenomena which exhibit some remarkable beauty of form or colour. In the zeal with which he devoted himself to the investigation of the laws of the subjective impressions of colour, he exposed his eyes to an excess of light, and

---

* *Statique expérimentale et théorique des Liquides soumis aux seules Forces moléculaires.* Par J. Plateau, Professeur à l'Université de Gand, &c.   (Paris, Gauthier-Villars; London, Trübner & Co.; Gand et Leipzig, F. Clemm.   1873.)

has ever since been blind. But in spite of this great loss he has continued for many years to carry on experiments such as those described in this book, on the forms of liquid masses and films, which he himself can never either see or handle, but from which he gathers the materials of science as they are furnished to him by the hands, eyes, and minds of devoted friends.

So perfect has been the co-operation with which these experiments have been carried out, that there is hardly a single expression in the book to indicate that the measures which he took and the colours with which he was charmed were observed by him, not in the ordinary way, but through the mediation of other persons.

Which, now, is the more poetical idea—the Etruscan boy blowing bubbles for himself, or the blind man of science teaching his friends how to blow them, and making out by a tedious process of question and answer the conditions of the forms and tints which he can never see ?

But we must now attempt to follow our author as he passes from phenomena to ideas, from experiment to theory.

The surface which forms the boundary between a liquid and its vapour is the seat of phenomena on the careful study of which depends much of our future progress in the knowledge of the constitution of bodies. To take the simplest case, that of a liquid, say water, placed in a vessel which it does not fill, but which contains nothing else. The water lies at the bottom of the vessel, and the upper part, originally empty, becomes rapidly filled with the vapour of water. The temperature and the pressure—the quantities on which the thermal and statical relations of any body to external bodies depend—are the same for the water and its vapour, but the energy of a milligramme of the vapour greatly exceeds that of a milligramme of the water. Hence the energy of a milligramme of water-substance is much greater when it happens to be in the upper part of the vessel in the state of vapour, than when it happens to be in the lower part of the vessel in the state of water.

Now we find by experiment that there is no difference between the phenomena in one part of the liquid and those in another part except in a region close to the surface and not more than a thousandth or perhaps a millionth of a millimetre thick. In the vapour also, everything is the same, except perhaps in a very thin stratum close to the surface. The change in the value of the energy takes place in the very narrow region between water and vapour. Hence the energy of a milligramme of water is the same all through the mass of the water except in a thin stratum close to the surface, where it is some-what greater; and the energy of a milligramme of vapour is the same all through the mass of vapour except close to the surface, where it is probably less.

The whole energy of the water is therefore, in the first place, that due to so many milligrammes of water; but besides this, since the water close to the surface has an excess of energy, a correction, depending on this excess, must be added. Thus we have, besides the energy of the water reckoned per milligramme, an additional energy to be reckoned per square millimetre of surface.

The energy of the vapour may be calculated in the same way at so much per milligramme, with a deduction of so much per square millimetre of surface. The quantity of vapour, however, which lies within the region in which the energy is beginning to change its value is so small that this deduction per square millimetre is always much smaller than the addition which has to be made on account of the liquid. Hence the whole energy of the system may be divided into three parts, one proportional to the mass of liquid, one to the mass of vapour, and the third proportional to the area of the surface which separates the liquid from the vapour.

If the system is displaced by an external agent in such a way that the area of the surface of the liquid is increased, the energy of the system is increased, and the only source of this increase of energy is the work done by the external agent. There is therefore a resistance to any motion which causes the extension of the surface of a liquid.

On the other hand, if the liquid moves in such a way that its surface diminishes, the energy of the system diminishes, and the diminution of energy appears in the form of work done on the external agent which allows the surface to diminish. Now a surface which tends to diminish in area, and which thus tends to draw together any solid framework which forms its boundary, is said to have surface-tension. Surface-tension is measured by the force acting on one millimetre of the boundary edge. In the case of water at 20° C., the tension is, according to M. Quincke, a force of 8·253 milligrammes weight per millimetre.

M. Plateau hardly enters into the theoretical deduction of the surface-tension from hypotheses respecting the constitution of bodies. We have there-fore thought it desirable to point out how the fact of surface-tension may be

50—2

deduced from the known fact that there is a difference in energy between a liquid and its vapour, combined with the hypothesis, that as a milligramme of the substance passes from the state of a liquid within the liquid mass, to that of a vapour outside it, the change of its energy takes place, not instantaneously, but in a continuous manner.

M. van der Waals, whose academic thesis, *Over de Continuiteit van den Gas en Vloeistoftoestand* *, is a most valuable contribution to molecular physics, has attempted to calculate approximately the thickness of the stratum within which this continuous change of energy is accomplished, and finds it for water about 0·0000003 millimetre.

Whatever we may think of these calculations, it is at least manifest that the only path in which we may hope to arrive at a knowledge of the size of the molecules of ordinary matter is to be traced among those phenomena which come into prominence when the dimensions of bodies are greatly reduced, as in the superficial layer of a liquid.

But it is in the experimental investigation of the effects of surface-tension on the form of the surface of a liquid that the value of M. Plateau's book is to be found. He uses two distinct methods. In the first he prepares a mixture of alcohol and water which has the same density as olive oil, then introducing some oil into the mixture and waiting till it has, by absorption of a small portion of alcohol into itself, become accommodated to its position, he obtains a mass of oil no longer under the action of gravity, but subject only to the surface-tension of its boundary. Its form is therefore, when undisturbed, spherical, but by means of rings, disks, &c., of iron, he draws out or compresses his mass of oil into a number of different figures, the equilibrium and stability of which are here investigated, both experimentally and theoretically.

The other method is the old one of blowing soap-bubbles. M. Plateau, however, has improved the art, first by finding out the best kind of soap and the best proportion of water, and then by mixing his soapy water with glycerine. Bubbles formed of this liquid will last for hours, and even days.

By forming a frame of iron wire and dipping it into this liquid he forms a film, the figure of which is that of the surface of minimum area which has the frame for its boundary. This is the case when the air is free on both sides of the film. If, however, the portions of air on the two sides of the film

---

* Leiden : A. W. Sijthoff, 1873.

are not in continuous communication, the film is no longer the surface of absolute minimum area, but the surface which, with the given boundary, and inclosing a given volume, has a minimum area.

M. Plateau has gone at great length into the interesting but difficult question of the conditions of the persistence of liquid films. He shews that the surface of certain liquids has a species of viscosity distinct from the interior viscosity of the mass. This surface-viscosity is very remarkable in a solution of saponine. There can be no doubt that a property of this kind plays an important part in determining the persistence or collapse of liquid films. M. Plateau, however, considers that one of the agents of destruction is the surface-tension, and that the persistence mainly depends on the degree in which the surface-viscosity counteracts the surface-tension. It is plain, however, that it is rather the inequality of the surface-tension than the surface-tension itself which acts as a destroying force.

It has not yet been experimentally ascertained whether the tension varies according to the thickness of the film. The variation of tension is certainly insensible in those cases which have been observed.

If, as the theory seems to indicate, the tension diminishes when the thickness of the film diminishes, the film must be unstable, and its actual persistence would be unaccountable. On the other hand, the theory has not as yet been able to account for the tension increasing as the thickness diminishes.

One of the most remarkable phenomena of liquid films is undoubtedly the formation of the black spots, which were described in 1672 by Hooke, under the name of holes.

Fusinieri has given a very exact account of this phenomenon as he observed it in a vertical film protected from currents of air. As the film becomes thinner, owing to the gradual descent of the liquid of which it is formed, certain portions become thinner than the rest, and begin to shew the colours of thin plates. These little spots of colour immediately begin to ascend, dragging after them a sort of train like the tail of a tadpole. These tadpoles, as Fusinieri calls them, soon begin to accumulate near the top of the film, and to range themselves in horizontal bands according to their colours, those which have the colour corresponding to the smallest thickness ascending highest.

In this way the colours become arranged in horizontal bands in beautiful gradation, exhibiting all the colours of Newton's scale. When the frame of the film is made to oscillate, these bands oscillate like the strata formed by a series of liquids of different densities. This shews that the film is subject to dynamical conditions similar to those of such a liquid system. The liquid is subject to the condition that the volume of each portion of it is invariable, and the motion arises from the fact that by the descent of the denser portions (which is necessarily accompanied by the rise of the rarer portions) the gravitational potential energy of the system is diminished. In the case of the film, the condition which determines that the descent of the thicker portions shall entail the rise of the thinner portions must be that each portion of the film offers a special resistance to an increase or diminution of area. This resistance probably forms a large part of the superficial viscosity investigated by M. Plateau, which retards the motion of his magnetic needle, and evidently is far greater than the viscosity of figure, in virtue of which the film resists a shearing motion.

The coloured bands gradually descend from the top of the film, presenting at first a continuous gradation of colour, but soon a remarkable black, or nearly black, band begins to form at the top of the film, and gradually to extend itself downwards. The lower boundary of this black band is sharply defined. There is not a continuous gradation of colour according to the arrangement in Newton's table, but the black appears in immediate contact with the white or even the yellow of the first order, and M. Fusinieri has even observed it in contact with bands of the third order.

Nothing can shew more distinctly that there is some remarkable change in the physical properties of the film, when it is of a thickness somewhat greater than that of the black portion. And in fact the black part of the film is in many other respects different from the rest. It is easy, as Leidenfrost tells us, to pass a solid point through the thicker part of the film, and to withdraw it, without bursting the film, but if anything touches the black part, the film is shattered at once. The black portion does not appear to possess the mobility which is so apparent in the coloured parts. It behaves more like a brittle solid, such as a Prince Rupert's drop, than a fluid. Its edges are often very irregular, and when the curvature of the film is made to vary, the black portions sometimes seem to resist the change, so that their surface has no longer the same continuous curvature as the rest of the bubble. We have thus numerous indications of the great assistance which molecular science is likely to derive from the study of liquid films of extreme tenuity.

We have no time or inclination to discuss M. Plateau's work in a critical spirit. The directions for making the experiments are very precise, and if sometimes they appear tedious on account of repetitions, we must remember that it is by words, and words alone, that the author can learn the details of the experiment which he is performing by means of the hands of his friends, and that the repetition of phrases must in his case take the place of the ordinary routine of a careful experimenter. The description of the results of mathematical investigation, which is a most difficult but at the same time most useful species of literary composition, is a notable feature of this book, and could hardly be better done. The mathematical researches of Lindelöf, Lamarle, Scherk, Riemann, &c., on surfaces of minimum area, deserve to be known to others besides professed mathematicians, and M. Plateau deserves our thanks for giving us an intelligible account of them, and still more for shewing us how to make them visible with his improved soap-suds.

In the speculative part of the book, where the author treats of the causes of the phenomena, there is of course more room for improvement, as there always must be when a physicist is pushing his way into the unknown regions of molecular science. In such matters everything human, at least in our century, must be very imperfect, but for the same reason any real progress, however small, is of the greater value.

[From *Nature*, Vol. **x**.]

LXVII. *Grove's " Correlation of Physical Forces*."*

THERE are few instances in which anyone whose life has not been exclusively scientific has made such valuable contributions to science as those of Sir W. R. Grove. His nitric acid battery, to the invention of which he was led, not by accident, but by a course of reasoning, which in the year 1839 was as new as it was original, is a contribution to science the value of which is proved by its still surviving and continuing in daily use in every laboratory as the most powerful generator of electric currents, while hundreds of batteries invented since that of Grove have fallen into disuse, and become extinct in the struggle for scientific existence.

The gas battery, though not of such practical importance, is still of great scientific interest, and the collection which we have before us of those contributions to science which took the form of papers, tempts us to indulge in speculations as to the magnitude of the results which would have accrued to science if so powerful a mind could have been continuously directed with undivided energy towards some of the great questions of physics.

But the main feature of the volume is that from which it takes its name, the essay on the Correlation of Physical Forces, the views contained in which were first advanced in a lecture at the London Institution in January 1842, printed by the proprietors, and subsequently more fully developed in a course of lectures in 1843, published in abstract in the *Literary Gazette*. This essay has a value peculiar to itself. Though it has long ago accomplished the main point of its scientific mission to the world, it will always retain its place in

---

* *The Correlation of Physical Forces.* Sixth edition. With other Contributions to Science. By the Hon. Sir W. R. Grove, M.A., F.R.S., one of the judges of the Court of Common Pleas. (London: Longmans, 1874.)

the memory of the student of human thought, as one of the documents which serve for the construction of the history of science.

It is not by discoveries only, and the registration of them by learned societies, that science is advanced. The true seat of science is not in the volume of Transactions, but in the living mind, and the advancement of science consists in the direction of men's minds into a scientific channel; whether this is done by the announcement of a discovery, the assertion of a paradox, the invention of a scientific phrase, or the exposition of a system of doctrine. It is for the historian of science to determine the magnitude and direction of the impulse communicated by either of these means to human thought.

But what we require at any given epoch for the advancement of science is not merely to set men thinking, but to produce a concentration of thought in that part of the field of science which at that particular season ought to be cultivated. In the history of science we find that effects of this kind have often been produced by suggestive books, which put into a definite, intelligible, and communicable form, the guiding ideas that are already working in the minds of men of science, so as to lead them to discoveries, but which they cannot yet shape into a definite statement.

In the first half of the present century, when what is now called the principle of the conservation of energy was as yet unknown by name, it "flung its vague shadow back from the depths of futurity," and those who had greater or less understanding of the times sketched out with greater or less clearness their view of the form into which science was shaping itself.

Some of these addressed themselves to the advanced cultivators of science, speaking, of course, in learned phraseology; but others appealed to a larger audience, and spoke in language which they could understand. Mrs Somerville's book on the "Connection of the Physical Sciences" was published in 1834, and had reached its eighth edition in 1849. This fact is enough to shew that there already existed a widespread desire to be able to form some notion of physical science as a whole.

But when we examine her book in order to find out the nature of the connexion of the physical sciences, we are at first tempted to suppose that it is due to the art of the bookbinder, who has bound into one volume such a quantity of information about each of them. What we find, in fact, is a series of expositions of different sciences, but hardly a word about their connexion. The little that is said about this connexion has reference to the mutual dependence of the different sciences on each other, a knowledge of the elements of one being essential to the successful prosecution of another. Thus physical astronomy requires a knowledge of dynamics, and the practical astronomer must learn a certain amount of optics in order to understand atmospheric refraction and the adjustment of telescopes. The sciences are also shewn to have a common method, namely, mathematical analysis; so that analytical methods invented for the investigation of one science are often useful in another.

The unity shadowed forth in Mrs Somerville's book is therefore a unity of the method of science, not a unity of the processes of nature.

Sir W. Grove's essay may be fairly called a popular book, as it has reached its sixth edition. It is, therefore, not merely a record of the speculations of the author, but an index of the state of scientific thought among a large number of readers. It has not the universal facility and occasional felicity of exposition which distinguish Mrs Somerville's writings. No one could use it as a text-book of any science, or even as an aid to the cultivation of the art of scientific conversation. The design of the book is to shew that of the various forms of energy existing in nature, any one may be transformed into any other, the one form appearing as the other disappears. This is what is meant in the essay by the "correlation of the physical forces," and the whole essay is an exposition of this fact, each of the physical forces in turn being taken as the starting-point, and employed as the source of all the others.

We are sorry that we are not at present able to refer to the early reviews of the essay as indicating the reception given to the doctrine by the literary and scientific public at the time of its original publication. It has certainly exercised a very considerable effect in moulding the mass of what is called scientific opinion, that is to say, the influence which determines what a scientific man shall say when he has to make a statement about a science which he does not understand. Many things in the essay which were then considered contrary to scientific opinion, and were therefore objected to, have since then become themselves part of scientific opinion, so that the objections now appear unintelligible to the rising generation of the scientific public.

Helmholtz's essay "On the Conservation of Force," published in 1847, undoubtedly masters a far greater step in science, but the immediate influence was confined to a small number of trained men of science, and it had little direct effect on the public mind.

The various papers of Mayer contain matter calculated to awaken an interest in the transformation of energy even in persons not exclusively devoted to science, but they were long unknown in this country, and produced little direct effect, even in Germany, at the time of their publication.

The rapid development of thermodynamics, and of other applications of the principle of the conservation of energy, at the beginning of the second half of this century, belongs to a later stage of the history of science than that with which we have to do.

To form a just estimate of the value of Sir W. Grove's work we must regard it as the instrument by which certain scientific ideas were diffused over a large area, in language sufficiently appropriate to prevent misapprehension, and yet sufficiently familiar to be listened to by persons who would recoil with horror from any statement in which literary convention is sacrificed to precision.

It is worth while, however, to take note of the progress of evolution by which the words of ordinary language are gradually becoming differentiated and rendered scientifically precise. The fathers of dynamical science found a number of words in common use expressive of action and the results of action, such as force, power, action, impulse, impetus, stress, strain, work, energy, &c. They also had in their minds a number of ideas to be expressed, and they appropriated these words as they best could to express these ideas. But the equivalent words Force *Vis*, *Kraft*, came most easily to hand, so that we find them compelled to carry almost all the ideas above mentioned, while the other words which might have borne a portion of the load were long left out of scientific language, and retained only their more or less vague meanings as ordinary words.

Thus we have the expressions *Vis acceleratrix*, *Vis motrix*, *Vis viva*, *Vis mortua*, and even *Vis inertiæ*, in every one of which, except the second and fourth, the word *Vis* is used in a sense radically different from that in which it is used in the other expressions.

Confusion may perhaps be avoided in scientific works when read by scientific students, by means of a careful appropriation of epithets such as those which distinguish the meanings of the word *Vis*, but as soon as science becomes popularised, unless its nomenclature is reformed and arranged upon a better principle, the ideas of popular science will be more confused than those of so-called popular ignorance.

Thus the "Physical Forces," whose correlation is discussed in the essay before us, are Motion, Heat, Electricity, Light, Magnetism, Chemical Affinity, and "other modes of force." According to the definition of force, as it has been

51—2

laid down during the last two centuries in treatises on dynamics, not one of these, except perhaps chemical affinity, can be admitted as a force. According to that definition, "force is that which produces change of motion, and is measured by the change of motion produced."

Newton himself reminds us that force exists only so long as it acts. Its effects may remain, but the force itself is essentially transitive. Hence, when we meet with such phrases as, Conservation of Force, Persistence of Force, and the like, we must suppose the word Force to be used in a sense radically different from that adopted by scientific men from Newton downwards. In all these cases, and in the phrase "The Physical Forces" as applied to heat, we are now, thanks to Dr Thomas Young, able to use the word Energy instead of Force, for this word, according to its scientific definition as "the capacity for performing work," is applicable to all these cases. The confusion has extended even to the metaphorical use of the word Force. Thus, it may be a legitimate metaphor to speak of the force of public opinion as being brought to bear on a statesman so as to exert an overpowering pressure upon him, because here we have an action tending to produce motion in a particular direction; but when we speak of "the Queen's Forces," we use the term in a sense as unscientific as when we speak of the Physical Forces. The author, in his concluding remarks, points out the confusion of terms which embarrassed him in his endeavours to enunciate scientific propositions, on account of the imperfection of scientific language. This, he tells us, "cannot be avoided without a neology which I have not the presumption to introduce or the authority to enforce."

Such a confession, proceeding from so great a master of the art of "putting things," is a most valuable testimony to the importance of the study and special cultivation of scientific language; and a comparison of many passages in the essay with the corresponding statements in more recent books of far inferior power, will shew how much may be gained by the successful introduction of appropriate neologies. What appeared mysterious and even paradoxical to the giant, labouring among rough-hewn words, dwindles into a truism in the eyes of the child, born heir to the palace of truth, for the erection of which the giant has furnished the materials.

Thus the appropriation of the word "Mass" to denote the quantity of matter as defined by the amount of force required to produce a given acceleration, has placed the students of the present day on a very different level from

those who had to puzzle out the meaning of the phrase *Vis inertiæ* by combining the explanation of *Vis* as force, with that of *inertia* as laziness. In the same way the word "stress" as an equivalent for "action and reaction," and as a generic name for pressure, tension, &c., will save future generations a great deal of trouble; and the distinction between the possession of energy and the act of doing work, which is now so familiar to us, would have obviated several objections to the doctrine of the essay, which are founded on statements in which the production of one form of energy and the maintenance of another are treated as if they were operations of the same kind. We read at p. 163:—
Thus, "a voltaic battery, decomposing water in a voltameter, while the same current is employed at the same time to make (maintain) an electromagnet, gives nevertheless in the voltameter an equivalent of gas, or decomposes an equivalent of an electrolyte for each equivalent of decomposition in the battery cells, and will give the same ratios if the electro-magnet be removed."

Here the maintenance of a magnet is a thing of a different order from the decomposition of an electrolyte; the first is maintenance of energy, the other is doing work. This is well explained in the essay; but if appropriate language had been used from the first, the objection could never have been put into form.

[From *Nature*, Vol. x.]

LXVIII. *On the application of Kirchhoff's Rules for Electric Circuits to the Solution of a Geometrical Problem.*

THE geometrical problem is as follows :—Let it be required to arrange a system of points so that the straight lines joining them into rows and columns shall form a network such that the sum of the squares of all these joining lines shall be a minimum, the first and last points of the first and last row being any four points given in space. The network may be regarded as a kind of extensible surface, each thread of which has a tension in each segment proportioned to the length of the segment. The problem is thus expressed as a statical problem, but the direct solution would involve the consideration of a large number of unknown quantities.

This number may be greatly reduced by means of the analogy between this problem and the electrical problem of determining the currents and potentials in the case of a network of wire having square meshes, one corner of which is kept at a unit potential, while that of the other three corners is zero. This problem having been solved by Kirchhoff's method, the position of any point P in the geometrical problem with reference to the given points A, B, C, D, is by finding the values of the potentials p_a, p_b, p_c, p_d of the corresponding point in the electric problem when the corners a, b, c, d respectively are those of unit potential. The position of P is then found by supposing p_a, p_b, p_c, p_d placed at A, B, C, D respectively, and determining P as the centre of gravity of the four masses.

[From *Nature*, Vol. x.]

LXIX. *Van der Waals on the Continuity of the Gaseous and Liquid States**.

THAT the same substance at the same temperature and pressure can exist in two very different states, as a liquid and as a gas, is a fact of the highest scientific importance, for it is only by the careful study of the difference between these two states, the conditions of the substance passing from one to the other, and the phenomena which occur at the surface which separates a liquid from its vapour, that we can expect to obtain a dynamical theory of liquids. A dynamical theory of "perfect" gases is already in existence; that is to say, we can explain many of the physical properties of bodies when in an extremely rarefied state by supposing their molecules to be in rapid motion, and that they act on one another only when they come very near one another. A molecule of a gas, according to this theory, exists in two very different states during alternate intervals of time. During its encounter with another molecule, an intense force is acting between the two molecules, and producing changes in the motion of both. During the time of describing its free path, the molecule is at such a distance from other molecules that no sensible force acts between them, and the centre of mass of the molecule is therefore moving with constant velocity and in a straight line.

If we define as a perfect gas a system of molecules so sparsely scattered that the aggregate of the time which a molecule spends in its encounters with other molecules is exceedingly small compared with the aggregate of the time which it spends in describing its free paths, it is not difficult to work out the dynamical theory of such a system. For in this case the vast majority of the molecules at any given instant are describing their free paths, and only a small

---

* *Over de Continuiteit van den Gas en Vloeistoftoestand. Academisch proefschrift.* Door Johannes Diderik van der Waals. (Leiden : A. W. Sijthoff, 1873.)

fraction of them are in the act of encountering each other. We know that during an encounter action and reaction are equal and opposite, and we assume, with Clausius, that on an average of a large number of encounters the proportion in which the kinetic energy of a molecule is divided between motion of translation of its centre of mass and motions of its parts relative to this point approaches some definite value. This amount of knowledge is by no means sufficient as a foundation for a complete dynamical theory of what takes place during each encounter, but it enables us to establish certain relations between the changes of velocity of two molecules before and after their encounter.

While a molecule is describing its free path, its centre of mass is moving with constant velocity in a straight line. The motions of parts of the molecule relative to the centre of mass depend, when it is describing its free path, only on the forces acting between these parts, and not on the forces acting between them and other molecules which come into play during an encounter. Hence the theory of the motion of a system of molecules is very much simplified if we suppose the space within which the molecules are free to move to be so large that the number of molecules which at any instant are in the act of encountering other molecules is exceedingly small compared with the number of molecules which are describing their free paths. The dynamical theory of such a system is in complete agreement with the observed properties of gases when in an extremely rare condition.

But if the space occupied by a given quantity of gas is diminished more and more, the lengths of the free paths of its molecules will also be diminished, and the number of molecules which are in the act of encounter will bear a larger proportion to the number of those which are describing free paths, till at length the properties of the substance will be determined far more by the nature of the mutual action between the encountering molecules than by the nature of the motion of a molecule when describing its free path. And we actually find that the properties of the substance become very different after it has reached a certain degree of condensation. In the rarefied state its properties may be defined with considerable accuracy in terms of the laws of Boyle, Charles, Gay-Lussac, Dulong and Petit, &c., commonly called the "gaseous laws." In the condensed state the properties of the substance are entirely different, and no mode of stating these properties has yet been discovered having a simplicity and a generality at all approaching to that of the "gaseous laws." According to the dynamical theory this is to be expected, because in the condensed state the properties of the substance depend on the mutual action of molecules when engaged in close encounter, and this is determined by the particular constitution of the encountering molecules. We cannot therefore extend the dynamical theory from the rarer to the denser state of substances without at the same time obtaining some definite conception of the nature of the action between molecules when they are so closely packed that each molecule is at every instant so near to several others that forces of great intensity are acting between them.

The experimental data for the study of the mutual action of molecules are principally of two kinds. In the first place we have the experiments of Regnault and others on the relation between the density, temperature, and pressure of various gases. The field of research has been recently greatly enlarged by Dr Andrews in his exploration of the properties of carbonic acid at very high pressures. Experiments of this kind, combined with experiments on specific heat, on the latent heat of expansion, or on the thermometric effect on gases passing through porous plugs, furnish us with the complete theory of the substance, so far as pure thermodynamics can carry us.

For the further study of molecular action we require experiments on the rate of diffusion. There are three kinds of diffusion—that of matter, that of visible motion, and that of heat. The inter-diffusion of gases of different kinds, and the viscosity and thermal conductivity of a gaseous medium, pure or mixed, enable us to estimate the amount of deviation which each molecule experiences on account of its encounter with other molecules.

M. Van der Waals, in entering on this very difficult inquiry, has shewn his appreciation of its importance in the present state of science ; many of his investigations are conducted in an extremely original and clear manner ; and he is continually throwing out new and suggestive ideas ; so that there can be no doubt that his name will soon be among the foremost in molecular science.

He does not, however, seem to be equally familiar, as yet, with all parts of the subject, so that in some places, where he has borrowed results from Clausius and others, he has applied them in a manner which appears to me erroneous.

He begins with the very remarkable theorem of Clausius, that in stationary motion the mean kinetic energy of the system is equal to the mean virial. As in this country the importance of this theorem seems hardly to be appreciated, it may be as well to explain it a little more fully.

When the motion of a material system is such that the sum of the moments of inertia of the system about three axes at right angles to each other through its centre of mass does not vary by more than small quantities from a constant value, the system is said to be in a state of stationary motion. The motion of the solar system satisfies this condition, and so does the motion of the molecules of a gas contained in a vessel.

The kinetic energy of a particle is half the product of its mass into the square of its velocity, and the kinetic energy of a system is the sum of the kinetic energy of its parts.

When an attraction or repulsion exists between two points, half the product of this stress into the distance between the two points is called the Virial of the stress, and is reckoned positive when the stress is an attraction, and negative when it is a repulsion. The virial of a system is the sum of the virial of the stresses which exist in it.

If the system is subjected to the external stress of the pressure of the sides of a vessel in which it is contained, the amount of virial due to this external stress is three halves of the product of the pressure into the volume of the vessel.

The virial due to internal stresses must be added to this.

The theorem of Clausius may now be written—

$$\tfrac{1}{2}\Sigma\,(m\overline{v^2}) = \tfrac{3}{2}pV + \tfrac{1}{2}\Sigma\Sigma\,(Rr).$$

The left-hand member denotes the kinetic energy.

On the right hand, in the first term, p is the external pressure on unit of area, and V is the volume of the vessel.

The second term represents the virial arising from the action between every pair of particles, whether belonging to different molecules or to the same molecule. R is the attraction between the particles, and r is the distance between them. The double symbol of summation is used because every pair of points must be taken into account, those between which there is no stress contributing, of course, nothing to the virial.

As an example of the generality of this theorem, we may mention that in any framed structure consisting of struts and ties, the sum of the products of the pressure in each strut into its length, exceeds the sum of the products of the tension of each tie into its length, by the product of the weight of the whole structure into the height of its centre of gravity above the foundations. (See a paper on "Reciprocal Figures, &c." *Trans. R. S. Edin.*, Vol. XXVI. p. 14. 1870.)*

In gases the virial is very small compared with the kinetic energy. Hence, if the kinetic energy is constant, the product of the pressure and the volume remains constant. This is the case for a gas at constant temperature. Hence we might be justified in conjecturing that the temperature of any one gas is determined by the kinetic energy of unit of mass.

The theory of the exchange of the energy of agitation from one body to another is one of the most difficult parts of molecular science. If it were fully understood, the physical theory of temperature would be perfect. At present we know the conditions of thermal equilibrium only in the case of gases in which encounters take place between only a pair of molecules at once. In this case the condition of thermal equilibrium is that the mean kinetic energy due to the agitation of the centre of mass of a molecule is the same, whatever be the mass of the molecule, the mean velocity being consequently less for the more massive molecules.

With respect to substances of more complicated constitution, we know, as yet, nothing of the physical condition on which their temperature depends, though the researches of Boltzmann on this subject are likely to result in some valuable discoveries.

M. Van der Waals seems, therefore, to be somewhat too hasty in assuming that the temperature of a substance is in every case measured by the energy of agitation of its individual molecules, though this is undoubtedly the case with substances in the gaseous state.

Assuming, however, for the present that the temperature is measured by the mean kinetic energy of a molecule, we obtain the means of determining the virial by observing the deviation of the product of the pressure and volume from the constant value given by Boyle's law.

It appears by Dr Andrews' experiments that when the volume of carbonic acid is diminished, the temperature remaining constant, the product of the volume and pressure at first diminishes, the rate of diminution becoming more and more rapid as the density increases. Now, the virial depends on the number of pairs of molecules which are at a given instant acting on one another, and this number in unit of volume is proportional to the square of the density. Hence the part of the pressure depending on the virial increases

* [Vol. II. p. 176.]

as the square of the density, and since, in the case of carbonic acid, it diminishes the pressure, it must be of the positive sign, that is, it must arise from *attraction* between the molecules.

But if the volume is still further diminished, at a certain point liquefaction begins, and from this point till the gas is all liquefied no increase of pressure takes place. As soon, however, as the whole substance is in the liquid condition, any further diminution of volume produces a great rise of pressure, so that the product of pressure and volume increases rapidly. This indicates negative virial, and shews that the molecules are now acting on each other by *repulsion*.

This is what takes place in carbonic acid below the temperature of 30·92° C. Above that temperature there is first a positive and then a negative virial, but no sudden liquefaction.

Similar phenomena occur in all the liquefiable gases. In other gases we are able to trace the existence of attractive force at ordinary pressures, though the compression has not yet been carried so far as to shew any repulsive force. In hydrogen the repulsive force seems to prevail even at ordinary pressures. This gas has never been liquefied, and it is probable that it never will be liquefied, as the attractive force is so weak.

We have thus evidence that the molecules of gases attract each other at a certain small distance, but when they are brought still nearer they repel each other. This is quite in accordance with Boscovich's theory of atoms as massive centres of force, the force being a function of the distance, and changing from attractive to repulsive, and back again several times, as the distance diminishes. If we suppose that when the force begins to be repulsive it increases very rapidly as the distance diminishes, so as to become enormous if the distance is less by a very small quantity than that at which the force first begins to be repulsive, the phenomena will be precisely the same as those of smooth elastic spheres.

M. Van der Waals makes his molecules elastic spheres, which, when not in contact, attract each other. His treatment of the "molecular pressure" arising from their attraction seems ingenious, and on the whole satisfactory, though he has not attempted a complete calculation of the attractive virial in terms of the law of force.

His treatment of the repulsive virial, however, shews a departure from the principles on which his investigation is founded. He considers the effect of the size of the molecules in diminishing the length of their "free paths," and he shews that this effect, in the case of very rare gases, is the same as if the volume of the space in ·which the molecules are free to move had been diminished by four times the sum of the volumes of the molecules themselves. He then substitutes for V, the volume of the vessel in Clausius' formula, this volume diminished by four times the molecular volume, and thus obtains the equation—

$$\left(p + \frac{a}{V^2}\right)(V - b) = R\left(1 + at\right),$$

where p is the externally applied pressure, $\frac{a}{V^2}$ is the molecular pressure arising from attraction between the molecules, which varies as the square of the density, or inversely as the square of the volume. The first factor is thus what he considers the total effective pressure. V is the volume of the vessel, and b is four times the volume of the molecules. The second factor is therefore the "effective volume" within which the molecules are free to move.

The right-hand member expresses the kinetic energy, represented by the absolute temperature, multiplied by a quantity, R, constant for each gas.

The results obtained by M. Van der Waals by a comparison of this equation with the determinations of Regnault and Andrews are very striking, and would almost persuade us that the equation represents the true state of the case. But though this agreement would be strong evidence in favour of the accuracy of an empirical formula devised to represent the experimental results, the equation of M. Van der Waals, professing as it does to be derived from the dynamical theory, must be subjected to a much more severe criticism.

It appears to me that the equation does not agree with the theorem of Clausius on which it is founded.

In that theorem p is the pressure of the sides of the vessel, and V is the volume of the vessel. Neither of these quantities is subject to correction.

The assumption that the kinetic energy is determined by the temperature is true for perfect gases, and we have no evidence that any other law holds for gases, even near their liquefying point.

The only source of deviation from Boyle's law is therefore to be looked for in the term $\frac{1}{2}\Sigma\Sigma(Rr)$, which expresses the virial. The effect of the repulsion of the molecules, causing them to act like elastic spheres, is therefore to be found by calculating the virial of this repulsion.

Neglecting the effect of attraction, I find that the effect of the impulsive repulsion reduces the equation of Clausius to the form—

$$pV = \tfrac{1}{3}\Sigma\,(m\overline{v^2})\left\{1 - 2\log\cdot\left(1 - 8\frac{\rho}{\sigma} + 17\frac{\rho^2}{\sigma^2} - \&c.\right)\right\},$$

where σ is the density of the molecules and ρ the mean density of the medium.

The form of this equation is quite different from that of M. Van der Waals, though it indicates the effect of the impulsive force in increasing the pressure. It takes no account of the attractive force, a full discussion of which would carry us into considerable difficulties.

At a constant temperature the effect of the attractive virial is to diminish the pressure by a quantity varying as the square of the density, as long as the encounters of the molecules are, on the whole, between two at a time, and not between three or more. The effect of the attraction in deflecting the paths of the molecules is to make the number of molecules which at any given instant are at distances between r and $r+dr$ of each other greater than the number in an equal volume at a greater distance in the proportion of the velocities corresponding to these distances. As the temperature rises, the volume being constant, the ratio of these velocities approaches to unity, so that the distribution of molecules according to distance becomes more uniform, and the virial is thus diminished.

If there is a virial arising from repulsive forces acting through a finite distance, a rise of temperature will increase the amount of this kind of virial.

Hence a rise of temperature at constant volume will produce a greater increase of pressure than that given by the law of Charles.

The isothermal lines at higher temperatures will exhibit less of the diminution of pressure due to attraction, and as the density increases will shew more of the increase of pressure due to repulsion.

I must not, however, while taking exception to part of the work of M. Van der Waals, forget to add that to him alone are due the suggestions which led me to examine the theory of virial more carefully in order to explore the continuity of the liquid and the gaseous states.

I cannot now enter into the comparison of his theoretical results with the experiments of Andrews, but I would call attention to the able manner in which he expounds the theory of capillarity, and to the remarkable phenomena of the surface-tension of gases which he tells (p. 38) has been observed by

Bosscha in tobacco smoke. As tobacco smoke is simply warm air with a slight excess of carbonic acid carrying solid particles along with it, the change of properties at the surface of the cloud must be very slight compared with that at the surface where two really different gases first come together. If, therefore, the phenomenon observed by Bosscha is a true instance of surface-tension, we may expect to discover much more striking phenomena at the meeting-place of different gases, if we can make our observations before the surface of discontinuity has been obliterated by the inter-diffusion of the gases.

[From *Cambridge Philosophical Society Proceedings*, Vol. II. 365.]

LXX. *On the Centre of Motion of the Eye.*

THE series of positions which the eye assumes as it is rolled horizontally have been investigated by Donders (Donders and Doijer, *Derde Jaarlijksch Verslag betr. het Nederlandsch Gasthuis voor Ooglijders.* Utrecht, 1862), and recently by Mr J. L. Tupper (*Proc. R. S.,* June 18, 1874). The chief difficulty in the investigation consists in fixing the head while the eyeball moves. The only satisfactory method of obtaining a system of co-ordinates fixed with reference to the skull is that adopted by Helmholtz (*Handbuch der Physiologischen Optik,* p. 517), and described in his Croonian Lecture.

A piece of wood, part of the upper surface of which is covered with warm sealingwax, is placed between the teeth and bitten hard till the sealingwax sets and forms a cast of the upper teeth. By inserting the teeth into their proper holes in the sealingwax the piece of wood may at any time be placed in a determinate position relatively to the skull.

By this device of Helmholtz the patient is relieved from the pressure of screws and clamps applied to the skin of his head, and he becomes free to move his head as he likes, provided he keeps the piece of wood between his teeth.

If we can now adjust another piece of wood so that it shall always have a determinate position with respect to the eyeball, we may study the motion of the one piece of wood with respect to the other as the eye moves about.

For this purpose a small mirror is fixed to a board, and a dot is marked on the mirror. If the eye, looking straight at the image of its own pupil in the mirror, sees the dot in the centre of the pupil, the normal to the mirror through the dot is the visual axis of the eye—a determinate line.

A right-angled prism is fixed to the board near the eye in such a position that the eye sees the image of its own cornea in profile by reflexion, first at the prism, and then at the mirror. A vertical line is drawn with black sealingwax on the surface of the prism next the eye, and the board is moved towards or from the eye till this line appears as a tangent to the front of the cornea, while the dot still is seen to cover the centre of the image of the pupil. The only way in which the position of the board can now vary with respect to the eye is by turning round the line of vision as an axis, and this is prevented by the board being laid on a horizontal platform carried by the teeth.

If now the eye is brought into two different positions and the board moved on the platform, so as to be always in the same position relative to the eye, we have to find the centre about which the board might have turned so as to get from one position to the other.

For this purpose two holes are made in the platform, and a needle thrust through the holes is made to prick a card fastened to the upper board. We thus obtain two pairs of points, AB for the first position, and ab for the second.

The ordinary rule for determining the centre of motion is to draw lines bisecting Aa and Bb at right angles. The intersection of these is the centre of motion. This construction fails when the centre of motion is in or near the line AB, for then the two lines coincide. In this case we may produce AB and ab till they meet, and draw a line bisecting the angle externally. This line will pass through the centre of motion as well as the other two, and when they coincide it intersects them at right angles.

[From *Nature*, Vol. XI.]

LXXI. *On the Dynamical Evidence of the Molecular Constitution of Bodies*.*

WHEN any phenomenon can be described as an example of some general principle which is applicable to other phenomena, that phenomenon is said to be explained. Explanations, however, are of very various orders, according to the degree of generality of the principle which is made use of. Thus the person who first observed the effect of throwing water into a fire would feel a certain amount of mental satisfaction when he found that the results were always similar, and that they did not depend on any temporary and capricious antipathy between the water and the fire. This is an explanation of the lowest order, in which the class to which the phenomenon is referred consists of other phenomena which can only be distinguished from it by the place and time of their occurrence, and the principle involved is the very general one that place and time are not among the conditions which determine natural processes. On the other hand, when a physical phenomenon can be completely described as a change in the configuration and motion of a material system, the dynamical explanation of that phenomenon is said to be complete. We cannot conceive any further explanation to be either necessary, desirable, or possible, for as soon as we know what is meant by the words configuration, motion, mass, and force, we see that the ideas which they represent are so elementary that they cannot be explained by means of anything else.

The phenomena studied by chemists are, for the most part, such as have not received a complete dynamical explanation.

Many diagrams and models of compound molecules have been constructed. These are the records of the efforts of chemists to imagine configurations of material systems by the geometrical relations of which chemical phenomena may

---

* A lecture delivered at the Chemical Society, Feb. 18, by Prof. Clerk-Maxwell, F.R.S.

be illustrated or explained. No chemist, however, professes to see in these diagrams anything more than symbolic representations of the various degrees of closeness with which the different components of the molecule are bound together.

In astronomy, on the other hand, the configurations and motions of the heavenly bodies are on such a scale that we can ascertain them by direct observation. Newton proved that the observed motions indicate a continual tendency of all bodies to approach each other, and the doctrine of universal gravitation which he established not only explains the observed motions of our system, but enables us to calculate the motions of a system in which the astronomical elements may have any values whatever.

When we pass from astronomical to electrical science, we can still observe the configuration and motion of electrified bodies, and thence, following the strict Newtonian path, deduce the forces with which they act on each other; but these forces are found to depend on the distribution of what we call electricity. To form what Gauss called a "construirbar Vorstellung" of the invisible process of electric action is the great desideratum in this part of science.

In attempting the extension of dynamical methods to the explanation of chemical phenomena, we have to form an idea of the configuration and motion of a number of material systems, each of which is so small that it cannot be directly observed. We have, in fact, to determine, from the observed external actions of an unseen piece of machinery, its internal construction.

The method which has been for the most part employed in conducting such inquiries is that of forming an hypothesis, and calculating what would happen if the hypothesis were true. If these results agree with the actual phenomena, the hypothesis is said to be verified, so long, at least, as some one else does not invent another hypothesis which agrees still better with the phenomena.

The reason why so many of our physical theories have been built up by the method of hypothesis is that the speculators have not been provided with methods and terms sufficiently general to express the results of their induction in its early stages. They were thus compelled either to leave their ideas vague and therefore useless, or to present them in a form the details of which could be supplied only by the illegitimate use of the imagination.

In the meantime the mathematicians, guided by that instinct which teaches them to store up for others the irrepressible secretions of their own minds, had developed with the utmost generality the dynamical theory of a material system.

Of all hypotheses as to the constitution of bodies, that is surely the most warrantable which assumes no more than that they are material systems, and proposes to deduce from the observed phenomena just as much information about the conditions and connections of the material system as these phenomena can legitimately furnish.

When examples of this method of physical speculation have been properly set forth and explained, we shall hear fewer complaints of the looseness of the reasoning of men of science, and the method of inductive philosophy will no longer be derided as mere guess-work.

It is only a small part of the theory of the constitution of bodies which has as yet been reduced to the form of accurate deductions from known facts. To conduct the operations of science in a perfectly legitimate manner, by means of methodised experiment and strict demonstration, requires a strategic skill which we must not look for, even among those to whom science is most indebted for original observations and fertile suggestions. It does not detract from the merit of the pioneers of science that their advances, being made on unknown ground, are often cut off, for a time, from that system of communications with an established base of operations, which is the only security for any permanent extension of science.

In studying the constitution of bodies we are forced from the very beginning to deal with particles which we cannot observe. For whatever may be our ultimate conclusions as to molecules and atoms, we have experimental proof that bodies may be divided into parts so small that we cannot perceive them.

Hence, if we are careful to remember that the word particle means a small part of a body, and that it does not involve any hypothesis as to the ultimate divisibility of matter, we may consider a body as made up of particles, and we may also assert that in bodies or parts of bodies of measurable dimensions, the number of particles is very great indeed.

The next thing required is a dynamical method of studying a material system consisting of an immense number of particles, by forming an idea of their configuration and motion, and of the forces acting on the particles, and deducing from the dynamical theory those phenomena which, though depending on the configuration and motion of the invisible particles, are capable of being observed in visible portions of the system.

The dynamical principles necessary for this study were developed by the fathers of dynamics, from Galileo and Newton to Lagrange and Laplace; but the special adaptation of these principles to molecular studies has been to a great extent the work of Prof. Clausius of Bonn, who has recently laid us under still deeper obligations by giving us, in addition to the results of his elaborate calculations, a new dynamical idea, by the aid of which I hope we shall be able to establish several important conclusions without much symbolical calculation.

The equation of Clausius, to which I must now call your attention, is of the following form:

$$pV = \tfrac{2}{3}T - \tfrac{2}{3}\Sigma\Sigma(\tfrac{1}{2}Rr).$$

Here p denotes the pressure of a fluid, and V the volume of the vessel which contains it. The product pV, in the case of gases at constant temperature, remains, as Boyle's Law tells us, nearly constant for different volumes and pressures. This member of the equation, therefore, is the product of two quantities, each of which can be directly measured.

The other member of the equation consists of two terms, the first depending on the motion of the particles, and the second on the forces with which they act on each other.

The quantity T is the kinetic energy of the system, or, in other words, that part of the energy which is due to the motion of the parts of the system.

The kinetic energy of a particle is half the product of its mass into the square of its velocity, and the kinetic energy of the system is the sum of the kinetic energy of its parts.

In the second term, r is the distance between any two particles, and R is the attraction between them. (If the force is a repulsion or a pressure, R is to be reckoned negative.)

The quantity $\tfrac{1}{2}Rr$, or half the product of the attraction into the distance across which the attraction is exerted, is defined by Clausius as the virial of the attraction. (In the case of pressure or repulsion, the virial is negative.)

The importance of this quantity was first pointed out by Clausius, who, by giving it a name, has greatly facilitated the application of his method to physical exposition.

The virial of the system is the sum of the virials belonging to every pair of particles which exist in the system. This is expressed by the double sum

$\Sigma\Sigma\left(\frac{1}{2}Rr\right)$, which indicates that the value of $\frac{1}{2}Rr$ is to be found for every pair of particles, and the results added together.

Clausius has established this equation by a very simple mathematical process, with which I need not trouble you, as we are not studying mathematics to-night. We may see, however, that it indicates two causes which may affect the pressure of the fluid on the vessel which contains it: the motion of its particles, which tends to increase the pressure, and the attraction of its particles, which tends to increase the pressure.

We may therefore attribute the pressure of a fluid either to the motion of its particles or to a repulsion between them.

Let us test by means of this result of Clausius the theory that the pressure of a gas arises entirely from the repulsion which one particle exerts on another, these particles, in the case of gas in a fixed vessel, being really at rest.

In this case the virial must be negative, and since by Boyle's Law the product of pressure and volume is constant, the virial also must be constant, whatever the volume, in the same quantity of gas at constant temperature. It follows from this that Rr, the product of the repulsion of two particles into the distance between them, must be constant, or in other words that the repulsion must be inversely as the distance, a law which Newton has shewn to be inadmissible in the case of molecular forces, as it would make the action of the distant parts of bodies greater than that of contiguous parts. In fact, we have only to observe that if Rr is constant, the virial of every pair of particles must be the same, so that the virial of the system must be proportional to the number of pairs of particles in the system—that is, to the square of the number of particles, or in other words to the square of the quantity of gas in the vessel. The pressure, according to this law, would not be the same in different vessels of gas at the same density, but would be greater in a large vessel than in a small one, and greater in the open air than in any ordinary vessel.

The pressure of a gas cannot therefore be explained by assuming repulsive forces between the particles.

It must therefore depend, in whole or in part, on the motion of the particles.

If we suppose the particles not to act on each other at all, there will be no virial, and the equation will be reduced to the form

$$Vp = \tfrac{2}{3}T.$$

If M is the mass of the whole quantity of gas, and c is the mean square of the velocity of a particle, we may write the equation—

$$Vp = \tfrac{1}{3}Mc^2$$

or in words, the product of the volume and the pressure is one-third of the mass multiplied by the mean square of the velocity. If we now assume, what we shall afterwards prove by an independent process, that the mean square of the velocity depends only on the temperature, this equation exactly represents Boyle's Law.

But we know that most ordinary gases deviate from Boyle's Law, especially at low temperatures and great densities. Let us see whether the hypothesis of forces between the particles, which we rejected when brought forward as the sole cause of gaseous pressure, may not be consistent with experiment when considered as the cause of this deviation from Boyle's Law.

When a gas is in an extremely rarefied condition, the number of particles within a given distance of any one particle will be proportional to the density of the gas. Hence the virial arising from the action of one particle on the rest will vary as the density, and the whole virial in unit of volume will vary as the square of the density.

Calling the density ρ, and dividing the equation by V, we get—

$$p = \tfrac{1}{3}\rho c^2 - \tfrac{2}{3}A\rho^2$$

where A is a quantity which is nearly constant for small densities.

Now, the experiments of Regnault shew that in most gases, as the density increases the pressure falls below the value calculated by Boyle's Law. Hence the virial must be positive; that is to say, the mutual action of the particles must be in the main attractive, and the effect of this action in diminishing the pressure must be at first very nearly as the square of the density.

On the other hand, when the pressure is made still greater the substance at length reaches a state in which an enormous increase of pressure produces but a very small increase of density. This indicates that the virial is now negative, or, in other words, the action between the particles is now, in the main, repulsive. We may therefore conclude that the action between two particles at any sensible distance is quite insensible. As the particles approach each other the action first shews itself as an attraction, which reaches a maximum, then diminishes, and at length becomes a repulsion so great that no attainable force can reduce the distance of the particles to zero.

The relation between pressure and density arising from such an action between the particles is of this kind.

As the density increases from zero, the pressure at first depends almost entirely on the motion of the particles, and therefore varies almost exactly as the pressure, according to Boyle's Law. As the density continues to increase, the effect of the mutual attraction of the particles becomes sensible, and this causes the rise of pressure to be less than that given by Boyle's Law. If the temperature is low, the effect of attraction may become so large in proportion to the effect of motion that the pressure, instead of always rising as the density increases, may reach a maximum, and then begin to diminish.

At length, however, as the average distance of the particles is still further diminished, the effect of repulsion will prevail over that of attraction, and the pressure will increase so as not only to be greater than that given by Boyle's Law, but so that an exceedingly small increase of density will produce an enormous increase of pressure.

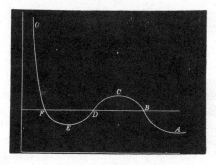

Hence the relation between pressure and volume may be represented by the curve $ABCDEFG$, where the horizontal ordinate represents the volume, and the vertical ordinate represents the pressure.

As the volume diminishes, the pressure increases up to the point C, then diminishes to the point E, and finally increases without limit as the volume diminishes.

We have hitherto supposed the experiment to be conducted in such a way that the density is the same in every part of the medium. This, however, is impossible in practice, as the only condition we can impose on the medium from without is that the whole of the medium shall be contained within a certain vessel. Hence, if it is possible for the medium to arrange itself so that part has one density and part another, we cannot prevent it from doing so.

Now the points B and F represent two states of the medium in which the pressure is the same but the density very different. The whole of the medium may pass from the state B to the state F, not through the intermediate states CDE, but by small successive portions passing directly from the state B to the state F. In this way the successive states of the medium as a whole will be represented by points on the straight line BF, the point B representing it when entirely in the rarefied state, and F representing it when entirely condensed. This is what takes place when a gas or vapour is liquefied.

Under ordinary circumstances, therefore, the relation between pressure and volume at constant temperature is represented by the broken line $ABFG$. If, however, the medium when liquefied is carefully kept from contact with vapour, it may be preserved in the liquid condition and brought into states represented by the portion of the curve between F and E. It is also possible that methods may be devised whereby the vapour may be prevented from condensing, and brought into states represented by points in BC.

The portion of the hypothetical curve from C to E represents states which are essentially unstable, and which cannot therefore be realised.

Now let us suppose the medium to pass from B to F along the hypothetical curve $BCDEF$ in a state always homogeneous, and to return along the straight line FB in the form of a mixture of liquid and vapour. Since the temperature has been constant throughout, no heat can have been transformed into work. Now the heat transformed into work is represented by the excess of the area FDE over BCD. Hence the condition which determines the maximum pressure of the vapour at given temperature is that the line BF cuts off equal areas from the curve above and below.

The higher the temperature, the greater the part of the pressure which depends on motion, as compared with that which depends on forces between the particles. Hence, as the temperature rises, the dip in the curve becomes less marked, and at a certain temperature the curve, instead of dipping, merely becomes horizontal at a certain point, and then slopes upward as before. This point is called the critical point. It has been determined for carbonic acid by the masterly researches of Andrews. It corresponds to a definite temperature, pressure and density.

At higher temperatures the curve slopes upwards throughout, and there is nothing corresponding to liquefaction in passing from the rarest to the densest state.

The molecular theory of the continuity of the liquid and gaseous states forms the subject of an exceedingly ingenious thesis by Mr Johannes Diderick van der Waals*, a graduate of Leyden. There are certain points in which I think he has fallen into mathematical errors, and his final result is certainly not a complete expression for the interaction of real molecules, but his attack on this difficult question is so able and so brave, that it cannot fail to give a notable impulse to molecular science. It has certainly directed the attention of more than one inquirer to the study of the Low-Dutch language in which it is written.

The purely thermodynamical relations of the different states of matter do not belong to our subject, as they are independent of particular theories about molecules. I must not, however, omit to mention a most important American contribution to this part of thermodynamics by Prof. Willard Gibbs†, of Yale College, U.S., who has given us a remarkably simple and thoroughly satisfactory method of representing the relations of the different states of matter by means of a model. By means of this model, problems which had long resisted the efforts of myself and others may be solved at once.

Let us now return to the case of a highly rarefied gas in which the pressure is due entirely to the motion of its particles. It is easy to calculate the mean square of the velocity of the particles from the equation of Clausius, since the volume, the pressure, and the mass are all measurable quantities. Supposing the velocity of every particle the same, the velocity of a molecule of oxygen would be 461 metres per second, of nitrogen 492, and of hydrogen 1844, at the temperature of 0° C.

The explanation of the pressure of a gas on the vessel which contains it by the impact of its particles on the surface of the vessel has been suggested at various times by various writers. The fact, however, that gases are not observed to disseminate themselves through the atmosphere with velocities at all approaching those just mentioned, remained unexplained, till Clausius, by a

---

* *Over de continuiteit van den gas en vloeistoftoestand.* (Leiden : A. W. Sijthoff, 1873.)

† "A method of geometrical representation of the thermodynamic properties of substances by means of surfaces." *Transactions of the Connecticut Academy of Arts and Sciences,* Vol. II. Part 2.

thorough study of the motions of an immense number of particles, developed the methods and ideas of modern molecular science.

To him we are indebted for the conception of the mean length of the path of a molecule of a gas between its successive encounters with other molecules. As soon as it was seen how each molecule, after describing an exceedingly short path, encounters another, and then describes a new path in a quite different direction, it became evident that the rate of diffusion of gases depends not merely on the velocity of the molecules, but on the distance they travel between each encounter.

I shall have more to say about the special contributions of Clausius to molecular science. The main fact, however, is, that he opened up a new field of mathematical physics by shewing how to deal mathematically with moving systems of innumerable molecules.

Clausius, in his earlier investigations at least, did not attempt to determine whether the velocities of all the molecules of the same gas are equal, or whether, if unequal, there is any law according to which they are distributed. He therefore, as a first hypothesis, seems to have assumed that the velocities are equal. But it is easy to see that if encounters take place among a great number of molecules, their velocities, even if originally equal, will become unequal, for, except under conditions which can be only rarely satisfied, two molecules having equal velocities before their encounter will acquire unequal velocities after the encounter. By distributing the molecules into groups according to their velocities, we may substitute for the impossible task of following every individual molecule through all its encounters, that of registering the increase or decrease of the number of molecules in the different groups.

By following this method, which is the only one available either experimentally or mathematically, we pass from the methods of strict dynamics to those of statistics and probability.

When an encounter takes place between two molecules, they are transferred from one pair of groups to another, but by the time that a great many encounters have taken place, the number which enter each group is, on an average, neither more nor less than the number which leave it during the same time. When the system has reached this state, the numbers in each group must be distributed according to some definite law.

As soon as I became acquainted with the investigations of Clausius, I endeavoured to ascertain this law.

The result which I published in 1860 has since been subjected to a more strict investigation by Dr Ludwig Boltzmann, who has also applied his method to the study of the motion of compound molecules. The mathematical investigation, though, like all parts of the science of probabilities and statistics, it is somewhat difficult, does not appear faulty. On the physical side, however, it leads to consequences, some of which, being manifestly true, seem to indicate that the hypotheses are well chosen, while others seem to be so irreconcilable with known experimental results, that we are compelled to admit that something essential to the complete statement of the physical theory of molecular encounters must have hitherto escaped us.

I must now attempt to give you some account of the present state of these investigations, without, however, entering into their mathematical demonstration.

I must begin by stating the general law of the distribution of velocity among molecules of the same kind.

If we take a fixed point in this diagram and draw from this point a line representing in direction and magnitude the velocity of a molecule, and make a dot at the end of the line, the position of the dot will indicate the state of motion of the molecule.

If we do the same for all the other molecules, the diagram will be dotted all over, the dots being more numerous in certain places than in others.

The law of distribution of the dots may be shewn to be the same as that which prevails among errors of observation or of adjustment.

The dots in the diagram before you may be taken to represent the velocities of molecules, the different observations of the position of the same star, or the bullet-holes round the bull's-eye of a target, all of which are distributed in the same manner.

The velocities of the molecules have values ranging from zero to infinity, so that in speaking of the average velocity of the molecules we must define what we mean.

The most useful quantity for purposes of comparison and calculation is called the "velocity of mean square." It is that velocity whose square is the average of the squares of the velocities of all the molecules.

This is the velocity given above as calculated from the properties of different gases. A molecule moving with the velocity of mean square has a kinetic energy equal to the average kinetic energy of all the molecules in the medium, and if a single mass equal to that of the whole quantity of gas were moving with this velocity, it would have the same kinetic energy as the gas actually has, only it would be in a visible form and directly available for doing work.

If in the same vessel there are different kinds of molecules, some of greater mass than others, it appears from this investigation that their velocities will be so distributed that the average kinetic energy of a molecule will be the same, whether its mass be great or small.

Diagram of Velocities.

Here we have perhaps the most important application which has yet been made of dynamical methods to chemical science. For, suppose that we have two gases in the same vessel. The ultimate distribution of agitation among the molecules is such that the average kinetic energy of an individual molecule is the same in either gas. This ultimate state is also, as we know, a state of equal temperature. Hence the condition that two gases shall have the same temperature is that the average kinetic energy of a single molecule shall be the same in the two gases.

Now, we have already shewn that the pressure of a gas is two-thirds of the kinetic energy in unit of volume. Hence, if the pressure as well as the temperature be the same in the two gases, the kinetic energy per unit of volume is the same, as well as the kinetic energy per molecule. There must, therefore, be the same number of molecules in unit of volume in the two gases.

This result coincides with the law of equivalent volumes established by Gay Lussac. This law, however, has hitherto rested on purely chemical evidence, the relative masses of the molecules of different substances having been deduced from the proportions in which the substances enter into chemical combination. It is now demonstrated on dynamical principles. The molecule is defined as that small portion of the substance which moves as one lump during the motion of agitation. This is a purely dynamical definition, independent of any experiments on combination.

The density of a gaseous medium, at standard temperature and pressure, is proportional to the mass of one of its molecules as thus defined.

We have thus a safe method of estimating the relative masses of molecules of different substances when in the gaseous state. This method is more to be depended on than those founded on electrolysis or on specific heat, because our knowledge of the conditions of the motion of agitation is more complete than our knowledge of electrolysis, or of the internal motions of the constituents of a molecule.

I must now say something about these internal motions, because the greatest difficulty which the kinetic theory of gases has yet encountered belongs to this part of the subject.

We have hitherto considered only the motion of the centre of mass of the molecule. We have now to consider the motion of the constituents of the molecule relative to the centre of mass.

If we suppose that the constituents of a molecule are atoms, and that each atom is what is called a material point, then each atom may move in three different and independent ways, corresponding to the three dimensions of space, so that the number of variables required to determine the position and configuration of all the atoms of the molecule is three times the number of atoms.

It is not essential, however, to the mathematical investigation to assume that the molecule is made up of atoms. All that is assumed is that the position and configuration of the molecule can be completely expressed by a certain number of variables.

Let us call this number n.

Of these variables, three are required to determine the position of the centre of mass of the molecule, and the remaining $n-3$ to determine its configuration relative to its centre of mass.

To each of the n variables corresponds a different kind of motion.

The motion of translation of the centre of mass has three components.

The motions of the parts relative to the centre of mass have $n-3$ components.

The kinetic energy of the molecule may be regarded as made up of two parts—that of the mass of the molecule supposed to be concentrated at its centre of mass, and that of the motions of the parts relative to the centre of mass. The first part is called the energy of translation, the second that of rotation and vibration. The sum of these is the whole energy of motion of the molecule.

The pressure of the gas depends, as we have seen, on the energy of translation alone. The specific heat depends on the rate at which the whole energy, kinetic and potential, increases as the temperature rises.

Clausius had long ago pointed out that the ratio of the increment of the whole energy to that of the energy of translation may be determined if we know by experiment the ratio of the specific heat at constant pressure to that at constant volume.

He did not however, attempt to determine à priori the ratio of the two parts of the energy, though he suggested, as an extremely probable hypothesis, that the average values of the two parts of the energy in a given substance always adjust themselves to the same ratio. He left the numerical value of this ratio to be determined by experiment.

In 1860 I investigated the ratio of the two parts of the energy on the hypothesis that the molecules are elastic bodies of invariable form. I found, to my great surprise, that whatever be the shape of the molecules, provided they are not perfectly smooth and spherical, the ratio of the two parts of the energy must be always the same, the two parts being in fact equal.

This result is confirmed by the researches of Boltzmann, who has worked out the general case of a molecule having n variables.

He finds that while the average energy of translation is the same for molecules of all kinds at the same temperature, the whole energy of motion is to the energy of translation as n to 3.

For a rigid body $n = 6$, which makes the whole energy of motion twice the energy of translation.

But if the molecule is capable of changing its form under the action of impressed forces, it must be capable of storing up potential energy, and if the forces are such as to ensure the stability of the molecule, the average potential energy will increase when the average energy of internal motion increases.

Hence, as the temperature rises, the increments of the energy of translation, the energy of internal motion, and the potential energy are as 3, $(n-3)$, and e respectively, where e is a positive quantity of unknown value depending on the law of the force which binds together the constituents of the molecule.

When the volume of the substance is maintained constant, the effect of the application of heat is to increase the whole energy. We thus find for the specific heat of a gas at constant volume—

$$\frac{1}{2J} \frac{p_0 V_0}{273^0} (n+e).$$

where p_0 and V_0 are the pressure and volume of unit of mass at zero centigrade, or 273^0 absolute temperature, and J is the dynamic equivalent of heat. The specific heat at constant pressure is

$$\frac{1}{2J} \frac{p_0 V_0}{273^0} (n+2+e).$$

In gases whose molecules have the same degree of complexity the value of n is the same, and that of e *may* be the same.

If this is the case, the specific heat is inversely as the specific gravity, according to the law of Dulong and Petit, which is, to a certain degree of approximation, verified by experiment.

But if we take the actual values of the specific heat as found by Regnault and compare them with this formula, we find that $n+e$ for air and several other gases cannot be more than 4·9. For carbonic acid and steam it is greater. We obtain the same result if we compare the ratio of the calculated specific heats

$$\frac{2+n+e}{n+e}$$

with the ratio as determined by experiment for various gases, namely, 1·408.

And here we are brought face to face with the greatest difficulty which the molecular theory has yet encountered, namely, the interpretation of the equation $n + e = 4\cdot9$.

If we suppose that the molecules are atoms—mere material points, incapable of rotatory energy or internal motion—then n is 3 and e is zero, and the ratio of the specific heats is $1\cdot66$, which is too great for any real gas.

But we learn from the spectroscope that a molecule can execute vibrations of constant period. It cannot therefore be a mere material point, but a system capable of changing its form. Such a system cannot have less than six variables. This would make the greatest value of the ratio of the specific heats $1\cdot33$, which is too small for hydrogen, oxygen, nitrogen, carbonic oxide, nitrous oxide, and hydrochloric acid.

But the spectroscope tells us that some molecules can execute a great many different kinds of vibrations. They must therefore be systems of a very considerable degree of complexity, having far more than six variables. Now, every additional variable introduces an additional amount of capacity for internal motion without affecting the external pressure. Every additional variable, therefore, increases the specific heat, whether reckoned at constant pressure or at constant volume.

So does any capacity which the molecule may have for storing up energy in the potential form. But the calculated specific heat is already too great when we suppose the molecule to consist of two atoms only. Hence every additional degree of complexity which we attribute to the molecule can only increase the difficulty of reconciling the observed with the calculated value of the specific heat.

I have now put before you what I consider to be the greatest difficulty yet encountered by the molecular theory. Boltzmann has suggested that we are to look for the explanation in the mutual action between the molecules and the ætherial medium which surrounds them. I am afraid, however, that if we call in the help of this medium, we shall only increase the calculated specific heat, which is already too great.

The theorem of Boltzmann may be applied not only to determine the distribution of velocity among the molecules, but to determine the distribution of the molecules themselves in a region in which they are acted on by external forces. It tells us that the density of distribution of the molecules at a point where the potential energy of a molecule is ψ, is proportional to $e^{-\frac{\psi}{\kappa\theta}}$ where θ is the absolute temperature, and κ is a constant for all gases. It follows from this, that if several gases in the same vessel are subject to an external force like that of gravity, the distribution of each gas is the same as if no other gas were present. This result agrees with the law assumed by Dalton, according to which the atmosphere may be regarded as consisting of two independent atmospheres, one of oxygen, and the other of nitrogen; the density of the oxygen diminishing faster than that of the nitrogen, as we ascend.

This would be the case if the atmosphere were never disturbed, but the effect of winds is to mix up the atmosphere and to render its composition more uniform than it would be if left at rest.

Another consequence of Boltzmann's theorem is, that the temperature tends to become equal throughout a vertical column of gas at rest.

In the case of the atmosphere, the effect of wind is to cause the temperature to vary as that of a mass of air would do if it were carried vertically upwards, expanding and cooling as it ascends.

But besides these results, which I had already obtained by a less elegant method and published in 1866, Boltzmann's theorem seems to open up a path into a region more purely chemical. For if the gas consists of a number of similar systems, each of which may assume different states having different amounts of energy, the theorem tells us that the number in each state is proportional to $e^{-\frac{\psi}{\kappa\theta}}$ where ψ is the energy, θ the absolute temperature, and κ a constant.

It is easy to see that this result ought to be applied to the theory of the states of combination which occur in a mixture of different substances. But as it is only during the present week that I have made any attempt to do so, I shall not trouble you with my crude calculations.

I have confined my remarks to a very small part of the field of molecular investigation. I have said nothing about the molecular theory of the diffusion of matter, motion, and energy, for though the results, especially in the diffusion of matter and the transpiration of fluids are of great interest to many chemists, and though from them we deduce important molecular data, they belong to a part of our study the data of which, depending on the conditions of the encounter of two molecules, are necessarily very hypothetical. I have thought it better to exhibit the evidence that the parts of fluids are in motion, and to describe the manner in which that motion is distributed among molecules of different masses.

To shew that all the molecules of the same substance are equal in mass, we may refer to the methods of dialysis introduced by Graham, by which two gases of different densities may be separated by percolation through a porous plug.

If in a single gas there were molecules of different masses, the same process of dialysis, repeated a sufficient number of times, would furnish us with two portions of the gas, in one of which the average mass of the molecules would be greater than in the other. The density and the combining weight of these two portions would be different. Now, it may be said that no one has carried out this experiment in a sufficiently elaborate manner for every chemical substance. But the processes of nature are continually carrying out experiments of the same kind; and if there were molecules of the same substance nearly alike, but differing slightly in mass, the greater molecules would be selected in preference to form one compound, and the smaller to form another. But hydrogen is of the same density, whether we obtain it from water or from a hydrocarbon, so that neither oxygen nor carbon can find in hydrogen molecules greater or smaller than the average.

The estimates which have been made of the actual size of molecules are founded on a comparison of the volumes of bodies in the liquid or solid state, with their volumes in the gaseous state. In the study of molecular volumes we meet with many difficulties, but at the same time there are a sufficient number of consistent results to make the study a hopeful one.

The theory of the possible vibrations of a molecule has not yet been studied as it ought, with the help of a continual comparison between the dynamical theory and the evidence of the spectroscope. An intelligent student, armed with the calculus and the spectroscope, can hardly fail to discover some important fact about the internal constitution of a molecule.

The observed transparency of gases may seem hardly consistent with the results of molecular investigations.

A model of the molecules of a gas consisting of marbles scattered at distances bearing the proper proportion to their diameters, would allow very little light to penetrate through a hundred feet.

But if we remember the small size of the molecules compared with the length of a wave of light, we may apply certain theoretical investigations of Lord Rayleigh's about the mutual action between waves and small spheres, which shew that the transparency of the atmosphere, if affected only by the presence of molecules, would be far greater than we have any reason to believe it to be.

A much more difficult investigation, which has hardly yet been attempted, relates to the electric properties of gases. No one has yet explained why dense gases are such good insulators, and why, when rarefied or heated, they permit the discharge of electricity, whereas a perfect vacuum is the best of all insulators.

It is true that the diffusion of molecules goes on faster in a rarefied gas, because the mean path of a molecule is inversely as the density. But the electrical difference between dense and rare gas appears to be too great to be accounted for in this way.

But while I think it right to point out the hitherto unconquered difficulties of this molecular theory, I must not forget to remind you of the numerous facts which it satisfactorily explains. We have already mentioned the gaseous laws, as they are called, which express the relations between volume, pressure, and temperature, and Gay Lussac's very important law of equivalent volumes. The explanation of these may be regarded as complete. The law of molecular specific heats is less accurately verified by experiment, and its full explanation depends on a more perfect knowledge of the internal structure of a molecule than we as yet possess.

But the most important result of these inquiries is a more distinct conception of thermal phenomena. In the first place, the temperature of the medium is measured by the average kinetic energy of translation of a single molecule of the medium. In two media placed in thermal communication, the temperature as thus measured tends to become equal.

In the next place, we learn how to distinguish that kind of motion which we call heat from other kinds of motion. The peculiarity of the motion called heat is that it is perfectly irregular; that is to say, that the direction and magnitude of the velocity of a molecule at a given time cannot be expressed as depending on the present position of the molecule and the time.

In the visible motion of a body, on the other hand, the velocity of the centre of mass of all the molecules in any visible portion of the body is the observed velocity of that portion, though the molecules may have also an irregular depending agitation on account of the body being hot.

In the transmission of sound, too, the different portions of the body have a motion which is generally too minute and too rapidly alternating to be directly observed. But in the motion which constitutes the physical phenomenon of sound, the velocity of each portion of the medium at any time can be expressed as depending on the position and the time elapsed; so that the motion of a medium during the passage of a sound-wave is regular, and must be distinguished from that which we call heat.

If, however, the sound-wave, instead of travelling onwards in an orderly manner and leaving the medium behind it at rest, meets with resistances which fritter away its motion into irregular agitations, this irregular molecular motion becomes no longer capable of being propagated swiftly in one direction as sound, but lingers in the medium in the form of heat till it is communicated to colder parts of the medium by the slow process of conduction.

The motion which we call light, though still more minute and rapidly alternating than that of sound, is, like that of sound, perfectly regular, and therefore is not heat. What was formerly called Radiant Heat is a phenomenon physically identical with light.

When the radiation arrives at a certain portion of the medium, it enters it and passes through it, emerging at the other side. As long as the medium is engaged in transmitting the radiation it is in a certain state of motion, but as soon as the radiation has passed through it, the medium returns to its former state, the motion being entirely transferred to a new portion of the medium.

Now, the motion which we call heat can never of itself pass from one body to another unless the first body is, during the whole process, hotter than the second. The motion of radiation, therefore, which passes entirely out of one portion of the medium and enters another, cannot be properly called heat.

We may apply the molecular theory of gases to test those hypotheses about the luminiferous æther which assume it to consist of atoms or molecules.

Those who have ventured to describe the constitution of the luminiferous æther have sometimes assumed it to consist of atoms or molecules.

The application of the molecular theory to such hypotheses leads to rather startling results.

In the first place, a molecular æther would be neither more nor less than a gas. We may, if we please, assume that its molecules are each of them equal to the thousandth or the millionth part of a molecule of hydrogen, and that they can traverse freely the interspaces of all ordinary molecules. But, as we have seen, an equilibrium will establish itself between the agitation of the ordinary molecules and those of the æther. In other words, the æther and the bodies in it will tend to equality of temperature, and the æther will be subject to the ordinary gaseous laws as to pressure and temperature.

Among other properties of a gas, it will have that established by Dulong and Petit, so that the capacity for heat of unit of volume of the æther must be equal to that of unit of volume of any ordinary gas at the same pressure. Its presence, therefore, could not fail to be detected in our experiments on specific heat, and we may therefore assert that the constitution of the æther is not molecular.

[From the *Proceedings of the London Mathematical Society*, Vol. VI. No. 83.]

LXXII. *On the Application of Hamilton's Characteristic Function to the Theory of an Optical Instrument symmetrical about its axis.*

[Read *April* 8th, 1875.]

When a ray of light passes from the point (x_1, y_1, z_1) to the point (x_2, y_2, z_2) through any series of media, the line-integral $V = \int \mu ds$ may be defined as the distance which light would travel in vacuum in the same time as it travels from (x_1, y_1, z_1) to (x_2, y_2, z_2).

Calling this the reduced distance between (x_1, y_1, z_1) and (x_2, y_2, z_2), Hamilton's Characteristic Function may be defined as the value of the reduced distance between two points expressed in terms of the co-ordinates of these points.

It is not necessary that the co-ordinates of the two points should be referred to the same system of axes. In treating of optical instruments we shall reckon z_1 and z_2 in opposite directions along the axis, and from different planes of reference. We shall, however, make the axes of x_1 and x_2 parallel to each other in what follows.

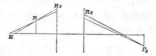

Let a ray from the point $P_1 (x_1, 0, z_1)$ pass through the first plane of reference at the point $R_1 (a_1, b_1, 0)$, through the second plane of reference at $R_2 (a_2, b_2, 0)$, and reach the point $P_2 (x_2, 0, z_2)$;

then, putting
and
$$\left. \begin{array}{l} \overline{P_1 R_1}^2 = (x_1 - a_1)^2 + b_1^2 + z_1^2 = r_1^2 \\ \overline{P_2 R_2}^2 = (x_2 - a_2)^2 + b_2^2 + z_2^2 = r_2^2 \end{array} \right\} \quad \dots\dots\dots\dots\dots(1),$$

and the characteristic function from R_1 to $R_2 = V$ (a function of a_1, b_1, a_2, b_2), the reduced path from P_1 to P_2 is

$$U = \mu_1 r_1 + V + \mu_2 r_2 \quad\dots\dots\dots\dots\dots\dots (2).$$

This quantity is stationary with respect to variations of a_1, b_1, a_2, b_2; therefore, differentiating with respect to these variables, we get

$$\left.\begin{aligned}
\mu_1 \frac{a_1 - x_1}{r_1} + \frac{dV}{da_1} = 0, \quad \mu_1 \frac{b_1}{r_1} + \frac{dV}{db_1} = 0 \\
\mu_2 \frac{a_2 - x_2}{r_2} + \frac{dV}{da_2} = 0, \quad \mu_2 \frac{b_2}{r_2} + \frac{dV}{db_2} = 0
\end{aligned}\right\} \quad\dots\dots\dots\dots (3).$$

If P_1 and P_2 are conjugate foci for rays in the plane of xz, the reduced path is stationary in passing from one ray to the next by simultaneous variation of a_1 and a_2.

Hence
$$\left.\begin{aligned}
\left[\mu_1 \left(\frac{1}{r_1} - \frac{(a_1 - x_1)^2}{r_1^3} \right) + \frac{d^2V}{da_1^2} \right] da_1 + \frac{d^2V}{da_1 da_2} da_2 = 0 \\
\left[\mu_2 \left(\frac{1}{r_2} - \frac{(a_2 - x_2)^2}{r_2^3} \right) + \frac{d^2V}{da_2^2} \right] da_2 + \frac{d^2V}{da_1 da_2} da_1 = 0
\end{aligned}\right\} \quad\dots\dots\dots(4).$$

Eliminating da_1 and da_2 from these equations, and putting θ for the angle between the ray and the axis, we find

$$\left(\frac{\mu_1}{r_1} \cos^2\theta_1 + \frac{d^2V}{da_1^2} \right) \left(\frac{\mu_2}{r_2} \cos^2\theta_2 + \frac{d^2V}{da_2^2} \right) = \left(\frac{d^2V}{da_1 da_2} \right)^2 \quad\dots\dots\dots\dots (5),$$

an equation connecting the values of r_1 and r_2 for conjugate primary focal lines formed by rays in the plane of xz.

For rays in a plane perpendicular to that of xz, we obtain the relation of r_1' and r_2' for the secondary focal lines, by passing from one ray to the next by simultaneous variation of b_1 and b_2,

$$\left.\begin{aligned}
\left(\frac{\mu}{r_1'} + \frac{d^2V}{db_1^2} \right) db_1 + \frac{d^2V}{db_1 db_2} db_2 = 0 \\
\left(\frac{\mu_2}{r_2'} + \frac{d^2V}{db_2^2} \right) db_2 + \frac{d^2V}{db_1 db_2} db_1 = 0
\end{aligned}\right\} \quad\dots\dots\dots\dots\dots (6),$$

whence
$$\left(\frac{\mu_1}{r_1'} + \frac{d^2V}{db_1^2} \right) \left(\frac{\mu_2}{r_2'} + \frac{d^2V}{db_2^2} \right) = \left(\frac{d^2V}{db_1 db_2} \right)^2 \quad\dots\dots\dots\dots (7).$$

The form of this equation differs from that for the primary focal lines only by the omission of $\cos^2 \theta$, and by substituting b for a.

From these equations we obtain the following values of the cardinal points of the ray in the primary and secondary plane:

$$\text{Let} \qquad \left. \begin{array}{llll} A=\dfrac{d^2V}{da_1{}^2}, & B=\dfrac{d^2V}{da_1 da_2}, & C=\dfrac{d^2V}{da_2{}^2}, & D=\dfrac{1}{B^2-AC} \\[2mm] A'=\dfrac{d^2V}{db_1{}^2}, & B'=\dfrac{d^2V}{db_1 db_2}, & C'=\dfrac{d^2V}{db_2{}^2}, & D'=\dfrac{1}{B'^2-A'C'} \end{array} \right\} \dots\dots (8).$$

	Primary.	Secondary.
Value of r_1 at 1st principal focus	$g_1 = \mu_1 CD \cos^2 \theta_1$	$g_1' = \mu_1 C'D'$
Value of r_2 at 2nd principal focus	$g_2 = \mu_2 AD \cos^2 \theta_2$	$g_2' = \mu_2 A'D'$
1st principal focal length	$f_1 = \mu_1 BD \cos \theta_1 \cos \theta_2$	$f_1' = \mu_1 B'D'$
2nd principal focal length	$f_2 = \mu_2 BD \cos \theta_1 \cos \theta_2$	$f_2' = \mu_2 B'D'$

$$\dots\dots(9).$$

In tracing the axis of the pencil, we may, as a first approximation, neglect the square of θ.

Let it cross the axis before incidence at H_1, and after emergence at H_2, where H_1 is $\dfrac{1}{a}f_1$ beyond the first principal focus, and H_2 is af_2 beyond the second principal focus.

Let it cut the first and second principal planes at a distance ξ from the axis. Then, since these planes are at distances f_1 and f_2 within the principal foci,

$$\tan \theta_1 = \frac{\xi}{f_1} \frac{a}{1+a}, \qquad \tan \theta_2 = \frac{\xi}{f_2} \frac{1}{1+a} \dots\dots\dots\dots(10),$$

$$a_1 = \frac{\xi}{1+a} \left(\frac{C}{B} a + 1 \right), \qquad a_2 = \frac{\xi}{1+a} \left(\frac{A}{B} + a \right) \dots\dots\dots\dots(11).$$

Let the object and image be respectively $\dfrac{1}{\beta} f_1$ and βf_1 beyond the principal foci,

$$z_1 = f_1 \left(\frac{C}{B} + \frac{1}{\beta} \right), \qquad z_2 = f_2 \left(\frac{A}{B} + \beta \right) \dots\dots\dots\dots\dots(12),$$

$$x_1 = \frac{\xi}{1+a} \left(1 - \frac{a}{\beta} \right), \qquad x_2 = \frac{\xi}{1+a} (a - \beta) \dots\dots\dots\dots(13).$$

We shall next determine the relation between the curvature of the object and that of the image.

Let their curvatures be concave towards the instrument, their radii being R_1 and R_2 respectively, then,

$$z_1 = f_1 \left(\frac{C}{B} + \frac{1}{\beta} \right) - \frac{x_1^2}{2R_1} + \&\text{c.}, \quad z_2 = f_2 \left(\frac{A}{B} + \beta \right) - \frac{x_2^2}{2R_1} + \&\text{c.} \dots\dots\dots(14).$$

We must now insert these values in equation (5), but, for the sake of simplicity, we shall suppose the planes of reference to pass through the principal foci.

We now find
$$f_1 = \frac{\mu_1}{B}, \quad f_2 = \frac{\mu_2}{B} \dots\dots\dots\dots\dots\dots\dots\dots(15),$$

$$z_1 = \frac{1}{\beta} f_1 - \frac{x_1^2}{2R_1}, \quad z_2 = \beta f_2 - \frac{x_2^2}{2R_1} \dots\dots\dots\dots\dots(16),$$

$$a_1 = \frac{\xi}{1+a}, \quad a_2 = \frac{\xi a}{1+a} \dots\dots\dots\dots\dots\dots(17).$$

Hamilton's function for a symmetrical instrument is of the form

$$\begin{aligned} V = \quad & \tfrac{1}{2}\mathfrak{A} \left(a_1^2 + b_1^2 \right) + \mathfrak{B} \left(a_1 a_2 + b_1 b_2 \right) + \tfrac{1}{2}\mathfrak{C} \left(a_2^2 + b_2^2 \right) \\ & + \tfrac{1}{4}a \left(a_1^2 + b_1^2 \right)^2 + \tfrac{1}{2}b \left(a_1 a_2 + b_1 b_2 \right)^2 + \tfrac{1}{4}c \left(a_2^2 + b_2^2 \right)^2 \\ & + p \left(a_1 a_2 + b_1 b_2 \right) \left(a_2^2 + b_2^2 \right) + \tfrac{1}{2}q \left(a_1^2 + b_1^2 \right) \left(a_2^2 + b_2^2 \right) \\ & + r \left(a_1^2 + b_1^2 \right) \left(a_1 a_2 + b_1 b_2 \right) \dots\dots\dots\dots\dots(18). \end{aligned}$$

Differentiating, and making b_1 and b_2 zero, we find

$$\left. \begin{aligned} A &= \mathfrak{A} + 3aa_1^2 + 6ra_1 a_2 + (b+q)\, a_2^2 \\ B &= \mathfrak{B} + 3ra_1^2 + (2b+2q)\, a_1 a_2 + 3pa_2^2 \\ C &= \mathfrak{C} + (b+q)\, a_1^2 + 6pa_1 a_2 + 3ca_2^2 \end{aligned} \right\} \dots\dots\dots\dots(19),$$

$$\left. \begin{aligned} A' &= \mathfrak{A} + aa_1^2 + 2ra_1 a_2 + qa_2^2 \\ B' &= \mathfrak{B} + ra_1^2 + ba_1 a_2 + pa_2^2 \\ C' &= \mathfrak{C} + qa_1^2 + 2paa_2^2 + ca_2^2 \end{aligned} \right\} \dots\dots\dots\dots(20).$$

If the planes of reference pass through the principal foci,

$$\mathfrak{A} = 0 \quad \text{and} \quad \mathfrak{C} = 0 \dots\dots\dots\dots\dots\dots(21).$$

Substituting in equations (5) and (7), and putting

$$U = \frac{2}{(a-\beta)^2} \left\{ \mathfrak{B}\beta \left(\frac{a^2}{\mu_1^2} + \frac{1}{\mu_2^2} \right) - \frac{1}{\mathfrak{B}^2} \left[a + \tfrac{1}{2}b\,(a-\beta)^2 + ca^2\beta^2 \right. \right. \\ \left. \left. - 2pa\beta(a-\beta) - 2qa\beta + 2r\,(a-\beta) \right] \right\} \dots\dots(22),$$

$$W = 2 \left(\frac{a+\beta}{a-\beta} \right)^2 \frac{1}{\mathfrak{B}^2} \left(\tfrac{1}{2}b - q \right) \dots\dots\dots\dots\dots(23),$$

we find $\qquad \dfrac{1}{\mu_1 R_1} + \dfrac{1}{\mu_2 R_2} = 3U + W$ for the primary image .... (24),

$$\frac{1}{\mu_1 R_1'} + \frac{1}{\mu_2 R_2'} = U + W \text{ for the secondary image} ....(25).$$

The condition of distinctness is $U = 0$.

That the image of a flat object may be flat as well as distinct,

$$U = 0 \text{ and } W = 0 ....(26).$$

Form of the Characteristic Function for a Spherical Refracting Surface.

Let the planes of reference pass through the principal foci.

Let $BC = s$ be the radius, then

$$AB = \frac{\mu_1 s}{\mu_2 - \mu_1}, \quad BA_2 = \frac{\cdot \mu_2 s}{\mu_2 - \mu_1}.$$

If the co-ordinates of P_1 are $a_1, \ b_1, \ -\dfrac{\mu_1 s}{\mu_2 - \mu_1},$

$$P_2 \quad ,, \quad a_2, \ b_2, \ \frac{\mu_2 s}{\mu_2 - \mu_1},$$

$$P \quad ,, \quad a, \ b, \ z,$$

and if $P_1 P = r_1$ and $PP_2 = r_2$, then

$$V = \mu_1 r_1 + \mu_2 r_2,$$

under the condition that V is stationary with respect to variations of a and b, when

$$a^2 + b^2 + (s - z)^2 = s^2.$$

This gives the following values of a and b:

$$a = a_1 + a_2 + \lambda_1 a_1 + \lambda_2 a_2 + \&c.,$$

$$b = b_1 + b_2 + \lambda_1 b_1 + \lambda_2 b_2 + \&c.,$$

when

$$\lambda_1 = \frac{1}{2s^2 \mu_1{}^2 \mu_2{}^2} \{\mu_1{}^3 (a_1{}^2 + b_1{}^2) + 2\mu_1{}^2 \mu_2 (a_1 a_2 + b_1 b_2) + \mu_2 (\mu_1{}^2 - \mu_1 \mu_2 + \mu_2{}^2) (a_2{}^2 + b_2{}^2)\},$$

$$\lambda_2 = \frac{1}{2s^2 \mu_1{}^2 \mu_2{}^2} \{\mu_1 (\mu_1{}^2 - \mu_1 \mu_2 + \mu_2{}^2) (a_1{}^2 + b_1{}^2) + 2\mu_1 \mu_2{}^2 (a_1 a_2 + b_1 b_2) + \mu_2{}^3 (a_2{}^2 + b_2{}^2)\};$$

56—2

whence we get, as the value of V to terms of the fourth order,

$$V = s \frac{\mu_1^2 + \mu_2^2}{\mu_2 - \mu_1} - \frac{1}{s}(\mu_2 - \mu_1)(a_1a_2 + b_1b_2)$$

$$+ \frac{\mu_2 - \mu_1}{8s^3\mu_1^2\mu_2^2} \left\{ \begin{array}{l} \mu_1^2(3\mu_1^2 + \mu_2^2)(a_1^2 + b_1^2)^2 + 8\mu_1\mu_2^2(\mu_1^2 + \mu_2^2)(a_1a_2 + b_1b_2)^2 \\ + \mu_2^2(\mu_1^2 + 3\mu_2^2)(a_2^2 + b_2^2)^2 \\ + 4\mu_2(\mu_1^3 + 2\mu_1\mu_2^2 + \mu_2^3)(a_1a_2 + b_1b_2)(a_2^2 + b_2^2) \\ + \mu_1\mu_2(7\mu_1^2 - 6\mu_1\mu_2 + 7\mu_2^2)(a_1^2 + b_1^2)(a_2^2 + b_2^2) \\ + 4\mu_1(\mu_1^3 + 2\mu_1^2\mu_2 + \mu_2^3)(a_1^2 + b_1^2)(a_1a_2 + b_1b_2) \end{array} \right\}.$$

Hence the coefficients in the general equations (18), (19), (20), (22), (23) are as follows :

$$\mathfrak{A} = 0, \qquad \mathfrak{B} = \frac{\mu_2 - \mu_1}{s}, \qquad \mathfrak{C} = 0,$$

$$a = \frac{1}{2}\frac{\mu_2 - \mu_1}{s^3\mu_2^2}(3\mu_1^2 + \mu_2^2), \quad b = 2\frac{\mu_2 - \mu_1}{s^3\mu_1\mu_2}(\mu_1^2 + \mu_2^2), \quad c = \frac{1}{2}\frac{\mu_2 - \mu_1}{s^3\mu_1^2}(\mu_1^2 + 3\mu_2^2),$$

$$p = \frac{1}{2}\frac{\mu_2 - \mu_1}{s^3\mu_1^2\mu_2}(\mu_1^3 + 2\mu_1\mu_2^2 + \mu_2^3), \quad q = \frac{1}{4}\frac{\mu_2 - \mu_1}{s^3\mu_1\mu_2^2}(7\mu_1^2 - 6\mu_1\mu_2 + 7\mu_2^2),$$

$$r = \frac{1}{2}\frac{\mu_2 - \mu_1}{s^3\mu_1\mu_2^2}(\mu_1^3 + 2\mu_1^2\mu_2 + \mu_2^3).$$

[From the *Encyclopædia Britannica*.]

LXXIII. *Atom.*

ATOM (ἄτομος) is a body which cannot be cut in two. The atomic theory is a theory of the constitution of bodies, which asserts that they are made up of atoms. The opposite theory is that of the homogeneity and continuity of bodies, and asserts, at least in the case of bodies having no apparent organisation, such, for instance, as water, that as we can divide a drop of water into two parts which are each of them drops of water, so we have reason to believe that these smaller drops can be divided again, and the theory goes on to assert that there is nothing in the nature of things to hinder this process of division from being repeated over and over again, times without end. This is the doctrine of the infinite divisibility of bodies, and it is in direct contradiction with the theory of atoms.

The atomists assert that after a certain number of such divisions the parts would be no longer divisible, because each of them would be an atom. The advocates of the continuity of matter assert that the smallest conceivable body has parts, and that whatever has parts may be divided.

In ancient times Democritus was the founder of the atomic theory, while Anaxagoras propounded that of continuity, under the name of the doctrine of homœomeria (Ὁμοιομέρια), or of the similarity of the parts of a body to the whole. The arguments of the atomists, and their replies to the objections of Anaxagoras, are to be found in Lucretius.

In modern times the study of nature has brought to light many properties of bodies which appear to depend on the magnitude and motions of their ultimate constituents, and the question of the existence of atoms has once more become conspicuous among scientific inquiries.

We shall begin by stating the opposing doctrines of atoms and of continuity before giving an outline of the state of molecular science as it now exists. In the earliest times the most ancient philosophers whose speculations are known to us seem to have discussed the ideas of number and of continuous magnitude, of space and time, of matter and motion, with a native power of thought which has probably never been surpassed. Their actual knowledge, however, and their scientific experience were necessarily limited, because in their days the records of human thought were only beginning to accumulate. It is probable that the first exact notions of quantity were founded on the consideration of number. It is by the help of numbers that concrete quantities are practically measured and calculated. Now, number is discontinuous. We pass from one number to the next *per saltum*. The magnitudes, on the other hand, which we meet with in geometry, are essentially continuous. The attempt to apply numerical methods to the comparison of geometrical quantities led to the doctrine of incommensurables, and to that of the infinite divisibility of space. Meanwhile, the same considerations had not been applied to time, so that in the days of Zeno of Elea time was still regarded as made up of a finite number of "moments," while space was confessed to be divisible without limit. This was the state of opinion when the celebrated arguments against the possibility of motion, of which that of Achilles and the tortoise is a specimen, were propounded by Zeno, and such, apparently, continued to be the state of opinion till Aristotle pointed out that time is divisible without limit, in precisely the same sense that space is. And the slowness of the development of scientific ideas may be estimated from the fact that Bayle does not see any force in this statement of Aristotle, but continues to admire the paradox of Zeno. (Bayle's *Dictionary*, art. "Zeno".) Thus the direction of true scientific progress was for many ages towards the recognition of the infinite divisibility of space and time.

It was easy to attempt to apply similar arguments to matter. If matter is extended and fills space, the same mental operation by which we recognise the divisibility of space may be applied, in imagination at least, to the matter which occupies space. From this point of view the atomic doctrine might be regarded as a relic of the old numerical way of conceiving magnitude, and the opposite doctrine of the infinite divisibility of matter might appear for a time the most scientific. The atomists, on the other hand, asserted very strongly the distinction between matter and space. The atoms, they said, do not fill up the universe; there are void spaces between them. If it were not so, Lucretius tells us, there could be no motion, for the atom which gives way first must have some empty place to move into.

"Quapropter locus est intactus, inane, vacansque.
Quod si non esset, nulla ratione moveri
Res possent; namque, officium quod corporis exstat,
Officere atque obstare, id in omni tempore adesset
Omnibus: haud igitur quicquam procedere posset,
Principium quoniam cedendi nulla daret res." *De Rerum Natura*, I. 335.

The opposite school maintained then, as they have always done, that there is no vacuum—that every part of space is full of matter, that there is a universal plenum, and that all motion is like that of a fish in the water, which yields in front of the fish because the fish leaves room for it behind.

"Cedere squamigeris latices nitentibus aiunt
Et liquidas aperire vias, quia post loca pisces
Linquant, quo possint cedentes confluere undæ." I. 373.

In modern times Descartes held that, as it is of the essence of matter to be extended in length, breadth, and thickness, so it is of the essence of extension to be occupied by matter, for extension cannot be an extension of nothing.

"Ac proinde si quæratur quid fiet, si Deus auferat omne corpus quod in aliquo vase continetur, et nullum aliud in ablati locum venire permittat? respondendum est, vasis latera sibi invicem hoc ipso fore contigua. Cum enim inter duo corpora nihil interjacet, necesse est ut se mutuo tangant, ac manifeste repugnat ut distent, sive ut inter ipsa sit distantia, et tamen ut ista distantia sit nihil; quia omnis distantia est modus extensionis, et ideo sine substantia extensa esse non potest."

Principia, II. 18.

This identification of extension with substance runs through the whole of Descartes's works, and it forms one of the ultimate foundations of the system of Spinoza. Descartes, consistently with this doctrine, denied the existence of atoms as parts of matter, which by their own nature are indivisible. He seems to admit, however, that the Deity might make certain particles of matter indivisible in this sense, that no creature should be able to divide them. These particles, however, would be still divisible by their own nature, because the Deity cannot diminish his own power, and therefore must retain his power of dividing them. Leibnitz, on the other hand, regarded his monad as the ultimate element of everything.

There are thus two modes of thinking about the constitution of bodies, which have had their adherents both in ancient and in modern times. They correspond to the two methods of regarding quantity—the arithmetical and the geometrical. To the atomist the true method of estimating the quantity of matter in a body is to count the atoms in it. The void spaces between the atoms count for nothing. To those who identify matter with extension, the volume of space occupied by a body is the only measure of the quantity of matter in it.

Of the different forms of the atomic theory, that of Boscovich may be taken as an example of the purest monadism. According to Boscovich matter is made up of atoms. Each atom is an indivisible point, having position in space, capable of motion in a continuous path, and possessing a certain mass, whereby a certain amount of force is required to produce a given change of motion. Besides this the atom is endowed with potential force, that is to say, that any two atoms attract or repel each other with a force depending on their distance apart. The law of this force, for all distances greater than say the thousandth of an inch, is an attraction varying as the inverse square of the distance. For smaller distances the force is an attraction for one distance and a repulsion for another, according to some law not yet discovered. Boscovich himself, in order to obviate the possibility of two atoms ever being in the same place, asserts that the ultimate force is a repulsion which increases without limit as the distance diminishes without limit, so that two atoms can never coincide. But this seems an unwarrantable concession to the vulgar opinion that two bodies cannot co-exist in the same place. This opinion is deduced from our experience of the behaviour of bodies of sensible size, but we have no experimental evidence that two atoms may not sometimes coincide. For instance, if oxygen and hydrogen combine to form water, we have no experimental evidence that the molecule of oxygen is not in the very same place with the two molecules of hydrogen. Many persons cannot get rid of the opinion that all matter is extended in length, breadth, and depth. This is a prejudice of the same kind with the last, arising from our experience of bodies consisting of immense multitudes of atoms. The system of atoms, according to Boscovich, occupies a certain region of space in virtue of the forces acting between the component atoms of the system and any other atoms when brought near them. No other system of atoms can occupy the same region of space at the same time, because, before it could do so, the mutual action of the atoms would have caused a repulsion between the two systems insuperable by any force which we can command. Thus, a number of soldiers with firearms may occupy an extensive region to the exclusion of the enemy's armies, though the space filled by their bodies is but small. In this way Boscovich explained the apparent extension of bodies consisting of atoms, each of which is devoid of extension. According to Boscovich's theory, all action between bodies is action at a distance. There is no such thing in nature as actual contact between two bodies. When two bodies are said in ordinary language to be in contact, all that is meant is that they are so near together that the repulsion between the nearest pairs of atoms belonging to the two bodies is very great.

Thus, in Boscovich's theory, the atom has continuity of existence in time and space. At any instant of time it is at some point of space, and it is never in more than one place at a time. It passes from one place to another along a continuous path. It has a definite mass which cannot be increased or diminished. Atoms are endowed with the power of acting on one another by attraction or repulsion, the amount of the force depending on the distance between them. On the other hand, the atom itself has no parts or dimensions. In its geometrical aspect it is a mere geometrical point. It has no extension in space. It has not the so-called property of Impenetrability, for two atoms may exist in the same place. This we may regard as one extreme of the various opinions about the constitution of bodies.

The opposite extreme, that of Anaxagoras—the theory that bodies apparently homogeneous and continuous are so in reality—is, in its extreme form, a theory incapable of development. To explain the properties of any substance by this theory is impossible. We can only admit the observed properties of such substance as ultimate facts. There is a certain stage, however, of scientific progress in which a method corresponding to this theory is of service. In hydrostatics, for instance, we define a fluid by means of one of its known properties, and from this definition we make the system of deductions which constitutes the science of hydrostatics. In this way the science of hydrostatics may be built upon an experimental basis, without any consideration of the constitution of a fluid as to whether it is molecular or continuous. In like manner, after the French mathematicians had attempted, with more or less ingenuity, to construct a theory of elastic solids from the hypothesis that they consist of atoms in equilibrium under the action of their mutual forces, Stokes and others shewed that all the results of this hypothesis, so far at least as they agreed with facts, might be deduced from the postulate that elastic bodies exist, and from the hypothesis that the smallest portions into which we can divide them are sensibly homogeneous. In this way the principle of continuity, which is the basis of the method of Fluxions and the whole of modern mathematics, may be applied to the analysis of problems connected with material bodies by assuming them, for the purpose of this analysis, to be homogeneous. All that is required to make the results applicable to the real case is that the smallest portions of the substance of which we take any notice shall be sensibly of the same kind. Thus, if a railway contractor has to make a tunnel through a hill of gravel, and if one cubic yard of the gravel is so like another cubic yard that for the purposes of the contract they may be taken as equivalent, then, in estimating the work required to remove the gravel from the tunnel, he may, without fear of error, make his calculations as if the gravel were a continuous substance. But if a worm has to make his way through the gravel, it makes the greatest possible difference to him whether he tries to push right against a piece of gravel, or directs his course through one of the intervals between the pieces; to him, therefore, the gravel is by no means a homogeneous and continuous substance.

In the same way, a theory that some particular substance, say water, is homogeneous and continuous may be a good working theory up to a certain point, but may fail when we come to deal with quantities so minute or so attenuated that their heterogeneity of structure comes into prominence. Whether this heterogeneity of structure is or is not consistent with homogeneity and continuity of substance is another question.

The extreme form of the doctrine of continuity is that stated by Descartes, who maintains that the whole universe is equally full of matter, and that this matter is all of one kind, having no essential property besides that of extension. All the properties which we perceive in matter he reduces to its parts being movable among one another, and so capable of all the varieties which we can perceive to follow from the motion of its parts (*Principia*, II. 23). Descartes's own attempts to deduce the different qualities and actions of bodies in this way are not of much value. More than a century was required to invent methods of investigating the conditions of the motion of systems of bodies such as Descartes imagined. But the hydrodynamical discovery of Helmholtz that a vortex in a perfect liquid possesses certain permanent characteristics, has been applied by Sir W. Thomson to form a theory of vortex atoms in a homogeneous, incompressible, and frictionless liquid, to which we shall return at the proper time.

Outline of Modern Molecular Science, and in particular of the Molecular Theory of Gases.

We begin by assuming that bodies are made up of parts, each of which is capable of motion, and that these parts act on each other in a manner consistent with the principle of the conservation of energy. In making these assumptions, we are justified by the facts that bodies may be divided into smaller parts, and that all bodies with which we are acquainted are conservative systems, which would not be the case unless their parts were also conservative systems.

We may also assume that these small parts are in motion. This is the most general assumption we can make, for it includes, as a particular case, the theory that the small parts are at rest. The phenomena of the diffusion of gases and liquids through each other shew that there may be a motion of the small parts of a body which is not perceptible to us.

We make no assumption with respect to the nature of the small parts— whether they are all of one magnitude. We do not even assume them to have extension and figure. Each of them must be measured by its mass, and any two of them must, like visible bodies, have the power of acting on one another when they come near enough to do so. The properties of the body, or medium, are determined by the configuration and motion of its small parts.

The first step in the investigation is to determine the amount of motion which exists among the small parts, independent of the visible motion of the medium as a whole. For this purpose it is convenient to make use of a general theorem in dynamics due to Clausius.

When the motion of a material system is such that the time average of the quantity $\Sigma\,(mx^2)$ remains constant, the state of the system is said to be that of stationary motion. When the motion of a material system is such that the sum of the moments of inertia of the system, about three axes at right angles through its centre of mass, never varies by more than small quantities from a constant value, the system is said to be in a state of stationary motion.

The kinetic energy of a particle is half the product of its mass into the square of its velocity, and the kinetic energy of a system is the sum of the kinetic energy of all its parts.

57—2

When an attraction or repulsion exists between two points, half the product of this stress into the distance between the two points is called the *virial* of the stress, and is reckoned positive when the stress is an attraction, and negative when it is a repulsion. The virial of a system is the sum of the virials of the stresses which exist in it. If the system is subjected to the external stress of the pressure of the sides of a vessel in which it is contained, this stress will introduce an amount of virial $\frac{3}{2}pV$, where p is the pressure on unit of area and V is the volume of the vessel.

The theorem of Clausius may now be stated as follows :—In a material system in a state of stationary motion the time-average of the kinetic energy is equal to the time-average of the virial. In the case of a fluid enclosed in a vessel

$$\tfrac{1}{2}\Sigma\left(m\overline{v^2}\right) = \tfrac{3}{2}pV + \tfrac{1}{2}\Sigma\Sigma\left(Rr\right),$$

where the first term denotes the kinetic energy, and is half the sum of the product of each mass into the mean square of its velocity. In the second term, p is the pressure on unit of surface of the vessel, whose volume is V, and the third term expresses the virial due to the internal actions between the parts of the system. A double symbol of summation is used, because every pair of parts between which any action exists must be taken into account. We have next to shew that in gases the principal part of the pressure arises from the motion of the small parts of the medium, and not from a repulsion between them.

In the first place, if the pressure of a gas arises from the repulsion of its parts, the law of repulsion must be inversely as the distance. For, consider a cube filled with the gas at pressure p, and let the cube expand till each side is n times its former length. The pressure on unit of surface according to Boyle's law is now $\dfrac{p}{n^3}$, and since the area of a face of the cube is n^2 times what it was, the whole pressure on the face of the cube is $\dfrac{1}{n}$ of its original value. But since everything has been expanded symmetrically, the distance between corresponding parts of the air is now n times what it was, and the force is n times less than it was. Hence the force must vary inversely as the distance.

But Newton has shewn (*Principia*, Book I. Prop. 93) that this law is inadmissible, as it makes the effect of the distant parts of the medium on a particle greater than that of the neighbouring parts. Indeed, we should arrive at the conclusion that the pressure depends not only on the density of the air but on the form and dimensions of the vessel which contains it, which we know not to be the case.

If, on the other hand, we suppose the pressure to arise entirely from the motion of the molecules of the gas, the interpretation of Boyle's law becomes very simple. For, in this case

$$pV = \tfrac{1}{3}\Sigma \left(m\overline{v^2}\right).$$

The first term is the product of the pressure and the volume, which according to Boyle's law is constant for the same quantity of gas at the same temperature. The second term is two-thirds of the kinetic energy of the system, and we have every reason to believe that in gases when the temperature is constant the kinetic energy of unit of mass is also constant. If we admit that the kinetic energy of unit of mass is in a given gas proportional to the absolute temperature, this equation is the expression of the law of Charles as well as of that of Boyle, and may be written—

$$pV = R\theta,$$

where θ is the temperature reckoned from absolute zero, and R is a constant. The fact that this equation expresses with considerable accuracy the relation between the volume, pressure, and temperature of a gas when in an extremely rarified state, and that as the gas is more and more compressed the deviation from this equation becomes more apparent, shews that the pressure of a gas is due almost entirely to the motion of its molecules when the gas is rare, and that it is only when the density of the gas is considerably increased that the effect of direct action between the molecules becomes apparent.

The effect of the direct action of the molecules on each other depends on the number of pairs of molecules which at a given instant are near enough to act on one another. The number of such pairs is proportional to the square of the number of molecules in unit of volume, that is, to the square of the density of the gas. Hence, as long as the medium is so rare that the encounter between two molecules is not affected by the presence of others, the deviation from Boyle's law will be proportional to the square of the density. If the action between the molecules is on the whole repulsive, the pressure will be greater than that given by Boyle's law. If it is, on the whole, attractive, the pressure will be less than that given by Boyle's law. It appears, by the experiments of Regnault and others, that the pressure does deviate from Boyle's law when the density of the gas is increased. In the case of carbonic acid and other gases which are easily liquefied, this deviation is very great. In all cases, however, except that of hydrogen, the pressure is less than that given by Boyle's law, shewing that the virial is on the whole due to *attractive* forces between the molecules.

Another kind of evidence as to the nature of the action between the molecules is furnished by an experiment made by Dr Joule. Of two vessels, one was exhausted and the other filled with a gas at a pressure of 20 atmospheres; and both were placed side by side in a vessel of water, which was constantly stirred. The temperature of the whole was observed. Then a communication was opened between the vessels, the compressed gas expanded to twice its volume, and the work of expansion, which at first produced a strong current in the gas, was soon converted into heat by the internal friction of the gas. When all was again at rest, and the temperature uniform, the temperature was again observed. In Dr Joule's original experiments the observed temperature was the same as before. In a series of experiments, conducted by Dr Joule and Sir W. Thomson on a different plan, by which the thermal effect of free expansion can be more accurately measured, a slight cooling effect was observed in all the gases examined except hydrogen. Since the temperature depends on the velocity of agitation of the molecules, it appears that when a gas expands without doing external work the velocity of agitation is not much affected, but that in most cases it is slightly diminished. Now, if the molecules during their mutual separation act on each other, their velocity will increase or diminish according as the force is repulsive or attractive. It appears, therefore, from the experiments on the free expansion of gases, that the force between the molecules is small but, on the whole, attractive.

Having thus justified the hypothesis that a gas consists of molecules in motion, which act on each other only when they come very close together during an encounter, but which, during the intervals between their encounters which constitute the greater part of their existence, are describing free paths, and are not acted on by any molecular force, we proceed to investigate the motion of such a system.

The mathematical investigation of the properties of such a system of molecules in motion is the foundation of molecular science. Clausius was the first to express the relation between the density of the gas, the length of the free paths of its molecules, and the distance at which they encounter each other. He assumed, however, at least in his earlier investigations, that the velocities of all the molecules are equal. The mode in which the velocities are distributed was first investigated by the present writer, who shewed that in the moving system the velocities of the molecules range from zero to infinity, but that the number of molecules whose velocities lie within given limits can be expressed by a formula identical with that which expresses in the theory of errors the number of errors of observation lying within corresponding limits. The proof of this theorem has been carefully investigated by Boltzmann[1], who has strengthened it where it appeared weak, and to whom the method of taking into account the action of external forces is entirely due.

The mean kinetic energy of a molecule, however, has a definite value, which is easily expressed in terms of the quantities which enter into the expression for the distribution of velocities. The most important result of this investigation is that when several kinds of molecules are in motion and acting on one another, the mean kinetic energy of a molecule is the same whatever be its mass, the molecules of greater mass having smaller mean velocities. Now, when gases are mixed their temperatures become equal. Hence we conclude that the physical condition which determines that the temperature of two gases shall be the same is that the mean kinetic energies of agitation of the individual molecules of the two gases are equal. This result is of great importance in the theory of heat, though we are not yet able to establish any similar result for bodies in the liquid or solid state.

In the next place, we know that in the case in which the whole pressure of the medium is due to the motion of its molecules, the pressure on unit of area is numerically equal to two-thirds of the kinetic energy in unit of volume. Hence, if equal volumes of two gases are at equal pressures the kinetic energy is the same in each. If they are also at equal temperatures the mean kinetic energy of each molecule is the same in each. If, therefore, equal volumes of two gases are at equal temperatures and pressures, the number of molecules in each is the same, and therefore, the masses of the two kinds of molecules are in the same ratio as the densities of the gases to which they belong.

This statement has been believed by chemists since the time of Gay-Lussac, who first established that the weights of the chemical equivalents of

* *Sitzungsberichte der K. K. Akad.*, Wien, 8th Oct. 1868.

different substances are proportional to the densities of these substances when in the form of gas. The definition of the word molecule, however, as employed in the statement of Gay-Lussac's law is by no means identical with the definition of the same word as in the kinetic theory of gases. The chemists ascertain by experiment the ratios of the masses of the different substances in a compound. From these they deduce the chemical equivalents of the different substances, that of a particular substance, say hydrogen, being taken as unity. The only evidence made use of is that furnished by chemical combinations. It is also assumed, in order to account for the facts of combination, that the reason why substances combine in definite ratios is that the molecules of the substances are in the ratio of their chemical equivalents, and that what we call combination is an action which takes place by a union of a molecule of one substance to a molecule of the other.

This kind of reasoning, when presented in a proper form and sustained by proper evidence, has a high degree of cogency. But it is purely chemical reasoning; it is not dynamical reasoning. It is founded on chemical experience, not on the laws of motion.

Our definition of a molecule is purely dynamical. A molecule is that minute portion of a substance which moves about as a whole, so that its parts, if it has any, do not part company during the motion of agitation of the gas. The result of the kinetic theory, therefore, is to give us information about the relative masses of molecules considered as moving bodies. The consistency of this information with the deductions of chemists from the phenomena of combination, greatly strengthens the evidence in favour of the actual existence and motion of gaseous molecules.

Another confirmation of the theory of molecules is derived from the experiments of Dulong and Petit on the specific heat of gases, from which they deduced the law which bears their name, and which asserts that the specific heats of equal weights of gases are inversely as their combining weights, or, in other words, that the capacities for heat of the chemical equivalents of different gases are equal. We have seen that the temperature is determined by the kinetic energy of agitation of each molecule. The molecule has also a certain amount of energy of internal motion, whether of rotation or of vibration, but the hypothesis of Clausius, that the mean value of the internal energy always bears a proportion fixed for each gas to the energy of agitation, seems highly probable and consistent with experiment. The whole kinetic energy is therefore equal to the energy of agitation multiplied by a certain factor. Thus the energy communicated to a gas by heating it is divided in a certain proportion between the energy of agitation and that of the internal motion of each molecule. For a given rise of temperature the energy of agitation, say of a million molecules, is increased by the same amount whatever be the gas. The heat spent in raising the temperature is measured by the increase of the whole kinetic energy. The thermal capacities, therefore, of equal numbers of molecules of different gases are in the ratio of the factors by which the energy of agitation must be multiplied to obtain the whole energy. As this factor appears to be nearly the same for all gases of the same degree of atomicity, Dulong and Petit's law is true for such gases.

Another result of this investigation is of considerable importance in relation to certain theories[*], which assume the existence of æthers or rare media consisting of molecules very much smaller than those of ordinary gases. According to our result, such a medium would be neither more nor less than a gas. Supposing its molecules so small that they can penetrate between the molecules of solid substances such as glass, a so-called vacuum would be full of this rare gas at the observed temperature, and at the pressure, whatever it may be, of the ætherial medium in space. The specific heat, therefore, of the medium in the so-called vacuum will be equal to that of the same volume of any other gas at the same temperature and pressure. Now, the purpose for which this molecular æther is assumed in these theories is to act on bodies by its pressure, and for this purpose the pressure is generally assumed to be very great. Hence, according to these theories, we should find the specific heat of a so-called vacuum very considerable compared with that of a quantity of air filling the same space.

We have now made a certain definite amount of progress towards a complete molecular theory of gases. We know the mean velocity of the molecules of each gas in metres per second, and we know the relative masses of the molecules of different gases. We also know that the molecules of one and the same gas are all equal in mass. For if they are not, the method of dialysis, as employed by Graham, would enable us to separate the molecules of smaller mass from those of greater, as they would stream through porous substances with greater velocity. We should thus be able to separate a gas, say hydrogen, into two portions, having different densities and other physical properties,

* See Gustav Hansemann, *Die Atome und ihre Bewegungen.* 1871. (H. G. Mayer.)

different combining weights, and probably different chemical properties of other kinds. As no chemist has yet obtained specimens of hydrogen differing in this way from other specimens, we conclude that all the molecules of hydrogen are of sensibly the same mass, and not merely that their mean mass is a statistical constant of great stability.

But as yet we have not considered the phenomena which enable us to form an estimate of the actual mass and dimensions of a molecule. It is to Clausius that we owe the first definite conception of the free path of a molecule and of the mean distance travelled by a molecule between successive encounters. He shewed that the number of encounters of a molecule in a given time is proportional to the velocity, to the number of molecules in unit of volume, and to the square of the distance between the centres of two molecules when they act on one another so as to have an encounter. From this it appears that if we call this distance of the centres the diameter of a molecule, and the volume of a sphere having this diameter the volume of a molecule, and the sum of the volumes of all the molecules the molecular volume of the gas, then the diameter of a molecule is a certain multiple of the quantity obtained by diminishing the free path in the ratio of the molecular volume of the gas to the whole volume of the gas. The numerical value of this multiple differs slightly, according to the hypothesis we assume about the law of distribution of velocities. It also depends on the definition of an encounter. When the molecules are regarded as elastic spheres we know what is meant by an encounter, but if they act on each other at a distance by attractive or repulsive forces of finite magnitude, the distance of their centres varies during an encounter, and is not a definite quantity. Nevertheless, the above statement of Clausius enables us, if we know the length of the mean path and the molecular volume of gas, to form a tolerably near estimate of the diameter of the sphere of the intense action of a molecule, and thence of the number of molecules in unit of volume and the actual mass of each molecule. To complete the investigation we have, therefore, to determine the mean path and the molecular volume. The first numerical estimate of the mean path of a gaseous molecule was made by the present writer from data derived from the internal friction of air. There are three phenomena which depend on the length of the free path of the molecules of a gas. It is evident that the greater the free path the more rapidly will the molecules travel from one part of the medium to another, because their direction will not be so often altered by encounters with other molecules. If the molecules in different parts of the medium are of different kinds, their progress from one part of the medium to another can be easily traced by analysing portions of the medium taken from different places. The rate of diffusion thus found furnishes one method of estimating the length of the free path of a molecule. This kind of diffusion goes on not only between the molecules of different gases, but among the molecules of the same gas, only in the latter case the results of the diffusion cannot be traced by analysis. But the diffusing molecules carry with them in their free paths the momentum and the energy which they happen at a given instant to have. The diffusion of momentum tends to equalise the apparent motion of different parts of the medium, and constitutes the phenomenon called the internal friction or viscosity of gases. The diffusion of energy tends to equalise the temperature of different parts of the medium, and constitutes the phenomenon of the conduction of heat in gases.

These three phenomena—the diffusion of matter, of motion, and of heat in gases—have been experimentally investigated,—the diffusion of matter by Graham and Loschmidt, the diffusion of motion by Oscar Meyer and Clerk Maxwell, and that of heat by Stefan.

These three kinds of experiments give results which in the present imperfect state of the theory and the extreme difficulty of the experiments, especially those on the conduction of heat, may be regarded as tolerably consistent with each other. At the pressure of our atmosphere, and at the temperature of melting ice, the mean path of a molecule of hydrogen is about the 10,000th of a millimetre, or about the fifth part of a wave-length of green light. The mean path of the molecules of other gases is shorter than that of hydrogen.

The determination of the molecular volume of a gas is subject as yet to considerable uncertainty. The most obvious method is that of compressing the gas till it assumes the liquid form. It seems probable, from the great resistance of liquids to compression, that their molecules are about the same distance from each other as that at which two molecules of the same substance in the gaseous form act on each other during an encounter. If this is the case, the molecular volume of a gas is somewhat less than the volume of the liquid into which it would be condensed by pressure, or, in other words, the density of the molecules is somewhat greater than that of the liquid.

Now, we know the relative weights of different molecules with great accuracy, and, from a knowledge of the mean path, we can calculate their relative diameters approximately. From these we can deduce the relative densities of different kinds of molecules. The relative densities so calculated have been compared by Lorenz Meyer with the observed densities of the liquids into which the gases may be condensed, and he finds a remarkable correspondence between them. There is considerable doubt, however, as to the relation between the molecules of a liquid and those of its vapour, so that till a larger number of comparisons have been made, we must not place too much reliance on the calculated densities of molecules. Another, and perhaps a more refined, method is that adopted by M. Van der Waals, who deduces the molecular volume from the deviations of the pressure from Boyle's law as the gas is compressed.

The first numerical estimate of the diameter of a molecule was that made by Loschmidt in 1865 from the mean path and the molecular volume. Independently of him and of each other, Mr Stoney, in 1868, and Sir W. Thomson, in 1870, published results of a similar kind—those of Thomson being deduced not only in this way, but from considerations derived from the thickness of soap bubbles, and from the electric action between zinc and copper.

The diameter and the mass of a molecule, as estimated by these methods, are, of course, very small, but by no means infinitely so. About two millions of molecules of hydrogen in a row would occupy a millimetre, and about two hundred million million million of them would weigh a milligramme. These numbers must be considered as exceedingly rough guesses; they must be corrected by more extensive and accurate experiments as science advances; but the main result, which appears to be well established, is that the determination of the mass of a molecule is a legitimate object of scientific research, and that this mass is by no means immeasurably small.

Loschmidt illustrates these molecular measurements by a comparison with the smallest magnitudes visible by means of a microscope. Nobert, he tells us, can draw 4000 lines in the breadth of a millimetre. The intervals between these lines can be observed with a good microscope. A cube, whose side is the 4000th of a millimetre, may be taken as the *minimum visibile* for observers of the present day. Such a cube would contain from 60 to 100 million molecules of oxygen or of nitrogen; but since the molecules of organised substances contain on an average about 50 of the more elementary atoms, we may assume that the smallest organised particle visible under the microscope contains about two million molecules of organic matter. At least half of every living organism consists of water, so that the smallest living being visible under the microscope dóes not contain more than about a million organic molecules. Some exceedingly simple organism may be supposed built up of not more than a million similar molecules. It is impossible, however, to conceive so small a number sufficient to form a being furnished with a whole system of specialised organs.

Thus molecular science sets us face to face with physiological theories. It forbids the physiologist from imagining that structural details of infinitely small dimensions can furnish an explanation of the infinite variety which exists in the properties and functions of the most minute organisms.

A microscopic germ is, we know, capable of development into a highly organised animal. Another germ, equally microscopic, becomes, when developed, an animal of a totally different kind. Do all the differences, infinite in number, which distinguish the one animal from the other, arise each from some difference in the structure of the respective germs? Even if we admit this as possible, we shall be called upon by the advocates of Pangenesis to admit still greater marvels. For the microscopic germ, according to this theory, is no mere individual, but a representative body, containing members collected from every rank of the long-drawn ramification of the ancestral tree, the number of these members being amply sufficient not only to furnish the hereditary characteristics of every organ of the body and every habit of the animal from birth to death, but also to afford a stock of latent gemmules to be passed on in an inactive state from germ to germ, till at last the ancestral peculiarity which it represents is revived in some remote descendant.

Some of the exponents of this theory of heredity have attempted to elude the difficulty of placing a whole world of wonders within a body so small and so devoid of visible structure as a germ, by using the phrase structureless germs*. Now, one material system can differ from another only in the configuration and motion which it has at a given instant. To explain differences of function and development of a germ without assuming differences of structure is, therefore, to admit that the properties of a germ are not those of a purely material system.

The evidence as to the nature and motion of molecules, with which we have hitherto been occupied, has been derived from experiments upon gaseous

* See F. Galton, "On Blood Relationship," *Proc. Roy. Soc.*, June 13, 1872.

media, the smallest sensible portion of which contains millions of millions of molecules. The constancy and uniformity of the properties of the gaseous medium is the direct result of the inconceivable irregularity of the motion of agitation of its molecules. Any cause which could introduce regularity into the motion of agitation, and marshal the molecules into order and method in their evolutions, might check or even reverse that tendency to diffusion of matter, motion, and energy, which is one of the most invariable phenomena of nature, and to which Thomson has given the name of the dissipation of energy.

Thus, when a sound-wave is passing through a mass of air, this motion is of a certain definite type, and if left to itself the whole motion is passed on to other masses of air, and the sound-wave passes on, leaving the air behind it at rest. Heat, on the other hand, never passes out of a hot body except to enter a colder body, so that the energy of sound-waves, or any other form of energy which is propagated so as to pass wholly out of one portion of the medium and into another, cannot be called heat.

We have now to turn our attention to a class of molecular motions, which are as remarkable for their regularity as the motion of agitation is for its irregularity.

It has been found, by means of the spectroscope, that the light emitted by incandescent substances is different according to their state of condensation. When they are in an extremely rarefied condition the spectrum of their light consists of a set of sharply-defined bright lines. As the substance approaches a denser condition the spectrum tends to become continuous, either by the lines becoming broader and less defined, or by new lines and bands appearing between them, till the spectrum at length loses all its characteristics and becomes identical with that of solid bodies when raised to the same temperature.

Hence the vibrating systems, which are the source of the emitted light, must be vibrating in a different manner in these two cases. When the spectrum consists of a number of bright lines, the motion of the system must be compounded of a corresponding number of types of harmonic vibration.

In order that a bright line may be sharply defined, the vibratory motion which produces it must be kept up in a perfectly regular manner for some hundreds or thousands of vibrations. If the motion of each of the vibrating bodies is kept up only during a small number of vibrations, then, however regular may be the vibrations of each body while it lasts, the resultant disturbance of the luminiferous medium, when analysed by the prism, will be found to contain, besides the part due to the regular vibrations, other motions, depending on the starting and stopping of each particular vibrating body, which will become manifest as a diffused luminosity scattered over the whole length of the spectrum. A spectrum of bright lines, therefore, indicates that the vibrating bodies when set in motion are allowed to vibrate in accordance with the conditions of their internal structure for some time before they are again interfered with by external forces.

It appears, therefore, from spectroscopic evidence that each molecule of a rarefied gas is, during the greater part of its existence, at such a distance from all other molecules that it executes its vibrations in an undisturbed and regular manner. This is the same conclusion to which we were led by considerations of another kind at p. 452.

We may therefore regard the bright lines in the spectrum of a gas as the result of the vibrations executed by the molecules while describing their free paths. When two molecules separate from one another after an encounter, each of them is in a state of vibration, arising from the unequal action on different parts of the same molecule during the encounter. Hence, though the centre of mass of the molecule describing its free path moves with uniform velocity, the parts of the molecule have a vibratory motion with respect to the centre of mass of the whole molecule, and it is the disturbance of the luminiferous medium communicated to it by the vibrating molecules which constitutes the emitted light.

We may compare the vibrating molecule to a bell. When struck, the bell is set in motion. This motion is compounded of harmonic vibrations of many different periods, each of which acts on the air, producing notes of as many different pitches. As the bell communicates its motion to the air, these vibrations necessarily decay, some of them faster than others, so that the sound contains fewer and fewer notes, till at last it is reduced to the fundamental note of the bell*. If we suppose that there are a great many bells precisely similar to each other, and that they are struck, first one and then another, in a perfectly irregular manner, yet so that, on an average, as many bells are struck in one second of time as in another, and also in such a way

---

* Part of the energy of motion is, in the case of the bell, dissipated in the substance of the bell in virtue of the viscosity of the metal, and assumes the form of heat, but it is not necessary, for the purpose of illustration, to take this cause of the decay of vibrations into account.

that, on an average, any one bell is not again struck till it has ceased to vibrate, then the audible result will appear a continuous sound, composed of the sound emitted by bells in all states of vibration, from the clang of the actual stroke to the final hum of the dying fundamental tone.

But now let the number of bells be reduced while the same number of strokes are given in a second. Each bell will now be struck before it has ceased to vibrate, so that in the resulting sound there will be less of the fundamental tone and more of the original clang, till at last, when the peal is reduced to one bell, on which innumerable hammers are continually plying their strokes all out of time, the sound will become a mere noise, in which no musical note can be distinguished.

In the case of a gas we have an immense number of molecules, each of which is set in vibration when it encounters another molecule, and continues to vibrate as it describes its free path. The molecule is a material system, the parts of which are connected in some definite way, and from the fact that the bright lines of the emitted light have always the same wave-lengths, we learn that the vibrations corresponding to these lines are always executed in the same periodic time, and therefore the force tending to restore any part of the molecule to its position of equilibrium in the molecule must be proportional to its displacement relative to that position.

From the mathematical theory of the motion of such a system, it appears that the whole motion may be analysed into the following parts, which may be considered each independently of the others :—In the first place, the centre of mass of the system moves with uniform velocity in a straight line. This velocity may have any value. In the second place, there may be a motion of rotation, the angular momentum of the system about its centre of mass remaining during the free path constant in magnitude and direction. This angular momentum may have any value whatever, and its axis may have any direction. In the third place, the remainder of the motion is made up of a number of component motions, each of which is an harmonic vibration of a given type. In each type of vibration the periodic time of vibration is determined by the nature of the system, and is invariable for the same system. The relative amount of motion in different parts of the system is also determinate for each type, but the absolute amount of motion and the phase of the vibration of each type are determined by the particular circumstances of the last encounter, and may vary in any manner from one encounter to another.

The values of the periodic times of the different types of vibration are given by the roots of a certain equation, the form of which depends on the nature of the connections of the system. In certain exceptionally simple cases, as, for instance, in that of a uniform string stretched between two fixed points, the roots of the equation are connected by simple arithmetical relations, and if the internal structure of a molecule had an analogous kind of simplicity, we might expect to find in the spectrum of the molecule a series of bright lines, whose wave-lengths are in simple arithmetical ratios.

But if we suppose the molecule to be constituted according to some different type, as, for instance, if it is an elastic sphere, or if it consists of a finite number of atoms kept in their places by attractive and repulsive forces, the roots of the equation will not be connected with each other by any simple relations, but each may be made to vary independently of the others by a suitable change of the connections of the system. Hence, we have no right to expect any definite numerical relations among the wave-lengths of the bright lines of a gas.

The bright lines of the spectrum of an incandescent gas are therefore due to the harmonic vibrations of the molecules of the gas during their free paths. The only effect of the motion of the centre of mass of the molecule is to alter the time of vibration of the light as received by a stationary observer. When the molecule is coming towards the observer, each successive impulse will have a shorter distance to travel before it reaches his eye, and therefore the impulses will appear to succeed each other more rapidly than if the molecule were at rest, and the contrary will be the case if the molecule is receding from the observer. The bright line corresponding to the vibration will therefore be shifted in the spectrum towards the blue end when the molecule is approaching, and towards the red end when it is receding from the observer. By observations of the displacement of certain lines in the spectrum, Dr Huggins and others have measured the rate of approach or of recession of certain stars with respect to the earth, and Mr Lockyer has determined the rate of motion of tornadoes in the sun. But Lord Rayleigh has pointed out that according to the dynamical theory of gases the molecules are moving hither and thither with so great velocity that, however narrow and sharply-defined any bright line due to a single molecule may be, the displacement of the line towards the blue by the approaching molecules, and towards the red by the receding molecules, will produce a certain amount of widening and blurring of the line in the spectrum, so that there is a limit to the sharpness of definition of the lines of a gas. The widening of the lines due to this cause will be in proportion to the velocity of agitation of the molecules. It will be greatest for the molecules of smallest mass, as those of hydrogen, and it will increase with the temperature. Hence the measurement of the breadth of the hydrogen lines, such as C or F in the spectrum of the solar prominences, may furnish evidence that the temperature of the sun cannot exceed a certain value.

On the Theory of Vortex Atoms.

The equations which form the foundations of the mathematical theory of fluid motion were fully laid down by Lagrange and the great mathematicians of the end of last century, but the number of solutions of cases of fluid motion which had been actually worked out remained very small, and almost all of these belonged to a particular type of fluid motion, which has been since named the irrotational type. It had been shewn, indeed, by Lagrange, that a perfect fluid, if its motion is at any time irrotational, will continue in all time coming to move in an irrotational manner, so that, by assuming that the fluid was at one time at rest, the calculation of its subsequent motion may be very much simplified.

It was reserved for Helmholtz to point out the very remarkable properties of rotational motion in a homogeneous incompressible fluid devoid of all viscosity. We must first define the physical properties of such a fluid. In the first place, it is a material substance. Its motion is continuous in space and time, and if we follow any portion of it as it moves, the mass of that portion remains invariable. These properties it shares with all material substances. In the next place, it is incompressible. The form of a given portion of the fluid may change, but its volume remains invariable; in other words, the density of the fluid remains the same during its motion. Besides this, the fluid is homogeneous, or the density of all parts of the fluid is the same. It is also continuous, so that the mass of the fluid contained within any closed surface is always *exactly* proportional to the volume contained within that surface. This is equivalent to asserting that the fluid is not made up of molecules; for, if it were, the mass would vary in a discontinuous manner as the volume increases continuously, because first one and then another molecule would be included within the closed surface. Lastly, it is a perfect fluid, or, in other words, the stress between one portion and a contiguous portion is always normal to the surface which separates these portions, and this whether the fluid is at rest or in motion.

We have seen that in a molecular fluid the interdiffusion of the molecules causes an interdiffusion of motion of different parts of the fluid, so that the action between contiguous parts is no longer normal but in a direction tending to diminish their relative motion. Hence the perfect fluid cannot be molecular.

All that is necessary in order to form a correct mathematical theory of a material system is that its properties shall be clearly defined and shall be consistent with each other. This is essential; but whether a substance having such properties actually exists is a question which comes to be considered only when we propose to make some practical application of the results of the mathematical theory. The properties of our perfect liquid are clearly defined and consistent with each other, and from the mathematical theory we can deduce remarkable results, some of which may be illustrated in a rough way by means of fluids which are by no means perfect in the sense of not being viscous, such, for instance, as air and water.

The motion of a fluid is said to be irrotational when it is such that if a spherical portion of the fluid were suddenly solidified, the solid sphere so formed would not be rotating about any axis. When the motion of the fluid is rotational the axis and angular velocity of the rotation of any small part of the fluid are those of a *small* spherical portion suddenly solidified.

The mathematical expression of these definitions is as follows:—Let u, v, w be the components of the velocity of the fluid at the point (x, y, z), and let

$$a = \frac{dv}{dz} - \frac{dw}{dy}, \quad \beta = \frac{dw}{dx} - \frac{du}{dz}, \quad \gamma = \frac{du}{dy} - \frac{dv}{dx} \quad \dots\dots\dots\dots (1),$$

then a, β, γ are the components of the velocity of rotation of the fluid at the point (x, y, z). The axis of rotation is in the direction of the resultant of a, β, and γ; and the velocity of rotation, ω, is measured by this resultant.

A line drawn in the fluid, so that at every point of the line

$$\frac{1}{a}\frac{dx}{ds} = \frac{1}{\beta}\frac{dy}{ds} = \frac{1}{\gamma}\frac{dz}{ds} = \frac{1}{\omega} \quad \dots\dots\dots\dots\dots\dots\dots(2),$$

where s is the length of the line up to the point x, y, z, is called a vortex line. Its direction coincides at every point with that of the axis of rotation of the fluid.

We may now prove the theorem of Helmholtz, that the points of the fluid which at any instant lie in the same vortex line continue to lie in the same vortex line during the whole motion of the fluid.

The equations of motion of a fluid are of the form

$$\rho \frac{\delta u}{\delta t} + \frac{dp}{dx} + \rho \frac{dV}{dx} = 0 \quad \ldots\ldots\ldots\ldots\ldots\ldots\ldots (3),$$

when ρ is the density, which in the case of our homogeneous incompressible fluid we may assume to be unity, the operator $\frac{\delta}{\delta t}$ represents the rate of variation of the symbol to which it is prefixed at a point which is carried forward with the fluid, so that

$$\frac{\delta u}{\delta t} = \frac{du}{dt} + u \frac{du}{dx} + v \frac{du}{dy} + w \frac{du}{dz} \quad \ldots\ldots\ldots\ldots\ldots\ldots (4),$$

p is the pressure, and V is the potential of external forces. There are two other equations of similar form in y and z. Differentiating the equation in y with respect to z, and that in z with respect to y, and subtracting the second from the first, we find

$$\frac{d}{dz} \frac{\delta v}{\delta t} - \frac{d}{dy} \frac{\delta w}{\delta t} = 0 \quad \ldots\ldots\ldots\ldots\ldots\ldots\ldots\ldots (5).$$

Performing the differentiations and remembering equations (1) and also the condition of incompressibility,

$$\frac{du}{dx} + \frac{dv}{dy} + \frac{dw}{dz} = 0 \quad \ldots\ldots\ldots\ldots\ldots\ldots\ldots (6),$$

we find

$$\frac{\delta a}{\delta t} = a \frac{du}{dx} + \beta \frac{du}{dy} + \gamma \frac{du}{dz} \quad \ldots\ldots\ldots\ldots\ldots\ldots(7).$$

Now, let us suppose a vortex line drawn in the fluid so as always to begin at the same particle of the fluid. The components of the velocity of this point are u, v, w. Let us find those of a point on the moving vortex line at a distance ds from this point where

$$ds = \omega d\sigma \quad \ldots\ldots\ldots\ldots\ldots\ldots\ldots\ldots\ldots\ldots (8).$$

The co-ordinates of this point are

$$x + ad\sigma, \quad y + \beta d\sigma, \quad z + \gamma d\sigma \dots\dots\dots\dots\dots (9),$$

and the components of its velocity are

$$u + \frac{\delta a}{\delta t} d\sigma, \quad v + \frac{\delta \beta}{\delta t} d\sigma, \quad w + \frac{\delta \gamma}{\delta t} d\sigma \dots\dots\dots\dots\dots(10).$$

Consider the first of these components. In virtue of equation (7) we may write it

$$u + \frac{du}{dx} ad\sigma + \frac{du}{dy} \beta d\sigma + \frac{du}{dz} \gamma d\sigma \dots\dots\dots\dots\dots (11),$$

or

$$u + \frac{du}{dx} \frac{dx}{d\sigma} d\sigma + \frac{du}{dy} \frac{dy}{d\sigma} d\sigma + \frac{du}{dz} \frac{dz}{d\sigma} d\sigma \dots\dots\dots\dots(12),$$

or

$$u + \frac{du}{d\sigma} d\sigma \dots\dots\dots\dots\dots\dots\dots\dots (13).$$

But this represents the value of the component u of the velocity of the fluid itself at the same point, and the same thing may be proved of the other components.

Hence the velocity of the second point on the vortex line is identical with that of the fluid at that point. In other words, the vortex line swims along with the fluid, and is always formed of the same row of fluid particles. The vortex line is therefore no mere mathematical symbol, but has a physical existence continuous in time and space.

By differentiating equations (1) with respect to x, y, and z respectively, and adding the results, we obtain the equation—

$$\frac{da}{dx} + \frac{d\beta}{dy} + \frac{d\gamma}{dz} = 0 \dots\dots\dots\dots\dots\dots(14).$$

This is an equation of the same form with (6), which expresses the condition of flow of a fluid of invariable density. Hence, if we imagine a fluid, quite independent of the original fluid, whose components of velocity are a, β, γ, this imaginary fluid will flow without altering its density.

Now, consider a closed curve in space, and let vortex lines be drawn in both directions from every point of this curve. These vortex lines will form a tubular surface, which is called a vortex tube or a vortex filament. Since the imaginary fluid flows along the vortex lines without change of density, the quantity which in unit of time flows through any section of the same vortex tube must be the same. Hence, at any section of a vortex tube the product of the area of the section into the mean velocity of rotation is the same. This quantity is called the *strength* of the vortex tube.

A vortex tube cannot begin or end within the fluid; for, if it did, the imaginary fluid, whose velocity components are a, β, γ, would be generated from nothing at the beginning of the tube, and reduced to nothing at the end of it. Hence, if the tube has a beginning and an end, they must lie on the surface of the fluid mass. If the fluid is infinite the vortex tube must be infinite, or else it must return into itself.

We have thus arrived at the following remarkable theorems relating to a finite vortex tube in an infinite fluid:—(1) It returns into itself, forming a closed ring. We may therefore describe it as a vortex *ring*. (2) It always consists of the same portion of the fluid. Hence its volume is invariable. (3) Its strength remains always the same. Hence the velocity of rotation at any section varies inversely as the area of that section, and that of any segment varies directly as the length of that segment. (4) No part of the fluid which is not originally in a state of rotational motion can ever enter into that state, and no part of the fluid whose motion is rotational can ever cease to move rotationally. (5) No vortex tube can ever pass through any other vortex tube, or through any of its own convolutions. Hence, if two vortex tubes are linked together, they can never be separated, and if a single vortex tube is knotted on itself, it can never become untied. (6) The motion at any instant of every part of the fluid, including the vortex rings themselves, may be accurately represented by conceiving an electric current to occupy the place of each vortex ring, the strength of the current being proportional to that of the ring. The magnetic force at any point of space will then represent in direction and magnitude the velocity of the fluid at the corresponding point of the fluid.

These properties of vortex rings suggested to Sir William Thomson* the possibility of founding on them a new form of the atomic theory. The conditions which must be satisfied by an atom are—permanence in magnitude, capability of internal motion or vibration, and a sufficient amount of possible characteristics to account for the difference between atoms of different kinds.

The small hard body imagined by Lucretius, and adopted by Newton, was invented for the express purpose of accounting for the permanence of the pro-

---

* "On Vortex Atoms," *Proc. Roy. Soc. Edin.*, 18th February, 1867.

perties of bodies. But it fails to account for the vibrations of a molecule as revealed by the spectroscope. We may indeed suppose the atom elastic, but this is to endow it with the very property for the explanation of which, as exhibited in aggregate bodies, the atomic constitution was originally assumed. The massive centres of force imagined by Boscovich may have more to recommend them to the mathematician, who has no scruple in supposing them to be invested with the power of attracting and repelling according to any law of the distance which it may please him to assign. Such centres of force are no doubt in their own nature indivisible, but then they are also, singly, incapable of vibration. To obtain vibrations we must imagine molecules consisting of many such centres, but, in so doing, the possibility of these centres being separated altogether is again introduced. Besides, it is in questionable scientific taste, after using atoms so freely to get rid of forces acting at sensible distances, to make the whole function of the atoms an action at insensible distances.

On the other hand, the vortex ring of Helmholtz, imagined as the true form of the atom by Thomson, satisfies more of the conditions than any atom hitherto imagined. In the first place, it is quantitatively permanent, as regards its volume and its strength,—two independent quantities. It is also qualitatively permanent as regards its degree of implication, whether " knottedness" on itself or "linkedness" with other vortex rings. At the same time, it is capable of infinite changes of form, and may execute vibrations of different periods, as we know that molecules do. And the number of essentially different implications of vortex rings may be very great without supposing the degree of implication of any of them very high.

But the greatest recommendation of this theory, from a philosophical point of view, is that its success in explaining phenomena does not depend on the ingenuity with which its contrivers "save appearances," by introducing first one hypothetical force and then another. When the vortex atom is once set in motion, all its properties are absolutely fixed and determined by the laws of motion of the primitive fluid, which are fully expressed in the fundamental equations. The disciple of Lucretius may cut and carve his solid atoms in the hope of getting them to combine into worlds; the follower of Boscovich may imagine new laws of force to meet the requirements of each new phenomenon; but he who dares to plant his feet in the path opened up by Helmholtz and Thomson has no such resources. His primitive fluid has no other properties than inertia, invariable density, and perfect mobility, and the method by which the motion of this fluid is to be traced is pure mathematical analysis. The difficulties of this method are enormous, but the glory of surmounting them would be unique.

There seems to be little doubt that an encounter between two vortex atoms would be in its general character similar to those which we have already described. Indeed, the encounter between two smoke rings in air gives a very lively illustration of the elasticity of vortex rings.

But one of the first, if not the very first desideratum in a complete theory of matter is to explain—first, mass, and second, gravitation. To explain mass may seem an absurd achievement. We generally suppose that it is of the essence of matter to be the receptacle of momentum and energy, and even Thomson, in his definition of his primitive fluid, attributes to it the possession of mass. But according to Thomson, though the primitive fluid is the only true matter, yet that which we call matter is not the primitive fluid itself, but a mode of motion of that primitive fluid. It is the mode of motion which constitutes the vortex rings, and which furnishes us with examples of that permanence and continuity of existence which we are accustomed to attribute to matter itself. The primitive fluid, the only true matter, entirely eludes our perceptions when it is not endued with the mode of motion which converts certain portions of it into vortex rings, and thus renders it molecular.

In Thomson's theory, therefore, the mass of bodies requires explanation. We have to explain the inertia of what is only a mode of motion, and inertia is a property of matter, not of modes of motion. It is true that a vortex ring at any given instant has a definite momentum and a definite energy, but to shew that bodies built up of vortex rings would have such momentum and energy as we know them to have is, in the present state of the theory, a very difficult task.

It may seem hard to say of an infant theory that it is bound to explain gravitation. Since the time of Newton, the doctrine of gravitation has been admitted and expounded, till it has gradually acquired the character rather of an ultimate fact than of a fact to be explained.

It seems doubtful whether Lucretius considers gravitation to be an essential property of matter, as he seems to assert in the very remarkable lines—

> "Nam si tantundem est in lanæ glomere, quantum
> Corporis in plumbo est, tantundem pendere par est :
> Corporis officium est quoniam premere omnia deorsum."—*De Rerum Natura*, I. 361.

If this is the true opinion of Lucretius, and if the downward flight of the atoms arises, in his view, from their own gravity, it seems very doubtful whether he attributed the weight of sensible bodies to the impact of the atoms. The latter opinion is that of Le Sage, of Geneva, propounded in his *Lucrèce Newtonien*, and in his *Traité de Physique Mécanique*, published, along with a second treatise of his own, by Pierre Prevost, of Geneva, in 1818[*]. The theory of Le Sage is that the gravitation of bodies towards each other is caused by the impact of streams of atoms flying in all directions through space. These atoms he calls ultramundane corpuscules, because he conceives them to come in all directions from regions far beyond that part of the system of the world which is in any way known to us. He supposes each of them to be so small that a collision with another ultramundane corpuscule is an event of very rare occurrence. It is by striking against the molecules of gross matter that they discharge their function of drawing bodies towards each other. A body placed by itself in free space and exposed to the impacts of these corpuscules would be bandied about by them in all directions, but because, on the whole, it receives as many blows on one side as on another, it cannot thereby acquire any sensible velocity. But if there are two bodies in space, each of them will screen the other from a certain proportion of the corpuscular bombardment, so that a smaller number of corpuscules will strike either body on that side which is next the other body, while the number of corpuscules which strike it in other directions remains the same.

Each body will therefore be urged towards the other by the effect of the excess of the impacts it receives on the side furthest from the other. If we take account of the impacts of those corpuscules only which come directly from infinite space, and leave out of consideration those which have already struck mundane bodies, it is easy to calculate the result on the two bodies, supposing their dimensions small compared with the distance between them.

The force of attraction would vary directly as the product of the areas of the sections of the bodies taken normal to the distance and inversely as the square of the distance between them.

Now, the attraction of gravitation varies as the product of the *masses* of the bodies between which it acts, and inversely as the square of the distance between them. If, then, we can imagine a constitution of bodies such that

---

[*] See also *Constitution de la Matière*, &c., par le P. Leray, Paris, 1869.

the effective areas of the bodies are proportional to their masses, we shall make the two laws coincide. Here, then, seems to be a path leading towards an explanation of the law of gravitation, which, if it can be shewn to be in other respects consistent with facts, may turn out to be a royal road into the very arcana of science.

Le Sage himself shews that, in order to make the effective area of a body, in virtue of which it acts as a screen to the streams of ultramundane corpuscules, proportional to the mass of the body, whether the body be large or small, we must admit that the size of the solid atoms of the body is exceedingly small compared with the distances between them, so that a very small proportion of the corpuscules are stopped even by the densest and largest bodies. We may picture to ourselves the streams of corpuscules coming in every direction, like light from a uniformly illuminated sky. We may imagine a material body to consist of a congeries of atoms at considerable distances from each other, and we may represent this by a swarm of insects flying in the air. To an observer at a distance this swarm will be visible as a slight darkening of the sky in a certain quarter. This darkening will represent the action of the material body in stopping the flight of the corpuscules. Now, if the proportion of light stopped by the swarm is very small, two such swarms will stop nearly the same amount of light, whether they are in a line with the eye or not, but if one of them stops an appreciable proportion of light, there will not be so much left to be stopped by the other, and the effect of two swarms in a line with the eye will be less than the sum of the two effects separately.

Now, we know that the effect of the attraction of the sun and earth on the moon is not appreciably different when the moon is eclipsed than on other occasions when full moon occurs without an eclipse. This shews that the number of the corpuscules which are stopped by bodies of the size and mass of the earth, and even the sun, is very small compared with the number which pass straight through the earth or the sun without striking a single molecule. To the streams of corpuscules the earth and the sun are mere systems of atoms scattered in space, which present far more openings than obstacles to their rectilinear flight.

Such is the ingenious doctrine of Le Sage, •by which he endeavours to explain universal gravitation. Let us try to form some estimate of this continual bombardment of ultramundane corpuscules which is being kept up on all sides of us.

We have seen that the sun stops but a very small fraction of the corpuscules which enter it. The earth, being a smaller body, stops a still smaller proportion of them. The proportion of those which are stopped by a small body, say a 1 lb. shot, must be smaller still in an enormous degree, because its thickness is exceedingly small compared with that of the earth.

Now, the weight of the ball, or its tendency towards the earth, is produced, according to this theory, by the excess of the impacts of the corpuscules which come from above over the impacts of those which come from below, and have passed through the earth. Either of these quantities is an exceedingly small fraction of the momentum of the whole number of corpuscules which pass through the ball in a second, and their difference is a small fraction of either, and yet it is equivalent to the weight of a pound. The velocity of the corpuscules must be enormously greater than that of any of the heavenly bodies, otherwise, as may easily be shewn, they would act as a resisting medium opposing the motion of the planets. Now, the energy of a moving system is half the product of its momentum into its velocity. Hence the energy of the corpuscules, which by their impacts on the ball during one second urge it towards the earth, must be a number of foot-pounds equal to the number of feet over which a corpuscule travels in a second, that is to say, not less than thousands of millions. But this is only a small fraction of the energy of all the impacts which the atoms of the ball receive from the innumerable streams of corpuscules which fall upon it in all directions.

Hence the rate at which the energy of the corpuscules is spent in order to maintain the gravitating property of a single pound, is at least millions of millions of foot-pounds per second.

What becomes of this enormous quantity of energy? If the corpuscules, after striking the atoms, fly off with a velocity equal to that which they had before, they will carry their energy away with them into the ultramundane regions. But if this be the case, then the corpuscules rebounding from the body in any given direction will be both in number and in velocity exactly equivalent to those which are prevented from proceeding in that direction by being deflected by the body, and it may be shewn that this will be the case whatever be the shape of the body, and however many bodies may be present in the field. Thus, the rebounding corpuscules exactly make up for those which are deflected by the body, and there will be no excess of the impacts on any other body in one direction or another.

60—2

The explanation of gravitation, therefore, falls to the ground if the corpuscules are like perfectly elastic spheres, and rebound with a velocity of separation equal to that of approach. If, on the other hand, they rebound with a smaller velocity, the effect of attraction between the bodies will no doubt be produced, but then we have to find what becomes of the energy which the molecules have brought with them but have not carried away.

If any appreciable fraction of this energy is communicated to the body in the form of heat, the amount of heat so generated would in a few seconds raise it, and in like manner the whole material universe, to a white heat.

It has been suggested by Sir W. Thomson that the corpuscules may be so constructed as to carry off their energy with them, provided that part of their kinetic energy is transformed, during impact, from energy of translation to energy of rotation or vibration. For this purpose the corpuscules must be material systems, not mere points. Thomson suggests that they are vortex atoms, which are set into a state of vibration at impact, and go off with a smaller velocity of translation, but in a state of violent vibration. He has also suggested the possibility of the vortex corpuscule regaining its swiftness and losing part of its vibratory agitation by communion with its kindred corpuscules in infinite space.

We have devoted more space to this theory than it seems to deserve, because it is ingenious, and because it is the only theory of the cause of gravitation which has been so far developed as to be capable of being attacked and defended. It does not appear to us that it can account for the temperature of bodies remaining moderate while their atoms are exposed to the bombardment. The temperature of bodies must tend to approach that at which the average kinetic energy of a molecule of the body would be equal to the average kinetic energy of an ultramundane corpuscule.

Now, suppose a plane surface to exist which stops *all* the corpuscules. The pressure on this plane will be $p = NMu^2$ where M is the mass of a corpuscule, N the number in unit of volume, and u its velocity normal to the plane. Now, we know that the very greatest pressure existing in the universe must be much less than the pressure p, which would be exerted against a body which stops all the corpuscules. We are also tolerably certain that N, the number of corpuscules which are at any one time within unit of volume, is small compared with the value of N for the molecules of ordinary bodies. Hence, Mu^2 must be enormous compared with the corresponding quantity for ordinary bodies, and it follows that the impact of the corpuscules would raise all bodies to an enormous temperature. We may also observe that according to this theory the habitable universe, which we are accustomed to regard as the scene of a magnificent illustration of the conservation of energy as the fundamental principle of all nature, is in reality maintained in working order only by an enormous expenditure of external power, which would be nothing less than ruinous if the supply were drawn from anywhere else than from the infinitude of space, and which, if the contrivances of the most eminent mathematicians should be found in any respect defective, might at any moment tear the whole universe atom from atom.

We must now leave these speculations about the nature of molecules and the cause of gravitation, and contemplate the material universe as made up of molecules. Every molecule, so far as we know, belongs to one of a definite number of species. The list of chemical elements may be taken as representing the known species which have been examined in the laboratories. Several of these have been discovered by means of the spectroscope, and more may yet remain to be discovered in the same way. The spectroscope has also been applied to analyse the light of the sun, the brighter stars, and some of the nebulæ and comets, and has shewn that the character of the light emitted by these bodies is similar in some cases to that emitted by terrestrial molecules, and in others to light from which the molecules have absorbed certain rays. In this way a considerable number of coincidences have been traced between the systems of lines belonging to particular terrestrial substances and corresponding lines in the spectra of the heavenly bodies.

The value of the evidence furnished by such coincidences may be estimated by considering the degree of accuracy with which one such coincidence may be observed. The interval between the two lines which form Fraunhofer's line D is about the five hundredth part of the interval between B and G on Kirchhoff's scale. A discordance between the positions of two lines amounting to the tenth part of this interval, that is to say, the five thousandth part of the length of the bright part of the spectrum, would be very perceptible in a spectroscope of moderate power. We may define the power of the spectroscope to be the number of times which the smallest measurable interval is contained in the length of the visible spectrum. Let us denote this by p. In the case we have supposed p will be about 5000.

If the spectrum of the sun contains n lines of a certain degree of intensity, the probability that any one line of the spectrum of a gas will coincide with one of these n lines is

$$1 - \left(1 - \frac{1}{p}\right)^n = \frac{n}{p}\left(1 - \frac{n-1}{2}\frac{1}{p} + \&c.\right),$$

and when p is large compared with n, this becomes nearly $\frac{n}{p}$. If there are r lines in the spectrum of the gas, the probability that each and every one shall coincide with a line in the solar spectrum is approximately $\frac{n^r}{p^r}$. Hence, in the case of a gas whose spectrum contains several lines, we have to compare the results of two hypotheses. If a large amount of the gas exists in the sun, we have the strongest reason for expecting to find all the r lines in the solar spectrum. If it does not exist, the probability that r lines out of the n observed lines shall coincide with the lines of the gas is exceedingly small. If, then, we find all the r lines in their proper places in the solar spectrum, we have very strong grounds for believing that the gas exists in the sun. The probability that the gas exists in the sun is greatly strengthened if the character of the lines as to relative intensity and breadth is found to correspond in the two spectra.

The absence of one or more lines of the gas in the solar spectrum tends of course to weaken the probability, but the amount to be deducted from the probability must depend on what we know of the variation in the relative intensity of the lines when the temperature and the pressure of the gas are made to vary.

Coincidences observed, in the case of several terrestrial substances, with several systems of lines in the spectra of the heavenly bodies, tend to increase the evidence for the doctrine that terrestrial substances exist in the heavenly bodies, while the discovery of particular lines in a celestial spectrum which do not coincide with any line in a terrestrial spectrum does not much weaken the general argument, but rather indicates either that a substance exists in the heavenly body not yet detected by chemists on earth, or that the temperature of the heavenly body is such that some substance, undecomposable by our methods, is there split up into components unknown to us in their separate state.

We are thus led to believe that in widely-separated parts of the visible universe molecules exist of various kinds, the molecules of each kind having their various periods of vibration either identical, or so nearly identical that our spectroscopes cannot distinguish them. We might argue from this that these molecules are alike in all other respects, as, for instance, in mass. But it is sufficient for our present purpose to observe that the same kind of molecule, say that of hydrogen, has the same set of periods of vibration, whether we procure the hydrogen from water, from coal, or from meteoric iron, and that light, having the same set of periods of vibration, comes to us from the sun, from Sirius, and from Arcturus.

The same kind of reasoning which led us to believe that hydrogen exists in the sun and stars, also leads us to believe that the molecules of hydrogen in all these bodies had a common origin. For a material system capable of vibration may have for its periods of vibration any set of values whatever. The probability, therefore, that two material systems, quite independent of each other, shall have, to the degree of accuracy of modern spectroscopic measurements, the same set of periods of vibration, is so very small that we are forced to believe that the two systems are not independent of each other. When, instead of two such systems, we have innumerable multitudes all having the same set of periods, the argument is immensely strengthened.

Admitting, then, that there is a real relation between any two molecules of hydrogen, let us consider what this relation may be.

We may conceive of a mutual action between one body and another tending to assimilate them. Two clocks, for instance, will keep time with each other if connected by a wooden rod, though they have different rates if they were disconnected. But even if the properties of a molecule were as capable of modification as those of a clock, there is no physical connection of a sufficient kind between Sirius and Arcturus.

There are also methods by which a large number of bodies differing from each other may be sorted into sets, so that those in each set more or less resemble each other. In the manufacture of small shot this is done by making the shot roll down an inclined plane. The largest specimens acquire the greatest velocities, and are projected farther than the smaller ones. In this way the various pellets, which differ both in size and in roundness, are sorted into different kinds, those belonging to each kind being nearly of the same size, and those which are not tolerably spherical being rejected altogether.

If the molecules were originally as various as these leaden pellets, and were afterwards sorted into kinds, we should have to account for the disappearance of all the molecules which did not fall under one of the very limited number of kinds known to us; and to get rid of a number of indestructible bodies, exceeding by far the number of the molecules of all the recognised kinds, would be one of the severest labours ever proposed to a cosmogonist.

It is well known that living beings may be grouped into a certain number of species, defined with more or less precision, and that it is difficult or impossible to find a series of individuals forming the links of a continuous chain between one species and another. In the case of living beings, however, the generation of individuals is always going on, each individual differing more or less from its parents. Each individual during its whole life is undergoing modification, and it either survives and propagates its species, or dies early, accordingly as it is more or less adapted to the circumstances of its environment. Hence, it has been found possible to frame a theory of the distribution of organisms into species by means of generation, variation, and discriminative destruction. But a theory of evolution of this kind cannot be applied to the case of molecules, for the individual molecules neither are born nor die, they have neither parents nor offspring, and so far from being modified by their environment, we find that two molecules of the same kind, say of hydrogen, have the same properties, though one has been compounded with carbon and buried in the earth as coal for untold ages, while the other has been "occluded" in the iron of a meteorite, and after unknown wanderings in the heavens has at last fallen into the hands of some terrestrial chemist.

The process by which the molecules become distributed into distinct species is not one of which we know any instances going on at present, or of which we have as yet been able to form any mental representation. If we suppose that the molecules known to us are built up each of some moderate number of atoms, these atoms being all of them exactly alike, then we may attribute the limited number of molecular species to the limited number of ways in which the primitive atoms may be combined so as to form a permanent system.

But though this hypothesis gets rid of the difficulty of accounting for the independent origin of different species of molecules, it merely transfers the difficulty from the known molecules to the primitive atoms. How did the atoms come to be all alike in those properties which are in themselves capable of assuming any value?

If we adopt the theory of Boscovich, and assert that the primitive atom is a mere centre of force, having a certain definite mass, we may get over the difficulty about the equality of the mass of all atoms by laying it down as a doctrine which cannot be disproved by experiment, that mass is not a quantity capable of continuous increase or diminution, but that it is in its own nature discontinuous, like number, the atom being the unit, and all masses being multiples of that unit. We have no evidence that it is possible for the ratio of two masses to be an incommensurable quantity, for the incommensurable quantities in geometry are supposed to be traced out in a continuous medium. If matter is atomic, and therefore discontinuous, it is unfitted for the construction of perfect geometrical models, but in other respects it may fulfil its functions.

But even if we adopt a theory which makes the equality of the mass of different atoms a result depending on the nature of mass rather than on any quantitative adjustment, the correspondence of the periods of vibration of actual molecules is a fact of a different order.

We know that radiations exist having periods of vibration of every value between those corresponding to the limits of the visible spectrum, and probably far beyond these limits on both sides. The most powerful spectroscope can detect no gap or discontinuity in the spectrum of the light emitted by incandescent lime.

The period of vibration of a luminous particle is therefore a quantity which in itself is capable of assuming any one of a series of values, which, if not mathematically continuous, is such that consecutive observed values differ from each other by less than the ten thousandth part of either. There is, therefore, nothing in the nature of time itself to prevent the period of vibration of a molecule from assuming any one of many thousand different observable values. That which determines the period of any particular kind of vibration is the relation which subsists between the corresponding type of displacement and the force of restitution thereby called into play, a relation involving constants of space and time as well as of mass.

It is the equality of these space- and time-constants for all molecules of the same kind which we have next to consider. We have seen that the very different circumstances in which different molecules of the same kind have been placed have not, even in the course of many ages, produced any appreciable difference in the values of these constants. If, then, the various processes of nature to which these molecules have been subjected since the world began have not been able in all that time to produce any appreciable difference between the constants of one molecule and those of another, we are forced to conclude that it is not to the operation of any of these processes that the uniformity of the constants is due.

The formation of the molecule is therefore an event not belonging to that order of nature under which we live. It is an operation of a kind which is not, so far as we are aware, going on on earth or in the sun or the stars, either now or since these bodies began to be formed. It must be referred to the epoch, not of the formation of the earth or of the solar system, but of the establishment of the existing order of nature, and till not only these worlds and systems, but the very order of nature itself is dissolved, we have no reason to expect the occurrence of any operation of a similar kind.

In the present state of science, therefore, we have strong reasons for believing that in a molecule, or if not in a molecule, in one of its component atoms, we have something which has existed either from eternity or at least from times anterior to the existing order of nature. But besides this atom, there are immense numbers of other atoms of the same kind, and the constants of each of these atoms are incapable of adjustment by any process now in action. Each is physically independent of all the others.

Whether or not the conception of a multitude of beings existing from all eternity is in itself self-contradictory, the conception becomes palpably absurd when we attribute a relation of quantitative equality to all these beings. We are then forced to look beyond them to some common cause or common origin to explain why this singular relation of equality exists, rather than any one of the infinite number of possible relations of inequality.

Science is incompetent to reason upon the creation of matter itself out of nothing. We have reached the utmost limit of our thinking faculties when we have admitted that, because matter cannot be eternal and self-existent, it must have been created. It is only when we contemplate not matter in itself, but the form in which it actually exists, that our mind finds something on which it can lay hold.

That matter, as such, should have certain fundamental properties, that it should have a continuous existence in space and time, that all action should be between two portions of matter, and so on, are truths which may, for aught we know, be of the kind which metaphysicians call necessary. We may use our knowledge of such truths for purposes of deduction, but we have no data for speculating on their origin.

But the equality of the constants of the molecules is a fact of a very different order. It arises from a particular distribution of matter, a *collocation*, to use the expression of Dr Chalmers, of things which we have no difficulty in imagining to have been arranged otherwise. But many of the ordinary instances of collocation are adjustments of constants, which are not only arbitrary in their own nature, but in which variations actually occur; and when it is pointed out that these adjustments are beneficial to living beings, and are therefore instances of benevolent design, it is replied that those variations which are not conducive to the growth and multiplication of living beings tend to their destruction, and to the removal thereby of the evidence of any adjustment not beneficial.

The constitution of an atom, however, is such as to render it, so far as we can judge, independent of all the dangers arising from the struggle for existence. Plausible reasons may, no doubt, be assigned for believing that if the constants had varied from atom to atom through any sensible range, the bodies formed by aggregates of such atoms would not have been so well fitted for the construction of the world as the bodies which actually exist. But as we have no experience of bodies formed of such variable atoms this must remain a bare conjecture.

Atoms have been compared by Sir J. Herschel to manufactured articles, on account of their uniformity. The uniformity of manufactured articles may be traced to very different motives on the part of the manufacturer. In certain cases it is found to be less expensive as regards trouble, as well as cost, to make a great many objects exactly alike than to adapt each to its special requirements. Thus, shoes for soldiers are made in large numbers without any designed adaptation to the feet of particular men. In another class of cases the uniformity is intentional, and is designed to make the manufactured article more valuable. Thus, Whitworth's bolts are made in a certain number of sizes, so that if one bolt is lost, another may be got at once, and accurately fitted to its place. The identity of the arrangement of the words in the different copies of a document or book is a matter of great practical importance, and it is more perfectly secured by the process of printing than by that of manuscript copying.

In a third class not a part only but the whole of the value of the object arises from its exact conformity to a given standard. Weights and measures belong to this class, and the existence of many well-adjusted material standards

61—2

of weight and measure in any country furnishes evidence of the existence of
a system of law regulating the transactions of the inhabitants, and enjoining
in all professed measures a conformity to the national standard.

There are thus three kinds of usefulness in manufactured articles—cheap-
ness, serviceableness, and quantitative accuracy. Which of these was present
to the mind of Sir J. Herschel we cannot now positively affirm, but it was
at least as likely to have been the last as the first, though it seems more
probable that he meant to assert that a number of exactly similar things cannot
be each of them eternal and self-existent, and must therefore have been made,
and that he used the phrase "manufactured article" to suggest the idea of
their being made in great numbers.

[From the *Encyclopædia Britannica*.]

LXXIV. *Attraction.*

THAT the different parts of a material system influence each other's motions is a matter of daily observation. In some cases we cannot discover any material connection extending from the one body to the other. We call these cases of action at a distance, to distinguish them from those in which we can trace a continuous material bond of union between the bodies. The mutual action between two bodies is called stress. When the mutual action tends to bring the bodies nearer, or to prevent them from separating, it is called tension or attraction. When it tends to separate the bodies, or to prevent them from approaching, it is called pressure or repulsion. The names tension and pressure are used when the action is seen to take place through a medium. Attraction and repulsion are reserved for cases of action at a distance. The configuration of a material system can always be defined in terms of the mutual distances of the parts of the system. Any change of configuration must alter one or more of these distances. Hence the force which produces or resists such a change may be resolved into attractions or repulsions between those parts of the system whose distance is altered.

There has been a great deal of speculation as to the cause of such forces, one of them, namely, the pressure between bodies in contact, being supposed to be more easily conceived than any other kind of stress. Many attempts have therefore been made to resolve cases of apparent attraction and repulsion at a distance into cases of pressure. At one time the possibility of attraction at a distance was supposed to be refuted by asserting that a body cannot act where it is not, and that therefore all action between different portions of matter must be by direct contact. To this it was replied that we have no evidence that real contact ever takes place between two bodies, and that, in fact, when bodies are pressed against each other and in apparent contact, we

may sometimes actually measure the distance between them, as when one piece
of glass is laid on another, in which case a considerable pressure must be applied to bring the surfaces near enough to shew the black spot of Newton's
rings, which indicates a distance of about a ten thousandth of a millimetre. If,
in order to get rid of the idea of action at a distance, we imagine a material medium through which the action is transmitted, all that we have done
is to substitute for a single action at a great distance a series of actions at
smaller distances between the parts of the medium, so that we cannot even
thus get rid of action at a distance.

The study of the mutual action between the parts of a material system
has, in modern times, been greatly simplified by the introduction of the idea
of the energy of the system. The energy of the system is measured by the
amount of work which it can do in overcoming external resistances. It depends
on the present configuration and motion of the system, and not on the manner
in which the system has acquired that configuration and motion. A complete
knowledge of the manner in which the energy of the system depends on its
configuration and motion, is sufficient to determine all the forces acting between
the parts of the system. For instance, if the system consists of two bodies,
and if the energy depends on the distance between them, then if the energy
increases when the distance increases, there must be attraction between the
bodies, and if the energy diminishes when the distance increases, there must
be repulsion between them. In the case of two gravitating masses m and m'
at a distance r, the part of the energy which depends on r is $-\dfrac{mm'}{r}$. We
may therefore express the fact that there is attraction between the two bodies
by saying that the energy of the system consisting of the two bodies increases
when their distance increases. The question, therefore, Why do the two bodies
attract each other? may be expressed in a different form. Why does the
energy of the system increase when the distance increases?

But we must bear in mind that the scientific or science-producing value of
the efforts made to answer these old standing questions is not to be measured
by the prospect they afford us of ultimately obtaining a solution, but by their
effect in stimulating men to a thorough investigation of nature. To propose a
scientific question presupposes scientific knowledge, and the questions which
exercise men's minds in the present state of science may very likely be such
that a little more knowledge would shew us that no answer is possible. The

scientific value of the question, How do bodies act on one another at a distance? is to be found in the stimulus it has given to investigations into the properties of the intervening. medium.

Newton, in his *Principia*, deduces from the observed motions of the heavenly bodies the fact that they attract one another according to a definite law. This he gives as a result of strict dynamical reasoning, and by it he shews how not only the more conspicuous phenomena, but all the apparent irregularities of the celestial motions are the calculable results of a single principle. In his *Principia* he confines himself to the demonstration and development of this great step in the science of the mutual action of bodies. He says nothing there about the means by which bodies gravitate towards each other. But his mind did not rest at this point. We know that he did not believe in the direct action of bodies at a distance.

"It is inconceivable that inanimate brute matter should, without the mediation of something else which is not material, operate upon and affect other matter without mutual contact, as it must do if gravitation in the sense of Epicurus be essential and inherent in it...That gravity should be innate, inherent, and essential to matter, so that one body can act upon another at a distance, through a vacuum, without the mediation of anything else, by and through which their action and force may be conveyed from one to another, is to me so great an absurdity, that I believe no man, who has in philosophical matters a competent faculty of thinking, can ever fall into it."—*Letter to Bentley.*

And we also know that he sought for the mechanism of gravitation in the properties of an æthereal medium diffused over the universe.

"It appears, from his letters to Boyle, that this was his opinion early, and if he did not publish it sooner it proceeded from hence only, that he found he was not able, from experiment and observation, to give a satisfactory account of this medium and the manner of its operation in producing the chief phenomena of nature*."

In his *Optical Queries*, indeed, he shews that if the pressure of this medium is less in the neighbourhood of dense bodies than at great distances from them, dense bodies will be drawn towards each other, and that if the diminution of pressure is inversely as the distance from the dense body the law will be that of gravitation. The next step, as he points out, is to account for this inequality of pressure in the medium; and as he was not able to do this, he left the explanation of the cause of gravity as a problem to succeeding ages. As regards gravitation the progress made towards the solution of the problem since the time of Newton has been almost imperceptible. Faraday

* Maclaurin's account of Sir Isaac Newton's discoveries.

shewed that the transmission of electric and magnetic forces is accompanied by phenomena occurring in every part of the intervening medium. He traced the lines of force through the medium; and he ascribed to them a tendency to shorten themselves and to separate from their neighbours, thus introducing the idea of stress in the medium in a different form from that suggested by Newton; for, whereas Newton's stress was a hydrostatic pressure in every direction, Faraday's is a tension along the lines of force, combined with a pressure in all normal directions. By shewing that the plane of polarisation of a ray of light passing through a transparent medium in the direction of the magnetic force is made to rotate, Faraday not only demonstrated the action of magnetism on light, but by using light to reveal the state of magnetisation of the medium, he "illuminated," to use his own phrase, " the lines of magnetic force."

From this phenomenon Thomson afterwards proved, by strict dynamical reasoning, that the transmission of magnetic force is associated with a rotatory motion of the small parts of the medium. He shewed, at the same time, how the centrifugal force due to this motion would account for magnetic attraction.

A theory of this kind is worked out in greater detail in Clerk Maxwell's *Treatise on Electricity and Magnetism.* It is there shewn that, if we assume that the medium is in a state of stress, consisting of tension along the lines of force and pressure in all directions at right angles to the lines of force, the tension and the pressure being equal in numerical value and proportional to the square of the intensity of the field at the given point,· the observed electrostatic and electromagnetic forces will be completely accounted for.

The next step is to account for this state of stress in the medium. In the case of electromagnetic force we avail ourselves of Thomson's deduction from Faraday's discovery stated above. We assume that the small parts of the medium are rotating about axes parallel to the lines of force. The centrifugal force due to this rotation produces the excess of pressure perpendicular to the lines of force. The explanation of electrostatic stress is less satisfactory, but there can be no doubt that a path is now open by which we may trace to the action of a medium all forces which, like the electric and magnetic forces, vary inversely as the square of the distance, and are attractive between bodies of different names, and repulsive between bodies of the same names.

The force of gravitation is also inversely as the square of the distance, but it differs from the electric and magnetic forces in this respect, that the bodies between which it acts cannot be divided into two opposite kinds, one positive and the other negative, but are in respect of gravitation all of the same kind, and that the force between them is in every case attractive. To account for such a force by means of stress in an intervening medium, on the plan adopted for electric and magnetic forces, we must assume a stress of an opposite kind from that already mentioned. We must suppose that there is a pressure in the direction of the lines of force, combined with a tension in all directions at right angles to the lines of force. Such a state of stress would, no doubt, account for the observed effects of gravitation. We have not, however, been able hitherto to imagine any physical cause for such a state of stress. It is easy to calculate the amount of this stress which would be required to account for the actual effects of gravity at the surface of the earth. It would require a pressure of 37,000 tons weight on the square inch in a vertical direction, combined with a tension of the same numerical value in all horizontal directions. The state of stress, therefore, which we must suppose to exist in the invisible medium, is 3000 times greater than that which the strongest steel could support.

Another theory of the mechanism of gravitation, that of Le Sage, who attributes it to the impact of "ultramundane corpuscles," has been already discussed in the article Atom, *supra*, p. 473.

Sir William Thomson* has shewn that if we suppose all space filled with a uniform incompressible fluid, and if we further suppose either that material bodies are always generating and emitting this fluid at a constant rate, the fluid flowing off to infinity, or that material bodies are always absorbing and annihilating the fluid, the deficiency flowing in from infinite space, then, in either of these cases, there would be an attraction between any two bodies inversely as the square of the distance. If, however, one of the bodies were a generator of the fluid and the other an absorber of it, the bodies would repel each other.

Here, then, we have a hydrodynamical illustration of action at a distance, which is so far promising that it shews how bodies of the same kind may attract each other. But the conception of a fluid constantly flowing out of a body without any supply from without, or flowing into it without any way of escape, is so contradictory to all our experience, that an hypothesis, of which it is an essential part, cannot be called an *explanation* of the phenomenon of gravitation.

* *Proceedings of the Royal Society of Edinburgh*, 7th Feb. 1870.

Dr Robert Hooke, a man of singular inventive power, in 1671 endeavoured to trace the cause of gravitation to waves propagated in a medium. He found that bodies floating on water agitated by waves were drawn towards the centre of agitation*. He does not appear, however, to have followed up this observation in such a way as to determine completely the action of waves on an immersed body.

Professor Challis has investigated the mathematical theory of the effect of waves of condensation and rarefaction in an elastic fluid on bodies immersed in the fluid. He found the difficulties of the investigation to be so great that he has not been able to arrive at numerical results. He concludes, however, that the effect of such waves would be to attract the body towards the centre of agitation, or to repel it from that centre, according as the wave's length is very large or very small compared with the dimensions of the body. Practical illustrations of the effect of such waves have been given by Guyot, Schellbach, Guthrie, and Thomson†.

A tuning-fork is set in vibration, and brought near a delicately suspended light body. The body is immediately attracted towards the tuning-fork. If the tuning-fork is itself suspended, it is seen to be attracted towards any body placed near it.

Sir W. Thomson has shewn that this action can in all cases be explained by the general principle that in fluid motion the average pressure is least where the average energy of motion is greatest. Now, the wave-motion is greatest nearest the tuning-fork, the pressure is therefore least there; and the suspended body being pressed unequally on opposite sides, moves from the side of greater pressure to the side of less pressure, that is towards the tuning-fork. He has also succeeded in producing repulsion in the case of a small body lighter than the surrounding medium.

It is remarkable that of the three hypotheses, which go some way towards a physical explanation of gravitation, every one involves a constant expenditure of work. Le Sage's hypothesis of ultramundane corpuscles does so, as we have shewn in the article ATOM. That of the generation or absorption of fluid requires, not only constant expenditure of work in emitting fluid under pressure, but actual creation and destruction of matter. That of waves requires some agent in a remote part of the universe capable of generating the waves.

---

* *Posthumous Works*, edited by R. Waller, pp. xiv. and 184
† *Philosophical Magazine*, June, 1871.

According to such hypotheses we must regard the processes of nature not as illustrations of the great principle of the conservation of energy, but as instances in which, by a nice adjustment of powerful agencies not subject to this principle, an apparent conservation of energy is maintained. Hence, we are forced to conclude that the explanation of the cause of gravitation is not to be found in any of these hypotheses.

[From *Cambridge Philosophical Society's Proceedings*, Vol. II. 1876.]

LXXV. *On Bow's method of drawing diagrams in graphical statics with illustrations from Peaucellier's linkage.*

THE use of Diagrams is a particular instance of that method of symbols which is so powerful an aid in the advancement of science.

A diagram differs from a picture in this respect, that in a diagram no attempt is made to represent those features of the actual material system which are not the special objects of our study.

Thus when we are studying the internal equilibrium of a particular piece of a structure or a machine, we require to know its shape and dimensions, and the specification of these may often be made easier by means of a drawing of the piece.

But when we are studying the equilibrium of a framework composed of such pieces jointed together, in which each piece acts only by tension or by pressure between its extremities, it is not necessary to know whether a particular piece is straight or curved or what may be the form of its section. In order, therefore, to exhibit the structure of the frame in the most elementary manner we may draw it as a skeleton in which the different joints are connected by straight lines. The tension or pressure of each piece may be indicated on such a diagram by numbers attached to the line which represents that piece in the diagram. The stresses in the frame would thus be indicated in a way which is geometrical as regards the position and direction of the forces, but arithmetical as regards their magnitude.

But a purely geometrical representation of a force has been made use of from the earliest beginnings of mechanics as a science. The force is represented by a straight line drawn from the point of application of the force, in the direction of the force, and containing as many units of length as there are units of force in the force. The end of the line is marked by an arrow-head to shew in which direction the force acts.

According to this method each force is drawn in its proper position in the diagram which represents the configuration of the system. Such a diagram might be useful as a record of the results of calculation of the magnitude of the forces, but it would be of no use in enabling us to test the correctness of the calculation. It would be of less use than the diagram in which the magnitudes of the forces were indicated by numbers.

But we have a geometrical method of testing the equilibrium of any set of forces acting at a point by drawing in series a set of lines parallel and proportional to these forces. If these lines form a closed polygon the forces are in equilibrium. We might thus form a set of polygons of forces, one for each joint of the frame. But in so doing we give up the principle of always drawing the line representing a force from its point of application, for all the sides of a polygon cannot pass through the same point as the forces do.

We also represent every stress twice over, for it appears as a side of both the polygons corresponding to the two joints between which it acts.

But if we can arrange the polygons in such a way that the sides of any two polygons which represent the same force coincide with each other, we may form a diagram in which every stress is represented in direction and magnitude, though not in position, by a single line, which is the common boundary of the two polygons which represent the points of concourse of the pieces of the frame.

Here we have a pure diagram of forces, in which no attempt is made to represent the configuration of the material system, and in which every force is not only represented in direction and magnitude by a straight line, but the equilibrium of the forces is manifest by inspection, for we have only to examine whether each polygon is closed or not.

The relations between the diagram of the frame and the diagram of stress are as follows :

To every piece in the frame corresponds a line in the diagram of stress which represents in magnitude and direction the stress acting on that piece.

To every joint of the frame corresponds a closed polygon in the diagram, and the forces acting at that joint are represented by the sides of the polygon taken in a certain cyclical order. The cyclical order of the sides of two adjacent polygons is such that their common side is traced in opposite directions in going round the two polygons.

When to every point of concourse of the lines in the diagram of stress corresponds a closed polygon in the skeleton of the frame, the two diagrams are said to be reciprocal.

The first extensions of the method of diagrams of forces to other cases than that of the funicular polygon were given by Rankine in his *Applied Mechanics* (1857).

The method was independently applied to a large number of cases by Mr W. P. Taylor, a practical draughtsman in the office of the well-known contractor Mr J. B. Cochrane. I pointed out the reciprocal properties of the diagram in 1864, and in 1870 shewed the relations of this method to Airy's function of stress and other mathematical methods.

Prof. Fleeming Jenkin has given a number of applications of the method to practice, *Trans. R. S. E.*, Vol. xxv.

Cremona * has deduced the construction of the reciprocal figures from the theory of the two linear components of a wrench.

Culmann in his *Graphische Statik* makes great use of diagrams of forces, some of which, however, are not reciprocal.

M. Maurice Levy in his *Statique Graphique* (Paris, 1874) has treated the whole subject in an elementary and complete manner.

Mr R. H. Bow, C.E., F.R.S.E., in a recent work *On the Economics of Construction in relation to Framed Structures* (Spon, 1873), has materially simplified the process of drawing a diagram of stress reciprocal to. a given frame acted on by any system of equilibrating external forces.

Instead of lettering the joints of the frame as is generally done, or the pieces of the frame as was my own custom, he places a letter in each of the polygonal areas enclosed by the pieces of the frame, and also in each of the divisions of the surrounding space as separated by the lines of action of the external forces.

When one piece of the frame crosses another, the point of intersection is treated as if it were a real joint, and the stresses of each of the intersecting pieces are represented twice in the diagram of stress, as the opposite sides of the parallelogram which represents the forces at the point of intersection. Thus the point V in figures 1 and 3, p. 495, is represented by the parallelogram $BDCE$ in figure 2, and the point A in figure 2 is represented by the parallelogram $PRQS$ in figures 1 and 3.

* *Le figure reciproche nella statica grafica* (Milano, 1872).

Peaucellier's linkage consists of the four equal pieces forming the jointed rhombus $PQRS$ together with two equal arms OS and OR.

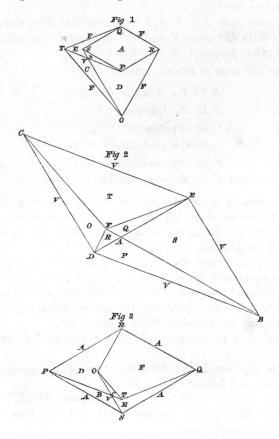

When these arms are longer than the sides of the rhombus the linkage is said to be positive; when they are shorter the linkage is said to be negative.

When Peaucellier's linkage is employed as a machine it is acted on by three forces, applied respectively at the fulcrum O, and the two tracing poles Q and S.

These three forces, if in equilibrium, must meet in some point T. We may therefore suppose them to be stresses in three new pieces OT, QT, ST, which will complete the frame.

Let us suppose that both O and T are outside the rhombus, and that OS intersects PT in the point V, and let us apply Bow's method to construct the diagram of stress reciprocal to this frame.

If we letter the areas as follows, putting

A for the rhombus $PRQS$,

B for the triangle PSV,

C for the triangle OTV,

D for the quadrilateral $ORPV$,

E for the quadrilateral $QSVT$,

and F for the space outside the frame,

then, in the diagram of stress, the stresses of the four sides of the rhombus will meet in A, and since the opposite sides of the rhombus are parallel, the lines EA and AD will be in one straight line, and the lines BA and AF will also be in a straight line.

Also since in the frame the pieces OR and OS are equal, the angles ORP, PSV are equal, and the corresponding angles FDA, ABE must be equal, and therefore the quadrilateral $BEFD$ can be inscribed in a circle, and therefore the angles FEA, DBA are equal, and the corresponding angles in the frame TQS, SPV are equal, and therefore PT is equal to QT.

If, therefore, O is in one diagonal of the rhombus, T must be in the other diagonal.

The diagram of stress is completed by drawing EC parallel to BD, and DC parallel to BE, and joining FC.

This diagram therefore consists of a parallelogram $BDCE$, a diagonal ED, a point F in the circle passing through FBD, and four lines drawn from F to the angles of the parallelogram.

If we now begin with the diagram of stress, and proceed to construct a frame reciprocal to it, the form of the frame will be different according to the cyclical direction in which the sides of the rhombus $PRQS$ are lettered. If in the one case we have the points O and T both outside the rhombus as in fig. 1, in the other O and T will both be within the rhombus as in fig. 3.

The stresses in the corresponding pieces of fig. 1 and fig. 3 are all equal if they are equal in any pair of them.

If in the frames represented in fig. 1 and fig. 3, we consider that the pieces OS and TP cross one another at V without intersecting, we have six points O, P, Q, R, S, T joined by nine lines. Now in general if p points in a plane are joined by $2p-3$ lines the figure is simply stiff, that is to say the form of the figure is determined by the lengths of the lines, and there are no necessary relations between the lengths of the lines.

But in Peaucellier's linkage the length of any line, as OT, is determined when those of the other eight are given. For if a is the length of a side of the rhombus, b the length of either arm OR or OS, c the length of either arm TP or TQ, then if $OT=d$,

$$d^2 = b^2 + c^2 - a^2.$$

Hence if any one of the nine pieces of the linkage be removed, the motion of the remaining eight will be the same as before, and a given stress in any one of the nine will produce stresses in each of the other eight which are determinate in magnitude when the configuration of the linkage is given, though they alter during the motion of the linkage.

[From the *Proceedings of the Cambridge Philosophical Society*, Vol. II., 1876.]

LXXVI. *On the Equilibrium of Heterogeneous Substances.*

THE thermodynamical problem of the equilibrium of heterogeneous substances was first attacked by Kirchoff in 1855, who studied the properties of mixtures of sulphuric acid with water, and the density of the vapour in equilibrium with the mixture. His method has recently been adopted by C. Neumann in his *Vorlesungen über die mechanische Theorie der Wärme* (Leipzig, 1875). Neither of these writers, however, makes use of two of the most valuable concepts in Thermodynamics, namely, the intrinsic energy and the entropy of the substance.

It is probably for this reason that their methods do not readily give an explanation of those states of equilibrium which are stable in themselves, but which the contact of certain substances may render unstable.

I therefore wish to point out to the Society the methods adopted by Professor J. Willard Gibbs of Yale College, published in the *Transactions of the Academy of Sciences of Connecticut*, which seem to me to throw a new light on Thermodynamics.

He considers the intrinsic energy (ϵ) of a homogeneous mass consisting of n kinds of component matter to be a function of $n+2$ variables, namely, the volume of the mass v, its entropy η, and the n masses, m_1, $m_2 \ldots m_n$, of its component substances.

Each of these variables represents a physical quantity, the value of which, for a material system, is the sum of its values for the parts of the system.

By differentiating the energy with respect to each of these variables (considered as independent), we obtain a set of $n+2$ differential coefficients which represent the intensity of various properties of the substance. Thus,

$\dfrac{d\epsilon}{dv} = -p$, where p is the pressure of the substance;

$\dfrac{d\epsilon}{d\eta} = \theta$, where θ is the temperature on the thermodynamic scale;

$\dfrac{d\epsilon}{dm_1} = \mu_1$, where μ_1 is the potential of the component (m_1) with respect to the compound mass.

Each of the component substances has therefore a potential with respect to the whole mass.

The idea of the potential of a substance is, I believe, due to Prof. Gibbs. His definition is as follows:—

If to any homogeneous mass we suppose an infinitesimal quantity of any substance to be added, the mass remaining homogeneous, and its entropy and volume remaining unchanged, the increase of the energy of the mass, divided by the mass of the substance added, is the *potential* of that substance in the mass considered.

The condition of the stable equilibrium of the mass is expressed by Prof. Gibbs in either of the two following ways:

I. *For the equilibrium of any isolated system it is necessary and sufficient that in all possible variations of the state of the system which do not alter its energy, the variation of its entropy shall either vanish or be negative.*

II. *For the equilibrium of any isolated system it is necessary and sufficient that in all possible variations of the state of the system which do not alter its entropy, the variation of the energy shall either vanish or be positive.*

The variations here spoken of must not involve the transportation of any matter through any finite distance.

It follows from this that the quantities θ, p, $\mu_1 \ldots \mu_n$ must have the same values in all parts of the mass. For if not, heat will flow from places of higher to places of lower temperature, the mass as a whole will move from places of higher to places of lower pressure, and each of the several component substances will pass from places where its potential is higher to places where it is lower, if it can do so continuously.

Hence Prof. Gibbs shews that if Θ, P, $M_1 \ldots M_n$ are the values of θ, p, $\mu_1 \ldots \mu_n$ for a given phase of the compound, and if the quantity

$$K = \epsilon - \Theta\eta + Pv - M_1 m_1 - \&c. - M_n m_n,$$

63—2

is zero for the given fluid, and is positive for every other phase of the same components, the condition of the given fluid will be stable.

If this condition holds for all variations of the variables the fluid will be absolutely stable, but if it holds only for *small* variations but not for certain finite variations, then the fluid will be stable when not in contact with matter in any of those phases for which K is positive, but if matter in any one of these phases is in contact with it, its equilibrium will be destroyed, and a portion will pass into the phase of the substance with which it is in contact.

Thus in Professor F. Guthrie's experiments, a solution of chloride of calcium of 37 per cent. was cooled to a temperature somewhat below $-37°$ C. without solidification.

In this state, however, the contact of three different solids determines three different kinds of solidification. A piece of ice causes ice to separate from the fluid. A piece of the cryohydrate of chloride of calcium determines the formation of cryohydrate from the fluid, and the anhydrous salt causes a precipitation of anhydrous salt.

The phase of the fluid is such that K is positive for all phases differing slightly from its own phase, and its equilibrium is therefore stable, but for certain widely different phases, namely, ice, cryohydrate and anhydrous salt, K is negative.

If none of these substances are in contact with the fluid, the fluid cannot alter in phase without a transport of matter through a finite .distance, and is therefore stable; but if any one of them is in contact with the fluid, part of the fluid is enabled to pass into a phase in which K is negative. The conditions of consistent phases are that the values of θ, p, $\mu_1 \ldots \mu_n$, and K are equal for all phases which can coexist in equilibrium, the surface of contact being plane.

This was illustrated by Mr Main's experiments on co-existent phases of mixtures of chloroform, alcohol and water.

[From *Nature*, Vol. XIV.]

LXXVII. *Diffusion of Gases through Absorbing Substances.*

THE importance of the exact ˙study of the motions of gases, not only as a method of distinguishing one gas from another, but as likely to increase our knowledge of the dynamical theory of gases, was pointed out by Thomas Graham. Graham himself studied the most important phenomena, and distinguished from each other those in which the principal effect is due to different properties of gases.

The motion of large masses of the gas approximates to that of a perfect fluid having the same density and pressure as the gas. This is the case with the motion of a single gas when it flows through a large hole in a thin plate from one vessel into another in which the pressure is less. The result in this case is found to be in accordance with the principles of the dynamics of fluids. This was approximately established by Graham, and the more accurate formula, in which the thermodynamic properties of the gas are taken into account, has been verified by the experiments of Joule and Thomson. (*Proc. R. S.*, May, 1856.)

When the orifice is exceedingly small, it appears from the molecular theory of gases that the total discharge may be calculated by supposing that there are two currents in opposite directions, the quantity flowing in each current being the same as if it had been discharged into a vacuum.

For different gases the volume discharged in a given time, reduced to standard pressure and temperature, is proportional to—

$$\frac{p}{\sqrt{s\theta}}$$

where p is the actual pressure, s is the specific gravity, and θ the temperature reckoned from $-274°$ C.

When the gases in the two vessels are different, each gas is discharged according to this law independently of the other.

These phenomena, however, can be observed only when the thickness of the plate and the diameter of the aperture are very small.

When this is the case, the distance is very small between a point in the first vessel where the mixed gas has a certain composition, and a point in the second vessel where the mixed gas has a quite different composition, so that the velocity of diffusion through the hole between these two points is large compared with the velocity of flow of the mixed gas arising from the difference of the total pressures in the two vessels.

When the hole is of sensible magnitude this distance is larger, because the region of mixed gases extends further from the hole, and the effects of diffusion become completely masked by the effect of the current of the gas in mass, arising from the difference of the total pressures in the two vessels. In this latter case the discharge depends only on the nature of the gas in the vessel of greater pressure, and on the resultant pressures in the two vessels. It consists entirely of the gas of the first vessel, and there is no appreciable counter current of the gas of the other vessel.

Hence the experiments on the double current must be made either through a single very small aperture, as in Graham's first experiment with a glass vessel accidentally cracked, or through a great number of apertures, as in Graham's later experiments with porous septa of plaster of Paris or of plumbago.

With such septa the following phenomena are observed :—

When the gases on the two sides of the septum are different, but have the same pressure, the reduced volumes of the gases diffused in opposite directions through the septum are inversely as the square roots of their specific gravities.

If one or both of the vessels is of invariable volume, the interchange of gas will cause an inequality of pressure, the pressure becoming greater in the vessel which contains the heavier gas.

If a vessel contains a mixture of gases, the gas diffused from the vessel through a porous septum will contain a larger proportion of the lighter gas, and the proportion of the heavier gas remaining in the vessel will increase during the process.

The rate of flow of a gas through a long capillary tube depends upon the viscosity or internal friction of the gas, a property quite independent of its specific gravity.

The phenomena of diffusion studied by Dr v. Wroblewski are quite distinct from any of these. The septum through which the gas is observed to pass is apparently quite free from pores, and is indeed quite impervious to certain gases, while it allows others to pass.

It was the opinion of Graham that the substance of the septum is capable of entering into a more or less intimate combination with the substance of the gas; that on the side where the gas has greatest pressure the process of combination is always going on; that at the other side, where the pressure of the gas is smaller, the substance of the gas is always becoming dissociated from that of the septum; while in the interior of the septum those parts which are richer in the substance of the gas are communicating it to those which are poorer.

The rate at which this diffusion takes place depends therefore on the power of the gas to combine with the substance of the septum. Thus if the septum be a film of water or a soap-bubble, those gases will pass through it most rapidly which are most readily absorbed by water, but if the septum be of caoutchouc the order of the gases will be different. The fact discovered by St Claire-Deville and Troost that certain gases can pass through plates of red-hot metals, was explained by Graham in the same manner.

Franz Exner * has studied the diffusion of gases through soap-bubbles, and finds the rate of diffusion is directly as the absorption-coefficient of the gas, and inversely as the square root of the specific gravity.

Stefan † in his first paper on the diffusion of gases has shewn that a law of this form is to be expected, but he says that he will not go further into the problem of the motion of gases in absorbing medium, as it ought to form the subject of a separate investigation.

Dr v. Wroblewski has confined himself to the investigation of the relation between the rate of diffusion and the pressure of the diffusing gas on the two sides of the membrane. The membrane was of caoutchouc, 0·0034 cm. thick. It was almost completely impervious to air. The rate at which carbonic acid diffused through the membrane was proportional to the pressure of that gas, and was independent of the pressure of the air on the other side of the

---

* *Pogg. Ann.*, Bd. 155.

† *Ueber das Gleichgewicht u. d. Diffusion von Gasgemengen.* Sitzb. der k. Akad. (Wien), Jan. 5, 1871.

membrane, provided this air was from carbonic acid.   The connexion between
this result and Henry's law of absorption is pointed out.

The time of diffusion of hydrogen through caoutchouc is 3·6 times that of
an equal volume of carbonic acid.   The diffusion of a mixture of hydrogen and
carbonic acid takes place as if each gas diffused independently of the other
at a rate proportional to the part of the pressure which is due to that gas.

We hope that Dr v. Wroblewski will continue his researches, and make
a complete investigation of the phenomena of diffusion through absorbing substances.

[From the *Kensington Museum Handbook*, pp. 1—21.]

LXXVIII. *General considerations concerning Scientific Apparatus.*

1. EXPERIMENTS.

THE aim of Physical Science is to observe and interpret natural phenomena.

Of natural phenomena, some—as, for example, those of astronomy—are not subject to our control, and in the study of these we can make use only of the method of Observation. When, however, we can cause the phenomenon to be repeated under various conditions, we are in possession of a much more powerful method of investigation—that of Experiment.

An Experiment, like every other event which takes place, is a natural phenomenon; but in a Scientific Experiment the circumstances are so arranged that the relations between a particular set of phenomena may be studied to the best advantage.

In designing an Experiment the agents and phenomena to be studied are marked off from all others and regarded as the Field of Investigation. All agents and phenomena not included within this field are called Disturbing Agents, and their effects Disturbances; and the experiment must be so arranged that the effects of these disturbing agents on the phenomena to be investigated shall be as small as possible.

We may afterwards change the field of our investigation, and include within it those phenomena which in our former investigation we regarded as disturbances. The experiments must now be designed so as to bring into prominence the phenomena which we formerly tried to get rid of. When we have in this way ascertained the laws of the disturbances, we shall be better prepared to make a more thorough investigation of what we began by regarding as the principal phenomena.

Thus, in experiments where we endeavour to detect or to measure a force by observing the motion which it produces in a movable body, we regard Friction as a disturbing agent, and we arrange the experiment so that the motion to be observed may be impeded as little as possible by friction.

2. APPARATUS.

Everything which is required in order to make an experiment is called Apparatus.

A piece of apparatus constructed specially for the performance of experiments is called an Instrument.

Apparatus may be designed to produce and exhibit a particular phenomenon, to eliminate the effects of disturbing agents, to regulate the physical conditions of the phenomenon, or to measure the magnitude of the phenomenon itself.

In many experiments, special apparatus is required for all these purposes, but certain pieces of apparatus are used in a great variety of experiments, and there are whole classes of instruments which have certain principles of construction in common.

Thus, in all instruments in which motion is to be produced there must be a prime mover or driving power, and a train of mechanism to connect the prime mover with the body to be moved; and in many cases additional apparatus is necessary—such as a break to destroy the superfluous energy of the prime mover, or a reservoir to store up its energy when not required; and we may have special apparatus to measure the force transmitted, the velocity produced, or the work done, or to regulate them by automatic governors.

We may make a somewhat similar classification of the functions of apparatus belonging to other physical sciences—such as Electricity, Heat, Light, Sound, &c.

3. GENERAL PRINCIPLE OF THE CONSTRUCTION OF APPARATUS.

There are certain primary requisites, however, which are common to all instruments, and which therefore are to be carefully considered in designing or selecting them. The fundamental principle is, that the construction of the instrument should be adapted to the use that is to be made of it, and in particular, that the parts intended to be fixed should not be liable to become displaced; that those which ought to be movable should not stick fast; that parts which have to be observed should not be covered up or kept in the dark; and that pieces intended to have a definite form should not be disfigured by warping, straining, or wearing.

It is therefore desirable, before we enter on the classification of instruments according to the phenomena with which they are connected, to point ' out a few of the principles which must be attended to in all instruments.

Each solid piece of an instrument is intended to be either fixed or movable, and to have a certain definite shape. It is acted on by its own weight, and other forces, but it ought not to be subjected to unnecessary stresses, for these not only diminish its strength, but (what for scientific purposes may be much more injurious) they alter its figure, and may, by their unexpected changes during the course of an experiment, produce disturbance or confusion in the observations we have to make.

We have, therefore, to consider the methods of relieving the pieces of an instrument from unnecessary strain, of securing for the fixed parts a determinate position, and of ensuring that the movable parts shall move freely, yet without shake.

This we may do by attending to the well-known fact in kinematics—"A RIGID BODY HAS SIX DEGREES OF FREEDOM."

A rigid body is one whose form does not vary. The pieces of our instruments are solid, but not rigid. They are liable to change of form under stress, but such change of form is not desirable, except in certain special parts, such as springs.

Hence, if a solid piece is constrained in more than six ways it will be subject to internal stress, and will become strained or distorted, and this in a manner which, without the most exact micrometrical measurements, it would be impossible to specify.

In instruments which are exposed to rough usage it may sometimes be advisable to secure a piece from becoming loose, even at the risk of straining and jamming it; but in apparatus for accurate work it is essential that the bearings of every piece should be properly defined, both in number and in position.

4. METHODS OF PLACING AN INSTRUMENT IN A DEFINITE POSITION.

When an instrument is intended to stand in a definite position on a fixed base it must have six bearings, so arranged that if one of the bearings were removed the direction in which the corresponding point of the instrument would be left free to move by the other bearings must be as nearly as possible normal to the tangent plane at the bearing.

(This condition implies that, of the normals to the tangent planes at the bearings, no two coincide; no three are in one plane, and either meet in a point or are parallel; no four are in one plane, or meet in a point, or are parallel, or, more generally, belong to the same system of generators of an hyperboloid of one sheet. The conditions for five normals and for six are more complicated.)*

These conditions are satisfied by the well-known method of forming on the fixed base three V grooves, whose sides are inclined 45° to the base, and whose directions meet in a point at angles of 120°. The instrument has three feet; the end of each foot is, roughly speaking, conical, but so rounded off that it bears against the two sides of the groove, and cannot reach the bottom. The instrument has thus six solid bearings, and is kept in its place by its weight, without being subjected to any unnecessary strain.

Sir William Thomson, who has bestowed much attention on this subject, has adopted a somewhat different arrangement in some of his instruments. A triangular hole, like that formed by pressing an angle of a cube into a mass of clay, is formed in the base, and a V groove is cut in a direction passing through the centre of the hole. The three feet of the instrument are all rounded, but of different lengths. The longest stands in the triangular hole, and has three bearings; the second stands in the V groove, and has two bearings; and the third stands on the horizontal plane of the base, and has one bearing. There are thus six bearings in all. This method, though it does not give so large a margin of stability as the method of three grooves, has this advantage, that as each of the three feet is differently formed, it is impossible to put any but the proper foot into the hole without detecting the mistake.

5. BEARINGS OF MIRRORS.

In mounting mirrors it is especially important to attend to the number and position of their bearings, for any stress on the mirror spoils its figure, and renders it useless for accurate work.

---

* See Ball on the *Theory of Screws.*

For small mirrors it is best to make one face of the mirror rest against three solid bearings, and to keep it in contact with these by three spring bearings placed exactly opposite to them against the other face of the mirror. These will prevent any displacement of the mirror out of its proper plane. The bearings against the edges of the mirror, by which it is prevented from shifting in its own plane, are, in the case of small mirrors, of less importance.

When the mirror is large, as in the case of the speculum of a large telescope, a greater number of bearings is required to prevent the mirror from becoming strained by its own weight; but in all cases the number of *fixed* bearings at the back of the mirror must be three and only three, otherwise any warping of the framework will entirely spoil the figure of the surface.

6. BEARINGS OF STANDARDS OF LENGTH.

It is of the greatest importance that the standard measure of length, by which the national unit of length is defined, should not be exposed to strain.

The box in which the standard yard is kept in the Exchequer Chamber is provided with bearings, the positions of which have been arranged so that the bar may rest on them with as little strain throughout its substance as is consistent with the fact that it is a heavy body.

7. ON THE BEARINGS OF MOVABLE PARTS.

The most important kinds of motion with one degree of freedom are, (1) Rotation round an axis; (2) Motion of translation without rotation; and (3) Screw motion, in which a definite rotation about an axis corresponds to a definite motion of translation along that axis.

For one degree of freedom five solid bearings are required, the sixth condition being supplied by that part of the instrument which regulates the motion of the piece.

The construction of pieces capable of rotation about an axis is better understood than any other department of mechanism.

In astronomical instruments, four of the bearings are supplied by the two Y's on which the cylindrical end-pieces of the axle rest, and the fifth by the longitudinal pressure of a bearing against one end of the axle, or a shoulder formed upon it. The weight of the instrument is generally sufficient to keep it in contact with its bearings; but when the weight is so great that the pressure on the bearings is likely to injure them, the greater part of the weight is supported by auxiliary bearings, the pressure of which is regulated by counterpoises or springs, leaving only a moderate pressure to be borne by the true bearings.

8. Translation.

Motion of translation in a fixed direction, without rotation.

This kind of motion is required for pieces which slide along straight fixed pieces, as the verniers and microscopes of measuring apparatus, such as cathetometers and micrometers, the slide-rests of lathes, the pistons of steam-engines and pumps, &c.

When a tripod stand is to have a motion of this kind in a horizontal plane, two of its feet may be made to slide in a V groove, while the third rests on the horizontal plane.

When a cylindrical rod is to have a longitudinal motion, it must be made to bear against two fixed Y's, and must be prevented from rotating on its axis by a bearing, connected either with the cylinder or the fixed piece, which slides on a surface whose plane passes through the axis of the cylinder.

When, as in cathetometers and other measuring apparatus, a piece has to slide along a bar, the five bearings of the piece may be arranged so that three of them form a triangle on one face of the bar, while the two others rest against an adjacent face of the bar, the line joining these two being in the direction of motion. These bearings may be kept tight, without the possibility of jamming, by means of spring bearings against the other sides of the bar.

9. Parallel Motion by Linkwork.

In all these methods of guiding a piece by sliding contact, there is a considerable waste of energy by friction. In many cases, however, this is of little moment, compared with the errors depending on the necessary imperfection of the guiding surfaces, arising not only from original defects of workmanship but from straining and wearing during use.

It is true that great advances have been made, and notably by Sir J. Whitworth, in the art of forming truly plane and cylindric surfaces; but even these are liable to become altered, not only by wear but by strain and by inequalities of temperature, so that it is never safe to depend upon the perfect accuracy of the fitting of a large bearing surface, except when the pressure is very great.

In linkwork, on the other hand, the relative motion of any two pieces at their mutual bearing is one of pure rotation about a well-turned axle. The extent of the sliding surfaces is thus reduced to a minimum, so that less power is lost by friction, and the workmanship of such bearings can be brought much nearer to perfection than that of any other kind of fittings. Hence, in all prime movers and other machines, in which waste of power by friction is to be avoided, and even in those in which great accuracy is required, it is desirable, if it is possible, to guide the motion by linkwork.

The so-called "Parallel Motion" invented by James Watt was the first attempt to guide a motion of translation by means of linkwork; but though the motion as thus guided is very nearly rectilinear, it is not exactly so. Various other contrivances have been invented since the time of Watt, as, for instance, that fitted to the engines of the *Gorgon* by Mr Seaward; but all of them involved either a deviation from true rectilinear motion, or a sliding contact on a plane surface, and it was generally supposed by mathematicians that a true rectilinear motion, guided by pure linkwork, was a geometrical impossibility.

It was in the year 1864 that M. Peaucellier published his invention of an exact parallel motion by pure linkwork, and thus opened up the path to a very great extension of the science of mechanism, and its practical applications. The linkwork motions constructed by M. Garcia, Mr Penrose, and others, and the extensions of the theory of linkwork by Sylvester, Hart, and Kempe, are now well known, but they could not be fully described within our present limits.

10. Screw Motion.

The adjustments of instruments are to a great extent made by means of screws. In the case of levelling screws, which bear the weight of an instrument, the thread of the screw is always in contact with its proper bearing in the nut; but in micrometer screws it is necessary to secure this contact by means of a spring. This spring is sometimes made to bear against the end of the screw, or a shoulder turned upon it; but this arrangement causes a variable pressure as the screw moves forward. A much better arrangement is to make the spring bear, not against the screw itself, but against a nut which is free to move on the screw, but which is prevented from turning round by a proper bearing. This movable nut always remains at the same distance from the fixed one, so that the pressure of the spring remains constant. This is the arrangement of the micrometer screws in Sir W. Thomson's electrometers.

11. On Contrivances for securing Freedom of Motion.

In many instruments there is a movable part or indicator, the position or motion of which is to be observed in order to deduce therefrom some conclusion with respect to the force which acts upon it. This force may be the weight of a body, or an attractive or repulsive force of any kind; but, besides the force we are investigating, the resistance called Friction is always acting as a disturbing force.

If the magnitude and direction of the force of friction were at all times accurately known, this would be of less consequence; but the amount of friction is liable to sudden alterations, owing to causes which we can often neither suspect nor detect, so that the only way in which we can make any approach to accuracy is by diminishing as much as possible the effect of friction. The modes by which this is effected are of two kinds. Whenever there is sliding contact, there is friction; and wherever there is complete freedom of motion there must be sliding contact; but by making the extent of the sliding motion small compared with the motion of the indicating part, we may reduce the effect of friction to a very small part of the whole effect.

This is done in rotating parts by diminishing the size of the axle, and by supporting it on friction-wheels; and in toothed wheels by keeping the bearings of the teeth as near as possible to the line of centres, or more perfectly by cutting the teeth obliquely, as in Hooke's teeth.* A compass needle is balanced on a fine point, and the extent of the bearing is so small that a very small force applied to either end of the needle is sufficient to turn it round.

In all these instances the effect of friction is reduced by diminishing the extent of the sliding motion.

In balances and other levers the bearing of the lever is in the form of a prism, called a knife-edge, having an angle of about 120°; the edge of this

* Communicated to the Royal Society in 1666. See Willis's *Principles of Mechanism*, 1870, p. 53.

prism is accurately ground to a straight line, and rests on a plane horizontal surface of agate.

The relative motion in this case is one of rolling contact.

In another class of instruments sliding and rolling are entirely done away with, and sufficient freedom of motion is secured by the pliability of certain solid parts.

Thus many pendulums are hung, not on knife-edges, but on pieces of watch-spring, and torsion balances are suspended by metallic wires or by silk fibres. The motion of the piece is then affected by the elastic force of the suspension apparatus, but this force is much more regular in its action than friction, and its effects can be accurately taken account of, and a proper correction applied to the observed result.

12. The Torsion Rod, or Balance of Torsion.

The balance of torsion has been of the greatest benefit to modern science in the measurement of small forces. The first instrument of the kind was that constructed by the Rev. John Michell, formerly Woodwardian Professor of Geology at Cambridge, in order to observe the effect of the attraction of a pair of large lead balls on a pair of smaller balls hung from the extremities of the rod of the balance. Michell, however, died before he had opportunity to make the experiment, and his apparatus came into the hands of Professor F. J. H. Wollaston, and was transmitted by him to Henry Cavendish. Cavendish greatly improved the apparatus,* and successfully measured the attraction of the balls, and thus determined the density of the earth.†

The experiment has since been repeated by Reich and Baily. In the meantime, however, independently of Michell, and before Cavendish had actually used the instrument, Coulomb‡ had invented a torsion balance, by which he established the laws of the attraction and repulsion of electrified and magnetic bodies.

---

* Cavendish's apparatus now belongs to the Royal Institution.

† *Philosophical Transactions,* 1798.

‡ *Mém. de l'Academie,* 1784, &c.

13. Bifilar Suspension.

The elastic force of torsion of a wire, though much more regular than the force of friction, is subject to alterations arising from hitherto unknown causes, but probably depending on facts in the previous history of the wire, such as its having been subjected to twists and other strains before it was hung up. Hence it is sometimes better to employ another mode of suspension, in which the force of restitution depends principally on the weight of the suspended parts.

The body is suspended by two wires or fibres, which are close together and nearly vertical, and are so connected by a pulley that their tensions are equal. The body is in equilibrium when the two fibres are in the same plane. When the body is turned about a vertical axis, the tension of the fibres produces a force tending to turn the body back towards its position of equilibrium; and this force is very regular in its action, and may be accurately determined by proper experiments.

This arrangement, which is called the Bifilar suspension, was invented by Gauss and Weber for their magnetic apparatus. It was afterwards used by Baily in his experiments on the attraction of balls.

14. Methods of Reading.

The observed position of the indicating part of an instrument is recorded as the "Reading." To ascertain the position of the indicating part of the instrument various methods have been adopted. The commonest method is to make the indicating part in the form of a light needle, the point of which moves near a graduated circle. The position of the needle is estimated by observing the position of its point with respect to the divisions of the scale. By giving the needle two points at opposite extremities of a diameter, and observing the position of both points, we may eliminate the errors arising from the want of coincidence between the centre of the graduated circle and the axis of motion of the needle.

This is the method adopted in ordinary magnetic compasses. As it is necessary for freedom of motion that the point of the needle should not be in actual contact with the graduated limb, the reading will be affected by any change in the position of the eye of the observer. The error thus introduced is called the error of Parallax. In some instruments, therefore, the observation is made through an eye-hole in a definite position. A better plan, however, is to place a plane mirror under the needle, and in taking the reading to place the eye so that the needle appears to cover its own reflexion in the mirror.

15. Spiegel-Ablesung, or Mirror-Reading.

A still more accurate method is that invented by Poggendorff, and used by Gauss and Weber in their magnetic observations. A small plane mirror is attached to the indicating piece, so as to turn with it about its axis, which we may suppose vertical. A divided scale is placed so as to be perpendicular to this axis, and so that a normal to the scale at its middle point passes through the axis. The image of this scale by reflexion in the mirror is observed by means of a telescope having a vertical wire in the plane of distinct vision. As the indicating piece turns about its axis, the image of the scale passes across the field of view of the telescope, and the coincidence of the image of any division of the scale with the vertical wire of the telescope may be observed.

The error of parallax is entirely got rid of by this method, for the two optical images whose relative position is observed are in the same plane.

Another method of using the mirror is to reverse the direction of the rays of light by removing the eye-piece of the telescope, and putting the flame of a lamp in its place. The light emerging from the object-glass falls on the mirror, and is reflected so as to form on the scale a somewhat confused image of the flame, with a distinct image of the vertical wire crossing it. The reading is made by observing the position on the scale of the image of the vertical wire. In many instruments the telescope is dispensed with, and the mirror is a concave one, as in Thomson's reflecting galvanometer.

Some German writers distinguish this method of using the mirror and scale with a lamp as the *objective* method, the method in which the observer looks through the telescope being called the *subjective* method. The objective method is the only one adapted for the photographic registration of the readings.

16. Ramsden's Ghost.

To ascertain the exact position of an instrument with respect to a plumb-line without touching the line, Ramsden fixed a convex lens to a part of his

65—2

instrument, and placed a wire so that when the instrument was in its proper position the image of the plumb-line formed by the lens exactly coincided with the fixed wire. By moving the instrument till this coincidence was observed, the instrument was adjusted to its proper position. This contrivance was long known as "Ramsden's Ghost." It is, in fact, a simple form of the reading microscope; and there is no better method of ascertaining that a delicately-suspended object is exactly in its proper place.

17. COLLIMATING TELESCOPE.

If two telescopes are made to face one another, and if the cross-wires of the first, as seen through the second, appear to coincide with the cross-wires of the second, the optic axes of the two instruments are parallel. This mode of ascertaining parallelism is used in practical astronomy, and is called the method of collimating telescopes, or of collimators.

It is also used in the Kew portable magnetometer. The magnet is hollow, and carries a lens at one end and a scale at the other, at the principal focus of the lens. The magnet is thus a collimating telescope, and is observed by means of a telescope mounted on a divided circle. The disadvantage of this method is, that when the magnet is deflected, the scale soon passes out of the field of view, and the observer has to shift his telescope, in order to get a new reading.

18. THREE CLASSES OF READINGS.

We may, in fact, arrange instruments in three classes, according to the method of reading them.

In the self-recording class the observer leaves the instrument to itself, and examines the record at his own convenience.

In those which depend on eye observations alone, the observer must be there to look at the indicator of the instrument, but he does not touch it.

In the third class, which depend on eye and hand, the observer, before taking the reading, must make some adjustment of the instrument.

19. FUNCTIONS OF INSTRUMENTS.

The foregoing remarks apply to the constituent parts of instruments, without reference to the special department of science to which they belong.

The classification of special instruments will be best understood if we arrange those belonging to each department of science according to their respective functions; some of these functions having instruments corresponding to them in several departments of science, while others are peculiar to one department.

All the physical sciences relate to the passage of energy, under its various forms, from one body to another; but Optics and Acoustics are often represented as relating to the sensations of sight and hearing. These two sciences, in fact, have a physiological as well as a physical aspect, and therefore some parts of them have less analogy with the purely dynamical sciences.

The most important functions belonging to instruments, or elements of instruments, are as follows :—

1. The Source of energy. The energy involved in the phenomenon we are studying is not, of course, produced from nothing, but it enters the apparatus at a particular place, which we may call the Source.
2. The channels or distributors of energy, which carry it to the places where it is required to do work.
3. The restraints, which prevent it from doing work when it is not required.
4. The reservoirs in which energy is stored up till it is required.
5. Apparatus for allowing superfluous energy to escape.
6. Regulators for equalising the rate at which work is done.
7. Indicators, or movable pieces, which are acted on by the forces under investigation.
8. Fixed scales on which the position of the indicator is read off.

Thus in solid machinery we have—

1. Prime movers.
2. Trains of mechanism.
3. Fixed framework.
4. Fly-wheels, springs, weights raised.
5. Friction breaks.
6. Governors, pendulums, balance springs in watches.
7. Dynamometers, Strophometers, Watt's indicator, chronographs, &c.
8. Scales for these indicators. Standards of length and mass. Astronomical standard of time.

For the phenomena depending on fluid pressure we have—

1. Pumps, condensing and rarifying syringes, Örsted's Piezometer, Andrews's apparatus for high pressure.
2. Pipes and tubes.
3. Packing, washers, caoutchouc tubes, paraffin joints; fusion and other methods of making joints tight.
4. Air chambers, water reservoirs, vacuum chambers.
5. Safety valves.
6. Governors by Siemens and others, Cavaillé-Col's regulator for organ blast.
7. Pressure-gauges, barometers, manometers, sphygmographs, &c.; areometers, and specific gravity bottles; current meters, gas meters.
8. Scales for these gauges.

For thermal phenomena—

1. Furnaces, blow-pipe flames, freezing mixtures, solar and electric heat.
2. Hot water pipes, copper conductors.
3. Non-conducting packing, cements, clothing, &c.; steam-jackets, and ice-jackets.
4. Regenerators, heaters, &c.
5. Condensers and safety valves.
6. Thermostats, (1) by regulation of gas; (2) by boiling a liquid of known composition.
7. Thermometers. Pyrometers, Thermoelectric Pile, Siemens' resistance thermometer; Calorimeters.
8. Standard temperatures: as those of melting ice, boiling water, &c.

For electric phenomena—

1. Electric machines, frictional machine, electrophorus, Holtz' machine; voltaic batteries, thermo-electric batteries, magneto-electric machines.
2. Wires and other metallic conductors; armatures of magnets.
3. Insulators.
4. Leyden jars and other "condensers;" secondary batteries or cells of polarization; magnets, and electro-magnets.
5. Rheostats, lightning conductors, &c.
6. Guthrie's voltastat, regulators of electric lamps, &c.

7. Electroscopes and electrometers, Coulomb's torsion balance, voltameters, galvanometers and electrodynamometers, magnetometers.

8. Standards of resistance, capacity, electro-motive force, &c., as the Ohm, the microfarad, L. Clark's voltaic constant cell.

From the physical, as distinguished from the physiological point of view, the science of Acoustics relates to the excitement of vibrations and the propagation of waves in solids, liquids, and gases, and that of Optics to the excitement of vibrations, and the propagation of radiation, in the luminiferous medium.

From the physiological point of view, only those waves in ordinary matter are considered which excite in us the sensation of Sound, though waves which do not excite this sensation can be detected and studied by appropriate methods.

In the physiological treatment of Optics, only those radiations are considered which excite in us the sensation of Light, though other radiations can be detected and studied by their thermal, chemical, and even mechanical effects.

VIBRATIONS AND WAVES.

PHYSICAL ASPECT OF ACOUSTICS.

1. Sources. Vibrations of various bodies.
   Air—Organ pipes, resonators and other wind instruments.
   Reed instruments.
   The Siren.

Strings . . .	Harp, &c.
Membranes . . .	Drum, &c.
Plates . . .	Gong, &c.
Rods . . .	Tuning-fork, &c.

2. Distributors. Air . . Speaking tubes, stethoscopes, &c.
   Wood, . Sounding rods.
   Metal, . Wires.

3. Pugging of floors, &c.

4. Reservoirs. Resonators, Organ Pipes, Sounding-boards.

5. Dampers of pianofortes.

6. Regulators. Organ Swell.

7. Detectors, the ear; Sensitive Flames, Membranes, Phonautographs, &c.

8. Tuning-forks, pitch-pipes, and musical scales.

HEARING.

PHYSIOLOGICAL ASPECT OF ACOUSTICS.

Apparatus for determining the conditions—

1. Of the audibility of sounds.
2. Of the perception of the distinction of sounds.
3. Of the harmony or discord of simultaneous sounds.
4. Of the melodious succession of sounds.
5. Of the timbre of sounds, and of the distinction of vowel sounds.
6. Of the time required for the perception of the sensation of sound.

RADIATION.

PHYSICAL ASPECT OF OPTICS.

1. Sources of Radiation. Heated bodies, solid, liquid, and gaseous.
   Solid. Heated by a blow-pipe as in the oxy-hydrogen limelight.
   Heated by their own combustion, as in the magnesium light and glowing coals.
   Heated by an electric current, as the carbon electrodes of the electric lamp.
   Heated by concentrated radiation from other sources, as in the phenomenon called Calescence.
   Liquid, as in hot fused metals and other bodies.
   Gaseous. Heated by their own combustion, as in flames.
   Heated by a Bunsen burner, as the sodium light.
   Heated by the voltaic arc.
   Heated by the induction spark.
2. Distributors. Burning mirrors and lenses, condensing lenses for solar microscopes, magic lanterns, &c., lighthouse apparatus; telescopes, microscopes, &c.
3. Selectors. Absorbing media and coloured bodies in general, prisms and spectroscopes, ruled gratings, &c. : tourmalines, Nicol's prisms, and other polarizers.

4. Phosphorescent, fluorescent, and calescent bodies.
5. Opaque screens, diaphragms, and slits.
6. Regulators. The iris of the eye.
7. Photometers, photographic apparatus, actinometer, thermopile, Bunsen and Roscoe's photometer, selenium photometer, Crookes' radiometer, and other instruments.
8. Fraunhofer's lines of reference, and maps of the spectrum. Standard sperm candle, burning 120 grains of sperm per hour.

SIGHT.

PHYSIOLOGICAL ASPECT OF OPTICS.

Apparatus for determining the conditions of—

1. The visibility of objects, with respect to size, illumination, &c.
2. The perception of the distinction of objects.
3. The perception of colour, as depending on the composition of the light coming from the object.

Apparatus for comparing the intensity of luminous impressions, as depending on the intensity of the exciting cause and on the time during which it has acted, and for tracing the course of the development of a luminous impression from its first excitation to its final decay and extinction.

Ophthalmometers, for measuring the dimensions of the eye and determining its motions; and for ascertaining the two limits of distinct vision.

Ophthalmoscopes, for illuminating and observing the interior of the eye.

BIOLOGICAL APPARATUS.

1. For measuring the ingesta, egesta, and weight of living beings.
2. For testing the strength of animals and measuring the work done by them.
3. For measuring the heat which they generate.
4. For determining the conditions of fatigue of muscles.
5. For investigating the phenomena of the propagation of impulses through the nerves, and of the excitement of muscular action.

6. For tracing and registering the rhythmic action of the circulatory and respiratory operations—cardiographs, sphygmographs, stethoscopes, &c.

7. Marey's apparatus for registering the paces of men, horses, &c., and the actions of birds and insects during flight.

8. Instruments for illuminating and rendering visible parts within the living body—ophthalmoscopes, laryngoscopes, &c.—and arrangements for transmitting light through parts of the living body.

9. Instruments for varying the electrical state of the body—induction coils, &c.

10. Instruments for determining the electric state of living organs—galvanometers with proper electrodes, electrometers, &c.

LXXIX. *Instruments connected with Fluids.*

IN countries where the fertility of the soil is capable of being greatly increased by artificial irrigation, the attention of all ingenious persons is naturally directed to devising means whereby the labour of raising water may be diminished. Hence we find that in China and in India, but especially in Egypt, great progress was made in the art of producing and guiding the motion of water.

The first pump worked by a piston of which we have any account seems to be that invented by Ctesibius of Alexandria, about 130 B.C.

The construction of this pump, as described by Vitruvius, resembles that of the modern fire-engine. It had two barrels, which discharged the water alternately into a closed vessel, the upper part of which contained air. This air-chamber acted as a reservoir of energy, and equalised the pressure under which the water was emitted from the discharge pipe.

Hero, a scholar of Ctesibius, invented a number of ingenious machines. He delighted in curious combinations of siphons, by which fountains were made to play under unusual circumstances. We should call such machines toys, but though to us they have no longer any scientific value, we must regard them as among the first instances of apparatus constructed not in order to minister directly to man's necessities or luxuries, but to excite or to satisfy his curiosity with respect to the more unusual phenomena of nature.

From the time of Ctesibius and Hero to that of Galileo (1600) pumps were constructed chiefly for useful, as distinguished from scientific, purposes, and considerable skill was developed in the art of forming the barrel and piston so as to work with a certain degree of accuracy.

Galileo shewed that the reason why water ascends in a sucking pump is not that Nature abhors a vacuum, but that the pressure of the atmosphere acts on the free surface of the water, and that this pressure will force the

66—2

water only to a height of 34 feet; for when this height is reached, the water rises no further, and this shews either that the pressure of the atmosphere is balanced by that of the column of water, or else that Nature has become reconciled to a vacuum.

From this time the production of a vacuum became the scientific object aimed at by a great number of inventors. Torricelli, the pupil of Galileo, in 1642, made the greatest step in this direction, by filling with mercury a tube closed at one end and then inverting the tube with its open end in a vessel of mercury. If the tube was long enough the mercury fell, leaving an empty space at the top of the tube. The vacuum obtained by filling a vessel with mercury and removing the mercury without admitting any other matter is hence called the Torricellian vacuum. Torricelli, therefore, gave us at once the mercury-pump and the barometer, though the subsequent history of these two instruments is very different.

A little before 1654 Otto Von Guericke, of Magdeburg, first applied the principle of the common pump to the production of a vacuum. The fitting of the pistons of the pumps of those days, however, though sufficiently water-tight, was by no means air-tight. He therefore began by filling a vessel with water and then removing the water by a water-pump. In his experiments he met with many failures, but he continued to improve his apparatus till he could not only exhibit most of the phenomena now shewn in exhausted receivers, but till he had discovered the reason of the imperfection of the vacuum when water was used to keep the pump air-tight.

"In the year 1658 Hooke finished an air-pump for Boyle, in whose laboratory he was an assistant; it was more convenient than Guericke's, but the vacuum was not so perfect; yet Boyle's numerous and judicious experiments gave to the exhausted receiver of the air-pump the name of the Boylean vacuum, by which it was long known in the greatest part of Europe. Hooke's air-pump had two barrels, and with some improvements by Hauksbee it remained in use until the introduction of Smeaton's pump, which, however, has not wholly superseded it*."

The history of the air-pump after this time relates chiefly to the contrivances for insuring the working of the valves when the pressure of the remaining air is no longer sufficient to effect it, and to methods of rendering

---

* Thomas Young's *Lectures on Nat. Phil.* (1807). Lecture xxx.

the working parts air-tight without introducing substances the vapour of which would continue to fill the otherwise empty space.

There is one form of air-pump, however, which we must notice, as in it all packing and lubricating substances are dispensed with. This is the air-pump constructed by M. Deleuil, of Paris*, in which the pistons are solid cylinders of considerable length, and are not made to fit tightly in the barrels of the pump. No grease or lubricating substance is used, and the pistons work easily and smoothly in the barrels. The space between the piston and the barrel contains air, but the internal friction of the air in this narrow space is so great that the rate at which it leaks into the exhausted part of the barrel is not comparable with the rate at which the pump is exhausting the air from the receiver. It has been shewn by the present writer that the internal friction of air is not diminished even when its density is greatly reduced. It is for this reason that this pump works satisfactorily up to a very considerable degree of exhaustion.

Pumps of the type already described are still used for the rapid exhaustion of large vessels, but since the physical properties of extremely rarefied gases have become the object of scientific research, the original method of Torricelli has been revived under various forms.

Thus we have one set of mercury-pumps in which the mercury is alternately made to fill a certain chamber completely and to drive out whatever gas may be in it, and then to flow back leaving the chamber empty.

Sprengel's pump is the type of the other set. The working part is a vertical glass tube longer than the height of the barometer, and so narrow that a small portion of mercury placed in it is compelled by its surface-tension to fill the whole section of the tube. The mercury is introduced into this tube from a funnel at the top through a small India-rubber tube regulated by a pinch-cock, so that the mercury falls in small detached portions, each of which drives before it any air which may be in the tube till it escapes into a mercury-trough, into which the bottom of the tube dips.

The vessel to be exhausted is connected to a tube which enters at the side of the vertical tube near the top. Any air or other gas which may be in the vessel expands into the vacuum left in the vertical tube between successive portions of the falling mercury, and is driven down the tube by the next portion of mercury into the mercury-trough, where it may be collected.

* *Comptes Rendus*, t. lx. p. 571. Carl's Repertorium.

As long as the rarefaction of the air is not very great the quantity of air which is included between successive portions of mercury is sufficient to act as a sort of buffer, but as the rarefaction increases the portions of mercury come together more abruptly, and produce a sound which becomes sharper as the vacuum becomes more perfect.

After the mercury-pump has been in action for some hours the quantity of matter remaining in the vessel is very small. If the tubes have been joined by means of caoutchouc connections there is a trace of gaseous matter emitted by the caoutchouc. It is therefore necessary, when a very perfect vacuum is desired, to make all the joints "hermetical" by fusing the glass. Still, however, there remains a trace of matter. The vapour of mercury is, of course, present, and the sides of the glass vessel retain water very strongly, and part with it very slowly, when all other matter is removed.

By passing a little strong sulphuric acid through the pump along with the mercury, vapours both of mercury and of water may be in great measure removed.

MM. Kundt and Warburg have got rid of an additional quantity of water-substance by heating the vessel to as high a temperature as the glass will bear while the pump was kept in action.

A method which has been long in use for getting a good vacuum is to place in the vessel a stick of fused potash, and to fill it with carbonic acid, and, after exhausting as much as possible, to seal up the vessel. The potash is then heated, and when it has again become cold, most of the remaining carbonic acid has combined with the potash.

Another method, employed by Professor Dewar, is to place in a compartment of the vessel a piece of freshly heated cocoa-nut charcoal, and to heat it strongly during the last stages of the exhaustion by the mercury-pump. The vessel is then sealed up, and as the charcoal cools it absorbs a very large proportion of the gases remaining in the vessel.

The interior of the vessel, after exhaustion, is found to be possessed of very remarkable properties.

One of these properties furnishes a convenient test of the completeness of the exhaustion. The vessel is provided with two metallic electrodes, the ends of which within the vessel are within a quarter of an inch of each other. When the vessel contains air at the ordinary pressure a considerable electromotive force is required to produce an electric discharge across this interval. As the exhaustion proceeds the resistance to the discharge diminishes till the pressure is reduced to that of about a millimetre of mercury. When, however, the exhaustion is made very perfect the discharge cannot be made to take place between the electrodes within the vessel, and the spark actually passes through several inches of air outside the vessel before it will leap the small interval in the empty vessel. A vacuum, therefore, is a stronger insulator of electricity than any other medium.

MM. Kundt and Warburg have experimented on the viscosity of the air remaining after exhaustion, and on its conductivity for heat. They find that it is only when the exhaustion is very perfect that the viscosity and conductivity begin sensibly to diminish, even when the stratum of the medium experimented on is very thin.

But the most remarkable phenomenon hitherto observed in an empty space is that discovered by Mr Crookes. A light body is delicately suspended in an exhausted vessel, and the radiation from the sun, or any other source of light or heat, is allowed to fall on it. The body is apparently repelled and moves away from the side on which the radiation falls.

This action is the more energetic the greater the perfection of the vacuum. When the pressure amounts to a millimetre or two the repulsion becomes very feeble, and at greater pressures an apparent attraction takes place, which, however, cannot be compared either in regularity or in intensity to the repulsion in a good vacuum.

From these instances we may see what important scientific discoveries may be looked for in consequence of improvements in the methods of obtaining a vacuum.

[From *Nature*, Vol. XIV.]

LXXX. *Whewell's Writings and Correspondence.*

WE frequently hear the complaint that as the boundaries of science are widened its cultivators become less of philosophers and more of specialists, each confining himself with increasing exclusiveness to the area with which he is familiar. This is probably an inevitable result of the development of science, which has made it impossible for any one man to acquire a thorough knowledge of the whole, while each of its sub-divisions is now large enough to afford occupation for the useful work of a lifetime. The ablest cultivators of science are agreed that the student, in order to make the most of his powers, should ascertain in what field of science these powers are most available, and that he should then confine his investigations to this field, making use of other parts of science only in so far as they bear upon his special subject.

Accordingly we find that Dr Whewell, in his article in the *Encyclopædia Metropolitana*, on "Archimedes and Greek Mathematics," says of Eratosthenes, who, like himself, was philologer, geometer, astronomer, poet, and antiquary: "It is seldom that one person attempts to master so many subjects without incurring the charge and perhaps the danger of being superficial."

It is probably on account of the number and diversity of the kinds of intellectual work in which Dr Whewell attained eminence that his name is most widely known. Of his actual performances the "History" and the "Philosophy of the Inductive Sciences" are the most characteristic, and this because his practical acquaintance with a certain part of his great subject enabled him the better to deal with those parts which he had studied only in books, and to describe their relations in a more intelligent manner than those authors who have devoted themselves entirely to the general aspect of human knowledge without being actual workers in any particular department of it.

But the chief characteristic of Dr Whewell's intellectual life seems to have been the energy and perseverance with which he pursued the development of each of the great ideas which had in the course of his life presented itself to him. Of these ideas some might be greater than others, but all were large.

The special pursuit, therefore, to which he devoted himself was the elaboration and the expression of the ideas appropriate to different branches of knowledge. The discovery of a new fact, the invention of a theory, the solution of a problem, the filling up of a gap in an existing science, were interesting to him not so much for their own sake as additions to the general stock of knowledge, as for their illustrative value as characteristic instances of the processes by which all human knowledge is developed.

To watch the first germ of an appropriate idea as it was developed either in his own mind or in the writings of the founders of the sciences, to frame appropriate and scientific words in which the idea might be expressed, and then to construct a treatise in which the idea should be largely developed and the appropriate words copiously exemplified—such seems to have been the natural channel of his intellectual activity in whatever direction it overflowed. When any of his great works had reached this stage he prepared himself for some other labour, and if new editions of his work were called for, the alterations which he introduced often rather tended to destroy than to complete the unity of the original plan.

Mr Todhunter has given us an exhaustive account of Dr Whewell's writings and scientific work, and in this we may easily trace the leading ideas which he successively inculcated as a writer. We can only share Mr Todhunter's regret that it is only as a writer that he appears in this book, and it is to be hoped that the promised account of his complete life as a man may enable us to form a fuller conception of the individuality and unity of his character, which it is hard to gather from the multifarious collection of his books.

Dr Whewell first appears before us as the author of a long series of text-books on Mechanics. His position as a tutor of his College, and the interest which he took in University education, may have induced him to spend more time in the composition of elementary treatises than would otherwise have been congenial to him, but in the prefaces to the different editions, as well as in the introductory chapters of each treatise, he shews that sense of the intellectual and educational value of the study of first principles which distinguishes all his writings. It is manifest from his other writings, that the composition of these text-books, involving as it did a thorough study of the fundamental science of Dynamics, was a most appropriate training for his subsequent labours in the survey of the sciences in their widest extent.

"It has always appeared to me," says Mr Todhunter, "that Mr Whewell would have been of great benefit to students if he had undertaken a critical revision of the technical language of Mechanics. This language was formed to a great extent by the early writers at an epoch when the subject was imperfectly understood, and many terms were used without well-defined meanings. Gradually the language has been improved, but it is still open to objection."

In after years, when his authority in scientific terminology was widely recognised, we find Faraday, Lyell, and others applying to him for appropriate expressions for the subject-matter of their discoveries, and receiving in reply systems of scientific terms which have not only held their place in technical treatises, but are gradually becoming familiar to the ordinary reader.

"Is it not true," Dr Whewell asks in his Address to the Geological Society, "in our science as in all others, that a technical phraseology is real wealth, because it puts in our hands a vast treasure of foregone generalisations?"

Perhaps, however, he felt it less difficult to induce scientific men to adopt a new term for a new idea than to persuade the students and teachers of a University to alter the phraseology of a time-honoured study.

But even in the elementary treatment of Dynamics, if we compare the text-books of different dates, we cannot fail to recognise a marked progress. Those by Dr Whewell were far in advance of any former text-books as regards logical coherence and scientific accuracy, and if many of those which have been published since have fallen behind in these respects, most of them have introduced some slight improvement in terminology which has not been allowed to be lost.

Dr Whewell's opinion with respect to the evidence of the fundamental doctrines of mechanics is repeatedly inculcated in his writings. He considered that experiment was necessary in order to suggest these truths to the mind, but that the doctrine when once fairly set before the mind is apprehended by it as strictly true, the accuracy of the doctrine being in no way dependent on the accuracy of observation of the result of the experiment.

He therefore regarded experiments on the laws of motion as illustrative experiments, meant to make us familiar with the general aspect of certain phenomena, and not as experiments of research from which the results are to be deduced by careful measurement and calculation.

Thus experiments on the fall of bodies may be regarded as experiments of research into the laws of gravity. We find by careful measurements of times and distances that the intensity of the force of gravity is the same whatever be the motion of the body on which it acts. We also ascertain the direction and magnitude of this force on different bodies and in different places. All this can only be done by careful measurement, and the results are affected by all the errors of observation to which we are liable.

The same experiments may be also taken as illustrations of the laws of motion. The performance of the experiments tends to make us familiar with these laws, and to impress them on our minds. But the laws of motion cannot be proved to be accurate by a comparison of the observations which we make, for it is only by taking the laws for granted that we have any basis for our calculations. We may ascertain, no doubt, by experiment, that the acceleration of a body acted on by gravity is the same whatever be the motion of that body, but this does not prove that a constant force produces a constant acceleration, but only that gravity is a force, the intensity of which does not depend on the velocity of the body on which it acts.

The truth of Dr Whewell's principle is curiously illustrated by a case in which he persistently contradicted it. In a paper communicated to the Philosophical Society of Cambridge, and reprinted at the end of his *Philosophy of the Inductive Sciences*, Dr Whewell conceived that he had proved, *à priori*, that all matter must be heavy. He was well acquainted with the history of the establishment of the law of gravitation, and knew that it was only by careful experiments and observations that Newton ascertained that the effect of gravitation on two equal masses is the same whatever be the chemical nature of the bodies, but in spite of this he maintained that it is contrary not only to observation but to reason, that any body should be repelled instead of attracted by another, whereas it is a matter of daily experience, that any two bodies when they are brought near enough, repel each other.

The fact seems to be that, finding the word weight employed in ordinary language to denote the quantity of matter in a body, though in scientific language it denotes the tendency of that body to move downwards, and at the same time supposing that the word mass in its scientific sense was not yet sufficiently established to be used without danger in ordinary language, Dr Whewell endeavoured to make the word weight carry the meaning of the word mass. Thus he tells us that " the weight of the whole compound must be equal to the weights of the separate elements."

On this Mr Todhunter very properly observes:

"Of course there is no practical uncertainty as to this principle; but Dr Whewell seems to allow his readers to imagine that it is of the same nature as the axiom that 'two straight lines cannot inclose a space.' There is, however, a wide difference between them, depending on a fact which Dr Whewell has himself recognised in another place (see vol. I. p. 224). The truth is, that *strictly* speaking the weight of the whole compound is not equal to the weight of the separate elements; for the weight depends upon the position of the compound particles, and in general by altering the position of the particles, the resultant effect which we call weight is altered, though it may be to an inappreciable extent."

It is evident that what Dr Whewell should have said was: "The mass of the whole compound must be equal to the sum of the masses of the separate elements." This statement all would admit to be strictly true, and yet not a single experiment has ever been made in order to verify it. All chemical measurements are made by comparing the weights of bodies, and not by comparing the forces required to produce given changes of motion in the bodies; and as we have just been reminded by Mr Todhunter, the method of comparing quantities of matter by weighing them is not strictly correct.

Thus, then, we are led by experiments which are not only liable to error, but which are to a certain extent erroneous in principle, to a statement which is universally acknowledged to be strictly true. Our conviction of its truth must therefore rest on some deeper foundation than the experiments which suggested it to our minds. The belief in and the search for such foundations is, I think, the most characteristic feature of all Dr Whewell's work.

[From the *British Association Report*, 1876.]

LXXXI. *On Ohm's Law.*

THE service rendered to electrical science by Dr G. S. Ohm can only be rightly estimated when we compare the language of those writers on electricity who were ignorant of Ohm's law with that of those who have understood and adopted it.

By the former, electric currents are said to vary as regards both their "quantity" and their "intensity," two qualities the nature of which was very imperfectly explained by tedious and vague expositions.

In the writings of the latter, after the elementary terms "Electromotive Force," "Strength of Current," and "Electric Resistance" have been defined, the whole doctrine of currents becomes distinct and plain.

Ohm's law may be stated thus:

The electromotive force which must act on a homogeneous conductor in order to maintain a given steady current through it, is numerically equal to the product of the resistance of the conductor into the strength of the current through it. If, therefore, we define the resistance of a conductor as the ratio of the numerical value of the electromotive force to the numerical value of the strength of the current, Ohm's law asserts that this ratio is constant— that is, that its value does not depend on that of the electromotive force or of the current.

The resistance, as thus defined, depends on the nature and form of the conductor, and on its physical condition as regards temperature, strain, &c.; but if Ohm's law is true, it does not depend on the strength of the current.

Ohm's law must, at least at present, be considered a purely empirical one. No attempt to deduce it from pure dynamical principles has as yet been successful; indeed Weber's latest theoretical investigations* on this subject have led him to suspect that Ohm's law is not true, but that, as the electro-

* *Pogg. Ann.* 1875.

motive force increases without limit, the current increases slower and slower, so that the "resistance," as defined by Ohm's law, would increase with the electromotive force. On the other hand, Schuster* has described experiments which lead him to suspect a deviation from Ohm's law, but in the opposite direction, the resistance being smaller for great currents than for small ones.

Lorentz†, of Leyden, has also proposed a theory according to which Ohm's law would cease to be true for rapidly varying currents. The rapidity of variation, however, which, as he supposes, would cause a perceptible deviation from Ohm's law, must be comparable with the rate of vibration of light, so that it would be impossible by any experiments other than optical ones to test this theory.

The conduction of electricity through a resisting medium is a process in which part of the energy of an electric current, flowing in a definite direction, is spent in imparting to the molecules of the medium that irregular agitation which we call heat. To calculate from any hypothesis as to the molecular constitution of the medium at what rate the energy of a given current would be spent in this way, would require a far more perfect knowledge of the dynamical theory of bodies than we at present possess. It is only by experiment that we can ascertain the laws of processes of which we do not understand the dynamical theory.

We therefore define, as the resistance of a conductor, the ratio of the numerical value of the electromotive force to that of the strength of the current, and we have to determine by experiment the conditions which affect the value of this ratio.

Thus if E denotes the electromotive force acting from one electrode of the conductor to the other, C the strength of the current flowing through the conductor, and R the resistance of the current, we have *by definition*

$$R = \frac{E}{C};$$

and if H is the heat generated in the time t, and if J is the dynamical equivalent of heat, we have by the principle of conservation of energy

$$JH = ECt = RC^2t = \frac{E^2}{R}\,t.$$

---

* *Report of British Association*, 1874.
† *Over de Terugkaatsing en Breking van het Licht.* Leiden, 1875.

The quantity R, which we have defined as the resistance of the conductor, can be determined only by experiment. Its value may therefore, for any thing we know, be affected by each and all of the physical conditions to which the conductor may be subjected.

Thus we know that the resistance is altered by a change of the temperature of the conductor, and also by mechanical strain and by magnetization.

The question which is now before us is whether the current itself is or is not one of the physical conditions which may affect the value of the resistance; and this question we cannot decide except by experiment.

Let us therefore assume that the resistance of a given conductor at a given temperature is a function of the strength of the current. Since the resistance of a conductor is the same for the same current in whichever direction the current flows, the expression for the resistance can contain only even powers of the current.

Let us suppose, therefore, that the resistance of a conductor of unit length and unit section is

$$r\left(1 + sc^2 + s'c^4 + \&c.\right),$$

where r is the resistance corresponding to an infinitely small current, and c is the current through unit of section, and s, s', &c. are small coefficients to be determined by experiment. The coefficients s, s', &c. represent the deviations from Ohm's law. If Ohm's law is accurate, these coefficients are zero; also if e is the electromotive force acting on this conductor,

$$e = rc\left(1 + sc^2 + s'c^4 + \&c.\right).$$

Now let us consider another conductor of the same substance whose length is L and whose section is A; then if E is the electromotive force on this conductor, and e that on unit of length,

$$E = Le.$$

Also if C be the current through the conductor and c that through unit of area,

$$C = Ac.$$

Hence the resistance of this conductor will be

$$R = \frac{E}{C} = \frac{Lr}{A}\left(1 + \frac{sC^2}{A^2} + \frac{s'C^4}{A^4} + \&c.\right).$$

Now let us suppose two conductors of the same material but of different dimensions arranged in series and the same current passed through both:

$$R_1 = \frac{L_1 r}{A_1}\left(1 + \frac{sC^2}{A_1^2} + \&c.\right),$$

$$R_2 = \frac{L_2 r}{A_2}\left(1 + \frac{sC^2}{A_2^2} + \&c.\right),$$

where the suffixes indicate to which conductor the quantities belong. The ratio of the resistances is

$$\frac{R_1}{R_2} = \frac{L_1}{A_1}\frac{A_2}{L_2}\left\{1 + sC^2\left(\frac{1}{A_1^2} - \frac{1}{A_2^2}\right) + \&c.\right\}.$$

Hence if Ohm's law is not true, and if, therefore, any of the quantities s, s', &c. have sensible values, the ratio of the resistances will depend on the strength of the current.

Now the ratio of two resistances may be measured with great accuracy by means of Wheatstone's bridge.

We therefore arrange the bridge so that one branch of the current passes first through a very fine wire a few centimetres long, and then through a much longer and thicker wire of about the same resistance. The other branch of the current passes through two resistances, equal to each other, but much greater than the other two, so that very little of the heating-effect of the current is produced in these auxiliary resistances.

The bridge is formed by connecting the electrodes of a galvanometer, one to the junction of the fine wire and the thick one, and the other to a point between the other two resistances.

We have thus a method of testing the ratio of the resistances of the fine wire to that of the thick one; and by passing through the bridge sometimes a feeble current and sometimes a powerful one, we might ascertain if the ratio differed in the two cases.

But this direct method is rendered useless by the fact that the current generates heat, which raises the temperature of both wires, but that of the thin wire most rapidly; and this makes it impossible to compare the effects of strong and weak currents through a conductor at one and the same temperature.

It is also useless to work with weak currents, as the effect depends on the square of the current, and is so small as to have escaped observation in all ordinary experiments.

Again, if we were to use a single very strong current acting for a very short time, we should not be able to observe the galvanometer in a satisfactory manner. In fact it was found in the experiment that currents which lasted for a sixtieth part of a second produced a heating-effect which interfered with the measurements. The experiment was therefore arranged so that a strong current and a weak one were passed through the bridge alternately; and when the bridge was so arranged that the galvanometer was in equilibrium, the direction of the weaker current was reversed. If Ohm's law were not true, the condition of equilibrium for strong currents would be different from that for weaker ones, so that when the weak currents were reversed there would be no longer equilibrium. Since, in point of fact, the reversal of the weaker currents did not affect the equilibrium, it follows that the bridge was in equilibrium for the weaker currents as well as for the stronger ones, and therefore the conditions were the same for both, and Ohm's law is true to within the limits of error of the experiment*.

[* The mode in which the actual strength of the currents was measured and the limits of error ascertained are described in the Report which follows the above by Mr Chrystal, now Professor of Mathematics at Edinburgh University.]

[From *Nature*, Vol. xiv.]

LXXXII. *On the protection of buildings from lightning.*

MOST of those who have given directions for the construction of lightning-conductors have paid great attention to the upper and lower extremities of the conductor. They recommend that the upper extremity of the conductor should extend somewhat above the highest part of the building to be protected, and that it should terminate in a sharp point, and that the lower extremity should be carried as far as possible into the conducting strata of the ground, so as to "make" what telegraph engineers call "a good earth."

The electrical effect of such an arrangement is to *tap*, as it were, the gathering charge by facilitating a quiet discharge between the atmospheric accumulation and the earth. The erection of the conductor will cause a somewhat greater number of discharges to occur at the place than would have occurred if it had not been erected; but each of these discharges will be smaller than those which would have occurred without the conductor. It is probable, also, that fewer discharges will occur in the region surrounding the conductor.

It appears to me that these arrangements are calculated rather for the benefit of the surrounding country and for the relief of clouds labouring under an accumulation of electricity, than for the protection of the building on which the conductor is erected.

What we really wish is to prevent the possibility of an electric discharge taking place within a certain region, say in the inside of a gunpowder manufactory. If this is clearly laid down as our object, the method of securing it is equally clear.

An electric discharge cannot occur between two bodies, unless the difference of their potentials is sufficiently great, compared with the distance between them. If, therefore, we can keep the potentials of all bodies within a certain region equal, or nearly equal, no discharge will take place between them. We may secure this by connecting all these bodies by means of good conductors, such as copper wire ropes, but it is not necessary to do so, for it may be shewn by experiment that if every part of the surface surrounding a certain region is at the same potential, every point within that region must be at the same potential, provided no charged body is placed within the region.

It would, therefore, be sufficient to surround our powder-mill with a conducting material, to sheathe its roof, walls, and ground-floor with thick sheet copper, and then no electrical effect could occur within it on account of any thunderstorm outside. There would be no need of any earth connection. We might even place a layer of asphalte between the copper floor and the ground, so as to insulate the building. If the mill were then struck with lightning, it would remain charged for some time, and a person standing on the ground outside and touching the wall might receive a shock, but no electrical effect would be perceived inside, even on the most delicate electrometer. The potential of everything inside with respect to the earth would be suddenly raised or lowered as the case might be, but electric potential is not a physical condition, but only a mathematical conception, so that no physical effect would be perceived.

It is therefore not necessary to connect large masses of metal such as engines, tanks, &c., to the walls, if they are entirely within the building. If, however, any conductor, such as a telegraph wire or a metallic supply-pipe for water or gas comes into the building from without, the potential of this conductor may be different from that of the building, unless it is connected with the conducting-shell of the building. Hence the water or gas supply pipes, if any enter the building, must be connected to the system of lightning conductors, and since to connect a telegraph wire with the conductor would render the telegraph useless, no telegraph from without should be allowed to enter a powder-mill, though there may be electric bells and other telegraphic apparatus entirely within the building.

I have supposed the powder-mill to be entirely sheathed in thick sheet copper. This, however, is by no means necessary in order to prevent any sensible electrical effect taking place within it, supposing it struck by lightning. It is quite sufficient to inclose the building with a network of a good conducting substance. For instance, if a copper wire, say No. 4, B.W.G. (0·238 inches diameter), were carried round the foundation of the house, up each of the corners and gables and along the ridges, this would probably be a sufficient

68—2

protection for an ordinary building against any thunderstorm in this climate. The copper wire may be built into the wall to prevent theft, but should be connected to any outside metal such as lead or zinc on the roof, and to metal rain-water pipes. In the case of a powder-mill it might be advisable to make the network closer by carrying one or two additional wires over the roof and down the walls to the wire at the foundation. If there are water or gas-pipes which enter the building from without, these must be connected with the system of conducting-wires, but if there are no such metallic connections with distant points, it is not necessary to take any pains to facilitate the escape of the electricity into the earth.

Still less is it advisable to erect a tall conductor with a sharp point in order to relieve the thunder-clouds of their charge.

It is hardly necessary to add, that it is not advisable, during a thunder-storm, to stand on the roof of a house so protected, or to stand on the ground outside and lean against the wall.

[From the *Encyclopædia Britannica*.]

LXXXIII.　*Capillary Action.*

A TUBE, the bore of which is so small that it will only admit a hair (*capilla*), is called a capillary tube. When such a tube of glass, open at both ends, is placed vertically with its lower end immersed in water, the water is observed to rise in the tube, and to stand within the tube at a higher level than the water outside. The action between the capillary tube and the water has been called Capillary Action, and the name has been extended to many other phenomena which have been found to depend on properties of liquids and solids similar to those which cause water to rise in capillary tubes.

The forces which are concerned in these phenomena are those which act between neighbouring parts of the same substance, and which are called forces of cohesion, and those which act between portions of matter of different kinds, which are called forces of adhesion. These forces are quite insensible between two portions of matter separated by any distance which we can directly measure. It is only when the distance becomes exceedingly small that these forces become perceptible. Quincke* has made experiments to determine the greatest distance at which the effect of these forces is sensible, and he finds for various substances distances about the twenty-thousandth part of a millimetre.

Poggendorff† tells us that Leonardo da Vinci‡ must be considered as the discoverer of capillary phenomena.

The first accurate observations of the capillary action of tubes and glass plates were made by Hauksbee§. He ascribes the action to an attraction between the glass and the liquid. He observed that the effect was the same in thick tubes as in thin, and concluded that only those particles of the glass which are very near the surface have any influence on the phenomenon.

---

* *Pogg. Ann.*, cxxxvii. p. 402.　　　† *Pogg. Ann.*, ci. p. 551.　　　‡ Died 1519.
§ *Physico-Mechanical Experiments*, London, 1709, pp. 139—169; and *Phil. Trans.*, 1711 and 1712.

Dr Jurin* shewed that the height at which the liquid is suspended depends on the section of the tube at the surface of the liquid, and is independent of the form of the lower part of the tube. He considered that the suspension of the liquid is due to "the attraction of the periphery or section of the surface of the tube to which the upper surface of the water is contiguous and coheres." From this he shews that the rise of the liquid in tubes of the same substance is inversely proportional to their radii.

Newton devotes the 31st query in the last edition of his *Opticks* to molecular forces, and instances several examples of the cohesion of liquids, such as the suspension of mercury in a barometer tube at more than double the height at which it usually stands. This arises from its adhesion to the tube, and the upper part of the mercury sustains a considerable tension, or negative pressure, without the separation of its parts. He considers the capillary phenomena to be of the same kind, but his explanation is not sufficiently explicit with respect to the nature and the limits of the action of the attractive force.

It is to be observed that, while these early speculators ascribe the phenomena to attraction, they do not distinctly assert that this attraction is sensible only at insensible distances, and that for all distances which we can directly measure the force is altogether insensible. The idea of such forces, however, had been distinctly formed by Newton, who gave the first example of the calculation of the effect of such forces in his theorem on the alteration of the path of a light-corpuscle when it enters or leaves a dense body.

Clairaut† appears to have been the first to shew the necessity of taking account of the attraction between the parts of the fluid itself in order to explain the phenomena. He does not, however, recognise the fact that the distance at which the attraction is sensible is not only small but altogether insensible.

Segner‡ introduced the very important idea of the surface-tension of liquids, which he ascribed to attractive forces, the sphere of whose action is so small "ut nullo adhuc sensu percipi potuerit." In attempting to calculate the effect of this surface-tension in determining the form of a drop of the liquid, Segner took account of the curvature of a meridian section of the drop, but neglected the effect of the curvature in a plane at right angles to this section.

---

* *Phil. Trans.*, 1718, No. 355, p. 739, and 1719, No. 363, p. 1083.

† Clairaut, *Théorie de la Figure de la Terre*, Paris, 1808, pp. 105, 128.

‡ Segner, *Comment. Soc. Reg. Götting.*, I. (1751), p. 301.

But the idea of surface-tension introduced by Segner had a most important effect on the subsequent development of the theory. We may regard it as a physical fact established by experiment in the same way as the laws of the elasticity of solid bodies. We may investigate the forces which act between finite portions of a liquid in the same way as we investigate the forces which act between finite portions of a solid. The experiments on solids lead to certain laws of elasticity expressed in terms of coefficients, the values of which can be determined only by experiments on each particular substance. Various attempts have also been made to deduce these laws from particular hypotheses as to the action between the molecules of the elastic substance. We may therefore regard the theory of elasticity as consisting of two parts. The first part establishes the laws of the elasticity of a finite portion of the solid subjected to a homogeneous strain, and deduces from these laws the equations of the equilibrium and motion of a body subjected to any forces and displacements. The second part endeavours to deduce the facts of the elasticity of a finite portion of the substance from hypotheses as to the motion of its constituent molecules and the forces acting between them.

In like manner we may by experiment ascertain the general fact that the surface of a liquid is in a state of tension similar to that of a membrane stretched equally in all directions, and prove that this tension depends only on the nature and temperature of the liquid and not on its form, and from this as a secondary physical principle we may deduce all the phenomena of capillary action. This is one step of the investigation. The next step is to deduce this surface-tension from an hypothesis as to the molecular constitution of the liquid and of the bodies that surround it. The scientific importance of this step is to be measured by the degree of insight which it affords or promises into the molecular constitution of real bodies by the suggestion of experiments by which we may discriminate between rival molecular theories.

In 1756 Leidenfrost * shewed that a soap-bubble tends to contract, so that if the tube with which it was blown is left open the bubble will diminish in size and will expel through the tube the air which it contains. He attributed this force, however, not to any general property of the surfaces of liquids, but to the fatty part of the soap which he supposed to separate itself from

---

* *De aquæ communis nonnullis qualitatibus tractatus*, Duisburg.

the other constituents of the solution, and to form a thin skin on the outer face of the bubble.

In 1787 Monge * asserted that "by supposing the adherence of the particles of a fluid to have a sensible effect only at the surface itself and in the direction of the surface it would be easy to determine the curvature of the surfaces of fluids in the neighbourhood of the solid boundaries which contain them; that these surfaces would be *lineariæ* of which the tension, constant in all directions, would be everywhere equal to the adherence of two particles, and the phenomena of capillary tubes would then present nothing which could not be determined by analysis." He applied this principle of surface-tension to the explanation of the apparent attractions and repulsions between bodies floating on a liquid.

In 1802 Leslie † gave the first correct explanation of the rise of a liquid in a tube by considering the effect of the attraction of the solid on the very thin stratum of the liquid in contact with it. He does not, like the earlier speculators, suppose this attraction to act in an upward direction so as to support the fluid directly. He shews that the attraction is everywhere normal to the surface of the solid. The direct effect of the attraction is to increase the pressure of the stratum of the fluid in contact with the solid, so as to make it greater than the pressure in the interior of the fluid. The result of this pressure if unopposed is to cause this stratum to spread itself over the surface of the solid as a drop of water is observed to do when placed on a clean horizontal glass plate, and this even when gravity opposes the action, as when the drop is placed on the under surface of the plate. Hence a glass tube plunged into water would become wet all over were it not that the ascending liquid film carries up a quantity of other liquid which coheres to it, so that when it has ascended to a certain height the weight of the column balances the force by which the film spreads itself over the glass. This explanation of the action of the solid is equivalent to that by which Gauss afterwards supplied the defect of the theory of Laplace, except that, not being expressed in terms of mathematical symbols, it does not indicate the mathematical relation between the attraction of individual particles and the final result. Leslie's theory was afterwards treated according to Laplace's mathematical methods by James Ivory in the article on capillary action, under the

* *Mémoires de l'Acad. des Sciences,* 1787, p. 506.
† *Philosophical Magazine,* 1802, Vol. xiv. p. 193.

heading "Fluids, Elevation of," in the supplement to the fourth edition of the *Encyclopædia Britannica*, published in 1819.

In 1804 Thomas Young* founded the theory of capillary phenomena on the principle of surface-tension. He also observed the constancy of the angle of contact of a liquid surface with a solid, and shewed how from these two principles to deduce the phenomena of capillary action. His essay contains the solution of a great number of cases, including most of those afterwards solved by Laplace, but his methods of demonstration, though always correct, and often extremely elegant, are sometimes rendered obscure by his scrupulous avoidance of mathematical symbols. Having applied the secondary principle of surface-tension to the various particular cases of capillary action, Young proceeds to deduce this surface-tension from ulterior principles. He supposes the particles to act on one another with two different kinds of forces, one of which, the attractive force of cohesion, extends to particles at a greater distance than those to which the repulsive force is confined. He further supposes that the attractive force is constant throughout the minute distance to which it extends, but that the repulsive force increases rapidly as the distance diminishes. He thus shews that at a curved part of the surface, a superficial particle would be urged towards the centre of curvature of the surface, and he gives reasons for concluding that this force is proportional to the sum of the curvatures of the surface in two normal planes at right angles to each other.

The subject was next taken up by Laplace†. His results are in many respects identical with those of Young, but his methods of arriving at them are very different, being conducted entirely by mathematical calculations. The form into which he has thrown his investigation seems to have deterred many able physicists from the inquiry into the ulterior cause of capillary phenomena, and induced them to rest content with deriving them from the fact of surface-tension. But for those who wish to study the molecular constitution of bodies it is necessary to study the effect of forces which are sensible only at insensible distances; and Laplace has furnished us with an example of the method of this study which has never been surpassed. Laplace investigates the force acting on the fluid contained in an infinitely slender canal normal to the surface of the fluid arising from the attraction of the parts of the fluid out-

---

* Essay on the "Cohesion of Fluids," *Philosophical Transactions*, 1805, p. 65.

† *Mecanique Celeste*, supplement to the tenth book, published in 1806.

side the canal. He thus finds for the pressure at a point in the interior of the fluid an expression of the form

$$p = K + \frac{1}{2} H \left(\frac{1}{R} + \frac{1}{R'} \right),$$

where K is a constant pressure, probably very large, which, however, does not influence capillary phenomena, and therefore cannot be determined from observation of such phenomena; H is another constant on which all capillary phenomena depend; and R and R' are the radii of curvature of any two normal sections of the surface at right angles to each other.

In the first part of our own investigation we shall adhere to the symbols used by Laplace, as we shall find that an accurate knowledge of the physical interpretation of these symbols is necessary for the further investigation of the subject. In the *Supplement to the Theory of Capillary Action*, Laplace deduces the equation of the surface of the fluid from the condition that the resultant force on a particle at the surface must be normal to the surface. His explanation, however, of the rise of a liquid in a tube is based on the *assumption* of the constancy of the angle of contact for the same solid and fluid, and of this he has nowhere given a satisfactory proof. In this supplement Laplace gives many important applications of the theory, and compares the results with the experiments of Gay-Lussac.

The next great step in the treatment of the subject was made by Gauss*. The principle which he adopts is that of virtual velocities, a principle which under his hands was gradually transforming itself into what is now known as the principle of the conservation of energy. Instead of calculating the direction and magnitude of the resultant force on each particle arising from the action of neighbouring particles, he forms a single expression which is the aggregate of all the potentials arising from the mutual action between pairs of particles. This expression has been called the force-function. With its sign reversed it is now called the potential energy of the system. It consists of three parts, the first depending on the action of gravity, the second on the mutual action between the particles of the fluid, and the third on the action between the particles of the fluid and the particles of a solid or fluid in contact with it.

The condition of equilibrium is that this expression (which we may for the sake of distinctness call the potential energy) shall be a minimum. This

---

* *Principia generalia Theoriæ Figuræ Fluidorum in statu Æquilibrii* (Göttingen, 1830), or *Werke*, v. 29 (Göttingen, 1867).

condition when worked out gives not only the equation of the free surface in the form already established by Laplace, but the conditions of the angle of contact of this surface with the surface of a solid.

Gauss thus supplied the principal defect in the great work of Laplace. He also pointed out more distinctly the nature of the assumptions which we must make with respect to the law of action of the particles in order to be consistent with observed phenomena. He did not, however, enter into the explanation of particular phenomena, as this had been done already by Laplace. He points out, however, to physicists the advantages of the method of Segner and Gay-Lussac, afterwards carried out by Quincke, of measuring the dimensions of large drops of mercury on a horizontal or slightly concave surface, and those of large bubbles of air in transparent liquids resting against the under side of a horizontal plate of a substance wetted by the liquid.

In 1831 Poisson published his *Nouvelle Théorie de l'Action Capillaire.* He maintains that there is a rapid variation of density near the surface of a liquid, and he gives very strong reasons, which have been only strengthened by subsequent discoveries, for believing that this is the case. He then proceeds to an investigation of the equilibrium of a fluid on the hypothesis of uniform density, and he arrives at the conclusion that on this hypothesis none of the observed capillary phenomena would take place, and that, therefore, Laplace's theory, in which the density is supposed uniform, is not only insufficient but erroneous. In particular he maintains that the constant pressure K, which occurs in Laplace's theory, and which on that theory is very large, must be in point of fact very small, but the equation of equilibrium from which he concludes this is itself defective. Laplace assumes that the liquid has uniform density, and that the attraction of its molecules extends to a finite though insensible distance. On these assumptions his results are certainly right, and are confirmed by the independent method of Gauss, so that the objections raised against them by Poisson fall to the ground. But whether the assumption of uniform density be physically correct is a very different question, and Poisson has done good service to science in shewing how to carry on the investigation on the hypothesis that the density very near the surface is different from that in the interior of the fluid.

The result, however, of Poisson's investigation is practically equivalent to that already obtained by Laplace. In both theories the equation of the liquid surface is the same, involving a constant H, which can be determined only by experiment. The only difference is in the manner in which this quantity H depends on the law of the molecular forces and the law of density near the surface of the fluid, and as these laws are unknown to us we cannot obtain any test to discriminate between the two theories.

We have now described the principal forms of the theory of capillary action during its earlier development. In more recent times the method of Gauss has been modified so as to take account of the variation of density near the surface, and its language has been translated in terms of the modern doctrine of the conservation of energy [*].

M. Plateau [†], who has himself made the most elaborate study of the phenomena of surface-tension, has adopted the following method of getting rid of the effects of gravity: He forms a mixture of alcohol and water of the same density as olive oil. He then introduces a quantity of oil into the mixture. It assumes the form of a sphere under the action of surface-tension alone. He then, by means of rings of iron-wire, disks, and other contrivances, alters the form of certain parts of the surface of the oil. The free portions of the surface then assume new forms depending on the equilibrium of surface-tension. In this way he has produced a great many of the forms of equilibrium of a liquid under the action of surface-tension alone, and compared them with the results of mathematical investigation. He has also greatly facilitated the study of liquid films by shewing how to form a liquid, the films of which will last for twelve or even for twenty-four hours. The debt which science owes to M. Plateau is not diminished by the fact that, while investigating these beautiful phenomena, he has never himself seen them. He lost his sight long ago in the pursuit of science, and has ever since been obliged to depend on the eyes and the hands of others.

M. Van der Mensbrugghe [‡] has also devised a great number of beautiful illustrations of the phenomena of surface-tension, and has shewn their connection with the experiments of Mr Tomlinson on the figures formed by oils dropped on the clean surface of water.

---

[*] See Prof. Betti, *Teoria della Capillarità: Nuovo Cimento*, 1867 ; a memoir by M. Stahl, "Ueber einige Punckte in der Theorie der Capillarerscheinungen," *Pogg. Ann.*, cxxxix. p. 239 (1870) ; and M. Van der Waal's *Over de Continuiteit van den Gas- en Vloeistoftoestand*. The student will find a good account of the subject from a mathematical point of view in Professor Challis's " Report on the Theory of Capillary Attraction," *Brit. Ass. Report*, iv. p. 253 (1834).

[†] M. Plateau, *Statique experimentale et théorique des liquides*.

[‡] *Mém. de l'Acad. Roy. de Belgique*, xxxvii. (1873).

M. Dupré in his 5th, 6th, and 7th Memoirs on the Mechanical Theory of Heat (*Ann. de Chimie et de Physique*, 1866 to 1868) has done much towards applying the principles of thermodynamics to capillary phenomena, and the experiments of his son are exceedingly ingenious and well devised, tracing the influence of surface-tension in a great number of very different circumstances, and deducing from independent methods the numerical value of the surface-tension. The experimental evidence which M. Dupré has obtained bearing on the molecular structure of liquids must be very valuable, even if many of our present opinions on this subject should turn out to be erroneous.

M. Quincke* has made a most elaborate series of experiments on the tension of the surfaces separating one liquid from another and from air.

M. Lüdtge† has experimented on liquid films, and has shewn how a film of a liquid of high surface-tension is replaced by a film of lower surface-tension. He has also experimented on the effects of the thickness of the film, and has come to the conclusion that the thinner a film is, the greater is its tension. This result, however, has been tested by M. Van der Mensbrugghe, who finds that the tension is the same for the same liquid whatever be the thickness, as long as the film does not burst. The phenomena of very thin liquid films deserve the most careful study, for it is in this way that we are most likely to obtain evidence by which we may test the theories of the molecular structure of liquids.

Sir W. Thomson‡ has investigated the effect of the curvature of the surface of a liquid on the thermal equilibrium between the liquid and the vapour in contact with it. He has also calculated the effect of surface-tension on the propagation of waves on the surface of a liquid, and has determined the minimum velocity of a wave, and the velocity of the wind when it is just sufficient to disturb the surface of still water§.

Theory of Capillary Action.

When two different fluids are placed in contact, they may either diffuse into each other or remain separate. In some cases diffusion takes place to a limited extent, after which the resulting mixtures do not mix with each other.

---

* *Pogg. Ann.*, cxxxix. (1870), p. 1.   † *Ibid.* p. 620.
‡ *Proceedings R. S.*, Edinburgh, February 7, 1870.
§ *Philosophical Magazine*, November, 1871.

The same substance may be able to exist in two different states at the same temperature and pressure, as when water and its saturated vapour are contained in the same vessel. The conditions under which the thermal and mechanical equilibrium of two fluids, two mixtures, or the same substance in two physical states in contact with each other, is possible belong to thermodynamics. All that we have to observe at present is that, in the cases in which the fluids do not mix of themselves, the potential energy of the system must be greater when the fluids are mixed than when they are separate.

It is found by experiment that it is only very close to the bounding surface of a liquid that the forces arising from the mutual action of its parts have any resultant effect on one of its particles. The experiments of Quincke and others seem to shew that the extreme range of the forces which produce capillary action lies between a thousandth and a twenty thousandth part of a millimetre.

We shall use the symbol ϵ to denote this extreme range, beyond which the action of these forces may be regarded as insensible. If χ denotes the potential energy of unit of mass of the substance, we may treat χ as sensibly constant except within a distance ϵ of the bounding surface of the fluid. In the interior of the fluid it has the uniform value χ_0. In like manner the density, ρ, is sensibly equal to the constant quantity ρ_0, which is its value in the interior of the liquid, except within a distance ϵ of the bounding surface. Hence if V is the volume of a mass M of liquid bounded by a surface whose area is S, the integral

$$M = \iiint \rho\, dx dy dz \quad\dots\dots\dots\dots\dots\dots\dots\dots (1),$$

where the integration is to be extended throughout the volume V, may be divided into two parts by considering separately the thin shell or skin extending from the outer surface to a depth ϵ, within which the density and other properties of the liquid vary with the depth, and the interior portion of the liquid within which its properties are constant.

Since ϵ is a line of insensible magnitude compared with the dimensions of the mass of liquid and the principal radii of curvature of its surface, the volume of the shell whose surface is S and thickness ϵ will be $S\epsilon$, and that of the interior space will be $V - S\epsilon$.

If we suppose a normal ν less than ϵ to be drawn from the surface S into the liquid, we may divide the shell into elementary shells whose thickness is $d\nu$, in each of which the density and other properties of the liquid will be constant.

The volume of one of these shells will be $Sd\nu$. Its mass will be $S\rho d\nu$. The mass of the whole shell will therefore be $S\int_0^\epsilon \rho d\nu$, and that of the interior part of the liquid $(V - S\epsilon)\rho_0$. We thus find for the whole mass of the liquid

$$M = V\rho_0 - S\int_0^\epsilon (\rho_0 - \rho)\, d\nu \quad\dots\dots\dots\dots\dots (2).$$

To find the potential energy we have to integrate

$$E = \iiint \chi\rho\, dx\, dy\, dz \quad\dots\dots\dots\dots\dots (3).$$

Substituting $\chi\rho$ for ρ in the process we have just gone through, we find

$$E = V\chi_0\rho_0 - S\int_0^\epsilon (\chi_0\rho_0 - \chi\rho)\, d\nu \quad\dots\dots\dots\dots (4).$$

Multiplying equation (2) by χ_0, and subtracting it from (4),

$$E - M\chi_0 = \chi_0 S\int_0^\epsilon (\chi - \chi_0)\, \rho d\nu \quad\dots\dots\dots\dots (5).$$

In this expression M and χ_0 are both constant, so that the variation of the right hand side of the equation is the same as that of the energy E, and expresses that part of the energy which depends on the area of the bounding surface of the liquid. We may call this the surface energy.

The symbol χ expresses the energy of unit of mass of the liquid at a depth ν within the bounding surface. When the liquid is in contact with a rare medium, such as its own vapour or any other gas, χ is greater than χ_0, and the surface energy is positive. By the principle of the conservation of energy, any displacement of the liquid by which its energy is diminished will tend to take place of itself. Hence if the energy is the greater, the greater the area of the exposed surface, the liquid will tend to move in such a way as to diminish the area of the exposed surface, or in other words, the exposed surface will tend to diminish if it can do so consistently with the other conditions. This tendency of the surface to contract itself is called the surface-tension of liquids.

M. Dupré has described an arrangement by which the surface-tension of a liquid film may be illustrated.

A piece of sheet metal is cut out in the form AA (fig. 1). A very fine slip of metal is laid on it in the position BB, and the whole is dipped into

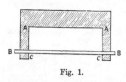

Fig. 1.

a solution of soap, or M. Plateau's glycerine mixture. When it is taken out the rectangle $AACC$ is filled up by a liquid film. This film, however, tends to contract on itself, and the loose strip of metal BB will, if it is let go, be drawn up towards AA, provided it is sufficiently light and smooth.

Let T be the surface-energy per unit of area; then the energy of a surface of area S will be ST. If, in the rectangle $AACC$, $AA = a$, and $CC = b$, its area is $S = ab$, and its energy Tab. Hence if F is the force by which the slip BB is pulled towards AA,

$$F = \frac{d}{db} Tab = Ta \dots\dots\dots\dots\dots\dots\dots\dots\dots\dots\dots(6),$$

or the force arising from the surface-tension acting on a length a of the strip is Ta, so that T represents the surface-tension acting transversely on every unit of length of the periphery of the liquid surface. Hence if we write

$$T = \int_0^\epsilon (\chi - \chi_0)\, \rho\, d\nu \dots\dots\dots\dots\dots\dots(7),$$

we may define T either as the surface-energy per unit of area, or as the surface-tension per unit of contour, for the numerical values of these two quantities are equal.

If the liquid is bounded by a dense substance, whether liquid or solid, the value of χ may be different from its value when the liquid has a free surface. If the liquid is in contact with another liquid, let us distinguish quantities belonging to the two liquids by suffixes. We shall then have

$$E_1 - M_1\chi_{01} = S \int_0^{\epsilon_1} (\chi_1 - \chi_{01})\, \rho_1\, d\nu_1 \dots\dots\dots\dots\dots(8),$$

$$E_2 - M_2\chi_{02} = S \int_0^{\epsilon_2} (\chi_2 - \chi_{02})\, \rho_2\, d\nu_2 \dots\dots\dots\dots\dots(9).$$

Adding these expressions, and dividing the second member by S, we obtain for the tension of the surface of contact of the two liquids

$$T_{1,2} = \int_0^{\epsilon_1} (\chi_1 - \chi_{01})\, \rho_1\, d\nu_1 + \int_0^{\epsilon_2} (\chi_2 - \chi_{02})\, \rho_2\, d\nu_2 \dots\dots\dots\dots(10).$$

If this quantity is positive, the surface of contact will tend to contract, and the liquids will remain distinct. If, however, it were negative, the displacement of the liquids which tends to enlarge the surface of contact would be aided by the molecular forces, so that the liquids, if not kept separate by gravity, would at length become thoroughly mixed. No instance, however, of a phenomenon of this kind has been discovered, for those liquids which mix of themselves do so by the process of diffusion, which is a molecular motion, and not by the spontaneous puckering and replication of the bounding surface, as would be the case if T were negative.

It is probable, however, that there are many cases in which the integral belonging to the less dense fluid is negative. If the denser body be solid we can often demonstrate this; for the liquid tends to spread itself over the surface of the solid, so as to increase the area of the surface of contact, even although in so doing it is obliged to increase the free surface in opposition to the surface-tension. Thus water spreads itself out on a clean surface of glass.

This shews that $\int_0^e (\chi - \chi_0) \rho d\nu$ must be negative for water in contact with glass.

On the Tension of Liquid Films.

The method already given for the investigation of the surface-tension of a liquid, all whose dimensions are sensible, fails in the case of a liquid film, such as a soap-bubble. In such a film it is possible that no part of the liquid may be so far from the surface as to have the potential and density corresponding to what we have called the interior of a liquid mass, and measurements of the tension of the film when drawn out to different degrees of thinness may possibly lead to an estimate of the range of the molecular forces, or at least of the depth within a liquid mass, at which its properties become sensibly uniform. We shall therefore indicate a method of investigating the tension of such films.

Let S be the area of the film, M its mass, and E its energy; σ the mass, and e the energy of unit of area; then

$$M = S\sigma \dots\dots\dots\dots\dots\dots\dots\dots\dots\dots\dots(11),$$
$$E = Se \dots\dots\dots\dots\dots\dots\dots\dots\dots\dots(12).$$

Let us now suppose that by some change in the form of the boundary of the film its area is changed from S to $S+dS$. If its tension is T the work required to effect this increase of surface will be TdS, and the energy of the film will be increased by this amount. Hence

$$TdS = dE$$
$$= Sde + edS \dotfill (13).$$

But since M is constant,

$$dM = Sd\sigma + \sigma dS = 0 \dotfill (14).$$

Eliminating dS from equations (13) and (14), and dividing by S, we find

$$T = e - \sigma \frac{de}{d\sigma} \dotfill (15).$$

In this expression σ denotes the mass of unit of area of the film, and e the energy of unit of area.

If we take the axis of z normal to either surface of the film, the radius of curvature of which we suppose to be very great compared with its thickness c, and if ρ is the density, and χ the energy of unit of mass at depth z, then

$$\sigma = \int_0^c \rho dz \dotfill (16),$$

and

$$e = \int_0^c \chi \rho dz \dotfill (17).$$

Both ρ and χ are functions of z, the values of which remain the same when $z - c$ is substituted for z. If the thickness of the film is greater than 2ϵ, there will be a stratum of thickness $c - 2\epsilon$ in the middle of the film, within which the values of ρ and χ will be ρ_0 and χ_0. In the two strata on either side of this the law, according to which ρ and χ depend on the depth, will be the same as in a liquid mass of large dimensions. Hence in this case

$$\sigma = (c - 2\epsilon)\rho_0 + 2\int_0^\epsilon \rho d\nu \dotfill (18),$$

$$e = (c - 2\epsilon)\chi_0\rho_0 + 2\int_0^\epsilon \chi\rho d\nu \dotfill (19),$$

$$\frac{d\sigma}{dc} = \rho_0, \quad \frac{de}{dc} = \chi_0\rho_0, \quad \therefore \frac{de}{d\sigma} = \chi_0,$$

$$T = 2\int_0^\epsilon \chi\rho\,d\nu - 2\chi_0\int_0^\epsilon \rho\,d\nu,$$

$$= 2\int_0^\epsilon (\chi - \chi_0)\,\rho\,d\nu \dots\dots\dots\dots\dots\dots\dots\dots\dots\dots\dots(20).$$

Hence the tension of a thick film is equal to the sum of the tensions of its two surfaces as already calculated (equation 7). On the hypothesis of uniform density we shall find that this is true for films whose thickness exceeds ϵ.

The symbol χ is defined as the energy of unit of mass of the substance. A knowledge of the absolute value of this energy is not required, since in every expression in which it occurs it is under the form $\chi - \chi_0$, that is to say, the difference between the energy in two different states. The only cases, however, in which we have experimental values of this quantity are when the substance is either liquid and surrounded by similar liquid, or gaseous and surrounded by similar gas. It is impossible to make direct measurements of the properties of particles of the substance within the insensible distance ϵ of the bounding surface.

When a liquid is in thermal and dynamical equilibrium with its vapour, then if ρ' and χ' are the values of ρ and χ for the vapour, and ρ_0 and χ_0 those for the liquid,

$$\chi' - \chi_0 = JL - p\left(\frac{1}{\rho'} - \frac{1}{\rho_0}\right) \dots\dots\dots\dots\dots\dots\dots (21),$$

where J is the dynamical equivalent of heat, L is the latent heat of unit of mass of the vapour, and p is the pressure. At points in the liquid very near its surface it is probable that χ is greater than χ_0, and at points in the gas very near the surface of the liquid it is probable that χ is less than χ', but this has not as yet been ascertained experimentally. We shall therefore endeavour to apply to this subject the methods used in Thermodynamics, and where these fail us we shall have recourse to the hypotheses of molecular physics.

70—2

We have next to determine the value of χ in terms of the action between one particle and another. Let us suppose that the force between two particles m and m' at the distance f is

$$F = mm'\left(\phi(f) + \frac{C}{f^2}\right) \quad\ldots\ldots\ldots\ldots\ldots\ldots\ldots\ldots(22),$$

being reckoned positive when the force is attractive. The actual force between the particles arises in part from their mutual gravitation, which is inversely as the square of the distance. This force is expressed by $mm'\dfrac{C}{f^2}$. It is easy to shew that a force subject to this law would not account for capillary action. We shall, therefore, in what follows, consider only that part of the force which depends on $\phi(f)$, where $\phi(f)$ is a function of f which is insensible for all sensible values of f, but which becomes sensible and even enormously great when f is exceedingly small.

If we next introduce a new function of f and write

$$\int_f^\infty \phi(f)\,df = \Pi(f) \quad\ldots\ldots\ldots\ldots\ldots\ldots\ldots (23),$$

then $mm'\Pi(f)$ will represent (1) the work done by the attractive force on the particle m, while it is brought from an infinite distance from m' to the distance f from m'; or (2) the attraction of a particle m on a narrow straight rod resolved in the direction of the length of the rod, one extremity of the rod being at a distance f from m, and the other at an infinite distance, the mass of unit of length of the rod being m'. The function $\Pi(f)$ is also insensible for sensible values of f, but for insensible values of f it may become sensible and even very great.

If we next write

$$\int_z^\infty f\Pi(f)\,df = \psi(z) \quad\ldots\ldots\ldots\ldots\ldots\ldots\ldots\ldots(24),$$

then $2\pi m\sigma\psi(z)$ will represent (1) the work done by the attractive force while a particle m is brought from an infinite distance to a distance z from an infinitely thin stratum of the substance whose mass per unit of area is σ; (2) the attraction of a particle m placed at a distance z from the plane surface of an infinite solid whose density is σ.

Let us examine the case in which the particle m is placed at a distance z from a curved stratum of the substance, whose principal radii of curvature are R_1 and R_2. Let P (fig. 2) be the particle and PB a normal to the surface. Let the plane of the paper be a normal section of the surface of the stratum at the point B, making an angle ω with the section whose radius of curvature is R_1. Then if O is the centre of curvature in the plane of the paper, and $BO = u$,

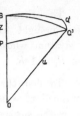

Fig. 2.

$$\frac{1}{u} = \frac{\cos^2 \omega}{R_1} + \frac{\sin^2 \omega}{R_2} \quad \dots \dots \dots \dots \dots \dots \dots (25),$$

Let $\qquad POQ = \theta, \quad PO = r, \quad PQ = f, \quad BP = z,$

$$f^2 = u^2 + r^2 - 2ur \cos \theta \quad \dots \dots \dots \dots \dots \dots (26).$$

The element of the stratum at Q may be expressed by

$$\sigma u^2 \sin \theta \, d\theta \, d\omega,$$

or expressing $d\theta$ in terms of df by (26),

$$\sigma \frac{u}{r} f \, df \, d\omega.$$

Multiplying this by m and by Πf, we obtain for the work done by the attraction of this element when m is brought from an infinite distance to P,

$$m\sigma \frac{u}{r} f \, \Pi \left(f \right) df \, d\omega.$$

Integrating with respect to f from $f = z$ to $f = a$, where a is a line very great compared with the extreme range of the molecular force, but very small compared with either of the radii of curvature, we obtain for the work

$$\int m\sigma \frac{u}{r} \{ \psi \left(z \right) - \psi \left(a \right) \} \, d\omega,$$

and since $\psi \left(a \right)$ is an insensible quantity we may omit it. We may also write

$$\frac{u}{r} = 1 + \frac{z}{u} + \&c.,$$

since z is very small compared with u, and expressing u in terms of ω by (25), we find

$$\int_0^{2\pi} m\sigma \psi \left(z \right) \left\{ 1 + z \left(\frac{\cos^2 \omega}{R_1} + \frac{\sin^2 \omega}{R_2} \right) \right\} \, d\omega = 2\pi m\sigma \psi \left(z \right) \left\{ 1 + \frac{1}{2} z \left(\frac{1}{R_1} + \frac{1}{R_2} \right) \right\}.$$

This then expresses the work done by the attractive forces when a particle m is brought from an infinite distance to the point P at a distance z from a stratum whose surface-density is σ, and whose principal radii of curvature are R_1 and R_2.

To find the work done when m is brought to the point P in the neighbourhood of a solid body, the density of which is a function of the depth ν below the surface, we have only to write instead of σ ρdz, and to integrate

$$2\pi m \int_z^\infty \rho\psi(z)\, dz + \pi m \left(\frac{1}{R_1} + \frac{1}{R_2}\right)\int_z^\infty \rho z\psi(z)\, dz,$$

where, in general, we must suppose ρ a function of z. This expression, when integrated, gives (1) the work done on a particle m while it is brought from an infinite distance to the point P, or (2) the attraction on a long slender column normal to the surface and terminating at P, the mass of unit of length of the column being m. In the form of the theory given by Laplace, the density of the liquid was supposed to be uniform. Hence if we write

$$K = 2\pi \int_0^\infty \psi(z)\, dz, \quad H = 2\pi \int_0^\infty z\psi(z)\, dz,$$

the pressure of a column *of the fluid itself* terminating at the surface will be

$$\rho^2 \left\{ K + \frac{1}{2} H \left(\frac{1}{R_1} + \frac{1}{R_2}\right) \right\},$$

and the work done by the attractive forces when a particle m is brought to the surface of the fluid from an infinite distance will be

$$m\rho \left\{ K + \frac{1}{2} H \left(\frac{1}{R_1} + \frac{1}{R_2}\right) \right\}.$$

If we write

$$\int_z^\infty \psi(z)\, dz = \theta(z),$$

then $2\pi m\rho\theta(z)$ will express the work done by the attractive forces, while a particle m is brought from an infinite distance to a distance z from the plane surface of a mass of the substance of density ρ and infinitely thick. The function $\theta(z)$ is insensible for all sensible values of z. For insensible values it may become sensible, but it must remain finite even when $z = 0$, in which case $\theta(0) = K$.

If χ' is the potential energy of unit of mass of the substance in vapour, then at a distance z from the plane surface of the liquid

$$\chi = \chi' - 2\pi\rho\theta(z).$$

At the surface

$$\chi = \chi' - 2\pi\rho\theta(0).$$

At a distance z within the surface

$$\chi = \chi' - 4\pi\rho\theta(0) + 2\pi\rho\theta(z).$$

If the liquid forms a stratum of thickness c, then

$$\chi = \chi' - 4\pi\rho\theta(0) + 2\pi\rho\theta(z) + 2\pi\rho\theta(z - c).$$

The surface-density of this stratum is $\sigma = c\rho$. The energy per unit of area is

$$e = \int_0^c \chi\rho\,dz,$$

$$= c\rho\{\chi' - 4\pi\rho\theta(0)\} + 2\pi\rho^2\int_0^c \theta(z)\,dz + 2\pi\rho^2\int_0^c \theta(c - z)\,dz.$$

Since the two sides of the stratum are similar the last two terms are equal, and

$$e = c\rho\{\chi' - 4\pi\rho\theta(0)\} + 4\pi\rho^2\int_0^c \theta(z)\,dz.$$

Differentiating with respect to c, we find

$$\frac{d\sigma}{dc} = \rho,$$

$$\frac{de}{dc} = \rho\{\chi' - 4\pi\rho\theta(0)\} + 4\pi\rho^2\theta(c).$$

Hence the surface-tension

$$T = e - \sigma\frac{de}{d\sigma},$$

$$= 4\pi\rho^2\left\{\int_0^c \theta(z)\,dz - c\theta(c)\right\}.$$

Integrating the first term within brackets by parts, it becomes

$$c\theta(c) - 0\theta(0) - \int_0^c z\frac{d\theta}{dz}\,dz.$$

Remembering that $\theta(0)$ is a finite quantity, and that $\dfrac{d\theta}{dz} = -\psi(z)$, we find

$$T = 4\pi\rho^2 \int_0^c z\psi(z)\,dz.$$

When c is greater than ϵ this is equivalent to $2H$ in the equation of Laplace. Hence the tension is the same for all films thicker than ϵ, the range of the molecular forces. For thinner films

$$\frac{dT}{dc} = 4\pi\rho^2 c\psi(c).$$

Hence if $\psi(c)$ is positive, the tension and the thickness will increase together. Now $2\pi m\rho\psi(c)$ represents the attraction between a particle m and the plane surface of an infinite mass of the liquid, when the distance of the particle outside the surface is c. Now, the force between the particle and the liquid is certainly, on the whole, attractive; but if between any two small values of c it should be repulsive, then for films whose thickness lies between these values the tension will increase as the thickness diminishes, but for all other cases the tension will diminish as the thickness diminishes.

We have given several examples in which the density is assumed to be uniform, because Poisson has asserted that capillary phenomena would not take place unless the density varied rapidly near the surface. In this assertion we think he was mathematically wrong, though in his own hypothesis that the density does actually vary, he was probably right. In fact, the quantity $4\pi\rho^2 K$, which we may call with Van der Waals the molecular pressure, is so great for most liquids (5000 atmospheres for water), that in the parts near the surface, where the molecular pressure varies rapidly, we may expect considerable variation of density, even when we take into account the smallness of the compressibility of liquids.

The pressure at any point of the liquid arises from two causes, the external pressure P to which the liquid is subjected, and the pressure arising from the mutual attraction of its molecules. If we suppose that the number of molecules within the range of the attraction of a given molecule is very large, the part of the pressure arising from attraction will be proportional to the square of the number of molecules in unit of volume, that is, to the square of the density. Hence we may write

$$p = P + A\rho^2 \quad\dotfill\quad (1),$$

where A is a constant. But by the equations of equilibrium of the liquid

$$dp = -\rho d\chi \dots\dots\dots\dots\dots\dots\dots (2).$$

Hence

$$-\rho d\chi = 2A\rho d\rho \dots\dots\dots\dots\dots\dots (3),$$

and

$$\chi' - \chi = 2A\rho - 2B \dots\dots\dots\dots\dots\dots (4),$$

where B is another constant.

Near the plane surface of a liquid we may assume ρ a function of z. We have then for the value of χ at the point where $z = c$,

$$\chi' - \chi = 2\pi \int_{c-\epsilon}^{c+\epsilon} \rho(z)\,\psi(z-c)\,dz \dots\dots\dots\dots\dots(5),$$

where ϵ is the range beyond which the attraction of a mass of liquid bounded by a plane surface becomes insensible. The value of χ depends, therefore, on those values only of ρ which correspond to strata for which z is nearly equal to c. We may, therefore, expand ρ in terms of $z - c$, or writing x for $z - c$,

$$\rho = \rho_c + x\left(\frac{d\rho}{dz}\right)_{(c)} + \frac{x^2}{2}\left(\frac{d^2\rho}{dz^2}\right)_{(c)} + \&c. \dots\dots\dots\dots\dots (6),$$

where the suffix (c) denotes that in the quantity to which it is applied after differentiation, z is to be made equal to c. We may now write

$$\chi' - \chi = 2\pi\rho_{(c)}\int_{-\epsilon}^{+\epsilon} \psi(x)\,dx + 2\pi\left(\frac{d\rho}{dz}\right)_{(c)}\int_{-\epsilon}^{+\epsilon} x\psi(x)\,dx$$

$$+ 2\pi\left(\frac{d^2\rho}{dz^2}\right)_{(c)}\frac{1}{2}\int x^2\psi(x)\,dx + \&c. \dots\dots\dots (7).$$

The function $\psi(x)$ has equal values for $+x$ and $-x$. Hence $\int_{-\epsilon}^{+\epsilon} x^n\psi(x)\,dx$ vanishes if n is odd.

But if we write

$$K = \pi\int_{-\epsilon}^{+\epsilon} \psi(x)\,dx, \quad L = \frac{1}{2}\pi\int_{-\epsilon}^{+\epsilon} x^2\psi(x)\,dx,$$

$$M = \frac{1}{1.2.3.4}\pi\int_{-\epsilon}^{+\epsilon} x^4\psi(x)\,dx, \&c.$$

$$\chi' - \chi = 2K\rho + 2L\frac{d^2\rho}{dz^2} + 2M\frac{d^4\rho}{dz^4} + \&c.$$

This is the expression for χ on the hypothesis that the value of ρ can be expanded in a series of powers of $z - c$ within the limits $z - \epsilon$ and $z + \epsilon$. It is only when the point P is within the distance ϵ of the surface of the liquid that this ceases to be possible.

If we now substitute for χ its value from equation (4), we obtain

$$2A\rho - 2B = 2K\rho + 2L\frac{d^2\rho}{dz^2} + 2M\frac{d^4\rho}{dz^4} + \&c.,$$

a linear differential equation in ρ, the solution of which is

$$\rho = \frac{B}{A-K} + C_1 e^{n_1 z} + C_2 e^{n_2 z} + C_3 e^{n_3 z} + C_4 e^{n_4 z},$$

where n_1, n_2, n_3, n_4 are the roots of the equation

$$Mn^4 + Ln^2 + K - A = 0.$$

The coefficient M is less than $\epsilon^2 L$, where ϵ is the range of the attractive force. Hence we may consider M very small compared with L. If we neglect M altogether,

$$n_1 = \sqrt{\frac{A-K}{L}}, \quad n_2 = -\sqrt{\frac{A-K}{L}}.$$

If we assume a quantity a such that $a^2 K = 2L$, we may call a the *average range of the molecular forces*. If we also take b, so that $bn = 1$, we may call b the *modulus of the variation of the density near the surface*.

Our calculation hitherto has been made on the hypothesis that a is small when compared with b, and in that case we have found that $a^2 : b^2 :: A - K : K$.

But it appears from experiments on liquids that $A - K$ is in general large when compared with K, and sometimes very large. Hence we conclude, first, that the hypothesis of our calculation is incorrect, and, secondly, that the phenomena of capillary action do not in any very great degree depend on the variation of density near the surface, but that the principal part of the force depends on the finite range of the molecular action.

In the following table, $A\rho$ is half the cubical elasticity of the liquid, and $K\rho$ the molecular pressure, both expressed in atmospheres (the absolute value of an atmosphere being one million in centimetre-gramme-second measure, see below, p. 589). ρ is the density, T the surface-tension, and a the average range of the molecular action, as calculated by Van der Waals from the values of T and K.

The unit in which a is expressed is 1 cm. $\times 10^{-9}$; a is therefore the twenty-millionth part of a centimetre for mercury, the thirty-millionth for water, and the forty-millionth part for alcohol. Quincke, however, found by direct experiment that certain molecular actions were sensible at a distance of a two-hundred-thousandth part of a centimetre, so that we cannot regard any of these numbers as accurate.

	$A\rho$	$K\rho$	ρ	T	a
Ether	4600	1300	·73	18	29
Alcohol	5500	2100	·79	25·5	25
Bisulphide of Carbon...	16000	2900	1·27	32·1	23
Water.....................	22200	5000	1	81	31
Mercury	542000	22500	13·54	540	49

On Surface-tension.

Definition.—*The tension of a liquid surface across any line drawn on the surface is normal to the line, and is the same for all directions of the line, and is measured by the force across an element of the line divided by the length of that element.*

Experimental Laws of Surface-tension.

1. For any given liquid surface, as the surface which separates water from air, or oil from water, the surface-tension is the same at every point of the surface and in every direction. It is also practically independent of the curvature of the surface, although it appears from the mathematical theory that there is a slight increase of tension where the mean curvature of the surface is concave, and a slight diminution where it is convex. The amount of this increase and diminution is too small to be directly measured, though it has a certain theoretical importance in the explanation of the equilibrium of the superficial layer of the liquid where it is inclined to the horizon.

2. The surface-tension diminishes as the temperature rises, and when the temperature reaches that of the critical point at which the distinction between the liquid and its vapour ceases, it has been observed by Andrews that the

71—2

capillary action also vanishes. The early writers on capillary action supposed that the diminution of capillary action was due simply to the change of density corresponding to the rise of temperature, and, therefore, assuming the surface-tension to vary as the square of the density, they deduced its variations from the observed dilatation of the liquid by heat. This assumption, however, does not appear to be verified by the experiments of Brunner and Wolff on the rise of water in tubes at different temperatures.

3. The tension of the surface separating two liquids which do not mix cannot be deduced by any known method from the tensions of the surfaces of the liquids when separately in contact with air.

When the surface is curved, the effect of the surface-tension is to make the pressure on the concave side exceed the pressure on the convex side by $T\left(\dfrac{1}{R_1}+\dfrac{1}{R_2}\right)$, where T is the intensity of the surface-tension and R_1, R_2 are the radii of curvature of any two sections normal to the surface and to each other.

If three fluids which do not mix are in contact with each other, the three surfaces of separation meet in a line, straight or curved.

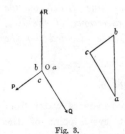

Fig. 3.

Let O (fig. 3) be a point in this line, and let the plane of the paper be supposed to be normal to the line at the point O. The three angles between the tangent planes to the three surfaces of separation at the point O are completely determined by the tensions of the three surfaces. For if in the triangle abc the side ab is taken so as to represent on a given scale the tension of the surface of contact of the fluids a and b, and if the other sides bc and ca are taken so as to represent on the same scale the tensions of the surfaces between b and c and between c and a respectively, then the condition of equilibrium at O for the corresponding tensions R, P, and Q is that the angle ROP shall be the supplement of abc, POQ of bca, and, therefore, QOR of cab. Thus the angles at which the surfaces of separation meet are the same at all parts of the line of concourse of the three fluids. When three films of the same liquid meet, their tensions are equal, and, therefore, they make angles of 120° with each other. The froth of soap-suds or beat-up eggs consists of a multitude of small films which meet each other at angles of 120°.

If four fluids, a, b, c, d, meet in a point O, and if a tetrahedron $ABCD$ is formed so that its edge AB represents the tension of the surface of contact of the liquids a and b, BC that of b and c, and so on; then if we place this tetrahedron so that the face ABC is normal to the tangent at O to the line of concourse of the fluids abc, and turn it so that the edge AB is normal to the tangent plane at O to the surface of contact of the fluids a and b, then the other three faces of the tetrahedron will be normal to the tangents at O to the other three lines of concourse of the liquids, and the other five edges of the tetrahedron will be normal to the tangent planes at O to the other five surfaces of contact.

If six films of the same liquid meet in a point the corresponding tetrahedron is a regular tetrahedron, and each film, where it meets the others, has an angle whose cosine is $-\frac{1}{3}$. Hence if we take two nets of wire with hexagonal meshes, and place one on the other so that the point of concourse of three hexagons of one net coincides with the middle of a hexagon of the other, and if we then, after dipping them in Plateau's liquid, place them horizontally, and gently raise the upper one, we shall develop a system of plane laminæ arranged as the walls and floors of the cells are arranged in a honeycomb. We must not, however, raise the upper net too much, or the system of films will become unstable.

When a drop of one liquid, B, is placed on the surface of another, A, the phenomena which take place depend on the relative magnitude of the three surface-tensions corresponding to the surface between A and air, between B and air, and between A and B. If no one of these tensions is greater than the sum of the other two, the drop will assume the form of a lens, the angles which the upper and lower surfaces of the lens make with the free surface of A and with each other being equal to the external angles of the triangle of forces. Such lenses are often seen formed by drops of fat floating on the surface of hot water, soup, or gravy. But when the surface-tension of A exceeds the sum of the tensions of the surfaces of contact of B with air and with A, it is impossible to construct the triangle of forces, so that equilibrium becomes impossible. The edge of the drop is drawn out by the surface-tension of A with a force greater than the sum of the tensions of the two surfaces of the drop. The drop, therefore, spreads itself out, with great velocity, over the surface of A till it covers an enormous area, and is reduced to such extreme tenuity that it is not probable that it retains the same properties of surface-tension which it has in a large mass. Thus a drop of train oil will spread itself over the surface of the sea till it shews the colours of thin plates. These rapidly descend in Newton's scale and at last disappear, shewing that the thickness of the film is less than the tenth part of the length of a wave of light. But even when thus attenuated, the film may be proved to be present, since the surface-tension of the liquid is considerably less than that of pure water. This may be shewn by placing another drop of oil on the surface. This drop will not spread out like the first drop, but will take the form of a flat lens with a distinct circular edge, shewing that the surface-tension of what is still apparently pure water is now less than the sum of the tensions of the surfaces separating oil from air and water.

The spreading of drops on the surface of a liquid has formed the subject of a very extensive series of experiments by Mr Tomlinson. M. Van der Mensbrugghe has also written a very complete memoir on this subject*.

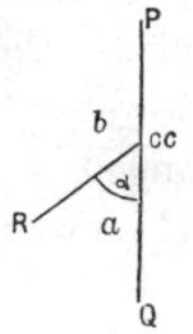

Fig. 4.

When a solid body is in contact with two fluids, the surface of the solid cannot alter its form, but the angle at which the surface of contact of the two fluids meets the surface of the solid depends on the values of the three surface-tensions. If a and b are the two fluids and c the solid then the equilibrium of the tensions at the point O depends only on that of thin components parallel to the surface, because the surface-tensions normal to the surface are balanced by the resistance of the solid. Hence if the angle ROQ (fig. 4) at which the surface of contact OP meets the solid is denoted by a,

$$T_{bc} - T_{ca} - T_{ab} \cos a = 0,$$

whence

$$\cos a = \frac{T_{bc} - T_{ca}}{T_{ab}}.$$

As an experiment on the angle of contact only gives us the difference of the surface-tensions at the solid surface, we cannot determine their actual value. It is theoretically probable that they are often negative, and may be called surface-pressures.

The constancy of the angle of contact between the surface of a fluid and a solid was first pointed out by Dr Young, who states that the angle of contact between mercury and glass is about 140°. Quincke makes it 128° 52'.

* *Sur la Tension Superficielle des Liquides*, Bruxelles, 1873.

If the tension of the surface between the solid and one of the fluids exceeds the sum of the other two tensions, the point of contact will not be in equilibrium, but will be dragged towards the side on which the tension is greatest. If the quantity of the first fluid is small it will stand in a drop on the surface of the solid without wetting it. If the quantity of the second fluid is small it will spread itself over the surface and wet the solid. The angle of contact of the first fluid is 180° and that of the second is zero.

If a drop of alcohol be made to touch one side of a drop of oil on a glass plate, the alcohol will appear to chase the oil over the plate, and if a drop of water and a drop of bisulphide of carbon be placed in contact in a horizontal capillary tube, the bisulphide of carbon will chase the water along the tube. In both cases the liquids move in the direction in which the surface-pressure at the solid is least.

On the Rise of a Liquid in a Tube.

Let a tube (fig. 5) whose internal radius is r, made of a solid substance c, be dipped into a liquid a. Let us suppose that the angle of contact for this liquid with the solid c is an acute angle. This implies that the tension of the free surface of the solid c is greater than that of the surface of contact of the solid with the liquid a. Now consider the tension of the free surface of the liquid a. All round its edge there is a tension T acting at an angle a with the vertical. The circumference of the edge is $2\pi r$, so that the resultant of this tension is a force $2\pi r T \cos a$ acting vertically upwards on the liquid. Hence

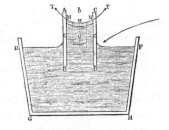

Fig. 5.

the liquid will rise in the tube till the weight of the vertical column between the free surface and the level of the liquid in the vessel balances the resultant of the surface-tension. The upper surface of this column is not level, so that the height of the column cannot be directly measured, but let us assume that h is the mean height of the column, that is to say, the height of a column of equal weight, but with a flat top. Then if r is the radius of the tube at the top of the column, the volume of the suspended column is $\pi r^2 h$, and its weight is $\pi\rho g r^2 h$, when ρ is its density and g the intensity of gravity. Equating this force with the resultant of the tension

$$\pi\rho g r^2 h = 2\pi r T \cos\alpha,$$

or
$$h = \frac{2T\cos\alpha}{\rho g r}.$$

Hence the mean height to which the fluid rises is inversely as the radius of the tube. For water in a clean glass tube the angle of contact is zero, and

$$h = \frac{2T}{\rho g r}.$$

For mercury in a glass tube the angle of contact is 128° 52′, the cosine of which is negative. Hence when a glass tube is dipped into a vessel of mercury, the mercury within the tube stands at a lower level than outside it.

Rise of a Liquid between Two Plates.

When two parallel plates are placed vertically in a liquid the liquid rises between them. If we now suppose fig. 5 to represent a vertical section perpendicular to the plates, we may calculate the rise of the liquid. Let l be the breadth of the plates measured perpendicularly to the plane of the paper, then the length of the line which bounds the wet and the dry parts of the plates inside is l for each surface, and on this the tension T acts at an angle α to the vertical. Hence the resultant of the surface-tension is $2lT\cos\alpha$. If the distance between the inner surfaces of the plates is a, and if the mean height of the film of fluid which rises between them is h, the weight of fluid raised is $\rho g h l a$. Equating the forces—

$$\rho g h l a = 2lT\cos\alpha,$$

whence
$$h = \frac{2T\cos\alpha}{\rho g a}.$$

This expression is the same as that for the rise of a liquid in a tube, except that instead of r, the radius of the tube, we have a the distance of the plates.

FORM OF THE CAPILLARY SURFACE.

The form of the surface of a liquid acted on by gravity is easily determined if we assume that near the part considered the line of contact of the surface of the liquid with that of the solid bounding it is straight and horizontal, as it is when the solids which constrain the liquid are bounded by surfaces formed by horizontal and parallel generating lines. This will be the case, for instance, near a flat plate dipped into the liquid. If we suppose these generating lines to be normal to the plane of the paper then all sections of the solids parallel to this plane will be equal and similar to each other, and the section of the surface of the liquid will be of the same form for all such sections.

Let us consider the portion of the liquid between two parallel sections distant one unit of length. Let P_1, P_2 (fig. 6) be two points of the surface; θ_1, θ_2, the inclination of the surface to the horizon at P_1 and P_2; y_1, y_2 the heights of P_1 and P_2 above the level of the liquid at a distance from all solid bodies. The pressure at any point of the liquid which is above this level is negative unless another fluid as, for instance, the air, presses on the upper surface, but it is only the difference of pressures with which we have to do, because two equal pressures on opposite sides of the surface produce no effect.

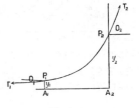

Fig. 6.

We may, therefore, write for the pressure at a height y

$$p = -\rho g y,$$

where ρ is the density of the liquid, or if there are two fluids the excess of the density of the lower fluid over that of the upper one.

The forces acting on the portion of liquid $P_1 P_2 A_2 A_1$ are—first, the horizontal pressures, $-\frac{1}{2}\rho g y_1^2$ and $\frac{1}{2}\rho g y_2^2$; second, the surface-tension T acting at P_1 and P_2 in directions inclined θ_1 and θ_2 to the horizon. Resolving horizontally we find—

$$T\left(\cos\theta_2 - \cos\theta_1\right) + \tfrac{1}{2}g\rho\left(y_2^2 - y_1^2\right) = 0,$$

whence

$$\cos\theta_2 = \cos\theta_1 - \tfrac{1}{2}g\rho y_1^2 + \tfrac{1}{2}\frac{g\rho}{T}y_2^2,$$

or if we suppose P_1 fixed and P_2 variable, we may write

$$\cos \theta = \tfrac{1}{2} \frac{g \rho y^2}{T} + \text{constant}.$$

This equation gives a relation between the inclination of the curve to the horizon and the height above the level of the liquid.

Resolving vertically we find that the weight of the liquid raised above the level must be equal to $T (\sin \theta_2 - \sin \theta_1)$, and this is therefore equal to the area $P_1 P_2 A_2 A_1$ multiplied by $g\rho$. The form of the capillary surface is identical with that of the "elastic curve," or the curve formed by a uniform spring originally straight, when its ends are acted on by equal and opposite forces applied either to the ends themselves or to solid pieces attached to them. Drawings of

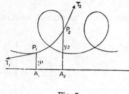

Fig. 7.

the different forms of the curve may be found in Thomson and Tait's *Natural Philosophy*, Vol. I. p. 455.

We shall next consider the rise of a liquid between two plates of different materials for which the angles of contact are a_1 and a_2, the distance between the plates being a, a small quantity. Since the plates are very near one another we may use the following equation of the surface as an approximation:—

$$y = h_1 + Ax + Bx^2$$
$$h_2 = h_1 + Aa + Ba^2,$$

whence

$$\cot a_1 = -A$$

$$\cot a_2 = A + 2Ba$$

$$T (\cos a_1 + \cos a_2) = \rho g a (h_1 + \tfrac{1}{2} Aa + \tfrac{1}{3} B A^2),$$

whence we obtain

$$h_1 = \frac{T}{\rho g a} (\cos a_1 + \cos a_2) + \frac{a}{6} (2 \cot a_1 - \cot a_2),$$

$$h_2 = \frac{T}{\rho g a} (\cos a_1 + \cos a_2) + \frac{a}{6} (2 \cot a_2 - \cot a_1).$$

Let X be the force which must be applied in a horizontal direction to either plate to keep it from approaching the other, then the forces acting on the first plate are $T + X$ in the negative direction, and $T \sin a_1 + \frac{1}{2} g \rho h_1^2$ in the positive direction. Hence

$$X = \frac{1}{2} g \rho h_1^2 - T (1 - \sin a_1).$$

For the second plate

$$X = \frac{1}{2} g \rho h_2^2 - T (1 - \sin a_2).$$

Hence

$$X = \frac{1}{4} g \rho (h_1^2 + h_2^2) - T \{ 1 - \frac{1}{2} (\sin a_1 + \sin a_2) \},$$

or, substituting the values of h_1 and h_2,

$$X = \frac{1}{2} \frac{T^2}{\rho g a^2} (\cos a_1 + \cos a_2)^2 - T \{ 1 - \frac{1}{2} (\sin a_1 + \sin a_2) - \frac{1}{12} (\cos a_1 + \cos a_2)(\cot a_1 + \cot a_2) \},$$

the remaining terms being negligible when a is small. The force, therefore, with which the two plates are drawn together consists first of a positive part, or in other words an attraction, varying inversely as the square of the distance, and second, of a negative part or repulsion independent of the distance. Hence in all cases except that in which the angles a_1 and a_2 are supplementary to each other, the force is attractive when a is small enough, but when $\cos a_1$ and $\cos a_2$ are of different signs, as when the liquid is raised by one plate, and depressed by the other, the first term may be so small that the repulsion indicated by the second term comes into play. The fact that a pair of plates which repel one another at a certain distance may attract one another at a smaller distance was deduced by Laplace from theory, and verified by the observations of the Abbé Haüy.

A Drop between Two Plates.

If a small quantity of a liquid which wets glass be introduced between two glass plates slightly inclined to each other, it will run towards that part where the glass plates are nearest together. When the liquid is in equilibrium it forms a thin film, the outer edge of which is all of the same thickness. If d is the distance between the plates at the edge of the film and Π the atmospheric pressure, the pressure of the liquid in the film is $\Pi - \dfrac{2T \cos a}{d}$, and if A is the area of the film between the plates and B its circumference, the plates will be pressed together with a force

$$\frac{2AT \cos a}{d} + BT \sin a,$$

72—2

and this, whether the atmosphere exerts any pressure or not. The force thus produced by the introduction of a drop of water between two plates is enormous, and is often sufficient to press certain parts of the plates together so powerfully as to bruise them or break them. When two blocks of ice are placed loosely together so that the superfluous water which melts from them may drain away, the remaining water draws the blocks together with a force sufficient to cause the blocks to adhere by the process called Regelation.

In many experiments bodies are floated on the surface of water in order that they may be free to move under the action of slight horizontal forces. Thus Newton placed a magnet in a floating vessel and a piece of iron in another in order to observe their mutual action, and Ampère floated a voltaic battery with a coil of wire in its circuit in order to observe the effects of the earth's magnetism on the electric circuit. When such floating bodies come near the edge of the vessel they are drawn up to it, and are apt to stick fast to it. There are two ways of avoiding this inconvenience. One is to grease the float round its water-line so that the water is depressed round it. This, however, often produces a worse disturbing effect, because a thin film of grease spreads over the water and increases its surface-viscosity. The other method is to fill the vessel with water till the level of the water stands a little higher than the rim of the vessel. The float will then be repelled from the edge of the vessel. Such floats, however, should always be made so that the section taken at the level of the water is as small as possible.

PHENOMENA ARISING FROM THE VARIATION OF THE SURFACE-TENSION.

Pure water has a higher surface-tension than that of any other substance liquid at ordinary temperatures except mercury. Hence any other liquid if mixed with water diminishes its surface-tension. For example, if a drop of alcohol be placed on the surface of water, the surface-tension will be diminished from 80, the value for pure water, to 25, the value for pure alcohol. The surface of the liquid will therefore no longer be in equilibrium, and a current will be formed at and near the surface from the alcohol to the surrounding water, and this current will go on as long as there is more alcohol at one part of the surface than at another. If the vessel is deep, these currents will be balanced by counter currents below them, but if the depth of the water is only two or three millimetres, the surface-current will sweep away the whole of the water, leaving a dry spot where the alcohol was dropped in. This phenomenon was first described and explained by Professor James Thomson, who also explained a phenomenon, the converse of this, called the "tears of strong wine."

If a wine glass be half-filled with port wine the liquid rises a little up the side of the glass as other liquids do. The wine, however, contains alcohol and water, both of which evaporate, but the alcohol faster than the water, so that the superficial layer becomes more watery. In the middle of the vessel the superficial layer recovers its strength by diffusion from below, but the film adhering to the side of the glass becomes more watery, and therefore has a higher surface-tension than the surface of the stronger wine. It therefore creeps up the side of the glass dragging the strong wine after it, and this goes on till the quantity of fluid dragged up collects into a drop and runs down the side of the glass.

The motion of small pieces of camphor floating on water arises from the gradual solution of the camphor. If this takes place more rapidly on one side of the piece of camphor than on the other side, the surface-tension becomes weaker where there is most camphor in solution, and the lump, being pulled unequally by the surface-tensions, moves off in the direction of the strongest tension, namely, towards the side on which least camphor is dissolved.

If a drop of ether is held near the surface of water the vapour of ether condenses on the surface of the water, and surface-currents are formed flowing in every direction away from under the drop of ether.

If we place a small floating body in a shallow vessel of water and wet one side of it with alcohol or ether, it will move off with great velocity and skim about on the surface of the water, the part wet with alcohol being always the stern.

The surface-tension of mercury is greatly altered by slight changes in the state of the surface. The surface-tension of pure mercury is so great that it is very difficult to keep it clean, for every kind of oil or grease spreads over it at once.

But the most remarkable effects of change of surface-tension are those produced by what is called the electric polarization of the surface. The tension of the surface of contact of mercury and dilute sulphuric acid depends on the electromotive force acting between the mercury and the acid. If the electromotive force is from the acid to the mercury the surface-tension increases; if it is from the mercury to the acid, it diminishes. Faraday observed that a large drop of mercury, resting on the flat bottom of a vessel containing dilute acid, changes its form in a remarkable way when connected with one of the electrodes of a battery, the other electrode being placed in the acid. When the mercury is made positive it becomes dull and spreads itself out; when it is made negative it gathers itself together and becomes bright again. M. Lippmann, who has made a careful investigation of the subject, finds that exceedingly small variations of the electromotive force produce sensible changes in the surface-tension. The effect of one Daniell's cell is to increase the tension from 30·4 to 40·6. He has constructed a capillary electrometer by which differences of electric potential less than 0·01 of that of a Daniell's cell can be detected by the difference of the pressure required to force the mercury to a given point of a fine capillary tube. He has also constructed an apparatus in which this variation in the surface-tension is made to do work and drive a machine. He has also found that this action is reversible, for when the area of the surface of contact of the acid and mercury is made to increase, an electric current passes from the mercury to the acid, the amount of electricity which passes while the surface increases by one square centimetre being sufficient to decompose ·000013 grammes of water.

On the Forms of Liquid Films which are Figures of Revolution.

A Spherical Soap-bubble.

A soap-bubble is simply a small quantity of soap-suds spread out so as to expose a large surface to the air. The bubble, in fact, has two surfaces, an outer and an inner surface, both exposed to air. It has, therefore, a certain amount of surface-energy depending on the area of these two surfaces. Since in the case of thin films the outer and inner surfaces are approximately equal, we shall consider the area of the film as representing either of them, and shall use the symbol T to denote the energy of unit of area of the film, both surfaces being taken together. If T' is the energy of a single surface of the liquid, T the energy of the film is $2T'$. When by means of a tube we blow air into the inside of the bubble we increase its volume and therefore its surface, and at the same time we do work in forcing air into it, and thus increase the energy of the bubble.

That the bubble has energy may be shewn by leaving the end of the tube open. The bubble will contract, forcing the air out, and the current of air blown through the tube may be made to deflect the flame of a candle. If the bubble is in the form of a sphere of radius r this material surface will have an area

$$S = 4\pi r^2 \quad \text{...................................... (1).}$$

If T be the energy corresponding to unit of area of the film the surface-energy of the whole bubble will be

$$ST = 4\pi r^2 T \quad \text{.................................... (2).}$$

The increment of this energy corresponding to an increase of the radius from r to $r+dr$ is therefore

$$TdS = 8\pi r T dr \quad \text{................................. (3).}$$

Now this increase of energy was obtained by forcing in air at a pressure greater than the atmospheric pressure, and thus increasing the volume of the bubble.

Let Π be the atmospheric pressure and $\Pi + p$ the pressure of the air within the bubble. The volume of the sphere is

$$V = \tfrac{4}{3}\pi r^3 \quad \text{..................................... (4),}$$

and the increment of volume is

$$dV = 4\pi r^2 dr \quad \text{...................................(5).}$$

Now if we suppose a quantity of air already at the pressure $\Pi + p$, the work done in forcing it into the bubble is pdV. Hence the equation of work and energy is

$$pdV = Tds \quad \text{.................................... (6),}$$

or

$$4\pi p r^2 dr = 8\pi r dr T \quad \text{................................. (7),}$$

or

$$p = 2T\frac{1}{r} \quad \text{..................................... (8).}$$

This, therefore, is the excess of the pressure of the air within the bubble over that of the external air, and it is due to the action of the inner and outer surfaces of the bubble. We may conceive this pressure to arise from the tendency which the bubble has to contract, or in other words from the surface-tension of the bubble.

If to increase the area of the surface requires the expenditure of work, the surface must resist extension, and if the bubble in contracting can do work, the surface must tend to contract. The surface must therefore act like a sheet of india-rubber when extended both in length and breadth, that is, it must exert surface-tension. The tension of the sheet of india-rubber, however, depends on the extent to which it is stretched, and may be different in different directions, whereas the tension of the surface of a liquid remains the same however much the film is extended, and the tension at any point is the same in all directions.

The intensity of this surface-tension is measured by the stress which it exerts across a line of unit length. Let us measure it in the case of the spherical soap-bubble by considering the stress exerted by one hemisphere of the bubble on the other, across the circumference of a great circle. This stress is balanced by the pressure p acting over the area of the same great circle: it is therefore equal to $\pi r^2 p$. To determine the intensity of the surface-tension we have to divide this quantity by the length of the line across which it acts, which is in this case the circumference of a great circle $2\pi r$. Dividing $\pi r^2 p$ by this length we obtain $\frac{1}{2}pr$ as the value of the intensity of the surface-tension, and it is plain from equation 8 that this is equal to T. Hence the numerical value of the intensity of the surface-tension is equal to the numerical value of the surface-energy per unit of surface. We must remember that since the film has two surfaces the surface-tension of the film is double the tension of the surface of the liquid of which it is formed.

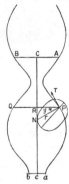

Fig. 8.

To determine the relation between the surface-tension and the pressure which balances it when the form of the surface is not spherical, let us consider the following case :—

Let fig. 8 represent a section through the axis Cc of a soap-bubble in the form of a figure of revolution bounded by two circular disks AB and ab, and having the meridian section APa. Let PQ be an imaginary section normal to the axis. Let the radius of this section PR be y, and let PT, the tangent at P, make an angle α with the axis.

Let us consider the stresses which are exerted across this imaginary section by the lower part on the upper part. If the internal pressure exceeds the external pressure by p, there is in the first place a force $\pi y^2 p$ acting upwards arising from the pressure p over the area of the section. In the next place, there is the surface-tension acting downwards, but at an angle a with the vertical, across the circular section of the bubble itself, whose circumference is $2\pi y$, and the downward force is therefore $2\pi y T \cos a$.

Now these forces are balanced by the external force which acts on the disk ACB, which we may call F. Hence equating the forces which act on the portion included between ACB and PRQ

$$\pi y^2 p - 2\pi y T \cos a = -F \dots\dots\dots\dots\dots (9).$$

If we make $CR = z$, and suppose z to vary, the shape of the bubble of course remaining the same, the values of y and of a will change, but the other quantities will be constant. In studying these variations we may if we please take as our independent variable the length s of the meridian section AP reckoned from A. Differentiating equation 9 with respect to s we obtain, after dividing by 2π as a common factor

$$py \frac{dy}{ds} - T \cos a \frac{dy}{ds} + Ty \sin a \frac{da}{ds} = 0 \dots\dots\dots\dots (10).$$

Now
$$\frac{dy}{ds} = \sin a \dots\dots\dots\dots\dots (11).$$

The radius of curvature of the meridian section is

$$R_1 = -\frac{ds}{da} \dots\dots\dots\dots\dots (12).$$

The radius of curvature of a normal section of the surface at right angles to the meridian section is equal to the part of the normal cut off by the axis, which is

$$R_2 = PN = \frac{y}{\cos a} \dots\dots\dots\dots\dots (13).$$

Hence dividing equation 10 by $y \sin a$, we find

$$p = T \left(\frac{1}{R_1} + \frac{1}{R_2} \right) \dots\dots\dots\dots (14).$$

This equation, which gives the pressure in terms of the principal radii of curvature, though here proved only in the case of a surface of revolution, must be true of all surfaces. For the curvature of any surface at a given point may be completely defined in terms of the positions of its principal normal sections and their radii of curvature.

Before going further we may deduce from equation 9 the nature of all the figures of revolution which a liquid film can assume. Let us first determine the nature of a curve, such that if it is rolled on the axis its origin will trace out the meridian section of the bubble. Since at any instant the rolling curve is rotating about the point of contact with the axis, the line drawn from this point of contact to the tracing point must be normal to the direction of motion of the tracing point. Hence if N is the point of contact, NP must be normal to the traced curve. Also, since the axis is a tangent to the rolling curve, the ordinate PR is the perpendicular from the tracing point P on the tangent. Hence the relation between the radius vector and the perpendicular on the tangent of the rolling curve must be identical with the relation between the normal PN and the ordinate PR of the traced curve. If we write r for PN, then $y = r \cos a$, and equation 9 becomes

$$y^2 \left(2 \frac{T}{pr} - 1 \right) = \frac{F}{\pi p}.$$

This relation between y and r is identical with the relation between the perpendicular from the focus of a conic section on the tangent at a given point and the focal distance of that point, provided the transverse and conjugate axes of the conic are $2a$ and $2b$ respectively, where

$$a = \frac{T}{p}, \text{ and } b^2 = \frac{F}{\pi p}.$$

Hence the meridian section of the film may be traced by the focus of such a conic, if the conic is made to roll on the axis.

On the Different Forms of the Meridian Line.

(1) When the conic is an ellipse the meridian line is in the form of a series of waves, and the film itself has a series of alternate swellings and contractions as represented in figs. 8 and 9. This form of the film is called the unduloid.

(1 *a*.) When the ellipse becomes a circle, the meridian line becomes a straight line parallel to the axis, and the film passes into the form of a cylinder of revolution.

(1 *b*.) As the ellipse degenerates into the straight line joining its foci, the contracted parts of the unduloid become narrower, till at last the figure becomes a series of spheres in contact.

In all these cases the internal pressure exceeds the external by $\dfrac{2T}{a}$ where a is the semi-transverse axis of the conic. The resultant of the internal pressure and the surface-tension is equivalent to a tension along the axis, and the numerical value of this tension is equal to the force due to the action of this pressure on a circle whose diameter is equal to the conjugate axis of the ellipse.

(2) When the conic is a parabola the meridian line is a catenary (fig. 10), the internal pressure is equal to the external pressure, and the tension along the axis is equal to $2\pi Tm$ where m is the distance of the vertex from the focus.

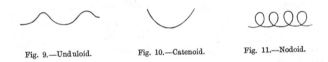

Fig. 9.—Unduloid.   Fig. 10.—Catenoid.   Fig. 11.—Nodoid.

(3) When the conic is a hyperbola the meridian line is in the form of a looped curve (fig. 11). The corresponding figure of the film is called the nodoid. The resultant of the internal pressure and the surface-tension is equivalent to a pressure along the axis equal to that due to a pressure p acting on a circle whose diameter is the conjugate axis of the hyperbola.

When the conjugate axis of the hyperbola is made smaller and smaller, the nodoid approximates more and more to the series of spheres touching each other along the axis. When the conjugate axis of the hyperbola increases without limit, the loops of the nodoid are crowded on one another, and each becomes more nearly a ring of circular section, without, however, ever reaching this form. The only closed surface belonging to the series is the sphere.

73—2

These figures of revolution have been studied mathematically by Poisson[*], Goldschmidt[†], Lindelöf and Moigno[‡], Delaunay[||], Lamarle[§], Beer[¶], and Mannheim[**], and have been produced experimentally by Plateau[††] in the two different ways already described.

The limiting conditions of the stability of these figures have been studied both mathematically and experimentally. We shall notice only two of them, the cylinder and the catenoid.

STABILITY OF THE CYLINDER.

The cylinder is the limiting form of the unduloid when the rolling ellipse becomes a circle. When the ellipse differs infinitely little from a circle, the equation of the meridian line becomes approximately $y = a + c \sin \dfrac{x}{a}$ where c is small. This is a simple harmonic wave-line, whose mean distance from the axis is a, whose wave-length is $2\pi a$, and whose amplitude is c. The internal pressure corresponding to this unduloid is as before $p = \dfrac{T}{a}$. Now consider a portion of a cylindric film of length x terminated by two equal disks of radius r and containing a certain volume of air. Let one of these disks be made to

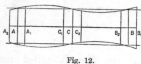

Fig. 12.

approach the other by a small quantity dx. The film will swell out into the convex part of an unduloid, having its largest section midway between the disks, and we have to determine whether the internal pressure will be greater or less than before. If A and C (fig. 12) are the disks, and if x the

---

[*] *Nouvelle théorie de l'action capillaire* (1831).

[†] *Determinatio superficiei minimæ rotatione curvæ data duo puncta jungentis circa datum axem ortæ* (Göttingen, 1831).

[‡] *Leçons de calcul des variations* (Paris, 1861).

[||] "Sur la surface de révolution dont la courbure moyenne est constante," *Liouville's Journal*, vi.

[§] "Théorie géométrique des rayons et centres de courbure," *Bullet. de l'Acad. de Belgique*, 1857.

[¶] *Tractatus de Theoria Mathematica Phænomenorum in Liquidis actione gravitatis detractis observatorum* (Bonn, 1857).

[**] *Journal l'Institut*, No. 1260.

[††] *Statique expérimentale et théorique des liquides.*

distance between the disks is equal to πr half the wave-length of the harmonic curve, the disks will be at the points where the curve is at its mean distance from the axis, and the pressure will therefore be $\dfrac{T}{r}$ as before. If A_1, C_1 are the disks, so that the distance between them is less than πr, the curve must be produced beyond the disks before it is at its mean distance from the axis. Hence in this case the mean distance is less than r, and the pressure will be greater than $\dfrac{T}{r}$. If, on the other hand, the disks are at A_2 and C_2, so that the distance between them is greater than πr, the curve will reach its mean distance from the axis before it reaches the disks. The mean distance will therefore be greater than r, and the pressure will be less than $\dfrac{T}{r}$. Hence if one of the disks be made to approach the other, the internal pressure will be increased if the distance between the disks is less than half the circumference of either, and the pressure will be diminished if the distance is greater than this quantity. In the same way we may shew that if the distance between the disks is increased, the pressure will be diminished or increased according as the distance is less or more than half the circumference of either.

Now let us consider a cylindric film contained between two equal fixed disks A and B, and let a third disk, C, be placed midway between. Let C be slightly displaced towards A. If AC and CB are each less than half the circumference of a disk the pressure on C will increase on the side of A and diminish on the side of B. The resultant force on C will therefore tend to oppose the displacement and to bring C back to its original position. The equilibrium of C is therefore stable. It is easy to shew that if C had been placed in any other position than the middle, its equilibrium would have been stable. Hence the film is stable as regards longitudinal displacements. It is also stable as regards displacements transverse to the axis, for the film is in a state of tension, and any lateral displacement of its middle parts would produce a resultant force tending to restore the film to its original position. Hence if the length of the cylindric film is less than its circumference, it is in stable equilibrium. But if the length of the cylindric film is greater than its circumference, and if we suppose the disk C to be placed midway between A and B, and to be moved towards A, the pressure on the side next A will diminish, and that on the side next B will increase, so that the resultant force will tend to increase the displacement, and the equilibrium of the disk C is therefore unstable. Hence the equilibrium of a cylindric film whose length is greater than its circumference is unstable. Such a film, if ever so little disturbed, will begin to contract at one section and to expand at another, till its form ceases to resemble a cylinder, if it does not break up into two parts which become ultimately portions of spheres.

Instability of a Jet of Liquid.

When a liquid flows out of a vessel through a circular opening in the bottom of the vessel, the form of the stream is at first nearly cylindrical though its diameter gradually diminishes from the orifice downwards on account of the increasing velocity of the liquid. But the liquid after it leaves the vessel is subject to no forces except gravity, the pressure of the air, and its own surface-tension. Of these gravity has no effect on the form of the stream except in drawing asunder its parts in a vertical direction, because the lower parts are moving faster than the upper parts. The resistance of the air produces little disturbance until the velocity becomes very great. But the surface-tension, acting on a cylindric column of liquid whose length exceeds the limit of stability, begins to produce enlargements and contractions in the stream as soon as the liquid has left the orifice, and these inequalities in the figure of the column go on increasing till it is broken up into elongated fragments. These fragments as they are falling through the air continue to be acted on by surface-tension. They therefore shorten themselves, and after a series of oscillations in which they become alternately elongated and flattened, settle down into the form of spherical drops.

This process, which we have followed as it takes place on an individual portion of the falling liquid, goes through its several phases at different distances from the orifice, so that if we examine different portions of the stream as it descends, we shall find next the orifice the unbroken column, then a series of contractions and enlargements, then elongated drops, then flattened drops, and so on till the drops become spherical.

STABILITY OF THE CATENOID.

When the internal pressure is equal to the external, the film forms a surface of which the mean curvature at every point is zero. The only surface of revolution having this property is the catenoid formed by the revolution of a catenary about its directrix. This catenoid, however, is in stable equilibrium only when the portion considered is such that the tangents to the catenary at its extremities intersect before they reach the directrix.

To prove this, let us consider the catenary as the form of equilibrium of a chain suspended between two fixed points A and B. Suppose the chain hanging between A and B to be of very great length, then the tension at A or B will be very great. Let the chain be hauled in over a peg at A. At first the tension will diminish, but if the process be continued the tension will reach a minimum value and will afterwards increase to infinity as the chain between A and B approaches to the form of a straight line. Hence for every tension greater than the minimum tension there are two catenaries passing through A and B. Since the tension is measured by the height above the directrix these two catenaries have the same directrix. Every catenary lying between them has its directrix higher, and every catenary lying beyond them has its directrix lower than that of the two catenaries.

Now let us consider the surfaces of revolution formed by this system of catenaries revolving about the directrix of the two catenaries of equal tension. We know that the radius of curvature of a surface of revolution in the plane normal to the meridian plane is the portion of the normal intercepted by the axis of revolution.

The radius of curvature of a catenary is equal and opposite to the portion of the normal intercepted by the directrix of the catenary. Hence a catenoid whose directrix coincides with the axis of revolution has at every point its principal radii of curvature equal and opposite, so that the mean curvature of the surface is zero.

The catenaries which lie between the two whose direction coincides with the axis of revolution generate surfaces whose radius of curvature convex towards the axis in the meridian plane is less than the radius of concave curvature. The mean curvature of these surfaces is therefore convex towards the axis. The catenaries which lie beyond the two generate surfaces whose radius of curvature convex towards the axis in the meridian plane is greater than the radius of concave curvature. The mean curvature of these surfaces is, therefore, concave towards the axis.

Now if the pressure is equal on both sides of a liquid film, if its mean curvature is zero, it will be in equilibrium. This is the case with the two catenoids. If the mean curvature is convex towards the axis the film will move from the axis. Hence if a film in the form of the catenoid which is nearest the axis is ever so slightly displaced from the axis it will move further from the axis till it reaches the other catenoid.

If the mean curvature is concave towards the axis the film will tend to approach the axis. Hence if a film in the form of the catenoid which is nearest the axis be displaced towards the axis, it will tend to move further towards the axis and will collapse. Hence the film in the form of the catenoid which is nearest the axis is in unstable equilibrium under the condition that it is exposed to equal pressures within and without. If, however, the circular ends of the catenoid are closed with solid disks, so that the volume of air contained between these disks and the film is determinate, the film will be in stable equilibrium however large a portion of the catenary it may consist of.

The criterion as to whether any given catenoid is stable or not may be obtained as follows.

Let $PABQ$ and $ApqB$ (fig. 13) be two catenaries having the same direc-

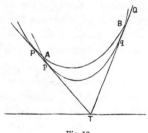

Fig. 13.

trix and intersecting in A and B. Draw Pp and Qq touching both catenaries, Pp and Qq will intersect at T, a point in the directrix; for since any catenary with its directrix is a similar figure to any other catenary with its directrix, if the directrix of the one coincides with that of the other the centre of similitude must lie on the common directrix. Also, since the curves at P and p are equally inclined to the directrix, P and p are corresponding points and the line Pp must pass through the centre of similitude. Similarly Qq must pass through the centre of similitude. Hence T, the point of intersection of Pp and Qq, must be the centre of similitude and must be on the common directrix. Hence the tangents at A and B to the upper catenary must intersect above the directrix, and the tangents at A and B to the lower catenary must intersect below the directrix. The condition of stability of a catenoid is therefore that the tangents at the extremities of its generating catenary must intersect before they reach the directrix.

STABILITY OF A PLANE SURFACE.

We shall next consider the limiting conditions of stability of the horizontal surface which separates a heavier fluid above from a lighter fluid below. Thus, in an experiment of M. Duprez*, a vessel containing olive oil is placed with its mouth downwards in a vessel containing a mixture of alcohol and water, the mixture being denser than the oil. The surface of separation is in this case horizontal and stable, so that the equilibrium is established of itself. Alcohol is then added very gradually to the mixture till it becomes lighter than the oil. The equilibrium of the fluids would now be unstable if it were not for the tension of the surface which separates them, and which, when the orifice of the vessel is not too large, continues to preserve the stability of the equilibrium.

When the equilibrium at last becomes unstable, the destruction of equilibrium takes place by the lighter fluid ascending in one part of the orifice and the heavier descending in the other. Hence the displacement of the surface to which we must direct our attention is one which does not alter the volume of the liquid in the vessel, and which therefore is upward in one part of the surface and downward in another. The simplest case is that of a rectangular orifice in a horizontal plane, the sides being a and b.

Let the surface of separation be originally in the plane of the orifice, and let the co-ordinates x and y be measured from one corner parallel to the sides a and b respectively, and let z be measured upwards. Then if ρ be the density of the upper liquid, and σ that of the lower liquid, and P the original pressure at the surface of separation, then when the surface receives an upward displacement z, the pressure above it will be $P - \rho gz$, and that below it will be $P - \sigma gz$, so that the surface will be acted on by an upward pressure $(\rho - \sigma) gz$. Now if the displacement z be everywhere very small, the curvature in the planes parallel to xz and yz will be $\dfrac{d^2z}{dx^2}$ and $\dfrac{d^2z}{dy^2}$ respectively; and if T is

---

* "Sur un cas particulier de l'équilibre des liquides," par F. Duprez, *Nouveaux Mém. de l'Acad. de Belgique*, 1851 et 1854.

the surface-tension the whole upward force will be

$$T\left(\frac{d^2z}{dx^2} + \frac{d^2z}{dy^2}\right) + (\rho - \sigma)\,gz.$$

If this quantity is of the same sign as z, the displacement will be increased, and the equilibrium will be unstable. If it is of the opposite sign from z, the equilibrium will be stable. The limiting condition may be found by putting it equal to zero. One form of the solution of the equation, and that which is applicable to the case of a rectangular orifice, is

$$z = C \sin px \sin qy.$$

Substituting in the equation we find the condition

$$(p^2 + q^2)\,T - (\rho - \sigma)\,g = \begin{cases} +^{ve} & \text{stable.} \\ 0 & \text{neutral.} \\ -^{ve} & \text{unstable.} \end{cases}$$

That the surface may coincide with the edge of the orifice, which is a rectangle, whose sides are a and b, we must have

$$pa = m\pi, \quad qb = n\pi,$$

when m and n are integral numbers. Also, if m and n are both unity, the displacement will be entirely positive, and the volume of the liquid will not be constant. That the volume may be constant, either n or m must be an even number. We have, therefore, to consider the conditions under which

$$\pi^2\left(\frac{m^2}{a^2} + \frac{n^2}{b^2}\right) T - (\rho - \sigma)\,g$$

cannot be made negative. Under these conditions the equilibrium is stable for all small displacements of the surface. The smallest admissible value of $\frac{m^2}{a^2} + \frac{n^2}{b^2}$ is $\frac{4}{a^2} + \frac{1}{b^2}$, where a is the longer side of the rectangle. Hence the condition of stability is that

$$\pi^2\left(\frac{4}{a^2} + \frac{1}{b^2}\right) T - (\rho - \sigma)\,g$$

is a positive quantity. When the breadth b is less than $\sqrt{\dfrac{\pi^2 T}{(\rho - \sigma)\,g}}$ the length a may be unlimited.

When the orifice is circular of radius a, the limiting value of a is $\sqrt{\dfrac{T}{g\rho}}\,z$, where z is the least root of the equation

$$\frac{2}{z}J^{1}{}_{(z)}=1-\frac{z^{2}}{2\,.\,4}+\frac{z^{4}}{2\,.\,4^{2}\,.\,6}-\frac{z^{6}}{2\,.\,4^{2}\,.\,6^{2}\,.\,8}+\&\text{c.},=0.$$

The least root of this equation is

$$z=3\cdot83171.$$

If h is the height to which the liquid will rise in a capillary tube of unit radius, then the diameter of the largest orifice is

$$2a=3\cdot8317\sqrt{2h}$$
$$=5\cdot4188\sqrt{h}.$$

M. Duprez found from his experiments

$$2a=5\cdot485\sqrt{h}.$$

Effect of Surface-tension on the Velocity of Waves[*].

When a series of waves are propagated on the surface of a liquid, the surface-tension has the effect of increasing the pressure at the crests of the waves and diminishing it in the troughs. If the wave-length is λ, the equation of the surface is

$$y=b\sin 2\pi\frac{x}{\lambda}.$$

The pressure due to the surface-tension T is

$$p=-T\frac{d^{2}y}{dx^{2}}=\frac{4\pi^{2}}{\lambda^{2}}Ty.$$

This pressure must be added to the pressure due to gravity $g\rho y$. Hence the waves will be propagated as if the intensity of gravity had been

$$f=g+\frac{4\pi^{2}}{\lambda^{2}}\frac{T}{\rho}$$

instead of g. Now it is shewn in hydrodynamics that the velocity of propagation of waves in deep water is that acquired by a heavy body falling through half the radius of the circle whose circumference is the wave-length, or

$$v=\sqrt{\frac{f\lambda}{2\pi}}$$
$$=\sqrt{\frac{\lambda g}{2\pi}+\frac{2\pi T}{\lambda\rho}}.$$

[*] See Sir W. Thomson, "Hydrokinetic Solutions and Observations," *Phil. Mag.*, Nov. 1871.

This velocity is a minimum when

$$\lambda = 2\pi \sqrt{\frac{T}{g\rho}},$$

and the minimum value is

$$v = \sqrt[4]{4\frac{Tg}{\rho}}.$$

For waves whose length from crest to crest is greater than λ, the principal force concerned in the motion is that of gravitation. For waves whose length is less than λ the principal force concerned is that of surface-tension. Sir William Thomson proposes to distinguish the latter kind of waves by the name of ripples.

When a small body is partly immersed in a liquid originally at rest, and moves horizontally with constant velocity V, waves are propagated through the liquid with various velocities according to their respective wave-lengths. In front of the body the relative velocity of the fluid and the body varies from V where the fluid is at rest, to zero at the cutwater on the front surface of the body. The waves produced by the body will travel forwards faster than the body till they reach a distance from it at which the relative velocity of the body and the fluid is equal to the velocity of propagation corresponding to the wave-length. The waves then travel along with the body at a constant distance in front of it. Hence at a certain distance in front of the body there is a series of waves which are stationary with respect to the body. Of these, the waves of minimum velocity form a stationary wave nearest to the front of the body. Between the body and this first wave the surface is comparatively smooth. Then comes the stationary wave of minimum velocity, which is the most marked of the series. In front of this is a double series of stationary waves, the gravitation waves forming a series increasing in wave-length with their distance in front of the body, and the surface-tension waves or ripples diminishing in wave-length with their distance from the body, and both sets of waves rapidly diminishing in amplitude with their distance from the body.

If the current-function of the water referred to the body considered as origin is ψ, then the equation of the form of the crest of a wave of velocity w, the crest of which travels along with the body, is

$$d\psi = wds$$

where ds is an element of the length of the crest. To integrate this equation for a solid of given form is probably difficult, but it is easy to see that at some distance on either side of the body, where the liquid is sensibly at rest, the crest of the wave will approximate to an asymptote inclined to the path of the body at an angle whose sine is $\frac{w}{V}$, where w is the velocity of the wave and V is that of the body.

The crests of the different kinds of waves will therefore appear to diverge as they get further from the body, and the waves themselves will be less and less perceptible. But those whose wave-length is near to that of the wave of minimum velocity will diverge less than any of the others, so that the most marked feature at a distance from the body will be the two long lines of ripples of minimum velocity. If the angle between these is 2θ, the velocity of the body is $w \sec \theta$, where w for water is about 23 centimetres per second.

TABLES OF SURFACE-TENSION.

In the following tables the units of length, mass, and time are the centimetre, the gramme, and the second, and the unit of force is that which if it acted on one gramme for one second would communicate to it a velocity of one centimetre per second:—

Table of Surface-Tension at 20° C. (Quincke).

Liquid.	Specific Gravity.	Tension of surface separating the liquid from			Angle of contact with glass in presence of		
		Air.	Water.	Mercury.	Air.	Water.	Mercury.
Water..........................	1	81	...	418	25° 32′	...	26° 8′
Mercury.........................	13·5432	540	418	...	51° 8′	26° 8′	...
Bisulphide of Carbon..............	1·2687	32·1	41·75	372·5	32° 16′	13° 8′	...
Chloroform........................	1·4878	30·6	29·5	399	...	..	...
Alcohol	0·7906	25·5	...	399	25° 12′	..	...
Olive Oil........................	0·9136	36·9	20·56	335	21° 50′	17°	47° 2′
Turpentine	0·8867	29·7	11·55	250·5	37° 44′	37° 44′	47° 2′
Petroleum	0·7977	31·7	27·8	284	36° 20′	42° 46′	...
Hydrochloric Acid.................	1·1	70·1	...	377	...	...	...
Solution of Hyposulphite of Soda	1·1248	77·5	...	442·5	23° 20′	...	10° 42′

Olive oil and alcohol, 12·2.
Olive oil and aqueous alcohol (sp. g. ·9231, tension of free surface 25·5), 6·8, angle 87° 48′.

Quincke has determined the surface-tension of a great many substances near their point of fusion or solidification. His method was that of observing the form of a large drop standing on a plane surface. If K is the height of the flat surface of the drop, and k that of the point where its tangent plane is vertical, then

$$T = \tfrac{1}{2} (K - k)^2 g\rho.$$

Surface-Tensions of Liquids at their Point of Solidification. From Quincke.

Substance.	Temperature of Solidification.	Surface-Tension.
Platinum	2000° C.	1658
Gold	1200°	983
Zinc	360°	860
Tin	230°	587
Mercury	− 40°	577
Lead	330°	448
Silver	1000°	419
Bismuth	265°	382
Potassium	58°	364
Sodium	90°	253
Antimony	432°	244
Borax	1000°	212
Carbonate of Soda	1000°	206
Chloride of Sodium	...	114
Water	0°	86·2
Selenium	217°	70·4
Sulphur	111°	41·3
Phosphorus	43°	41·1
Wax	68°	33·4

Quincke finds that for several series of substances the surface-tension is nearly proportional to the density, so that if we call $(K-k)^2 = \dfrac{2T}{g\rho}$ the specific cohesion, we may state the general results of his experiments as follows:—

The bromides and iodides have a specific cohesion about half that of mercury. The nitrates, chlorides, sugars, and fats, as also the metals, lead, bismuth, and antimony, have a specific cohesion nearly equal to that of mercury. Water, the carbonates and sulphates, and probably phosphates, and the metals, platinum, gold, silver, cadmium, tin, and copper have a specific cohesion double that of mercury. Zinc, iron, and palladium, three times that of mercury, and sodium, six times that of mercury.

Relation of Surface-tension to Temperature.

It appears from the experiments of Brunner and of Wolff on the ascent of water in tubes that at the temperature $t°$ centigrade

$T = 75\text{·}20\,(1 - 0\text{·}00187t)\,;$

$\quad = 76\text{·}08\,(1 - 0\text{·}002t + 0\text{·}00000415t^2)$, for a tube ·02346 cm. diameter (Wolff);

$\quad = 77\text{·}34\,(1 - 0\text{·}00181t)$, for a tube ·03098 cm. diameter (Wolff).

Sir W. Thomson has applied the principles of Thermodynamics to determine the thermal effects of increasing or diminishing the area of the free surface of a liquid, and has shewn that in order to keep the temperature constant while the area of the surface increases by unity, an amount of heat must be supplied to the liquid which is dynamically equivalent to the product of the absolute temperature into the decrement of the surface-tension per degree of temperature. We may call this the *latent heat of surface-extension.*

It appears from the experiments of Brunner and Wolff that at ordinary temperatures the latent heat of extension of the surface of water is dynamically equivalent to about half the mechanical work done in producing the surface-extension.

[From *Nature*, Vol. xv.]

LXXXIV. *Hermann Ludwig Ferdinand Helmholtz.*

THE contributions made by Helmholtz to mathematics, physics, physiology, psychology, and æsthetics, are well known to all cultivators of these various subjects. Most of those who have risen to eminence in any one of these sciences have done so by devoting their whole attention to that science exclusively, so that it is only rarely that the cultivators of different branches can be of service to each other by contributing to one science the skill they have acquired by the study of another.

Hence the ordinary growth of human knowledge is by accumulation round a number of distinct centres. The time, however, must sooner or later arrive when two or more departments of knowledge can no longer remain independent of each other, but must be fused into a consistent whole. But though men of science may be profoundly convinced of the necessity of such a fusion, the operation itself is a most arduous one. For though the phenomena of nature are all consistent with each other, we have to deal not only with these, but with the hypotheses which have been invented to systematise them ; and it by no means follows that because one set of observers have laboured with all sincerity to reduce to order one group of phenomena, the hypotheses which they have formed will be consistent with those by which a second set of observers have explained a different set of phenomena. Each science may appear tolerably consistent within itself, but before they can be combined into one, each must be stripped of the daubing of untempered mortar by which its parts have been prematurely made to cohere.

Hence the operation of fusing two sciences into one generally involves much criticism of established methods, and the explosion of many pieces of fancied knowledge which may have been long held in scientific reputation.

Most of those physical sciences which deal with things without life have either undergone this fusion or are in a fair state of preparation for it, and the form which each finally assumes is that of a branch of dynamics.

Hermann L. F. Helmholtz

Engraved by C. H. Jeens, from a Photograph.

Many cultivators of the biological sciences have been impressed with the conviction that for an adequate study of their subject a thorough knowledge of dynamical science is essential. But the manner in which some of them have cut and pared at the facts in order to bring the phenomena within the range of their dynamics, has tended to throw discredit on all attempts to apply dynamical methods to biology.

We purpose to make a few remarks on a portion of the scientific work of Helmholtz, who is himself the most illustrious example not merely of extensive acquaintance with science combined with thoroughness, but of a thoroughness which of itself demands the mastery of many sciences, and in so doing makes its mark on each.

Hermann Ludwig Ferdinand Helmholtz was born August 31, 1821, at Potsdam, where his father, Ferdinand Helmholtz, was Professor of the Gymnasium. His mother, Caroline Penn, was of an emigrated English family. His father's means would not admit of his studying science otherwise than as a medical student. He therefore became a military surgeon, and continued in that position till the end of 1848, when he was appointed Assistant of the Anatomical Museum of Berlin, and Teacher of Anatomy at the Academy of Arts. In the following year he went to Königsberg, in Prussia, as Professor of Physiology. In 1856 he became Professor of Anatomy and Physiology at the University of Bonn; in 1859, Professor of Physiology at the University of Heidelberg; and, in 1871, Professor of Natural Philosophy to the University of Berlin.

It was during his career as a military surgeon that he published his celebrated essay on *The Conservation of Energy.*

The science of dynamics has been so long established, that it is hardly conceivable that any addition to its fundamental principles should yet remain to be made. But in the application of pure dynamics to actual bodies a great deal remains to be done. The great work for the men of science of the present age is to extend our knowledge of the motion of matter from those instances in which we can see and measure the motion to those in which our senses are unable to trace it. For this purpose we must avail ourselves of such principles of dynamics as are applicable to cases in which the precise nature of the motion cannot be directly observed, and we must also discover methods of observation by which effects which indicate the nature of the unseen motion may be measured. It is unnecessary here to refer to the labours of the different men of science who, each in his own way, have contributed by experiment, calculation, or speculation, to the establishment of the principle of the conservation of energy; but there can be no doubt that a very great impulse was communicated to this research by the publication in 1847, of Helmholtz's essay *Ueber die Erhaltung der Kraft*, which we must now (and correctly, as a matter of science) translate *Conservation of Energy*, though in the translation which appeared in Taylor's *Scientific Memoirs*, the word *Kraft* was translated *Force* in accordance with the ordinary literary usage of that time.

In this essay Helmholtz shewed that if the forces acting between material bodies were equivalent to attractions or repulsions between the particles of these bodies, the intensity of which depends only on the distance, then the configuration and motion of any material system would be subject to a certain equation, which, when expressed in words, is the principle of the conservation of energy.

Whether this equation applies to actual material systems is a matter which experiment alone can decide, but the search for what was called the perpetual motion has been carried on for so long, and always in vain, that we may now appeal to the united experience of a large number of most ingenious men, any one of whom, if he had once discovered a violation of the principle, would have turned it to most profitable account.

Besides this, if the principle were in any degree incorrect, the ordinary processes of nature, carried on as they are incessantly and in all possible combinations, would be certain now and then to produce observable and even startling phenomena, arising from the accumulated effects of any slight divergence from the principle of conservation.

But the scientific importance of the principle of the conservation of energy does not depend merely on its accuracy as a statement of fact, nor even on the remarkable conclusions which may be deduced from it, but on the fertility of the methods founded on this principle.

Whether our work is to form a science by the colligation of known facts, or to seek for an explanation of obscure phenomena by devising a course of experiments, the principle of the conservation of energy is our unfailing guide. It gives us a scheme by which we may arrange the facts of any physical science as instances of the transformation of energy from one form to another. It also indicates that in the study of any new phenomenon our first inquiry must be, How can this phenomenon be explained as a transformation of energy?

What is the original form of the energy? What is its final form? and What are the conditions of transformation?

To appreciate the full scientific value of Helmholtz's little essay on this subject, we should have to ask those to whom we owe the greatest discoveries in thermodynamics and other branches of modern physics, how many times they have read it over, and how often during their researches they felt the weighty statements of Helmholtz acting on their minds like an irresistible driving-power.

We come next to his researches on the eye and on vision, as they are given in his book on Physiological Optics. Every modern oculist will admit that the ophthalmoscope, the original form of which was invented by Helmholtz, has substituted observation for conjecture in the diagnosis of diseases of the inner parts of the eye, and has enabled operations on the eye to be made with greater certainty.

But though the ophthalmoscope is an indispensable aid to the oculist, a knowledge of optical principles is of still greater importance. Whatever optical information he had was formerly obtained from text-books, the only practical object of which seemed to be to explain the construction of telescopes. They were full of very inelegant mathematics, and most of the results were quite inapplicable to the eye.

The importance to the physiologist and the physician of a thorough knowledge of physical principles has often been insisted on, but unless the physical principles are presented in a form which can be directly applied to the complex structures of the living body, they are of very little use to him; but Helmholtz, Donders, and Listing, by the application to the eye of Gauss's theory of the cardinal points of an instrument, have made it possible to acquire a competent knowledge of the optical effects of the eye by a few direct observations.

But perhaps the most important service conferred on science by this great work consists in the way in which the study of the eye and vision is made to illustrate the conditions of sensation and of voluntary motion. In no department of research is the combined and concentrated light of all the sciences more necessary than in the investigation of sensation. The purely subjective school of psychologists used to assert that for the analysis of sensation no apparatus was required except what every man carries within himself, for, since a sensation can exist nowhere except in our own consciousness, the only possible method for the study of sensations must be an unbiased contemplation of our

75—2

own frame of mind. Others might study the conditions under which an impulse is propagated along a nerve, and might suppose that while doing so they were studying sensations, but though such a procedure leaves out of account the very essence of the phenomenon, and treats a fact of consciousness as if it were an electric current, the methods which it has suggested have been more fertile in results than the method of self-contemplation has ever been.

But the best results are obtained when we employ all the resources of physical science so as to vary the nature and intensity of the external stimulus, and then consult consciousness as to the variation of the resulting sensation. It was by this method that Johannes Müller established the great principle that the difference in the sensations due to different senses does not depend upon the actions which excite them, but upon the various nervous arrangements which receive them. Hence the sensation due to a particular nerve may vary in intensity, but not in quality, and therefore the analysis of the infinitely various states of sensation of which we are conscious must consist in ascertaining the number and nature of those simple sensations which, by entering into consciousness each in its own degree, constitute the actual state of feeling at any instant.

If, after this analysis of sensation itself, we should find by anatomy an apparatus of nerves arranged in natural groups corresponding in number to the elements of sensation, this would be a strong confirmation of the correctness of our analysis, and if we could devise the means of stimulating or deadening each particular nerve in our own bodies, we might even make the investigation physiologically complete.

The two great works of Helmholtz on *Physiological Optics* and on the *Sensations of Tone*, form a splendid example of this method of analysis applied to the two kinds of sensation which furnish the largest proportion of the raw materials for thought.

In the first of these works the colour-sensation is investigated and shewn to depend upon three variables or elementary sensations. Another investigation, in which exceedingly refined methods are employed, is that of the motions of the eyes. Each eye has six muscles by the combined action of which its angular position may be varied in each of its three components, namely, in altitude and azimuth as regards the optic axis, and rotation about that axis. There is no material connection between these muscles or their nerves which would cause the motion of one to be accompanied by the motion of any other, so that the three motions of one eye are mechanically independent of the three motions of the other eye. Yet it is well known that the motions of the axis of one eye are always accompanied by corresponding motions of the other. This takes place even when we cover one eye with the fingers. We feel the cornea of the shut eye rolling under our fingers as we roll the open eye up or down, or to left or right; and indeed we are quite unable to move one eye without a corresponding motion of the other.

Now though the upward and downward motions are effected by corresponding muscles for both eyes, the motions to right and left are not so, being produced by the inner muscle of one eye along with the outer muscle of the other, and yet the combined motion is so regular, that we can move our eyes quite freely while maintaining during the whole motion the condition that the optic axes shall intersect at some point of the object whose motions we are following. Besides this, the motion of each eye about its optic axis is found to be connected in a remarkable way with the motion of the axis itself.

The mode in which Helmholtz discusses these phenomena, and illustrates the conditions of our command over the motions of our bodies, is well worth the attention of those who are conscious of no limitation of their power of moving in a given manner any organ which is capable of that kind of motion.

In his other great work on the *Sensation of Tone as a Physiological Basis for the Theory of Music*, he illustrates the conditions under which our senses are trained in a yet clearer manner. We quote from Mr Ellis's translation, p. 95 :—

"Now practice and experience play a far greater part in the use of our senses than we are usually inclined to assume, and since, as just remarked, our sensations derived from the senses are primarily of importance only for enabling us to form a correct conception of the world without us, our practice in the observation of these sensations usually does not extend in the slightest degree beyond what is necessary for this purpose. We are certainly only far too much disposed to believe that we must be immediately conscious of all that we feel and of all that enters into our sensations. This natural belief, however, is founded only on the fact that we are always immediately conscious, without taking any special trouble, of everything necessary for the practical purpose of forming a correct acquaintance with external nature, because during our whole life we have been daily and hourly using our organs of sense and collecting results of experience for this precise object."

Want of space compels us to leave out of consideration that paper on Vortex Motion, in which he establishes principles in pure hydrodynamics which had escaped the penetrative power of all the mathematicians who preceded him, including Lagrange himself; and those papers on electrodynamics where he reduces to an intelligible and systematic form the laborious and intricate investigations of several independent theorists, so as to compare them with each other and with experiment.

But we must not dwell on isolated papers, each of which might have been taken for the work of a specialist, though few, if any, specialists could have treated them in so able a manner. We prefer to regard Helmholtz as the author of the two great books on Vision and Hearing, and now that we are no longer under the sway of that irresistible power which has been bearing us along through the depths of mathematics, anatomy, and music, we may venture to observe from a safe distance the whole figure of the intellectual giant as he sits on some lofty cliff watching the waves, great and small, as each pursues its independent course on the surface of the sea below.

"I must own," he says, "that whenever I attentively observe this spectacle, it awakens in me a peculiar kind of intellectual pleasure, because here is laid open before the bodily eye what, in the case of the waves of the invisible atmospheric ocean, can' be rendered intelligible only to the eye of the understanding, and by the help of a long series of complicated propositions."— (*Tonempfindungen*, p. 42.)

Helmholtz is now in Berlin, directing the labours of able men of science in his splendid laboratory. Let us hope that from his present position he will again take a comprehensive view of the waves and ripples of our intellectual progress, and give us from time to time his idea of the meaning of it all.

[From the *Proceedings of the Cambridge Philosophical Society,* Vol. III. 1877.]

LXXXV.   *On a Paradox in the Theory of Attraction.*

LET A_1A_2 be a straight line, P a point in the same, X_1, X_2 corresponding points in the segments PA_1, PA_2.

Let the distances of these points from the origin O measured in the positive

$$O \qquad A_2 \quad\underset{a}{\rule{2.5cm}{0.4pt}}\quad X_2 \quad P \quad X_1 \quad A_1$$

direction be a_1, a_2, p, x_1, x_2, respectively, and let the equation of correspondence between x_1 and x_2 be

$$\frac{1}{x_1 - p} - \frac{1}{a_1 - p} = \frac{1}{p - x_2} - \frac{1}{p - a_2} \quad\dots\dots\dots\dots\dots(1).$$

If x_1 and x_2 vary simultaneously,

$$\frac{dx_1}{(x_1 - p)^2} = -\frac{dx_2}{(p - x_2)^2} \quad\dots\dots\dots\dots\dots\dots\dots(2).$$

Hence x_1 and x_2 move in opposite directions, and the lengths of the corresponding elements dx_1 and dx_2 (considered both positive) are as the squares of their respective distances from the point P.

If therefore AB is a uniform rod of matter attracting inversely as the square of the distance, the attractions of the corresponding elements on a particle at the point P will be equal and opposite.

Now by giving values to x_1, varying continuously from a_1 to p, we may obtain a corresponding series of values of x_2, varying from a_2 to p, and since every corresponding pair of elements dx_1 and dx_2 exert equal and opposite attractions on a particle at P, we might conclude that the attraction of the whole segment A_1P on a particle at P is equal and opposite to that of the segment A_2P on the same particle.

But it is still more evident that if A_2P is the greater of the two segments, and if we cut off $Pa = PA_1$ the attractions of Pa and PA_1 on the particle at P will be equal and opposite. But the attraction of PA_2 exceeds that of Pa by the attraction of the part aA_2, therefore the attraction of PA_2 exceeds that of PA_1 by a finite quantity, contrary to our first conclusion.

Hence our first conclusion is wrong, and for this reason. The attractions of any two corresponding segments A_1X_1 and A_2X_2 are exactly equal, but however near the corresponding points X_1 and X_2 approach to P, the attraction of each of the parts X_1P and X_2P on P is infinite, but that of X_2P exceeds that of X_1P by a constant quantity, equal to the attraction of A_2a on P.

This method of corresponding elements leads to a very simple investigation of the distribution on straight lines, circular and elliptic disks and solid spheres and ellipsoids of fluids repelling according to any power of the distance.

The problem has been already solved by Green* in a far more general manner, but at the same time by a far more intricate method.

We have, as before, for corresponding values of x_1 and x_2

$$\frac{1}{x_1 - p} - \frac{1}{a_1 - p} = \frac{1}{p - x_2} - \frac{1}{p - a_2} \quad \ldots\ldots\ldots\ldots\ldots\ldots(1).$$

Transposing

$$\frac{1}{x_1 - p} + \frac{1}{p - a_2} = \frac{1}{p - x_2} + \frac{1}{a_1 - p} \quad \ldots\ldots\ldots\ldots\ldots(2).$$

Multiplying

$$\frac{(x_1 - a_1)(x_1 - a_2)}{(x_1 - p)^2(a_1 - p)(p - a_2)} = \frac{(a_2 - x_2)(a_1 - x_2)}{(p - x_2)^2(a_1 - p)(p - a_2)} \quad \ldots\ldots\ldots(3).$$

If we write

$$(a_1 - x_1)(x_1 - a_2) = y_1^2 \quad \ldots\ldots\ldots\ldots\ldots\ldots\ldots(4),$$

$$(a_1 - x_2)(x_2 - a_2) = y_2^2 \quad \ldots\ldots\ldots\ldots\ldots\ldots\ldots(5),$$

we find from equation (3)

$$\frac{x_1 - p}{y_1} = \frac{p - x_2}{y_2} \quad \ldots\ldots\ldots\ldots\ldots\ldots\ldots\ldots(6).$$

Let ρ_1, ρ_2 be the densities and s_1, s_2 the sections of the rod at the corresponding points X_1 and X_2, and let the repulsion of the matter of the

---

* George Green. "Mathematical Investigations concerning the laws of the Equilibrium of Fluids analogous to the electric fluid, with other similar researches." *Transactions of the Cambridge Philosophical Society*, 1833. (Read Nov. 12, 1832.) Ferrers' Edition of Green's Papers, p. 119.

rod vary inversely as the nth power of the distance, then the condition of equilibrium of a particle at P under the action of the elements dx_1 and $-dx_2$ is

$$\rho_1 s_1 dx_1 \, (x_1 - p)^{-n} = - \rho_2 s_2 dx_2 \, (p - x_2)^{-n} \dots\dots\dots\dots\dots(7).$$

Eliminating dx_1 and dx_2 by means of equation (2), we find

$$\rho_1 s_1 (x_1 - p)^{2-n} = \rho_2 s_2 \, (p - x_2)^{2-n} \dots\dots\dots\dots\dots(8),$$

and from this by means of equation (6) we obtain

$$\rho_1 s_1 y_1^{2-n} = \rho_2 s_2 y_2^{2-n} \dots\dots\dots\dots\dots\dots\dots(9),$$

as the condition of equilibrium between the elements.

The condition of equilibrium is therefore satisfied for every pair of elements by making

$$\rho s y^{2-n} = \text{constant} = C \quad \dots\dots\dots\dots\dots\dots(10).$$

In a uniform rod s is constant, so that the distribution of density is given by the equation

$$\rho = C y^{n-2} \dots\dots\dots\dots\dots\dots\dots\dots(11).$$

If $n = 2$, as in the case of electricity, the density is uniform.

We have already shewn that when the density is uniform a particle not at the middle of the rod cannot be in equilibrium, but on the other hand any finite deviation from uniformity of density would be inconsistent with equilibrium. We may therefore assert that the distribution of the fluid when in equilibrium is not absolutely uniform, but is least at the middle of the rod, while at the same time the deviation from uniformity is less than any assignable quantity.

If the force is independent of the distance, $n = 0$ and

$$\rho = C y^{-2} \dots\dots\dots\dots\dots\dots\dots\dots(12),$$

or if r is the distance from the middle of the rod, $2l$ being the length of the rod,

$$\rho = \frac{C}{l^2 - r^2} \dots\dots\dots\dots\dots\dots\dots\dots..(13).$$

If C were finite, the whole mass would be infinite. Hence if the mass of fluid in the rod is finite it must be concentrated into two equal masses and placed at the two ends of the rod.

Let us next consider a disk on which two chords are drawn intersecting at the point P at a small angle θ, and let corresponding elements be taken of the two sectors so formed.

In this case the section of either sector is proportional to the distance of the element from the point of intersection, and therefore the two sections are proportional to the values of y at the two elements. Hence if ρy^{3-n} is constant, the particle at the point of intersection will be in equilibrium.

If the edge of the disk is the ellipse whose equation is

$$1 - \frac{\xi^2}{a^2} - \frac{\eta^2}{b^2} = 0 \dots\dots\dots\dots\dots\dots\dots(14),$$

and if at any point within it

$$1 - \frac{\xi^2}{a^2} - \frac{\eta^2}{b^2} = p^2 \dots\dots\dots\dots\dots\dots\dots(15),$$

and if the length of a diameter parallel to the given chord is $2d$, then the value of y for any point of the chord is

$$y = pd \dots\dots\dots\dots\dots\dots\dots\dots(16).$$

Hence if
$$p = Cp^{n-3} \dots\dots\dots\dots\dots\dots\dots(17),$$

a particle placed at any point of the disk will be in equilibrium under the action of any pair of sectors formed by chords intersecting at that point, and therefore it will be absolutely in equilibrium.

When as in the case of electricity, $n = 2$,

$$\rho = Cp^{-1} \dots\dots\dots\dots\dots\dots\dots(18),$$

the known law of distribution of density.

If the repulsion were inversely as the distance, the fluid would be accumulated in the circumference of the disk, leaving the rest entirely empty.

If the force were inversely as the cube of the distance, the density would be uniform over the surface of the disk.

Lastly, let us consider a solid ellipsoid, the equation of the surface being

$$1 - \frac{\xi^2}{a^2} - \frac{\eta^2}{b^2} - \frac{\zeta^2}{c^2} = 0,$$

and at any point within it let

$$1 - \frac{\xi^2}{a^2} - \frac{\eta^2}{b^2} - \frac{\zeta^2}{c^2} = p^2.$$

At any point of a chord drawn parallel to a diameter whose length is $2d$ the value of y is pd.

If we consider a double cone of small angular aperture whose vertex is at a given point, and whose axis is this chord, the sections at two corresponding elements are in the ratio of the squares of the distances of the elements from the given point, and therefore in the ratio of the values of p^2 at these elements. Hence the condition to be satisfied is

$$\rho p^{4-n} = C, \text{ a constant.}$$

If this condition be fulfilled the fluid will be in equilibrium at every point of the ellipsoid.

If $n = 2$, $$\rho = Cp^{-2}$$

is the condition of equilibrium. But if C is finite the whole mass of the fluid in the ellipsoid if distributed according to this law of density would be infinite. Hence if the whole quantity of fluid is finite it must be accumulated entirely on the surface, and the interior will be entirely empty, as we know already.

If the force is inversely as the fourth power of the distance the density within the ellipsoid will be uniform.

[From the *Proceedings of the Cambridge Philosophical Society*, Vol. III. 1877.]

LXXXVI. *On Approximate Multiple Integration between Limits by Summation.*

It is often desirable to obtain the approximate value of an integral taken between limits in cases in which, though we can ascertain the value of the quantity to be integrated for any given values of the variables, we are not able to express the integral as a mathematical function of the variables.

A method of deducing the result of a single integration between limits from the values of the quantity corresponding to a series of equidistant values of the independent variable was invented by Cotes in 1707, and given in his Lectures in 1709. Newton's tract *Methodus Differentialis* (see Horsley's edition of Newton's Works (1779), Vol. I. p. 521) was published in 1711.

Cotes' rules are given in his *Opera Miscellanea*, edited by Dr Robert Smith, and placed at the end of his *Harmonia Mensurarum*. He gives the proper multipliers for the ordinates up to eleven ordinates, but he gives no details of the method by which he ascertained the values of these multipliers.

Gauss, in his *Methodus nova Integralium Valores per Approximationem Inveniendi* (Göttingische gelehrte Anzeigen, 1814, Sept. 26, or Werke, III. 202) shews how to calculate Cotes' multipliers, and goes on to investigate the case in which the values of the independent variable are not supposed to be equidistant, but are chosen so as with a given number of values to obtain the highest degree of approximation.

He finds that by a proper choice of the values of the variable the value of the integral may be calculated to the same degree of approximation as would be obtained by means of double the number of equidistant values.

The equation, the roots of which give the proper values of the variable, is identical in form with that which gives the zero values of a zonal spherical harmonic.

Double Integration.

There is a particular kind of double integration which can be treated in a somewhat similar manner, namely, when the quantity to be integrated is a function of a linear function of the two independent variables.

Thus if

$$I = \int_{x_1}^{x_2} \int_{y_1}^{y_2} u \, dx \, dy \dots\dots\dots(1),$$

where u is a function of r, and

$$r = a + bx + cy \dots\dots\dots(2),$$

let

$$x = \tfrac{1}{2}(x_2 + x_1) + \tfrac{1}{2} p (x_2 - x_1) \dots\dots\dots(3),$$

$$y = \tfrac{1}{2}(y_2 + y_1) + \tfrac{1}{2} q (y_2 - y_1) \dots\dots\dots(4),$$

$$I = \tfrac{1}{4}(x_2 - x_1)(y_2 - y_1) \int_{-1}^{1}\int_{-1}^{1} u \, dp \, dq \dots\dots\dots(5).$$

If we write

$$r_0 = a + \tfrac{1}{2} b (x_2 + x_1) + \tfrac{1}{2} c (y_2 + y_1) \dots\dots\dots(6),$$

$$\beta = \tfrac{1}{2} b (x_2 - x_1) \dots\dots\dots(7),$$

$$\gamma = \tfrac{1}{2} c (y_2 - y_1) \dots\dots\dots(8),$$

$$\zeta = \beta p + \gamma q \dots\dots\dots(9),$$

we may consider u as a function of ζ of the form

$$u = A_0 + A_1 \zeta + A_2 \zeta^2 + \&c. \dots\dots\dots(10),$$

$$\tfrac{1}{4}\int_{-1}^{1}\int_{-1}^{1} u \, dp \, dq = A_0 + \tfrac{1}{3} A_2 (\beta^2 + \gamma^2) + A_4 (\tfrac{1}{5}\beta^4 + \tfrac{1}{9}\beta^2\gamma^2 + \tfrac{1}{5}\gamma^4) + \&c. \dots (11).$$

Now let u_0 be the value of u corresponding to $\zeta = 0$,

$\qquad\qquad u_1$ and u'_1 $\qquad\qquad\qquad\qquad\qquad \zeta = \pm \zeta_1,$

$\qquad\qquad u_2$ and u'_2 $\qquad\qquad\qquad\qquad\qquad \zeta = \pm \zeta_2,$

and if we assume

$$I = (x_2 - x_1)(y_2 - y_1)\{R_0 u_0 + R_1 (u_1 + u'_1) + R_2 (u_2 + u'_2) + \&c.\} \dots\dots(12),$$

$$I = (x_2 - x_1)(y_2 - y_1)\{(R_0 + 2R_1 + 2R_2 + \&c.) A_0 + (2R_1\zeta_1^2 + 2R_2\zeta_2^2 + \&c.) A_2 + \&c.\} \dots (13),$$

then since the form of the function u, and therefore the values of the coefficients A_0, A_1, A_2, &c. must be considered entirely arbitrary, we may equate the coefficients of A_0, &c. in equations (11) and (13) as follows:

$$R_0 + 2R_1 + 2R_2 + \text{&c.} \quad = 1 \qquad\qquad\qquad\qquad\qquad\quad = B_0,$$

$$2R_1\zeta_1^2 + 2R_2\zeta_2^2 + \text{&c.} = \tfrac{1}{3}\beta^2 + \tfrac{1}{3}\gamma^2 \qquad\qquad\qquad\quad = B_1,$$

$$2R_1\zeta_1^4 + 2R_2\zeta_2^4 + \text{&c.} = \tfrac{1}{5}\beta^4 + \tfrac{1}{3}\beta^2\gamma^2 + \tfrac{1}{5}\gamma^4 \qquad\qquad = B_2,$$

$$2R_1\zeta_1^6 + 2R_2\zeta_2^6 + \text{&c.} = \tfrac{1}{7}\beta^6 + \beta^4\gamma^2 + \beta^2\gamma^4 + \tfrac{1}{7}\gamma^6 \qquad = B_3,$$

$$2R_1\zeta_1^8 + 2R_2\zeta_2^8 + \text{&c.} = \tfrac{1}{9}\beta^8 + \tfrac{4}{3}\beta^6\gamma^2 + \tfrac{14}{5}\beta^4\gamma^4 + \tfrac{4}{3}\beta^2\gamma^6 + \tfrac{1}{9}\gamma^8 = B_4,$$

&c.

If we write S_1 for the sum of all the values of $\qquad\zeta^2$,

$\qquad\qquad\quad S_2$ for the sum of all products such as ζ_1^2, ζ_2^2,

$\qquad\qquad\quad S_3 \dots\dots\dots\dots\dots\dots\dots\dots\dots\dots\dots\dots\dots, \zeta_1^2,\ \zeta_2^2,\ \zeta_3^2,$

then for r terms

$$B_1S_r - B_2S_{r-1} + B_3S_{r-2} - \text{&c.}\ (-)^r B_{r+1} = 0,$$

$$B_2S_r - B_3S_{r-1} + B_4S_{r-2} - \text{&c.}\ (-)^r B_{r+2} = 0,$$

$$\dots\dots\dots\dots\dots\dots\dots\dots\dots\dots\dots\dots\dots\dots\dots\dots$$

$$B_{r+1}S_r - B_{r+2}S_{r-1} + B_{r+3}S_{r-2} - \text{&c.}\ (-)^r B_{2r+1} = 0,$$

a set of r equations, from which the quantities R_1, R_2 have been eliminated, and from which we may determine the r quantities $S_1 \dots S_r$, and the values of ζ are then given as the roots of the equation

$$\zeta^{2r} - S_1\zeta^{2r-2} + S_2\zeta^{2r-4} - \text{&c.}\ (-)^r S_r = 0.$$

Thus if we have three values of ζ they should be

$$\zeta_0 = 0, \qquad \zeta_1 = \pm\left[3\beta^4 + 10\beta^2\gamma^2 + 3\gamma^4\right]^{\frac{1}{2}}\left[5\beta^2 + 5\gamma^2\right]^{-\frac{1}{2}},$$

$$R_0 = \tfrac{4}{3}\,\frac{\beta^4 + 5\beta^2\gamma^2 + \gamma^4}{3\beta^4 + 10\beta^2\gamma^2 + 3\gamma^4}, \qquad R_1 = \tfrac{5}{6}\,\frac{\beta^4 + 2\beta^2\gamma^2 + \gamma^4}{3\beta^4 + 10\beta^2\gamma^2 + 3\gamma^4}.$$

If $\beta = \gamma = 1$,

$$\zeta_0 = 0, \qquad \zeta_1 = \pm\sqrt{\tfrac{8}{5}},$$

$$R_0 = \tfrac{7}{12}, \qquad R_1 = \tfrac{5}{24}.$$

When the quantity to be integrated is a perfectly general function of the variables we must proceed in a different manner.

We may begin as before by transforming the double integral into one between the limits ± 1 for both variables, so that

$$I = \int_{x_1}^{x_2}\int_{y_1}^{y_2} u\,dx\,dy = \tfrac{1}{4}(x_2 - x_1)(y_2 - y_1)\int_{-1}^{1}\int_{-1}^{1} u\,dp\,dq \quad\ldots\ldots\ldots\ldots(1).$$

Let $\Sigma(u_n)$ denote the sum of the eight values of u corresponding to the following eight systems of values of p and q,

$$(a_n, b_n),\ (a_n, -b_n),\ (-a_n, b_n),\ (-a_n, -b_n);$$

$$(b_n, a_n),\ (b_n, -a_n),\ (-b_n, a_n),\ (-b_n, -a_n),$$

and let us assume that the value of the integral is of the form

$$I = \tfrac{1}{4}(x_2 - x_1)(y_2 - y_1)\{R_0\Sigma(u_0) + R_1\Sigma(u_1) + \&c. + R_n\Sigma(u_n)\} \quad\ldots\ldots\ldots(2).$$

The values of the coefficients R, a and b are to be deduced from equations formed by equating the sum of the terms in $p^a q^\beta$ in this expression with the integral

$$\int_{-1}^{+1}\int_{-1}^{+1} p^a q^\beta\,dp\,dq = \frac{4}{(a+1)(\beta+1)} \quad\ldots\ldots\ldots\ldots\ldots(3).$$

Only those terms in which both a and β are even will require to be considered, for the symmetrical distribution of the values of p and q ensures that the terms in which either a or β is odd must disappear.

Also since the expression is symmetrical with respect to p and q, the term in $p^\beta q^a$ will give an equation identical with that in $p^a q^\beta$.

We may therefore write down the equations at once, leaving out the factor $p^a q^\beta$ common to each term, but writing it at the side to indicate how the equation was obtained. There are $a+1$ equations in the first group, in which $\beta = 0$,

$$p^0 q^0 \qquad\qquad \Sigma[2R_n] \qquad\qquad = 4,$$

$$p^2 q^0 \qquad\qquad \Sigma[R_n(p_n^2 + q_n^2)] \qquad = \tfrac{4}{3},$$

$$p^4 q^0 \qquad\qquad \Sigma[R_n(p_n^4 + q_n^4)] \qquad = \tfrac{4}{5},$$

$$p^{2a} q^0 \qquad\qquad \Sigma[R_n(p_n^{2a} + q_n^{2a})] = \frac{4}{2a+1}.$$

There are $a-1$ equations in the second group, in which $\beta = 2$,

p^2q^2 $\qquad\qquad \Sigma\left[2R_np_n^2q_n^2\right] \qquad = \dfrac{4}{3.3}.$

p^4q^2 $\qquad\qquad \Sigma\left[R_np_n^2q_n^2(p_n^2+q_n^2)\right] \qquad = \dfrac{4}{5.3}.$

$p^{2a-2}q^2$ $\qquad\quad \Sigma\left[R_np_n^2q_n^2(p_n^{2a-4}+q_n^{2a-4})\right] = \dfrac{4}{(2a-1).3}.$

There will be $a-3$ equations in which $\beta = 4$, and so on. Hence if a is even, the whole number of equations is

$$\left(\frac{a}{2}+1\right)^2.$$

If a is odd, the number is

$$\frac{(a+1)(a+3)}{4}.$$

To satisfy these equations we have in general, for each group of values of u, three disposable quantities, R, p and q.

If, however, the central ordinate be selected it will constitute the first group, and will introduce only one disposable quantity, namely R_o.

Also, if ordinates lying on the axes of p or of q be chosen, the groups so formed contain only two disposable quantities, one of the ordinates being zero.

Also for ordinates lying on the diagonals, $q=p$, so that for these also there are only two disposable quantities.

Thus if $a=3$, the number of equations is $\dfrac{4.6}{4}=6$; and if we select the central ordinate, giving one disposable quantity, a group of four points on the axes, giving two disposable quantities, and a group of eight points giving three disposable quantities, we shall be able to satisfy the six equations, and to form an expression for the integral which will be correct for any function not exceeding the seventh degree.

We assume

$$\int_{-1}^{1}\int_{-1}^{1} udpdq = Pu_o + Q\Sigma(u_{p,o}) + R\Sigma(u_{q,r}) \quad\dots\dots\dots\dots\dots(4).$$

The equations are

$$P + 4Q + 8R = 4,$$
$$Qp^2 + 2R(q^2 + r^2) = \tfrac{2}{3},$$
$$Qp^4 + 2R(q^4 + r^4) = \tfrac{2}{5},$$
$$Qp^6 + 2R(q^6 + r^6) = \tfrac{2}{7},$$
$$2Rq^2r^2 = \tfrac{1}{9},$$
$$Rq^2r^2(q^2 + r^2) = \tfrac{1}{15}.$$

The solution of these equations gives

$$p^2 = \tfrac{12}{35}, \qquad\qquad p = \pm 0.5855571,$$
$$q^2 = \tfrac{3}{5}\left[1 + \left(\tfrac{6}{31}\right)^{\frac{1}{2}}\right], \qquad q = \pm 0.9294971,$$
$$r^2 = \tfrac{3}{5}\left[1 - \left(\tfrac{6}{31}\right)^{\frac{1}{2}}\right], \qquad r = \pm 0.57969554,$$
$$P = \tfrac{8}{162}, \qquad Q = \tfrac{98}{162}, \qquad R = \tfrac{31}{162}.$$

The positions of the thirteen points are given in the annexed figure.

TRIPLE INTEGRATION.

In extending this method to triple integration we meet with the curious result, that in certain cases the solution indicates that we are to employ values of the function some of which correspond to values of the variables outside the limits of integration.

Thus if we endeavour to determine twenty-seven sets of values of x, y and z, with a corresponding set of multipliers, so as to express the value of the triple integral in the form

$$\int_{-a}^{a}\int_{-b}^{b}\int_{-c}^{c} u\,dxdydz = abc\{Ou_o + P\Sigma(u_p) + Q\Sigma(u_q) + R\Sigma(u_r)\}\ldots\ldots(1),$$

where u_o denotes the value of u when $x=y=z=0$;

$\Sigma(u)$ denotes the sum of the six values of u for which

$$x = \pm pa,\quad 0,\quad\quad 0,$$
$$y = 0,\quad\quad \pm pd,\quad 0,$$
$$z = 0,\quad\quad 0,\quad\quad \pm pc;$$

$\Sigma(u_q)$ denotes the sum of the twelve values of u for which

$$x = 0,\quad\quad \pm qa,\quad \pm qa,$$
$$y = \pm qb,\quad 0,\quad\quad \pm qb,$$
$$z = \pm qc,\quad \pm qc,\quad 0;$$

and $\Sigma(u_r)$ denotes the sum of the eight values of u for which

$$x = \pm ra,$$
$$y = \pm rb,$$
$$z = \pm rc,$$

where the signs may be taken in any order.

The equations to be satisfied in order that equation (1) may be satisfied for any function of x, y and z of not more than seven dimensions are

$$O + 6P + 12Q + 8R = 8,$$
$$2Pp^2 + 8Qq^2 + 8Rr^2 = \tfrac{8}{3},$$
$$2Pp^4 + 8Qq^4 + 8Rr^4 = \tfrac{8}{5},$$
$$2Pp^6 + 8Qq^6 + 8Rr^6 = \tfrac{8}{7},$$
$$4Qq^4 + 8Rr^4 = \tfrac{8}{9},$$
$$4Qq^6 + 8Rr^6 = \tfrac{8}{15},$$
$$8Rr^6 = \tfrac{8}{27}.$$

The solution of these equations gives two systems of values:

$$First\ System.\qquad\qquad\qquad Second\ System.$$

$$\frac{1}{p_1^2} = 1 + (\tfrac{5}{33})^{\frac{1}{2}}, \qquad\qquad \frac{1}{p_2^2} = 1 - (\tfrac{5}{33})^{\frac{1}{2}}.$$

$$\frac{1}{q_1^2} = \tfrac{5}{7}\left[2 - (\tfrac{11}{15})^{\frac{1}{2}}\right], \qquad\qquad \frac{1}{q_2^2} = \tfrac{5}{7}\left[2 + (\tfrac{11}{15})^{\frac{1}{2}}\right].$$

$$\frac{1}{r_1^2} = \tfrac{1}{7}\left[13 + 4(\tfrac{11}{15})^{\frac{1}{2}}\right], \qquad\qquad \frac{1}{r_2^2} = \tfrac{1}{7}\left[13 - 4(\tfrac{11}{15})^{\frac{1}{2}}\right].$$

$$p_1 = 0\text{·}969773, \qquad\qquad\qquad p_2 = 2\text{·}638430.$$

$$q_1 = 1\text{·}119224, \qquad\qquad\qquad q_2 = 0\text{·}602526.$$

$$r_1 = 0\text{·}652817, \qquad\qquad\qquad r_2 = 0\text{·}855044.$$

$$O_1 = -2\text{·}856446, \qquad\qquad\quad O_2 = -7\text{·}999462.$$

$$P_1 = \ \ 1\text{·}106789, \qquad\qquad\quad P_2 = \ \ 0\text{·}000513.$$

$$Q_1 = \ \ 0\text{·}032304, \qquad\qquad\quad Q_2 = \ \ 1\text{·}238514.$$

$$R_1 = \ \ 0\text{·}478508, \qquad\qquad\quad R_2 = \ \ 0\text{·}094777.$$

In the first system q_1 is greater than unity, and in the second system p_2 is greater than unity, so that in either case one set of the values of u corresponds to values of the variables outside of the limits of integration.

This, of course, renders the method useless in determining the integral from the *measured* values of the quantity u, as when we wish to determine the weight of a brick from the specific gravities of samples taken from 27 selected places in the brick, for we are directed by the method to take some of the samples from places outside the brick.

But this is not the case contemplated in the mathematical enunciation. All that we have proved is that if u be a function of x, y, z of not more than seven dimensions, our method will lead to a correct value, and of course we can determine the value of such a function for any values of the variables, whether they lie within the limits of integration or not.

[From the *Proceedings of the Cambridge Philosophical Society.* Vol. III. Pt. III.]

LXXXVII. *On the Unpublished Electrical Papers of the* Hon. HENRY CAVENDISH.

CAVENDISH published only two papers relating to electricity, "An attempt to explain some of the principal Phænomena of Electricity by Means of an Elastic Fluid" (*Phil. Trans.* 1771, pp. 584—677), and "An account of some Attempts to imitate the Effects of the Torpedo by Electricity" (*Phil. Trans.* for 1776, pp. 196—225). He left behind him, however, some twenty packets of manuscript on mathematical and experimental electricity. These were placed by the then Earl of Burlington, now Duke of Devonshire, in the hands of the late Sir William Snow Harris, who appears to have made "an abstract of them with a commentary of great value on their contents." This was sent to Dr George Wilson when he was preparing his Life of Cavendish (*Works of the Cavendish Society,* Vol. I. London, 1851). It was afterwards returned to Sir W. S. Harris, but I have not been able to learn whether it is still in existence. The Cavendish manuscripts, however, were placed in my hands by the Duke of Devonshire in 1874, and they are now almost ready for publication.

They may be divided into three classes:

(A) Mathematical propositions, intended to follow those in the paper of 1771, and numbered accordingly. Some of these are important as shewing the clear ideas of Cavendish with respect to what we now call charge, potential, and the capacity of a conductor; but the great improvements in the mathematical treatment of electricity since the time of Cavendish have rendered others superfluous.

We come next to an account of the experiments on which the mathematical theory was founded. This is a manuscript fully prepared for the press, and since it refers to the second part of the published paper of 1771 as "the second part of this Work," it must have been intended to be published as a book, along with a reprint of that paper. It contains no dates, but as it refers to experiments which we know were made in 1773, it must have been written after that time, but I do not think later than 1775.

It forms a scientifically arranged treatise on electricity. A manuscript entitled "Thoughts concerning electricity" seems to form a kind of introduction to this treatise, for it contains several important definitions and hypotheses which are not afterwards repeated.

Next comes the fundamental experiment, in which it is proved that a conducting sphere insulated within a hollow conducting sphere does not become charged when the hollow sphere is charged and the inner sphere is made to communicate with it.

Cavendish proves that if this is the case, the law of force must be that of the inverse square, and also that if the index instead of being 2 had been $2 \pm \frac{1}{59}$, his method would have detected the charge on the inner sphere.

The experiment has been repeated this summer by Mr MacAlister of St John's College with a delicate quadrant electrometer capable of detecting a charge many thousand times smaller than Cavendish could detect by his straw electrometer, so that we may now assert that the index cannot exceed or fall short of 2 by the millionth of a unit.

The second experiment is a repetition of this, using one parallelopiped within another instead of the two spheres.

He then describes his apparatus for comparing the charges of different bodies, or, as we should say, their capacities.

He first shews (Exp. 3) that the charge, communicated to a body connected to another body at a great distance by a fine wire, does not depend on the form of the wire, or on the point where it touches the body.

Exp. 4 is on the capacities of bodies of the same shape and size but of different substances.

Exp. 5 compares the capacity of two circles with that of another of twice the diameter.

Exp. 6 compares the capacity of two short wires with that of a long one.

Exp. 7 compares the capacities of bodies of different forms, the most important of which are a disk and a sphere.

Exp. 8 compares the charge of the middle of three parallel plates with that of the outer plates

In the next part of his researches he investigates the capacities of condensers formed of plates of different kinds of glass, rosin, wax, shellac, &c. coated with disks of tinfoil, and also of plates of air between two flat conductors. He finds that the electricity spreads on the surface of the plate beyond the tinfoil coatings, and he investigates most carefully the extent of this spreading, and how it depends on the strength of the electrification.

After correcting for the spreading, he finds that for coated plates of the same substance the observed capacity is proportional to the computed capacity, but it is always several times greater than the computed capacity, except in the case of plates of air. Cavendish thus anticipated Faraday in the discovery of the specific inductive capacity of dielectrics, and in the measurement of this quantity for different substances.

For these experiments Cavendish constructed a large number of coated plates with capacities so arranged that by combining them he could measure the capacity of any conductor from a sphere 12·1 inches diameter to his large battery of 49 Leyden jars. He expressed the capacity of any conductor in what he calls "inches of electricity," that is to say the *diameter* of a sphere of equal capacity expressed in inches.

The details and dates of the experiments referred to in this work are contained in three volumes of experiments in the years 1771, 1772 and 1773, in a separate collection of "*Measurements*" and in a paper entitled "*Results*," in which the experiments of different days are compared together. Besides these there are experiments of other kinds which are not described in the treatise.

The most important of these experiments are those on the electric resistance of different substances, which were continued to the year 1781.

He compares the resistance of solutions of sea salt of various strengths from saturation to 1 in 20000, and measures the diminution of resistance as the temperature rises. He also compares the resistance of solutions of sea salt with that of solutions containing chemical equivalents of other salts in the same quantity of water. He finds the resistance of distilled water to be very great, and much greater for fresh distilled water than for distilled water kept for some time in a glass bottle.

I have compared Cavendish's results with those recently obtained by Kohlrausch, and find them all within 10 per cent. and many much nearer.

Cavendish also investigates the relation between the resistance and the velocity of the current, and finds the power of the velocity to be by different experiments 1·08, 1·03, 0·976 and 1, and he finally concludes that the resistance is as the first power of the velocity, thus anticipating Ohm's Law.

The general accuracy of these results is the more remarkable when we consider the method by which they were obtained, forty years before the invention of the galvanometer.

Every comparison of two resistances was made by Cavendish by connecting one end of each resistance-tube with the external coatings of a set of equally charged Leyden jars and touching the jars in succession with a piece of metal held in one hand, while with a piece of metal in the other hand he touched alternately the ends of the two resistances. He thus compared the sensation of the shock felt when the one or the other resistance in addition to the resistance of his body was placed in the path of the discharge. His results therefore are derived from the comparison of the sensations produced by an enormous number of shocks passed through his own body.

The skill which he thus acquired in the discrimination of shocks was so great that he is probably accurate even when he tells us that the shock when taken through a long thin copper wire wound on a large reel was sensibly greater than when taken direct. The experiment is certainly worth repeating, to determine whether the intensification of the physiological effect on account of the oscillatory character of the discharge through a coil would in any case compensate for the weakening effect of the resistance of the coil. But I have not hitherto succeeded in obtaining this result. Indeed on comparing the shock through two coils of equal resistance, one of which had far more self-induction than the other, I found the shock sensibly feebler through the coil of large self-induction.

[From the *Encyclopædia Britannica*.]

LXXXVIII. *Constitution of Bodies.*

THE question whether the smallest parts of which bodies are composed are finite in number, or whether, on the other hand, bodies are infinitely divisible, relates to the *ultimate* constitution of bodies, and is treated of in the article ATOM.

The mode in which elementary substances combine to form compound substances is called the *chemical* constitution of bodies, and is treated of in CHEMISTRY.

The mode in which sensible quantities of matter, whether elementary or compound, are aggregated together so as to form a mass having certain observed properties, is called the *physical* constitution of bodies.

Bodies may be classed in relation to their physical constitution by considering the effects of internal stress in changing their dimensions. When a body can exist in equilibrium under the action of a stress which is not uniform in all directions it is said to be solid.

When a body is such that it cannot be in equilibrium unless the stress at every point is uniform in all directions, it is said to be fluid.

There are certain fluids, any portion of which, however small, is capable of expanding indefinitely, so as to fill any vessel, however large. These are called gases. There are other fluids, a small portion of which, when placed in a large vessel, does not at once expand so as to fill the vessel uniformly, but remains in a collected mass at the bottom, even when the pressure is removed. These fluids are called liquids.

When a liquid is placed in a vessel so large that it only occupies a part of it, part of the liquid begins to evaporate, or in other words it passes into the state of a gas, and this process goes on either till the whole of the liquid is evaporated, or till the density of the gaseous part of the substance has reached a certain limit. The liquid and the gaseous portions of the substance are then in equilibrium. If the volume of the vessel be now made smaller, part of the gas will be condensed as a liquid, and if it be made larger, part of the liquid will be evaporated as a gas.

The processes of evaporation and condensation, by which the substance passes from the liquid to the gaseous, and from the gaseous to the liquid state, are discontinuous processes, that is to say, the properties of the substance are very different just before and just after the change has been effected. But this difference is less in all respects the higher the temperature at which the change takes place, and Cagniard de la Tour in 1822[*] first shewed that several substances, such as ether, alcohol, bisulphide of carbon, and water, when heated to a temperature sufficiently high, pass into a state which differs from the ordinary gaseous state as much as from the liquid state. Dr Andrews has since[†] made a complete investigation of the properties of carbonic acid both below and above the temperature at which the phenomena of condensation and evaporation cease to take place, and has thus explored as well as established the continuity of the liquid and gaseous states of matter.

For carbonic acid at a temperature, say of $0°$ C., and at the ordinary pressure of the atmosphere, is a gas. If the gas be compressed till the pressure rises to about 40 atmospheres, condensation takes place, that is to say, the substance passes in successive portions from the gaseous to the liquid condition.

If we examine the substance when part of it is condensed, we find that the liquid carbonic acid at the bottom of the vessel has all the properties of a liquid, and is separated by a distinct surface from the gaseous carbonic acid which occupies the upper part of the vessel.

But we may transform gaseous carbonic acid at $0°$ C. into liquid carbonic acid at $0°$ C. without any abrupt change, by first raising the temperature of the gas above $30°.92$ C. which is the *critical* temperature, then raising the pressure to about 80 atmospheres, and then cooling the substance, still at high pressure, to zero.

During the whole of this process the substance remains perfectly homogeneous. There is no surface of separation between two forms of the substance, nor can any sudden change be observed like that which takes place when the gas is condensed into a liquid at low temperatures; but at the end of the

---

[*] *Annales de Chimie*, 2ᵐᵉ série, XXI. et XXII.
[†] *Phil. Trans.* 1869, p. 575.

process the substance is undoubtedly in the liquid state, for if we now diminish the pressure to somewhat less than 40 atmospheres the substance will exhibit the ordinary distinction between the liquid and the gaseous state, that is to say, part of it will evaporate, leaving the rest at the bottom of the vessel, with a distinct surface of separation between the gaseous and the liquid parts.

The passage of a substance between the liquid and the solid state takes place with various degrees of abruptness. Some substances, such as some of the more crystalline metals, seem to pass from a completely fluid to a completely solid state very suddenly. In some cases the melted matter appears to become thicker before it solidifies, but this may arise from a multitude of solid crystals being formed in the still liquid mass, so that the consistency of the mass becomes like that of a mixture of sand and water, till the melted matter in which the crystals are swimming becomes all solid.

There are other substances, most of them colloidal, such that when the melted substance cools it becomes more and more viscous, passing into the solid state with hardly any discontinuity. This is the case with pitch.

The theory of the consistency of solid bodies will be discussed in the article ELASTICITY, but the manner in which a solid behaves when acted on by stress furnishes us with a system of names of different degrees and kinds of solidity.

A fluid, as we have seen, can support a stress only when it is uniform in all directions, that is to say, when it is of the nature of a hydrostatic pressure.

There are a great many substances which so far correspond to this definition of a fluid that they cannot remain in permanent equilibrium if the stress within them is not uniform in all directions.

In all existing fluids, however, when their motion is such that the shape of any small portion is continually changing, the internal stress is not uniform in all directions, but is of such a kind as to tend to check the relative motion of the parts of the fluid.

This capacity of having inequality of stress called into play by inequality of motion is called viscosity. All real fluids are viscous, from treacle and tar to water and ether and air and hydrogen.

When the viscosity is very small the fluid is said to be mobile, like water and ether.

When the viscosity is so great that a considerable inequality of stress, though it produces a continuously increasing displacement, produces it so slowly that we can hardly see it, we are often inclined to call the substance a solid, and even a hard solid. Thus the viscosity of cold pitch or of asphalt is so great that the substance will break rather than yield to any sudden blow, and yet if it is left for a sufficient time it will be found unable to remain in equilibrium under the slight inequality of stress produced by its own weight, but will flow like a fluid till its surface becomes level.

If, therefore, we define a fluid as a substance which cannot remain *in permanent equilibrium* under a stress not equal in all directions, we must call these substances fluids, though they are so viscous that we can walk on them without leaving any footprints.

If a body, after having its form altered by the application of stress, tends to recover its original form when the stress is removed, the body is said to be elastic.

The ratio of the numerical value of the stress to the numerical value of the strain produced by it is called the *coefficient of elasticity*, and the ratio of the strain to the stress is called the *coefficient of pliability*.

There are as many kinds of these coefficients as there are kinds of stress and of strains or components of strains produced by them.

If, then, the values of the coefficients of elasticity were to increase without limit, the body would approximate to the condition of a rigid body.

We may form an elastic body of great pliability by dissolving gelatine or isinglass in hot water and allowing the solution to cool into a jelly. By diminishing the proportion of gelatine the coefficient of elasticity of the jelly may be diminished, so that a very small force is required to produce a large change of form in the substance.

When the deformation of an elastic body is pushed beyond certain limits depending on the nature of the substance, it is found that when the stress is removed it does not return exactly to its original shape, but remains permanently deformed. These limits of the different kinds of strain are called the limits of perfect elasticity.

There are other limits which may be called the limits of cohesion or of tenacity, such that when the deformation of the body reaches these limits the body breaks, tears asunder, or otherwise gives way, and the continuity of its substance is destroyed.

A body which can have its form permanently changed without any flaw or break taking place is called *mild*. When the force required is small the

78—2

body is said to be *soft;* when it is great the body is said to be *tough.* A body which becomes flawed or broken before it can be permanently deformed is called *brittle.* When the force required is great the body is said to be *hard.*

The stiffness of a body is measured by the force required to produce a given amount of deformation.

Its strength is measured by the force required to break or crush it.

We may conceive a solid body to approximate to the condition of a fluid in several different ways.

If we knead fine clay with water, the more water we add the softer does the mixture become till at last we have water with particles of clay slowly subsiding through it. This is an instance of a mechanical mixture the constituents of which separate of themselves. But if we mix bees-wax with oil, or rosin with turpentine, we may form permanent mixtures of all degrees of softness, and so pass from the solid to the fluid state through all degrees of viscosity.

We may also begin with an elastic and somewhat brittle substance like gelatine, and add more and more water till we form a very weak jelly which opposes a very feeble resistance to the motion of a solid body, such as a spoon, through it. But even such a weak jelly may not be a true fluid, for it may be able to withstand a very small force, such as the weight of a small mote. If a small mote or seed is enclosed in the jelly, and if its specific gravity is different from that of the jelly, it will tend to rise to the top or sink to the bottom. If it does not do so we conclude that the jelly is not a fluid but a solid body, very weak, indeed, but able to sustain the force with which the mote tends to move.

It appears, therefore, that the passage from the solid to the fluid state may be conceived to take place by the diminution without limit either of the coefficient of rigidity, or of the ultimate strength against rupture, as well as by the diminution of the viscosity. But whereas the body is not a true fluid till the ultimate strength, or the coefficient of rigidity, is reduced to zero, it is not a true solid as long as the viscosity is not infinite.

Solids, however, which are not viscous in the sense of being capable of an unlimited amount of change of form, are yet subject to alterations depending on the time during which stress has acted on them. In other words, the stress at any given instant depends, not only on the strain at that instant, but on the previous history of the body. Thus the stress is somewhat greater when the strain is increasing than when it is diminishing, and if the strain is continued for a long time, the body, when left to itself, does not at once return to its original shape, but appears to have taken a set, which, however, is not a permanent set, for the body slowly creeps back towards its original shape with a motion which may be observed to go on for hours and even weeks after the body is left to itself.

Phenomena of this kind were pointed out by Weber and Kohlrausch (*Pogg. Ann.* Bd. 54, 119 and 128), and have been described by O. E. Meyer (*Pogg. Ann.* Bd. 131, 108), and by Maxwell (*Phil. Trans.* 1866, p. 249), and a theory of the phenomena has been proposed by Dr L. Boltzmann (*Wiener Sitzungs-berichte*, 8th October 1874).

The German writers refer to the phenomena by the name of "elastische Nachwirkung," which might be translated "elastic reaction" if the word reaction were not already used in a different sense. Sir W. Thomson speaks of the viscosity of elastic bodies.

The phenomena are most easily observed by twisting a fine wire suspended from a fixed support, and having a small mirror suspended from the lower end, the position of which can be observed in the usual way by means of a tele-scope and scale. If the lower end of the wire is turned round through an angle not too great, and then left to itself, the mirror makes oscillations, the extent of which may be read off on the scale. These oscillations decay much more rapidly than if the only retarding force were the resistance of the air, shewing that the force of torsion in the wire must be greater when the twist is increasing than when it is diminishing. This is the phenomenon described by Sir W. Thomson under the name of the viscosity of elastic solids. But we may also ascertain the middle point of these oscillations, or the point of temporary equilibrium when the oscillations have subsided, and trace the varia-tions of its position.

If we begin by keeping the wire twisted, say for a minute or an hour, and then leave it to itself, we find that the point of temporary equilibrium is displaced in the direction of twisting, and that this displacement is greater the longer the wire has been kept twisted. But this displacement of the point of equilibrium is not of the nature of a permanent set, for the wire, if left to itself, creeps back towards its original position, but always slower and slower. This slow motion has been observed by the writer going on for more than a week, and he also found that if the wire was set in vibration the motion of the point of equilibrium was more rapid than when the wire was not in vibration.

We may produce a very complicated series of motions of the lower end of the wire by previously subjecting the wire to a series of twists. For instance, we may first twist it in the positive direction, and keep it twisted for a day, then in the negative direction for an hour, and then in the positive direction for a minute. When the wire is left to itself the displacement, at first positive, becomes negative in a few seconds, and this negative displacement increases for some time. It then diminishes, and the displacement becomes positive, and lasts a longer time, till it too finally dies away.

The phenomena are in some respects analogous to the variations of the surface temperature of a very large ball of iron which has been heated in a furnace for a day, then placed in melting ice for an hour, then in boiling water for a minute, and then exposed to the air; but a still more perfect analogy may be found in the variations of potential of a Leyden jar which has been charged positively for a day, negatively for an hour, and positively again for a minute*.

The effects of successive magnetization on iron and steel are also in many respects analogous to those of strain and electrification†.

The method proposed by Boltzmann for representing such phenomena mathematically is to express the actual stress, $L_{(t)}$, in terms not only of the actual strain, $\theta_{(t)}$, but of the strains to which the body has been subjected during all previous time.

His equation is of the form

$$L_t = K\theta_t - \int_0^\infty \psi(\omega)\,\theta_{t-\omega}\,d\omega,$$

where ω is the interval of time reckoned backwards from the actual time t to the time $t-\omega$, when the strain $\theta_{t-\omega}$ existed, and $\psi(\omega)$ is some function of that interval.

We may describe this method of deducing the actual state from the previous states as the historical method, because it involves a knowledge of the previous history of the body. But this method may be transformed into another,

---

* See Dr Hopkinson, "On the Residual Charge of the Leyden Jar," *Proc. R. S.* xxiv. 408, March 30, 1876.

† See Wiedemann's *Galvanismus*, vol. ii. p. 567.

in which the present state is not regarded as influenced by any state which has ceased to exist. For if we expand $\theta_{t-\omega}$ by Taylor's theorem,

$$\theta_{t-\omega} = \theta_t - \omega \frac{d\theta}{dt} + \frac{\omega^2}{1\cdot 2} \frac{d^2\theta}{dt^2} - \&c.$$

and if we also write

$$A = \int_0^\infty \psi(\omega)\, d\omega, \qquad B = \int_0^\infty \omega\psi(\omega)\, d\omega, \qquad C = \int_0^\infty \frac{\omega^2}{1\cdot 2} \psi(\omega)\, d\omega, \quad \&c.$$

then equation (1) becomes

$$L = (K - A)\,\theta + B\frac{d\theta}{dt} - C\frac{d^2\theta}{dt^2} + \&c.$$

where no symbols of time are subscribed, because all the quantities refer to the present time.

This expression of Boltzmann's, however, is not in any sense a physical theory of the phenomena; it is merely a mathematical formula which, though it represents some of the observed phenomena, fails to express the phenomenon of permanent deformation. Now we know that several substances, such as gutta-percha, India-rubber, &c., may be permanently stretched when cold, and yet when afterwards heated to a certain temperature they recover their original form. Gelatine also may be dried when in a state of strain, and may recover its form by absorbing water.

We know that the molecules of all bodies are in motion. In gases and liquids the motion is such that there is nothing to prevent any molecule from passing from any part of the mass to any other part; but in solids we must suppose that some, at least, of the molecules merely oscillate about a certain mean position, so that, if we consider a certain group of molecules, its configuration is never very different from a certain stable configuration, about which it oscillates.

This will be the case even when the solid is in a state of strain, provided the amplitude of the oscillations does not exceed a certain limit, but if it exceeds this limit the group does not tend to return to its former configuration, but begins to oscillate about a new configuration of stability, the strain in which is either zero, or at least less than in the original configuration.

The condition of this breaking up of a configuration must depend partly on the amplitude of the oscillations, and partly on the amount of strain in the original configuration; and we may suppose that different groups of molecules, even in a homogeneous solid, are not in similar circumstances in this respect.

Thus we may suppose that in a certain number of groups the ordinary agitation of the molecules is liable to accumulate so much that every now and then the configuration of one of the groups breaks up, and this whether it is in a state of strain or not. We may in this case assume that in every second a certain proportion of these groups break up, and assume configurations corresponding to a strain uniform in all directions.

If all the groups were of this kind, the medium would be a viscous fluid.

But we may suppose that there are other groups, the configuration of which is so stable that they will not break up under the ordinary agitation of the molecules unless the average strain exceeds a certain limit, and this limit may be different for different systems of these groups.

Now if such groups of greater stability are disseminated through the substance in such abundance as to build up a solid framework, the substance will be a solid, which will not be permanently deformed except by a stress greater than a certain given stress.

But if the solid also contains groups of smaller stability and also groups of the first kind which break up of themselves, then when a strain is applied the resistance to it will gradually diminish as the groups of the first kind break up, and this will go on till the stress is reduced to that due to the more permanent groups. If the body is now left to itself, it will not at once return to its original form, but will only do so when the groups of the first kind have broken up so often as to get back to their original state of strain.

This view of the constitution of a solid, as consisting of groups of molecules some of which are in different circumstances from others, also helps to explain the state of the solid after a permanent deformation has been given to it. In this case some of the less stable groups have broken up and assumed new configurations, but it is quite possible that others, more stable, may still retain their original configurations, so that the form of the body is determined by the equilibrium between these two sets of groups; but if, on account of rise of temperature, increase of moisture, violent vibration, or any other cause, the breaking up of the less stable groups is facilitated, the more stable groups may again assert their sway, and tend to restore the body to the shape it had before its deformation.

[From the *Encyclopædia Britannica*.]

LXXXIX. *Diffusion.*

SOME liquids, such as mercury and water, when placed in contact with each other do not mix at all, but the surface of separation remains distinct, and exhibits the phenomena described under CAPILLARY ACTION. Other pairs of liquids, such as chloroform and water, mix, but only in certain proportions. The chloroform takes up a little water, and the water a little chloroform; but the two mixed liquids will not mix with each other, but remain in contact separated by a surface shewing capillary phenomena. The two liquids are then in a state of equilibrium with each other. The conditions of the equilibrium of heterogeneous substances have been investigated by Professor J. Willard Gibbs in a series of papers published in the *Transactions of the Connecticut Academy of Arts and Sciences*, Vol. III. part I. p. 108. Other pairs of liquids, and all gases, mix in all proportions.

When two fluids are capable of being mixed, they cannot remain in equilibrium with each other; if they are placed in contact with each other the process of mixture begins of itself, and goes on till the state of equilibrium is attained, which, in the case of fluids which mix in all proportions, is a state of uniform mixture.

This process of mixture is called diffusion. It may be easily observed by taking a glass jar half full of water and pouring a strong solution of a coloured salt, such as sulphate of copper, through a long-stemmed funnel, so as to occupy the lower part of the jar. If the jar is not disturbed we may trace the process of diffusion for weeks, months, or years, by the gradual rise of the colour into the upper part of the jar, and the weakening of the colour in the lower part.

This, however, is not a method capable of giving accurate measurements of the composition of the liquid at different depths in the vessel. For more exact determinations we may draw off a portion from a given stratum of the mixed liquid, and determine its composition either by chemical methods or by its specific gravity, or any other property from which its composition may be deduced.

But as the act of removing a portion of the fluid interferes with the process of diffusion, it is desirable to be able to ascertain the composition of any stratum of the mixture without removing it from the vessel. For this purpose Sir W. Thomson places in the jar a number of glass beads of different densities, which indicate the densities of the strata in which they are observed to float. The principal objection to this method is, that if the liquids contain air or any other gas, bubbles are apt to form on the glass beads, so as to make them float in a stratum of less density than that marked on them.

M. Voit has observed the diffusion of cane-sugar in water by passing a ray of plane-polarized light horizontally through the vessel, and determining the angle through which the plane of polarization is turned by the solution of sugar. This method is of course applicable only to those substances which cause rotation of the plane of polarized light.

Another method is to place the diffusing liquids in a hollow glass prism, with its refracting edge vertical, and to determine the deviation of a ray of light passing through the prism at different depths. The ray is bent downwards on account of the variable density of the mixture, as well as towards the thicker part of the prism; but by making it pass as near the edge of the prism as possible, the vertical component of the refraction may be made very small; and by placing the prism within a vessel of water having parallel sides of glass, we can get rid of the constant part of the deviation, and are able to use a prism of large angle, so as to increase the part due to the diffusing substance. At the same time we can more easily control and register the temperature.

The laws of diffusion were first investigated by Graham. The diffusion of gases has recently been observed with great accuracy by Loschmidt, and that of liquids by Fick and by Voit.

Diffusion as a Molecular Motion.

If we observe the process of diffusion with our most powerful microscopes, we cannot follow the motion of any individual portions of the fluids. We cannot point out one place in which the lower fluid is ascending, and another in which the upper fluid is descending. There are no currents visible to us, and the motion of the material substances goes on as imperceptibly as the conduction of heat or of electricity. Hence the motion which constitutes diffusion must be distinguished from those motions of fluids which we can trace by means of floating motes. It may be described as a motion of the fluids, not *in mass* but by *molecules*.

When we reason upon the hypothesis that a fluid is a continuous homogeneous substance, it is comparatively easy to define its density and velocity; but when we admit that it may consist of molecules of different kinds, we must revise our definitions. We therefore define these quantities by considering that part of the medium which at a given instant is within a certain small region surrounding a given point. This region must be so small that the properties of the medium as a whole are sensibly the same throughout the region, and yet it must be so large as to include a large number of molecules. We then define the density of the medium at the given point as the mass of the medium within this region divided by its volume, and the velocity of the medium as the momentum of this portion of the medium divided by its mass.

If we consider the motion of the medium relative to an imaginary surface supposed to exist within the region occupied by the medium, and if we define the flow of the medium through the surface as the mass of the medium which in unit of time passes through unit of area of the surface, then it follows from the above definitions that the velocity of the medium resolved in the direction of the normal to the surface is equal to the flow divided by the density. If we suppose the surface itself to move with the same velocity as the fluid, and in the same direction, there will be no flow through it.

Having thus defined the density, velocity, and flow of the medium as a whole, or, as it is sometimes expressed, "in mass," we may now consider one of the fluids which constitute the medium, and define its density, velocity, and flow in the same way. The velocity of this fluid may be different from that of the medium in mass, and its velocity relative to that of the medium is the velocity of diffusion which we have to study.

Diffusion of Gases according to the Kinetic Theory.

So many of the phenomena of gases are found to be explained in a consistent manner by the kinetic theory of gases, that we may describe with considerable probability of correctness the kind of motion which constitutes diffusion in gases. We shall therefore consider gaseous diffusion in the light of the kinetic theory before we consider diffusion in liquids.

A gas, according to the kinetic theory, is a collection of particles or molecules which are in rapid motion, and which, when they encounter each other, behave pretty much as elastic bodies, such as billiard balls, would do if no energy were lost in their collisions. Each molecule travels but a very small distance between one encounter and another, so that it is every now and then altering its velocity both in direction and magnitude, and that in an exceedingly irregular manner.

The result is that the velocity of any molecule may be considered as compounded of two velocities, one of which, called the velocity of the medium, is the same for all the molecules, while the other, called the velocity of agitation, is irregular both in magnitude and in direction, though the average magnitude of the velocity may be calculated, and any one direction is just as likely as any other.

The result of this motion is, that if in any part of the medium the molecules are more numerous than in a neighbouring region, more molecules will pass from the first region to the second than in the reverse direction, and for this reason the density of the gas will tend to become equal in all parts of the vessel containing it, except in so far as the molecules may be crowded towards one direction by the action of an external force such as gravity. Since the motion of the molecules is very swift, the process of equalization of density in a gas is a very rapid one, its velocity of propagation through the gas being that of sound.

Let us now consider two gases in the same vessel, the proportion of the gases being different in different parts of the vessel, but the pressure being everywhere the same. The agitation of the molecules will still cause more molecules of the first gas to pass from places where that gas is dense to places where it is rare than in the opposite direction, but since the second gas is dense where the first one is rare, its molecules will be for the most part travelling in the opposite direction. Hence the molecules of the two gases will encounter each other, and every encounter will act as a check to the process of equalization of the density of each gas throughout the mixture.

The interdiffusion of two gases in a vessel is therefore a much slower process than that by which the density of a single gas becomes equalized, though it appears from the theory that the final result is the same, and that each gas is distributed through the vessel in precisely the same way as if no other gas had been present, and this even when we take into account the effect of gravity.

If we apply the ordinary language about fluids to a single gas of the mixture, we may distinguish the forces which act on an element of volume as follows :—

1st. Any external force, such as gravity or electricity.

2nd. The difference of the pressure *of the particular gas* on opposite sides of the element of volume. [The pressure due to other gases is to be considered of no account.]

3rd. The resistance arising from the percolation of the gas through the other gases which are moving with different velocity.

The resistance due to encounters with the molecules of any other gas is proportional to the velocity of the first gas relative to the second, to the product of their densities, and to a coefficient which depends on the nature of the gases and on the temperature. The equations of motion of one gas of a mixture are therefore of the form

$$\rho_1 \frac{\delta_1 u_1}{\delta t} + \frac{dp_1}{dx} - X_1\rho_1 + C_{12}\rho_1\rho_2(u_1 - u_2) + C_{13}\rho_1\rho_3(u_1 - u_3) + \&c. = 0,$$

where the symbol of operation $\frac{\delta_1}{\delta t}$ prefixed to any quantity denotes the time-variation of that quantity at a point which moves along with that medium which is distinguished by the suffix $(_1)$, or more explicitly

$$\frac{\delta_1}{\delta t} = \frac{d}{dt} + u_1\frac{d}{dx} + v_1\frac{d}{dy} + w_1\frac{d}{dz}.$$

In the state of ultimate equilibrium $u_1 = u_2 = \&c. = 0$, and the equation is reduced to

$$\frac{dp_1}{dx} - X\rho_1 = 0,$$

which is the ordinary form of the equations of equilibrium of a single fluid.

Hence, when the process of diffusion is complete, the density of each gas at any point of the vessel is the same as if no other gas were present.

If V_1 is the potential of the force which acts on the gas, and if in the equation $p_1 = k_1 \rho_1$, k_1 is constant, as it is when the temperature is uniform, then the equation of equilibrium becomes

$$k_1 \frac{d\rho_1}{dx} + \frac{dV_1}{dx} \rho_1 = 0,$$

the solution of which is

$$\rho_1 = A_1 e^{-\frac{V_1}{k_1}}.$$

Hence if, as in the case of gravity, V is the same for all gases, but k is different for different gases, the composition of the mixture will be different in different parts of the vessel, the proportion of the heavier gases, for which k is smaller, being greater at the bottom of the vessel than at the top. It would be difficult, however, to obtain experimental evidence of this difference of composition except in a vessel more than 100 metres high, and it would be necessary to keep the vessel free from inequalities of temperature for more than a year, in order to allow the process of diffusion to advance to a state even half-way towards that of ultimate equilibrium. The experiment might, however, be made in a few minutes by placing a tube, say 10 centimetres long, on a whirling apparatus, so that one end shall be close to the axis, while the other is moving at the rate, say, of 50 metres per second. Thus if equal volumes of hydrogen and carbonic acid were used, the proportion of hydrogen to carbonic acid would be about $\frac{1}{134}$ greater at the end of the tube nearest the axis. The experimental verification of the result is important, as it establishes a method of effecting the partial separation of gases without the selective action of chemical agents.

Let us next consider the case of diffusion in a vertical cylinder. Let m_1 be the mass of the first gas in a column of unit area extending from the bottom of the vessel to the height x, and let v_1 be the volume which this mass would occupy at unit pressure, then

$$k_1 m_1 = v_1,$$

$$\rho_1 = \frac{dm_1}{dx}, \qquad \rho_1 u_1 = -\frac{dm_1}{dt},$$

$$p_1 = \frac{dv_1}{dx}, \qquad p_1 u_1 = -\frac{dv_1}{dt};$$

and the equation of motion becomes

$$\frac{1}{k_1\left|\frac{dv_1}{dx}\right|^2}\left\{\frac{d^2v_1}{dx^2}\overline{\frac{dv_1}{dt}}\right|^2 - \frac{d^2v_1}{dt^2}\overline{\frac{dv_1}{dx}}\right|^2\right\} + \frac{d^2v_1}{dx^2} - \frac{X}{k_1}\frac{dv_1}{dx}$$

$$+ \frac{C_{12}}{k_1k_2}\left\{\frac{dv_2}{dt}\frac{dv_1}{dx} - \frac{dv_1}{dt}\frac{dv_2}{dx}\right\} + \&\text{c.} = 0.$$

If we add the corresponding equations together for all the gases, we find that the terms in C_{12} destroy each other, and that if the medium is not affected with sensible currents the first term of each equation may be neglected. In ordinary experiments we may also neglect the effect of gravity, so that we get

$$\frac{d^2}{dx^2}(v_1 + v_2) = 0,$$

or

$$v_1 + v_2 = px,$$

where p is the uniform pressure of the mixed medium. Hence

$$\frac{dv_2}{dt} = -\frac{dv_1}{dt} \quad \text{and} \quad \frac{dv_2}{dx} = p - \frac{dv_1}{dx},$$

and the equation becomes

$$\frac{d^2v_1}{dx^2} = \frac{C_{12}}{k_1k_2}p\frac{dv_1}{dt},$$

an equation, the form of which is identical with the well-known equation for the conduction of heat. We may write it

$$\frac{dv_1}{dt} = D\frac{d^2v_1}{dx^2}.$$

D is called the coefficient of diffusion. It is equal to

$$\frac{k_1k_2}{C_{12}p}.$$

It therefore varies inversely as the total pressure of the medium, and if the coefficient of resistance, C_{12}, is independent of the temperature, it varies directly as the product k_1k_2, i.e., as the square of the absolute temperature. It is probable, however, that the effect of temperature is not so great as this would make it.

In liquids D probably depends on the proportion of the ingredients of the mixed medium as well as on the temperature. The dimensions of D are $L^2 T^{-1}$, where L is the unit of length and T the unit of time.

The values of the coefficients of diffusion of several pairs of gases have been determined by Loschmidt*. They are referred in the following table to the centimetre and the second as units, for the temperature 0° C. and the pressure of 76 centimetres of mercury.

	D
Carbonic acid and air	0·1423
Carbonic acid and hydrogen . . .	0·5558
Oxygen and hydrogen	0·7214
Carbonic acid and oxygen	0·1409
Carbonic acid and carbonic oxide . .	0·1406
Carbonic acid and marsh gas . . .	0·1586
Carbonic acid and nitrous oxide . . .	0·0983
Sulphurous acid and hydrogen . . .	0·4800
Oxygen and carbonic oxide . . .	0·1802
Carbonic oxide and hydrogen . . .	0·6422

Diffusion in Liquids.

The nature of the motion of the molecules in liquids is less understood than in gases, but it is easy to see that if there is any irregular displacement among the molecules in a mixed liquid, it must, on the whole, tend to cause each component to pass from places where it forms a large proportion of the mixture to places where it is less abundant. It is also manifest that any relative motion of two constituents of the mixture will be opposed by a resistance arising from the encounters between the molecules of these components. The value of this resistance, however, depends, in liquids, on more complicated conditions than in gases, and for the present we must regard it as a function of all the physical properties of the mixture at the given place, that is to say, its temperature and pressure, and the proportions of the different components of the mixture.

* Imperial Academy of Vienna, 10th March, 1870.

The coefficient of interdiffusion of two liquids must therefore be considered as depending on all the physical properties of the mxiture according to laws which can be ascertained only by experiment.

Thus Fick has determined the coefficient of diffusion for common salt in water to be 0·00000116, and Voit has found that of cane-sugar to be 0·00000365.

It appears from these numbers that in a vessel of the same size the process of diffusion of liquids requires a greater number of days to reach a given stage than the process of diffusion of gases in the same vessel requires seconds.

When we wish to mix two liquids, it is not sufficient to place them in the same vessel, for if the vessel is, say, a metre in depth, the lighter liquid will lie above the denser, and it will be many years before the mixture becomes even sensibly uniform. We therefore stir the two liquids together, that is to say, we move a solid body through the vessel, first one way, then another, so as to make the liquid contents eddy about in as complicated a manner as possible. The effect of this is that the two liquids, which originally formed two thick horizontal layers, one above the other, are now disposed in thin and excessively convoluted strata, which, if they could be spread out, would cover an immense area. The effect of the stirring is thus to increase the area over which the process of diffusion can go on, and to diminish the distance between the diffusing liquids; and since the time required for diffusion varies as the square of the thickness of the layers, it is evident that by a moderate amount of stirring the process of mixture which would otherwise require years may be completed in a few seconds. That the process is not instantaneous is easily ascertained by observing that for some time after the stirring the mixture appears full of streaks, which cause it to lose its transparency. This arises from the different indices of refraction of different portions of the mixture which have been brought near each other by stirring. The surfaces of separation are so drawn out and convoluted, that the whole mass has a woolly appearance, for no ray of light can pass through it without being turned many times out of its path.

Graham observed that the diffusion both of liquids and gases takes place through porous solid bodies, such as plugs of plaster of Paris or plates of pressed plumbago, at a rate not very much less than when no such body is interposed, and this even when the solid partition is amply sufficient to check all ordinary currents, and even to sustain a considerable difference of pressure on its opposite sides.

But there is another class of cases in which a liquid or a gas can pass through a diaphragm, which is not, in the ordinary sense, porous. For instance, when carbonic acid gas is confined in a soap bubble it rapidly escapes. The gas is absorbed at the inner surface of the bubble, and forms a solution of carbonic acid in water. This solution diffuses from the inner surface of the bubble, where it is strongest, to the outer surface, where it is in contact with air, and the carbonic acid evaporates and diffuses out into the atmosphere. It is also found that hydrogen and other gases can pass through a layer of caoutchouc. Graham shewed that it is not through pores, in the ordinary sense, that the motion takes place, for the ratios are determined by the chemical relations between the gases and the caoutchouc, or the liquid film.

According to Graham's theory, the caoutchouc is a colloïd substance,—that is, one which is capable of combining, in a temporary and very loose manner, with indeterminate proportions of certain other substances, just as glue will form a jelly with various proportions of water. Another class of substances, which Graham called crystalloïd, are distinguished from these by being always of definite composition, and not admitting of these temporary associations. When a colloïd body has in different parts of its mass different proportions of water, alcohol, or solutions of crystalloïd bodies, diffusion takes place through the colloïd body, though no part of it can be shewn to be in the liquid state.

On the other hand, a solution of a colloïd substance is almost incapable of diffusion through a porous solid, or another colloïd body. Thus, if a solution of gum and salt in water is placed in contact with a solid jelly of gelatine and alcohol, alcohol will be diffused into the gum, and salt and water will be diffused into the gelatine, but the gum and the gelatine will not diffuse into each other.

There are certain metals whose relations to certain gases Graham explained by this theory. For instance, hydrogen can be made to pass through iron and palladium at a high temperature, and carbonic oxide can be made to pass through iron. The gases form colloïdal unions with the metals, and are diffused through them as water is diffused through a jelly. Root has lately found that hydrogen can pass through platinum, even at ordinary temperatures.

By taking advantage of the different velocities with which different liquids and gases pass through parchment-paper and other solid bodies, Graham was enabled to effect many remarkable analyses. He called this method the method of Dialysis.

Diffusion and Evaporation, Condensation, Solution, and Absorption.

The rate of evaporation of liquids is determined principally by the rate of diffusion of the vapour through the air or other gas which lies above the liquid. Indeed, the coefficient of diffusion of the vapour of a liquid through air can be determined in a rough but easy manner by placing a little of the liquid in a test tube, and observing the rate at which its weight diminishes by evaporation day by day. For at the surface of the liquid the density of the vapour is that corresponding to the temperature, whereas at the mouth of the test tube the air is nearly pure. Hence, if p be the pressure of the vapour corresponding to the temperature, and $p = k\rho$, and if m be the mass evaporated in time t, and diffused into the air through a distance h *, then

$$D = \frac{khm}{pt}.$$

This method is not, of course, applicable to vapours which are rarer than the superincumbent gas.

The solution of a salt in a liquid goes on in the same way, and so does the absorption of a gas by a liquid.

These processes are all accelerated by currents, for the reason already explained.

The processes of evaporation and condensation go on much more rapidly when no air or other non-condensible gas is present. Hence the importance of the air-pump in the steam engine.

Relation between Diffusion of Matter and Diffusion of Heat.

The same motion of agitation of the molecules of gases which causes two gases to diffuse through each other also causes two portions of the same gas to diffuse through each other, although we cannot observe this kind of diffusion, because we cannot distinguish the molecules of one portion from those of the

---

* h should be taken equal to the height of the tube above the surface of the liquid, together with about $\frac{2}{5}$ of the diameter of the tube.—See Clerk Maxwell's *Electricity*, Art. 309.

other when they are once mixed. If, however, the molecules of one portion have any property whereby they can be distinguished from those of the other, then that property will be communicated from one part of the medium to an adjoining part, and that either by convection—that is by the molecules themselves passing out of one part into the other, carrying the property with them—or by transmission—that is by the property being communicated from one molecule to another during their encounters. The chemical properties by which different substances are recognized are inseparable from their molecules, so that the diffusion of such properties can take place only by the transference of the molecules themselves, but the momentum of a molecule in any given direction and its energy are also properties which may be different in different molecules, but which may be communicated from one molecule to another. Hence the diffusion of momentum and that of energy through the medium can take place in two different ways, whereas the diffusion of matter can take place only in one of these ways.

In gases the great majority of the particles, at any instant, are describing free paths, and it is therefore possible to shew that there is a simple numerical relation between the coefficients of the three kinds of diffusion,—the diffusion of matter, the lateral diffusion of velocity (which is the phenomenon known as the internal friction or viscosity of fluids), and the diffusion of energy (which is called the conduction of heat). But in liquids the majority of the molecules are engaged at close quarters with one or more other molecules, so that the transmission of momentum and of energy takes place in a far greater degree by communication from one molecule to another, than by convection by the molecules themselves. Hence the ratios of the coefficient of diffusion to those of viscosity and thermal conductivity are much smaller in liquids than in gases.

Theory of the Wet Bulb Thermometer.

The temperature indicated by the wet bulb thermometer is determined in great part by the relation between the coefficients of diffusion and thermal conductivity. As the water evaporates from the wet bulb heat must be supplied to it by convection, conduction, or radiation. This supply of heat will not be sufficient to maintain the temperature constant till the temperature of the wet bulb has sunk so far below that of the surrounding air and other bodies that the flow of heat due to the difference of temperature is equal to the latent heat of the vapour which leaves the bulb.

The use of the wet bulb thermometer as a means of estimating the humidity of the atmosphere was employed by Hutton[*] and Leslie[†], but the formula by which the dew-point is commonly deduced from the readings of the wet and dry thermometers was first given by Dr Apjohn[‡].

Dr Apjohn assumes that, when the temperature of the wet bulb is stationary, the heat required to convert the water into vapour is given out by portions of the surrounding air in cooling from the temperature of the atmosphere to that of the wet bulb, and that the air thus cooled becomes saturated with the vapour which it receives from the bulb.

Let m be the mass of a portion of air at a distance from the wet bulb, θ_0 its temperature, p_0 the pressure due to the aqueous vapour in it, and P the whole pressure.

If σ is the specific gravity of aqueous vapour (referred to air), then the mass of water in this portion of air is $\frac{p_0}{P} \sigma m$.

Let this portion of air communicate with the wet bulb till its temperature sinks to θ_1, that of the wet bulb, and the pressure of the aqueous vapour in it rises to p_1, that corresponding to the temperature θ_1.

The quantity of vapour which has been communicated to the air is

$$(p_1 - p_0) \frac{\sigma m}{P},$$

and if L is the latent heat of vapour at the temperature θ_1, the quantity of heat required to produce this vapour is

$$(p_1 - p_0) \frac{\sigma m}{P} L.$$

According to Apjohn's theory, this heat is supplied by the mixed air and vapour in cooling from θ_0 to θ_1.

If S is the specific heat of the air (which will not be sensibly different from that of dry air), this quantity of heat is

$$(\theta_0 - \theta_1) mS.$$

---

[*] Playfair's "Life of Hutton," *Edinburgh Transactions*, Vol. v. p. 67, note.

[†] *Encyc. Brit.*, 8th ed. Vol. I. "Dissertation Fifth," p. 764.

[‡] *Trans. Royal Irish Academy*, 1834.

Equating the two values we obtain

$$p_0 = p_1 - \frac{PS}{L\sigma}(\theta_0 - \theta_1).$$

Here p_0 is the pressure of the vapour in the atmosphere. The temperature—for which this is the maximum pressure—is the dew-point, and p_1 is the maximum pressure corresponding to the temperature θ_1 of the wet bulb. Hence this formula, combined with tables of the pressure of aqueous vapour, enables us to find the dew-point from observations of the wet and dry bulb thermometers.

We may call this the convection theory of the wet bulb, because we consider the temperature and humidity of a portion of air brought from a distance to be affected directly by the wet bulb without communication either of heat or of vapour with other portions of air.

Dr Everett has pointed out as a defect in this theory, that it does not explain how the air can either sink in temperature or increase in humidity unless it comes into absolute contact with the wet bulb. Let us, therefore, consider what we may call the conduction and diffusion theory in calm air, taking into account the effects of radiation.

The steady conduction of heat is determined by the conditions—

$\theta = \theta_0$ at a great distance from the bulb,

$\theta = \theta_1$ at the surface of the bulb,

$\nabla^2\theta = 0$ at any point of the medium.

The steady diffusion of vapour is determined by the conditions—

$p = p_0$ at a great distance from the bulb,

$p = p_1$ at the surface of the bulb,

$\nabla^2 p = 0$ at any point of the medium.

Now, if the bulb had been an electrified conductor, the conditions with respect to the potential would have been

$V = 0$ at a great distance,

$V = V_1$ at the surface,

$\nabla^2 V = 0$ at any point outside the bulb.

Hence the solution of the electrical problem leads to that of the other two. For if V is the potential at any point,

$$\theta = \theta_0 + (\theta_1 - \theta_0)\frac{V}{V_1}, \qquad p = p_0 + (p_1 - p_0)\frac{V}{V_1}.$$

If E is the electric charge of the conductor,

$$4\pi E = -\iint \frac{dV}{d\nu}\, dS,$$

where the double integral is extended over the surface of the bulb, and $d\nu$ is an element of a normal to the surface.

If H is the flow of heat in unit of time from the bulb,

$$H = -K\iint \frac{d\theta}{d\nu}\, dS,$$

and if Q is the flow of aqueous vapour from the bulb,

$$Q = -\frac{D}{k}\iint \frac{dp}{d\nu}\, dS,$$

where k is the ratio of the pressure of aqueous vapour to its density.

If C is the electrical capacity of the bulb, $E = CV_1$,

$$H = 4\pi CK (\theta_1 - \theta_0), \qquad Q = 4\pi C\frac{D}{k} (p_1 - p_0).$$

The heat which leaves the bulb by radiation to external objects at temperature θ_0 may be written

$$h = AR (\theta_1 - \theta_0),$$

where A is the surface of the bulb and R the coefficient of radiation of unit of surface.

When the temperature becomes constant

$$LQ + H + h = 0,$$

$$p_0 = -p_1 \frac{PS}{L\sigma}\left\{\frac{K}{D} + \frac{AR}{4\pi C\rho SD}\right\}(\theta_0 - \theta_1).$$

This formula gives the result of the theory of diffusion, conduction, and radiation in a still atmosphere. It differs from the formula of the convection theory only by the factor in the last term.

The first part of this factor $\dfrac{K}{D}$ is certainly less than unity, and probably about ·77.

If the bulb is spherical and of radius r, $A = 4\pi r^2$ and $C = r$, so that the second part is $\dfrac{Rr}{\rho SD}$.

Hence, the larger the wet bulb, the greater will be the ratio of the effect of radiation to that of conduction. If, on the other hand, the air is in motion, this will increase both conduction and diffusion, so as to increase the ratio of the first part to the second. By comparing actual observations of the dew-point with Apjohn's formula, it has been found that the factor should be somewhat greater than unity. According to our theory it ought to be greater if the bulb is larger, and smaller if there is much wind.

Relation between Diffusion and Electrolytic Conduction.

Electrolysis (see separate article) is a molecular movement of the constituents of a compound liquid in which, under the action of electromotive force, one of the components travels in the positive and the other in the negative direction, the flow of each component, when reckoned in electrochemical equivalents, being in all cases numerically equal to the flow of electricity.

Electrolysis resembles diffusion in being a molecular movement of two currents in opposite directions through the same liquid; but since the liquid is of the same composition throughout, we cannot ascribe the currents to the molecular agitation of a medium whose composition varies from one part to another as in ordinary diffusion, but we must ascribe it to the action of the electromotive force on particles having definite charges of electricity.

The force, therefore, urging an electro-chemical equivalent of either component, or *ion*, as it is called, in a given direction is numerically equal to the electromotive force at a given point of the electrolyte, and is therefore comparable with any ordinary force. The resistance which prevents the current from rising above a certain value is that arising from the encounters of the molecules of the ion with other molecules as they struggle forward through the liquid, and this depends on their relative velocity, and also on the nature of the ion, and of the liquid through which it has to flow.

The average velocity of the ions will therefore increase, till the resistance they meet with is equal to the force which urges them forward, and they will thus acquire a definite velocity proportional to the electric force at the point, but depending also on the nature of the liquid.

If the resistance of the liquid to the passage of the ion is the same for different strengths of solution, the velocity of the ion will be the same for different strengths, but the quantity of it, and therefore the quantity of electricity which passes in a given time, will be proportional to the strength of the solution.

Now, Kohlrausch has determined the conductivity of the solutions of many electrolytes in water, and he finds that for very weak solutions the conductivity is proportional to the strength. When the solution is strong the liquid through which the ions struggle can no longer be considered sensibly the same as pure water, and consequently this proportionality does not hold good for strong solutions.

Kohlrausch has determined the actual velocity in centimetres per second of various ions in weak solutions under an electro-motive force of unit value. From these velocities he has calculated the conductivities of weak solutions of electrolytes different from those of which he made use in calculating the velocity of the ions, and he finds the results consistent with direct experiments on those electrolytes.

It is manifest that we have here important information as to the resistance which the ion meets with in travelling through the liquid. It is not easy, however, to make a numerical comparison between this resistance and any results of ordinary diffusion, for, in the first place, we cannot make experiments on the diffusion of ions. Many electrolytes, indeed, are decomposed by the current into components, one or both of which are capable of diffusion, but these components, when once separated out of the electrolyte, are no longer ions—they are no longer acted on by electric force, or charged with definite quantities of electricity. Some of them, as the metals, are insoluble, and therefore incapable of diffusion; others, like the gases, though soluble in the liquid electrolyte, are not, when in solution, acted on by the current.

Besides this, if we accept the theory of electrolysis proposed by Clausius, the molecules acted on by the electro-motive force are not the whole of the molecules which form the constituents of the electrolyte, but only those which at a given instant are in a state of dissociation from molecules of the other kind, being forced away from them temporarily by the violence of the molecular agitation. If these dissociated molecules form a small proportion of the whole, the velocity of their passage through the medium must be much greater than the mean velocity of the whole, which is the quantity calculated by Kohlrausch.

On Processes by which the Mixture and Separation of Fluids can be effected in a Reversible Manner.

A physical process is said to be reversible when the material system can be made to return from the final state to the original state under conditions which at every stage of the reverse process differ only infinitesimally from the conditions at the corresponding stage of the direct process.

All other processes are called irreversible.

Thus the passage of heat from one body to another is a reversible process if the temperature of the first body exceeds that of the second only by an infinitesimal quantity, because by changing the temperature of either of the bodies by an infinitesimal quantity, the heat may be made to flow back again from the second body to the first.

But if the temperature of the first body is higher than that of the second by a finite quantity, the passage of heat from the first body to the second is not a reversible process, for the temperature of one or both of the bodies must be altered by a finite quantity before the heat can be made to flow back again.

In like manner the interdiffusion of two gases is in general an irreversible process, for in order to separate the two gases the conditions must be very considerably changed. For instance, if carbonic acid is one of the gases, we can separate it from the other by means of quicklime; but the absorption of carbonic acid by quicklime at ordinary temperatures and pressures is an irreversible process, for in order to separate the carbonic acid from the lime it must be raised to a high temperature.

In all reversible processes the substances which are in contact must be in complete equilibrium throughout the process; and Professor Gibbs has shewn the condition of equilibrium to be that not only the temperature and the pressure of the two substances must be the same, but also that the *potential* of each of the component substances must be the same in both compounds, and that there is an additional condition which we need not here specify.

Now, we may obtain complete equilibrium between quicklime and the mixture containing carbonic acid if we raise the whole to a temperature at which the pressure of dissociation of the carbonic acid in carbonate of lime is equal to the pressure of the carbonic acid in the mixed gases. By altering the temperature or the pressure very slowly we may cause carbonic acid to pass from the mixture to the lime, or from the lime to the mixture, in such a manner that the conditions of the system differ only by infinitesimal quantities at the corresponding stages of the direct and the inverse processes. The same thing may be done at lower temperatures by means of potash or soda.

If one of the gases can be condensed into a liquid, and if during the condensation the pressure is increased or the temperature diminished so slowly that the liquid and the mixed gases are always very nearly in equilibrium, the separation and mixture of the gases can be effected in a reversible manner.

The same thing can be done by means of a liquid which absorbs the gases in different proportions, provided that we can maintain such conditions as to temperature and pressure as shall keep the system in equilibrium during the whole process.

If the densities of the two gases are different, we can effect their partial separation by a reversible process which does not involve any of the actions commonly called chemical. We place the mixed gases in a very long horizontal tube, and we raise one end of the tube till the tube is vertical. If this is done so slowly that at every stage of the process the distribution of the two gases is sensibly the same as it would be at the same stage of the reverse process, the process will be reversible, and if the tube is long enough the separation of the gases may be carried to any extent.

In the *Philosophical Magazine* for 1876, Lord Rayleigh has investigated the thermodynamics of diffusion, and has shewn that if two portions of different gases are given at the same pressure and temperature, it is possible, by mixing them by a reversible process, to obtain a certain quantity of work. At the end of the process the two gases are uniformly mixed, and occupy a volume equal to the sum of the volumes they occupied when separate, but the temperature and pressure of the mixture are lower than before.

The work which can be gained during the mixture is equal to that which would be gained by allowing first one gas and then the other to expand from its original volume to the sum of the volumes; and the fall of temperature and pressure is equal to that which would be produced in the mixture by taking away a quantity of heat equivalent to this work.

If the diffusion takes place by an irreversible process, such as goes on when the gases are placed together in a vessel, no external work is done, and there is no fall of temperature or of pressure during the process.

We may arrive at this result by a method which, if not so instructive as that of Lord Rayleigh, is more general, by the use of a physical quantity called by Clausius the Entropy of the system.

The entropy of a body in equilibrium is a quantity such that it remains constant if no heat enters or leaves the body, and such that in general the quantity of heat which enters the body is

$$\int \theta d\phi,$$

where ϕ is the entropy, and θ the absolute temperature.

The entropy of a material system is the sum of the entropy of its parts.

In reversible processes the entropy of the system remains unchanged, but in all irreversible processes the entropy of the system increases.

The increase of entropy involves a diminution of the available energy of the system, that is to say, the total quantity of work which can be obtained from the system. This is expressed by Sir W. Thomson by saying that a certain amount of energy is *dissipated*.

The quantity of energy which is dissipated in a given process is equal to

$$\theta_0(\phi_2 - \phi_1),$$

where ϕ_1 is the entropy at the beginning, and ϕ_2 that at the end of the process, and θ_0 is the temperature of the system in its ultimate state, when no more work can be got out of it.

When we can determine the ultimate temperature we can calculate the amount of energy dissipated by any process; but it is sometimes difficult to do this, whereas the increase of entropy is determined by the known states of the system at the beginning and end of the process.

The entropy of a volume v_1 of a gas at pressure p_1 and temperature θ_1 exceeds its entropy where its volume is v_0 and its temperature θ_0 by the quantity

$$\frac{p_1 v_1}{\theta_1} \left\{ \frac{1}{\gamma - 1} \log \frac{\theta_1}{\theta_0} + \log \frac{v_1}{v_0} \right\}.$$

Hence if volumes v_1 and v_2 of two gases at the same temperature and pressure are mixed so as to occupy a volume $v_1 + v_2$ at the same temperature and pressure, the entropy of the system increases during the process by the quantity

$$\frac{p}{\theta}\left\{v_1 \log \frac{v_1 + v_2}{v_1} + v_2 \log \frac{v_1 + v_2}{v_2}\right\}.$$

Since in this case the temperature does not change during the process, we may calculate the quantity of energy dissipated by multiplying the gain of entropy by the temperature, and we thus find for the dissipation

$$pv_1 \log \frac{v_1 + v_2}{v_1} + pv_2 \log \frac{v_1 + v_2}{v_2},$$

or the sum of the work which would be done by the two portions of gas if each expanded under constant temperature to the volume $v_1 + v_2$.

It is greatest when the two volumes are equal, in which case it is $1 \cdot 386\, pv$, where p is the pressure and v the volume of one of the portions.

Let us now suppose that we have in a vessel two separate portions of gas of equal volume, and at the same pressure and temperature, with a movable partition between them. If we remove the partition the agitation of the molecules will carry them from one side of the partition to the other in an irregular manner, till ultimately the two portions of gas will be thoroughly and uniformly mixed together. This motion of the molecules will take place whether the two gases are the same or different, that is to say, whether we can distinguish between the properties of the two gases or not.

If the two gases are such that we can separate them by a reversible process, then, as we have just shewn, we might gain a definite amount of work by allowing them to mix under certain conditions; and if we allow them to mix by ordinary diffusion, this amount of work is no longer available, but is dissipated for ever. If, on the other hand, the two portions of gas are the same, then no work can be gained by mixing them, and no work is dissipated by allowing them to diffuse into each other.

It appears, therefore, that the process of diffusion does not involve dissipation of energy if the two gases are the same, but that it does if they can be separated from each other by a reversible process.

Now, when we say that two gases are the same, we mean that we cannot distinguish the one from the other by any known reaction. It is not probable, but it is possible, that two gases derived from different sources, but hitherto supposed to be the same, may hereafter be found to be different, and that a method may be discovered of separating them by a reversible process. If this should happen, the process of interdiffusion which we had formerly supposed not to be an instance of dissipation of energy would now be recognized as such an instance.

It follows from this that the idea of dissipation of energy depends on the extent of our knowledge. Available energy is energy which we can direct into any desired channel. Dissipated energy is energy which we cannot lay hold of and direct at pleasure, such as the energy of the confused agitation of molecules which we call heat. Now, confusion, like the correlative term order, is not a property of material things in themselves, but only in relation to the mind which perceives them. A memorandum-book does not, provided it is neatly written, appear confused to an illiterate person, or to the owner who understands it thoroughly, but to any other person able to read it appears to be inextricably confused. Similarly the notion of dissipated energy could not occur to a being who could not turn any of the energies of nature to his own account, or to one who could trace the motion of every molecule and seize it at the right moment. It is only to a being in the intermediate stage, who can lay hold of some forms of energy while others elude his grasp, that energy appears to be passing inevitably from the available to the dissipated state.

[From the *Encyclopædia Britannica*.]

XC. *Diagrams.*

A DIAGRAM is a figure drawn in such a manner that the geometrical relations between the parts of the figure help us to understand relations between other objects. A few have been selected for description in this article on account of their greater geometrical significance.

Diagrams may be classed according to the manner in which they are intended to be used, and also according to the kind of analogy which we recognize between the diagram and the thing represented.

Diagrams of Illustration.

The diagrams in mathematical treatises are intended to help the reader to follow the mathematical reasoning. The construction of the figure is defined in words so that even if no figure were drawn the reader could draw one for himself. The diagram is a good one if those features which form the subject of the proposition are clearly represented. The accuracy of the drawing is therefore of smaller importance than its distinctness.

Metrical Diagrams.

Diagrams are also employed in an entirely different way—namely, for purposes of measurement. The plans and designs drawn by architects and engineers are used to determine the value of certain real magnitudes by measuring certain distances on the diagram. For such purposes it is essential that the drawing be as accurate as possible.

We therefore class diagrams as diagrams of illustration, which merely suggest certain relations to the mind of the spectator, and diagrams drawn to scale, from which measurements are intended to be made.

Methods in which diagrams are used for purposes of measurement are called Graphical methods.

Diagrams of illustration, if sufficiently accurate, may be used for purposes of measurement; and diagrams for measurement, if sufficiently clear, may be used for purposes of demonstration.

There are some diagrams or schemes, however, in which the form of the parts is of no importance, provided their connections are properly shewn. Of this kind are the diagrams of electrical connections, and those belonging to that department of geometry which treats of the degrees of cyclosis, periphraxy, linkedness, and knottedness.

Diagrams purely Graphic and mixed Symbolic and Graphic.

Diagrams may also be classed either as purely graphical diagrams, in which no symbols are employed except letters or other marks to distinguish particular points of the diagrams, and mixed diagrams, in which certain magnitudes are represented, not by the magnitudes of parts of the diagram, but by symbols, such as numbers written on the diagram.

Thus in a map the height of places above the level of the sea is often indicated by marking the number of feet above the sea at the corresponding places on the map.

There is another method in which a line called a contour line is drawn through all the places in the map whose height above the sea is a certain number of feet, and the number of feet is written at some point or points of this line.

By the use of a series of contour lines, the height of a great number of places can be indicated on a map by means of a small number of written symbols. Still this method is not a purely graphical method, but a partly symbolical method of expressing the third dimension of objects on a diagram in two dimensions.

Diagrams in Pairs.

In order to express completely by a purely graphical method the relations of magnitudes involving more than two variables, we must use more than one diagram. Thus in the arts of construction we use plans and elevations and sections through different planes, to specify the form of objects having three dimensions.

In such systems of diagrams we have to indicate that a point in one diagram corresponds to a point in another diagram. This is generally done by marking the corresponding points in the different diagrams with the same letter. If the diagrams are drawn on the same piece of paper we may indicate corresponding points by drawing a line from one to the other, taking care that this line of correspondence is so drawn that it cannot be mistaken for a real line in either diagram.

In the stereoscope the two diagrams, by the combined use of which the form of bodies in three dimensions is recognized, are projections of the bodies taken from two points so near each other that, by viewing the two diagrams simultaneously, one with each eye, we identify the corresponding points intuitively.

The method in which we simultaneously contemplate two figures, and recognize a correspondence between certain points in the one figure and certain points in the other, is one of the most powerful and fertile methods hitherto known in science. Thus in pure geometry the theories of similar, reciprocal, and inverse figures have led to many extensions of the science. It is sometimes spoken of as the method or principle of Duality.

DIAGRAMS IN KINEMATICS.

The study of the motion of a material system is much assisted by the use of a series of diagrams representing the configuration, displacement, and acceleration of the parts of the system.

Diagram of Configuration.

In considering a material system it is often convenient to suppose that we have a record of its position at any given instant in the form of a diagram of configuration.

The position of any particle of the system is defined by drawing a straight line or vector from the origin, or point of reference, to the given particle. The position of the particle with respect to the origin is determined by the magnitude and direction of this vector.

If in the diagram we draw from the origin (which need not be the same point of space as the origin for the material system) a vector equal and parallel to the vector which determines the position of the particle, the end of this vector will indicate the position of the particle in the diagram of configuration.

If this is done for all the particles, we shall have a system of points in the diagram of configuration, each of which corresponds to a particle of the material system, and the relative positions of any pair of these points will be the same as the relative positions of the material particles which correspond to them.

We have hitherto spoken of two origins or points from which the vectors are supposed to be drawn—one for the material system, the other for the diagram. These points, however, and the vectors drawn from them, may now be omitted, so that we have on the one hand the material system and on the other a set of points, each point corresponding to a particle of the system, and the whole representing the configuration of the system at a given instant.

This is called a diagram of configuration.

Diagram of Displacement.

Let us next consider two diagrams of configuration of the same system, corresponding to two different instants.

We call the first the initial configuration and the second the final configuration, and the passage from the one configuration to the other we call the displacement of the system. We do not at present consider the length of time during which the displacement was effected, nor the intermediate stages through which it passed, but only the final result—a change of configuration. To study this change we construct a diagram of displacement.

Let A, B, C be the points in the initial diagram of configuration, and A', B', C' be the corresponding points in the final diagram of configuration.

From o, the origin of the diagram of displacement, draw a vector oa equal and parallel to AA', ob equal and parallel to BB', oc to CC', and so on.

The points, a, b, c, &c., will be such that the vector ab indicates the displacement of b relative to a, and so on. The diagram containing the points a, b, c, &c., is therefore called the diagram of displacement.

In constructing the diagram of displacement we have hitherto assumed that we know the absolute displacements of the points of the system. For we are required to draw a line equal and parallel to AA', which we cannot do unless we know the absolute final position of A, with respect to its initial position. In this diagram of displacement there is therefore, besides the points a, b, c, &c., an *origin*, o, which represents a point absolutely fixed in space. This is necessary because the two configurations do not exist at the same time; and therefore to express their relative position we require to know a point which remains the same at the beginning and end of the time.

But we may construct the diagram in another way which does not assume a knowledge of absolute displacement or of a point fixed in space.

Assuming any point and calling it a, draw ak parallel and equal to B_1A_1 in the initial configuration, and from k draw kb parallel and equal to A_2B_2 in the final configuration. It is easy to see that the position of the point b relative to a will be the same by this construction as by the former construction, only we must observe that in this second construction we use only vectors such as A_1B_1, A_2B_2, which represent the relative position of points both of which exist simultaneously, instead of vectors such as A_1A_2, B_1B_2, which express the position of a point at one instant relative to its position at a former instant, and which therefore cannot be determined by observation, because the two ends of the vector do not exist simultaneously.

It appears therefore that the diagram of displacements, when drawn by the first construction includes an origin o, which indicates that we have assumed a knowledge of absolute displacements. But no such point occurs in the second construction, because we use such vectors only as we can actually observe. Hence the diagram of displacements *without an origin* represents neither more nor less than all we can ever know about the displacement of the material system.

Diagram of Velocity.

If the relative velocities of the points of the system are constant, then the diagram of displacement corresponding to an interval of a unit of time between the initial and the final configuration is called a diagram of relative velocity.

If the relative velocities are not constant, we suppose another system in which the velocities are equal to the velocities of the given system at the given instant and continue constant for a unit of time. The diagram of displacements for this imaginary system is the required diagram of relative velocities of the actual system at the given instant.

It is easy to see that the diagram gives the velocity of any one point relative to any other, but cannot give the absolute velocity of any of them.

Diagram of Acceleration.

By the same process by which we formed the diagram of displacements from the two diagrams of initial and final configuration, we may form a diagram of changes of relative velocity from the two diagrams of initial and final velocities. This diagram may be called that of total accelerations in a finite interval of time.

By the same process by which we deduced the diagram of velocities from that of displacements we may deduce the diagram of rates of acceleration from that of total acceleration.

We have mentioned this system of diagrams in elementary kinematics because they are found to be of use especially when we have to deal with material systems containing a great number of parts, as in the kinetic theory of gases. The diagram of configuration then appears as a region of space swarming with points representing molecules, and the only way in which we can investigate it is by considering the number of such points in unit of volume in different parts of that region, and calling this the *density* of the gas.

In like manner the diagram of velocities appears as a region containing points equal in number but distributed in a different manner, and the number of points in any given portion of the region expresses the number of molecules whose velocities lie within given limits. We may speak of this as the velocity-density.

Path and Hodograph.

When the number of bodies in the system is not so great, we may construct diagrams each of which represents some property of the whole course of the motion.

Thus if we are considering the motion of one particle relative to another, the point on the diagram of configuration which corresponds to the moving particle will trace out a continuous line called the path of the particle.

On the diagram of velocity the point corresponding to the moving particle will trace another continuous line called the hodograph of the particle.

The hodograph was invented and used with great success by Sir W. R. Hamilton as a method of studying the motions of bodies.

DIAGRAMS OF STRESS.

Graphical methods are peculiarly applicable to statical questions, because the state of the system is constant, so that we do not need to construct a series of diagrams corresponding to the successive states of the system.

The most useful of these applications relates to the equilibrium of plane framed structures. Two diagrams are used, one called the diagram of the frame and the other called the diagram of stress.

The structure itself consists of a number of separable pieces or links jointed together at their extremities. In practice these joints have friction, or may be made purposely stiff, so that the force acting at the extremity of a piece may not pass exactly through the axis of the joint; but as it is unsafe to make the stability of the structure depend in any degree upon the stiffness of joints, we assume in our calculations that all the joints are perfectly smooth, and therefore that the force acting on the end of any link passes through the axis of the joint.

The axes of the joints of the structure are represented by points in the diagram of the frame.

The link which connects two joints in the actual structure may be of any shape, but in the diagram of the frame it is represented by a straight line joining the points representing the two joints.

If no force acts on the link except the two forces acting through the centres of the joints, these two forces must be equal and opposite, and their direction must coincide with the straight line joining the centres of the joints.

If the force acting on either extremity of the link is directed towards the other extremity, the stress on the link is called pressure and the link is called a strut. If it is directed away from the other extremity, the stress on the link is called tension and the link is called a tie.

In this case, therefore, the only stress acting in a link is a pressure or a tension in the direction of the straight line which represents it in the diagram of the frame, and all that we have to do is to find the magnitude of this stress.

In the actual structure, gravity acts on every part of the link, but in the diagram we substitute for the actual weight of the different parts of the link, two weights which have the same resultant acting at the extremities of the link.

We may now treat the diagram of the frame as composed of links without weight, but loaded at each joint with a weight made up of portions of the weights of all the links which meet in that joint.

If any link has more than two joints we may substitute for it in the diagram an imaginary stiff frame, consisting of links, each of which has only two joints.

The diagram of the frame is now reduced to a system of points, certain pairs of which are joined by straight lines, and each point is in general acted on by a weight or other force acting between it and some point external to the system.

To complete the diagram we may represent these external forces as links, that is to say, straight lines joining the points of the frame to points external to the frame. Thus each weight may be represented by a link joining the point of application of the weight with the centre of the earth.

But we can always construct an imaginary frame having its joints in the lines of action of these external forces, and this frame, together with the real frame and the links representing external forces, which join points in the one frame to points in the other frame, make up together a complete self-strained system in equilibrium, consisting of points connected by links acting by pressure or tension. We may in this way reduce any real structure to the case of a system of points with attractive or repulsive forces acting between certain pairs of these points, and keeping them in equilibrium.

The direction of each of these forces is sufficiently indicated by that of the line joining the points, so that we have only to determine its magnitude.

We might do this by calculation, and then write down on each link the pressure or the tension which acts in it.

We should in this way obtain a mixed diagram in which the stresses are represented graphically as regards direction and position, but symbolically as regards magnitude.

But we know that a force may be represented in a purely graphical manner by a straight line in the direction of the force containing as many units of length as there are units of force in the force. The end of this line is marked with an arrow head to shew in which direction the force acts.

According to this method each force is drawn in its proper position in the diagram of configuration of the frame. Such a diagram might be useful as a record of the result of calculation of the magnitude of the forces, but it would be of no use in enabling us to test the correctness of the calculation.

But we have a graphical method of testing the equilibrium of any set of forces acting at a point. We draw in series a set of lines parallel and proportional to these forces. If these lines form a closed polygon the forces are in equilibrium. We might in this way form a series of polygons of forces, one for each joint of the frame. But in so doing we give up the principle of drawing the line representing a force from the point of application of the force, for all the sides of the polygon cannot pass through the same point, as the forces do.

We also represent every stress twice over, for it appears as a side of both the polygons corresponding to the two joints between which it acts.

But if we can arrange the polygons in such a way that the sides of any two polygons which represent the same stress coincide with each other, we may form a diagram in which every stress is represented in direction and magnitude, though not in position, by a single line which is the common boundary of the two polygons which represent the joints at the extremities of the corresponding piece of the frame.

We have thus obtained a pure diagram of stress in which no attempt is made to represent the configuration of the material system, and in which every force is not only represented in direction and magnitude by a straight line, but the equilibrium of the forces at any joint is manifest by inspection, for we have only to examine whether the corresponding polygon is closed or not.

The relations between the diagram of the frame and the diagram of stress are as follows :—

To every link in the frame corresponds a straight line in the diagram of stress which represents in magnitude and direction the stress acting in that link.

To every joint in the frame corresponds a closed polygon in the diagram, and the forces acting at that joint are represented by the sides of the polygon taken in a certain cyclical order. The cyclical order of the sides of the two adjacent polygons is such that their common side is traced in opposite directions in going round the two polygons.

The direction in which any side of a polygon is traced is the direction of the force acting on that joint of the frame which corresponds to the polygon, and due to that link of the frame which corresponds to the side.

This determines whether the stress of the link is a pressure or a tension.

If we know whether the stress of any one link is a pressure or a tension, this determines the cyclical order of the sides of the two polygons corresponding to the ends of the links, and therefore the cyclical order of all the polygons, and the nature of the stress in every link of the frame.

Definition of Reciprocal Diagrams.

When to every point of concourse of the lines in the diagram of stress corresponds a closed polygon in the skeleton of the frame, the two diagrams are said to be reciprocal.

The first extensions of the method of diagrams of forces to other cases than that of the funicular polygon were given by Rankine in his *Applied Mechanics* (1857). The method was independently applied to a large number of cases by Mr W. P. Taylor, a practical draughtsman in the office of the well-known contractor Mr J. B. Cochrane, and by Professor Clerk Maxwell in his lectures in King's College, London. In the *Phil. Mag.* for 1864 the latter pointed out the reciprocal properties of the two diagrams, and in a paper on "Reciprocal Figures, Frames, and Diagrams of Forces," *Trans. R. S. Edinburgh*, Vol. XXVI. (1870), he shewed the relation of the method to Airy's function of stress and to other mathematical methods.

Professor Fleeming Jenkin has given a number of applications of the method to practice (*Trans. R. S. Edin.*, Vol. XXV.).

Cremona (*Le figure reciproche nella statica grafica*, Milan, 1872) has deduced the construction of reciprocal figures from the theory of the two components of a wrench as developed by Möbius.

Culmann, in his *Graphische Statik*, makes great use of diagrams of forces, some of which, however, are not reciprocal.

M. Maurice Levy in his *Statique Graphique* (Paris, 1874) has treated the whole subject in an elementary but copious manner.

Mr R. H. Bow, C.E., F.R.S.E., in his work on *The Economics of Construction in relation to Framed Structures*, 1873, has materially simplified the process of drawing a diagram of stress reciprocal to a given frame acted on by a system of equilibrating external forces.

Instead of lettering the joints of the frame, as is usually done, or the links of the frame, as was the writer's custom, he places a letter in each of the polygonal areas inclosed by the links of the frame, and also in each of the divisions of surrounding space as separated by the lines of action of the external forces.

When one link of the frame crosses another, the point of apparent intersection of the links is treated as if it were a real joint, and the stresses of each of the intersecting links are represented twice in the diagram of stress, as the opposite sides of the parallelogram which corresponds to the point of intersection.

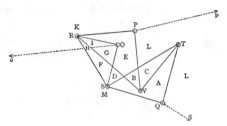

Fig. 1. Diagram of Configuration.

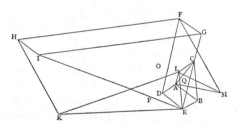

Fig. 2. Diagram of Stress.

This method is followed in the lettering of the diagram of configuration (fig. 1), and the diagram of stress (fig. 2) of the linkwork which Professor Sylvester has called a quadruplane.

In fig. 1 the real joints are distinguished from the places where one link appears to cross another by the little circles O, P, Q, R, S, T, V.

The four links $RSTV$ form a "contraparallelogram" in which $RS = TV$ and $RV = ST$.

The triangles ROS, RPV, TQS are similar to each other. A fourth triangle (TNV), not drawn in the figure, would complete the quadruplane. The four points O, P, N, Q form a parallelogram whose angle POQ is constant and equal to $\pi - SOR$. The product of the distances OP and OQ is constant.

The linkwork may be fixed at O. If any figure is traced by P, Q will trace the inverse figure, but turned round O through the constant angle POQ.

In the diagram forces Pp, Qq are balanced by the force Oo at the fixed point. The forces Pp and Qq are necessarily inversely as OP and OQ, and make equal angles with those lines.

Every closed area formed by the links or the external forces in the diagram of configuration is marked by a letter which corresponds to a point of concourse of lines in the diagram of stress.

The stress in the link which is the common boundary of two areas is represented in the diagram of stress by the line joining the points corresponding to those areas.

When a link is divided into two or more parts by lines crossing it, the stress in each part is represented by a different line for each part, but as the stress is the same throughout the link these lines are all equal and parallel. Thus in the figure the stress in RV is represented by the four equal and parallel lines HI, FG, DE, and AB.

If two areas have no part of their boundary in common the letters corresponding to them in the diagram of stress are not joined by a straight line. If, however, a straight line were drawn between them, it would represent in direction and magnitude the resultant of all the stresses in the links which are cut by any line, straight or curved, joining the two areas.

For instance the areas F and C in fig. 1 have no common boundary, and the points F and C in fig. 2 are not joined by a straight line. But every path from the area F to the area C in fig. 1 passes through a series of other areas, and each passage from one area into a contiguous area corresponds to a line drawn in the diagram of stress. Hence the whole path from F to C in fig. 1 corresponds to a path formed of lines in fig. 2 and extending from F to C, and the resultant of all the stresses in the links cut by the path is represented by FC in fig. 2.

Automatic Description of Diagrams.

There are many other kinds of diagrams in which the two co-ordinates of a point in a plane are employed to indicate the simultaneous values of two related quantities.

If a sheet of paper is made to move, say horizontally, with a constant known velocity, while a tracing point is made to move in a vertical straight line, the height varying as the value of any given physical quantity, the point will trace out a curve on the paper from which the value of that quantity at any given time may be determined.

This principle is applied to the automatic registration of phenomena of all kinds, from those of meteorology and terrestrial magnetism to the velocity of cannon-shot, the vibrations of sounding bodies, the motions of animals, voluntary and involuntary, and the currents in electric telegraphs.

Indicator-Diagram.

In Watt's indicator for steam-engines the paper does not move with a constant velocity, but its displacement is proportional to that of the piston of the engine, while that of the tracing point is proportional to the pressure of the steam. Hence the co-ordinates of a point of the curve traced on the diagram represent the volume and the pressure of the steam in the cylinder. The indicator-diagram not only supplies a record of the pressure of the steam at each stage of the stroke of the engine, but indicates the work done by the steam in each stroke by the area inclosed by the curve traced on the diagram.

The indicator-diagram was invented by James Watt as a method of estimating the work done by an engine. It was afterwards used by Clapeyron to illustrate the theory of heat, and this use of it was greatly developed by Rankine in his work on the steam-engine.

The use of diagrams in thermodynamics has been very completely illustrated by Prof. J. Willard Gibbs (*Connecticut Acad. Sci.*, Vol. III.), but though his methods throw much light on the general theory of diagrams as a method of study, they belong rather to thermodynamics than to the present subject.

[From *Nature*, Vol. XVII.]

XCI. *Tait's " Thermodynamics."*

THIS book, as we are told in the preface, has grown out of two articles contributed in 1864 by Prof. Tait to the *North British Review.* This journal, about that time, inserted a good many articles in which scientific subjects were discussed in scientific language, and in which, instead of the usual attempts to conciliate the unscientific reader by a series of relapses into irrelevant and incoherent writing, his attention was maintained by awakening a genuine interest in the subject.

The attempt was so far successful that the publishers of the *Review* were urged by men of science, especially engineers, to reprint these essays of Prof. Tait, but the *Review* itself soon afterwards became extinct.

Prof. Tait added to the two essays a mathematical sketch of the fundamental principles of thermodynamics, and in this form the book was published in 1868. In the present edition, though there are many additions and improvements, the form of the book is essentially the same.

Whether on account of these external circumstances, or from internal causes, it is impossible to compare this book either with so-called popular treatises or with those of a more technical kind.

In the popular treatise, whatever shreds of the science are allowed to appear, are exhibited in an exceedingly diffuse and attenuated form, apparently with the hope that the mental faculties of the reader, though they would reject any stronger food, may insensibly become saturated with scientific phraseology, provided it is diluted with a sufficient quantity of more familiar language. In this way, by simple reading, the student may become possessed of the phrases of the science without having been put to the trouble of thinking a single thought about it. The loss implied in such an acquisition can be estimated only by those who have been compelled to unlearn a science that they might at length begin to learn it.

The technical treatises do less harm, for no one ever reads them except under compulsion. From the establishment of the general equations to the end of the book, every page is full of symbols with indices and suffixes, so that there is not a paragraph of plain English on which the eye may rest.

Prof. Tait has not adopted either of these methods. He serves up his strong meat for grown men at the beginning of the book, without thinking it necessary to employ the language either of the nursery or of the school; while for younger students he has carefully boiled down the mathematical elements into the most concentrated form, and has placed the result at the end as a *bonne bouche*, so that the beginner may take it in all at once, and ruminate upon it at his leisure.

A considerable part of the book is devoted to the history of thermodynamics, and here it is evident that with Prof. Tait the names of the founders of his science call up the ideas, not so much of the scientific documents they have left behind them in our libraries, as of the men themselves, whether he recommends them to our reverence as masters in science, or bids us beware of them as tainted with error. There is no need of a garnish of anecdotes to enliven the dryness of science, for science has enough to do to restrain the strong human nature of the author, who is at no pains to conceal his own idiosyncrasies, or to smooth down the obtrusive antinomies of a vigorous mind into the featureless consistency of a conventional philosopher.

Thus, in the very first page of the book, he denounces all metaphysical methods of constructing physical science, and especially any *à priori* decisions as to what may have been or ought to have been. In the second page he does not indeed give us Aristotle's ten categories, but he lays down four of his own :— matter, force, position, and motion, to one of which he tells us, "it is evident that every distinct physical conception must be referred," and then before we have finished the page we are assured that heat does not belong to any of these four categories, but to a fifth, called energy.

This sort of writing, however unlike what we might expect from the conventional man of science, is the very thing to rouse the placid reader, and startle his thinking powers into action.

Prof. Tait next handles the caloric theory, but instead of merely shewing up its weak points and then dismissing it with contempt, he puts fresh life into it by giving (in the new edition) a characteristic extract from Dr Black's lectures, and proceeds to help the calorists out of some of their difficulties, by generously making over to them some excellent hints of his own.

The history of thermodynamics has an especial interest as the development of a science, within a short time and by a small number of men, from the condition of a vague anticipation of nature to that of a science with secure foundations, clear definitions, and distinct boundaries.

The earlier part of the history has already provoked a sufficient amount of discussion. We shall therefore confine our remarks to the methods employed for the advancement of the science by the three men who brought the theory to maturity.

Of the three founders of theoretical thermodynamics, Rankine availed himself to the greatest extent of the scientific use of the imagination. His imagination, however, though amply luxuriant, was strictly scientific. Whatever he imagined about molecular vortices, with their nuclei and atmospheres, was so clearly imaged in his mind's eye, that he, as a practical engineer, could see how it would work.

However intricate, therefore, the machinery might be which he imagined to exist in the minute parts of bodies, there was no danger of his going on to explain natural phenomena by any mode of action of this machinery which was not consistent with the general laws of mechanism. Hence, though the construction and distribution of his vortices may seem to us as complicated and arbitrary as the Cartesian system, his final deductions are simple, necessary, and consistent with facts.

Certain phenomena were to be explained. Rankine set himself to imagine the mechanism by which they might be produced. Being an accomplished engineer, he succeeded in specifying a particular arrangement of mechanism competent to do the work, and also in predicting other properties of the mechanism which were afterwards found to be consistent with observed facts.

As long as the training of the naturalist enables him to trace the action only of particular material systems without giving him the power of dealing with the general properties of all such systems, he must proceed by the method so often described in histories of science—he must imagine model after model of hypothetical apparatus till he finds one which will do the required work. If this apparatus should afterwards be found capable of accounting for many of the known phenomena, and not demonstrably inconsistent with any of them, he is strongly tempted to conclude that his hypothesis is a fact, at least until an equally good rival hypothesis has been invented. Thus Rankine*, long after an explanation of the properties of gases had been founded on the theory of the collisions of molecules, published what he supposed to be a proof that the phenomena of heat were invariably due to steady closed streams of continuous fluid matter.

The scientific career of Rankine was marked by the gradual development of a singular power of bringing the most difficult investigations within the range of elementary methods. In his earlier papers, indeed, he appears as if battling with chaos, as he swims, or sinks, or wades, or creeps, or flies,

> " And through the palpable obscure finds out
> His uncouth way ;"

but he soon begins to pave a broad and beaten way over the dark abyss, and his latest writings shew such a power of bridging over the difficulties of science, that his premature death must have been almost as great a loss to the diffusion of science as it was to its advancement.

The chapter on thermodynamics in his book on the steam-engine was the first published treatise on the subject, and is the only expression of his views addressed directly to students.

In this book he has disencumbered himself to a great extent of the hypothesis of molecular vortices, and builds principally on observed facts, though he, in common with Clausius, makes several assumptions, some expressed as axioms, others implied in definitions, which seem to us anything but self-evident. As an example of Rankine's best style we may take the following definition :—

" A PERFECT GAS is a substance in such a condition that the total pressure exerted by any number of portions of it, at a given temperature, against the sides of a vessel in which they are enclosed, is the sum of the pressures which each portion would exert if enclosed in the vessel separately at the same temperature."

Here we can form a distinct conception of every clause of the definition, but when we come to Rankine's Second Law of Thermodynamics we find that though, as to literary form, it seems cast in the same mould, its actual meaning is inscrutable.

* " On the Second Law of Thermodynamics," *Phil. Mag.* Oct. 1865, § 12, p. 244; but in his paper on the Thermal Energy of Molecular Vortices, *Trans. R. S. Edin.* xxv. p. 557 [1869], he admits that the explanation of gaseous pressure by the impacts of molecules has been proved + be possible.

"*The Second Law of Thermodynamics.*—If the total actual heat of a homogeneous and uniformly hot substance be conceived to be divided into any number of equal parts, the effects of those parts in causing work to be performed are equal."

We find it difficult enough, even in 1878, to attach any distinct meaning to the total actual heat of a body, and still more to conceive this heat divided into equal parts, and to study the action of each of these parts ; but as if our powers of deglutition were not yet sufficiently strained, Rankine follows this up with another statement of the same law, in which we have to assert our intuitive belief that—

"If the absolute temperature of any uniformly hot substance be divided into any number of equal parts, the effects of those parts in causing work to be performed are equal."

The student who thinks that he can form any idea of the meaning of this sentence is quite capable of explaining on thermodynamical principles what Mr Tennyson says of the great Duke :—

"Whose eighty winters freeze with one rebuke
All great self-seekers trampling on the right."

Prof. Clausius does not ask us to believe quite so much about the heat in hot bodies. In his first memoir, indeed, he boldly dismisses one supposed variety of heat from the science. Latent heat, he tells us, "is not only, as its name imports, hidden from our perceptions, but has actually no existence;" "it has been converted into work."

But though Clausius thus gets rid of all the heat which, after entering a body, is expended in doing work, either exterior or interior, he allows a certain quantity to remain in the body as heat, and this remnant of what should have been utterly destroyed lives on in a sort of smouldering existence, breaking out now and then with just enough vigour to mar the scientific coherence of what might have been a well compacted system of thermodynamics.

Prof. Tait tells us :—

"The source of all this sort of speculation, which is as old as the time of Crawford and Irvine—and which was countenanced to a certain extent even by Rankine—is the assumption that bodies must contain a certain quantity of actual, or thermometric, heat. We are quite ignorant of the condition of energy in bodies generally. We know how much goes in, and how much comes out, and we know whether at entrance or exit it is in the form of heat or of work. But that is all."

If we define thermodynamics, as I think we may now do, as the investigation of the dynamical and thermal properties of bodies, deduced entirely from what are called the First and Second laws of Thermodynamics, without any hypotheses as to the molecular constitution of bodies, all speculations as to how much of the energy in a body is in the form of heat are quite out of place.

Prof. Tait, however, does not seem to have noticed that Prof. Clausius, in a footnote to his sixth memoir *, tells us what he means by the heat in a body. In the middle of a sentence we read :—

"......the heat actually present in a unit weight of the substance in question—in other words, the *vis viva* of its molecular motions"......

Thus the doctrine that heat consists of the *vis viva* of molecular motions, and that it does not include the potential energy of molecular configuration— the most important doctrine, if true, in molecular science—is introduced in a footnote under cover of the unpretending German abbreviation "d.h."

Prof. Clausius is himself the principal founder of the kinetic theory of gases. The theory of the exchanges of the energy of collections of molecules was afterwards developed by Boltzmann to a much greater extent than had been done by Clausius, and it appears from his investigations that whether we suppose the molecules to be acted on by forces towards fixed centres or not, the condition of equilibrium of exchange of energy, or in other words the condition of equality of temperature of two bodies, is that the average kinetic energy of translation of a single molecule is the same in both bodies.

We may therefore define the temperature of a body as the average kinetic energy of translation of one of its molecules multiplied into a constant which is the same for all bodies. If we also define the total heat of the body as the sum of the whole kinetic energy of its molecules, then the total heat must be equal to the temperature multiplied into the number of molecules, and by the ratio of the whole kinetic energy to the energy of translation, and divided by the above constant.

The kinetic theory of gases has therefore a great deal to say about what Rankine and Clausius call the actual heat of a body, and if we suppose that molecules never coalesce or split up, but remain constant in number, then we may also assert, all experiments notwithstanding, that the real capacity for heat (as defined by Clausius) is constant for the same substance in all conditions.

---

* Hirst's translation, p. 230, German edition, 1864, p. 258, "wirklich vorhandene Wärme, d.h. die lebendige Kraft seiner Molecularbewegungen."

Rankine, indeed, probably biassed by the results of experiments, allowed that the real specific heat of a substance might be different in different states of aggregation, but Clausius has clearly shewn that this admission is illogical, and that if we admit any such changes, we had better give up real specific heat altogether.

Statements of this kind have their legitimate place in molecular science, where it is essential to specify the dynamical condition of the system, and to distinguish the kinetic energy of the molecules from the potential energy of their configuration; but they have no place in thermodynamics proper, in which we deal only with sensible masses and their sensible motions.

Both Rankine and Clausius have pointed out the importance of a certain function, the increase or diminution of which indicates whether heat is entering or leaving the body. Rankine calls it the thermodynamic function, and Clausius the entropy. Clausius, however, besides inventing the most convenient name for this function, has made the most valuable developments of the idea of entropy, and in particular has established the most important theorem in the whole science,—that when heat passes from one body to another at a lower temperature, there is always an increase of the sum of the entropy of the two bodies, from which it follows that the entropy of the universe must always be increasing.

He has also shewn that if the energy of a body is expressed as a function of the volume and the entropy, then its pressure (with sign reversed) and its temperature are the differential coefficients of the energy with respect to the volume and the entropy respectively, thus indicating the symmetrical relations of the five principal quantities in thermodynamics.

But Clausius, having begun by breaking up the energy of the body into its thermal and ergonal content, has gone on to break up its entropy into the transformational value of its thermal content and the disgregation.

Thus both the energy and the entropy, two quantities capable of direct measurement, are broken up into four quantities, all of them quite beyond the reach of experiment, and all this is owing to the actual heat which Clausius, after getting rid of the latent heat, suffered to remain in the body.

Sir William Thomson, the last but not the least of the three great founders, does not even consecrate a symbol to denote the entropy, but he was the first to clearly define the intrinsic energy of a body, and to him alone are due the ideas and the definitions of the available energy and the dissipation of energy. He has always been most careful to point out the exact extent of the assumptions and experimental observations on which each of his statements is based, and he avoids the introduction of quantities which are not capable of experimental measurement. It is therefore greatly to be regretted that his memoirs on the dynamical theory of heat have not been collected and reprinted in an accessible form, and completed by a formal treatise, in which his method of building up the science should be exhibited in the light of his present knowledge.

The touchstone of a treatise on thermodynamics is what is called the second law.

Rankine, as we have seen, founds it on statements which may or may not be true, but which cannot be considered as established in the present state of science.

The second law is introduced by Clausius and Thomson as an axiom on which to found Carnot's theorem that the efficiency of a reversible engine is at least as great as that of any other engine working between the same limits of temperature.

If an engine of greater efficiency exists, then, by coupling this engine with Carnot's engine reversed, it is possible to restore to the hot body as much heat as is taken from it, and at the same time to do a certain amount of work.

If with Carnot we suppose heat to be a substance, then this work would be performed in direct violation of the first law—the principle of the conservation of energy. But if we regard heat as a form of energy, we cannot apply this method of *reductio ad absurdum*, for the work may be derived from the heat taken from the colder body.

Clausius supposes all the work gained by the first engine to be expended in driving the second. There is then no loss or gain of heat on the whole, but heat is taken from the cold body, and an equal quantity communicated to the hot body, and this process might be carried on to an indefinite extent.

In order to assert the impossibility of such a process in a form of words having sufficient verisimilitude to be received as an axiom, Clausius, in his first memoir, simply says that this process "contradicts the general deportment of heat, which everywhere exhibits the tendency to equalize differences of temperature, and therefore to pass from the warmer to the colder body *."

---

* Und das widerspricht dem sonstigen Verhalten der Wärme, indem sie überall das Bestreben zeigt, vorkommende Temperaturdifferenzen auszugleichen und also aus den wärmeren Körpern in die kälteren überzugehen.

84—2

In its obvious and strict sense no axiom can be more irrefragable. Even in the hypothetical process, the impossibility of which it was intended to assert, every communication of heat is from a warmer to a colder body. When the heat is taken from the cold body it flows into the working substance which is at that time still colder. The working substance afterwards becomes hot, not by communication of heat to it, but by change of volume, and when it communicates heat to the hot body it is itself still hotter.

It is therefore hardly correct to assert that heat has been transmitted or transferred from the colder to the hotter body. There is undoubtedly a transfer of energy, but in what form this energy existed during its middle passage is a question for molecular science, not for pure thermodynamics.

In a note added in 1864 Clausius states the principle in a modified form, "that heat cannot of itself pass from a colder to a warmer body" * and finally, in the new edition of his *Theory of Heat* (1876) he substitutes for the words " of itself " the expression " without compensation†."

With respect to the first of these emendations we must remember that the words " of itself " are not intended to exclude the intervention of any kind of self-acting machinery, and it is easy, by means of an engine which takes in heat from a body at 200° C., and gives it out at 100° to drive a freezing machine so as to take heat from water at 0°, and so freeze' it, and also a friction break so as to generate heat in a body at 500°. It would therefore be necessary to exclude all bodies except the hot body, the cold body, and the working substance, in order to exclude exceptions to the principle.

By the introduction of the second expression, " without compensation," combined with a full interpretation of this phrase, the statement of the principle becomes complete and exact ; but in order to understand it we must have a previous knowledge of the theory of transformation-equivalents, or in other words of entropy, and it is to be feared that we shall have to be taught thermodynamics for several generations before we can expect beginners to receive as axiomatic the theory of entropy.

Thomson, in his " Third Paper on the Dynamical Theory of Heat " (*Trans. R. S. Edin.* xx. p. 265, read March 17, 1851), has stated the axiom as follows :—

* Dass die Wärme nicht von selbst aus einem kälteren in einem wärmeren Körper übergehen kann.

† Ein Wärmeübergang aus einem kälteren in einem wärmeren Körper kann nicht ohne Compensation Statt finden.

"It is impossible, by means of inanimate material agency, to derive mechanical effect from any portion of matter by cooling it below the temperature of the coldest of surrounding objects."

Without some further restriction this axiom cannot be considered as true, for by allowing air to expand we may derive mechanical effect from it by cooling it below the temperature of the coldest of surrounding objects.

If we make it a condition that the material agency is to be left in the same state at the end of the process as it was at first, and also that the mechanical effect is not to be derived from the pressure of the hot or of the cold body, the axiom will be rendered strictly true, but this brings us back to a simple re-assertion of Carnot's principle, except that it is extended from heat engines to all other kinds of inanimate material agency.

It is probably impossible to reduce the second law of thermodynamics to a form as axiomatic as that of the first law, for we have reason to believe that though true, its truth is not of the same order as that of the first law.

The first law is an extension to the theory of heat of the principle of conservation of energy, which can be proved mathematically true if real bodies consist of matter "as per definition," acted on by forces having potentials.

The second law relates to that kind of communication of energy which we call the transfer of heat as distinguished from another kind of communication of energy which we call work. According to the molecular theory the only difference between these two kinds of communication of energy is that the motions and displacements which are concerned in the communication of heat are those of molecules, and are so numerous, so small individually, and so irregular in their distribution, that they quite escape all our methods of observation; whereas when the motions and displacements are those of visible bodies consisting of great numbers of molecules moving altogether, the communication of energy is called work.

Hence we have only to suppose our senses sharpened to such a degree that we could trace the motions of molecules as easily as we now trace those of large bodies, and the distinction between work and heat would vanish, for the communication of heat would be seen to be a communication of energy of the same kind as that which we call work.

The second law must either be founded on our actual experience in dealing with real bodies of sensible magnitude, or else deduced from the molecular theory of these bodies, on the hypothesis that the behaviour of bodies consisting of millions of molecules may be deduced from the theory of the encounters of pairs of molecules, by supposing the relative frequency of different kinds of encounters to be distributed according to the laws of probability.

The truth of the second law is therefore a statistical, not a mathematical, truth, for it depends on the fact that the bodies we deal with consist of millions of molecules, and that we never can get hold of single molecules.

Sir William Thomson * has shewn how to calculate the probability of the occurrence within a given time of a given amount of deviation from the most probable distribution of a finite number of molecules of two different kinds in a vessel, and has given a numerical example of a particular case of the diffusion of gases.

The same method might be extended to the diffusion of heat by conduction, and the diffusion of motion by internal friction, which are also processes by which energy is dissipated in consequence of the motions and encounters of the molecules of the system.

The tendency of these motions and encounters is in general towards a definite state, in which there is an equilibrium of exchanges of the molecules and their momenta and energies between the different parts of the system.

If we restrict our attention to any one molecule of the system, we shall find its motion changing at every encounter in a most irregular manner.

If we go on to consider a finite number of molecules, even if the system to which they belong contains an infinite number, the average properties of this group, though subject to smaller variations than those of a single molecule, are still every now and then deviating very considerably from the theoretical mean of the whole system, because the molecules which form the group do not submit their procedure as individuals to the laws which prescribe the behaviour of the average or mean molecule.

Hence the second law of thermodynamics is continually being violated, and that to a considerable extent, in any sufficiently small group of molecules belonging to a real body. As the number of molecules in the group is increased, the deviations from the mean of the whole become smaller and less frequent; and when the number is increased till the group includes a sensible portion of the body, the probability of a measurable variation from the mean occurring in a finite number of years becomes so small that it may be regarded as practically an impossibility.

* " On the Kinetic Theory of the Dissipation of Energy," *Proc. R. S. Edin.*, February 16, 1874, Vol. VIII. p. 323, also in *Nature*, Vol. IX. p. 441.

This calculation belongs of course to molecular theory and not to pure thermodynamics, but it shews that we have reason for believing the truth of the second law to be of the nature of a strong probability, which, though it falls short of certainty by less than any assignable quantity, is not an absolute certainty.

Several attempts have been made to deduce the second law from purely dynamical principles, such as Hamilton's principle, and without the introduction of any element of probability. If we are right in what has been said above, no deduction of this kind, however apparently satisfactory, can be a sufficient explanation of the second law. Indeed some of them have already indicated their unsoundness by leading to determinations of physical quantities which have no existence, such as the periodic time of the alternations of the volume of particular gases*.

* Szily, *Phil. Mag.*, October, 1876 ; Clausius, *Pogg. Ann.* cxlii. p. 433 ; *Pogg. Ann.* cxlvi. p. 585, May, 1872 ; J. J. Müller, *Pogg. Ann.* clii. p. 105.

[From the *Proceedings of the London Mathematical Society*, Vol. IX.]

XCII. *On the Electrical Capacity of a long narrow Cylinder, and of a Disk of sensible Thickness.*

THE distribution of electricity in equilibrium on a straight line without breadth is a uniform one. We may expect, therefore, that the distribution on a cylinder will approximate to uniformity as the radius of the cylinder diminishes.

Let $2l$ be the length of the cylinder, and b its radius.

Let x be measured along the axis from the middle point of the axis, and let y be the distance of any point from the axis.

Let λ be the linear density on the curved surface of the cylinder; that is, let λdx be the charge on the annular element dx.

Let σ be the surface-density on the flat ends.

Then, at a point on the axis for which $\xi = x$, the potential (ψ) is

$$\psi = \int_{-l}^{+l} \lambda \left[(\xi - x)^2 + b^2\right]^{-\frac{1}{2}} dx + 2\pi \int_0^b \sigma \eta \left[(l - \xi)^2 + y^2\right]^{-\frac{1}{2}} dy + 2\pi \int_0^b \sigma \eta \left[(l + \xi)^2 + y^2\right]^{-\frac{1}{2}} dy,$$

the first integral being extended over the curved surface, and the other two over the positive and negative flat ends respectively.

If the electricity is in equilibrium in the cylinder, ψ must be constant for all points within the cylinder, and therefore for all points on the axis.

Also, by Art. 144 of *Electricity and Magnetism*, if ψ is constant for all points on the axis, it is constant for all points within the surface of the cylinder.

If we suppose λ and σ constant,

$$\psi = \lambda \log \frac{(f_1 + l - \xi)(f_2 + l + \xi)}{b^2} + 2\pi\sigma (f_1 + f_2 - 2l),$$

where f_1 and f_2 are the distances of the point (ξ) on the axis from the positive and negative edges of the curved surface.

At the middle of the axis,

$$\xi = 0, \quad \text{and} \quad f_1 = f_2 = \sqrt{l^2 + b^2},$$

$$\psi_{(0)} = 2\lambda \log \frac{f+l}{b} + 4\pi\sigma (f - l).$$

At either end of the axis, $\xi = l$, $f_1 = b$, $f_2 = 2l$, nearly,

$$\psi_{(l)} = \lambda \log \frac{4l}{b} + 2\pi\sigma b.$$

Just within the cylinder, when ξ is just less than l,

$$\frac{d\psi}{dx_{(l)}} = -\lambda \left(\frac{1}{b} - \frac{1}{f} \right) + 2\pi\sigma = 0 \quad \text{by hypothesis.}$$

Hence $2\pi b\sigma = \lambda,$

or the density on the end must be equal to that on the curved surface.

The whole charge is therefore $E = 2\pi b\sigma (2l + b)$.

The greatest potential is $\psi_{(0)} = 2\pi b\sigma \left(2 \log \frac{2l}{b} + \frac{b}{l} \right).$

The smallest potential is that at the curved edge, and is approximately

$$\psi_{(e)} = 2\pi b\sigma \left(\log \frac{4l}{b} + \frac{2}{\pi} \right);$$

and the capacity must lie between

$$\frac{E}{\psi_{(0)}} = \frac{2l + b}{2 \log \frac{2l}{b} + \frac{b}{l}} \quad \text{and} \quad \frac{E}{\psi_{(e)}} = \frac{2l + b}{\log \frac{4l}{b} + \frac{2}{\pi}}.$$

These are the limits between which Cavendish shews that the capacity must lie. When the cylinder is very narrow, the upper limit is nearly double the lower, so that we cannot obtain in this way any approximation to the true value.

To obtain an approximation, we may make use of the following method, in which we neglect the effect of the flat ends, and consider the cylinder as a hollow tube :—

Let Q be the potential energy of any arbitrary distribution of electricity on the cylinder,

$$Q = \tfrac{1}{2} \int_{-l}^{+l} \lambda \psi d\xi.$$

The charge is

$$E = \int_{-l}^{+l} \lambda d\xi.$$

Let us now suppose this charge to distribute itself so as to pass into the state of equilibrium; then the potential will become uniform, and equal, say, to ψ_0, and

$$Q_0 = \tfrac{1}{2} \psi_0 E.$$

If K is the capacity of the conductor,

$$E = K\psi_0, \quad \text{and} \quad K = \frac{1}{2} \frac{E^2}{Q_0}.$$

Since Q, the potential energy due to any arbitrary distribution of the charge, may be greater, but cannot be less, than Q_0, the energy of the same charge in equilibrium, the capacity may be greater, but cannot be less, than

$$\frac{1}{2} \frac{E^2}{Q} \quad \text{or} \quad \frac{\left[\int_{-l}^{+l} \lambda d\xi \right]^2}{\int_{-l}^{+l} \lambda \psi d\xi}.$$

This inferior limit of the capacity is greater than that derived from the maximum value of the potential, and, as we shall see, often gives a very close approximation to the truth. Thus, if we suppose, in the case of the cylinder, λ to be uniform,

$$E = 2\lambda l, \qquad Q = 2\lambda^2 l \left(\log \frac{f+2l}{b} - \frac{f-b}{2l} \right),$$

where $f^2 = 4l^2 + b^2$. For a long narrow cylinder,

$$K_0 > \frac{l}{\log \dfrac{4l}{b} - 1}.$$

To obtain a closer approximation, let us suppose the distribution to be of any form, and to be expressed in the form of a series of harmonics.

The potential due to any such distribution at a given point may be expressed in terms of spherical harmonics of the second kind. See Ferrers' *Spherical Harmonics*, Chap. v.

If we write
$$a = \frac{1}{2}\frac{r_2 + r_1}{l}, \quad \beta = \frac{1}{2}\frac{r_2 - r_1}{l},$$

where r_1 and r_2 are the distances of a given point from the ends of the line, and if the linear density is expressed by

$$\lambda = \Sigma A_i P_i\left(\frac{\xi}{l}\right),$$

where P_i is the zonal harmonic of degree i, then the potential at the given point (a, β) is
$$\psi = \Sigma A_i Q_i(a) P_i(\beta),$$

where Q_i is the zonal harmonic of the second kind, and is of the form

$$Q_i(a) = P_i(a) \log\frac{a+1}{a-1} + R_i(a),$$

where $R_i(a)$ is a rational function of a of $(i-1)$ degrees, and is such that $Q_i(a)$ vanishes when a is infinite, thus:

$$Q_0(a) = \log\frac{a+1}{a-1},$$

$$Q_1(a) = a\log\frac{a+1}{a-1} - 2,$$

$$Q_2(a) = \left(\frac{3}{2}a^2 - \frac{1}{2}\right)\log\frac{a+1}{a-1} - 3a,$$

$$Q_3(a) = \left(\frac{5}{2}a^3 - \frac{3}{2}a\right)\log\frac{a+1}{a-1} - 5a^2 + \frac{4}{3},$$

$$Q_4(a) = \left(\frac{5.7}{8}a^4 - \frac{3.5}{4}a^2 + \frac{3}{8}\right)\log\frac{a+1}{a-1} - \frac{5.7}{4}a^3 + \frac{5.11}{12}a.$$

At a point at a very small distance b from the line, if we write

$$L = \log\frac{r_1 + l - \xi}{b} + \log\frac{r_2 + l + \xi}{b},$$

the potential due to the distribution whose linear density is

$$\lambda_i = A_i P_i\left(\frac{x}{l}\right)$$

is approximately

$$\psi_i = A_i P_i\left(\frac{\xi}{l}\right)\left[L - 2\left(i - \frac{i(i-1)}{2.2} + \frac{i(i-1)(i-2)}{2.3.3} - \frac{i(i-1)(i-2)(i-3)}{2.3.4.4} + \&c.\right)\right];$$

85—2

thus, if

$$\lambda_0 = A_0,$$

$$\lambda_1 = A_1 \frac{x}{l},$$

$$\lambda_2 = A_2 \left(\frac{3}{2} \frac{x^2}{l^2} - \frac{1}{2} \right),$$

$$\lambda_3 = A_3 \left(\frac{5}{2} \frac{x^3}{l^3} - \frac{3}{2} \frac{x}{l} \right),$$

$$\lambda_4 = A_4 \left(\frac{5 \cdot 7}{8} \frac{x^4}{l^4} - \frac{3 \cdot 5}{4} \frac{x^2}{l^2} + \frac{3}{8} \right);$$

then approximately

$$\psi_0 = A_0 L,$$

$$\psi_1 = A_1 \frac{\xi}{l} (L - 2),$$

$$\psi_2 = A_2 \left(\frac{3}{2} \frac{\xi^2}{l^2} - \frac{1}{2} \right) (L - 3),$$

$$\psi_3 = A_3 \left(\frac{5}{2} \frac{\xi^3}{l^3} - \frac{3}{2} \frac{\xi}{l} \right) \left(L - \frac{11}{3} \right),$$

$$\psi_4 = A_4 \left(\frac{5 \cdot 7}{8} \frac{\xi^4}{l^4} - \frac{3 \cdot 5}{4} \frac{\xi^2}{l^2} + \frac{3}{8} \right) \left(L - \frac{25}{6} \right).$$

If we write $\mathcal{L}$ for $\log \dfrac{(4l^2 + b^2)^{\frac{1}{2}} + 2l}{b}$, or approximately $\mathcal{L} = \log \dfrac{4l}{b}$, we find, to the same degree of approximation,

$$\int \lambda_0 \psi_0 d\xi = 4 A_0^2 l (\mathcal{L} - 1),$$

$$\int \lambda_0 \psi_2 d\xi = \int \lambda_2 \psi_0 d\xi = -\tfrac{2}{3} A_0 A_2 l,$$

$$\int \lambda_2 \psi_2 d\xi = 2 A_2^2 l \left(\tfrac{2}{5} \mathcal{L} - \frac{101}{75} \right),$$

$$\int \lambda_0 \psi_4 d\xi = -\tfrac{1}{5} A_0 A_4 l,$$

$$\int \lambda_2 \psi_4 d\xi = -\tfrac{2}{7} A_2 A_4 l,$$

$$\int \lambda_4 \psi_4 d\xi = 2 A_4^2 l \left(\tfrac{2}{9} \mathcal{L} - \frac{6989}{5670} \right).$$

Determining A_2 so as to make $\int (\lambda_0 + \lambda_2)(\psi_0 + \psi_2)\, d\xi$ a minimum, and remembering that $E = 2lA_0$, we find

$$A_2 = A_0 \frac{5}{6} \cdot \frac{1}{\mathfrak{L} - \dfrac{101}{30}},$$

and we obtain as a second approximation

$$K_2 > \frac{l}{\mathfrak{L} - 1 - \dfrac{5}{36}\dfrac{1}{\mathfrak{L} - \dfrac{101}{30}}}.$$

Unless the length of the cylinder considerably exceeds 7·245 times its diameter, this approximation is of little use, for this ratio makes A_2 infinite. It shews, however, that when the ratio of the length to the diameter increases without limit, the electric density becomes more nearly uniform, and the expression for K_0 approximates to the true capacity.

We may go on to a third approximation by determining A_2 and A_4 so that $\int (\lambda_0 + \lambda_2 + \lambda_4)(\psi_0 + \psi_2 + \psi_4)\, d\xi$ shall be a minimum; whence

$$A_2 = A_0 \frac{5}{6} \frac{\mathfrak{L} - \dfrac{3373}{630}}{\left(\mathfrak{L} - \dfrac{101}{30}\right)\left(\mathfrak{L} - \dfrac{6989}{1260}\right) - \dfrac{45}{196}},$$

$$A_4 = A_0 \frac{9}{20} \frac{\mathfrak{L} - \dfrac{457}{210}}{\left(\mathfrak{L} - \dfrac{101}{30}\right)\left(\mathfrak{L} - \dfrac{6989}{1260}\right) - \dfrac{45}{196}},$$

and

$$K_4 > \frac{l}{\mathfrak{L} - 1 - \dfrac{5}{36}\dfrac{1}{\mathfrak{L} - \dfrac{101}{30}} - \dfrac{9}{400}\dfrac{\left(\mathfrak{L} - \dfrac{457}{210}\right)^2}{\left(\mathfrak{L} - \dfrac{101}{30}\right)\left[\left(\mathfrak{L} - \dfrac{101}{30}\right)\left(\mathfrak{L} - \dfrac{6989}{1260}\right) - \dfrac{45}{196}\right]}}.$$

When $\mathfrak{L}$ is very great, the distribution of electricity is expressed by the equation

$$\lambda = A_o \left[1 + \frac{1}{\mathfrak{L}} \frac{7}{32} \left\{ 9 \frac{x^4}{l^4} - 2 \frac{x^2}{l^2} - \frac{17}{15} \right\} \right],$$

which shews that, as the ratio of the length to the diameter increases, the density becomes more nearly uniform, and the deviation from uniformity becomes more confined to the parts near the ends of the cylinder.

To indicate the character of the approximation, I have calculated $\mathfrak{L}$ and the three terms of the denominator of K_4 for different values of the ratio of l to b. When this ratio is less than 100, the third term is unavailable.

$\frac{l}{b}$	$\mathfrak{L}$	1st term.	2nd term.	3rd term.
10	3·68888	. 2·68888	− 0·43151	
20	4·38203	. 3·38203	− 0·13680	
30	4·78749	. 3·78749	− 0·09775	
50	5·29832	. 4·29832	− 0·07191	
100	5·99146	. 4·99146	− 0·05291	− 0·13566
1000	8·29405	. 7·29405	− 0·02818	− 0·00892.

Examples of the application of the method to the calculation of the capacities of a cylinder in presence of a plane conducting surface, and in presence of another equal cylinder, will be given in the notes to the forthcoming edition of Cavendish's *Electrical Researches*, as illustrations of measurements made by Cavendish in 1771.

Electric Capacity of a Disk of sensible Thickness.

We may apply the same method to determine the capacity of a disk of radius a and thickness b, b being very small compared with a.

We may begin by supposing that the density on the flat surfaces is the same as when the disk is infinitely thin.

Let a and β be the elliptic co-ordinates of a given point with respect to the lower disk, or in other words let the greatest and least distances of the point from the edge of the disk be $a(a+\beta)$ and $a(a-\beta)$.

The distance of the given point from the axis is

$$r = aa\beta \dots\dots\dots\dots\dots\dots\dots\dots(1),$$

and its distance from the plane of the lower disk is

$$z = a\left(a^{2}-1\right)^{\frac{1}{2}}\left(1-\beta^{2}\right)^{\frac{1}{2}} \dots\dots\dots\dots(2).$$

If we write

$$a^{2}p^{2} = a^{2}-r^{2} \dots\dots\dots\dots\dots\dots(3),$$

then, if A_{2} is the charge of the upper disk, distributed as when undisturbed by the lower disk, the density at any point is

$$\sigma = \frac{A_{2}}{2\pi a^{2}p} \dots\dots\dots\dots\dots\dots(4).$$

If A_{1} is the charge of the lower disk, also undisturbed, the potential at the given point due to it is

$$\psi = A_{1}a^{-1}\operatorname{cosec}^{-1}a \dots\dots\dots\dots\dots(5),$$

or, if we write

$$a^{2} = \gamma^{2}+1 \dots\dots\dots\dots\dots\dots(6),$$

$$\psi = A_{1}a^{-1}\left(\frac{\pi}{2}-\tan^{-1}\gamma\right) \dots\dots\dots\dots(7).$$

We have next to find the relation between p and γ when the given point is in the upper disk, and therefore $z = b$.

Equation (2) becomes

$$b^{2} = a^{2}\gamma^{2}\left(1-\beta^{2}\right) \dots\dots\dots\dots\dots(8),$$

and

$$p^{2} = 1-a^{2}\beta^{2} \dots\dots\dots\dots\dots\dots(9),$$

or

$$p^{2} = \frac{b^{2}}{a^{2}\gamma^{2}}-\gamma^{2}+\frac{b^{2}}{a^{2}}\dots\dots\dots\dots\dots(10).$$

Since the given point is on the upper disk, and since b is small, p must be between 1 and 0, and γ between $\dfrac{b}{a}$ and $\left(\dfrac{b}{a}\right)^{\frac{1}{3}}$; and between those limits we may write, as a sufficient approximation for our purpose,

$$\tan^{-1}\gamma = \gamma = \frac{b}{a}\left[1+\left(\frac{b}{a}\right)^{\frac{1}{3}}\right]\left[p+\left(\frac{b}{a}\right)^{\frac{1}{3}}\right]^{-1} \dots\dots\dots(11).$$

We have now to find the value of the surface integral of the product of the density into the potential taken over the upper disk, or

$$\int 2\pi r\, dr\, \sigma\psi = A_{1}A_{2}a^{-1}\left(\frac{\pi}{2}-\int_{0}^{1}\tan^{-1}\gamma\, dp\right)\dots\dots\dots(12).$$

Substituting the value of $\tan^{-1}\gamma$ from (11), the integral in (12) becomes

$$A_1 A_2 a^{-1} \left\{ \frac{\pi}{2} - \frac{b}{a} \left[1 + \left(\frac{b}{a} \right)^{\frac{1}{2}} \right] \log \left[\left(\frac{a}{b} \right)^{\frac{1}{2}} + 1 \right] \right\} \quad \ldots\ldots\ldots\ldots(13).$$

The corresponding quantity for the action of the upper disk on itself is got by putting $A_1 = A_2$ and $b = 0$, and is

$$A_2^2 a^{-1} \frac{\pi}{2} \quad \ldots\ldots\ldots\ldots\ldots\ldots\ldots\ldots\ldots\ldots(14).$$

In the actual case, $A_1 = A_2 = \frac{1}{2} E$, when E is the whole charge; and the lower limit of the capacity is therefore

$$K > \frac{2a}{\pi - \dfrac{b}{a} \left[1 + \left(\dfrac{b}{a} \right)^{\frac{1}{2}} \right] \log \left[\left(\dfrac{a}{b} \right)^{\frac{1}{2}} + 1 \right]} \quad \ldots\ldots\ldots\ldots(15);$$

but since we have assumed that b is very small compared with a, we may express our result with sufficient accuracy in the form

$$K = \frac{2}{\pi} \left(a + \frac{1}{2\pi} b \log \frac{a}{b} \right) \quad \ldots\ldots\ldots\ldots\ldots\ldots\ldots(16),$$

or, the capacity of two equal disks is equal to that of a single disk whose circumference exceeds that of either disk by $b \log \frac{a}{b}$.

If the space between the disks is filled up, so as to form a single disk of sensible thickness, there will be a certain charge on the cylindric surface; but, at the same time, the charge on the inner sides of the disks will vanish, and that on the outer sides of the disks will be diminished, so that the capacity of a disk of sensible thickness is very little greater than that given by (16).

[From the *Philosophical Transactions of the Royal Society*, Part I. 1879.]

XCIII. *On Stresses in Rarified Gases arising from Inequalities of Temperature.*

1. IN this paper I have followed the method given in my paper "On the Dynamical Theory of Gases" (*Phil. Trans.*, 1867, p. 49). I have shewn that when inequalities of temperature exist in a gas, the pressure at a given point is not the same in all directions, and that the difference between the maximum and the minimum pressure at a point may be of considerable magnitude when the density of the gas is small enough, and when the inequalities of temperature are produced by small* solid bodies at a higher or lower temperature than the vessel containing the gas.

2. The nature of this stress may be thus defined:—Let the distance from a given point, measured in a given direction, be denoted by h; then the space-

---

* The dimensions of the bodies must be of the same order of magnitude as a certain length λ, which may be defined as the distance travelled by a molecule with its mean velocity during the time of relaxation of the medium.

The time of relaxation is the time in which inequalities of stress would disappear if the rate at which they diminish were to continue constant. Hence

$$\lambda = 2 \left(\frac{2p}{\pi\rho}\right)^{\frac{1}{2}} \cdot \frac{\mu}{p} = 2\mu \left(\frac{2}{\pi\rho p}\right)^{\frac{1}{2}}.$$

On the hypothesis that the encounters between the molecules resemble those between "rigid elastic" spheres, the free path of a molecule between two successive encounters has a definite meaning, and if l is its mean value,

$$l = \frac{3}{2} \mu \left(\frac{\pi}{2p\rho}\right)^{\frac{1}{2}} = \frac{3\pi}{8} \lambda = 1{\cdot}178\lambda.$$

So that the mean path of a molecule may be taken as representing what we mean by "small".

If the force between the molecules is supposed to be a continuous function of the distance, the free path of a molecule has no longer a definite meaning, and we must fall back on the quantity λ, as defined above.

variation of the temperature for a point moving along this line will be denoted by $\frac{d\theta}{dh}$, and the space-variation of this quantity along the same line by $\frac{d^2\theta}{dh^2}$.

There will, in general, be a particular direction of the line h for which $\frac{d^2\theta}{dh^2}$ is a maximum, another for which it is a minimum, and a third for which it is a maximum-minimum. These three directions are at right angles to each other, and are the axes of principal stress at the given point; and the part of the stress arising from inequalities of temperature is, in each of these principal axes,

$$3\,\frac{\mu^2}{\rho\theta}\,\frac{d^2\theta}{dh^2},$$

where μ is the coefficient of viscosity, ρ the density, and θ the absolute temperature.

3. Now for dry air at 15°C., $\mu = 1\cdot9 \times 10^{-4}$ in centimetre-gramme-second measure, and $\frac{3\mu^2}{\rho\theta} = \frac{1}{p}\,0\cdot315$, where p is the pressure, the unit of pressure being one dyne per square centimetre, or nearly one-millionth part of an atmosphere.

If a sphere of $2a$ centimetres in diameter is T degrees centigrade hotter than the air at large distances from it, then, when there is a steady flow of heat, the temperature at a distance of r centimetres from the centre will be

$$\theta = \theta_0 + \frac{Ta}{r}, \quad \text{and} \quad \frac{d^2\theta}{dr^2} = \frac{2Ta}{r^3}.$$

Hence, at a distance of r centimetres from the centre of the sphere, the pressure in the direction of the radius arising from inequality of temperature will be

$$\frac{Ta}{pr^3}\,0\cdot63 \text{ dynes per square centimetre.}$$

4. In Mr Crookes' experiments the pressure, p, was often so small that this stress would be capable, if it existed alone, of producing rapid motion in a radiometer.

Indeed, if we were to consider only the normal part of the stress exerted on solid bodies immersed in the gas, most of the phenomena observed by Mr Crookes could be readily explained.

5. Let us take the case of two small bodies symmetrical with respect to the axis joining their centres of figure. If both bodies are warmer than

the air at a distance from them, then, in any section perpendicular to the axis joining their centres, the point where it cuts this line will have the highest temperature, and there will be a flow of heat outwards from this axis in all directions.

Hence $\dfrac{d^2\theta}{dh^2}$ will be positive for the axis, and it will be a line of maximum pressure, so that the bodies will repel each other.

If both bodies are colder than the air at a distance, everything will be reversed; the axis will be a line of minimum pressure, and the bodies will attract each other.

If one body is hotter and the other colder than the air at a distance, the effect will be smaller, and it will depend on the relative sizes of the bodies, and on their exact temperatures, whether the action is attractive or repulsive.

6. If the bodies are two parallel disks very near to each other, the central parts will produce very little effect, because between the disks the temperature varies uniformly, and $\dfrac{d^2\theta}{dh^2}=0$. Only near the edges will there be any stress arising from inequality of temperature in the gas.

7. If the bodies are encircled by a ring having its axis in the line joining the bodies, then the repulsion between the two bodies, when they are warmer than the air in general, may be converted into attraction by heating the ring so as to produce a flow of heat inwards towards the axis.

8. If a body in the form of a cup or bowl is warmer than the air, the distribution of temperature in the surrounding gas is similar to the distribution of electric potential near a body of the same form, which has been investigated by Sir W. Thomson. Near the convex surface the value of $\dfrac{d^2\theta}{dh^2}$ is nearly the same as if the body had been a complete sphere, namely $2T\dfrac{1}{a^2}$, where T is the excess of temperature, and a is the radius of the sphere. Near the concave surface the variation of temperature is exceedingly small.

Hence the normal pressure will be greater on the convex surface than on the concave surface, and if we were to neglect the tangential pressures we might think this an explanation of the motion of Mr Crookes' cups.

Since the expressions for the stress are linear as regards the temperature, everything will be reversed when the cup is colder than the surrounding air.

9. In a spherical vessel, if the two polar regions are made hotter than the equatorial zone, the pressure in the direction of the axis will be greater than that parallel to the equatorial plane, and the reverse will be the case if the polar regions are made colder than the equatorial zone.

10. All such explanations of the observed phenomena must be subjected to careful criticism. They have been obtained by considering the normal stresses alone, to the exclusion of the tangential stresses, and it is much easier to give an elementary exposition of the former than of the latter. If, however, we go on to calculate the forces acting on any portion of the gas in virtue of the stresses on its surface, we find that when the flow of heat is steady, these forces are in equilibrium. Mr Crookes tells us that there is no molar current or wind in his radiometer vessels. It is not easy to prove this by experiment, but it is satisfactory to find that the system of stresses here described as arising from inequalities of temperature will not, when the flow of heat is steady, generate currents.

11. Consider, then, the case in which there are no currents of gas but a steady flow of heat, the condition of which is

$$\frac{d^2\theta}{dx^2} + \frac{d^2\theta}{dy^2} + \frac{d^2\theta}{dz^2} = 0.$$

(In the absence of external forces such as gravity, and if the gas in contact with solid bodies does not slide over them, this is always a solution of the equations, and it is the only permanent solution.) In this case the equations of motion shew that every particle of the gas is in equilibrium under the stresses acting on it. Hence, any finite portion of the gas is also in equilibrium; also, since the stresses are linear functions of the temperature, if we superpose one system of temperatures on another, we also superpose the corresponding systems of forces.

Now the system of temperatures due to a solid sphere of uniform temperature immersed in the gas, cannot of itself give rise to any force tending to move the sphere in one direction rather than in another. Let the sphere be placed within the finite portion of gas which, as we have said, is already in equilibrium. The equilibrium will not be disturbed. We may introduce any number of spheres at different temperatures into the portion of gas, so as to form a body of any shape, heated in any manner, and when the flow of heat has become steady the whole system will be in equilibrium.

12. How, then, are we to account for the observed fact that forces act between solid bodies immersed in rarified gases, and this, apparently, as long as inequalities of temperature are maintained?

I think we must look for an explanation in the phenomenon discovered in the case of liquids by Helmholtz and Piotrowski*, and for gases by Kundt and Warburg†, that the fluid in contact with the surface of a solid must slide over it with a finite velocity in order to produce a finite tangential stress.

The theoretical treatment of the boundary conditions between a gas and a solid is difficult, and it becomes more difficult if we consider that the gas close to the surface is probably in an unknown state of condensation. We shall therefore accept the results obtained by Kundt and Warburg on their experimental evidence.

They have found that the velocity of sliding of the gas over the surface due to a given tangential stress varies inversely as the pressure.

The coefficient of sliding for air on glass was found to be $G = \dfrac{8}{p}$ centimetres, where p is the pressure in millionths of an atmosphere. Hence at ordinary pressures G is insensible, but in the vessels exhausted by Mr Crookes it may be considerable.

Hence, if close to the surface of a solid there is a tangential stress S, acting on a surface parallel to that of the body in a direction h parallel to that surface, there will also be a sliding of the gas in contact with the solid over its surface in the direction h with a finite velocity $= \dfrac{SG}{\mu}$.

13. I have not attempted to enter on the calculation of the effect of this sliding motion, but it is easy to see that if we begin with the case in which there is no sliding, the instantaneous effect of permission being given

---

* *Wiener Sitzb.*, xl. 1860, p. 607.

† Pogg. *Ann.*, clv. 1875, p. 337.

to the gas to slide must be to diminish the action of all tangential stresses on the surface, without affecting the normal stresses, and in course of time to set up currents sweeping over the surfaces of solid bodies, thus completely destroying the simplicity of our first solution of the problem.

14.   When external forces, such as gravity, act on the gas, and when the thermal phenomena produce differences of density in different parts of the vessel, then the well-known convection currents are set up.   These also interfere with the simplicity of the problem and introduce very complicated effects.   All that we know is that the rarer the gas and the smaller the vessel the less is the effect of the convection currents, so that in Mr Crookes' experiments they play a very small part.

We now proceed to the calculations :—

(1)   *Encounter between Two Molecules.*

The motion of the two molecules after an encounter depends on their motion before the encounter, and is capable of being determined by purely dynamical methods.   If the encounter of the molecules does not cause rotation or vibration in the individual molecules, then the kinetic energy of the centres of mass of the two molecules must be the same after the encounter as it was before.

This will be true on the average, even if the molecules are complex systems capable of rotation and internal vibration, provided the temperature is constant.   If, however, the temperature is rising, the internal energy of the molecules is, on the whole, increasing, and therefore the energy of translation of their centres of mass must be, ·on an average, diminishing at every encounter. The reverse will be the case if the temperature is falling.

But however important this consideration may be in the theory of specific heat and that of the conduction of heat, it has only a secondary bearing on the question of the stresses in the medium ; and as it would introduce great complexity and much guesswork into our calculations, I shall suppose that the gas here considered is one the molecules of which do not take up any sensible amount of energy in the form of internal motion.   Kundt and Warburg* have shewn that this is the case with mercury gas.

* Pogg. *Ann.*, clvii. 1876, p. 353.

Let the masses of the molecule be M_1 and M_2, and their velocity-components ξ_1, η_1, ζ_1, and ξ_2, η_2, ζ_2 respectively. Let V be the velocity of M_1 relative to M_2.

Before the encounter let a straight line be drawn through M_1 parallel to V, and let a perpendicular b be drawn from M_2 to this line. The magnitude and direction of b and V will be constant as long as the motion is undisturbed.

During the encounter the two molecules act on each other. If the force acts in the line joining their centres of mass, the product bV will remain constant, and if the force is a function of the distance, V and therefore b will be of the same magnitude after the encounter as before it, but their directions will be turned in the plane of V and b through an angle 2θ, this angle being a function of b and V, which vanishes for values of b greater than the limit of molecular action. Let the plane through V and b make an angle ϕ with the plane through V parallel to x, then all values of ϕ are equally probable.

If ξ_1' be the value of ξ_1 after the encounter,

$$\xi_1' = \xi_1 + \frac{M_2}{M_1 + M_2} \left((\xi_2 - \xi_1) \, 2 \sin^2 \theta + [(\eta_2 - \eta_1)^2 + (\zeta_2 - \zeta_1)^2]^{\frac{1}{2}} \sin 2\theta \cos\phi \right) \dots (1).$$

When the two molecules are of the same kind, $\dfrac{M_2}{M_1 + M_2} = \frac{1}{2}$, and in the present investigation of a single gas we shall assume this to be the case.

If we use the symbol δ to indicate the increment of any quantity due to an encounter, and if we remember that all values of ϕ are equally probable, so that the average value of $\cos\phi$ and of $\cos^3\phi$ is zero, and that of $\cos^2\phi$ is $\frac{1}{2}$, we find

$$\delta \left(\xi_1 + \xi_2 \right) = 0 \dots (2)$$

$$\delta \left(\xi_1^2 + \xi_2^2 \right) = - \left[3 \left(\xi_2 - \xi_1 \right)^2 - V^2 \right] \sin^2 \theta \cos^2 \theta \dots (3)$$

$$\delta \left(\xi_1^3 + \xi_2^3 \right) = - \tfrac{3}{2} \left(\xi_1 + \xi_2 \right) \left[3 \left(\xi_2 - \xi_1 \right)^2 - V^2 \right] \sin^2 \theta \cos^2 \theta \dots (4).$$

From these by transformation of coordinates we find

$$\delta \left(\xi_1 \eta_1 + \xi_2 \eta_2 \right) = - 3 \left(\xi_2 - \xi_1 \right) \left(\eta_2 - \eta_1 \right) \sin^2 \theta \cos^2 \theta \dots (5)$$

$$\delta(\xi_1 \eta_1^2 + \xi_2 \eta_2^2) = - \tfrac{1}{2} \big[9 \left(\xi_1 \eta_1^2 + \xi_2 \eta_2^2 \right) - 3 \left(\xi_1 \eta_2^2 + \xi_2 \eta_1^2 \right)$$
$$- \left(\xi_1 + \xi_2 \right) \left(6 \eta_1 \eta_2 + V^2 \right) \big] \sin^2 \theta \cos^2 \theta \dots (6)$$

$$\delta \left(\xi_1 \eta_1 \zeta_1 + \xi_2 \eta_2 \zeta_2 \right) = - \tfrac{1}{2} \big[9 \left(\xi_1 \eta_1 \zeta_1 + \xi_2 \eta_2 \zeta_2 \right) - 3 (\xi_1 \eta_1 \zeta_2 + \xi_1 \eta_2 \zeta_1 + \xi_2 \eta_1 \zeta_1$$
$$+ \xi_2 \eta_1 \zeta_2 + \xi_2 \eta_2 \zeta_1) \big] \sin^2 \theta \cos^2 \theta \dots (7).$$

[Application of Spherical Harmonics to the Theory of Gases.

If we suppose the direction of the velocity of M_1 relative to M_2 to be indicated by the position of a point P on a sphere, which we may call the sphere of reference, then the direction of the relative velocity after the encounter will be indicated by a point P', the angular distance PP' being 2θ, so that the point P' lies in a small circle, every position in which is equally probable.

We have to calculate the effect of an encounter upon certain functions of the six velocity-components of the two molecules. These six quantities may be expressed in terms of the three velocity-components of the centre of mass of the two molecules (say u, v, w), the relative velocity of M_1 with respect to M_2 which we call V, and the two angular coordinates which indicate the direction of V. During the encounter, the quantities u, v, w and V remain the same, but the angular coordinates are altered from those of P to those of P' on the sphere of reference.

Whatever be the form of the function of ξ_1, η_1, ζ_1, ξ_2, η_2, ζ_2, we may consider it expressed in the form of a series of spherical harmonics of the angular coordinates, their coefficients being functions of u, v, w, V, and we have only to determine the effect of the encounter upon the value of the spherical harmonics, for their coefficients are not changed.

Let $Y^{(n)}$ be the value at P of the surface harmonic of order n in the series considered.

After the encounter, the corresponding term becomes what $Y^{(n)}$ becomes at the point P', and since all positions of P' in a circle whose centre is P are equally probable, the mean value of the function after the encounter must depend on the mean value of the spherical harmonic in this circle.

Now the mean value of a spherical harmonic of order n in a circle, the cosine of whose radius is μ, is equal to the value of the harmonic at the pole of the circle multiplied by $P^{(n)}(\mu)$, the zonal harmonic of order n, and amplitude μ.

Hence, after the encounter, $Y^{(n}$ becomes $Y^{(n)}P^{(n)}(\mu)$, and if F_n is the corresponding part of the function to be considered, and δF_n the increment of F_n arising from the encounter, $\delta F_n = F_n(P^{(n)}(\mu)-1)$.

This is the mean increment of F_n arising from an encounter in which $\cos 2\theta = \mu$. The rate of increment is to be found from this by multiplying it by the number of encounters of each molecule per second in which μ lies between μ and $\mu + d\mu$, and integrating for all values of μ from -1 to $+1$.

This operation requires, in general, a knowledge of the law of force between the molecules, and also a knowledge of the distribution of velocity among the molecules.

When, as in the present investigation, we suppose both the molecules to be of the same kind, and take both molecules into account in the final summation, the spherical harmonics of odd orders will disappear, so that if we restrict our calculations to functions of not more than three dimensions, the effect of the encounters will depend on harmonics of the second order only, in which case $P^{(2)}(\mu) - 1 = \frac{3}{2}(\mu^2 - 1) = -\frac{3}{2}\sin^2 2\theta$.—Note added May, 1879.]

(2) *Number of Encounters in Unit of Time.*

We now abandon the dynamical method and adopt the statistical method. Instead of tracing the path of a single molecule and determining the effects of each encounter on its velocity-components and their combinations, we fix our attention on a particular element of volume, and trace the changes in the average values of such combinations of components for all the molecules which at a given instant happen to be within it. The problem which now presents itself may be stated thus: to determine the distribution of velocities among the molecules of any element of the medium, the current-velocity and the temperature of the medium being given in terms of the coordinates and the time. The only case in which this problem has been actually solved is that in which the medium has attained to its ultimate state, in which the temperature is uniform and there are no currents.

Denoting by

$$dN = f_1(\xi, \eta, \zeta, x, y, z, t)\, d\xi d\eta d\zeta dx dy dz$$

the number of molecules of the kind M_1 which at a given instant are within the element of volume $dxdydz$, and whose velocity-components lie between the limits $\xi \pm \frac{1}{2}d\xi$, $\eta \pm \frac{1}{2}d\eta$, $\zeta \pm \frac{1}{2}d\zeta$, Boltzmann has shewn that the function f_1 must satisfy the equation

$$\frac{df_1}{dt} + \xi_1 \frac{df_1}{dx} + \eta_1 \frac{df_1}{dy} + \zeta_1 \frac{df_1}{dz} + X \frac{df_1}{d\xi_1} + Y \frac{df_1}{d\eta_1} + Z \frac{df_1}{d\zeta_1} +$$

$$+ \iiint d\xi_2 d\eta_2 d\zeta_2 \int b\,db \int d\phi\, V\,(f_1 f_2 - f_1' f_2') = 0 \quad\ldots\ldots\ldots(8)$$

where f_2, f_1', f_2' denote what f_1 becomes when in place of the velocity-components of M_1 before the encounter we put those of M_2 before the encounter, and those of M_1 and M_2 after the encounter, respectively, and the integration is extended to all values of ϕ and b and of ξ_2, η_2, ζ_2, the velocity-components of the second molecule M_2.

It is impossible, in general, to perform this integration without a knowledge, not only of the law of force between the molecules, but of the form of the functions f_1, f_2, f_1', f_2', which have themselves to be found by means of the equation.

It is only for particular cases, therefore, that the equation has hitherto been solved.

If the medium is surrounded by a surface through which no communication of energy can take place, then one solution of the equation is given by the conditions

$$f_1 f_2 - f_1' f_2' = 0,$$

and

$$\xi \frac{df}{dx} + \eta \frac{df}{dy} + \zeta \frac{df}{dz} + X \frac{df}{d\xi} + Y \frac{df}{d\eta} + Z \frac{df}{d\zeta} = 0,$$

which give

$$f_1 = A_1 e^{-h(2\psi_1 + \xi_1^2 + \eta_1^2 + \zeta_1^2)} \dots\dots\dots\dots\dots\dots\dots(9)$$

where ψ_1 is the potential of the force whose components are X_1, Y_1, Z_1, and A_1 is a constant which may be different for each kind of molecules in the medium, but h is the same for all kinds of molecules.

This is the complete solution of this problem, and is independent of any hypothesis as to the manner in which the molecules act on each other during an encounter. The quantity h which occurs in this expression may be determined by finding the mean value of ξ^2, which is $\frac{1}{2h}$. Now in the kinetic theory of gases,

$$\rho \overline{\xi^2} = p = R\rho\theta \dots\dots\dots\dots\dots\dots\dots\dots(10)$$

where p is the pressure, ρ the density, θ the absolute temperature, and R a constant for a given gas. Hence

$$\frac{1}{2h} = R\theta \dots\dots\dots\dots\dots\dots\dots\dots\dots(11).$$

We shall suppose, however, with Boltzmann, that in a medium in which there are inequalities of temperature and of velocity

$$dN = N \{1 + F(\xi, \eta, \zeta)\} f_0 (\xi, \eta, \zeta) \, d\xi d\eta d\zeta \ldots\ldots\ldots\ldots(12)$$

where F is a rational function of ξ, η, ζ, which we shall suppose not to contain terms of more than three dimensions, and f_0 is the same function as in equation (9).

Now consider two groups of molecules, each defined by the velocity-components, and let the two groups be distinguished by the suffixes $(_1)$ and $(_2)$. We have to estimate the number of encounters of a given kind between these two groups in a unit of volume in the time δt, those encounters only being considered for which the limits of b and ϕ are $b \pm \frac{1}{2}db$ and $\phi \pm \frac{1}{2}d\phi$.

Let us first suppose that both groups consist of mere geometrical points which do not interfere with each other's motion. The group dN_1 is moving through the group dN_2 with the relative velocity V, and we have to find how many molecules of the first group approach a molecule of the second group in a manner which would, if the molecules acted on each other, produce an encounter of the given kind. This will be the case for every molecule of the first group which passes through the area $bdbd\phi$ in the time δt. The number of such molecules is $dN_1 V b d b d\phi \delta t$ for every molecule of the second group, so that the whole number of pairs which pass each other within the given limits is

$$V b d b d\phi \, dN_1 dN_2 \delta t,$$

and if we take the time δt small enough, this will be the number of encounters of the real molecules in the time δt.

(3) Effect of the Encounters.

We have next to estimate the effect of these encounters on the average values of different functions of the velocity-components. The effect of an individual encounter on these functions for the pair of molecules concerned is given in equations (3), (4), (5), (6), (7), each of which is of the form

$$\delta P = Q \sin^2 \theta \cos^2 \theta \ldots\ldots\ldots\ldots\ldots\ldots(13)$$

where P and Q are functions of the velocity-components of the two molecules, and if we write $\bar{P}$ for the average value of P for the N molecules in unit of volume, then taking the sum of the effects of the encounters—

$$\Sigma \delta P = N \delta \bar{P} \dots\dots\dots\dots\dots\dots\dots(14).$$

We thus find

$$\frac{\delta P}{\delta t} = N \iiiint\!\!\iiiint Q \sin^2 \theta \cos^2 \theta \, V b \, db \, d\phi f_1 f_2 d\xi_1 d\eta_1 d\zeta_1 d\xi_2 d\eta_2 d\zeta_2 \quad \dots(15). \; .$$

Now, since θ is a function of b and V, the definite integral

$$V \int_0^{2\pi}\!\!\int_0^{\infty} b \sin^2 \theta \cos^2\theta \, db \, d\phi = B \dots\dots\dots\dots\dots(16)$$

will be a function of V only.

If the molecules are "rigid-elastic" spheres of diameter s,

$$B = \tfrac{1}{6}\pi s^2 V \dots\dots\dots\dots\dots\dots\dots(17).$$

If they repel each other with a force inversely as the fifth power of the distance, so that at a distance r the force is κr^{-5}, then

$$B = \left(\frac{2\kappa}{M}\right)^{\frac{1}{2}} A_2 \dots\dots\dots\dots\dots\dots(18)$$

where A_2 is the numerical quantity $1\cdot3682$. In this case B is independent of V.

The experiments of O. E. Meyer[*], Kundt and Warburg[†], Puluj[‡], Von Obermayer[§], Eilhard Wiedemann[||], and Holman[¶], shew that 'the viscosity of air varies according to a lower power of the absolute temperature than the first, probably the $0\cdot77$ power. If the viscosity had varied as the first power of the absolute temperature, B would have been independent of V. Though this is not the case, we shall assume, for the sake of being able to effect the integrations, that B is independent of V.

We shall find it convenient to write for B,

$$B = \frac{p}{3N\mu} \dots\dots\dots\dots\dots\dots(19)$$

where p is the hydrostatic pressure, N the number of molecules in unit of

[*] Pogg. *Ann.*, 1873, Bd. 148, p. 222.   [†] *Ibid.* 1876, Bd. 159, p. 403.
[‡] *Wiener Sitz.*, 1874 and 1876.   [§] *Ibid.* 1875.
[||] *Arch. des Sci. Phys. et Nat.*, 1876, t. 56, p. 273.
[¶] *American Academy of Arts and Sciences*, June 14, 1876. *Phil. Mag.*, s. 5, vol. 3, No. 16, Feb., 1877.

volume, and μ a new coefficient which we shall afterwards find to be the coefficient of viscosity.

Equation (15) may now be written

$$\frac{\delta P}{\delta t} = \frac{p}{3\mu} \iiint\iiint Q f_1 f_2 d\xi_1 d\eta_1 d\zeta_1 d\xi_2 d\eta_2 d\zeta_2 \quad\ldots\ldots\ldots\ldots(20)$$

where the integrations are all between the limits $-\infty$ and $+\infty$, and f_1 and f_2 are of the form

$$f = \{1 + F(\xi, \eta, \zeta)\} h^{\frac{3}{2}} \pi^{-\frac{3}{2}} e^{-h(\xi^2 + \eta^2 + \zeta^2)} \quad\ldots\ldots\ldots\ldots\ldots(21)$$

$F(\xi, \eta, \zeta)$ being small compared with unity.

We may write F in the form

$$\begin{aligned}
F = (2h)^{\frac{1}{2}} (\alpha\xi + \beta\eta + \gamma\zeta) + 2h \left(\tfrac{1}{2}\alpha^2\xi^2 + \tfrac{1}{2}\beta^2\eta^2 + \tfrac{1}{2}\gamma^2\zeta^2 + \beta\gamma\eta\zeta + \gamma\alpha\zeta\xi + \alpha\beta\xi\eta\right) \\
+ (2h)^{\frac{3}{2}} \left(\tfrac{1}{6}\alpha^3\xi^3 + \tfrac{1}{6}\beta^3\eta^3 + \tfrac{1}{6}\gamma^3\zeta^3 + \tfrac{1}{2}\alpha^2\beta\xi^2\eta + \tfrac{1}{2}\alpha^2\gamma\xi^2\zeta + \tfrac{1}{2}\beta^2\gamma\eta^2\zeta \right. \\
\left. + \tfrac{1}{2}\beta^2\alpha\eta^2\zeta + \tfrac{1}{2}\gamma^2\alpha\zeta^2\xi + \tfrac{1}{2}\gamma^2\beta\zeta^2\eta + \alpha\beta\gamma\xi\eta\zeta\right) \quad\ldots\ldots\ldots\ldots\ldots\ldots(22)
\end{aligned}$$

where each combination of the symbols $\alpha\beta\gamma$ is to be taken as a single independent symbol, and not as a product of the component symbols.

(4) *Mean Values of Combinations of* ξ, η, ζ.

To find the mean value of any function of ξ, η, ζ for all the molecules in the element, we must multiply this function by f, and integrate with respect to ξ, η, and ζ.

If the non-exponential factor of any term contains an odd power of any of the variables, the corresponding part of the integral will vanish, but if it contains only even powers, each even power, such as $2n$, will introduce a factor

$$R^n \theta^n (2n-1)(2n-3)\ldots\ldots 3\cdot 1$$

into the corresponding part of the integral.

First, let the function be 1, then

$$1 = \iiint f d\xi d\eta d\zeta \quad\ldots\ldots\ldots\ldots\ldots\ldots\ldots\ldots(23)$$

or

$$1 = 1 + \tfrac{1}{2} \left(a^2 + \beta^2 + \gamma^2 \right) \quad\quad\quad\quad (24)$$

which gives the condition

$$a^2 + \beta^2 + \gamma^2 = 0 \quad\quad\quad\quad (25).$$

Let us next find the mean value of ξ in the same way, denoting the result by the symbol $\bar{\xi}$,

$$\bar{\xi} = (R\theta)^{\frac{1}{2}} \left[a + \tfrac{1}{2} \left(a^3 + a\beta^2 + a\gamma^2 \right) \right] \quad\quad\quad\quad (26).$$

Since in what follows we shall denote the velocity-components of each molecule by $u+\xi$, $v+\eta$, $w+\zeta$, where u, v, w are the velocity-components of the centre of mass of all the molecules within the element, it follows that the mean values of ξ, η, ζ are each of them zero. We thus obtain the equations

$$\left. \begin{array}{l} a + \tfrac{1}{2} \left(a^3 + a\beta^2 + a\gamma^2 \right) = 0 \\ \beta + \tfrac{1}{2} \left(a^2\beta + \beta^3 + \beta\gamma \right) = 0 \\ \gamma + \tfrac{1}{2} \left(a^2\gamma + \beta^2\gamma + \gamma^3 \right) = 0 \end{array} \right\} \quad\quad\quad (27).$$

Remembering these conditions, we find that the mean values of combinations of two, three, and four dimensions are of the forms

$$\left. \begin{array}{l} \overline{\xi^2} \;\; = R\theta \left(1 + a^2 \right) \\ \overline{\xi\eta} \;\; = R\theta a\beta \end{array} \right\} \quad\quad\quad\quad (28)$$

$$\left. \begin{array}{l} \overline{\xi^3} \;\; = (R\theta)^{\frac{3}{2}} a^3 \\ \overline{\xi\eta^2} \;\; = (R\theta)^{\frac{3}{2}} a\beta^2 \\ \overline{\xi\eta\zeta} = (R\theta)^{\frac{3}{2}} a\beta\gamma \end{array} \right\} \quad\quad\quad\quad (29)$$

$$\left. \begin{array}{l} \overline{\xi^4} \;\; = 3R^2\theta^2 \left(1 + 2a^2 \right) \\ \overline{\xi^3\eta} \;\; = 3R^2\theta^2 a\beta \\ \overline{\xi^2\eta^2} = R^2\theta^2 \left(1 + a^2 + \beta^2 \right) \\ \overline{\xi^2\eta\zeta} = R^2\theta^2 \beta\gamma \end{array} \right\} \quad\quad\quad (30).$$

(5)   *Rates of Decay of these Mean Values.*

If any term of Q in equation (20) contains symbols belonging to one group alone of the molecules, the corresponding term of the integral may be found from the above table, but if it contains symbols belonging to both groups we must consider the sextuple integral (20). But we shall not find it necessary to do this for terms of not more than three dimensions, for in these, if both groups of symbols occur, the index of one of them must be odd, and the integral vanishes.

We thus find from equations (3), (4), (5), (6), and (7)

$$\frac{\delta}{\delta t} \, \alpha^2 \quad = -\frac{p}{\mu} \alpha^2 \quad\dots\dots\dots\dots\dots\dots\dots\dots\dots\dots\dots\dots (31)$$

$$\frac{\delta}{\delta t} \, \alpha\beta \quad = -\frac{p}{\mu} \alpha\beta \dots\dots\dots\dots\dots\dots\dots\dots\dots\dots\dots\dots\dots (32)$$

$$\frac{\delta}{\delta t} \, \alpha^3 \quad = \frac{1}{2}\frac{p}{\mu} \left(- 2\alpha^3 + \alpha\beta^2 + \alpha\gamma^2 \right) \dots\dots\dots\dots\dots\dots (33)$$

$$\frac{\delta}{\delta t} \, \alpha\beta^2 = \frac{1}{6}\frac{p}{\mu} \left(\alpha^3 - 8\alpha\beta^2 + \alpha\gamma^2 \right) \dots\dots\dots\dots\dots\dots\dots (34)$$

$$\frac{\delta}{\delta t} \, \alpha\beta\gamma = -\frac{3}{2}\frac{p}{\mu} \, \alpha\beta\gamma \dots\dots\dots\dots\dots\dots\dots\dots\dots\dots\dots (35).$$

[Any rational homogeneous function of ξ η ζ is either a solid harmonic, or a solid harmonic multiplied by a positive integral power of $(\xi^2 + \eta^2 + \zeta^2)$, or may be expressed as the sum of a number of terms of these forms.

If we express any one of these terms as a function of u, v, w, V and the angular coordinates of V, we can determine the rate of change of each of the spherical harmonics of the angular coordinates.

If we then transform the expression back to its original form as a function of ξ_1, η_1, ζ_1, ξ_2, η_2, ζ_2, and if we add the corresponding functions for both molecules, we shall obtain an expression for the rate of change of the original function.

Thus among the terms of two dimensions we have the five conjugate solid harmonics

$$\frac{1}{3} \left(2\xi^2 - \eta^2 - \zeta^2 \right),$$

$$\xi\eta, \qquad \xi\zeta,$$

$$\eta^2 - \zeta^2, \quad \eta\zeta.$$

The rate of increase of each of these arising from the encounters of the molecules is found by multiplying it by $-\dfrac{p}{\mu}$. We may therefore call $\dfrac{p}{\mu}$ the "modulus of the time of relaxation" of this class of functions.

The function $\xi^2 + \eta^2 + \zeta^2$ is not changed by the encounters.

Homogeneous functions of three dimensions are either solid harmonics of the third order or solid harmonics of the first order multiplied by $\xi^2 + \eta^2 + \zeta^2$, or combinations of these.

The time modulus for solid harmonics of the third order is $\dfrac{3}{2}\dfrac{p}{\mu}$.—Note added May, 1879.]

That of ξ, η, or ζ, multiplied by $\xi^2 + \eta^2 + \zeta^2$ is $\dfrac{2}{3}\dfrac{p}{\mu}$.

(6) *Effect of External Forces.*

The only effect of external forces is expressed by equations of the form

$$\frac{\partial u}{\partial t} = X \dotfill (36).$$

The average values of ξ, η, ζ and their combinations are not affected by external forces.

(7) *Variation of Mean Values within an Element of Volume.*

We have employed the symbol δ to denote the variation of any quantity within an element, arising either from encounters between molecules or from the action of external forces.

There is a third way, however, in which a variation may occur, namely, by molecules entering the element or leaving it, carrying their properties with them.

We shall use the symbol ∂ to denote the actual variation within a specified element.

If MQ is the average value of any quantity for each molecule within the element, then the quantity in unit of volume is ρQ. We have to trace the variation of ρQ.

We begin with an element of volume moving with the velocity-components U, V, W, then by the ordinary investigation of the "equation of continuity"

$$\frac{\partial}{\partial t}[Q\rho] + \frac{d}{dx}[Q(u+\xi-U)] + \frac{d}{dy}[Q(v+\eta-V)] + \frac{d}{dz}[Q(w+\zeta-W)] = \rho\frac{\delta}{\delta t}Q \ldots(37).$$

If after performing the differentiations we make $U=u$, $V=v$, $W=w$, the equation becomes for an element moving with the velocity (u, v, w)

$$\frac{\partial}{\partial t}(Q\rho) + \rho Q\left(\frac{du}{dx} + \frac{dv}{dy} + \frac{dw}{dz}\right) + \frac{d}{dx}(\rho Q\xi) + \frac{d}{dy}(\rho Q\eta) + \frac{d}{dz}(\rho Q\zeta) = \rho\frac{\delta}{\delta t}Q \ldots(38).$$

(8) *Equation of Density.*

Let us first make $Q=1$, then, since the mass of a molecule is invariable, the equation becomes

$$\frac{\partial\rho}{\partial t} + \rho\left(\frac{du}{dx} + \frac{dv}{dy} + \frac{dw}{dz}\right) = 0 \ldots\ldots\ldots\ldots\ldots\ldots(39),$$

which is the ordinary "equation of continuity."

Eliminating by means of this equation the second term of the general equation (38) we obtain the more convenient form—

$$\rho\frac{\partial Q}{\partial t} + \frac{d}{dx}(\rho Q\xi) + \frac{d}{dy}(\rho Q\eta) + \frac{d}{dz}(\rho Q\zeta) = \rho\frac{\delta Q}{\delta t} \ldots\ldots\ldots\ldots(40).$$

(9) *Equations of Motion.*

Putting $Q = u + \xi$, this equation becomes

$$\rho\frac{\partial u}{\partial t} + \frac{d}{dx}(\rho\xi^2) + \frac{d}{dy}(\rho\xi\eta) + \frac{d}{dz}(\rho\xi\zeta) = \rho X \ldots\ldots\ldots\ldots(41)$$

where any combination of the symbols ξ, η, ζ is to be taken as the average value of that combination.

Substituting their values as given in (28)

$$\rho\frac{\partial u}{\partial t} + R\frac{d}{dx}(\rho\theta) + R\left[\frac{d}{dx}(\rho\theta\alpha^2) + \frac{d}{dy}(\rho\theta\alpha\beta) + \frac{d}{dz}(\rho\theta\alpha\gamma)\right] = \rho X \ldots..(42),$$

which is one of the three ordinary equations of motion of a medium in which stresses exist.

(10) *Terms of Two Dimensions.*

Put $Q = (u + \xi)^2$. Since the resulting equation is true whatever be the values of u, v, w, we may, after differentiation, put each of these quantities equal to zero. We shall thus obtain the same result which we might have obtained by elimination between this and the former equations. We find

$$\rho \frac{\partial}{\partial t} \xi^2 + 2\rho \xi^2 \frac{du}{dx} + 2\rho \xi \eta \frac{du}{dy} + 2\rho \xi \zeta \frac{du}{dz} + \frac{d}{dx} (\rho \xi^3) + \frac{d}{dy} (\rho \xi^2 \eta) + \frac{d}{dz} (\rho \xi^2 \zeta) = \rho \frac{\delta}{\delta t} \xi^2 \dots (43),$$

or by substituting the mean values of these quantities from (29)

$$\rho \frac{\partial \theta}{\partial t} + \rho \frac{\partial}{\partial t} (\theta a^2) + 2\rho \theta \frac{du}{dx} + 2\rho \theta \left(a^2 \frac{du}{dx} + a\beta \frac{du}{dy} + a\gamma \frac{du}{dz} \right)$$

$$+ R^{\frac{1}{2}} \left[\frac{d}{dx} (\rho \theta^{\frac{3}{2}} a^3) + \frac{d}{dy} (\rho \theta^{\frac{3}{2}} a^2 \beta) + \frac{d}{dz} (\rho \theta^{\frac{3}{2}} a^2 \gamma) \right] = - \frac{R \rho^2 \theta^2}{\mu} a^2 \dots (44)$$

with two other equations of similar form.

Similarly we obtain by putting $Q = (u + \xi)(v + \eta)$

$$\rho \frac{\partial}{\partial t} (\theta a \beta) + \rho \theta \left(\frac{dv}{dx} + \frac{du}{dy} \right)$$

$$+ \rho \theta \left(a^2 \frac{dv}{dx} + a\beta \frac{dv}{dy} + a\gamma \frac{dv}{dz} + a\beta \frac{du}{dx} + \beta^2 \frac{du}{dy} + \beta\gamma \frac{du}{dz} \right)$$

$$+ R \left[\frac{d}{dx} (\rho \theta^{\frac{3}{2}} a^2 \beta) + \frac{d}{dy} (\rho \theta \, a\beta^2) + \frac{d}{dz} (\rho \theta^{\frac{3}{2}} a\beta\gamma) \right] = - \frac{R \rho^2 \theta^2}{\mu} a\beta \ \dots (45)$$

with two other equations of like form for $\beta\gamma$ and γa.

(11) *Terms of Three Dimensions.*

Putting $Q = (u + \xi)^3$ and in the final equation making $u = v = w = 0$ and eliminating $\frac{\partial u}{\partial t}$ by (41) we find

$$\rho \frac{\partial}{\partial t} \xi^3 + 3\rho \xi^3 \frac{du}{dx} + 3\rho \xi^2 \eta \frac{du}{dy} + 3\rho \xi^2 \zeta \frac{du}{dz}$$

$$+ \frac{d}{dx} (\rho \xi^4) + \frac{d}{dy} (\rho \xi^3 \eta) + \frac{d}{dz} (\rho \xi^3 \zeta)$$

$$- 3\xi^2 \left[\frac{d}{dx} (\rho \xi^2) + \frac{d}{dy} (\rho \xi \eta) + \frac{d}{dz} (\rho \xi \zeta) \right] = \rho \frac{\delta}{\delta t} \xi^3 \dots\dots\dots\dots (46),$$

which gives

$$R^{\frac{3}{2}}\rho\frac{\partial}{\partial t}\left(\theta^{\frac{3}{2}}a^2\right)+3\rho\left(R\theta\right)^{\frac{3}{2}}\left(a^3\frac{du}{dx}+a^2\beta\frac{du}{dy}+a^2\gamma\frac{du}{dz}\right)$$

$$+3R^2\rho\theta\frac{d\theta}{dx}+3R^2\rho\theta\left(a^2\frac{d\theta}{dx}+a\beta\frac{d\theta}{dy}+a\gamma\frac{d\theta}{dz}\right)+3R^2\rho\theta\frac{d}{dx}\left(a^2\theta\right)$$

$$-3R^2\theta a^2\left[\frac{d}{dx}\left(\rho\theta a^2\right)+\frac{d}{dy}\left(\rho\theta a\beta\right)+\frac{d}{dz}\left(\rho\theta a\gamma\right)\right]=\rho\left(R\theta\right)^{\frac{3}{2}}\frac{1}{2}\frac{p}{\mu}\left(-2a^3+a\beta^2+a\gamma^2\right)\ldots(47).$$

Since the combinations of $a\beta\gamma$ represent small numerical quantities, we may at this stage of the calculation, when we are dealing with terms of the third order, neglect terms involving them, except when they are multiplied by the large coefficient p/μ. The equation may then be written approximately :—

$$3R^2\rho\theta\frac{d\theta}{dx}=\rho\left(R\theta\right)^{\frac{3}{2}}\frac{1}{2}\frac{p}{\mu}\left(-2a^3+a\beta^2+a\gamma^2\right)\ldots\ldots\ldots\ldots(48).$$

Similarly, by putting $Q=(u+\xi)(v+\eta)^2$, we obtain the approximate equation

$$R^2\rho\theta\frac{d\theta}{dx}=\rho\left(R\theta\right)^{\frac{3}{2}}\frac{1}{6}\frac{p}{\mu}\left(a^3-8a\beta^2+a\gamma^2\right)\ldots\ldots\ldots\ldots(49),$$

and in the same way we find

$$R^2\rho\theta\frac{d\theta}{dx}=\rho\left(R\theta\right)^{\frac{3}{2}}\frac{1}{6}\frac{p}{\mu}\left(a^3+a\beta^2-8a\gamma^2\right)\ldots\ldots\ldots\ldots(50).$$

(12) *Approximate Values of Terms of Three Dimensions.*

From equations (48), (49), and (50), we find

$$a^3=-\frac{9}{2}\frac{\mu}{p}\left(\frac{R}{\theta}\right)^{\frac{1}{2}}\frac{d\theta}{dx},\quad a\beta^2=a\gamma^2=-\frac{3}{2}\frac{\mu}{p}\left(\frac{R}{\theta}\right)^{\frac{1}{2}}\frac{d\theta}{dx}$$

From which by substitution we obtain

$$\left.\begin{array}{l}\beta^3=-\frac{9}{2}\frac{\mu}{p}\left(\frac{R}{\theta}\right)^{\frac{1}{2}}\frac{d\theta}{dy},\quad a^2\beta=\beta\gamma^2=-\frac{3}{2}\frac{\mu}{p}\left(\frac{R}{\theta}\right)^{\frac{1}{2}}\frac{d\theta}{dy}\\[2mm]\gamma^3=-\frac{9}{2}\frac{\mu}{p}\left(\frac{R}{\theta}\right)^{\frac{1}{2}}\frac{d\theta}{dz},\quad a^2\gamma=\beta^2\gamma=-\frac{3}{2}\frac{\mu}{p}\left(\frac{R}{\theta}\right)^{\frac{1}{2}}\frac{d\theta}{dz}\end{array}\right\}\ldots\ldots\ldots\ldots(51).$$

The value of $a\beta\gamma$ is of a smaller order of magnitude, and we do not require it in this investigation.

(13) *Equation of Temperature.*

Adding the three equations of the form (44), and omitting terms containing small quantities of two dimensions, and also products of differential coefficients such as $\dfrac{d\mu}{dx}\dfrac{d\theta}{dx}$, we find

$$\frac{\partial\theta}{\partial t} = \frac{5}{2}\frac{\mu}{\rho}\left(\frac{d^2\theta}{dx^2} + \frac{d^2\theta}{dy^2} + \frac{d^2\theta}{dz^2}\right) + \frac{2}{3}\frac{\theta}{\rho}\frac{\partial\rho}{\partial t}\ \dotsb\dotsb(52).$$

The first term of the second member represents the rate of increase of temperature due to conduction of heat, as in Fourier's Theory, and the second term represents the increase of temperature due to increase of density. We must remember that the gas here considered is one for which the ratio of the specific heats is 1·6.

(14) *Stresses in the Gas.*

Subtracting one-third of the sum of the three equations from (44), we obtain

$$p\alpha^2 = -2\mu\frac{du}{dx} + \frac{2}{3}\mu\left(\frac{du}{dx} + \frac{dv}{dy} + \frac{dw}{dz}\right) + 3\frac{\mu^2}{\rho\theta}\frac{d^2\theta}{dx^2} + \frac{3}{2}\frac{\mu^2}{\rho\theta}\left(\frac{d^2\theta}{dx^2} + \frac{d^2\theta}{dy^2} + \frac{d^2\theta}{dz^2}\right)\ \dotsb(53).$$

This equation gives the excess of the normal pressure in x above the mean hydrostatic pressure p. The first two terms of the second member represent the effect of viscosity in a moving fluid, and are identical with those given by Professor Stokes (*Cambridge Transactions*, Vol. VIII., 1845, p. 297). The last two terms represent the part of the stress which arises from inequality of temperature, which is the special subject of this paper.

There are two other equations of similar form for the normal stresses in y and z.

The tangential stress in the plane xy is given by the equation

$$p\alpha\beta = -\mu\left(\frac{du}{dy} + \frac{dv}{dx}\right) + 3\frac{\mu^2}{\rho\theta}\frac{d^2\theta}{dxdy}\ \dotsb(54).$$

There are two other equations of similar form for the tangential stresses in the planes of yz and zx.

(15) *Final Equations of Motion.*

We are now prepared to complete the equations of motion by inserting in (42) the values of the quantities a^2, $a\beta$, $a\gamma$, and we find for the equation in x

$$\rho \frac{\partial u}{\partial t} + \frac{dp}{dx} - \mu \left(\frac{d^2u}{dx^2} + \frac{d^2u}{dy^2} + \frac{d^2u}{dz^2} \right) + \frac{1}{3} \mu \frac{d}{dx} \left(\frac{du}{dx} + \frac{dv}{dy} + \frac{dw}{dz} \right)$$

$$+ \frac{9}{2} \frac{\mu^2}{\rho\theta} \frac{d}{dx} \left(\frac{d^2\theta}{dx^2} + \frac{d^2\theta}{dy^2} + \frac{d^2\theta}{dz^2} \right) = \rho X \quad \dots\dots\dots\dots(55).$$

If we write

$$p' = p + \frac{1}{3} \mu \left(\frac{du}{dx} + \frac{dv}{dy} + \frac{dw}{dz} \right) + \frac{9}{2} \frac{\mu^2}{\rho\theta} \left(\frac{d^2\theta}{dx^2} + \frac{d^2\theta}{dy^2} + \frac{d^2\theta}{dz^2} \right) \quad \dots\dots\dots(56)$$

$$= p + \frac{9}{5} \frac{\mu}{\theta} \frac{\partial \theta}{\partial t} - \frac{23}{15} \frac{\mu}{\rho} \frac{\partial \rho}{\partial t} \dots\dots\dots\dots\dots\dots(57)$$

or, if the pressure p is constant, so that $\rho\partial\theta + \theta\partial\rho = 0$

$$p' = p + \frac{10}{3} \frac{\mu}{\theta} \frac{\partial \theta}{\partial t} \quad \dots\dots\dots\dots\dots\dots\dots\dots(58)$$

then the equation (55) may be written

$$\rho \frac{\partial u}{\partial t} + \frac{dp'}{dx} - \mu \left(\frac{d^2u}{dx^2} + \frac{d^2u}{dy^2} + \frac{d^2u}{dz^2} \right) = \rho X \quad \dots\dots\dots\dots(59).$$

If there are no external forces such as gravity, then one solution of the equations is

$$u = v = w = 0, \quad p' = \text{constant,}$$

and if the boundary conditions are such that this solution is consistent with them, it will become the actual solution as soon as the initial motions, if any exist, have subsided. This will be the case if no slipping is possible between the gas and solid bodies in contact with it.

But if such slipping is possible, then wherever in the above solution there is a tangential stress in the gas at the surface of a solid or liquid, there cannot be equilibrium, but the gas will begin to slide over the surface till the velocity of sliding has produced a frictional resistance equal and opposite to the tangential stress. When this is the case the motion may become steady.

I have not, however, attempted to enter into the calculation of the state of steady motion.

[I have recently applied the method of spherical harmonics, as described in the notes to sections (1) and (5), to carrying the approximations two orders higher. I expected that this would have involved the calculation of two new quantities, namely, the rates of decay of spherical harmonics of the fourth and sixth orders, but I found that, to the order of approximation required, all harmonics of the fourth and sixth orders may be neglected, so that the rate of decay of harmonics of the second order, the time-modulus of which is $\mu \div p$, determines the rate of decay of all functions of less than 6 dimensions.

The equations of motion, as here given (equation 55) contain the second derivatives of u, v, w, with respect to the coordinates, with the coefficient μ. I find that in the more approximate expression there is a term containing the fourth derivatives of u, v, w, with the coefficient $\mu^3 \div \rho p$.

The equations of motion also contain the third derivatives of θ with the coefficient $\mu^2 \div \rho \theta$. Besides these terms, there is another set consisting of the fifth derivatives of θ with the coefficient $\mu^4 \div \rho^2 p \theta$.

It appears from the investigation that the condition of the successful use of this method of approximation is that $l \dfrac{d}{dh}$ should be small, where $\dfrac{d}{dh}$ denotes differentiation with respect to a line drawn in any direction. In other words, the properties of the medium must not be sensibly different at points within a distance of each other, comparable with the "mean free path" of a molecule. —Note added June, 1879.]

APPENDIX.

(Added May, 1879.)

In the paper as sent in to the Royal Society, I made no attempt to express the conditions which must be satisfied by a gas in contact with a solid body, for I thought it very unlikely that any equations I could write down would be a satisfactory representation of the actual conditions, especially as it is almost certain that the stratum of gas nearest to a solid body is in a very different condition from the rest of the gas.

One of the referees, however, pointed out that it was desirable to make the attempt, and indicated several hypothetical forms of surfaces which might be tried. I have therefore added the following calculations, which are carried to the same degree of approximation as those for the interior of the gas.

It will be seen that the equations I have arrived at express both the fact that the gas may slide over the surface with a finite velocity, the previous investigations of which have been already mentioned;* and the fact that this velocity and the corresponding tangential stress are affected by inequalities of temperature at the surface of the solid, which give rise to a force tending to make the gas slide along the surface from colder to hotter places.

This phenomenon, to which Professor Osborne Reynolds has given the name of Thermal Transpiration, was discovered entirely by him. He was the first to point out that a phenomenon of this kind was a necessary consequence of the Kinetic Theory of Gases, and he also subjected certain actual phenomena, of a somewhat different kind, indeed, to measurement, and reduced his measurements by a method admirably adapted to throw light on the relations between gases and solids.

It was not till after I had read Professor Reynolds' paper that I began to reconsider the surface conditions of a gas, so that what I have done is simply to extend to the surface phenomena the method which I think most suitable for treating the interior of the gas. I think that this method is, in

* Sect. 12 of introduction.

some respects, better than that adopted by Professor Reynolds, while I admit that his method is sufficient to establish the existence of the phenomena, though not to afford an estimate of their amount.

The method which I have adopted throughout is a purely statistical one. It considers the mean values of certain functions of the velocities within a given element of the medium, but it never attempts to trace the motion of a molecule, not even so far as to estimate the length of its mean path. Hence all the equations are expressed in the forms of the differential calculus, in which the phenomena at a given place are connected with the space variations of certain quantities at that place, but in which no quantity appears which explicitly involves the condition of things at a finite distance from that place.

The particular functions of the velocities which are here considered are those of one, two, and three dimensions. These are sufficient to determine approximately the principal phenomena in a gas which is not very highly rarified, and in which the space-variations within distances comparable to λ are not very great.

The same method, however, can be extended to functions of higher degrees, and by a sufficient number of such functions any distribution of velocities, however abnormal, may be expressed. The labour of such an approximation is considerably diminished by the use of the method of spherical harmonics as indicated in the note to Section I. of the paper.

On the Conditions to be Satisfied by a Gas at the Surface of a Solid Body.

As a first hypothesis, let us suppose the surface of the body to be a perfectly elastic smooth fixed surface, having the apparent shape of the solid, without any minute asperities.

In this case, every molecule which strikes the surface will have the normal component of its velocity reversed, while the other components will not be altered by impact.

The rebounding molecules will therefore move as if they had come from an imaginary portion of gas occupying the space really filled by the solid, and such that the motion of every molecule close to the surface is the optical reflection in that surface of the motion of a molecule of the real gas.

In this case we may speak of the rebounding molecules close to the surface as constituting the *reflected* gas. All directed properties of the incident gas are reflected, or, as Professor Listing might say, *perverted* in the reflected gas; that is to say, the properties of the incident and the reflected gas are symmetrical with respect to the tangent plane of the surface.

The incident and reflected gas together constitute the actual gas close to the surface. The actual gas, therefore, cannot exert any stress on the surface, except in the direction of the normal, for the oblique components of stress in the incident and reflected gas will destroy one another.

Since gases can actually exert oblique stress against real surfaces, such surfaces cannot be represented as perfectly reflecting surfaces.

If a molecule, whose velocity is given in direction and magnitude, but whose line of motion is not given in position, strikes a fixed elastic sphere, its velocity after rebound may with equal probability be in any direction.

Consider, therefore, a stratum in which fixed elastic spheres are placed so far apart from one another that any one sphere is not to any sensible extent protected by any other sphere from the impact of molecules, and let the stratum be so deep that no molecule can pass through it without striking one or more of the spheres, and let this stratum of fixed spheres be spread over the surface of the solid we have been considering, then every molecule which comes from the gas towards the surface must strike one or more of the spheres, after which all directions of its velocity become equally probable.

When, at last, it leaves the stratum of spheres and returns into the gas, its velocity must of course be *from* the surface, but the probability of any particular magnitude and direction of the velocity will be the same as in a gas at rest with respect to the surface.

The distribution of velocity among the molecules which are leaving the surface will therefore be the same as if, instead of the solid, there were a portion of gas at rest, having the temperature of the solid, and a density such that the number of molecules which pass from it through the surface in a given time is equal to the number of molecules of the real gas outside which strike the surface.

To distinguish the molecules, which, after being entangled in the stratum of spheres, afterwards return into the surrounding gas, we shall call them, collectively, the *absorbed and evaporated* gas.

If the spheres are so near together that a considerable part of the surface of each sphere of the outer layer is shielded from the direct impact of the incident molecules by the spheres which lie next to it, then if we call that point of each sphere which lies furthest from the solid the *pole* of the sphere, a greater proportion of molecules will strike any one of the outer layer of spheres near its pole than near its equator, and the greater the obliquity of incidence of the molecule, the greater will be the probability that it will strike a sphere near its pole.

The direction of the rebounding molecule will no longer be with equal probability in all directions, but there will be a greater probability of the tangential part of its velocity being in the direction of the motion before impact, and of its normal part being opposite to the normal part before impact.

The condition of the molecules which leave the surface will therefore be intermediate between that of evaporated gas and that of reflected gas, approaching most nearly to evaporated gas at normal incidence and most nearly to reflected gas at grazing incidence.

If the spheres, instead of being hard elastic bodies, are supposed to act on the molecules at finite, though small distances, and if they are so close together that their spheres of action intersect, then the gas which leaves the surface will be still more like reflected gas, and less like evaporated gas.

We might also consider a surface on which there are a great number of minute asperities of any given form, but since in this case there is considerable difficulty in calculating the effect when the direction of rebound from the first impact is such as to lead to a second or third impact, I have preferred to treat the surface as something intermediate between a perfectly reflecting and a perfectly absorbing surface, and, in particular, to suppose that of every unit of area a portion f absorbs all the incident molecules, and afterwards allows them to evaporate with velocities corresponding to those in still gas at the temperature of the solid, while a portion $1-f$ perfectly reflects all the molecules incident upon it.

We shall begin by supposing that the surface is the plane yz, and that the gas is on that side of it for which x is positive.

The incident molecules are those which, close to the surface, have their normal component of velocity negative. We shall distinguish these molecules by the suffix $(_1)$. For these, and these only, ξ_1 is negative.

The rebounding molecules are those which have ξ positive. We shall distinguish them by the suffix $(_2)$. Those which are evaporated will be further distinguished by an accent.

Symbols without any mark refer to the whole gas, incident, reflected, and evaporated, close to the surface.

The quantity of gas which is incident on unit of surface in unit of time, is $-\rho_1\xi_1$.

Of this quantity the fraction $1-f$ is reflected, so that the sign of ξ is reversed, and the fraction f is evaporated, the mean value of ξ in evaporated gas being ξ', where the accent distinguishes symbols belonging to unpolarized gas at rest relative to the surface, and having the temperature, θ', of the solid.

Equating the quantity of gas which is incident on the absorbing part of the surface to that which is evaporated from it, we have

$$f\rho_1\xi_1 + f\rho_2'\xi_2' = 0 \dots\dots\dots\dots\dots\dots\dots\dots\dots\dots(60).$$

Equating the whole quantity of gas which leaves the surface to the reflected and evaporated portions

$$\rho_2\xi_2 = (f-1)\,\rho_1\xi_1 + f\rho_2'\xi_2' \dots\dots\dots\dots\dots\dots\dots(61).$$

If we next consider the momentum of the molecules in the direction of y, that of the incident molecules is $\rho_1\xi_1\eta_1$. A fraction $(1-f)$ of this is reflected and becomes $(1-f)\,\rho_1\xi_1\eta_1$, and a fraction f of it is absorbed and then evaporated, the mean value of η being now $-v$, namely, the velocity of the surface relatively to the gas in contact with it.

The momentum of the evaporated portion in the direction of y is therefore $-f\rho_2'\xi_2'v$, and this, together with the reflected portion, makes up the whole momentum which is leaving the surface, or

$$\rho_2\xi_2\eta_2 = (f-1)\,\rho_1\xi_1\eta_1 - f\rho_2'\xi_2'v \dots\dots\dots\dots\dots\dots(62).$$

Eliminating $f\rho_2'\xi_2'$ between equations (61) and (62)

$$(1-f)\,\rho_1\xi_1\eta_1 + \rho_2\xi_2\eta_2 + v\left[(1-f)\,\rho_1\xi_1 + \rho_2\xi_2\right] = 0 \dots\dots\dots\dots(63).$$

The values of functions of ξ, η and ζ for the incident molecules are to be found by multiplying the expression in equation (22) by the given function, and integrating with respect to ξ between the limits $-\infty$ and 0, and with respect to η and ζ between the limits $\pm\infty$.

The values of the same functions for the molecules which are leaving the surface are to be found by integrating with respect to ξ from 0 to ∞.

We must remember, however, that since there is an essential discontinuity in the conditions of the gas at the surface, the expression in equation (22) is a much less accurate approximation to the actual distribution of velocities in the gas close to the surface than it is in the interior of the gas. We must, therefore, consider the surface conditions at which we arrive in this way as liable to important corrections when we shall have discovered more powerful methods of attacking the problem.

For the present, however, we consider only terms of three dimensions or less, and we find

$$\left.\begin{aligned}\rho_1\xi_1 &= -\rho\,(2\pi)^{-\frac{1}{2}}\,(R\theta)^{\frac{1}{2}}\,(1+\tfrac{1}{2}a^2)\\ \rho_2\xi_2 &= \rho\,(2\pi)^{-\frac{1}{2}}\,(R\theta)^{\frac{1}{2}}\,(1+\tfrac{1}{2}a^2)\end{aligned}\right\}\quad\dots\dots\dots\dots\dots\dots(64)$$

$$\left.\begin{aligned}\rho_1\xi_1\eta_1 &= \tfrac{1}{2}\rho R\theta a\beta - \tfrac{1}{2}\rho\,(2\pi)^{-\frac{1}{2}}\,R\theta a^2\beta\\ \rho_2\xi_2\eta_2 &= \tfrac{1}{2}\rho R\theta a\beta + \tfrac{1}{2}\rho\,(2\pi)^{-\frac{1}{2}}\,R\theta a^2\beta\end{aligned}\right\}\quad\dots\dots\dots\dots(65).$$

Substituting these expressions in equation (63), and neglecting a^2 in comparison with unity, we find

$$(2-f)\,\rho R\theta a\beta + f\,(2\pi)^{-\frac{1}{2}}\,\rho R\theta a^2\beta + 2f(2\pi)^{-\frac{1}{2}}\,(1+\tfrac{1}{2}a^2)\,(R\theta)^{\frac{1}{2}}\,\rho v = 0 \;\dots(66).$$

If we write

$$G = \tfrac{1}{2}\mu\,(2\pi)^{\frac{1}{2}}\,(p\rho)^{-\frac{1}{2}}\left(\frac{2}{f}-1\right)\dots\dots\dots\dots\dots\dots(67)$$

and substitute for $a\beta$ and $a^2\beta$ their values as given in equations (54) and (51), and divide by $2\,(p\rho)^{\frac{1}{2}}$, equation (66) becomes

$$v - G\!\left(\frac{dv}{dx} - \frac{3}{2}\frac{\mu}{\rho\theta}\frac{d^2\theta}{dx\,dy}\right) - \frac{3}{4}\frac{\mu}{\rho\theta}\frac{d\theta}{dy} = 0 \;\dots\dots\dots\dots(68).$$

If there is no inequality of temperature, this equation is reduced to

$$v = G\,\frac{dv}{dx}\dots\dots\dots\dots\dots\dots\dots\dots\dots\dots\dots(69).$$

If, therefore, the gas at a finite distance from the surface is moving parallel to the surface, the gas in contact with the surface will be sliding over it with the finite velocity v, and the motion of the gas will be very nearly the same as if the stratum of depth G had been removed from the solid and filled with the gas, there being now no slipping between the new surface of the solid and the gas in contact with it.

The coefficient G was introduced by Helmholtz and Piotrowski under the name of *Gleitungs-coefficient*, or coefficient of slipping. The dimensions of G are those of a line, and its ratio to l, the mean free path of a molecule, is given by the equation

$$G = \frac{2}{3}\left(\frac{2}{f} - 1\right) l \quad \dots\dots\dots\dots\dots\dots\dots\dots(70).$$

Kundt and Warburg found that for air in contact with glass, $G = 2l$, whence we find $f = \frac{1}{2}$, or the surface acts as if it were half perfectly reflecting and half perfectly absorbent. If it were wholly absorbent, $G = \frac{2}{3}l$.

It is easy to write down the surface conditions for a surface of any form.

Let the direction-cosines of the normal ν be l, m, n, and let us write

$$\frac{d}{d\nu} \text{ for } l\frac{d}{dx} + m\frac{d}{dy} + n\frac{d}{dz}.$$

We then find as the surface conditions

$$\left.\begin{array}{l}
u - G\dfrac{d}{d\nu}[(1 - l^2)u - lmv - lnw] + \dfrac{3}{4}\dfrac{\mu}{\rho\theta}\left(\dfrac{d}{dx} - l\dfrac{d}{d\nu}\right)\left(\theta + 4G\dfrac{d\theta}{d\nu}\right) = 0 \\[2ex]
v - G\dfrac{d}{d\nu}[(1 - m^2)v - mnw - mlu] + \dfrac{3}{4}\dfrac{\mu}{\rho\theta}\left(\dfrac{d}{dy} - m\dfrac{d}{d\nu}\right)\left(\theta + 4G\dfrac{d\theta}{d\nu}\right) = 0 \\[2ex]
w - G\dfrac{d}{d\nu}[(1 - n^2)w - nlu - nmv] + \dfrac{3}{4}\dfrac{\mu}{\rho\theta}\left(\dfrac{d}{dz} - n\dfrac{d}{d\nu}\right)\left(\theta + 4G\dfrac{d\theta}{d\nu}\right) = 0
\end{array}\right\} \quad \dots(71).$$

In each of these equations the first term is one of the velocity-components of the gas in contact with the surface, which is supposed fixed; the second term depends on the slipping of the gas over the surface, and the third term indicates the effect of inequalities of temperature of the gas close to the surface, and shows that in general there will be a force urging the gas from colder to hotter parts of the surface.

Let us take as an illustration the case of a capillary tube of circular section, and for the sake of easy calculation we shall suppose that the motion is so slow, and the temperature varies so gradually along the tube that we may suppose the temperature uniform throughout any one section of the tube.

Taking the axis of the tube for that of z, we have for the condition of steady motion parallel to the axis

$$\frac{dp}{dz} = \mu\left(\frac{d^2w}{dx^2} + \frac{d^2w}{dy^2}\right) \quad \dots\dots\dots\dots\dots\dots\dots(72).$$

Since everything is symmetrical about the axis, if we write r^2 for x^2+y^2 we find as the solution of this equation

$$w = A + \frac{1}{4\mu}\frac{dp}{dz}r^2 \quad \dots\dots\dots\dots\dots\dots(73).$$

If Q denotes the quantity of gas which passes through a section of the tube in unit of time

$$Q = 2\pi\int\rho wrdr$$

$$= \pi\rho a^2\left(A + \frac{1}{8\mu}\frac{dp}{dz}a^2\right) \quad \dots\dots\dots\dots\dots(74).$$

At the inner surface of the tube we have $r=a$, and

$$w = A + \frac{1}{4\mu}\frac{dp}{dz}a^2$$

$$= \frac{Q}{\pi\rho a^2} + \frac{1}{8\mu}\frac{dp}{dz}a^2 \quad \dots\dots\dots\dots\dots(75)$$

also

$$\frac{dw}{d\nu} = -\frac{1}{2\mu}\frac{dp}{dz}a \quad \dots\dots\dots\dots\dots\dots(76).$$

The last of equations (71) may therefore be written

$$\frac{Q}{\pi\rho a^2} + \frac{1}{8\mu}(a^2 + 4Ga)\frac{dp}{dz} - \frac{3}{4}\frac{\mu}{\rho\theta}\frac{d\theta}{dz} = 0 \quad \dots\dots\dots\dots(77).$$

Equation (77) gives the relation between the quantity of gas which passes through any section of the tube, the rate of variation of pressure, and the rate of variation of temperature in passing along the axis of the tube.

If the pressure is uniform there will be a flow of gas from the colder to the hotter end of the tube, and if there is no flow of gas the pressure will increase from the colder to the hotter end of the tube.

These effects of the variation of temperature in a tube have been pointed out by Professor Osborne Reynolds as a result of the Kinetic Theory of Gases, and have received from him the name of Thermal Transpiration: a name in strict analogy with the use of the word Transpiration by Graham.

But the phenomenon actually observed by Professor Reynolds in his experiments was the passage of gas through a porous plate, not through a capillary tube; and the passage of gases through porous plates, as was shown by Graham, is of an entirely different kind from the passage of gases through capillary tubes, and is more nearly analogous to the flow of a gas through a small hole in a thin plate.

When the diameter of the hole and the thickness of the plate are both small compared with the length of the free path of a molecule, then, as Sir William Thomson has shown, any molecule which comes up to the hole on either side will be in very little danger of encountering another molecule before it has got fairly through to the other side.

Hence the flow of gas in either direction through the hole will take place very nearly in the same manner as if there had been a vacuum on the other side of the hole, and this whether the gas on the other side of the hole is of the same or of a different kind.

If the gas on the two sides of the plate is of the same kind but at different temperatures, a phenomenon will take place which we may call *thermal effusion*.

The velocity of the molecules is proportional to the square root of the absolute temperature, and the quantity which passes out through the hole is proportional to this velocity and to the density. Hence, on whichever side the product of the density into the square root of the temperature is greatest, more molecules will pass from that side than from the other through the hole, and this will go on till this product is equal on both sides of the hole. Hence the condition of equilibrium is that the density must be inversely as the square root of the temperature, and since the pressure is as the product of the density into the temperature, the pressure will be directly proportional to the square root of the absolute temperature.

The theory of thermal effusion through a small hole in a thin plate is therefore a very simple one. It does not involve the theory of viscosity at all.

The finer the pores of a porous plate, and the rarer the gas which effuses through it, the more nearly does the passage of gas through the plate correspond to what we have called effusion, and the less does it depend on the viscosity of the gas.

The coarser the pores of the plate and the denser the gas, the further does the phenomenon depart from simple effusion, and the more nearly does it approach to transpiration through a capillary tube, which depends altogether on viscosity.

To return to the case of transpiration through a capillary tube. When the temperature is uniform

$$Q = -\frac{\pi \rho a^4}{8\mu} \frac{dp}{dz} \left(1 + 4\frac{G}{a}\right) \quad \dots\dots\dots\dots\dots\dots(78).$$

By experiments on capillary tubes of glass, MM. Kundt and Warburg found* for the value of G for air at different pressures and at from 17° C. to 27° C.,

$$G = \frac{8}{p} \text{ centimetres} \dots\dots\dots\dots\dots\dots\dots(79)$$

where p is the pressure in dynes per square centimetre, which is nearly the same as in millionths of an atmosphere. For hydrogen on glass

$$G = \frac{15}{p} \text{ centimetres} \dots\dots\dots\dots\dots\dots(80).$$

When there is no flow of gas in a tube in which the temperature varies from end to end, the pressure is greater at the hot end than at the cold end. Putting $Q = 0$ we have

$$\frac{dp}{d\theta} = 6\frac{\mu^2}{\rho\theta} \frac{1}{a^2 + 4Ga} \quad \dots\dots\dots\dots\dots\dots(81).$$

The quantity $6\frac{\mu^2}{\rho\theta}$ is just double of that calculated in section (3) of the introduction, and is therefore in C.G.S. measure $0.63 \times p$ for dry air at 15° C. Let us suppose $a = 0.01$ centimetre, and the pressure 40 millimetres of mercury, then $G = .00016$ centimetre.

If one end of the tube is kept at 0° C. and the other at 100° C., the pressure at the hot end will exceed that at the cold end by about 1·2 millionths of an atmosphere.

The difference of pressure might be increased by using a tube of smaller bore and air of smaller density, but the effect is so small that though the theoretical proof of its existence seems satisfactory, an experimental verification of it would be difficult.

* Pogg. *Ann.*, July, 1876.

[From the *Cambridge Philosophical Society's Transactions*, Vol. XII.]

XCIV. *On Boltzmann's Theorem on the average distribution of energy in a system of material points.*

DR LUDWIG BOLTZMANN, in his "Studien über das Gleichgewicht der lebendigen Kraft zwischen bewegten materiellen Punkten" [*Sitzb. d. k. Akad. Wien*, Bd. LVIII., 8 Oct. 1868], has devoted his third section to the general solution of the problem of the equilibrium of kinetic energy among a finite number of material points. His method of treatment is ingenious, and, as far as I can see, satisfactory, but I think that a problem of such primary importance in molecular science ought to be scrutinized and examined on every side, so that as many persons as possible may be enabled to follow the demonstration, and to know on what assumptions it rests. This is more especially necessary when the assumptions relate to the degree of irregularity to be expected in the motion of a system whose motion is not completely known.

Mr H. W. Watson, in his Treatise on the Kinetic Theory of Gases*, has developed with great clearness the steps of the investigation of the distribution of energy among a set of particles which are supposed to act on each other only at very small distances. The particles may be acted on by external forces such as gravity, but it is expressly stipulated that the time during which a particle is encountering other particles is very small compared with the time during which there is no sensible action between it and other particles; and also that the time during which a particle is simultaneously within the distance of molecular action of more than one other particle may be neglected.

Now this method of treating the question, however necessary it may be in the subsequent investigation of the processes of diffusion, &c. in gases, is inapplicable to the theory of the equilibrium of temperature in liquids and

* *Clarendon Press Series*, 1876.

solids, for in these bodies the particles are never free from the action of neighbouring particles. It is true that in following the steps of the investigation, as given either by Boltzmann or by Watson, it is difficult, if not impossible, to see where the stipulation about the shortness and the isolation of the encounters is made use of. We may almost say that it is introduced rather for the sake of enabling the reader to form a more definite mental image of the material system than as a condition of the demonstration. Be this as it may, the presence of such a stipulation in the enunciation of the problem cannot fail to leave in the mind of the reader the impression of a corresponding limitation in the generality of the solution.

In the theorem of Boltzmann which we have now to consider there is no such limitation. The material points may act on each other at all distances, and according to any law which is consistent with the conservation of energy, and they may also be acted on by any forces external to the system provided these also are consistent with that law.

The only assumption which is necessary for the direct proof is that the system, if left to itself in its actual state of motion, will, sooner or later, pass through every phase which is consistent with the equation of energy.

Now it is manifest that there are cases in which this does not take place. The motion of a system not acted on by external forces satisfies six equations besides the equation of energy, so that the system cannot pass through those phases, which, though they satisfy the equation of energy, do not also satisfy these six equations.

Again, there may be particular laws of force, as for instance that according to which the stress between two particles is proportional to the distance between them, for which the whole motion repeats itself after a finite time. In such cases a particular value of one variable corresponds to a particular value of each of the other variables, so that phases formed by sets of values of the variables which do not correspond cannot occur, though they may satisfy the seven general equations.

But if we suppose that the material particles, or some of them, occasionally encounter a fixed obstacle such as the sides of a vessel containing the particles, then, except for special forms of the surface of this obstacle, each encounter will introduce a disturbance into the motion of the system, so that it will pass from one undisturbed path into another. The two paths must both satisfy the equation of energy, and they must intersect each other in the phase for which the conditions of encounter with the fixed obstacle are satisfied, but they are not subject to the equations of momentum. It is difficult in a case of such extreme complexity to arrive at a thoroughly satisfactory conclusion, but we may with considerable confidence assert that except for particular forms of the surface of the fixed obstacle, the system will sooner or later, after a sufficient number of encounters, pass through every phase consistent with the equation of energy.

I shall begin with the case in which the system is supposed to be contained within a fixed vessel, and shall afterwards consider the case of a free system, or of a system contained in a vessel rotating uniformly about an axis which itself moves uniformly in a straight line.

I have found it convenient, instead of considering one system of material particles, to consider a large number of systems similar to each other in all respects except in the initial circumstances of the motion, which are supposed to vary from system to system, the total energy being the same in all. In the statistical investigation of the motion, we confine our attention to the *number* of these systems which at a given time are in a phase such that the variables which define it lie within given limits.

If the number of systems which are in a given phase (defined with respect to configuration and velocity) does not vary with the time, the distribution of the systems is said to be *steady*.

It is shewn that if the distribution is steady, a certain function of the variables must be constant for all phases belonging to the same path. If the path passes through all phases consistent with the equation of energy, this function must be constant for all such phases. If however there are phases consistent with the equation of energy, but which do not belong to the same path, the value of the function may be different for such phases.

But whether we are able or not to prove that the constancy of this function is a necessary condition of a steady distribution, it is manifest that if the function is initially constant for all phases consistent with the equation of energy, it will remain so during the motion. This therefore is one solution, if not the only solution, of the problem of a steady distribution.

Now we know from the empirical laws of the diffusion of heat that the problem of the equilibrium of temperature in an isolated material system has one and only one solution.   But we have found one solution of the problem of equilibrium of energy in a system of material points in motion.   If, therefore, the real material system in which the equilibrium of temperature takes place is capable of being accurately represented by a system of material points (as defined in pure dynamics) acting on each other according to determinate, though unknown, laws, then the mathematical condition of the equilibrium of energy must be the dynamical representative of the physical condition of the equality of temperature.

It appears from the theorem that in the ultimate state of the system the average kinetic energy of two given portions of the system must be in the ratio of the number of degrees of freedom of those portions.   This, therefore, must be the condition of the equality of temperature of the two portions of the system.

Hence at a given temperature the total kinetic energy of a material system must be the product of the number of degrees of' freedom of that system into a constant which is the same for all substances at that temperature, being in fact the temperature on the thermodynamic scale multiplied by an absolute constant.

If the temperature, therefore, is raised by unity, the kinetic energy is increased by the product of the number of degrees of freedom into the absolute constant.

The observed specific heat of the body, expressed in dynamical measure, is the increment of the *total* energy when the temperature is increased by unity The observed specific heat cannot therefore be less than the product of the number of degrees of freedom into the absolute constant, unless the potential energy diminishes as the temperature rises.

Dynamical Specification of the motion.

We shall begin by supposing the material system to be of the most general type, having its configuration determined by the n variables $q_1, q_2 \ldots q_n$, and its motion determined by the corresponding momenta $p_1, p_2 \ldots p_n$.   The state of the system at any instant is completely defined if we know the values of these $2n$ variables for that instant.

We shall suppose the forces acting between the parts of the system to be of the most general kind consistent with the conservation of energy.   This may be expressed by defining V, the potential energy of the system, as a function of $q_1...q_n$, the variables which define the configuration.

The kinetic energy of the system is denoted by T. We shall suppose it to be expressed in terms of the q's and p's as in Hamilton's method. The total energy is denoted by

$$E = V + T \dots\dots\dots\dots\dots\dots\dots\dots\dots\dots(1),$$

and is a constant during the motion of the system.

Hamilton's equations of motion for this system are

$$\frac{\partial q_r}{\partial t} = \frac{dE}{dp_r} \dots\dots\dots\dots\dots\dots\dots\dots\dots(2),$$

$$\frac{\partial p_r}{\partial t} = -\frac{dE}{dq_r} \dots\dots\dots\dots\dots\dots\dots\dots\dots(3),$$

where q_r and p_r are the co-ordinate and the momentum corresponding to each other.

Let us now consider a finite motion of the system. Let the initial co-ordinates and momenta be distinguished by accented letters, and the final co-ordinates and momenta by the same letters unaccented.

To define completely such a motion requires $2n+1$ variables to be given. These may be the n initial co-ordinates, the n initial momenta, and the time occupied by the motion.

There is another method however in which the $2n+1$ variables are the n initial co-ordinates, the n final co-ordinates, and the total energy. When these quantities are given there are in general only a finite number of possible motions.

Definition of the "Action" of the system during the motion.

Twice the time integral of the kinetic energy, taken from the beginning to the end of the motion, and expressed in terms of the initial and final co-ordinates and of the total energy, is called the "Action" of the system during the motion. If we denote it by A,

$$A = \int 2T dt \dots\dots\dots\dots\dots\dots\dots\dots\dots(4),$$

and is expressed as a function of $q_1'...q_n'$, $q_1...q_n$, and E.

It is shewn in treatises on dynamics* that

$$\frac{dA}{dq_r'} = -p_r' \dots\dots\dots\dots(5),$$

and

$$\frac{dA}{dq_r} = p_r \dots\dots\dots\dots(6).$$

Hence

$$\frac{dp_r'}{dq_s} = -\frac{d^2A}{dq_r'dq_s} = -\frac{dp_s}{dq_r'} \dots\dots\dots(7).$$

The indices r and s in this equation may be the same or different.

Also if t' and t are the values of the time at the beginning and at the end of the motion,

$$\frac{dA}{dE} = t - t' \dots\dots\dots\dots(8).$$

Hence

$$\frac{dp_r}{dE} = -\frac{dt'}{dq_r} \quad (9) \quad \text{and} \quad \frac{dp_s'}{dE} = -\frac{dt}{dq_s'} \dots\dots\dots(10).$$

In the course of our investigation we shall have to compare the product of the differentials of the co-ordinates and momenta at the beginning of the motion with the corresponding product at the end of the motion. We shall write for brevity $ds = dq_1 \dots dq_n$ for the product of the differentials of the co-ordinates, and $d\sigma = dp_1 \dots dp_n$ for the product of the differentials of the momenta, and we shall use the product $ds' \, ds \, dE$ as a middle term in comparing $ds' \, d\sigma' \, dt'$ with $ds \, d\sigma \, dt$.

Now

$$ds' \, d\sigma' \, dt' = ds' \, ds \, dE \Sigma \pm \left(\frac{dp_1'}{dq_1} \dots\dots \frac{dp_n'}{dq_n} \frac{dt'}{dE} \right) \dots\dots\dots(11),$$

where

$$\Sigma \pm \left(\frac{dp_1'}{dq_1} \dots\dots \frac{dp_n'}{dq_n} \frac{dt'}{dE} \right)$$

denotes the functional determinant

$$\begin{vmatrix} \dfrac{dp_1'}{dq_1}, & \dots\dots \dfrac{dp_1'}{dq_n}, & \dfrac{dp_1'}{dE} \\ \dots\dots\dots\dots\dots \\ \dfrac{dp_n'}{dq_1}, & \dots\dots \dfrac{dp_n'}{dq_n}, & \dfrac{dp_n'}{dE} \\ \dfrac{dt'}{dq_1}, & \dots\dots \dfrac{dt'}{dq_n}, & \dfrac{dt'}{dE} \end{vmatrix} \dots\dots\dots(12).$$

* Thomson and Tait's *Natural Philosophy*, § 330.

Substituting for the elements of this determinant their values as given by equations (7), (9), and (10) it becomes

$$\begin{vmatrix} -\dfrac{dp_1}{dq_1''}, & \cdots & -\dfrac{dp_n}{dq_1''}, & -\dfrac{dt}{dq_1'} \\ & \cdots & & \\ -\dfrac{dp_1}{dq_n''}, & \cdots & -\dfrac{dp_n}{dq_n''}, & -\dfrac{dt}{dq_n'} \\ -\dfrac{dp_1}{dE'}, & \cdots & -\dfrac{dp_n}{dE'}, & -\dfrac{dt}{dE} \end{vmatrix} \quad \cdots\cdots\cdots(13).$$

Now the rows in this determinant are the same as the columns in the former one; the accented and unaccented letters being exchanged and the signs of all the elements changed. We may therefore express the relation between the two determinants in the abbreviated form

$$\Sigma \pm \left(\frac{dp_1'}{dq_1} \cdots \frac{dp_n'}{dq_n} \frac{dt'}{dE} \right) = (-)^{n+1} \Sigma \pm \left(\frac{dp_1}{dq_1'} \cdots \frac{dp_n}{dq_n'} \frac{dt}{dE} \right) \cdots\cdots(14).$$

Hence

$$ds' \, d\sigma' \, dt' = ds' \, ds \, dE \Sigma \pm \left(\frac{dp_1'}{dq_1} \cdots \frac{dp_n'}{dq_n} \frac{dt'}{dE} \right)$$

$$= (-)^{n+1} ds' \, ds \, dE \Sigma \pm \left(\frac{dp_1}{dq_1'} \cdots \frac{dp_n}{dq_n'} \frac{dt}{dE} \right)$$

$$= (-)^{n+1} d\sigma \, ds \, dt$$

$$= ds \, d\sigma \, dt \quad \cdots\cdots\cdots\cdots\cdots\cdots\cdots\cdots(15).$$

If we suppose the time, $t - t'$, to be given, $dt = dt'$ and

$$ds' \, d\sigma' = ds \, d\sigma \cdots\cdots\cdots\cdots\cdots\cdots(16),$$

or

$$dq_1' \cdots dq_n' \, dp_1' \cdots dp_n' = dq_1 \cdots dq_n \, dp_1 \cdots dp_n \quad \cdots\cdots(17).$$

The initial state of the system is a function of $2n$ variables. We have hitherto supposed these to be the n co-ordinates and the n momenta, but since the total energy E is a function of these variables we may substitute for one of the momenta, say p_1', its value in terms of the n co-ordinates, the $n-1$ remaining momenta, and E, and thus express every quantity we have to deal with in terms of the latter set of variables. Then since by equation (2)

$$\frac{dE}{dp_1'} = \frac{\partial q_1'}{\partial t} = \dot{q}_1' \quad \dots\dots\dots\dots\dots\dots\dots\dots(18),$$

$$dq_1'\dots\dots dq_n' dp_1'\dots\dots dp_n' = dq_1'\dots\dots dq_n' dp_2'\dots\dots dp_n' dE \frac{1}{q_1'}, \dots(19).$$

Similarly we find for the final state of the system

$$dq_1\dots\dots dq_n dp_1\dots\dots dp_n = dq_1\dots\dots dq_n dp_2\dots\dots dp_n dE \frac{1}{q_1} \dots\dots\dots(20).$$

The left-hand members of these equations have been proved equal, and in the right-hand members dE is the same at the beginning and end of the motion. Dividing out dE we find

$$dq_1'\dots\dots dq_n' dp_2'\dots\dots dp_n' \frac{1}{q_1'} = dq_1\dots\dots dq_n dp_2\dots\dots dp_n \frac{1}{q_1} \dots\dots(21).$$

This equation is applicable to the case in which the total energy is supposed not to vary from one particular instant of the motion to another, and in which, therefore, the $2n$ variables are no longer independent, but, being subject to the equation of energy, are reduced to $2n-1$.

Statistical Specification.

We have hitherto, in speaking of a phase of the motion of the system, supposed it to be defined by the values of the n co-ordinates and the n momenta. We shall call the phase so defined the phase (pq). We shall now adopt a wider definition by saying that the system is in the phase (a,b) whenever the values of the co-ordinates are such that q_1 is between b_1 and $b_1 + db_1$, q_2 between b_2 and $b_2 + db_2$, and so on; also p_2 between a_2 and $a_2 + da_2$, and so on. The limits of the first component of momentum, p_1, are not specified, because the value of p_1 is not independent of the other variables, being given in terms of E and the other $2n-1$ variables in virtue of the equation of energy.

The quantities a, b are of the same kind as p and q respectively, only they are not supposed to vary on account of the motion of the system. In the statistical method of investigation, we do not follow the system during its motion, but we fix our attention on a particular phase, and ascertain whether the system is in that phase or not, and also when it enters the phase and when it leaves it.

Boltzmann defines the probability of the system being in the phase (a,b) as the ratio of the aggregate time during which it is in that phase to the whole time of the motion, the whole time being supposed to be very great. I prefer to suppose that there are a great many systems the properties of which are the same, and that each of these is set in motion with a different set of values for the n co-ordinates and the $n-1$ momenta, the value of the total energy E being the same in all, and to consider the number of these systems which, at a given instant, are in the phase (a,b). The motion of each system is of course independent of the other systems.

Let N be the whole number of systems, and let the number of these which, at the time t, are in the phase (a,b) be denoted by $N(a_1, b, t)$. The aim of the statistical method is to express $N(a_1, b, t)$ as a function of N, of the co-ordinates and momenta with their limits, and of t. It is manifest that N can only enter the function as a factor, for the different systems do not act on each other. Also any differential as da or db can only enter as a factor, for the number of systems within any phase must vary in the ratio of the interval between the limits of that phase. We may therefore write

$$N(a_1bt) = Nf(a_2, \ldots \ldots a_n, \ b_1, \ldots \ldots b_n, \ t) \, da_2 \ldots \ldots da_n db_1 \ldots \ldots db_n \ldots \ldots (22),$$

where we have to determine the form of the function f.

We shall now follow the motion of these systems from the time t', when we begin to watch the motion, to the time t when we cease to watch it.

Since the systems which at the time t form the group $N(a_1, b, t)$ are individually the same systems which at the time t' formed the group $N(a_1', b', t')$ we have

$$N(a_1, b, t) = N(a_1', b', t') \ \ldots \ldots \ldots \ldots \ldots \ldots (23),$$

or $\qquad\qquad Nf(a_2 \ldots \ldots t) \, da_2 \ldots \ldots db_n = Nf(a_2' \ldots \ldots t') \, da_2' \ldots \ldots db_n' \ \ldots \ldots \ldots (24).$

But by equation (21)

$$da_2 \ldots \ldots db_n \, (\dot{b}_1)^{-1} = da_2' \ldots \ldots db_n' (\dot{b}_1')^{-1} \ \ldots \ldots \ldots \ldots (25).$$

Hence $\qquad\qquad f(a_2 \ldots \ldots t) \, \dot{b}_1 = f(a_2' \ldots \ldots t') \, \dot{b}_1' = C \ \ldots \ldots \ldots \ldots \ldots (26),$

where C is a constant for all phases of the same motion, and we may write

$$f(a_2 \ldots \ldots t) = C (\dot{b}_1)^{-1} \ldots \ldots \ldots \ldots \ldots \ldots \ldots (27),$$

and $\qquad\qquad N(a_1, b, t) = NC (\dot{b}_1)^{-1} \, da_2 \ldots \ldots db_n \ \ldots \ldots \ldots \ldots \ldots (28).$

If the distribution of the N systems in the different phases is such that the number in a given phase does not vary with the time, the distribution is said to be steady. The condition of this is that C must be constant for all phases belonging to the same path. It will require further investigation to determine whether or not this path necessarily includes all phases consistent with the equation of energy.

If, however, we assume that the original distribution of the systems according to the different phases is such that C is constant for all phases consistent with the equation of energy, and zero for all phases which that equation shows to be impossible, then the law of distribution will not change with the time, and C will be an absolute constant.

We have therefore found one solution of the problem of finding a steady distribution. Whether there may be other solutions remains to be investigated.

Let $N(b)$ denote the number of systems in which q_1 is between b_1 and $b_1 + db_1$, q_2 between b_2 and $b_2 + db_2$, and so on, and q_n between b_n and $b_n + db_n$, the momenta not being specified otherwise than by their being consistent with the equation of energy, then

$$N(b) = \int \dots \int N(a_1, \ b) \, da_2 \dots da_n \dots\dots\dots\dots\dots\dots(29),$$

the integration being extended to all values of the momenta consistent with the equation of energy.

To simplify the integration let us suppose the variables transformed so that the kinetic energy is expressed in terms of the squares of the component momenta,

$$T = \tfrac{1}{2}\left(\mu_1 a_1^2 + \mu_2 a_2^2 + \dots + \mu_n a_n^2\right) \dots\dots\dots\dots\dots(30),$$

where $a_1 \dots a_n$ are the transformed momenta, and $\mu_1 \dots \mu_n$ are functions of the co-ordinates, which we may call moments of mobility, and which, in the case of material points, are the reciprocals of the masses.

Now let us assume

$$\tfrac{1}{2}\mu_n A_n^2 = T = E - V \dots\dots\dots\dots\dots\dots\dots(31),$$

$$\mu_{n-1}A_{n-1}^2 = \mu_n\left(A_n^2 - a_n^2\right) \dots\dots\dots\dots\dots(32),$$

$$\mu_{n-2}A_{n-2}^2 = \mu_{n-1}\left(A_{n-1}^2 - a_{n-1}^2\right) \dots\dots\dots\dots(33),$$

$$\dots\dots\dots\dots\dots\dots\dots\dots\dots\dots\dots$$

$$\mu_2 A_2^2 = \mu_3\left(A_3^2 - a_3^2\right)\dots\dots\dots\dots\dots\dots\dots(34).$$

Then by the equation of energy

$$\mu_1 a_1^2 = \mu_2 (A_2^2 - a_2^2) \quad \dots\dots\dots\dots\dots\dots\dots\dots(35).$$

Of these quantities, A_n is a function of the co-ordinates only, because E is given and V is a function of the co-ordinates, A_{n-1} is a function of the co-ordinates and a_n, A_{n-2} of the co-ordinates and of a_n and a_{n-1}, and so on.

Also by equation (2)

$$\dot{b}_1 = \frac{dT}{da_1} = \mu_1 a_1$$

$$= (\mu_1 \mu_2)^{\frac{1}{2}} (A_2^2 - a_2^2)^{\frac{1}{2}} \quad \dots\dots\dots\dots\dots\dots\dots(36).$$

To integrate the expression

$$\iiint \dots \int C (\dot{b}_1)^{-1} da_2 \dots da_n,$$

we begin by integrating with respect to a_2, thus

$$\int C (\dot{b}_1)^{-1} da_2 = \int C (\mu_1 \mu_2)^{-\frac{1}{2}} (A_2^2 - a_2^2)^{-\frac{1}{2}} da_2 \quad \dots\dots\dots\dots(37),$$

the limits of integration being $\pm A_2$. The result is

$$\frac{\Gamma(\frac{1}{2}) \Gamma(\frac{1}{2})}{\Gamma(\frac{2}{2})} C (\mu_1 \mu_2)^{-\frac{1}{2}} A_2^0 \quad \dots\dots\dots\dots\dots\dots(38).$$

For the next integration we have

$$\int (\mu_2 A_2^2)^0 da_3 = \int_{-A_3}^{A_3} \{\mu_3 (A_3^2 - a_3^2)\}^0 da_3 = \frac{\Gamma\frac{1}{2}\Gamma\frac{2}{2}}{\Gamma\frac{3}{2}} A_3^{\frac{2}{2}} \quad \dots\dots\dots(39).$$

Hence after r integrations, r being any number less than n, the result is

$$NC \frac{(\Gamma(\frac{1}{2}))^{r+1}}{\Gamma\frac{r+1}{2}} (\mu_1 \mu_2 \dots \mu_{r+1})^{-\frac{1}{2}} [\mu_{r+1} A_{r+1}^2]^{\frac{r-1}{2}} da_{r+2} \dots da_r db_1 \dots db_n \quad \dots\dots(40).$$

Putting $r = n-1$ and remembering that $\mu_n A_n^2 = 2E - 2V$, we find

$$N(b) = NC \frac{[\Gamma(\frac{1}{2})]^n}{\Gamma(\frac{n}{2})} (\mu_1 \mu_2 \dots \mu_n)^{-\frac{1}{2}} [2E - 2V]^{\frac{n-2}{2}} \quad \dots\dots\dots\dots(41).$$

This is the number of systems whose configuration is specified by the variables $b_1 \dots b_n$, while the momenta may have any values consistent with the equation of energy.

The quantity $E - V$, which occurs in this equation, is, by equation (1), equal in magnitude to T, the kinetic energy of the system. The quantity T, however, is defined explicitly in terms of the velocities or the momenta of the system, whereas $E - V$ does not involve these quantities explicitly, but is expressed as a function of the configuration.

We shall find it convenient, however, especially in the study of more complicated problems, to remember that the number of systems in a given configuration is a function of the kinetic energy corresponding to that configuration.

If the kinetic energy is not expressed as a sum of squares, but in the more general form,

$$T = \tfrac{1}{2}[11]\, a_1^2 + [12]\, a_1 a_2 + \&c.$$
$$+ \tfrac{1}{2}[22]\, a_2^2 + [23]\, a_2 a_3 + \&c. \quad \dots\dots\dots\dots\dots(42),$$

where the quantities denoted by $[11]$ &c. are functions of the co-ordinates, which we may call the moments and products of mobility of the system; then since the discriminant

$$\Delta = \begin{vmatrix} [11], & [12], & \dots\dots & [1n] \\ [21], & [22], & \dots\dots & [2n] \\ \multicolumn{4}{c}{\dots\dots\dots\dots\dots\dots\dots\dots\dots} \\ [n1], & [n2], & \dots\dots & [nn] \end{vmatrix} \quad \dots\dots\dots\dots\dots\dots(43)$$

is an invariant, its value is the same when T is reduced to a sum of squares, in which case all the elements except those in the principal diagonal of the determinant vanish, and we have

$$\Delta = \mu_1 \mu_2 \dots \mu_n \quad \dots\dots\dots\dots\dots\dots\dots\dots(44),$$

and we may write the value of $N\,(b)$,

$$N\,(b) = NC \frac{(\Gamma(\tfrac{1}{2}))^n}{\Gamma\left(\dfrac{n}{2}\right)} \Delta^{-\tfrac{1}{2}} (2E - 2V)^{\tfrac{n-2}{2}} \, db_1 \dots db_n \dots\dots\dots\dots(45).$$

If the system consists of n' material particles, whose masses are $m_1 \dots m_{n'}$, then the number of degrees of freedom is $n = 3n'$ and

$$\mu_1 = \mu_2 = \mu_3 = m_1^{-1}, \quad \mu_4 = \mu_5 = \mu_6 = m_2^{-1} \text{ and so on} \dots\dots\dots(46).$$

Hence in this case we may write

$$N\,(b) = NC' \frac{(\Gamma(\tfrac{1}{2}))^{3n'}}{\Gamma\left(\dfrac{3n'}{2}\right)} (m_1 \dots m_{n'})^{\tfrac{3}{2}} [2E - 2V]^{\tfrac{3n'-2}{2}} \, db_1 \dots db_n \dots\dots\dots(47).$$

These expressions give the number of systems in a given configuration only when $E - V$ is positive for that configuration, for since the kinetic energy is necessarily positive, the potential energy cannot exceed the total energy. For configurations specified in such a way that if they existed V would be greater than E, the value of $N(b)$ is zero.

The value of $N(b)$ is also zero for configurations which, though they make V less than E, cannot be reached by a continuous path from the original configuration without passing through configurations which make V greater than E.

We shall return to this expression for the number of systems in a completely specified configuration, but in the mean time it will be useful to consider how many of these systems have one of their momenta, p_n, between given limits. In this way we shall be able to determine completely the average distribution of momentum among the variables without making any assumptions about the nature of the system which might limit the generality of our results.

In order to find the number of systems in the configuration (b) for which one of the momenta, say p_n, lies between a_n and $a_n + da_n$, we must stop before the last integration. Putting $r = n - 2$ in equation (40)

$$N(b_1 a_n) = NC \frac{\Gamma(\tfrac{1}{2})^{n-1}}{\Gamma\left(\dfrac{n-1}{2}\right)} (\mu_1 \dots \mu_{n-1})^{-\frac{1}{2}} (\mu_{n-1} A_{n-1}{}^2)^{\frac{n-3}{2}} da_n \, db_1 \dots db_n \dots \dots (48).$$

The whole number of systems in configuration (b) is given by (45). Hence the proportion of these systems for which a_n lies between a_n and $a_n + da_n$ is

$$\frac{2^{-\frac{1}{2}} \Gamma\left(\dfrac{n}{2}\right)}{\Gamma(\tfrac{1}{2}) \Gamma\left(\dfrac{n-1}{2}\right)} \frac{\left[E - V - \tfrac{1}{2}\mu_n a_n{}^2\right]^{\frac{n-3}{2}}}{\left[E - V\right]^{\frac{n-2}{2}}} \mu_n^{\frac{1}{2}} da_n \dots \dots \dots \dots (49).$$

If we write

$$\tfrac{1}{2}\mu_n a_n{}^2 = k_n \dots \dots \dots \dots \dots \dots \dots \dots \dots (50),$$

then k_n denotes the part of the kinetic energy arising from the momentum a_n. The proportion of the systems in configuration (b) for which k_n is between k_n and $k_n + dk_n$ is

$$\frac{\Gamma\left(\dfrac{n}{2}\right)}{\Gamma(\tfrac{1}{2}) \Gamma\left(\dfrac{n-1}{2}\right)} \frac{\left[E - V - k_n\right]^{\frac{n-3}{2}}}{\left[E - V\right]^{\frac{n-2}{2}}} k_n^{-\frac{1}{2}} dk_n \dots \dots \dots \dots (51).$$

Since any one of the variables may be taken for q_n, the law of distribution of values of the kinetic energy is the same for all the variables. The mean value of the kinetic energy corresponding to any variable is

$$K = \frac{1}{n}(E - V) = \frac{1}{n} T \quad \dots\dots\dots\dots\dots(52).$$

The maximum value is $\qquad T = nK \quad \dots\dots\dots\dots\dots\dots(53).$

The mean value of k^r is

$$\frac{1 \cdot 3 \dots 2r - 1}{n \cdot n + 2 \dots n + 2r - 2} n^r K^r \dots\dots\dots\dots\dots(54).$$

When n is very large, the expression (51) approximates to

$$\frac{1}{\sqrt{2\pi}} \frac{1}{K} e^{-\frac{k}{2K}} dk \quad \dots\dots\dots\dots\dots\dots(55).$$

Recapitulation.

The result of our investigation may therefore be stated as follows:

(α) We begin by considering a set of material systems which satisfy the general equations of dynamics (2) and (3), and the equation of energy (1). If in these systems the distribution of configurations satisfies equation (45), and the distribution of motion satisfies equation (51), these equations will continue to be satisfied during the subsequent motion of the system. One result of equation (51), to which we shall have to refer, is that the average kinetic energy corresponding to any one of the variables is the same for every one of the variables of the system.

(β) We now turn our attention to a system of real bodies enclosed in a rigid vessel impervious to matter and to heat. We know by experiment that in such a system the temperature cannot remain steady in every part unless the temperature of every part of the system is the same, and that this condition is necessary in whatever manner the configuration of the system may be varied by altering the position and mean density of the portions of sensible size into which we are able to divide it.

Now if the system of real bodies is a material system which satisfies the equations of dynamics, and if equations (45) and (51) are also satisfied, the condition of the system will, as we have shewn, (α), be steady in every respect, and therefore in respect of temperature.   Hence by (β) the temperature of every part of the system must be the same.

Therefore if equations (45) and (51) are satisfied, the condition of equality of temperature is also satisfied.

But the condition of equality of temperature does not depend on the configuration of the system, for though we can alter the configuration by external constraint we cannot prevent the temperature from becoming equalized. It does not depend, therefore, on equation (45). We must therefore conclude, that if equation (51) is satisfied, the condition of equality of temperature is also satisfied, or, in other words, that equation (51) is the condition of equality of temperature.

Hence when two parts of a system have the same temperature, the average kinetic energy corresponding to any one of the variables belonging to these parts must be the same.

If the system is a gas or a mixture of gases not acted on by external forces, the theorem that the average kinetic energy of a single molecule is the same for molecules of different gases is not sufficient to establish the condition of equilibrium of temperature between gases of different kinds such as oxygen and nitrogen, because when the gases are mixed we have no means of ascertaining the temperature of the oxygen or of the nitrogen separately. We can only ascertain the temperature of the mixture by putting a thermometer into it.

We cannot legitimately assert that the temperatures of the oxygen and of the nitrogen must be equal because they are in contact with each other, for the only way in which we can conceive the oxygen or the nitrogen as existing in the mixture is by picturing the medium as a system of molecules, and as soon as we begin to see the molecules distinctly, heat becomes resolved into motion.

But since our investigation is equally applicable to a system of any kind, provided only it satisfies the equations of dynamics, we may suppose it to consist of pure oxygen and pure nitrogen separated by a solid diaphragm, the solid diaphragm consisting of molecules capable of motion, but acting on each other with forces which are sufficient to prevent any molecule from getting far apart from its neighbours except under the action of disturbing forces greater than any which would occur in a system at the given temperature. In this system, though the oxygen and the nitrogen cannot mix, each can make an exchange of molecular energy with the surface molecules of the diaphragm, and exchanges of energy can go on within the solid diaphragm itself without any exchange of molecules between distant parts of the diaphragm.

Hence, in this system, the average kinetic energy of a molecule of oxygen will become equal to that of a molecule of nitrogen in the final state of the system, that is to say, when the temperatures of all parts of the system have become equal, and since in that final state we have pure oxygen on one side and pure nitrogen on the other, we can verify the equality of temperature by means of a thermometer, and we can now assert that the temperatures, not only of oxygen and nitrogen, but of all bodies, are equal when the average kinetic energy of a single molecule of each of these substances is the same.

Approximate value of the probability when V is small compared with E.

To find the number of systems the configuration of which is specified as regards the limits of certain of the variables while the other variables are left undetermined, we should have to integrate the expressions in equations (41), (45), or (47) with respect to each of the undetermined variables in succession, the integrations being extended to all values of these variables which are consistent with the equation of energy.

These integrations cannot be performed unless the potential energy of the system is a known function of the variables which determine its configuration. We cannot therefore in general continue the integration so as to determine the number of systems in which the limits are specified for some, but not all, of the variables.

But when the number of variables is very great, and when the potential energy of the specified configuration is very small compared with the total energy of the system, we may obtain a useful approximation to the value of $[E - V]^{\frac{n-2}{2}}$ in an exponential form, for if we write, as in equation (53), $E = nK$,

$$[E - V]^{\frac{n-2}{2}} = E^{\frac{n-2}{2}} e^{\frac{n-2}{2} \log \left(1 - \frac{V}{nK}\right)}$$

$$= E^{\frac{n-2}{2}} e^{-\frac{V}{2K}} \dots\dots\dots\dots\dots\dots\dots\dots\dots(56),$$

nearly, provided n is very great and V is small compared with E.   The expression is no longer approximate when V is nearly as great as E, and it does not vanish, as it ought to do, when $V = E$.

Hence when the potential energy of the system in the given configuration is very small compared with its kinetic energy, we may use the approximately correct statement, that the number of systems in a given configuration is inversely proportional to the exponential function, the index of which is half the potential energy of the system in the given configuration divided by the average kinetic energy corresponding to each variable of the system.

If we divide the system into any two parts, A and B, we may consider V, the potential energy of the whole system, as made up of three parts, V_A and V_B, the potential energy of A and B, each on itself, and W, that of B with respect to A.

When, as in the case of a gas, the parts of a system are in a great degree independent of each other, the average values of V_A and V_B may be treated as constants, and the variations of V will be the same as those of W, so that the variable part of the exponential function will be reduced to

$$e^{-\frac{W}{2K}} \dots\dots\dots\dots\dots\dots\dots\dots\dots\dots\dots\dots(57).$$

If we suppose that A denotes a single molecule of a particular kind of gas, and that B denotes all the other molecules, of whatever kind, in the system, then, since there are many molecules similar to A, we may pass, from the number of systems in which A is within a given element of volume, to the average number of molecules similar to A which are within that element, or, in other words, the average density of the gas A within that element.

We may therefore interpret the expression (57) as asserting that the density of a particular kind of gas at a given point is inversely proportional to the exponential function whose index is half the potential energy of a single molecule of the gas at that point, divided by the average kinetic energy corresponding to a variable of the system.

We must remember that since the centre of mass of a molecule is determined by *three* variables, the mean kinetic energy of agitation of the centre of mass of a molecule is *three* times the quantity K which denotes the mean kinetic energy of a single variable.

PART II. *A Free system.*

In a material system not acted on by external forces the motion satisfies six equations besides the equation of energy, so that we must not include in our integration all the phases which satisfy the equation of energy, but only those of them which also satisfy these six equations.

In what follows, we shall suppose the system to consist of n particles, whose masses are $m_1 \ldots m_n$, and whose co-ordinates x, y, z, and velocity-components u, v, w, are distinguished by the same suffix as the particle to which they belong.

Let us now consider a system consisting of s of these particles, and write

$$m_1 + m_2 + \&c. + m_s = M_s \ldots\ldots\ldots\ldots\ldots\ldots(58),$$

$$\left.\begin{aligned} m_1 x_1 + m_2 x_2 + \&c. + m_s x_s &= M_s X_s, \\ m_1 y_1 + m_2 y_2 + \&c. + m_s y_s &= M_s Y_s, \\ m_1 z_1 + m_2 z_2 + \&c. + m_s z_s &= M_s Z_s, \end{aligned}\right\} \ldots\ldots\ldots\ldots\ldots(59),$$

then M_s will be the mass of the minor system and X_s, Y_s, Z_s the co-ordinates of its centre of mass. If we also write

$$\left.\begin{aligned} m_1 u_1 + \&c. + m_s u_s &= M_s U_s, \\ m_1 v_1 + \&c. + m_s v_s &= M_s V_s, \\ m_1 w_1 + \&c. + m_s w_s &= M_s W_s, \end{aligned}\right\} \ldots\ldots\ldots\ldots\ldots\ldots(60),$$

$$\left.\begin{aligned} m_1(y_1 w_1 - z_1 v_1) + \&c. + m_s(y_s w_s - z_s v_s) &= F_s + M_s(Y_s W_s - Z_s V_s), \\ m_1(z_1 u_1 - x_1 w_1) + \&c. + m_s(z_s u_s - x_s w_s) &= G_s + M_s(Z_s U_s - X_s W_s), \\ m_1(x_1 v_1 - y_1 u_1) + \&c. + m_s(x_s v_s - y_s u_s) &= H_s + M_s(X_s V_s - Y_s U_s), \end{aligned}\right\} \ldots(61),$$

then U_s, V_s, W_s will be the velocity-components of the centre of mass, and F_s, G_s, H_s the components of angular momentum round this point.

We shall also write

$$\tfrac{1}{2} m_1 (u_1^2 + v_1^2 + w_1^2) + \&c. + \tfrac{1}{2} m_s (u_s^2 + v_s^2 + w_s^2) = T_s \ldots\ldots\ldots(62).$$

The seven conditions satisfied by the whole system are that the seven quantities U_n, V_n, W_n, F_n, G_n, H_n and E are constant during the motion.

Under these conditions the $3n$ momentum-components are not independent. We shall therefore transform equation (17) into one in which the differentials of the first seven velocity-components are replaced by the differentials of the seven constants.

The functional determinant is found by differentiating the seven quantities U_n, V_n, W_n, F_n, G_n, H_n and E with respect to the momenta m_1u_1, m_1v_1, m_1w_1; m_2u_2, m_2v_2, m_2w_2; and m_3u_3. We thus obtain

$$\begin{vmatrix} 1, & 0, & 0, & 0, & z_1, & -y_1, & u_1 \\ 0, & 1, & 0, & -z_1, & 0, & x_1, & v_1 \\ 0, & 0, & 1, & y_1, & -x_1, & 0, & w_1 \\ 1, & 0, & 0, & 0, & z_2, & -y_2, & u_2 \\ 0, & 1, & 0. & -z_2, & 0, & x_2, & v_2 \\ 0, & 0, & 1, & y_2, & -x_2, & 0, & w_2 \\ 1, & 0, & 0, & 0, & z_3, & -y_3, & u_3 \end{vmatrix} = \Delta \quad \dots\dots\dots\dots(63),$$

which we may write

$$\Delta = a\, r_{12}\, \dot{r}_{12} \dots\dots\dots\dots\dots\dots\dots\dots\dots(64),$$

where

$$a = (y_1 - y_2)(z_2 - z_3) - (y_2 - y_3)(z_1 - z_2) \dots\dots\dots\dots\dots(65),$$

or twice the projection on the plane of yz of the triangle whose vertices are m_1, m_2, and m_3, and

$$r_{12}\dot{r}_{12} = (u_1 - u_2)(x_1 - x_2) + (v_1 - v_2)(y_1 - y_2) + (w_1 - w_2)(z_1 - z_2)\dots\dots(66),$$

or the rate of increase of the distance between m_1 and m_2 multiplied into that distance.

In a system composed of material particles, each component of momentum is equal to the corresponding velocity-component multiplied into the mass of the particle. We may therefore write $p_1 = m_1u_1$ and so on, and since the masses are invariable we may omit them from both members of equation (17), and write it

$$dx_1' \dots dz_n'\, du_1' \dots dw_n' = dx_1 \dots dz_n du_1 \dots dw_n \dots\dots\dots\dots(67).$$

But $dUdVdWdFdGdHdE = m_1^3\, m_2^3\, m_3\, a'r_{12}'\dot{r}_{12}'\, du_1'dv_1'dw_1'du_2'dv_2'dw_2'du_3'$

$$= m_1^3\, m_2^3\, m_3\, ar_{12}\, \dot{r}_{12}\, du_1 \dots\dots du_3 \dots\dots\dots\dots(68).$$

Hence $\dfrac{dx_1' \dots dz_n' dv_3' \dots dw_n'}{m_1^3 m_2^3 m_3\, a'r_{12}'\dot{r}_{12}'} = \dfrac{dx_1 \dots dz_n dv_3 \dots dw_n}{m_1^3 m_2^3 m_3\, ar_{12} r_{12}} = C \dots\dots\dots\dots(69),$

and equation (29) becomes

$$N(b) = \int^{3n-7} C(m_1^3\, m_2^3\, m_3\, ar_{12}\, \dot{r}_{12})^{-1} dv_3 \dots dw_n \quad \dots\dots\dots\dots(70).$$

92—2

We shall find it useful in what follows to define the energy of internal motion as the excess of the whole kinetic energy of the system over that which it would have if it were moving like a rigid body with the same configuration, and the same components of momentum and of angular momentum.

If we suppose the internal motion of the system to be destroyed in a very short time by internal forces, so that the configuration is not sensibly altered during the process, then the work done by the system against these forces is the measure of the energy of internal motion.

Writing T for the kinetic energy referred to the origin, K for that of the mass moving with the velocity of the centre of mass, J for the kinetic energy due to the rotation of the system as a rigid body, and I for the energy of internal motion, we have

$$I = T - K - J \quad \dots\dots\dots\dots\dots\dots\dots\dots\dots\dots(71),$$

where

$$T = \Sigma \left[\tfrac{1}{2} m \left(u^2 + v^2 + w^2 \right) \right] \quad \dots\dots\dots\dots\dots\dots\dots(72),$$

$$K = \tfrac{1}{2} M \left(U^2 + V^2 + W^2 \right) \quad \dots\dots\dots\dots\dots\dots(73),$$

$$J = \tfrac{1}{2} \left(Fp + Gq + Hr \right) \quad \dots\dots\dots\dots\dots\dots\dots(74),$$

where p, q, r are the components of angular velocity with respect to the axes of x, y, z and are related to F, G, H by the equations

$$\left.\begin{aligned} Ap - Nq - Mr &= F, & aF - nG - mH &= p, \\ -Np + Bq - Lr &= G, & -nF + bG - lH &= q, \\ -Mp - Lq + Cr &= H, & -mF - lG + cH &= r, \end{aligned}\right\} \quad \dots\dots\dots(75).$$

where

$$\left.\begin{aligned} A &= \Sigma m \left[(y - Y)^2 + (z - Z)^2 \right] & L &= \Sigma m \, (y - Y)(z - Z) \\ B &= \Sigma m \left[(z - Z)^2 + (x - X)^2 \right] & M &= \Sigma m \, (z - Z)(x - X) \\ C &= \Sigma m \left[(x - X)^2 + (y - Y)^2 \right] & N &= \Sigma m \, (x - X)(y - Y) \end{aligned}\right\} \dots(76).$$

Writing for the sake of brevity

$$D = \begin{vmatrix} A, & -N, & -M \\ -N, & B, & -L \\ -M, & -L, & C \end{vmatrix}, \qquad d = \begin{vmatrix} a, & -n, & -m \\ -n, & b, & -l \\ -m, & -l, & c \end{vmatrix} \dots\dots\dots(77),$$

the relations between the moments and products of mobility and those of inertia will be given by equations of the forms

$$\left.\begin{aligned} aD &= BC - L^2 & Ad &= bc - l^2 \\ lD &= -MN - AL, & Ld &= -mn - al, \\ & Dd = 1. \end{aligned}\right\} \dots\dots\dots\dots(78).$$

If we write

$$\left.\begin{aligned}
\xi &= u - U + qz - ry \\
\eta &= v - V + rx - pz \\
\zeta &= w - W + py - qx
\end{aligned}\right\} \quad \dots\dots\dots\dots\dots\dots\dots(79),$$

then ξ, η, ζ will be the velocity-components of a particle with respect to axes passing through the centre of mass of the system and rotating with the angular velocity whose components are p, q, r. We may therefore call ξ, η, ζ the velocity-components of the internal motion. If the system were to become rigid, the internal motion would become zero. The energy of internal motion may be expressed in terms of ξ, η, ζ, thus :—

$$I = \Sigma \tfrac{1}{2} m (\xi^2 + \eta^2 + \zeta^2) \quad \dots\dots\dots\dots\dots\dots\dots(80).$$

We have now to express the energy of internal motion of a system of $s - 1$ particles in terms of the quantities U, V, W, F, G, H and T belonging to the system of s particles, together with the position and velocity of the sth particle.

To avoid the repetition of suffixes we shall distinguish quantities belonging to the minor system of $s - 1$ particles by accented letters, and quantities belonging to the complete system of s particles and the particle m_s by unaccented letters. We shall also write

$$\mu = \frac{Mm}{M'} .$$

We thus find

$$\left.\begin{aligned}
M' &= M - m \\
M'X' &= MX - mx \\
M'U' &= MU - mu, \\
F' &= F - \mu (y - Y)(w - W) + \mu (z - Z)(v - V) \\
A' &= A - \mu (y - Y)^2 - \mu (z - Z)^2 \\
L' &= L - \mu (y - Y)(z - Z) \\
T' &= T - \tfrac{1}{2} m (u^2 + v^2 + w^2) \\
K' &= K + \tfrac{1}{2} \mu [(U - u)^2 + (V - v)^2 + (W - w)^2] - \tfrac{1}{2} m (u^2 + v^2 + w^2).
\end{aligned}\right\} \dots(81).$$

Since the choice of the axes of reference is arbitrary, we may simplify the expressions by taking for origin the centre of mass of the system M, and for the axis of z the line passing through the particle m. We may also turn the axes of x and y about that of z till A becomes a maximum, the condition of which is

$$LM + CN = 0.$$

We shall also reckon velocities with reference to the centre of mass of the system M.

With these simplifications we find

$$\left.\begin{array}{lll} F' = F + \mu vz & G' = G - \mu uz & H' = H \\ A' = A - \mu z^2 & B' = B - \mu z^2 & C' = C \\ L' = L & M' = M & N' = N \\ a' = \dfrac{a}{1 - a\mu z^2}, & & l' = \dfrac{l'}{1 - b\mu z^2}, \\ b' = \dfrac{b}{1 - b\mu z^2}, & & m' = \dfrac{m}{1 - a\mu z^2}, \\ c' = c + \mu z^2 \left(\dfrac{l^2}{1 - b\mu z^2} + \dfrac{m^2}{1 - a\mu z^2} \right), & n' = n = 0, \\ \multicolumn{2}{c}{D' = D\,(1 - a\mu z^2)\,(1 - b\mu z^2).} \end{array}\right\} \dots(82).$$

We are now able to calculate the energy of rotation, J', of the minor system :

$$2J' = a'F''^2 + b'G''^2 + c'H''^2 - 2l'G'H' - 2m'H'F' - 2n'F''G' \dots\dots(83),$$

$$\left.\begin{array}{l} = 2J + \dfrac{1}{1 - a\mu z^2}\left[v^2 a\mu z^2 - 2v\mu z\,(Fa - Hm) + \mu z^2 (Fa - Hm)^2 \right] \\ + \dfrac{1}{1 - b\mu z^2}\left[u^2 b\mu z^2 + 2u\mu z\,(Gb - Hl) + \mu z^2 (Gb - Hl)^2 \right] \end{array}\right\} (84).$$

Combining these results and reducing we find for the energy of internal motion of the system M'

$$I' = I - \tfrac{1}{2}\mu\,(1 - b\mu z^2)^{-1}\,(u - Gb + Hl)^2 - \tfrac{1}{2}\mu\,(1 - a\mu z^2)^{-1}\,(v - Fa + Hl)^2 - \tfrac{1}{2}\mu w^2 \dots(85).$$

Hence

$$\iiint I'^{\frac{q}{2}}\,du\,dv\,dw = \frac{(\Gamma(\frac{1}{2}))^3 \Gamma\left(\dfrac{q+2}{2}\right)}{\Gamma\left(\dfrac{q+5}{2}\right)} \left(\frac{2}{\mu}\right)^{\frac{3}{2}} (1 - a\mu z^2)^{\frac{1}{2}}\,(1 - b\mu z^2)^{\frac{1}{2}} I^{\frac{q+3}{2}} \dots(86),$$

the integration being extended to all values of u. v, and w which make I' positive.

Now $(1 - a\mu z^2)\,(1 - b\mu z^2) = \dfrac{D'}{D}$, and this is an invariant.

Hence in general, whatever axes we choose,

$$\iiint [M_{s-1}{}^3 D_{s-1}]^{-\frac{1}{2}} I_{s-1}{}^{\frac{q}{2}} du_s dv_s dw_s = \frac{(\Gamma(\tfrac{1}{2}))^3 \Gamma\left(\dfrac{q+2}{2}\right)}{\Gamma\left(\dfrac{q+5}{2}\right)} [\tfrac{1}{2}m_s]^{-\frac{3}{2}} [M_s{}^3 D_s]^{-\frac{1}{2}} I_s^{\frac{q+3}{2}} \dots\dots(87).$$

For the system consisting of the two particles m_1 and m_2 the energy of rotation is

$$J_2 = \tfrac{1}{2}\frac{M_2}{m_1 m_2 r_{12}{}^2}(F_2{}^2 + G_2{}^2 + H_2{}^2)\dots\dots\dots\dots\dots(88),$$

and the energy of internal motion is

$$I_2 = \tfrac{1}{2}\frac{m_1 m_2}{M_2}\dot{r}_{12}{}^2 \dots\dots\dots\dots\dots\dots\dots(89).$$

Hence we may write equation (70)

$$N(b) = \int^{3n-7} C(m_1{}^3 m_2{}^3 m_3 a_1 r_2)^{-1}\left(2\frac{M_2}{m_1 m_2}\right)^{-\frac{1}{2}} I_2^{-\frac{1}{2}} dv_3 \dots dw_n \dots\dots\dots(90).$$

We have first to express I_2 in terms of quantities having the suffix $_3$.

If we make the plane of yz pass through the three particles m_1, m_2, m_3, so that the origin coincides with their centre of mass and has the same velocity, and the axis of z passes through m_3, then a is twice the area of the triangle whose vertices are m_1, m_2 and m_3,

$$F_2 = F_3 + \frac{M_3 m_3}{M_2} z_3 v_3, \qquad G_2 = G_3 - \frac{M_3 m_3}{M_2} z_3 u_3, \qquad H_2 = H_3 \dots\dots(91),$$

$$a m_3 u_3 = G_3 (y_1 - y_2) + H_3 (z_1 - z_2)\dots\dots\dots\dots\dots\dots(92),$$

$$I_2 = I_3 - \tfrac{1}{2}\frac{M_3 m_3}{M_2}\left(1 + \frac{M_3 m_3}{m_1 m_2}\frac{z_3{}^3}{r_{12}{}^3}\right)$$

$$\left[\left(u - \frac{M_2 G_3 z_3}{m_1 m_2 r_{12}{}^2 + M_3 m_3 z_3{}^2}\right)^2 + \left(v + \frac{M_2 F_3 z_3}{m_1 m_2 r_{12}{}^2 + M_3 m_3 z_3}\right)^2\right] - \tfrac{1}{2}\frac{M_3 m_3}{M_2} w^2 \dots(93).$$

We have now to integrate

$$\iint I^{-\frac{1}{2}} dv_3 dw_3,$$

extending the integration to all values of v_3 and w_3 which make I_2 positive, and remembering that equation (92) shews that u_3 is independent of v_3 and w_3. The result is

$$\iint I_2^{-\frac{1}{2}}\, dv_3 dw_3 = \frac{(\Gamma(\frac{1}{2}))^3}{\Gamma(\frac{3}{2})}\left[\frac{1}{4}\frac{M_3^2 m_3^2}{M_2^2} \cdot \frac{m_1 m_2 r_{12}^2 + M_3 m_3 z_3^2}{m_1 m_2 r_{12}^2}\right]^{-\frac{1}{2}} I_3^{\frac{1}{2}} \quad \dots\dots(94).$$

Now for the three particles m_1, m_2, m_3,

$$D_3 = \frac{m_1 m_2 m_3}{M_3^2}\left[r_{23}^2\, m_2 m_3 + r_{31}^2\, m_3 m_1 + r_{12}^2\, m_1 m_2\right]a^2 \dots\dots\dots\dots(95),$$

where r_{23}, r_{31} and r_{12} are the distances between the particles, and a is the area of the triangle $m_1 m_2 m_3$.

Also $\qquad r_{23}^2 m_2 m_3 + r_{31}^2 m_3 m_1 + r_{12}^2 m_1 m_2 = \dfrac{M_3}{M_2}(m_1 m_2 r_{12}^2 + M_3 m_3 z_3^2)\dots\dots\dots(96).$

We may now write equation (90) in the form

$$N(b) = \int^{3n-9} C\frac{(\Gamma\frac{1}{2})^3}{\Gamma(\frac{3}{2})}\left[\frac{1}{2}m_1^3 m_2^3 m_3^3 M_3^3 D_3\right]^{-\frac{1}{2}} I_3^{\frac{1}{2}}\, du_4\dots dw_n \dots\dots\dots(97).$$

Continuing the integration by equation (87) we find

$$N(b) = 2^{\frac{3n-8}{2}} C\frac{(\Gamma\frac{1}{2})^{3n-6}}{\Gamma\left(\dfrac{3n-6}{2}\right)}(m_1\dots m_n)^{-\frac{3}{2}} M_n^{-\frac{3}{2}} D_n^{-\frac{1}{2}} I_n^{\frac{3n-8}{2}} \dots\dots\dots(98),$$

where I_n is what we have defined as the energy of internal motion of the system, or the work which the system would do, in virtue of its motion, against the system of internal forces which would be called into play if the distances between the parts of the material system were in an insensibly small time to become invariable.

In order to determine the number of systems in a given configuration for which the velocity-components of the particle m_n lie between the limits $u \pm \frac{1}{2}du$, $v \pm \frac{1}{2}dv$, $w \pm \frac{1}{2}dw$, we must form the expression for $N(b, u_n, v_n, w_n)$ by stopping short before the last triple integration.

We thus find $N(b, u_n, v_n, w_n)$

$$= 2^{\frac{3n-11}{2}} C\frac{\{\Gamma(\frac{1}{2})\}^{3n-9}}{\Gamma\left(\dfrac{3n-9}{2}\right)}(m_1\dots m_{n-1})^{-\frac{3}{2}} M_{n-1}^{-\frac{3}{2}} D_{n-1}^{-\frac{1}{2}} I_{n-1}^{\frac{3n-11}{2}}\, du_n dv_n dw_n\dots(99).$$

If, as in equations (82) to (86), we suppose the origin of co-ordinates to be the centre of mass of the whole system, the axis of z to pass through the particle m_n, and the axes of x and y to be in the directions of the principal axes of the section of the momental ellipsoid normal to z, then writing

$$\xi = u - qz, \quad \eta = v + pz, \quad \zeta = w \dots\dots\dots\dots\dots(100),$$

so that ξ, η, ζ are the velocity-components of m_n relative to axes moving as the system would do if it were then to become rigid, with the angular velocity whose components are p, q, r, we may write

$$I_{n-1} = I_n - \tfrac{1}{2}\mu \left(1 - b\mu z^2\right)^{-1}\xi^2 - \tfrac{1}{2}\mu \left(1 - a\mu z^2\right)^{-1}\eta^2 - \tfrac{1}{2}\mu z^2 \dots\dots\dots(101).$$

The sum of the last three terms of this expression, with its sign taken positive, represents the part of the internal motion of the system which is due to the fact that the particle m_n is moving with the relative velocity whose components are ξ, η, ζ.

We may also define it as the work which would be done by the particle m_n against the internal forces of the system, if these forces were suddenly to become such as to render the whole system rigid in an infinitely short time.

Comparing this result with that obtained in equation (48), we see that the law of distribution of the velocities of the particle m_n is the same as what it would be in a fixed vessel containing $n-2$ particles, provided that we substitute for u^2, v^2, w^2 the quantities $(1 - b\mu z^2)^{-1}\xi^2$, $(1 - a\mu z^2)^{-1}\eta^2$, ζ^2 respectively.

Hence the mean square of the velocity in the direction of the line joining the particle with the centre of mass is the same at all points of the system, but the mean square of the velocity in other directions is less than this in the ratio of $1 - a\mu z^2$ to 1, where z is the perpendicular from the centre of mass on the line of relative motion of the particle, and a is the moment of mobility of the system about an axis through the centre of mass and normal to the plane through that centre and the line of motion.

When the product of the mass of the particle into the square of its distance from the centre is so small that it may be neglected in comparison with the moments of inertia of the system, then quantities like $a\mu z^2$ and $b\mu z^2$ may be neglected in respect of unity, and we may assert that the mean square of the relative velocity, for a particle of given mass, is the same in all directions and at all points of the system; but that for different particles it varies inversely as their masses; so that the average energy of motion relative to the moving axes is the same for particles of all kinds throughout the system.

We have already learned from equation (98) that in a free system of n particles the number of cases in which the system is in a given configuration, or, in other words, the probability of that configuration, is proportional to the $\frac{3n-8}{2}$ power of the energy of internal motion corresponding to that configuration.

We have next to consider the manner in which this probability depends on the position of a particular particle, say of the last particle, m_n.

Let $I_n^{(0)}$ denote the energy of internal motion of the complete system when m_n is at the centre of mass of the system and is without any velocity relative to that centre. It is manifest that in this case m_n contributes nothing towards the energy of internal motion.

Now let m_n be carried from the centre of mass to the point $(0, 0, z)$ and left there without any velocity (that is, let $u = v = w = 0$).

Let W be the work which must be done against the forces of the system to effect this transference, then since the total energy of the system and the three angular momenta must be maintained constant, we shall have after this displacement, for the energy of internal motion of the remaining $n - 1$ particles,

$$I_{n-1} = I_n^{(0)} - W \dots\dots\dots\dots\dots\dots\dots\dots(102).$$

But by equation (85)

$$I_n = I_{n-1} + \tfrac{1}{2}\mu\,(1 - b\mu z^2)^{-1}\,(u - qz)^2 + \tfrac{1}{2}\mu\,(1 - a\mu z^2)^{-1}\,(v + pz)^2 + \tfrac{1}{2}\mu w^2 \dots(103).$$

Substituting the value of I_{n-1} from equation (102), and remembering that $u = v = w = 0$, we find for the energy of internal motion in the new configuration

$$I_n = I_n^{(0)} - W + \tfrac{1}{2}\mu\,(1 - b\mu z^2)^{-1}\,q^2 z^2 + \tfrac{1}{2}\mu\,(1 - a\mu z^2)\,p^2 z^2 \dots\dots\dots(104).$$

The probability, therefore, of a configuration in which, the positions of all the other particles being given, that of m_n is varied, is proportional to $I_n^{\frac{3n-8}{2}}$, I_n being given by equation (104).

When, as in the case of a gas, there are a great many particles similar to m_n, we may speak of the density of the medium consisting of such particles in the element $dxdydz$. In this case, however, for reasons already given, neglect the quantities $a\mu z^2$ and $b\mu \dot{z}^2$, and we may write m for μ. We may also choose our axes in the manner which is most convenient. We shall therefore make the axis of z that round which the system, if it were rendered rigid, would rotate with velocity ω, and we shall suppose this axis to be vertical, as otherwise a steady motion under the action of gravity could not exist, and we shall denote the horizontal distance from this axis by r.

We may now write for the density of the gas at the point (z, r)

$$\rho = \rho_0 \left[1 + (2 I_n^{(0)})^{-1} (m\omega^2 r^2 - 2mgz) \right]^{\frac{3n-8}{2}} \quad \dotsc\dotsc\dotsc(105),$$

where ρ_0 is the density at the origin.

When n is a very large number and when the second term of the binomial is very small compared with unity, we may write for this the exponential expression

$$\rho = \rho_0 e^{\frac{3}{4}\frac{m n}{I}(\omega^2 r^2 - 2gz)} \quad \dotsc\dotsc\dotsc\dotsc\dotsc\dotsc(106).$$

If m_0 is the mass of a molecule of hydrogen, μm_0 will be the mass of a molecule of the kind of gas considered, where μ is the chemical equivalent of the gas.

Also if T is the temperature on the centigrade scale, and α the coefficient of dilatation of a perfect gas, then since the "velocity of mean square" of agitation of the molecules of hydrogen at $0°$C. is $1\cdot844 \times 10^5$ centimetres per second, the kinetic energy of agitation of a system containing n molecules of any kind will be

$$\tfrac{3}{2} m_0 n (1\cdot844)^2 10^{10} (1 + \alpha T),$$

and the difference between this and the energy of internal motion may be neglected.

We thus find for the density at any point

$$\rho = \rho_0 e^{\frac{\mu}{3}\cdot\frac{\omega^2 r^2 - 2gz}{(1\cdot844)^2 10^{10}(1+\alpha T)}} \quad \dotsc\dotsc\dotsc\dotsc\dotsc(107).$$

Let us now consider a tube of uniform section placed on a whirling table so that one end, A, of the tube coincides with the axis while the other end, B, revolves about the axis with the angular velocity ω. The linear velocity of B is ωr, and we shall suppose, for the sake of easy calculation, that this velocity is one-tenth of the velocity of agitation of the molecules of hydrogen.

The velocity of the end B would be 184·4 metres per second. If the tube contains hydrogen at 0°C., the ratio of the density of the gas at B to the density at A will be $e^{\frac{1}{200}}$, or approximately $1 + \frac{1}{200}$.

If it contains a gas whose chemical equivalent is μ, the ratio will be

$$1 + \frac{\mu}{200}.$$

If the tube contains hydrogen and carbonic acid, and if a certain volume of the tube at A contains 200 parts of hydrogen and 200 of carbonic acid, then an equal volume of the tube at B will contain 201 parts of hydrogen and 222 parts of carbonic acid.

The time during which the experiment would require to be continued in order to obtain a given degree of approximation to the ultimate distribution of the mixed gases varies as the square of the length of the tube.

Thus in Loschmidt's experiments on the diffusion of gases he used a tube about a metre long, and continued his experiments from half an hour to an hour in order to obtain the results from which he could best deduce the coefficient of diffusion.

In these experiments the inequalities of distribution of. hydrogen and carbonic acid were reduced to less than a third part of their original value in half an hour, and if the experiment had gone on for two hours the differences from the ultimate distribution would have been reduced to a hundredth part of their original value.

We may therefore consider two hours as ample time for an experiment on the ultimate distribution of these two gases in a tube one metre in length.

But if we make the whirling tube 20 centimetres long, the differences of distribution from the ultimate distribution would be reduced to a hundredth part of their original value in a twenty-fifth part of the time, that is to say in 4 minutes 48 seconds.

If it were found more convenient to have bulbs on the ends of the tubes, so as to be able to secure the gas at each end before it got mixed up by the violent commotion arising from the stopping of the whirling tube, we should have to allow a longer time for the whirling.

In order to obtain a similar distribution of the two gases in a vertical tube by the action of gravity the tube would require to be 1720 metres high, and in order to obtain the same degree of approximation to the ultimate distribution we should have to let the experiment go on for 675 years, carefully preserving the tube during that time from all inequalities of temperature, which, by causing convection-currents, would continually mix up the gases and prevent their partial separation.

[From *Nature*, Vol. XVIII.]

XCV. *The Telephone* (*Rede Lecture*).

WHEN, about two years ago, news came from the other side of the Atlantic that a method had been invented of transmitting, by means of electricity, the articulate sounds of the human voice, so as to be heard hundreds of miles away from the speaker, those of us who had reason to believe that the report had some foundation in fact, began to exercise our imaginations in picturing some triumph of constructive skill—something as far surpassing Sir William Thomson's Siphon Recorder in delicacy and intricacy as that is beyond a common bell-pull. When at last this little instrument appeared, consisting, as it does, of parts, everyone of which is familiar to us, and capable of being put together by an amateur, the disappointment arising from its humble appearance was only partially relieved on finding that it was really able to talk.

But perhaps the telephone, though simple in respect of its material and construction, may involve some recondite physical principle, the study of which might worthily occupy an hour's time of an academic audience: I can only say that I have not yet met anyone acquainted with the first elements of electricity who has experienced the slightest difficulty in understanding the physical process involved in the action of the telephone. I may even go further, and say that I have never seen a printed article on the subject, even in the columns of a newspaper, which shewed a sufficient amount of mis-apprehension to make it worth preserving—a proof that among scientific subjects the telephone possesses a very exceptional degree of lucidity.

However, if the telephone has something to say for itself, it would seem hardly necessary for me to take up your time with any tedious introduction. It is unfortunate, however, that up to the present time the telephone has kept all his more perfect utterances to be whispered into the privileged ear of a single listener. When he is older, he may get more accustomed to public speaking, but if we force him, in his present immature state, to exert his voice beyond what is good for him, it may sound rather too like the pot quarrelling with the kettle, and may call for the criticism with which Mr Tennyson's Princess complimented the disguised Prince on his "Song of the Swallow:"—

> "Not for thee, she said,
> O Bulbul, any rose of Gulistan
> Shall burst her veil: marsh divers rather, maid,
> Shall croak thee sister, or the meadow crake
> Grate her harsh kindred in the grass."

Is it for this, then, that we are to forsake the luncheons and lawn tennis and all the engrossing studies of the May Term, and to assemble in this solemn hall, where the very air seems thick with the accumulation of unsolved problems, or else redolent of the graces of innumerable congregations?

It is not by concentrating our minds on any problem, however important, but rather by encouraging them to expand, that we shall best fulfil the intention of Sir Robert Rede when he founded this lecture.

It would be as useless as it would be tedious to try to explain the various parts of this small instrument to persons in every part of the Senate House. I shall, therefore, consider the telephone as a material symbol of the widely separated departments of human knowledge, the cultivation of which has led, by as many converging paths, to the invention of this instrument by Professor Graham Bell.

For whatever may be said about the importance of aiming at depth rather than width in our studies, and however strong the demand of the present age may be for specialists, there will always be work, not only for those who build up particular sciences and write monographs on them, but for those who open up such communications between the different groups of builders as will facilitate a healthy interaction between them. And in a university we are especially bound to recognise not only the unity of science itself, but the communion of the workers in science. We are too apt to suppose that we are congregated here merely to be within reach of certain appliances of study, such as museums and laboratories, libraries and lecturers, so that each of us may study what he prefers. I suppose that when the bees crowd round the flowers it is for the sake of the honey that they do so, never thinking that it is the dust which they are carrying from flower to flower which is to render possible a more splendid array of flowers, and a busier crowd of bees, in the years to come. We cannot, therefore, do better than improve the shining hour in helping forward the cross-fertilization of the sciences.

Before we go further, I wish to express my obligation to Mr Garnett for the able assistance he has given me. He has not only collected the apparatus before you, but constructed some of it himself. But for him, I might have given you some second-hand information about telephones. He has made it possible for you to hear something yourselves. I have also to thank Mr Gower, who has brought his telephone harp, and Mr Middleton, who has contributed several instruments of his own invention.

We shall begin with the telephone in its most obvious aspect, as an instrument depending on certain physical principles.

The apparatus consists of two instruments, the transmitter and the receiver, doubly connected by a circuit capable of conducting electricity. The speaker talks to the transmitter at one end of the line, and at the other end of the line the listener puts his ear to the receiver, and hears what the speaker says.

The process in its two extreme stages is so exactly similar to the old-fashioned method of speaking and hearing that no preparatory practice is required on the part of either operator.

We must not, however, fall into the error of confounding the principle of the electric telephone with that of other contrivances for increasing the distance at which a conversation may be carried on. In all these the principle is the same as in the ordinary transmission of sound through the air. The different portions of matter which intervene between the speaker and the hearer take part, in succession, in a certain mechanical process. Each receives a certain motion from the portion behind it and communicates a precisely similar motion to the portion in front of it, in doing which it gives out all the energy it received, and is again reduced to rest.

The medium which takes part in this process may be the open air, or air confined in a long tube, or some other medium such as a brick wall, as when we hear what goes on in the next house, or a long wooden rod, or a metal wire, or even a stretched string. In all these it is by the actual motion of the successive portions of the medium that the message is transmitted.

In the electric telephone there is also a medium extending from the one instrument to the other. It is a copper wire, or rather two wires forming a closed circuit. But it is not by any motion of the copper that the message is transmitted. The copper remains at rest, but a variable electric current flows to and fro in the circuit.

It is this which distinguishes the electric telephone from the ordinary speaking tube, and from the transmission of vibrations along wooden rods by which Sir Charles Wheatstone used to cause musical instruments to sound in a mysterious manner without any visible performer.

On the other hand, we have to distinguish the principle of the articulating telephone from that of a great number of electrical contrivances which produce visible or audible signals at a distance. Most of these depend on the alternate transmission and interruption of an electric current. In some part of the circuit a piece of apparatus is introduced corresponding to this instrument which is called a key. Whenever two pieces of metal, called the contact pieces, touch each other, the current flows from the one to the other, and so round the circuit. Whenever the contact pieces are separated the current is interrupted, and the effects of this alternation of current and no current may be made to produce signals at any other part of the circuit.

In the Morse system of signalling, currents of longer and of shorter duration are called dashes and dots respectively, and by combinations of these the symbols of letters are formed. The rate at which these little currents succeed one another depends on the rate at which the operator can work the key, and may be increased by mechanical methods till the receiving clerk can no longer distinguish the symbols.

But the capability of the telegraph wire for transmitting signals is by no means exhausted; as the rapidity of the succession is increased, the ear ceases to distinguish them as separate signals, but begins to recognise the impression it receives as that of a musical tone, the pitch of which depends on the number of currents in a second.

Tuning forks driven by electricity were used by Helmholtz in his researches on the vowel sounds, and the periodically intermittent current which they furnish is recognised as a most valuable agent in physical and physiological research. The tuning forks are of the most massive construction, and the succession of currents goes on with the most inflexible regularity, so that whenever we have occasion to follow the march of a process which takes place in a short time, such as the vibration of a violin string or the twitch of a living muscle, the tuning fork becomes our appropriate timepiece.

Apparatus of this kind, however, the merit of which is its regularity, is quite incapable of adapting itself to the transmission of variable tones such as those of a melody.

The first successful attempt to transmit variable tones by electricity was made by Philip Reis, a teacher in a school at Friedrichsdorf, near Homburg. On October 21, 1861, Reis showed his instrument, which he called a telephone, to the Physical Society of Frankfort on the Main. He succeeded in transmitting melodies which were distinctly heard about the room.

The transmitter of Reis's telephone is essentially a make and break key of so delicate a construction that the sound-waves in the air are able to work it.

The air vibrations set in motion a stretched membrane like a drumhead, with a piece of platinum fastened to it. This piece of platinum, when vibrating, strikes against another piece of platinum, and so completes the circuit every time contact is made.

At every point of the circuit there is thus a series of currents corresponding in number to the vibrations of the drumhead, and by causing these to pass through the coil of an electromagnet, the armature of the electromagnet is attracted every time the current passes, and if the armature is attached to a resonator of any kind, the succession of tugs will set it in vibration, and cause it to emit a sound, the pitch of which is the same as that of the note sung into the transmitter at the other end of the line.

[Mr Gower here played the "March of the Men of Harlech" on the telephone harp placed in the Geological Museum. The instrument consists of a set of steel reeds worked by percussion, which make and break contact on the battery circuit, of which the primary wire of an induction coil forms part. The receivers are worked by the secondary current. There were four receivers, one of them Prof. Bell's original one, placed in different parts of the Senate-house.]

If the pitch of a sound were the only quality which we are able to distinguish, the problem of telephony would have received its complete solution in the instrument of Reis. But the human ear is so constructed, and we ourselves are so trained by continual practice, that we recognise distinctions in sound of a far more subtle character than that of pitch; and these finer distinctions have become so much more important for the purposes of human intercourse than the musical distinction of pitch, that many persons can detect the slightest variation in the pronunciation of a word who are comparatively indifferent to the variations of a melody.

Now, the telephone of Prof. Graham Bell is an articulating telephone, which can transmit not only melodies sung to it, but ordinary speech, and that so faithfully that we can often recognise the speaker by his voice as heard through the telephone. How is this effected? It is manifest that if by any means we can cause the tinned plate of the receiving instrument to vibrate in precisely the same manner as that of the transmitter, the impression on the ear will be exactly the same as if it had been placed at the back of the plate of the transmitter, and the words will be heard as if spoken at the other side of a tinned plate.

But this implies an exact correspondence, not only in the number of vibrations, but in the type of each vibration.

Now, if the electrical part of the process consisted merely of alternations between current and no current, the receiving instrument could never elicit from it the semblance of articulate speech. If the alternations were sufficiently regular, they would produce a sound of a recognisable pitch, which would be very rough music if the pitch were low, but might be less unendurable if the pitch were high; still, at the best, it would be like playing a violin with a saw instead of a bow.

What we want is not a sudden starting and stopping of the current, but a continuous rise and fall of the current, corresponding in every gradation and inflexion to the motion of the air agitated by the voice of the speaker.

Prof. Graham Bell has recounted the many unsuccessful attempts which he made to produce undulatory currents instead of mere intermittent ones. He had, of course, to give up altogether the method of making and breaking contact. Every method involving impact of any kind, whether between electric contact pieces or between the sounding parts of the instrument, introduces discontinuity of motion, and therefore precludes a faithful reproduction of speech.

In the ultimate form which the telephone in his hands assumed, the electric current is not merely regulated but actually generated by the aërial vibrations themselves.

The electric principle involved in Bell's telephone is that of the induction of electric currents discovered by Faraday in 1831. Faraday's own statement of this principle has been before the scientific world for nearly half a century, but has never been improved upon.

Consider first a conducting circuit, that is to say, a wire which after any number of convolutions returns into itself. Round such a circuit an electric current may flow, and will flow if there is an electromotive force to drive it.

Consider next a line of magnetic force, such a line as you see here made visible by sprinkling iron filings on a sheet of paraffin paper. This line, as Faraday also first showed, is a line returning into itself, or, as the mathematicians would say, it is a closed curve.

Now, if there are two closed curves in space, they must either embrace one another so as to be linked together, or they must not embrace each other.

If the line of force as well as the circuit were made of wire, and if it embraced the copper circuit, it would be impossible to unlink them without cutting one or other of the wires. But the line of force is more like one of Milton's spirits, which cannot

"In their liquid texture mortal wound
Receive, no more than can the fluid air."

Now, if the copper circuit or the lines of force move relatively to each other, then in general some of the lines of force which originally embraced the circuit will cease to embrace it, or else some of those which did not embrace it will become linked with it.

For every line of force which ceases to embrace the circuit there is a certain amount of positive electromotive force, which, if unopposed, will generate a current in the positive direction, and for every new line which embraces the circuit there is a negative electromotive force, causing a negative current.

In Bell's telephone the circuit forms a coil round a small core of soft iron fastened to the end of a steel magnet. Now lines of magnetic force pass more freely through iron than through any other substance. They will go out of their way in order to pass through iron instead of air. Hence a large proportion of the lines of force belonging to the magnet pass through the iron core, and, therefore, through the coil, even though there is no iron beyond the core, so that they have to complete their circuit through air.

But if another piece of soft iron is placed near the end of the core it will afford greater facilities for lines which have passed through the core to complete their circuit, and so the lines belonging to the magnet will crowd still closer together to take advantage of an easy passage through the core and the iron beyond it. If then the iron is moved nearer to the core, there will be an increase in the number of such lines, and, therefore, a negative current in the circuit. If it is moved away there will be a diminution in the number of lines, and a positive current in the circuit. This principle was employed by Page in the construction of one of the earliest magneto-electric machines, but it was reserved for Prof. Bell to discover that the vibrations of a tinned iron plate, set in motion by the voice, would produce such currents in the circuit as to set in motion a similar tinned plate at the other end of the line.

It will help us to appreciate the fertility of that germ of science which Faraday first detected and developed if we recollect that year after year he had employed the powerful batteries and magnets and delicate galvanometers of the Royal Institution to obtain evidence of what he all along hoped to discover —the production of a current in one circuit by a current in another, but all without success, till at last he detected the induced current as a transient phenomenon, to be observed only at the instant of making or breaking the primary circuit.

In less than half a century, and by the aid of no second Faraday, but in the course of the ordinary growth of scientific principles, this germ, so barely caught by Faraday, has developed on the one hand into the powerful currents which maintain the illumination of the lighthouses on our coasts; and on the other, into these currents of the telephone which produce an audible effect, though the engine that drives them is itself driven by the tremors of a child's voice.

Prof. Tait has recently measured the absolute strength of these telephone currents. He produced them by means of a tuning fork vibrating in front of the coil of the transmitter. Before the transmitted note ceased to be audible at the other end of the line he measured by means of a microscope the amplitude of the vibrations of the fork.

He then placed a very delicate galvanometer in the circuit and found what deflection was produced by a measured motion of the fork.

Finally he measured the deflection of the galvanometer produced by a small electromotive force of known magnitude. He thus found that the telephone currents produced an audible effect when reversed 500 times a second, though their strength was no greater than what a Grove's cell would send through a million megohms, about a thousand million times less than the currents used in ordinary telegraphic work.

One great beauty of Prof. Bell's invention is that the instruments at the two ends of the line are precisely alike. When the tin plate of the transmitter approaches the core of its bobbin it produces a current in the circuit, which has also to circulate round the bobbin of the receiver, and thus the core of the receiver is rendered more or less magnetic, and attracts its tin plate with greater or smaller force. Thus the tin plate of the receiver reproduces on a smaller scale, but with perfect fidelity, every motion of the tin plate of the transmitter.

This perfect symmetry of the whole apparatus—the wire in the middle, the two telephones at the end of the wire, and the two gossips at the ends of the telephones—may be very fascinating to a mere mathematician, but it would not satisfy an evolutionist of the Spencerian type, who would consider anything with both ends alike to be an organism of a very low type, which must have its functions differentiated before any satisfactory integration can take place.

Accordingly, many attempts have been made, by differentiating the function of the transmitter from that of the receiver, to overcome the principal limitation to the power of the telephone. As long as the human voice is the sole motive power of the apparatus it is manifest that what is heard at one end must be fainter than what is spoken at the other. But if the vibration set up by the voice is used no longer as the source of energy, but merely as a means of modulating the strength of a current produced by a voltaic battery, then there will be no necessary limitation of the intensity of the resulting sound, so that what is whispered to the transmitter may be proclaimed *ore rotundo* by the receiver.

A result of this kind has already been obtained by Mr Edison by means of a transmitter in which the sound vibrations produce a varying pressure on a piece of carbon, which forms part of the electric circuit. The greater the pressure, the smaller is the resistance due to the insertion of the carbon, and therefore the greater is the current in the circuit.

I have not yet seen Mr Edison's transmitter, but the microphone of Prof. Hughes is an application of carbon and other substances to the construction of a transmitter, which modulates the intensity of a battery current in more or less complete accordance with the sound-vibrations it receives. The energy of the sound produced is no longer limited by that of the original sound. All that the original sound does is to draw supplies of energy from the battery, so that a very feeble sound may give rise to a considerable effect. Thus, when a fly walks over the table of the microphone the sound of his tramp may be heard miles off.

Indeed, the microphone seems to open up several new lines of research. We shall have London physicians performing stethoscopic auscultations on patients in all parts of the kingdom. The Entomological Society have been much interested by Mr Wood-Mason's discovery of a stridulating apparatus in scorpions. Perhaps ere long a microphone, placed in a nest of tropical scorpions, may be connected up to a receiver in the apartments of the society, so as to give the members and their musical friends an opportunity of deciding whether the musical taste of the scorpion resembles that of the nightingale or that of the cat.

I have said that the telephone is an instance of the benefit to be derived from the cross-fertilization of the sciences. Now this is an operation which cannot be performed by merely collecting treatises on the different sciences, and binding them up into an encyclopædia. Science exists only in the mind, and the union of the sciences can take place only in a living person.

Now, Prof. Graham Bell, the inventor of the telephone, is not an electrician who has found out how to make a tin plate speak, but a speaker, who, to gain his private ends, has become an electrician. He is the son of a very remarkable man, Alexander Melville Bell, author of a book called "Visible Speech," and of other works relating to pronunciation. In fact, his whole life has been employed in teaching people to speak. He brought the art to such perfection that, though a Scotchman, he taught himself in six months to speak English, and I regret extremely that when I had the opportunity in Edinburgh I did not take lessons from him. Mr Melville Bell has made a complete analysis and classification of all the sounds capable of being uttered by the human voice, from the Zulu clicks to coughing and sneezing; and he has embodied his results in a system of symbols, the elements of which are not taken from any existing alphabet, but are founded on the different configurations of the organs of speech.

The capacities of this new mode of representing speech have been put to the test by Mr Alexander J. Ellis, author of "The Essentials of Phonetics," a gentleman who has studied the whole theory of speech acoustically, philologically, and historically. He describes the result in a letter to *The Reader*:—

"The mode of procedure was as follows:—Mr Bell sent his two sons, who were to read the writing, out of the room—it is interesting to know that the elder, who read all the words in this case, had only had five weeks' instruction in the use of the alphabet—and I dictated slowly and distinctly the sounds which I wished to be written. They consisted of a few words in Latin, pronounced first as at Eton, then as in Italy, and then according to some theoretical notions of how the Latins might have uttered them. Then came some English provincialisms and affected pronunciations, the words 'how odd' being given in several distinct ways. Suddenly German provincialisms were introduced; then discriminations of sounds often confused. Some Arabic, some Cockney English, with an introduced Arabic guttural, some mispronounced Spanish, and a variety of shades of vowels and diphthongs.

"The result was perfectly satisfactory—that is, Mr Bell wrote down my queer and purposely exaggerated pronunciations and mispronunciations, and delicate distinctions, in such a manner that his sons, not having heard them, so uttered them as to surprise me by the extremely correct echo of my own voice......Accent, tone, drawl, brevity, indistinctness were all reproduced with surprising accuracy. Being on the watch, I could, as it were, trace the alphabet in the lips of the readers. I think, then, that Mr Bell is justified in the somewhat bold title which he has assumed for his mode of writing— 'Visible speech.' I only hope that for the advantage of linguists, such an alphabet may soon be made accessible, and that, for the intercourse of nations, it may be adopted generally, at least for extra-European nations, as for the Chinese dialect and the several extremely diverse Indian languages, where such an alphabet would rapidly become a great social and political engine."

The inventor of the telephone was thus prepared, by early training in the practical analysis of the elements of speech, to associate whatever scientific knowledge he might afterwards acquire with those elementary sensations and actions, which each of us must learn from himself, because they lie too deep within us to be described to others. This training was put to a very severe test, when, at the request of the Boston Board of Education, Prof. Graham Bell conducted a series of experiments with his father's system in the Boston School for the Deaf and Dumb. I cannot conceive a nobler application of the scientific analysis of speech, than that by which it enables those to whom all sound is

> "expunged and rased
> And wisdom at one entrance quite shut out,"

not only to speak themselves, but to read by sight what other people are saying. The successful result of the experiments at Boston is not only the most valuable testimonial to the father's system of visible speech, but an honour which the inventor of the telephone may well consider as the highest he has attained.

An independent method of research into the process of speech was employed by Wheatstone, Willis, and Kempelen, the aim of which was to imitate the sounds of the human voice by means of artificial apparatus. This apparatus was in some cases modelled so as to represent as nearly as possible the form as well as the functions of the organs of speech, but it was found that an equally good imitation of the vocal sounds could be obtained from apparatus the form of which had no resemblance to the natural organs.

Several isolated facts of considerable importance were established by this method, but the whole theory of speaking and hearing has been so profoundly modified by Helmholtz and Donders, that much of what was advanced before their time has come to possess only an historical interest.

Among all the recent steps in the progress of science, I know none of which the truly scientific or science-producing consequences are likely to be so influential as the rise of a school of physiologists, who investigate the conditions of our sensations by producing on the external senses impressions, the physical conditions of which can be measured with precision, and then recording the verdict of consciousness as to the similarity or difference of the resulting sensations.

Prof. Helmholtz, in his recent address as Rector of the University of Berlin, lays great stress on that personal interaction between living minds, which I have already spoken of as essential to the life of a University. "I appreciate," he says, "at its full value this last advantage, when, looking back, I recall my student days, and the impression made upon us by a man like Johannes Müller, the physiologist. When one finds himself in contact with a man of the first order, the entire scale of one's intellectual conceptions is modified for life; contact with such a man is perhaps the most interesting thing life may have to offer."

Now, the form in which Johannes Müller stated what we may regard as the germ which fertilized the physiology of the senses is this, that the difference in the sensations due to different senses does not depend upon the actions which excite them, but upon the various nervous arrangements which receive them.

To accept this statement out of a book, as a matter of dead faith, may not be difficult to an easy-going student; but when caught like a contagion, as

Helmholtz caught it, from the lips of the living teacher, it has become the guiding principle of a life of research.

No man has done more than Helmholtz to open up paths of communication between isolated departments of human knowledge; and one of these, lying in a more attractive region than that of elementary psychology, might be explored under exceptionally favourable conditions, by some of the fresh minds now coming up to Cambridge.

Helmholtz, by a series of daring strides, has effected a passage for himself over that untrodden wild between acoustics and music—that Serbonian bog where whole armies of scientific musicians and musical men of science have sunk without filling it up.

We may not be able even yet to plant our feet in his tracts and follow him right across. That would require the seven league boots of the German colossus; but to help us in Cambridge we have the Board of Musical Studies, vindicating for music its ancient place in a liberal education. On the physical side we have Lord Rayleigh laying the foundation deep and strong in his *Theory of Sound*. On the æsthetic side we have the University Musical Society doing the practical work, and in the space between, those conferences of Mr Sedley Taylor, where the wail of the siren draws musician and mathematician together down into the depths of their sensational being, and where the gorgeous hues of the phoneidoscope are seen to seethe and twine and coil like the

> " Dragon boughs and elvish emblemings "

on the gates of that city where

> "an ye heard a music, like enow
> They are building still, seeing the city is built
> To music, therefore never built at all,
> And therefore built for ever."

The special educational value of this combined study of music and acoustics is that more than almost any other study it involves a continual appeal to what we must observe for ourselves.

The facts are things which must be felt; they cannot be learned from any description of them.

All this has been said more than two hundred years ago by one of our own prophets—William Harvey, of Gonville and Caius College. "For whosoever they be that read authors, and do not by the aid of their own senses, abstract true representations of the things themselves (comprehended in the author's expressions) they do not represent true ideas, but deceitful idols and phantasms, by which they frame to themselves certain shadows and chimæras, and all their theory and contemplation (which they call science) represents nothing but waking men's dreams and sick men's phrensies."

Prof. Maxwell was assisted in his practical demonstrations by Mr Garnett, of St John's College.

[From *Nature*, Vol. XIX.]

XCVI.—*Paradoxical Philosophy**

ON opening this book, the general appearance of the pages, and some of the phrases on which we happened to light made us somewhat doubtful whether it lay within our jurisdiction, as it is not the practice of *Nature* to review either novels or theological works.

In the dedication, however, the book is described as an account of the *Proceedings* of a learned society, a species of literature which we are under a special vow to rescue from oblivion, even when, as in this case, the proceedings are those of one of those jubilee meetings, in which learned men seem to aim rather at being lively than scientific.

On the title-page itself there is no name to indicate whether the author is one of those who by previous conviction have rendered themselves liable to our surveillance, but on the opposite page we find *The Unseen Universe; or, Physical Speculations on a Future State*, to which this book is a "Sequel," ascribed to the well-known names of Balfour Stewart and P. G. Tait.

Mr Browning has expressed his regret that the one volume in which Rafaelle wrote his sonnets, and the one angel which Dante was drawing when he was interrupted by "people of importance," are lost to the world. We shall therefore make the most of our opportunity when two eminent men of science, "driven," as they tell us, "by the exigencies of the subject," have laid down all the instruments of their art, shaken the very chalk from their hands, and, locking up their laboratories, have betaken themselves to those blissful country seats where Philonous long ago convinced Hylas that there can be no heat in the fire and no matter in the world; and where in more recent times, Peacock and Mallock have brought together in larger groups the more picturesque of contemporary opinions.

In this book we do not indeed catch those echoes of well-known voices in which the citizens of the "New Republic" tell us how they prefer to

* *Paradoxical Philosophy.* A Sequel to *The Unseen Universe* (London: Macmillan & Co., 1878).

regard themselves as thinking, taking care, all the while, that no actual thought shall disturb their enjoyment of the luxury of extravagant opinion. The members of the Paradoxical Society, with their guest, Dr Hermann Stoffkraft, are far too earnest to adopt this pose of mind, but they exhibit that sympathy in fundamentals overlaid with variety in opinions which is one of the main conditions of good-fellowship. Dr Stoffkraft, in spite of his name and of his office as the single-handed opponent of the thesis of the book, makes it his chief care so to brandish his materialistic weapons as not to hurt the feelings of his friends; and when, near the end of the book, he gets a little out of temper, it is about matters with which a materialist, as such, has no concern.

As the book is not a novel there is no literary reason for not telling "what became of the Doctor," as narrated in the last chapter. He goes to Strathkelpie Castle to take part in an investigation of spiritualistic phenomena. He begins by detecting the mode in which one young lady performs her spirit-rapping, but forthwith falls into an "electro-biological" courtship of another, and, this proving successful, he is persuaded by his wife and her priest to renounce the black arts in the lump as works of the foul fiend; and then we are told that, having quieted his spirit by a few evolutions in four dimensions, he has now settled down to compose his *Exposition of the Relations between Religion and Science*, which he intends to be a thoroughly matured production.

The Doctor—and, indeed, most of the other characters—are no mere materialised spirits, or opinions labelled with names of the *Euphranor* and *Alciphron* type. They do not reduce their subject to a *caput mortuum* by an exhaustive treatment, but take care, like well-bred people, to drop it and pass on to another before we have time to suspect that the last word has been said.

We cannot accuse the authors of leading us through the mazy paths of science only to entrap us into some peculiar form of theological belief. On the contrary, they avail themselves of the general interest in theological dogmas to imbue their readers at unawares with the newest doctrines of science. There must be many who would never have heard of Carnot's reversible engine, if they had not been led through its cycle of operations while endeavouring to explore the Unseen Universe. No book containing so much thoroughly scientific matter would have passed through seven editions in so short a time without the allurement of some more human interest.

Nor need we fear to draw down on *Nature* the admonition which fell on the inner ear of the poet—

> "Thou pratest here where thou art least ;
> This faith hath many a purer priest,
> And many an abler voice than thou."

For even those words and phrases which seemed at first sight to remove the book from the field of our criticism, are found on a nearer view to have acquired a new, and indeed a *paradoxical* sense, for which no right of sanctuary can be claimed.

The words on the title-page : "In te, Domine, speravi, non confundar in æternum," may recall to an ordinary reader the aspiration of the Hebrew Psalmist, the closing prayer of the "Te Deum," or the dying words of Francis Xavier ; and men of science, as such, are not to be supposed incapable either of the nobler hopes or of the nobler fears to which their fellow-men have attained. Here, however, we find these venerable words employed to express a conviction of the perpetual validity of the "Principle of Continuity," enforced by the tremendous sanction, that if at any place or at any time a single exception to that principle were to occur, a general collapse of every intellect in the universe would be the inevitable result.

There are other well-known words in which St Paul contrasts things seen with things unseen. These also are put in a prominent place by the authors of the *Unseen Universe*. What, then, is the Unseen to which they raise their thoughts ?

In the first place the luminiferous æther, the tremors of which are the dynamical equivalent of all the energy which has been lost by radiation from the various systems of grosser matter which it surrounds. In the second place a still more subtle medium, imagined by Sir William Thomson as possibly capable of furnishing an explanation of the properties of sensible bodies ; on the hypothesis that they are built up of ring vortices set in motion by some supernatural power in a frictionless liquid : beyond which we are to suppose an indefinite succession of media, not hitherto imagined by any one, each manifoldly more subtle than any of those preceding it. To exercise the mind in speculations on such media may be a most delightful employment for those who are intellectually fitted to indulge in it, though we cannot see why they should on that account appropriate the words of St Paul.

Nature is a journal of science, and one of the severest tests of a scientific mind is to discern the limits of the legitimate application of scientific methods. We shall therefore endeavour to keep within the bounds of science in speaking of the subject-matter of this book, remembering that there are many things in heaven and earth which, by the selection required for the application of our scientific methods, have been excluded from our philosophy.

No new discoveries can make the argument against the personal existence of man after death any stronger than it has appeared to be ever since men began to die, and no language can express it more forcibly than the words of the Psalmist :—

"His breath goeth forth, he returneth to his earth; in that very day his thoughts perish."

Physiology may supply a continually increasing number of illustrations of the dependence of our actions, mental as well as bodily, on the condition of our material organs, but none of these can render any more certain those facts about death which our earliest ancestors knew as well as our latest posterity can ever learn them.

Science has, indeed, made some progress in clearing away the haze of materialism which clung so long to men's notions about the soul, in spite of their dogmatic statements about its immateriality. No anatomist now looks forward to being able to demonstrate my soul by dissecting it out of my pineal gland, or to determine the quantity of it by the process of double weighing. The notion that the soul exerts force lingered longer. We find it even in the late Isaac Taylor's *Physical Theory of a Future State*. It was admitted that one body might set another in motion; but it was asserted that in every case, if we only trace the chain of phenomena far enough back, we must come to a body set in motion by the direct action of a soul.

It would be rash to assert that any experiments on living beings have as yet been conducted with such precision as to account for every foot-pound of work done by an animal in terms of the diminution of the intrinsic energy of the body and its contents; but the principle of the conservation of energy has acquired so much scientific weight during the last twenty years that no physiologist would feel any confidence in an experiment which shewed a considerable difference between the work done by an animal and the balance of the account of energy received and spent.

Science has thus compelled us to admit that that which distinguishes a living body from a dead one is neither a material thing, nor that more refined entity, a "form of energy." There are methods, however, by which the application of energy may be directed without interfering with its amount. Is the soul like the engine-driver, who does not draw the train himself, but, by means of certain valves, directs the course of the steam so as to drive the engine forward or backward, or to stop it?

The dynamical theory of a conservative material system shews us, however, that *in general* the present configuration and motion determine the whole course of the system, exceptions to this rule occurring only at the instants when the system passes through certain isolated and singular phases, at which a strictly infinitesimal force may determine the course of the system to any one of a finite number of equally possible paths, as the pointsman at a railway junction directs the train to one set of rails or another. Prof. B. Stewart has expounded a theory of this kind in his book on *The Conservation of Energy*, and MM. de St Venant and Boussinesq have examined the corresponding phase of some purely mathematical problems.

The science which rejoices in the name of "Psychophysik" has made considerable progress in the study of the phenomena which accompany our sensations and voluntary motions. We are taught that many of the processes which we suppose entirely under the control of our own will are subject to the strictest laws of succession, with which we have no power of interfering; and we are shewn how to verify the conclusions of the science by deducing from it methods of physical and mental training for ourselves and others.

Thus science strips off, one after the other, the more or less gross materialisations by which we endeavour to form an objective image of the soul, till men of science, speculating, in their non-scientific intervals, like other men on what science may possibly lead to, have prophesied that we shall soon have to confess that the soul is nothing else than a function of certain complex material systems.

Men of science, however, are but men, and therefore occasionally contemplate their souls from within. Those who, like Du Bois-Reymond, cannot admit that sensation or consciousness can be a function of a material system, are led to the conception of a double mind.

"On the one side the acting, inventing, unconscious material mind, which puts the muscles into motion, and determines the world's history; this is nothing else but the mechanics of atoms, and is subject to the causal law, and on the other side the inactive, contemplative, remembering, fancying, conscious, immaterial mind, which feels pleasure and pain, love, and hate; this one lies outside of the mechanics of matter, and cares nothing for cause and effect."

We might ask Prof. Du Bois-Reymond which of these it is that does right or wrong, and knows that it is his act, and that he is responsible for it, but we must go on to the other view of the case, which Dr Stoffkraft alludes to at p. 78, although by some law of the *Paradoxical*, he is not allowed to pursue a subject which might have afforded excellent sport to the Society.

"I feel myself compelled to believe," says the learned Doctor, "that all kinds of matter have their motions accompanied with certain simple sensations. In a word, all matter is, in some occult sense, alive."

This is what we may call the "levelling up" policy, and it has been expounded with great clearness by Prof. von Nägeli in a lecture, of which a translation was given in *Nature*, Vol. XVI. p. 531.

He can draw no line across the chain of being, and say that sensation and consciousness do not extend below that line. He cannot doubt that every molecule possesses something related, though distantly, to sensation, "since each one feels the presence, the particular condition, the peculiar forces of the other, and, accordingly, has the inclination to move, and under circumstances really begins to move—becomes alive as it were;"... "If, therefore, the molecules feel something which is related to sensation, then this must be pleasure if they can respond to attraction and repulsion, *i.e.* follow their inclination or disinclination; it must be displeasure if they are forced to execute some opposite movement, and it must be neither pleasure nor displeasure if they remain at rest."

Prof. von Nägeli must have forgotten his dynamics, or he would have remembered that the molecules, like the planets, move along like blessed gods. They cannot be disturbed from the path of their choice by the action of any forces, for they have a constant and perpetual will to render to every force precisely that amount of deflexion which is due to it. Their condition must, therefore, be one of unmixed and unbroken pleasure.

But even if a man were built up of thinking atoms would the thoughts of the man have any relation to the thoughts of the atoms? Those who try to account for mental processes by the combined action of atoms do so, not by the thoughts of the atoms, but by their motions.

Dr Stoffkraft explains the origin of consciousness at p. 77 and at p. 107. We recommend to his attention Mr Herbert Spencer's statement in his *Principles of Psychology*, § 179, where he shews in a most triumphant manner how, under certain circumstances, "there must arise a consciousness." Such statements, carefully studied, may contribute to the further progress of science in the path which we have been describing, by shewing more clearly that consciousness cannot be the result of a plexus of nervous communications any more than of a congeries of plastidule souls.

Personality is often spoken of as if it were another name for the continuity of consciousness as reproduced in memory, but it is impossible to deal with personality as if it were something objective that we could reason about. My knowledge that I am is quite independent of my recollection that I was, and also of my belief that, for a certain number of years, I have never ceased to be. But as soon as we plunge into the abysmal depths of personality we get beyond the limits of science, for all science, and, indeed, every form of human speech, is about objects capable of being known by the speaker and the hearer. Whenever we pretend to talk about the Subject we are really dealing with an Object under a false name, for the first proposition about the Subject, namely, "I am," cannot be used in the same sense by any two of us, and therefore can never become part of science at all.

The progress of science, therefore, so far as we have been able to follow it, has added nothing of importance to what has always been known about the physical consequences of death, but has rather tended to deepen the distinction between the visible part, which perishes before our eyes, and that which we are ourselves, and to shew that this personality, with respect to its nature as well as to its destiny, lies quite beyond the range of science.

[From *Encyclopaedia Britannica*.]

XCVII. *Ether.*

ETHER, or ÆTHER (αἰθήρ, probably from αἴθω, I burn, though Plato in his *Cratilus* (410, b) derives the name from its perpetual motion—ὅτι ἀεὶ θεῖ περὶ τὸν ἀέρα ῥέων, ἀειθεὴρ δικαίως ἂν καλοῖτο), a material substance of a more subtle kind than visible bodies, supposed to exist in those parts of space which are apparently empty.

The hypothesis of an æther has been maintained by different speculators for very different reasons. To those who maintained the existence of a plenum as a philosophical principle, nature's abhorrence of a vacuum was a sufficient reason for imagining an all-surrounding æther, even though every other argument should be against it. To Descartes, who made extension the sole essential property of matter, and matter a necessary condition of extension, the bare existence of bodies apparently at a distance was a proof of the existence of a continuous medium between them.

But besides these high metaphysical necessities for a medium, there were more mundane uses to be fulfilled by æthers. Æthers were invented for the planets to swim in, to constitute electric atmospheres and magnetic effluvia, to convey sensations from one part of our bodies to another, and so on, till all space had been filled three or four times over with æthers. It is only when we remember the extensive and mischievous influence on science which hypotheses about æthers used formerly to exercise, that we can appreciate the horror of æthers which sober-minded men had during the 18th century, and which, probably as a sort of hereditary prejudice, descended even to the late Mr John Stuart Mill.

The disciples of Newton maintained that in the fact of the mutual gravitation of the heavenly bodies, according to Newton's law, they had a complete quantitative account of their motions; and they endeavoured to follow out the path which Newton had opened up by investigating and measuring the attractions and repulsions of electrified and magnetic bodies, and the cohesive forces in the interior of bodies, without attempting to account for these forces.

Newton himself, however, endeavoured to account for gravitation by differences of pressure in an æther (see Art. ATTRACTION *, Vol. III. p. 64); .but he did not publish his theory, " because he was not able from experiment and observation to give a satisfactory account of this medium, and the manner of its operation in producing the chief phenomena of nature."

On the other hand, those who imagined æthers in order to explain phenomena could not specify the nature of the motion of these media, and could not prove that the media, as imagined by them, would produce the effects they were meant to explain. The only æther which has survived is that which was invented by Huygens to explain the propagation of light. The evidence for the existence of the luminiferous æther has accumulated as additional phenomena of light and other radiations have been discovered; and the properties of this medium, as deduced from the phenomena of light, have been found to be precisely those required to explain electromagnetic phenomena.

Function of the æther in the propagation of radiation.—The evidence for the undulatory theory of light will be given in full, under the Article on LIGHT, but we may here give a brief summary of it so far as it bears on the existence of the æther.

That light is not itself a substance may be proved from the phenomenon of interference. A beam of light from a single source is divided by certain optical methods into two parts, and these, after travelling by different paths, are made to reunite and fall upon a screen. If either half of the beam is stopped, the other falls on the screen and illuminates it, but if both are allowed to pass, the screen in certain places becomes dark, and thus shews that the two portions of light have destroyed each other.

Now, we cannot suppose that two bodies when put together can annihilate each other; therefore light cannot be a substance. What we have proved is that one portion of light can be the exact opposite of another portion, just as $+a$ is the exact opposite of $-a$, whatever a may be. Among physical quantities we find some which are capable of having their signs reversed, and others which are not. Thus a displacement in one direction is the exact opposite of an equal displacement in the opposite direction. Such quantities

* [p. 485 of the present vol.]

are the measures, not of substances, but always of processes taking place in a substance. We therefore conclude that light is not a substance but a process going on in a substance, the process going on in the first portion of light being always the exact opposite of the process going on in the other at the same instant, so that when the two portions are combined no process goes on at all. To determine the nature of the process in which the radiation of light consists, we alter the length of the path of one or both of the two portions of the beam, and we find that the light is extinguished when the difference of the length of the paths is an odd multiple of a certain small distance called a half wave-length. In all other cases there is more or less light; and when the paths are equal, or when their difference is a multiple of a whole wave-length, the screen appears four times as bright as when one portion of the beam falls on it. In the ordinary form of the experiment these different cases are exhibited simultaneously at different points of the screen, so that we see on the screen a set of fringes consisting of dark lines at equal intervals, with bright bands of graduated intensity between them.

If we consider what is going on at different points in the axis of a beam of light at the same instant, we shall find that if the distance between the points is a multiple of a wave-length the same process is going on at the two points at the same instant, but if the distance is an odd multiple of half a wave-length the process going on at one point is the exact opposite of the process going on at the other.

Now, light is known to be propagated with a certain velocity $(3 \cdot 004 \times 10^{10}$ centimetres per second in vacuum, according to Cornu). If, therefore, we suppose a movable point to travel along the ray with this velocity, we shall find the same process going on at every point of the ray as the moving point reaches it. If, lastly, we consider a fixed point in the axis of the beam, we shall observe a rapid alternation of these opposite processes, the interval of time between similar processes being the time light takes to travel a wave-length.

These phenomena may be summed up in the mathematical expression

$$u = A \cos (nt - px + a)$$

which gives u, the phase of the process, at a point whose distance measured from a fixed point in the beam is x, and at a time t.

We have determined nothing as to the nature of the process. It may be a displacement, or a rotation, or an electrical disturbance, or indeed any physical quantity which is capable of assuming negative as well as positive values. Whatever be the nature of the process, if it is capable of being expressed by an equation of this form, the process going on at a fixed point is called a *vibration;* the constant A is called the *amplitude;* the time $\dfrac{2\pi}{n}$ is called the *period;* and $nt - px + a$ is the phase.

The configuration at a given instant is called a *wave,* and the distance $\dfrac{2\pi}{p}$ is called the *wave-length.* The velocity of propagation is $\dfrac{n}{p}$. When we contemplate the different parts of the medium as going through the same process in succession, we use the word undulatory to denote this character of the process without in any way restricting its physical nature.

A further insight into the physical nature of the process is obtained from the fact that if the two rays are polarized, and if the plane of polarization of one of them be made to turn round the axis of the ray, then when the two planes of polarization are parallel the phenomena of interference appear as above described. As the plane turns round, the dark and light bands become less distinct, and when the planes of polarization are at right angles, the illumination of the screen becomes uniform, and no trace of interference can be discovered.

Hence the physical process involved in the propagation of light must not only be a directed quantity or vector capable of having its direction reversed, but this vector must be at right angles to the ray, and either in the plane of polarization or perpendicular to it. Fresnel supposed it to be a displacement of the medium perpendicular to the plane of polarization. Maccullagh and Neumann supposed it to be a displacement in the plane of polarization. The comparison of these two theories must be deferred till we come to the phenomena of dense media.

The process may, however, be an electromagnetic one, and as in this case the electric displacement and the magnetic disturbance are perpendicular to each other, either of these may be supposed to be in the plane of polarization.

All that has been said with respect to the radiations which affect our eyes, and which we call light, applies also to those radiations which do not produce a luminous impression on our eyes, for the phenomena of interference have been observed, and the wave-lengths measured, in the case of radiations, which can be detected only by their heating or by their chemical effects.

Elasticity, tenacity, and density of the æther.—Having so far determined the geometrical character of the process, we must now turn our attention to the medium in which it takes place. We may use the term æther to denote this medium, whatever it may be.

In the first place, it is capable of transmitting energy. The radiations which it transmits are able not only to act on our senses, which of itself is evidence of work done, but to heat bodies which absorb them; and by measuring the heat communicated to such bodies, the energy of the radiation may be calculated.

In the next place this energy is not transmitted instantaneously from the radiating body to the absorbing body, but exists for a certain time in the medium.

If we adopt either Fresnel's or Maccullagh's form of the undulatory theory, half of this energy is in the form of potential energy, due to the distortion of elementary portions of the medium, and half in the form of kinetic energy, due to the motion of the medium. We must therefore regard the æther as possessing elasticity similar to that of a solid body, and also as having a finite density. If we take Pouillet's estimate of $1·7633$ as the number of gramme-centigrade units of heat produced by direct sunlight falling on a square centi-metre in a minute, this is equivalent to $1·234 \times 10^6$ ergs per second. Dividing this by $3·004 \times 10^{10}$, the velocity of light in centimetres per second, we get for the energy in a cubic centimetre $4·1 \times 10^{-5}$ ergs. Near the sun the energy in a cubic centimetre would be about 46,000 times this, or $1·886$ ergs. If we further assume, with Sir W. Thomson, that the amplitude is not more than one hundredth of the wave-length, we have $Ap = \dfrac{2\pi}{100}$, or about $\dfrac{1}{16}$; so that we have—

Energy per cubic centimetre .... $= \frac{1}{2}\rho V^2 A^2 p^2 = 1·886$ ergs.*
Greatest tangential stress per square centimetre $= \rho V^2 A\,p = 30·176$ dynes.
Coefficient of rigidity of ether .... $= \rho V^2 \qquad = 842·8$.
Density of æther .... $= \rho \qquad\quad = 9·36 \times 10^{-19}$.

The coefficient of rigidity of steel is about 8×10^{11}, and that of glass $2·4 \times 10^{11}$.

* [The numbers in this column are incorrectly deduced from the data. They should be $1·886$, $60·352$, $965·632$ and $1·07 \times 10^{-18}$.]

If the temperature of the atmosphere were everywhere 0° C., and if it were in equilibrium about the earth supposed at rest, its density at an infinite distance from the earth would be 3×10^{-346} which is about 1.8×10^{287} times less than the estimated density of the æther. In the regions of interplanetary space the density of the æther is therefore very great compared with that of the attenuated atmosphere of interplanetary space, but the whole mass of æther within a sphere whose radius is that of the most distant planet is very small compared with that of the planets themselves*.

The æther distinct from gross matter.—When light travels through the atmosphere it is manifest that the medium through which the light is propagated is not the air itself, for in the first place the air cannot transmit transverse vibrations, and the normal vibrations which the air does transmit travel about a million times slower than light. Solid transparent bodies, such as glass and crystals, are no doubt capable of transmitting transverse vibrations, but the velocity of transmission is still hundreds of thousand times less than that with which light is transmitted through these bodies. We are therefore obliged to suppose that the medium through which light is propagated is something distinct from the transparent medium known to us, though it interpenetrates all transparent bodies and probably opaque bodies too.

The velocity of light, however, is different in different transparent media, and we must therefore suppose that these media take some part in the process, and that their particles are vibrating as well as those of the æther, but the energy of the vibrations of the gross particles must be very much smaller than that of the æther, for otherwise a much larger proportion of the incident light would be reflected when a ray passes from vacuum to glass or from glass to vacuum than we find to be the case.

Relative motion of the æther.—We must therefore consider the æther within dense bodies as somewhat loosely connected with the dense bodies, and we have next to inquire whether, when these dense bodies are in motion through the great ocean of æther, they carry along with them the æther they contain, or whether the æther passes through them as the water of the sea passes through the meshes of a net when it is towed along by a boat. If it were possible to determine the velocity of light by observing the time it takes to travel between one station and another on the earth's surface, we

---

* See Sir W. Thomson, *Trans. R. S. Edin.* Vol. xxi. p. 60.

might, by comparing the observed velocities in opposite directions, determine the velocity of the æther with respect to these terrestrial stations. All methods, however, by which it is practicable to determine the velocity of light from terrestrial experiments depend on the measurement of the time required for the double journey from one station to the other and back again, and the increase of this time on account of a relative velocity of the æther equal to that of the earth in its orbit would be only about one hundred millionth part of the whole time of transmission, and would therefore be quite insensible.

The theory of the motion of the æther is hardly sufficiently developed to enable us to form a strict mathematical theory of the aberration of light, taking into account the motion of the æther. Professor Stokes, however, has shewn that, on a very probable hypothesis with respect to the motion of the æther, the amount of aberration would not be sensibly affected by that motion.

The only practicable method of determining directly the relative velocity of the æther with respect to the solar system is to compare the values of the velocity of light deduced from the observation of the eclipses of Jupiter's satellites when Jupiter is seen from the earth at nearly opposite points of the ecliptic.

Arago proposed to compare the deviation produced in the light of a star after passing through an achromatic prism when the direction of the ray within the prism formed different angles with the direction of motion of the earth in its orbit. If the æther were moving swiftly through the prism, the deviation might be expected to be different when the direction of the light was the same as that of the æther, and when these directions were opposite.

The present writer* arranged the experiment in a more practicable manner by using an ordinary spectroscope, in which a plane mirror was substituted for the slit of the collimator. The cross wires of the observing telescope were illuminated. The light from any point of the wire passed through the object-glass and then through the prisms as a parallel pencil till it fell on the object-glass of the collimator, and came to a focus at the mirror, where it was reflected, and after passing again through the object-glass it formed a pencil passing through each of the prisms parallel to its original direction, so that the object-glass of the observing telescope brought it to a focus coinciding with the point of the cross wires from which it originally proceeded. Since

---

* *Phil. Trans.* CLVIII. (1868), p. 532. [Communicated by Prof. Maxwell to Dr Huggins and included by him in his paper on the spectra of some of the stars and nebulæ.]

the image coincided with the object, it could not be observed directly, but by diverting the pencil by partial reflection at a plane surface of glass, it was found that the image of the finest spider line could be distinctly seen, though the light which formed the image had passed twice through three prisms of 60°. The apparatus was first turned so that the direction of the light in first passing through the second prism was that of the earth's motion in its orbit. The apparatus was afterwards placed so that the direction of the light was opposite to that of the earth's motion. If the deviation of the ray by the prisms was increased or diminished for this reason in the first journey, it would be diminished or increased in the return journey, and the image would appear on one side of the object. When the apparatus was turned round it would appear on the other side. The experiment was tried at different times of the year, but only negative results were obtained. We cannot, however, conclude absolutely from this experiment that the æther near the surface of the earth is carried along with the earth in its orbit, for it has been shown by Professor Stokes * that according to Fresnel's hypothesis the relative velocity of the æther within the prism would be to that of the æther outside inversely as the square of the index of refraction, and that in this case the deviation would not be sensibly altered on account of the motion of the prism through the æther.

Fizeau†, however, by observing the change of the plane of polarization of light transmitted obliquely through a series of glass plates, obtained what he supposed to be evidence of a difference in the result when the direction of the ray in space was different, and Angström obtained analogous results by diffraction. The writer is not aware that either of these very difficult experiments has been verified by repetition.

In another experiment of M. Fizeau, which seems entitled to greater confidence, he has observed that the propagation of light in a stream of water takes place with greater velocity in the direction in which the water moves than in the opposite direction, but that the change of velocity is less than that which would be due to the actual velocity of the water, and that the phenomenon does not occur when air is substituted for water. This experiment seems rather to verify Fresnel's theory of the æther; but the whole question of the state of the luminiferous medium near the earth, and of its connexion with gross matter, is very far as yet from being settled by experiment.

* *Phil. Mag.* 1846, p. 53.   † *Ann. de Chimie et de Physique*, Feb. 1860.

Function of the æther in electromagnetic phenomena.—Faraday conjectured that the same medium which is concerned in the propagation of light might also be the agent in electromagnetic phenomena. "For my own part," he says, "considering the relation of a vacuum to the magnetic force, and the general character of magnetic phenomena external to the magnet, I am much more inclined to the notion that in the transmission of the force there is such an action, external to the magnet, than that the effects are merely attraction and repulsion at a distance. Such an action may be a function of the æther; for it is not unlikely that, if there be an æther, it should have other uses than simply the conveyance of radiation*." This conjecture has only been strengthened by subsequent investigations.

Electrical energy is of two kinds, electrostatic and electrokinetic. We have reason to believe that the former depends on a property of the medium in virtue of which an electric displacement elicits an electromotive force in the opposite direction, the electromotive force for unit displacement being inversely as the specific inductive capacity of the medium.

The electrokinetic energy, on the other hand, is simply the energy of the motion set up in the medium by electric currents and magnets, this motion not being confined to the wires which carry the currents, or to the magnet, but existing in every place where magnetic force can be found.

Electromagnetic Theory of Light.—The properties of the electromagnetic medium are therefore as far as we have gone similar to those of the luminiferous medium, but the best way to compare them is to determine the velocity with which an electromagnetic disturbance would be propagated through the medium. If this should be equal to the velocity of light, we would have strong reason to believe that the two media, occupying as they do the same space, are really identical. The data for making the calculation are furnished by the experiments made in order to compare the electromagnetic with the electrostatic system of units. The velocity of propagation of an electromagnetic disturbance in air, as calculated from different sets of data, does not differ more from the velocity of light in air, as determined by different observers, than the several calculated values of these quantities differ among each other.

If the velocity of propagation of an electromagnetic disturbance is equal to that of light in other transparent media, then in non-magnetic media the

---

* *Experimental Researches*, 3075.

specific inductive capacity should be equal to the square of the index of refraction.

Boltzmann* has found that this is very accurately true for the gases which he has examined. Liquids and solids exhibit a greater divergence from this relation, but we can hardly expect even an approximate verification when we have to compare the results of our sluggish electrical experiments with the alternations of light, which take place billions of times in a second.

The undulatory theory, in the form which treats the phenomena of light as the motion of an elastic solid, is still encumbered with several difficulties†.

The first and most important of these is that the theory indicates the possibility of undulations consisting of vibrations normal to the surface of the wave. The only way of accounting for the fact that the optical phenomena which would arise from these waves do not take place is to assume that the æther is incompressible.

The next is that, whereas the phenomena of reflection are best explained on the hypothesis that the vibrations are perpendicular to the plane of polarization, those of double refraction require us to assume that the vibrations are in that plane.

The third is that, in order to account for the fact that in a doubly refracting crystal the velocity of rays in any principal plane and polarized in that plane is the same, we must assume certain highly artificial relations among the coefficients of elasticity.

The electromagnetic theory of light satisfies all these requirements by the single hypothesis ‡ that the electric displacement is perpendicular to the plane of polarization. No normal displacement can exist, and in doubly refracting crystals the specific dielectric capacity for each principal axis is assumed to be equal to the square of the index of refraction of a ray perpendicular to that axis, and polarized in a plane perpendicular to that axis. Boltzmann§ has found that these relations are approximately true in the case of crystallized sulphur,

---

* *Wiener Sitzb.*, 23 April, 1874.

† See Prof. Stokes, "Report on Double Refraction," *British Ass. Report*, 1862, p. 253.

‡ *Over de theorie der terugkaatsing en breking van het licht,*—Academisch Proefschrift door H. A. Lorentz. Arnhem, K. van der Zande, 1875.

§ "Ueber die Verschiedenheit der Dielektricitätsconstante des krystallisirten Schwefels nach verschiedenen Richtungen," by Ludwig Boltzmann, *Wiener Sitzb.*, 8th Oct., 1874.

a body having three unequal axes. The specific dielectric capacity for these axes are respectively

$$4{\cdot}773 \qquad\qquad 3{\cdot}970 \qquad\qquad 3{\cdot}811$$

and the squares of the indices of refraction

$$4{\cdot}576 \qquad\qquad 3{\cdot}886 \qquad\qquad 3{\cdot}591$$

Physical constitution of the æther.—What is the ultimate constitution of the æther? is it molecular or continuous?

We know that the æther transmits transverse vibrations to very great distances without sensible loss of energy by dissipation. A molecular medium, moving under such conditions that a group of molecules once near together remain near each other during the whole motion, may be capable of transmitting vibrations without much dissipation of energy, but if the motion is such that the groups of molecules are not merely slightly altered in configuration but entirely broken up, so that their component molecules pass into new types of grouping, then in the passage from one type of grouping to another the energy of regular vibrations will be frittered away into that of the irregular agitation which we call heat.

We cannot therefore suppose the constitution of the æther to be like that of a gas, in which the molecules are always in a state of irregular agitation, for in such a medium a transverse undulation is reduced to less than one five-hundredth of its amplitude in a single wave-length. If the æther is molecular, the grouping of the molecules must remain of the same type, the configuration of the groups being only slightly altered during the motion.

Mr S. Tolver Preston* has supposed that the æther is like a gas whose molecules very rarely interfere with each other, so that their mean path is far greater than any planetary distances. He has not investigated the properties of such a medium with any degree of completeness, but it is easy to see that we might form a theory in which the molecules *never* interfere with each other's motion of translation, but travel in all directions with the velocity of light; and if we further suppose that vibrating bodies have the power of impressing on these molecules some vector property (such as rotation about an axis) which does not interfere with their motion of translation, and which is then carried along by the molecules, and if the alternation of the average

* *Phil. Mag.*, Sept. and Nov. 1877.

value of this vector for all the molecules within an element of volume be the process which we call light, then the equations which express this average will be of the same form as that which expresses the displacement in the ordinary theory.

It is often asserted that the mere fact that a medium is elastic or compressible is a proof that the medium is not continuous, but is composed of separate parts having void spaces between them. But there is nothing inconsistent with experience in supposing elasticity or compressibility to be properties of every portion, however small, into which the medium can be conceived to be divided, in which case the medium would be strictly continuous. A medium, however, though homogeneous and continuous as regards its density, may be rendered heterogeneous by its motion, as in Sir W. Thomson's hypothesis of vortex-molecules in a perfect liquid (see Art. ATOM)*.

The æther, if it is the medium of electromagnetic phenomena, is probably molecular, at least in this sense.

Sir W. Thomson† has shewn that the magnetic influence on light discovered by Faraday depends on the direction of motion of moving particles, and that it indicates a rotational motion in the medium when magnetized. See also Maxwell's *Electricity and Magnetism*, Art. 806, &c.

Now, it is manifest that this rotation cannot be that of the medium as a whole about an axis, for the magnetic field may be of any breadth, and there is no evidence of any motion the velocity of which increases with the distance from a single fixed line in the field. If there is any motion of rotation, it must be a rotation of very small portions of the medium each about its own axis, so that the medium must be broken up into a number of molecular vortices.

We have as yet no data from which to determine the size or the number of these molecular vortices. We know, however, that the magnetic force in the region in the neighbourhood of a magnet is maintained as long as the steel retains its magnetization, and as we have no reason to believe that a steel magnet would lose all its magnetization by the mere lapse of time, we conclude that the molecular vortices do not require a continual expenditure of work in order to maintain their motion, and that therefore this motion does not necessarily involve dissipation of energy.

* [p. 445 of the present volume.]   † *Proceedings of the Royal Society,* June, 1856.

No theory of the constitution of the æther has yet been invented which will account for such a system of molecular vortices being maintained for an indefinite time without their energy being gradually dissipated into that irregular agitation of the medium which, in ordinary media, is called heat.

Whatever difficulties we may have in forming a consistent idea of the constitution of the æther, there can be no doubt that the interplanetary and interstellar spaces are not empty, but are occupied by a material substance or body, which is certainly the largest, and probably the most uniform body of which we have any knowledge.

Whether this vast homogeneous expanse of isotropic matter is fitted not only to be a medium of physical interaction between distant bodies, and to fulfil other physical functions of which, perhaps, we have as yet no conception, but also, as the authors of the *Unseen Universe* seem to suggest, to constitute the material organism of beings exercising functions of life and mind as high or higher than ours are at present, is a question far transcending the limits of physical speculation.

[From *Nature*, Vol. xx.]

XCVIII. *Thomson and Tait's Natural Philosophy.*

THE year 1867 will long be remembered by natural philosophers as that of the publication of the first volume of "Thomson and Tait." They had long been waiting for the book, and in the preface the delay was accounted for by the necessity of anticipating the wants of the other three volumes, in which the remaining divisions of Natural Philosophy were to be treated. The reader was also reminded, that if in any passage he failed to appreciate the aim of the authors, the reason might be that what he was studying was in reality a prospective contrivance, the true aim of which would not become manifest until after the perusal of that part of the work for which it was designed to prepare the way.

What we have had before us now for twelve years was, the authors reminded us, strictly preliminary matter. The plan of the whole treatise could only be guessed at from the scale on which its foundations were constructed.

In these days, when so much of the science of our best men is dribbled out of them in the fragmentary and imperfectly elaborated form of the memoirs which they contribute to learned societies, and when the work of making books is relegated to professional bookmakers, who understand about as much of one subject as of another, it was something to find that even one man of known power had not shrunk from so great a work; it was more when it appeared that two men of mark were joined together in the undertaking; and when at last the plan of the work was described in the preface, and the scale on which its foundations were being laid was exhibited in the vast substructure of Preliminary Matter, the feeling with which we began to contemplate the mighty whole was one in which delight was almost overpowered by awe.

This feeling has been growing upon us during the twelve years we have been exploring the visible part of the work, marking its bulwarks and telling the rising generation what manner of a palace that must be, of which these are but the outworks and first line of defences, so that now, when we have before us the second edition of the first part of the first volume, we are impelled to risk the danger of criticising an unfinished work, and to say something about the plan of what is already before us.

The first thing which we observe in the arrangement of the work is the prominence given to kinematics, or the theory of pure motion, and the large space devoted under this heading to what has been hitherto considered part of pure geometry. The theory of the curvature of lines and surfaces, for example, has long been recognised as an important branch of geometry, but in treatises on motion it was regarded as lying as much outside of the subject as the four rules of arithmetic or the binomial theorem.

The guiding idea, however, which, though it has long exerted its influence on the best geometers, is now for the first time boldly and explicitly put forward, is that geometry itself is part of the science of motion, and that it treats, not of the relations between figures already existing in space, but of the process by which these figures are generated by the motion of a point or a line.

We no longer, for example, consider the line AB simply as a white stroke on a black board, and call it indifferently AB or BA, but we conceive it as the trace of the motion of a point from A to B, and we distinguish A as the beginning and B as the end of this trace.

This method of regarding geometrical figures seems to imply that the idea of motion underlies the idea of form, and is in accordance with the psychological doctrine which asserts that at any given instant the attention is confined to a single and indivisible percept, but that as time flows on the attention passes along a continuous series of such percepts, so that the path of investigation along which the mind proceeds may be described as a continuous line without breadth. Our knowledge, therefore, of whatever kind, may be compared to that which a blind man acquires of the form of solid bodies by stroking them with the point of his stick, and then filling up in his imagination the unexplored parts of the surface according to his own notions about continuity and probability. The rapidity, however, with which we make our exploration is such that we come to think that by a single glance we can thoroughly see the whole of that surface of a body which is turned towards us, if, indeed, we are not prepared to assert that we have seen the other side too, when after all, if our attention were to leave a trace behind it, as the point of the blind man's stick might do, this trace would appear as a mere line meandering over the surface in various directions, but leaving between its convolutions unexplored areas, the sum of which is still equal to, the whole surface.   We are at liberty no doubt to course over the surface and to subdivide the meshes of the network of lines in which we envelope it, and to conclude that there cannot be a hole in it of more than a certain diameter, but no amount of investigation will warrant the conclusion, which nevertheless we draw at once and without a scruple, that the surface is absolutely continuous and has no hole in it at all.   Even when, in a dark night, a flash of lightning discloses instantaneously a whole landscape with trees and buildings, we discover these things not at once, but by perusing at our leisure the picture which the sudden flash has photographed on our retina.

The reason why the phenomena of motion have been so long refused a place among the most universal and elementary subjects of instruction seems to be, that we have been relying too much on symbols and diagrams, to the neglect of the vital processes of sensation and thought.

It is no doubt much easier to represent in a diagram or a picture the instantaneous relations of things coexisting in space than to illustrate in a full and complete manner the simplest case of motion.   When we have drawn our diagram it remains on the paper, and the student may run his mind over the lines in any order which pleases him.   But when we are either perceiving real motions, or thinking about them without the aid or the encumbrance of a diagram, the mind is carried along the actual course of the motion, in a manner far more easy and natural than when it is rushing indiscriminately hither and thither along the lines of a diagram.

Having pursued kinematics from its elementary principles till its intricacies begin to be appalling, we resume the study of the elements of science in the opening of the chapter on "Dynamical Laws and Principles."   It is here that we first have to deal with something which claims the title of Matter, and our authors, one of whom never misses an opportunity of denouncing metaphysical reasoning, except when he has occasion to expound the peculiarities of the Unconditioned, make the following somewhat pusillanimous statement :—

"We cannot, of course, give a definition of *Matter* which will satisfy the metaphysician, but the naturalist may be content to know matter as *that which can be perceived by the senses, or as that which can be acted upon by, or can exert, force.*"

The authors proceed to throw out a hint about Force being a direct object of sense, and after telling us that the question *What is matter?* will be discussed in a future volume, in which also the Subjectivity of Force will be considered, they retire to watch the effect of the definition they have thrown into the camp of the naturalists.

Now all this seems to us very much out of place in a treatise on Dynamics. We have nothing of the kind in treatises on Geometry. We have no disquisitions as to whether it is by touch or by sight that we come to know in what way a triangle differs from a square. We have not even a caution that the diagrams of these figures in the book do not exactly correspond with their definitions. Even in kinematics, when our authors speak of the motion of points, lines, surfaces, and solids, though they introduce several modern phrases, the kind of motion they speak of is none other than that which Euclid recognises, when he treats of the generation of figures.

Why, then, should we have any change of method when we pass on from kinematics to abstract dynamics? Why should we find it more difficult to endow moving figures with mass than to endow stationary figures with motion? The bodies we deal with in abstract dynamics are just as completely known to us as the figures in Euclid. They have no properties whatever except those which we explicitly assign to them.

Again, at p. 222, the capacity of the student is called upon to accept the following statement :—

"Matter has an innate power of resisting external influences, so that every body, as far as it can, remains at rest or moves uniformly in a straight line."

Is it a fact that "matter" has any power, either innate or acquired, of resisting external influences? Does not every force which acts on a body always produce exactly that change in the motion of the body by which its value, as a force, is reckoned? Is a cup of tea to be accused of having an innate power of resisting the sweetening influence of sugar, because it persistently refuses to turn sweet unless the sugar is actually put into it?

But suppose we have got rid of this Manichæan doctrine of the innate depravity of matter, whereby it is disabled from yielding to the influence c

98—2

a moving force unless that force actually spends itself upon it, what sort of facts are left us to be the subject-matter of abstract dynamics?

We are supposed to have mastered so much of kinematics as to be able to describe all possible motions of points, lines, and figures. In so far as real bodies have figures and motions, we may apply kinematics to them.

The new idea appropriate to dynamics is that the motions of bodies are not independent of each other, but that, under certain conditions, dynamical transactions take place between two bodies, whereby the motions of both bodies are affected.

Every body and every portion of a body in dynamics is credited with a certain quantitative value, called its mass. The first part of our study must therefore be the distribution of mass in bodies. In every dynamical system there is a certain point, the position of which is determined by the distribution of mass. This point was called by Boscovich the centre of mass—a better name, we think, than centre of inertia, though either of these is free from the error involved in the term centre of gravity.

In every dynamical transaction between two bodies there must be something which determines the relation between the alteration of the motions of the two bodies. In other words, there must be some function of the motions of the two bodies which remains constant during the transaction. According to the doctrine of abstract dynamics it is the motion of the centre of mass of the two bodies which is not altered on account of any dynamical transaction between the bodies. This doctrine, if true of real bodies, gives us the means of ascertaining the ratio of the mass of any body to that of the body adopted as the standard of mass, provided we can observe the changes in the motions of the two bodies arising from an encounter between them.

We then confine our attention to one of the bodies, and estimate the magnitude of the transaction between the bodies by its effect in changing the *momentum* of that body, momentum being merely a term for a quantity mathematically defined in terms of mass and motion. The rate at which this change of momentum takes place is the numerical measure of the force acting on the body, and, for all the purposes of abstract dynamics, it *is* the force acting on the body.

We have thus vindicated for figures with mass, and, therefore, for force and stress, impulse and momentum, work and energy, their places in abstract science beside form and motion.

The phenomena of real bodies are found to correspond so exactly with the necessary laws of dynamical systems, that we cannot help applying the language of dynamics to real bodies, and speaking of the masses in dynamics as if they were real bodies or portions of matter.

We must be careful, however, to remember that what we sometimes, even in abstract dynamics, call matter, is not that unknown substratum of real bodies, against which Berkeley directed his arguments, but something as perfectly intelligible as a straight line or a sphere.

Real bodies may or may not have such a substratum, just as they may or may not have sensations, or be capable of happiness or misery, knowledge or ignorance, and the dynamical transactions between them may or may not be accompanied with the conscious effort which the word force suggests to us when we imagine one of the bodies to be our own, but so long as their motions are related to each other according to the conditions laid down in dynamics, we call them, in a perfectly intelligible sense, dynamical or material systems.

In this, the second edition, we notice a large amount of new matter, the importance of which is such that any opinion which we could form within the time at our disposal would be utterly inadequate. But there is one point of vital importance in which we observe a marked improvement, namely, in the treatment of the generalised equations of motion.

Whatever may be our opinion about the relation of mass, as defined in dynamics, to the matter which constitutes real bodies, the practical interest of the science arises from the fact that real bodies *do* behave in a manner strikingly analogous to that in which we have proved that the mass-systems of abstract dynamics *must* behave.

In cases like that of the planets, when the motions we have to account for can be actually observed, the equations of Maclaurin, which are simply a translation of Newton's laws into the Cartesian system of co-ordinates, are amply sufficient for our purpose. But when we have reason to believe that the phenomena which fall under our observation form but a very small part of what is really going on in the system, the question is not—what phenomena will result from the hypothesis that the system is of a certain specified kind? but—what is the most general specification of a material system consistent with the condition that the motions of those parts of the system which we can observe are what we find them to be?

It is to Lagrange, in the first place, that we owe the method which enables us to answer this question without asserting either more or less than all that can be legitimately deduced from the observed facts. But though this method has been in the hands of mathematicians since 1788, when the *Mécanique Analytique* was published, and though a few great mathematicians, such as Sir W. R. Hamilton, Jacobi, &c., have made important contributions to the general theory of dynamics, it is remarkable how slow natural philosophers at large have been to make use of these methods.

Now, however, we have only to open any memoir on a physical subject in order to see that these dynamical theorems have been dragged out of the sanctuary of profound mathematics in which they lay so long enshrined, and have been set to do all kinds of work, easy as well as difficult, throughout the whole range of physical science.

The credit of breaking up the monopoly of the great masters of the spell, and making all their charms familiar in our ears as household words, belongs in great measure to Thomson and Tait. The two northern wizards were the first who, without compunction or dread, uttered in their mother tongue the true and proper names of those dynamical concepts which the magicians of old were wont to invoke only by the aid of muttered symbols and inarticulate equations. And now the feeblest among us can repeat the words of power and take part in dynamical discussions which but a few years ago we should have left for our betters.

In the present edition we have for the first time an exposition of the general theory of a very potent form of incantation, called by our authors the Ignoration of Co-ordinates. We must remember that the co-ordinates of Thomson and Tait are not the mere scaffolding erected over space by Descartes, but the variables which determine the whole motion. We may picture them as so many independent driving-wheels of a machine which has as many degrees of freedom. In the cases to which the method of ignoration is applied there are certain variables of the system such that neither the kinetic nor the potential energy of the system depends on the value of these variables, though of course the kinetic energy depends on their momenta and velocities. The motion of the rest of the system cannot in any way depend on the particular values of these variables, and therefore the particular values of these variables cannot be ascertained by means of any observation of the motion of the rest of the system. We have therefore no right, from such observations, to assign to them any particular values, and the only scientific way of dealing with them is to ignore them.

But this is not all. Since these variables do not appear in the expression for the potential energy, there can be no force acting on them, and therefore their momenta are, each of them, constant, and their velocities are functions of the variables, but, since their own variables do not enter into the expressions, we may consider them as functions of the other variables, or, as they are here called, the retained co-ordinates, and of the constant momenta of the ignored co-ordinates.

From the velocities as thus expressed, together with the constant momenta, we obtain the contribution of the ignored co-ordinates to the kinetic energy of the system in terms of the retained co-ordinates and of the constant momenta of the ignored co-ordinates. This part of the kinetic energy, being independent of the velocities of the retained co-ordinates, is, as regards the retained co-ordinates, strictly *positional**, and may be considered for all experimental purposes as if it were a term of the potential energy. The other part of the kinetic energy is a homogeneous quadratic function of the velocities of the retained co-ordinates. In the final equations of motion neither the ignored co-ordinates nor their velocities appear, but everything is expressed in terms of the retained co-ordinates and their velocities, the coefficients, however, being, in general, functions of the constant momenta of the ignored co-ordinates.

We may regard this investigation as a mathematical illustration of the scientific principle that in the study of any complex object, we must fix our attention on those elements of it which we are able to observe and to cause to vary, and ignore those which we can neither observe nor cause to vary.

In an ordinary belfry, each bell has one rope which comes down through a hole in the floor to the bellringers' room. But suppose that each rope, instead of acting on one bell, contributes to the motion of many pieces of machinery, and that the motion of each piece is determined not by the motion of one rope alone, but by that of several, and suppose, further, that all this machinery is silent and utterly unknown to the men at the ropes, who can only see as far as the holes in the floor above them.

Supposing all this, what is the scientific duty of the men below? They have full command of the ropes, but of nothing else. They can give each rope any position and any velocity, and they can estimate its momentum

* The division of forces into motional and positional is introduced at p. 370.

stopping all the ropes at once, and feeling what sort of tug each rope gives. If they take the trouble to ascertain how much work they have to do in order to drag the ropes down to a given set of positions, and to express this in terms of these positions, they have found the potential energy of the system in terms of the known co-ordinates. If they then find the tug on any one rope arising from a velocity equal to unity communicated to itself or to any other rope, they can express the kinetic energy in terms of the co-ordinates and velocities.

These data are sufficient to determine the motion of every one of the ropes when it and all the others are acted on by any given forces. This is all that the men at the ropes can ever know. If the machinery above has more degrees of freedom than there are ropes, the co-ordinates which express these degrees of freedom must be ignored. There is no help for it.

Of course, if there are co-ordinates for which there are no ropes, but which enter into the expression for the energy, then, if the motion of these co-ordinates is periodic, there will be "adynamic vibrations" communicated to the ropes, and by these the men below will know that there is something peculiar going on above them. But if they pull the ropes in proper time, they can either quiet these adynamic vibrations or strengthen them, so that in this case these co-ordinates cannot be ignored.

There are other cases, however, in which the conditions for the ignoration of co-ordinates strictly apply. For instance, if an opaque and apparently rigid body contains in a cavity within it an accurately balanced body, mounted on frictionless pivots, and previously set in rapid rotation, the co-ordinate which expresses the angular position of this body is one which we are compelled to ignore, because we have no means of ascertaining it. An unscientific person on receiving this body into his hands would immediately conclude that it was bewitched. A disciple of the northern wizards would prefer to say that the body was subject to gyrostatic domination.

Of the sections on cycloidal motions of systems, we can only here say that the investigation of the constitution of molecules by means of their vibrations, as indicated by spectroscopic observations, will be greatly assisted by a thorough study of this part of the volume.

We have not space to say anything of what to many readers must be one of the most interesting parts of the book—that on continuous calculating machines, in which pure rolling friction is taken from the class of unavoidable evils, and raised to the rank of one of the most powerful aids to science. Rolling and sliding have been more than once combined in the hope of obtaining accurate measurements, but the combination is fatal to accuracy, and these new machines, one at least of which has been actually constructed and used, are the first in which pure rolling friction has had fair play given it as a method of mechanically accurate integration.

A method is also given of combining a number of disk, globe, and cylinder integrators, so as to form a machine the motions of two pieces of which are related to each other by a differential equation of any given form. These machines all work in a purely statical manner, that is, in such a way that the kinetic energy of the system is not an essential element in the practical theory of the machine (as in the case of pendulums, &c.), but has to be taken into account only in order to estimate the magnitude of the tangential forces at the points of contact which might, if great enough, produce slipping between the surfaces. Thus, by means of a machine, which will go as slowly as may be necessary to keep pace with our powers of thought, motions may be calculated, the phases of which in nature pass before us too rapidly to be followed by us.

In the original preface some indications were given of what we were to expect in the remaining three volumes of the work. We hope that the reason why this part of the preface is omitted in the new edition is that the work will now go on so steadily that it will be unnecessary to preface performance by promise.

[From *Encyclopaedia Britannica*.]

XCIX.—*Faraday*.

FARADAY, MICHAEL, chemist, electrician, and philosopher, was born at New-ington, Surrey, 22nd September, 1791, and died at Hampton Court, 25th August, 1867. His parents had migrated from Yorkshire to London, where his father worked as a blacksmith. Faraday himself became apprenticed to Mr Riebau, a bookbinder. The letters written to his friend Benjamin Abbott at this time give a lucid account of his aims in life, and of his methods of self-culture, when his mind was beginning to turn to the experimental study of nature. In 1812 Mr Dance, a customer of his master, took him to hear four lectures by Sir Humphry Davy. Faraday took notes of these lectures, and afterwards wrote them out in a fuller form. Under the encouragement of Mr Dance, he wrote to Sir H. Davy, enclosing these notes. "The reply was immediate, kind, and favourable." He continued to work as a journeyman bookbinder till 1st March, 1813, when, at the recommendation of Sir H. Davy, he was appointed assistant in the laboratory of the Royal Institution of Great Britain. He was appointed director of the laboratory 7th February, 1825; and in 1833 he was appointed Fullerton Professor of Chemistry in the Institution for life, without the obligation to deliver lectures. He thus remained in the Institu-tion 54 years. He accompanied Sir H. Davy on a tour through France, Italy, Switzerland, Tyrol, Geneva, etc. from October 13th, 1813, to April 23, 1815.

Faraday's earliest chemical work was in the paths opened by Davy, to whom he acted as assistant. He made a special study of chlorine, and discovered two new chlorides of carbon. He also made the first rough experiments on the diffusion of gases, a phenomenon first pointed out by Dalton, the physical importance of which has been more fully brought to light by Graham and Loschmidt. He succeeded in liquifying several gases; he investigated the alloys of steel, and produced several new kinds of glass intended for optical purposes.

A specimen of one of these heavy glasses afterwards became historically important as the substance in which Faraday detected the rotation of the plane of polarization of light when the glass was placed in the magnetic field, and also as the substance which was first repelled by the poles of the magnet. He also endeavoured with some success to make the general methods of chemistry, as distinguished from its results, the subject of special study and of popular exposition. See his work on *Chemical Manipulation*.

But Faraday's chemical work, however important in itself, was soon completely overshadowed by his electrical discoveries. The first experiment which he has recorded was the construction of a voltaic pile with seven halfpence, seven disks of sheet zinc, and six pieces of paper moistened with salt water. With this pile he decomposed sulphate of magnesia (first letter to Abbott, July 12, 1812). Henceforward, whatever other subjects might from time to time claim his attention, it was from among electrical phenomena that he selected those problems to which he applied the full force of his mind, and which he kept persistently in view, even when year after year his attempts to solve them had been baffled.

His first notable discovery was the production of the continuous rotation of magnets and of wires conducting the electric current round each other. The consequences deducible from the great discovery of Örsted (21st July, 1820) were still in 1821 apprehended in a somewhat confused manner even by the foremost men of science. Dr Wollaston indeed had formed the expectation that he could make the conducting wire rotate on its own axis, and in April, 1821, he came with Sir H. Davy to the laboratory of the Royal Institution to make an experiment. Faraday was not there at the time, but coming in afterwards he heard the conversation on the expected rotation of the wire.

In July, August, and September of that year Faraday, at the request of Mr Phillips, the editor of the *Annals of Philosophy*, wrote for that journal an historical sketch of electro-magnetism, and he repeated almost all the experiments he described. This led him in the beginning of September to discover the method of producing the continuous rotation of the wire round the magnet, and of the magnet round the wire. He did not succeed in making the wire or the magnet revolve on its own axis. This first success of Faraday in electromagnetic research became the occasion of the most painful, though unfounded, imputations against his honour. Into these we shall not enter, referring the reader to the *Life of Faraday*, by Dr Bence Jones.

99—2

We may remark, however, that although the fact of the tangential force between an electric current and a magnetic pole was clearly stated by Örsted, and clearly apprehended by Ampère, Wollaston, and others, the realization of the continuous rotation of the wire and the magnet round each other was a scientific puzzle requiring no mean ingenuity for its original solution. For on the one hand the electric current always forms a closed circuit, and on the other the two poles of the magnet have equal but opposite properties, and are inseparably connected, so that whatever tendency there is for one pole to circulate round the current in one direction is opposed by the equal tendency of the other pole to go round the other way, and thus the one pole can neither drag the other round the wire nor yet leave it behind. The thing cannot be done unless we adopt in some form Faraday's ingenious solution, by causing the current, in some part of its course, to divide into two channels, one on each side of the magnet, in such a way that during the revolution of the magnet the current is transferred from the channel in front of the magnet to the channel behind it, so that the middle of the magnet can pass across the current without stopping it, just as Cyrus caused his army to pass dryshod over the Gyndes by diverting the river into a channel cut for it in his rear.

We must now go on to the crowning discovery of the induction of electric currents.

In Dec. 1824 he had attempted to obtain an electric current by means of a magnet, and on three occasions he had made elaborate but unsuccessful attempts to produce a current in one wire by means of a current in another wire or by a magnet. He still persevered, and on the 29th August, 1831, he obtained the first evidence that an electric current can induce another in a different circuit. On September 23 he writes to his friend R. Phillips—"I am busy just now again on electromagnetism, and think I have got hold of a good thing, but can't say. It may be a weed instead of a fish that, after all my labour, I may at last pull up." This was his first successful experiment. In nine more days of experimenting he had arrived at the results described in his first series of "Experimental Researches" read to the Royal Society, November 24, 1841.

By the intense application of his mind he had brought the new idea, in ss than three months from its first development, to a state of perfect maturity. e magnitude and originality of Faraday's achievement may be estimated by tracing the subsequent history of his discovery. As might be expected, it was at once made the subject of investigation by the whole scientific world, but some of the most experienced physicists were unable to avoid mistakes in stating, in what they conceived to be more scientific language than Faraday's, the phenomena before them. Up to the present time the mathematicians who have rejected Faraday's method of stating his law as unworthy of the precision of their science have never succeeded in devising any essentially different formula which shall fully express the phenomena without introducing hypotheses about the mutual action of things which have no physical existence, such as elements of currents which flow out of nothing, then along a wire, and finally sink into nothing again.

After nearly half a century of labour of this kind, we may say that, though the practical applications of Faraday's discovery have increased and are increasing in number and value every year, no exception to the statement of these laws as given by Faraday has been discovered, no new law has been added to them, and Faraday's original statement remains to this day the only one which asserts no more than can be verified by experiment, and the only one by which the theory of the phenomena can be expressed in a manner which is exactly and numerically accurate, and at the same time within the range of elementary methods of exposition.

During his first period of discovery, besides the induction of electric currents, Faraday established the identity of the electrification produced in different ways; the law of the definite electrolytic action of the current; and the fact, upon which he laid great stress, that every unit of positive electrification is related in a definite manner to a unit of negative electrification, so that it is impossible to produce what Faraday called "an absolute charge of electricity" of one kind not related to an equal charge of the opposite kind.

He also discovered the difference of the capacities of different substances for taking part in electric induction, a fact which has only in recent years been admitted by continental electricians. It appears, however, from hitherto unpublished papers that Henry Cavendish had before 1773 not only discovered that glass, wax, rosin and shellac have higher specific inductive capacities than air, but had actually determined the numerical ratios of these capacities. This, of course, was unknown both to Faraday and to all other electricians of his time.

The first period of Faraday's electrical discoveries lasted 10 years. In 1841 he found that he required rest, and it was not till 1845 that he entered on his second great period of research, in which he discovered the effect of magnetism on polarized light, and the phenomena of diamagnetism.

Faraday had for a long time kept in view the possibility of using a ray of polarized light as a means of investigating the condition of transparent bodies when acted on by electric and magnetic forces. Dr. Bence Jones (*Life of Faraday*, vol. I. p. 362) gives the following note from his laboratory book, 10th September, 1822 :—

"Polarized a ray of lamp-light by reflexion, and endeavoured to ascertain whether any depolarizing action (was) exerted on it by water placed between the poles of a voltaic battery and in a glass cistern; one Wollaston's trough used; the fluids decomposed were pure water, weak solution of sulphate of soda, and strong sulphuric acid; none of them had any effect on the polarized light, either when out of or in the voltaic circuit, so that no particular arrangement of particles could be ascertained in this way."

Eleven years afterwards we find another entry in his note-book, on 2nd May, 1833 (*Life* by Dr Bence Jones, vol. ii. p. 29). He then tried, not only the effect of a steady current, but the effect on making and breaking contact.

"I do not think, therefore, that decomposing solutions or substances will be found to have (as a consequence of decomposition or arrangement for the time) any effect on the polarized ray. Should now try non-decomposing bodies, as solid nitre, nitrate of silver, borax, glass, etc. whilst solid, to see if any internal state induced, which by decomposition is destroyed, i.e. whether, when they cannot decompose, any state of electrical tension is present. My borate of glass good, and common electricity better than voltaic."

On May 6 he makes further experiments, and concludes—"Hence I see no reason to expect that any kind of structure or tension can be rendered evident, either in decomposing or non-decomposing bodies, in insulating or conducting states."

Experiments similar to the last-mentioned have recently been made by Dr Kerr, of Glasgow, who considers that he has obtained distinct evidence of action on a ray of polarized light when the electric force is perpendicular to the ray and inclined 45° to the plane of polarization. Many physicists, however, have found themselves unable to obtain Dr Kerr's result.

At last, in 1845, Faraday attacked the old problem, but this time with complete success. Before we describe this result we may mention that in 1862 he made the relation between magnetism and light the subject of his very last experimental work. He endeavoured, but in vain, to detect any change in the lines of the spectrum of a flame when the flame was acted on by a powerful magnet.

This long series of researches is an instance of his persistence. His energy is shewn in the way in which he followed up his discovery in the single instance in which he was successful. The first evidence which he obtained of the rotation of the plane of polarization of light under the action of magnetism was on the 13th September, 1845, the transparent substance being his own heavy glass.

He began to work on August 30, 1845, on polarized light passing through electrolytes. After three days he worked with common electricity, trying glass, heavy optical glass, quartz, Iceland spar, all without effect, as on former trials. On September 13 he worked with lines of magnetic force. Air, flint, glass, rock-crystal, calcareous spar, were examined but without effect.

"Heavy glass was experimented with. It gave no effects when the *same magnetic poles* or the *contrary* poles were on opposite sides (as respects the course of the polarized ray), nor when the same poles were on the same side either with the constant or intermitting current. But when contrary magnetic poles were on the same side there was an effect produced on the polarized ray, and thus magnetic force and light were proved to have relations to each other. This fact will most likely prove exceedingly fertile, and of great value in the investigation of the conditions of natural force."

He immediately goes on to examine other substances, but with "no effect," and he ends by saying, "Have got enough for to-day." On September 18 he "does an excellent day's work." During September he had four days of work, and in October six, and on 6th November he sent in to the Royal Society the 19th series of his "Experimental Researches," in which the whole conditions of the phenomena are fully specified. The negative rotation in ferromagnetic media is the only fact of importance which remains to be discovered afterwards (by Verdet in 1856).

But his work for the year was not yet over. On November 3, a new horseshoe magnet came home, and Faraday immediately began to experiment on the action in the polarized ray through gases, but with no effect. The following day he repeated an experiment which had given no result on October 6. A bar of heavy glass was suspended by silk between the poles of the new magnet. "When it was arranged, and had come to rest, I found I *could* affect it by the magnetic forces and give it position." By the 6th December he had sent in to the Royal Society the 20th, and on 24th December the 21st series of his "Researches," in which the properties of diamagnetic bodies are fully described. Thus these two great discoveries were elaborated, like his earlier one, in about three months.

The discovery of the magnetic rotation of the plane of polarized light, though it did not lead to such important practical applications as some of Faraday's earlier discoveries, has been of the highest value to science, as furnishing complete dynamical evidence that wherever magnetic force exists there is matter, small portions of which are rotating about axes parallel to the direction of that force.

We have given a few examples of the concentration of his efforts in seeking to identify the apparently different forces of nature, of his far-sightedness in selecting subjects for investigation, of his persistence in the pursuit of what he set before him, of his energy in working out the results of his discoveries, and of the accuracy and completeness with which he made his final statement of the laws of the phenomenon.

The characteristics of his scientific spirit lie on the surface of his work, and are manifest to all who read his writings. But there was another side of his character, to the cultivation of which he paid at least as much attention, and which was reserved for his friends, his family, and his church. His letters and his conversation were always full of whatever could awaken a healthy interest, and free from anything that might rouse ill-feeling. When, on rare occasions, he was forced out of the region of science into that of controversy, he stated the facts, and let them make their own way. He was entirely free from pride and undue self-assertion. During the growth of his powers he always thankfully accepted a correction, and made use of every expedient, however humble, which would make his work more effective in every detail. When at length he found his memory failing and his mental powers declining, he gave up, without ostentation or complaint, whatever parts of his work he could no longer carry on according to his own standard of efficiency. When he was no longer able to apply his mind to science, he remained content and happy in the exercise of those kindly feelings and warm affections which he had cultivated no less carefully than his scientific powers.

The parents of Faraday belonged to the very small and isolated Christian sect which is commonly called after Robert Sandeman. Faraday himself attended the meetings from childhood; at the early age of 30 he made public profession of his faith, and during two different periods he discharged the office of elder. His opinion with respect to the relation between his science and his religion is expressed in a lecture on mental education delivered in 1854, and printed at the end of his *Researches in Chemistry and Physics.*

"Before entering upon the subject, I must make one distinction which, however it may appear to others, is to me of the utmost importance. High as man is placed above the creatures around him, there is a higher and far more exalted position within his view; and the ways are infinite in which he occupies his thoughts about the fears, or hopes, or expectations of a future life. I believe that the truth of that future cannot be brought to his knowledge by any exertion of his mental powers, however exalted they may be; that it is made known to him by other teaching than his own, and is received through simple belief of the testimony given. Let no one suppose for an instant that the self-education I am about to commend, in respect of the things of this life, extends to any considerations of the hope set before us, as if man by reasoning could find out God. It would be improper here to enter upon the subject farther than to claim an absolute distinction between religious and ordinary belief. I shall be reproached with the weakness of refusing to apply those mental operations which I think good in respect of high things to the very highest. I am content to bear the reproach. Yet even in earthly matters I believe that 'the invisible things of Him from the creation of the world are clearly seen, being understood by the things that are made, even His eternal power and Godhead'; and I have never seen anything incompatible between those things of man which can be known by the spirit of man which is within him, and those higher things concerning his future which he cannot know, by that spirit."

Faraday gives the following note as to this lecture :—

"These observations were delivered as a lecture before His Royal Highness the Prince Consort and the members of the Royal Jnstitution on the 6th of May, 1854. They are so immediately connected in their nature and origin with my own experimental life, considered either as cause or consequence, that I have thought the close of this volume not an unfit place for their reproduction."

As Dr Bence Jones concludes—

"His standard of duty was supernatural. It was not founded on any intuitive ideas of right and wrong, nor was it fashioned upon any outward experiences of time and place, but it was formed entirely on what he held to be the revelation of the will of God in the written word, and throughout all his life his faith led him to act up to the very letter of it."

Published Works.—Chemical Manipulation, being Instructions to Students in Chemistry, 1 vol., John Murray, 1st edition 1827, 2nd 1830, 3rd 1842; *Experimental Researches in Electricity*, vols. I. and II., Richard and John Edward Taylor, vols. I. and II. 1844 and 1847; vol. III. 1844; vol. III., Richard Taylor and William Francis, 1855; *Experimental Researches in Chemistry and Physics*, Taylor and Francis, 1859; *Lectures on the Chemical History of a Candle* (edited by W. Crookes), Griffin, Bohn, and Co., 1861; *On the various Forces in Nature* (edited by W. Crookes), Chatto and Windus (no date).

Biographies.—Faraday as a Discoverer, by John Tyndall, Longmans, 1st edition 1868, 2nd edition 1870; *The Life and Letters of Faraday*, by Dr Bence Jones, Secretary of the Royal Institution, in 2 vols., Longmans, 1870; *Michael Faraday*, by J. H. Gladstone, Ph.D., F.R.S., Macmillan, 1872.

[From *British Association Report*.]

C.—*Reports on Special Branches of Science.*

REPORTS on special branches of science may be of several different types, corresponding to every stage of organisation, from the catalogue up to the treatise.

When a person is engaged in scientific research, it is desirable that he should be able to ascertain, with as little labour as possible, what has been written on the subject and who are the best authorities. The ordinary method is to get hold of the most recent German paper on the subject, to look up the references there given, and by following up the trail of each to find out who are the most influential authors on the subject. German papers have the most complete references because the machinery for docketing and arranging scientific papers is more developed in Germany than elsewhere.

The "Fortschritte der Physik" gave an annual list of all papers, good and bad, arranged in subjects, with abstracts of the more important ones. Wiedemann's "Beiblätter" is a more select assortment, given more in full.

I think it doubtful whether a publication of this kind, if undertaken by the British Association, would succeed. Lists of the titles of the proceedings of Societies and of the contents of periodicals are given in *Nature*. These are useful for strictly contemporary science, and I do not think that a more elaborate system of collection could be kept up for long.

The intending publisher of a discovery has to examine the whole mass of science to see whether he has been anticipated, but the student wishes to read only what is worth reading. What he requires is the names of the best authors. The selection or election of these is constantly done by skimming individual authors, who indicate by the names they quote the men whose opinions have had most influence. But a report on the history and present state of a science has for its main aim to enumerate the various authors and to point out their relative weight, and this has been very well done in several British Association Reports, some of which are nearly as old as the British Association.

There are some branches of science whose position with respect to the public, or else to the educational interest, is such that treatises or text-books can be published on commercial principles, either as books to be read by the free public, or to be got up by the school public.

There is little encouragement, however, for a scientific man to write a treatise so long as he can, with much less trouble, produce an original memoir, which will be much more readily received by a learned society than the treatise would have been by a publisher.

The systematisation of science is therefore carried on under difficulties when left to itself; and I think that the experience of the British Association warrants the belief that its action in asking men of science to furnish reports has conferred benefits on science which would not otherwise have accrued to it.

There are so many valuable reports in the published volumes that I shall indicate only a few, the selection being founded on the direction of my own work rather than on any less arbitrary principle.

First, when a branch of science contains abstruse calculations as well as interesting experiments, it is desirable that those who cultivate the experimental side should be conscious that certain things have been done by the mathematicians. The matter to be reported on in this case is not voluminous, but it is hard reading, and those who are not experts require a guide.

Thus, Professor Challis in 1834 gave a most useful report on the mathematical investigations by Young, Laplace, Poisson, and Gauss on Capillary Attraction, and Professor Stokes in 1862 reports on Theories of Double Refraction. This report may, indeed, be accepted as an instalment of the treatises which, if the desire of the scientific world were law, Professor Stokes would long ago have written. It is meant, no doubt, as a guide to other men's writings, but it is intelligible in itself without reference to those writings. Such a report is a full justification of the existence of the British Association, if it had done nothing else.

Another type of report is that of Professor Cayley on Dynamics (1857 and 1862). This seems intended rather as a guide in reading the original authors than as a self-interpreting document, though, of course, besides th

100—2

criticism and the methodical arrangement, there is much original light thrown on the mass of memoirs discussed in it. It will be many years before the value of this report will be superseded by treatises.

The Report of the Committee on Mathematical Tables deals with a subject which, though not so abstruse, is larger and drier than any of the preceding. It is, however, a most interesting as well as valuable report, and supplies information which would never have been printed unless the British Association had asked for the Report, and which never would have been obtained if the author of the report had not been available.

There are several other reports which are not mere reports, but rather original papers preceded by a historical sketch of the subject. No special encouragement is needed to get people to write reports of this kind.

[From the *Encyclopædia Britannica*.]

CI.—*Harmonic Analysis.*

HARMONIC ANALYSIS is the name given by Sir William Thomson and Professor Tait in their treatise on *Natural Philosophy* to a general method of investigating physical questions, the earliest applications of which seem to have been suggested by the study of the vibrations of strings and the analysis of these vibrations into their fundamental tone and its harmonics or overtones.

The motion of a uniform stretched string fixed at both ends is a periodic motion; that is to say, after a certain interval of time, called the fundamental period of the motion, the form of the string and the velocity of every part of it are the same as before, provided that the energy of the motion has not been sensibly dissipated during the period.

There are two distinct methods of investigating the motion of a uniform stretched string. One of these may be called the wave method, and the other the harmonic method. The wave method is founded on the theorem that in a stretched string of infinite length a wave of any form may be propagated in either direction with a certain velocity, V, which we may define as the "velocity of propagation." If a wave of any form travelling in the positive direction meets another travelling in the opposite direction, the form of which is such that the lines joining corresponding points of the two waves are all bisected in a fixed point in the line of the string, then the point of the string corresponding to this point will remain fixed, while the two waves pass it in opposite directions. If we now suppose that the form of the waves travelling in the positive direction is periodic, that is to say, that after the wave has travelled forward a distance l, the position of every particle of the string is the same as it was at first, then l is called the wave-length, and the time of travelling a wave-length is called the periodic time, which we sha denote by T, so that

$$l = VT.$$

If we now suppose a set of waves similar to these, but reversed in position, to be travelling in the opposite direction, there will be a series of points, distant $\frac{1}{2}l$ from each other, at which there will be no motion of the string; it will therefore make no difference to the motion of the string if we suppose the string fastened to fixed supports at any two of these points, and we may then suppose the parts of the string beyond these points to be removed, as it cannot affect the motion of the part which is between them. We have thus arrived at the case of a uniform string stretched between two fixed supports, and we conclude that the motion of the string may be completely represented as the resultant of two sets of periodic waves travelling in opposite directions, their wave-lengths being either twice the distance between the fixed points or a submultiple of this wave-length, and the form of these waves, subject to this condition, being perfectly arbitrary.

To make the problem a definite one, we may suppose the initial displacement and velocity of every particle of the string given in terms of its distance from one end of the string, and from these data it is easy to calculate the form which is common to all the travelling waves. The form of the string at any subsequent time may then be deduced by calculating the positions of the two sets of waves at that time, and compounding their displacements.

Thus in the wave-method the actual motion of the string is considered as the resultant of two wave-motions, neither of which is of itself, and without the other, consistent with the condition that the ends of the string are fixed. Each of the wave-motions is periodic with a wave-length equal to twice the distance between the fixed points, and the one set of waves is the reverse of the other in respect of displacement and velocity and direction of propagation; but, subject to these conditions, the form of the wave is perfectly arbitrary. The motion of a particle of the string, being determined by the two waves which pass over it in opposite directions, is of an equally arbitrary type.

In the harmonic method, on the other hand, the motion of the string is regarded as compounded of a series of vibratory motions which may be infinite in number, but each of which is perfectly definite in type, and is in fact a particular solution of the problem of the motion of a string with its ends fixed.

A simple harmonic motion is thus defined by Thomson and Tait (§ 53):—
·en a point Q moves uniformly in a circle, the perpendicular QP, drawn from

its position at any instant to a fixed diameter AA' of the circle, intersects the diameter in a point P whose position changes by a *simple harmonic motion*.

The amplitude of a simple harmonic motion is the range on one side or the other of the middle point of the course.

The period of a simple harmonic motion is the time which elapses from any instant until the moving-point again moves in the same direction through the same position.

The phase of a simple harmonic motion at any instant is the fraction of the whole period which has elapsed since the moving point last passed through its middle position in the positive direction.

In the case of the stretched string, it is only in certain particular cases that the motion of a particle of the string is a simple harmonic motion. In these particular cases the form of the string at any instant is that of a curve of sines having the line joining the fixed points for its axis, and passing through these two points, and therefore having for its wave-length either twice the length of the string or some submultiple of this wave-length. The amplitude of the curve of sines is a simple harmonic function of the time, the period being either the fundamental period or some submultiple of the fundamental period. Every one of these modes of vibration is dynamically possible by itself, and any number of them may coexist independently of each other.

By a proper adjustment of the initial amplitude and phase of each of these modes of vibration, so that their resultant shall represent the initial state of the string, we obtain a new representation of the whole motion of the string, in which it is seen to be the resultant of a series of simple harmonic vibrations whose periods are the fundamental period and its submultiples. The determination of the amplitudes and phases of the several simple harmonic vibrations so as to satisfy the initial conditions is an example of harmonic analysis.

We have thus two methods of solving the partial differential equation of the motion of a string. The first, which we have called the wave-method, exhibits the solution in the form containing an arbitrary function, the nature of which must be determined from the initial conditions. The second, or harmonic method, leads to a series of terms involving sines and cosines, the coefficient of which have to be determined. The harmonic method may be defined in more general manner as a method by which the solution of any actual problem may be obtained as the sum or resultant of a number of terms, each of which is a solution of a particular case of the problem. The nature of these particular cases is defined by the condition that any one of them must be conjugate to any other.

The mathematical test of conjugacy is that the energy of the system arising from two of the harmonics existing together is equal to the sum of the energy arising from the two harmonics taken separately. In other words, no part of the energy depends on the product of the amplitudes of two different harmonics. When two modes of motion of the same system are conjugate to each other, the existence of one of them does not affect the other.

The simplest case of harmonic analysis, that of which the treatment of the vibrating string is an example, is completely investigated in what is known as Fourier's Theorem.

Fourier's theorem asserts that any periodic function of a single variable period p, which does not become infinite at any phase, can be expanded in the form of a series consisting of a constant term, together with a double series of terms, one set involving cosines and the other sines of multiples of the phase.

Thus if $\phi(\xi)$ is a periodic function of the variable ξ having a period p, then it may be expanded as follows:

$$\phi(\xi) = A_0 + \Sigma_1^\infty A_i \cos \frac{2i\pi\xi}{p} + \Sigma_1^\infty B_i \sin \frac{2i\pi\xi}{p} \ldots\ldots(1).$$

The part of the theorem which is most frequently required, and which also is the easiest to investigate, is the determination of the values of the coefficients $A_0\ A_i\ B_i$. These are

$$A_0 = \frac{1}{p} \int_0^p \phi(\xi)\,d\xi\,;$$

$$A_i = \frac{2}{p} \int_0^p \phi(\xi) \cos \frac{2i\pi\xi}{p}\,d\xi\,;$$

$$B_i = \frac{2}{p} \int_0^p \phi(\xi) \sin \frac{2i\pi\xi}{p}\,d\xi.$$

This part of the theorem may be verified at once by multiplying both sides of (1) by $d\xi$, by $\cos\dfrac{2i\pi\xi}{p}\,d\xi$, or by $\sin\dfrac{2i\pi\xi}{p}\,d\xi$, and in each case integrating from 0 to p.

The series is evidently single-valued for any given value of ξ. It cannot therefore represent a function of ξ which has more than one value, or which becomes imaginary for any value of ξ. It is convergent, approaching to the true value of $\phi(\xi)$ for all values of ξ such that if ξ varies infinitesimally the function also varies infinitesimally.

Sir W. Thomson, availing himself of the disk, globe, and cylinder integrating machine invented by his brother, Professor James Thomson, has constructed a machine by which eight of the integrals required for the expression of Fourier's series can be obtained simultaneously from the recorded trace of any periodically variable quantity, such as the height of the tide, the temperature of the pressure of the atmosphere, or the intensity of the different components of terrestrial magnetism. If it were not on account of the waste of time, instead of having a curve drawn by the action of the tide, and the curve afterwards acted on by the machine, the time axis of the machine itself might be driven by a clock, and the tide itself might work the second variable of the machine, but this would involve the constant presence of an expensive machine at every tidal station.

It would not be devoid of interest, had we opportunity for it, to trace the analogy between these mathematical and mechanical methods of harmonic analysis and the dynamical processes which go on when a compound ray of light is analysed into its simple vibrations by a prism, when a particular overtone is selected from a complex tone by a resonator, and when the enormously complicated sound-wave of an orchestra, or even the discordant clamours of a crowd, are interpreted into intelligible music or language by the attentive listener, armed with the harp of three thousand strings, the resonance of which, as it hangs in the gateway of his ear, discriminates the multifold components of the waves of the aerial ocean.

INDEX TO VOL. II.